General Chemistry 142

University of Washington

7th EDITION

Steven S. Zumdahl I Donald J. DeCoste

Susan A. Zumdahl

CENGAGE
Learning·

Australia • Brazil • Japan • Korea • Mexico • Singapore • Spain • United Kingdom • United States

General Chemistry 142: University of Washington, 7th EDITION

Chemical Principles 7th Edition
Steven S. Zumdahl
Donald J. DeCoste

© 2013 Cengage Learning. All rights reserved.

Chemistry: An Atoms First Approach, 2nd Edition
Steven S. Zumdahl
Susan A. Zumdahl

© 2016 Cengage Learning. All rights reserved.

SSM CHEMICAL PRINCIPLES, 7th Edition
Steven S. Zumdahl
Donald J. DeCoste

© 2013 Cengage Learning. All rights reserved.

For product information and technology assistance, contact us at
Cengage Learning Customer & Sales Support, 1-800-354-9706
For permission to use material from this text or product,
submit all requests online at **cengage.com/permissions**
Further permissions questions can be emailed to
permissionrequest@cengage.com

This book contains select works from existing Cengage Learning resources and was produced by Cengage Learning Custom Solutions for collegiate use. As such, those adopting and/or contributing to this work are responsible for editorial content accuracy, continuity and completeness.

Compilation © 2015 Cengage Learning

ISBN: 9781305753648

WCN: 01-100-101

Cengage Learning
20 Channel Center Street
Boston, MA 02210
USA

Cengage Learning is a leading provider of customized learning solutions with office locations around the globe, including Singapore, the United Kingdom, Australia, Mexico, Brazil, and Japan. Locate your local office at:
www.international.cengage.com/region.

Cengage Learning products are represented in Canada by Nelson Education, Ltd.

For your lifelong learning solutions, visit **www.cengage.com/custom.**

Visit our corporate website at **www.cengage.com.**

Printed at CLDPC, USA, 12-18

Contents

Learning to Think Like a Chemist

Chemistry is a fascinating and important subject that is challenging to teach and even more challenging to learn. Making this complex subject accessible to students without distortion is the challenge of the chemical educator, especially at the introductory level. *Chemical Principles*, Seventh Edition, provides a rigorous but understandable introduction to chemistry. It emphasizes conceptual understanding, the importance of models, and thoughtful problem solving.

Chemical Principles is based on our experiences at the University of Illinois teaching an accelerated general chemistry course for chemical sciences majors and other students who require a rigorous introductory course. These students typically have excellent credentials and a genuine aptitude for chemistry but only limited understanding of the fundamental concepts of chemistry. Although they may know how to solve stoichiometry and gas problems when they arrive in our courses, these students typically lack a thorough appreciation for the chemical principles that underlie these applications. This is not because they had inadequate preparation in high school; instead, we believe it results from the nature of chemistry itself—a subject that requires several passes before real mastery can take place.

Our mission in writing this text was to produce a book that does not assume that students already know how to think like chemists. These students will eventually do complicated and rigorous thinking, but they must be brought to that point gradually. Thus this book covers the advanced topics (in gases, atomic theory, thermodynamics, and so on) that one expects in a course for chemical sciences majors, but it starts with the fundamentals and then builds to the level required for more complete understanding. Chemistry is not the result of an inspired vision. It is the product of countless observations and many attempts, using logic and trial and error, to account for these observations. In this book we develop key chemical concepts in the same way—to show the observations first and then discuss the models that have been constructed to explain the observed behavior. We hope students will practice "thinking like a chemist" by carefully studying the observations to see if they can follow the thought process, rather than just jumping ahead to the equation or model that will follow.

In *Chemical Principles,* Seventh Edition, we take advantage of the excellent math skills that these students typically possess. As a result, there are fewer work-out examples than would be found in most mainstream books. The end-of-chapter problems cover a wide range—from drill exercises to difficult problems, some of which would challenge the average senior chemistry major. Thus instructors can tailor the problem assignments to the level appropriate for their students.

This text maintains a student-friendly approach without being patronizing. In addition, to demonstrate the importance of chemistry in real life, we have incorporated throughout the book a number of applications and recent advances in essay form.

New to This Edition

We continue to be pleased that the previous editions of the text have been well received. In response to comments from users, however, we have made some significant changes for the seventh edition.

- We have added a new section, Section 3.4, "Conceptual Problem Solving," that emphasizes the importance of conceptual problem solving in which students are shown how to think their way through a problem. We discuss how to solve problems in a flexible, creative way based on understanding the fundamental ideas of chemistry and asking and answering key questions. The students will learn that this "big picture approach" produces more long-term, meaningful learning rather than simply memorizing specific steps that are soon forgotten.

- Using the general conceptual problem-solving approach outlined in the new Section 3.4, we have introduced a series of questions into many of the in-chapter *Examples*. This more active approach helps students think their way through the solution to the problem.

- Several Chemical Insights boxes are new in the seventh edition, and many have been revised, with up-to-date topics such as geoengineering, laser cooling, graphene, and nanogenerators.

- We have replaced 10% of the end-of-chapter questions and problems and have added more than 50 new visual problems.

- We have added a list of the key terms at the end of each chapter along with an outline that reviews each chapter (termed *For Review*).

- We have revised many of the figures in the textbook to better serve visual learners.

Organization

The early chapters in this book deal with chemical reactions. Stoichiometry is covered in Chapters 3 and 4, with special emphasis on reactions in aqueous solutions. The properties of gases are treated in Chapter 5, followed by coverage of gas phase equilibria in Chapter 6. Acid–base equilibria are covered in Chapter 7, and Chapter 8 deals with additional aqueous equilibria. Thermodynamics is covered in two chapters: Chapter 9 deals with thermochemistry and the first law of thermodynamics; Chapter 10 treats the topics associated with the second law of thermodynamics. The discussion of electrochemistry follows in Chapter 11. Atomic theory and quantum mechanics are covered in Chapter 12, followed by two chapters on chemical bonding and modern spectroscopy (Chapters 13 and 14). Chemical kinetics is discussed in Chapter 15, followed by coverage of solids and liquids in Chapter 16 and the physical properties of solutions in Chapter 17. A systematic treatment of the descriptive chemistry of the representative elements is given in Chapter 18 and of the transition metals in Chapter 19. Chapter 20 covers topics in nuclear chemistry, and Chapter 21 provides an introduction to organic chemistry and to the most important biomolecules.

Flexibility of Topic Order

We recognize that the order of the chapters in this text may not fit the order of the topics in your course. Therefore, we have tried to make the order as flexible as possible. In the courses that we have taught using the text, we have successfully used it in a very different order from the one the text follows. We would encourage you to use it in whatever order that serves your purposes.

Instructors have several options for arranging the material to complement their syllabi. For example, the section on gas phase and aqueous equilibria

(Chapters 6–8) could be moved to any point later in the course. The chapters on thermodynamics can be separated: Chapter 9 can be used early in the course with Chapter 10 later. In addition, the chapters on atomic theory and bonding (Chapters 12–14) can be used near the beginning of the course. In summary, an instructor who wants to cover atomic theory early and equilibrium later might prefer the following order of chapters: 1–5, 9, 12, 13, 14, 10, 11, 6, 7, 8, 15–21. An alternative order might be: 1–5, 9, 12, 13, 14, 6, 7, 8, 10, 11, 15–21. The point is that the chapters on atomic theory and bonding (12–14), thermodynamics (9, 10), and equilibrium (6, 7, 8) can be moved around quite easily. In addition, the kinetics chapter (Chapter 15) can be covered at any time after bonding. It is also possible to use Chapter 20 (on nuclear chemistry) much earlier—after Chapter 12, for example—if desired.

Two approaches for teaching atomic theory earlier and equilibrium later in the course

APPROACH 1

Chapter 1 *Chemists and Chemistry*
Chapter 2 *Atoms, Molecules, and Ions*
Chapter 3 *Stoichiometry*
Chapter 4 *Types of Chemical Reactions and Solution Stoichiometry*
Chapter 5 *Gases*
Chapter 9 *Energy, Enthalpy, and Thermochemistry*
Chapter 12 *Quantum Mechanics and Atomic Theory*
Chapter 13 *Bonding: General Concepts*
Chapter 14 *Covalent Bonding: Orbitals*
Chapter 10 *Spontaneity, Entropy, and Free Energy*
Chapter 11 *Electrochemistry*
Chapter 6 *Chemical Equilibrium*
Chapter 7 *Acids and Bases*
Chapter 8 *Applications of Aqueous Equilibria*
Chapter 15 *Chemical Kinetics*
Chapter 16 *Liquids and Solids*
Chapter 17 *Properties of Solutions*
Chapter 18 *The Representative Elements*
Chapter 19 *Transition Metals and Coordination Chemistry*
Chapter 20 *The Nucleus: A Chemist's View*
Chapter 21 *Organic and Biochemical Molecules*

APPROACH 2

Chapter 1 *Chemists and Chemistry*
Chapter 2 *Atoms, Molecules, and Ions*
Chapter 3 *Stoichiometry*
Chapter 4 *Types of Chemical Reactions and Solution Stoichiometry*
Chapter 5 *Gases*
Chapter 9 *Energy, Enthalpy, and Thermochemistry*
Chapter 12 *Quantum Mechanics and Atomic Theory*
Chapter 13 *Bonding: General Concepts*
Chapter 14 *Covalent Bonding: Orbitals*
Chapter 6 *Chemical Equilibrium*
Chapter 7 *Acids and Bases*
Chapter 8 *Applications of Aqueous Equilibria*
Chapter 10 *Spontaneity, Entropy, and Free Energy*
Chapter 11 *Electrochemistry*
Chapter 15 *Chemical Kinetics*
Chapter 16 *Liquids and Solids*
Chapter 17 *Properties of Solutions*
Chapter 18 *The Representative Elements*
Chapter 19 *Transition Metals and Coordination Chemistry*
Chapter 20 *The Nucleus: A Chemist's View*
Chapter 21 *Organic and Biochemical Molecules*

Mathematical Level

This text assumes a solid background in algebra. All of the mathematical operations required are described in Appendix One or are illustrated in worked-out examples. A knowledge of calculus is not required for use of this text. Differential and integral notions are used only where absolutely necessary and are explained when they are used.

Alternate Versions

**Hybrid Edition with Access (24 months) to OWL with Cengage YouBook
ISBN-10: 1-133-10984-5; ISBN-13: 978-1-133-10984-6**
This briefer version of *Chemical Principles* does not contain the end-of-chapter problems, which can be assigned in OWL.

Supporting Materials

OWL for General Chemistry

Printed Access OWL with YouBook (24 months) ISBN-10: 1-133-04411-5; ISBN-13: 978-1-133-04411-6

Instant Access OWL with YouBook (6 months) ISBN-10: 1-133-00149-1; ISBN-13: 978-1-133-00149-2

Instant Access OWL with YouBook (24 months) ISBN-10: 1-133-00150-5; ISBN-13: 978-1-133-00150-8

By Roberta Day and Beatrice Botch of the University of Massachusetts, Amherst, and William Vining of the State University of New York at Oneonta. **OWL** Online Web Learning offers more assignable, gradable content (including end-of chapter questions specific to this textbook) and more reliability and flexibility than any other system. OWL's powerful course management tools allow instructors to control due dates, number of attempts, and whether students see answers or receive feedback on how to solve problems. OWL includes the **Cengage YouBook**, an interactive and customizable Flash-based eBook. Instructors can publish web links, modify the textbook narrative as needed with the text edit tool, quickly reorder entire sections and chapters, and hide any content they don't teach to create an eBook that perfectly matches their syllabus. The Cengage YouBook includes animated figures, video clips, highlighting, notes, and more.

Developed by chemistry instructors for teaching chemistry, OWL is the only system specifically designed to support **mastery learning**, where students work as long as they need to master each chemical concept and skill. OWL has already helped hundreds of thousands of students master chemistry through a wide range of assignment types, including tutorials, interactive simulations, and algorithmically generated homework questions that provide instant, answer-specific feedback.

OWL is continually enhanced with online learning tools to address the various learning styles of today's students such as:

- **Quick Prep** Review courses that help students learn essential skills to succeed in General and Organic Chemistry
- **Jmol** Molecular visualization program for rotating molecules and measuring bond distances and angles
- **Go Chemistry®** Mini video lectures on key concepts that students can play on their computers or download to their video iPods, smart phones, or personal video players

In addition, when you become an OWL user, you can expect service that goes far beyond the ordinary. To learn more or to see a demo, please contact your Cengage Learning representative, or visit us at www.cengage.com/owl.

For the Instructor

PowerLecture Instructor's CD/DVD Package with ExamView®
ISBN-10: 1-111-98895-1; ISBN-13: 978-1-111-98895-1
This digital library and presentation tool includes:

- **PowerPoint® lecture slides** written for this text that instructors can customize by importing their own lecture slides or other materials.
- **Image libraries** that contain digital files for figures, photographs, and numbered tables from the text, as well as multimedia animations in a variety of digital formats. Use these files to print transparencies, create your own PowerPoint slides, and supplement your lectures.
- Digital files of the complete **Instructor's Manual** and **ExamView Test Bank**.

- Sample chapters from the **Study Guide,** by Paul Kelter (Northern Illinois University)
- Sample chapters from the **Student Solutions Manual,** by Tom Hummel (University of Illinois)
- **ExamView testing software** that enables you to create, deliver, and customize tests using the more than 2000 test bank questions written specifically for this text

Instructor Companion Site
Supporting materials are available to qualified adopters. Please consult your local Cengage Learning sales representative for details. Go to login.cengage.com, find this textbook, and choose Instructor Companion Site to see samples of these materials, request a desk copy, locate your sales representative, and download the WebCT or Blackboard versions of the Test Bank.

For the Student

Visit CengageBrain.com
To access these and additional course materials, please visit www.cengagebrain.com. At the CengageBrain.com home page, search for this textbook's ISBN (from the back cover of your book). This will take you to the product page where these resources can be found. (Instructors can log in at login.cengage.com.)

OWL Quick Prep for General Chemistry
Instant Access OWL Quick Prep for General Chemistry (90 days) ISBN-10: 0-495-56030-8; ISBN-13: 978-0-495-56030-2
Quick Prep is a self-paced online short course that helps students succeed in general chemistry. Students who completed Quick Prep through an organized class or self-study averaged almost a full letter grade higher in their subsequent general chemistry course than those who did not. Intended to be taken prior to the start of the semester, Quick Prep is appropriate for both underprepared students and for students who seek a review of basic skills and concepts. Quick Prep features an assessment quiz to focus students on the concepts they need to study to be prepared for general chemistry. Quick Prep is approximately 20 hours of instruction delivered through OWL with no textbook required and can be completed at any time in the student's schedule. Professors can package a printed access card for Quick Prep with the textbook, or students can purchase instant access at www.cengagebrain.com. To view an OWL Quick Prep demonstration and for more information, visit www.cengage.com/chemistry/quickprep.

Go Chemistry® for General Chemistry
ISBN-10: 0-495-38228-0; ISBN-13: 978-0-495-38228-7
Pressed for time? Missed a lecture? Need more review? Go Chemistry for General Chemistry is a set of 27 downloadable mini-video lectures. Developed by award-winning chemists, Go Chemistry helps you quickly review essential topics—whenever and wherever you want! Each video contains animations and problems and can be downloaded to your computer desktop or portable video player (like iPod or iPhone) for convenient self-study and exam review. Selected Go Chemistry videos have e-flashcards to briefly introduce a key concept and then test student understanding of the basics with a series of questions. OWL includes five Go Chemistry videos. Professors can package a printed access card for Go Chemistry with the textbook. Students can enter the ISBN above at www.cengagebrain.com to download two free videos or to purchase instant access to the 27-video set or to individual videos.

CengageBrain.com App

Now, students can prepare for class anytime and anywhere using the Cengage Brain.com application developed specifically for the Apple iPhone® and iPod touch®, which allows students to access free study materials—book-specific quizzes, flash cards, related Cengage Learning materials, and more—so they can study the way they want, when they want to . . . even on the go. To learn more about this complimentary application, please visit www.cengagebrain.com. Also available on iTunes.

Student Companion Site

This site includes a glossary, flashcards, an interactive periodic table, and samples of the Study Guide and Student Solutions Manual, which are all accessible from www.cengagebrain.com.

Acknowledgments

The successful completion of this book is due to the efforts of many people. Mary Finch, publisher, and Lisa Lockwood, executive editor, were extremely supportive of the revision. We also wish to thank Thomas Martin, developmental editor, who has a keen eye, good ideas, and is extremely organized and helpful. We are grateful to have worked with Sharon Donahue, photo researcher, who never fails in finding just the right photo.

We greatly appreciate the efforts of Tom Hummel from the University of Illinois, who managed the revision of the end-of-chapter exercises and problems and the solutions manuals. Tom's extensive knowledge of general chemistry and high standards of accuracy ensure the quality of the problems and solutions in this text. We are deeply grateful to Gretchen Adams, who created the interactive examples and interactive end-of-chapter exercises and problems. Gretchen is extremely creative, never misses a deadline, and is a real pleasure to work with. Special thanks go to Nicole Hamm, marketing manager, who knows the market and works very hard in support of this book.

Thanks to others who provided valuable assistance on this revision: Krista Mastroianni, editorial assistant; Lisa Weber, senior media editor; Stephanie VanCamp, media editor; Julie Stefani, marketing assistant; Megan Greiner, production editor (Graphic World); Teresa L. Trego, content project manager; and Maria Epes, art director.

Our sincerest appreciation goes to all of the reviewers whose feedback and suggestions contributed to the success of this project.

Seventh Edition Reviewers

Rosemary Bartoszek-Loza, *Ohio State University*
H. Floyd Davis, *Cornell University*
Darby Feldwinn, *University of California–Santa Barbara*
Burt Goldberg, *New York University*
Kandalam V. Ramanujachary, *Rowan University*
Philip J. Reid, *University of Washington*
Christopher P. Roy, *Duke University*

Sixth Edition Reviewers

Elizabeth Day, *University of the Pacific*
Ivan J. Dmochowski, *University of Pennsylvania*
Brian Enderle, *University of California, Davis*
Regina Frey, *Washington University, St. Louis*
Brian Frost, *University of Nevada*

Derek Gragson, *California Polytechnic State University*
Keith Griffiths, *University of Western Ontario*
Carl Hoeger, *University of California, San Diego*
Robert Kerber, *State University of New York, Stony Brook*
K. C. McGill, *Georgia College and State University*
Thomas G. Minehan, *California State University, Northridge*
John H. Nelson, *University of Nevada*
Robert Price, *City College of San Francisco*
Douglas Raynie, *South Dakota State University*
Philip J. Reid, *University of Washington*
Thomas Schleich, *University of California, Santa Cruz*
Robert Sharp, *University of Michigan*
Mark Sulkes, *Tulane University*
John H. Terry, *Cornell University*
Mark Thachuk, *University of British Columbia*
Michael R. Topp, *University of Pennsylvania*
Meishan Zhao, *University of Chicago*

Fifth Edition Reviewers

Alan L. Balch, *University of California, Davis*
David Erwin, *Rose-Hulman Institute of Technology*
Michael Hecht, *Princeton University*
Rosemary Marusak, *Kenyon College*
Patricia B. O'Hara, *Amherst College*
Ruben D. Parra, *DePaul University*
Philip J. Reid, *University of Washington*
Eric Scerri, *University of California, Los Angeles*
Robert Sharp, *University of Michigan*

About the Authors

STEVEN S. ZUMDAHL received his B.S. degree in Chemistry from Wheaton College (Illinois) in 1964 and his Ph.D. in Chemistry from the University of Illinois, Urbana, in 1968.

In over 35 years of teaching he has been a faculty member at the University of Colorado, Boulder; Parkland College (Illinois); and the University of Illinois, where he served as Professor and Associate Head and Director of Undergraduate Programs in Chemistry until he became Professor Emeritus in 2003. In 1994 Dr. Zumdahl received the National Catalyst Award from the Chemical Manufacturers Association in recognition of his contribution to chemical education in the United States.

Professor Zumdahl is known at the University of Illinois for his rapport with students and for his outstanding teaching ability. During his tenure at the University, he received the University of Illinois Award for Excellence in Teaching, the Liberal Arts and Sciences College Award for Distinguished Teaching, and the School of Chemical Sciences Teaching Award (five times).

Dr. Z., as he is known to his students, greatly enjoys "mechanical things," including bicycles and cars. He collects and restores classic automobiles, having a special enthusiasm for vintage Corvettes and Packards.

DONALD J. DECOSTE is Associate Director of General Chemistry at the University of Illinois, Urbana-Champaign, and has been teaching chemistry at the high school and college levels for 24 years. He earned his B.S. degree in Chemistry and Ph.D. from the University of Illinois, Urbana-Champaign. At UIUC he has developed chemistry courses for nonscience majors, preservice secondary teachers, and preservice elementary teachers. He teaches courses in introductory chemistry and the teaching of chemistry and has received the School of Chemical Sciences Teaching Award four times. Don has led workshops for secondary teachers and graduate student teaching assistants, discussing the methods and benefits of getting students more actively involved in class. When not involved in teaching and advising, Don enjoys spending time with his wife and three children.

Atoms, Molecules, and Ions

2

chapter

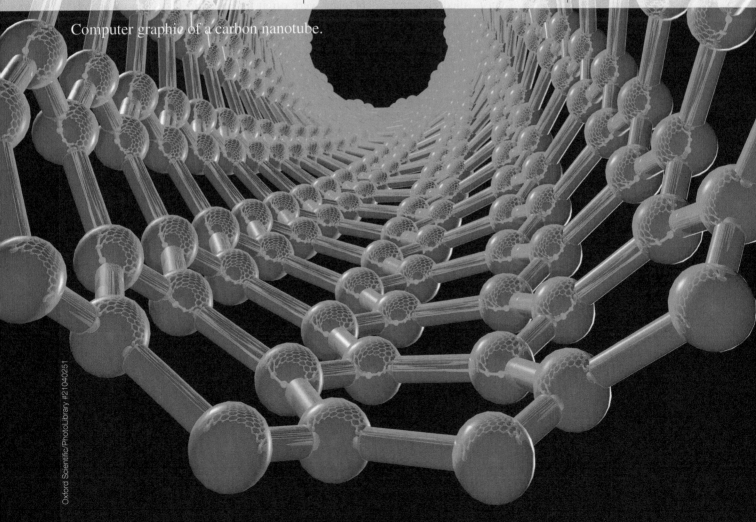

Computer graphic of a carbon nanotube.

In this chapter we present very briefly many of the fundamental concepts and some of the vocabulary of chemistry plus something about how the science developed. Depending on your specific background in chemistry, much of this material may be review. However, whatever your background, read this chapter carefully to be sure this material is fresh in your mind as we pursue the study of reaction chemistry in Chapters 3 and 4.

2.1 | The Early History of Chemistry

Chemistry has been important since ancient times. The processing of natural ores to produce metals for ornaments and weapons and the use of embalming fluids are two applications of chemical phenomena that were used before 1000 B.C.

The Greeks were the first to try to explain why chemical changes occur. By about 400 B.C. they had proposed that all matter was composed of four fundamental substances: fire, earth, water, and air. The Greeks also considered the question of whether matter is continuous, and thus infinitely divisible into smaller pieces, or composed of small indivisible particles. One supporter of the latter position was Democritus, who used the term *atomos* (which later became *atoms*) to describe these ultimate particles. However, because the Greeks had no experiments to test their ideas, no definitive conclusion about the divisibility of matter was reached.

The next 2000 years of chemical history were dominated by a pseudoscience called alchemy. Alchemists were often mystics and fakes who were obsessed with the idea of turning cheap metals into gold. However, this period also saw important discoveries: Elements such as mercury, sulfur, and antimony were discovered, and alchemists learned how to prepare the mineral acids.

The foundations of modern chemistry were laid in the sixteenth century with the development of systematic metallurgy (extraction of metals from ores) by a German, Georg Bauer, and the medicinal application of minerals by the Swiss alchemist Paracelsus.

The first "chemist" to perform truly quantitative experiments was Robert Boyle (1627–1691), an Irish scientist, who carefully measured the relationship between the pressure and volume of gases. When Boyle published his book *The Sceptical Chemist* in 1661, the quantitative sciences of physics and chemistry were born. In addition to his results on the quantitative behavior of gases, Boyle's other major contribution to chemistry consisted of his ideas about the chemical elements. Boyle held no preconceived notion about the number of elements. In his view a substance was an element unless it could be broken down into two or more simpler substances. As Boyle's experimental definition of an element became generally accepted, the list of known elements began to grow, and the Greek system of four elements finally died. Although Boyle was an excellent scientist, he was not always right. For example, he clung to the alchemist's views that metals were not true elements and that a way would eventually be found to change one metal to another.

The Priestley Medal is the highest honor given by the American Chemical Society. It is named for **Joseph Priestley,** who was born in England on March 13, 1733. He performed many important scientific experiments, one of which led to the discovery that a gas later identified as carbon dioxide could be dissolved in water to produce *seltzer.* Also, as a result of meeting Benjamin Franklin in London in 1766, Priestley became interested in electricity and was the first to observe that graphite was an electrical conductor. However, his greatest discovery occurred in 1774, when he isolated oxygen by heating mercuric oxide.

Because of his nonconformist political views, he was forced to leave England. He died in the United States in 1804.

The phenomenon of combustion evoked intense interest in the seventeenth and eighteenth centuries. The German chemist Georg Stahl (1660–1734) suggested that a substance he called phlogiston flowed out of the burning material. Stahl postulated that a substance burning in a closed container eventually stopped burning because the air in the container became saturated with phlogiston. Oxygen gas, discovered by Joseph Priestley (1733–1804), an English clergyman and scientist, was found to support vigorous combustion and was thus supposed to be low in phlogiston. In fact, oxygen was originally called "dephlogisticated air." It is important to note that the observations made by

Joseph Priestley did not contradict those made by Georg Stahl. However, Priestley's theory to explain what he saw was vastly different. As we stated in Chapter 1, *what* happens doesn't change, but our ideas about *why* a phenomenon occurs can change. Such is the nature of science.

2.2 | Fundamental Chemical Laws

By the late eighteenth century, combustion had been studied extensively; the gases carbon dioxide, nitrogen, hydrogen, and oxygen had been discovered; and the list of elements continued to grow. However, it was Antoine Lavoisier (1743–1794), a French chemist (Fig. 2.1), who finally explained the true nature of combustion, thus clearing the way for the tremendous progress that was made near the end of the eighteenth century. Lavoisier, like Boyle, regarded measurement as the essential operation of chemistry. His experiments, in which he carefully weighed the reactants and products of various reactions, suggested that *mass is neither created nor destroyed*. Lavoisier's discovery of this **law of conservation of mass** was the basis for the developments in chemistry in the nineteenth century.

Lavoisier's quantitative experiments showed that combustion involved oxygen (which Lavoisier named), not phlogiston. He also discovered that life was supported by a process that also involved oxygen and was similar in many ways to combustion. In 1789 Lavoisier published the first modern chemistry textbook, *Elementary Treatise on Chemistry*, in which he presented a unified picture of the chemical knowledge assembled up to that time. Unfortunately, in the same year the text was published, the French Revolution began. Lavoisier, who had been associated with collecting taxes for the government, was executed on the guillotine as an enemy of the people in 1794.

After 1800, chemistry was dominated by scientists who, following Lavoisier's lead, performed careful weighing experiments to study the course of chemical reactions and to determine the composition of various chemical compounds. One of these chemists, a Frenchman, Joseph Proust (1754–1826), showed that *a given compound always contains exactly the same proportion of elements by mass*. For example, Proust found that the substance copper car-

Figure 2.1

Antoine Lavoisier with his wife. Lavoisier was born in Paris on August 26, 1743. From the beginning of his scientific career, Lavoisier recognized the importance of accurate measurements. His careful weighings showed that mass is conserved in chemical reactions and that combustion involves reaction with oxygen. Also, he wrote the first modern chemistry textbook. He is often called the father of modern chemistry.

Because of his connection to a private tax-collecting firm, radical French revolutionaries demanded his execution, which occurred on the guillotine on May 8, 1794.

(Detail) *Antoine Laurent Lavoisier & His Wife* by Jacques Louis David, 1788. Image copyright © The Metropolitan Museum of Art/Art Resource, NY

Figure 2.2
John Dalton (1766–1844), an Englishman, began teaching at a Quaker school when he was 12. His fascination with science included an intense interest in meteorology (he kept careful daily weather records for 46 years), which led to an interest in the gases of the air and their ultimate components, atoms. Dalton is best known for his atomic theory, in which he postulated that the fundamental differences among atoms are their masses. He was the first to prepare a table of relative atomic weights.

Dalton was a humble man with several apparent handicaps: He was poor; he was not articulate; he was not a skilled experimentalist; and he was color-blind, a terrible problem for a chemist. Despite these disadvantages, he helped revolutionize the science of chemistry.

bonate is always 5.3 parts copper to 4 parts oxygen to 1 part carbon (by mass). The principle of the constant composition of compounds, originally called Proust's law, is now known as the **law of definite proportion.**

Proust's discovery stimulated John Dalton (1766–1844), an English schoolteacher (Fig. 2.2), to think about atoms. Dalton reasoned that if elements were composed of tiny individual particles, a given compound should always contain the same combination of these atoms. This concept explained why the same relative masses of elements were always found in a given compound.

But Dalton discovered another principle that convinced him even more of the existence of atoms. He noted, for example, that carbon and oxygen form two different compounds that contain different relative amounts of carbon and oxygen, as shown by the following data:

	Mass of Oxygen That Combines with 1 g of Carbon
Compound I	1.33 g
Compound II	2.66 g

Dalton noted that compound II contained twice as much oxygen per gram of carbon as compound I, a fact that could be easily explained in terms of atoms. Compound I might be CO, and compound II might be CO_2. This principle, which was found to apply to compounds of other elements as well, became known as the **law of multiple proportions:** *When two elements form a series of compounds, the ratios of the masses of the second element that combine with 1 gram of the first element can always be reduced to small whole numbers.*

These ideas are also illustrated by the compounds of nitrogen and oxygen, as shown by the following data:

	Mass of Nitrogen That Combines with 1 g of Oxygen
Compound I	1.750 g
Compound II	0.8750 g
Compound III	0.4375 g

which yield the following ratios:

$$\frac{I}{II} = \frac{1.750}{0.8750} = \frac{2}{1}$$

$$\frac{II}{III} = \frac{0.8750}{0.4375} = \frac{2}{1}$$

$$\frac{I}{III} = \frac{1.750}{0.4375} = \frac{4}{1}$$

The significance of these data is that compound I contains twice as much nitrogen (N) per gram of oxygen (O) as does compound II and that compound II contains twice as much nitrogen per gram of oxygen as does compound III. In terms of the numbers of atoms combining, these data can be explained by any of the following sets of formulas:

Compound I	N_2O		NO		N_4O_2
Compound II	NO	or	NO_2	or	N_2O_2
Compound III	NO_2		NO_4		N_2O_4

In fact, an infinite number of other possibilities exists. Dalton could not deduce absolute formulas from the available data on relative masses. However, the data on the composition of compounds in terms of the relative masses of the elements supported his hypothesis that each element consisted of a certain type of atom and that compounds were formed from specific combinations of atoms.

2.3 | Dalton's Atomic Theory

In 1808 Dalton published *A New System of Chemical Philosophy*, in which he presented his theory of atoms.

These statements are a modern paraphrase of Dalton's ideas.

> ### Dalton's Model
>
> 1. Each element is made up of tiny particles called atoms.
> 2. The atoms of a given element are identical; the atoms of different elements are different in some fundamental way or ways.
> 3. Chemical compounds are formed when atoms combine with one another. A given compound always has the same relative numbers and types of atoms.
> 4. Chemical reactions involve reorganization of the atoms—changes in the way they are bound together. The atoms themselves are not changed in a chemical reaction.

It is instructive to consider Dalton's reasoning on the relative masses of the atoms of the various elements. In Dalton's time, water was known to be composed of the elements hydrogen and oxygen, with 8 grams of oxygen present for every 1 gram of hydrogen. If the formula for water were OH, an oxygen atom would have to have eight times the mass of a hydrogen atom. However, if the formula for water were H_2O (two atoms of hydrogen for every oxygen atom), this would mean that each atom of oxygen is 16 times as heavy as *each* atom of hydrogen (since the ratio of the mass of one oxygen to that of *two* hydrogens is 8 to 1). Because the formula for water was not then known, Dalton could not specify the relative masses of oxygen and hydrogen unambiguously. To solve the problem, Dalton made a fundamental assumption: He decided that nature would be as simple as possible. This assumption led him to conclude that the formula for water should be OH. He thus assigned hydrogen a mass of 1 and oxygen a mass of 8.

mass (*m*): the quantity of matter in a body

weight: $m \times g$

Using similar reasoning for other compounds, Dalton prepared the first table of **atomic masses** (formerly called atomic weights by chemists, since mass is usually determined by comparison to a standard mass—a process called *weighing**). Many of the masses were later proved to be wrong because of Dalton's incorrect assumptions about the formulas of certain compounds, but the construction of a table of masses was an important step forward.

Although not recognized as such for many years, the keys to determining absolute formulas for compounds were provided in the experimental work of the French chemist Joseph Gay-Lussac (1778–1850) and by the hypothesis of an Italian chemist named Amedeo Avogadro (1776–1856). In 1809 Gay-Lussac performed experiments in which he measured (under the same conditions of temperature and pressure) the volumes of gases that reacted with one another. For example, Gay-Lussac found that 2 volumes of hydrogen react with 1 volume of oxygen to form 2 volumes of gaseous water and that 1 vol-

---

*Technically, weight is the force exerted on an object by gravitational attraction to a body such as the earth (weight = mass × acceleration due to gravity). It is mass (the quantity of matter in a body), not weight, that chemists use in their measurements, although the two terms are sometimes used interchangeably.

Joseph Louis Gay-Lussac (1778–1850), a French physicist and chemist, was remarkably versatile. Although he is now primarily known for his studies on the combining of volumes of gases, Gay-Lussac was instrumental in the studies of many of the other properties of gases. Some of Gay-Lussac's motivation to learn about gases arose from his passion for ballooning. In fact, he made ascents to heights of over 4 miles to collect air samples, setting altitude records that stood for approximately 50 years. Gay-Lussac also was the codiscoverer of boron and the developer of a process for manufacturing sulfuric acid. As chief assayer of the French mint, Gay-Lussac developed many techniques for chemical analysis and invented many types of glassware now used routinely in labs. Gay-Lussac spent his last 20 years as a lawmaker in the French government.

ume of hydrogen reacts with 1 volume of chlorine to form 2 volumes of hydrogen chloride.

In 1811 Avogadro interpreted these results by proposing that, *at the same temperature and pressure, equal volumes of different gases contain the same number of particles.* This assumption (called **Avogadro's hypothesis**) makes sense if the distances between the particles in a gas are very great compared with the sizes of the particles. Under these conditions the volume of a gas is determined by the number of molecules present, not by the size of the individual particles.

If Avogadro's hypothesis is correct, Gay-Lussac's result,

2 volumes of hydrogen react with 1 volume of oxygen
$$\longrightarrow \text{2 volumes of water vapor}$$

can be expressed as follows:

2 molecules of hydrogen react with 1 molecule of oxygen
$$\longrightarrow \text{2 molecules of water}$$

These observations can be explained best by assuming that gaseous hydrogen, oxygen, and chlorine are all composed of diatomic (two-atom) molecules: H_2, O_2, and Cl_2, respectively. Gay-Lussac's results can then be represented as shown in Fig. 2.3. (Note that this reasoning suggests that the formula for water is H_2O, not OH as Dalton believed.)

Unfortunately, Avogadro's interpretations were not accepted by most chemists. The main stumbling block seems to have been the prevailing belief that only atoms of different elements could attract each other to form molecules. Dalton and the other prominent chemists of the time assumed that identical atoms had no "affinity" for each other and thus would not form diatomic molecules.

Because no general agreement existed concerning the formulas for elements such as hydrogen, oxygen, and chlorine or for the compounds formed from these elements, chaos reigned in the first half of the nineteenth century. Although during this period chemists, such as the Swedish chemist Jöns Jakob Berzelius (1779–1848), made painstaking measurements of the masses of various elements that combined to form compounds, these results were interpreted in many different ways, depending on the assumptions about the formulas of the elements and compounds, and this led to many different tables of atomic masses. The situation was so confused that 19 different formulas for the com-

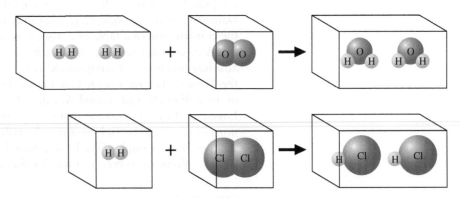

Figure 2.3

A representation of combining gases at the molecular level. The spheres represent atoms in the molecules, and the boxes represent the relative volumes of the gases.

pound acetic acid were given in a textbook written in 1861 by F. August Kekulé (1829–1896). In the next section we will see how this mess was finally cleaned up, primarily because of the leadership of the Italian chemist Stanislao Cannizzaro (1826–1910).

2.4 | Cannizzaro's Interpretation

Convinced that chemists had to find a way to agree on a common set of atomic masses, the German chemist F. August Kekulé organized the First International Chemical Congress held in 1860 at Karlsruhe, Germany. At this meeting the young Italian chemist Stanislao Cannizzaro presented his ideas so clearly and forcefully, both in formal and informal talks, that a consensus about atomic masses began to develop in the chemical community. Cannizzaro was guided by two main beliefs:

1. Compounds contained whole numbers of atoms as Dalton postulated.

2. Avogadro's hypothesis was correct—equal volumes of gases under the same conditions contain the same number of molecules.

Applications of Avogadro's hypothesis to Gay-Lussac's results of combining volumes of gas convinced Cannizzaro that hydrogen gas consisted of H_2 molecules. Thus he arbitrarily assigned the relative molecular mass of hydrogen (H_2) to be 2. He then set out to measure the relative molecular masses for other gaseous substances. He did so by comparing the mass of 1 liter of a given gas with the mass of 1 liter of hydrogen gas (both gases at the same conditions of temperature and pressure). For example, the ratio of the masses of 1-liter samples of oxygen and hydrogen gas is 16:

Both gases are at the same temperature and pressure.

$$\frac{\text{Mass of 1.0 L oxygen gas}}{\text{Mass of 1.0 L hydrogen gas}} = \frac{16}{1} = \frac{32}{2}$$

Since by Avogadro's hypothesis both samples of gas contain the same number of molecules, the mass of an oxygen molecule (which he assumed to be O_2) must be 32 relative to a mass of 2 for the H_2 molecule. Since each molecule contains two atoms, the relative atomic masses for oxygen and hydrogen are then 16 and 1, respectively. Using this same method, Cannizzaro found the relative molecular mass of carbon dioxide to be 44 (relative to 2 for H_2). Chemical analysis of carbon dioxide had shown it to contain 27% carbon (by mass). This percentage corresponds to $(0.27)(44 \text{ g})$, or 12 g, of carbon in 44 g of carbon dioxide, and 44 g − 12 g = 32 g of oxygen. Recall that the oxygen atom has a relative mass of 16. Thus if the formula of carbon dioxide is assumed to be CO_2, then the relative mass of carbon is 12 because $12 + 2(16) = 44$. However, if the formula of carbon dioxide is C_2O_2, then 12 represents the relative mass of two carbon atoms, giving carbon a relative mass of 6. Similarly, the formula C_3O_2 for carbon dioxide gives a relative mass of 4 for carbon. Thus the relative mass of the carbon atom cannot be determined from these data without knowing the formula for carbon dioxide. This is exactly the type of problem that had plagued chemists all along and was the reason for so many different mass tables.

Cannizzaro addressed this problem by obtaining the relative molecular masses of many other compounds containing carbon. For example, consider the data shown in Table 2.1. Notice from these data that the relative mass of carbon present in the compounds is always a multiple of 12. This observation strongly suggests that the relative mass of carbon is 12, which in turn would mean that the formula for carbon dioxide is CO_2.

Chemical Insights   Seeing Atoms

There are many pieces of evidence that convince us that matter is made up of atoms. Some of the most compelling evidence comes from scanning probe microscopy. This technique employs a microscopic tip, which responds to a surface to reveal its architecture. The principal methods of scanning probe microscopy are scanning tunneling microscopy (STM) and atomic force microscopy (AFM).

The scanning tunneling microscope was invented at IBM's Zurich Research Laboratory in Switzerland in the early 1980s by Gerd K. Binning and Heinrich Rohrer, who subsequently won the Nobel Prize in Physics for their work. STM uses an ultrasharp metal tip that is brought to within about 1 nm of the surface. A small voltage is applied to the tip, which produces current flow between the surface and the tip. This tunneling* current is strongly dependent on the distance of the tip from the surface. A feedback circuit, which senses the current flow, keeps the tip at a constant distance from the surface. The tip can also be used to move atoms around on the surface, as illustrated by the elliptical arrangement of cobalt atoms shown in Fig. 2.4.

AFM is similar in many ways to STM. In AFM, the attractive and repulsive forces acting on a tiny arm near the surface are measured, and a relief map is produced from the results.

Recently, IBM researcher Leo Gross and his coworkers have found that the image produced by AFM can be greatly improved by inserting a carbon monoxide (CO) molecule at the end of the gold AFM tip. This technique enables the AFM probe to produce a detailed image of an entire molecule such as pentacene ($C_{22}H_{14}$) as depicted in Figure 2.5.

*The term *tunneling* refers to the ability of electrons from the surface to escape even though they do not apparently possess enough energy to overcome the large potential energy holding them there. This quantum mechanical phenomenon is known as tunneling (the electron "tunnels through" the potential barrier).

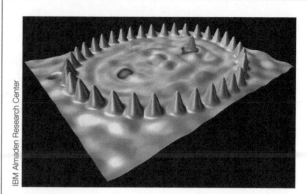

IBM Almaden Research Center

Figure 2.4
Image of a ring of cobalt atoms placed on a copper surface.

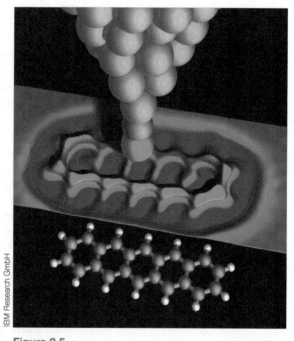

IBM Research GmbH

Figure 2.5
Top, A depiction of the EMF tip in which a CO ⬤⬤ molecule has been added to the tip (consisting of gold atoms). The image of the pentacene molecule is shown in blue, green, and red.
Bottom, A ball and stick model of the pentacene ($C_{22}H_{14}$) molecule (carbon atoms are black, hydrogen atoms are white)

Table 2.1

Relative Mass Data for Several Gases Containing Carbon

Compound	Relative Molecular Mass	Percent Carbon (by Mass)	Relative Mass of Carbon Present
Methane	16	75	12
Ethane	30	80	24
Propane	44	82	36
Butane	58	83	48
Carbon dioxide	44	27	12

EXAMPLE 2.1

The first four compounds listed in Table 2.1 contain only carbon and hydrogen. Predict the formulas for these compounds.

Solution Since the compounds contain only carbon and hydrogen, the percent hydrogen in each compound (by mass) is $100 - \%$ carbon. We can then find the relative mass of hydrogen present as follows:

$$\text{Relative mass of hydrogen} = \frac{\text{percent hydrogen}}{100} \times \text{relative molecular mass}$$

In tabular form the results are as follows:

Compound	Relative Molecular Mass	Percent Hydrogen	Relative Mass of Hydrogen
Methane	16	25	4
Ethane	30	20	6
Propane	44	18	8
Butane	58	17	10

Combining the preceding results with those from Table 2.1, we find that methane contains relative masses of carbon and hydrogen of 12 and 4, respectively. Using the relative atomic mass values of 12 and 1 for carbon and hydrogen gives a formula of CH_4 for methane. Similarly, the relative masses of carbon and hydrogen in ethane of 24 and 6, respectively, lead to a formula of C_2H_6 for ethane. Similar reasoning gives formulas for propane and butane of C_3H_8 and C_4H_{10}, respectively.

Cannizzaro's work was so convincing because he collected data on so many compounds. Although he couldn't absolutely prove that his atomic mass values were correct (because he had no way to verify absolutely the formulas of the compounds), the consistency of the large quantity of data he had collected eventually convinced virtually everyone that his interpretation made sense and that the relative values of atomic mass that he had determined were correct. The confusion was finally over. Chemistry had the universal (relative) mass standards that it needed.

It is worthwhile to note that Cannizzaro's work led to *approximate* values of the relative atomic masses. His goal was not to determine highly precise values for atomic masses but rather to pin down the approximate values (for example, to show that oxygen's relative mass was 16 rather than 8). The most precise values for atomic masses were determined by quantitative experiments

Stanislao Cannizzaro (1826–1910). Cannizzaro's work ended the confusion of atomic mass values.

in which the combining masses of elements were carefully measured, such as in the work of Berzelius.

In the next chapter we will have much more to say about atomic masses, including the origin of the very precise values used by today's chemists.

2.5 | Early Experiments to Characterize the Atom

On the basis of the work of Dalton, Gay-Lussac, Avogadro, Cannizzaro, and others, chemistry was beginning to make sense. The concept of atoms was clearly a good idea. Inevitably, scientists began to wonder about the nature of the atom. What is an atom made of, and how do the atoms of the various elements differ?

The Electron

The first important experiments that led to an understanding of the composition of the atom were done by the English physicist J. J. Thomson (1856–1940), who studied electrical discharges in partially evacuated tubes called *cathode-ray tubes* (Fig. 2.6) during the period from 1898 to 1903. Thomson found that when high voltage was applied to the tube, a "ray" he called a **cathode ray** (because it emanated from the negative electrode, or cathode) was produced. Because this ray was produced at the negative electrode and was repelled by the negative pole of an applied electric field (Fig. 2.7), Thomson postulated that the ray was a stream of negatively charged particles, now called **electrons.** From experiments in which he measured the deflection of the beam of electrons in a magnetic field, Thomson determined the *charge-to-mass ratio* of an electron:

$$\frac{e}{m} = -1.76 \times 10^8 \text{ C/g}$$

where *e* represents the charge on the electron in coulombs and *m* represents the electron mass in grams.

One of Thomson's primary goals in his cathode-ray tube experiments was to gain an understanding of the structure of the atom. He reasoned that since electrons could be produced from electrodes made of various types of metals, *all* atoms must contain electrons. Since atoms were known to be electrically neutral, Thomson further assumed that atoms also must contain some positive charge. Thomson postulated that an atom consisted of a diffuse cloud of positive charge with the negative electrons embedded randomly in it. This model,

Figure 2.6
A cathode-ray tube. The fast-moving electrons excite the gas in the tube, causing a glow between the electrodes. The green color in the photo is due to the response of the screen (coated with zinc sulfide) to the electron beam.

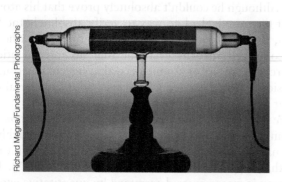

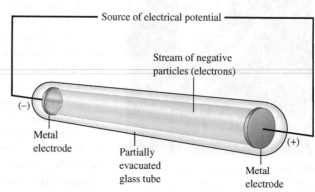

Source of electrical potential

Stream of negative particles (electrons)

(−)

Metal electrode

Partially evacuated glass tube

Metal electrode

(+)

Figure 2.7
Deflection of cathode rays by an applied electric field.

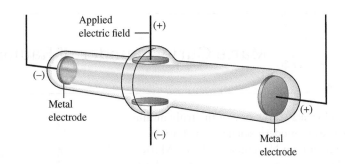

Applied electric field

(+)

(−)

Metal electrode

(−)

Metal electrode

(+)

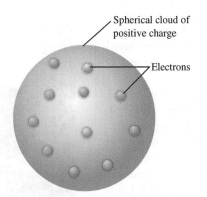

Spherical cloud of positive charge

Electrons

Figure 2.8
Thomson's plum pudding model.

C. Byatt-norman/ Shutterstock.com #19116133

A classic English plum pudding.

shown in Fig. 2.8, is often called the *plum pudding model* because the electrons are like raisins dispersed in a pudding (the positive-charge cloud), as in plum pudding, a favorite English dessert.*

In 1909 Robert Millikan (1868–1953), working at the University of Chicago, performed very clever experiments involving charged oil drops. These experiments allowed him to determine the magnitude of the electron charge (Fig. 2.9). With this value and the charge-to-mass ratio determined by Thomson, Millikan was able to calculate the mass of the electron as 9.11×10^{-31} kilogram.

Bettmann/Corbis #BE042343

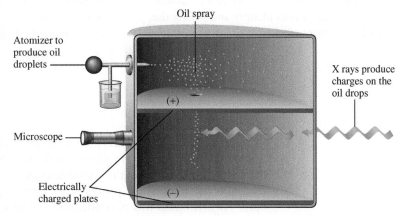

Oil spray

Atomizer to produce oil droplets

X rays produce charges on the oil drops

Microscope

(+)

Electrically charged plates

(−)

Figure 2.9
A schematic representation of the apparatus Millikan used to determine the charge on the electron. The fall of charged oil droplets due to gravity can be halted by adjusting the voltage across the two plates. The voltage and the mass of an oil drop can then be used to calculate the charge on the oil drop. Millikan's experiments showed that the charge on an oil drop is always a whole-number multiple of the electron charge.

*Although J. J. Thomson is generally given credit for this model, the idea was apparently first suggested by the English mathematician and physicist William Thomson (better known as Lord Kelvin and not related to J. J. Thomson).

Marie Curie: Founder of Radioactivity

Marie Sklodowska Curie, one of the truly monumental figures of modern science, was born in Warsaw, Poland, on November 7, 1867. Marie developed an early interest in chemistry, and it is interesting that Dmitri Mendeleev, creator of the periodic table and friend of Marie's father (a high school mathematics and physics teacher), predicted great success for the young woman when he met her in Warsaw.

To escape political persecution in Poland by the Russians, Marie emigrated in 1891 at the age of 24 to Paris, where she decided to pursue a degree in science at the Sorbonne Institute. While studying there, Marie met Pierre Curie, a well-respected physicist who, among other things, had studied the temperature dependence of magnetism, which led to the formulation of Curie's law. Marie and Pierre were married in 1895, after which Marie decided to pursue a doctorate in physics. As the subject of her doctoral thesis, she decided to study the strange radiation emitted by uranium ore, which had been accidentally discovered by Henri Becquerel. Marie was recruited for the task by Becquerel himself. As she began her studies, Madame Curie noticed that pitchblende produced more radiation than uranium, and she became convinced that an as-yet-unknown element in pitchblende was responsible for this "radioactivity"—a term that she coined.

The next step was to identify and isolate the radioactive element or elements in pitchblende.

Marie Sklodowska Curie (1867–1934) in her laboratory.

Bettmann/Corbis

Pierre interrupted his own research—he thought it would be for just a few weeks—to collaborate with his wife on the project. The Curies actually bor-

Radioactivity

In the late nineteenth century, scientists discovered that certain elements produce high-energy radiation. For example, in 1896 the French scientist Antoine Henri Becquerel accidentally found that the image of a piece of mineral containing uranium could be produced on a photographic plate in the absence of light. He attributed this phenomenon to a spontaneous emission of radiation by the uranium, which his student, Marie Curie, called **radioactivity.** Studies in the early twentieth century demonstrated three types of radioactive emission: gamma (γ) rays, beta (β) particles, and alpha (α) particles. A γ ray is high-energy "light"; a β particle is a high-speed electron; and an α particle has a 2+ charge—that is, a charge twice that of the electron and with the opposite sign. The mass of an α particle is 7300 times that of an electron.

rowed money to support themselves and convinced the Austrian government to send them 1 ton of pitchblende from the mines at Joachimsthal. After receiving this 5 cubic foot pile of "sand" from Austria, the Curies worked to chemically digest the ore. In this process they worked with batches as large as 40 pounds at a time in an improvised laboratory with a leaky roof. Working through the bitter winter of 1896 and all through 1897 (in which they had their first daughter, Iréne, who also became a prominent scientist), in July 1898 the Curies finally isolated a previously unknown element they named polonium after Marie's homeland. Although most people would be satisfied by discovering a new element 400 times more radioactive than uranium, the Curies kept working. By this time, the 1 ton of pitchblende had been concentrated to an amount that would fit into an ordinary flask. Marie continued to extract and crystallize increasingly smaller amounts of material. Finally, in November 1898 she obtained crystals of the salt of another new element that the Curies named radium, which turned out to be 900 times more radioactive than uranium.

For their work the Curies were awarded the Nobel Prize in Physics in 1903, sharing the award with Henri Becquerel. In 1904, Pierre was awarded a chair in physics at the Sorbonne. He was killed tragically on the streets of Paris on April 19, 1906, when he was knocked down by a cab and the wheels of a heavy van passing in the opposite direction ran over his head. After mourning for just a few weeks, Marie Curie decided to proceed with the research on radium. In an unprecedented action, she was awarded her late husband's chair and became the first woman to teach at the Sorbonne.

Marie Curie worked tirelessly to develop radioactivity as a new discipline in physics. With the help of five assistants, she studied the effects of radioactivity and developed the atomic theory of its origin. In 1911, Marie was awarded her second Nobel Prize, this time in chemistry, for the chemical processes discovered in the identification of radium and polonium and for the subsequent characterization of those elements. During World War I, she trained doctors in the new methods of radiology and, after learning to drive, personally transported medical equipment to hospitals. After the war, Madame Curie assumed leadership of the newly built Radium Institute in Paris. In 1920, a campaign was mounted in the United States to produce 1 gram of radium for Marie to support her research. She traveled to the United States to receive the precious vial of radium at the White House in 1921.

Marie Curie continued her studies of radioactivity until just before her death of leukemia in 1934. She was truly one of the greatest scientists of the twentieth century.

The Nuclear Atom

In 1911 Ernest Rutherford (Fig. 2.10), who performed many of the pioneering experiments to explore radioactivity, carried out an experiment to test Thomson's plum pudding model. The experiment involved directing α particles at a thin sheet of metal foil, as illustrated in Fig. 2.11. Rutherford reasoned that if Thomson's model were accurate, the massive α particles should crash through the thin foil like cannonballs through gauze, as shown in Fig. 2.12(a). He expected the α particles to travel through the foil with, at the most, very minor deflections in their paths. The results of the experiment were very different from those Rutherford anticipated. Although most of the α particles passed straight through, many of the particles were deflected at large angles, as shown in Fig. 2.12(b), and some were reflected, never hitting the detector. This

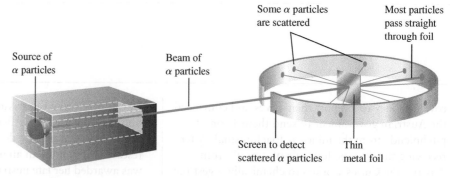

Figure 2.11

Rutherford's experiment on α-particle bombardment of metal foil. (Gold foil was used in the original experiments because it can be hammered into extremely thin sheets.)

Figure 2.10

Ernest Rutherford (1871–1937) was born on a farm in New Zealand. In 1895 he placed second in a scholarship competition to attend Cambridge University but was awarded the scholarship when the winner decided to stay home and get married. As a scientist in England, Rutherford did much of the early work on characterizing radioactivity. He named the α and β particles and the γ ray and coined the term *half-life* to describe an important attribute of radioactive elements. His experiments on the behavior of α particles striking thin metal foils led him to postulate the nuclear atom. He also invented the name *proton* for the nucleus of the hydrogen atom. He received the Nobel Prize in Chemistry in 1908.

outcome was a great surprise to Rutherford. (He wrote that this result was comparable to shooting a howitzer at a piece of paper and having the shell reflected back.)

Rutherford knew from these results that the plum pudding model for the atom could not be correct. The large deflections of the α particles could be caused only by a center of concentrated positive charge that contains most of the atom's mass, as illustrated in Fig. 2.12(b). Most of the α particles pass directly through the foil because the atom is mostly open space. The deflected α particles are those that had a "close encounter" with the massive positive center of the atom, and the few reflected α particles are those that made a "direct hit" on the much more massive positive center.

In Rutherford's mind these results could be explained only in terms of a **nuclear atom**—an atom with a dense center of positive charge (the **nucleus**) and electrons moving around the nucleus at a distance that is large relative to the nuclear radius.

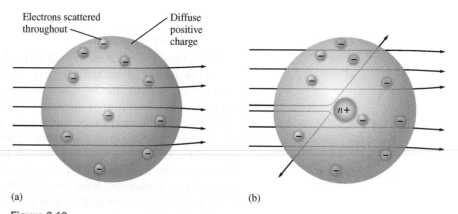

Figure 2.12

(a) The expected results of the metal foil experiment if Thomson's model were correct.
(b) Actual results.

2.6 | The Modern View of Atomic Structure: An Introduction

In the years since Thomson and Rutherford, a great deal has been learned about atomic structure. Because much of this material will be covered in detail in later chapters, only an introduction will be given here. The simplest view of the atom is that it consists of a tiny nucleus with a diameter of about 10^{-13} cm and electrons that move about the nucleus at an average distance of about 10^{-8} cm away from it (Fig. 2.13).

As we will see later, the chemistry of an atom mainly results from its electrons. For this reason chemists can be satisfied with a relatively crude nuclear model. The nucleus is assumed to contain **protons,** which have a positive charge equal in magnitude to the electron's negative charge, and **neutrons,** which have virtually the same mass as a proton but no charge. The masses and charges of the electron, proton, and neutron are shown in Table 2.2.

Two striking things about the nucleus are its small size, compared with the overall size of the atom, and its extremely high density. The tiny nucleus accounts for almost all of the atom's mass. Its great density is dramatically demonstrated by the fact that a piece of nuclear material about the size of a pea would have a mass of 250 million tons!

As with any theory in science, although it provides answers to questions, it also brings about more questions. An important question to consider at this point is, *"If all atoms are composed of these same components, why do different atoms have different chemical properties?"* The answer to this question lies in the number and the arrangement of the electrons. The electrons constitute most of the atomic volume and thus are the parts that "intermingle" when atoms combine to form molecules. Therefore, the number of electrons possessed by a given atom greatly affects its ability to interact with other atoms. As a result, the atoms of different elements, which have different numbers of protons and electrons, show different chemical behavior.

A sodium atom has 11 protons in its nucleus. Since atoms have no net charge, the number of electrons must equal the number of protons. Therefore, a sodium atom has 11 electrons moving around its nucleus. It is *always* true that a sodium atom has 11 protons and 11 electrons. However, each sodium atom also has neutrons in its nucleus, and different types of sodium atoms exist that have different numbers of neutrons. For example, consider the sodium atoms represented in Fig. 2.14. These two atoms are **isotopes,** or *atoms with*

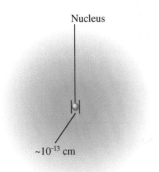

Nucleus

~10^{-13} cm

~10^{-8} cm

Figure 2.13
A nuclear atom viewed in cross section.

The *chemistry* of an atom arises from its electrons.

Table 2.2

The Mass and Charge of the Electron, Proton, and Neutron

Particle	Mass	Charge*
Electron	9.11×10^{-31} kg	1−
Proton	1.67×10^{-27} kg	1+
Neutron	1.67×10^{-27} kg	None

*The magnitude of the charge of the electron and the proton is 1.60×10^{-19} C.

Figure 2.14
Two isotopes of sodium. Both have 11 protons and 11 electrons, but they differ in the number of neutrons in their nuclei. Sodium-23 is the only naturally occurring form of sodium. Sodium-24 does not occur naturally but can be made artificially.

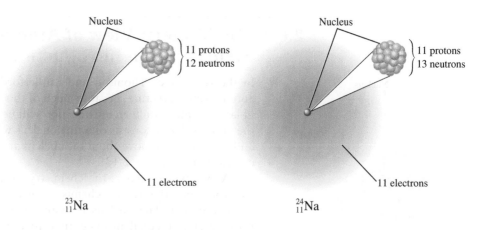

the same number of protons but different numbers of neutrons. Note that the symbol for one particular type of sodium atom is written

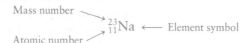

where the **atomic number,** Z (number of protons), is written as a subscript and the **mass number,** A (the total number of protons and neutrons), is written as a superscript. (The particular atom represented here is called "sodium-23." It has 11 electrons, 11 protons, and 12 neutrons.) Because the chemistry of an atom arises from its electrons, isotopes show almost identical chemical properties. In nature most elements contain a mixture of isotopes.

2.7 | Molecules and Ions

From a chemist's viewpoint, the most interesting characteristic of an atom is its ability to combine with other atoms to form compounds. It was John Dalton who first recognized that chemical compounds were collections of atoms, but he could not determine the structure of atoms or their means for binding to one another. During the twentieth century, scientists have learned that atoms have electrons and that these electrons participate in the bonding of one atom to another. We will discuss bonding thoroughly in Chapters 13 and 14; here we will consider some definitions that will be useful in the next few chapters.

The forces that hold atoms together in compounds are called **chemical bonds.** One way that atoms can form bonds is by *sharing electrons.* These bonds are called **covalent bonds,** and the resulting collection of atoms is called a **molecule.** Molecules can be represented in several different ways. The simplest method is the **chemical formula,** in which the symbols for the elements are used to indicate the types of atoms present and subscripts are used to indicate the relative numbers of atoms. For example, the formula for carbon dioxide is CO_2, meaning, of course, that each molecule contains 1 atom of carbon and 2 atoms of oxygen.

Familiar examples of molecules that contain covalent bonds are hydrogen (H_2), water (H_2O), oxygen (O_2), ammonia (NH_3), and methane (CH_4). More information about a molecule is given by its **structural formula,** in which the individual bonds are shown (indicated by lines). Structural formulas may or may not indicate the actual shape of the molecule. For example, water might be represented as

$$\text{H—O—H} \quad \text{or} \quad \overset{\text{O}}{\underset{\text{H} \qquad \text{H}}{}}$$

The structure on the right shows the actual shape of the water molecule, based on experimental evidence. Other examples of structural formulas are

Ammonia

Methane

In the actual structures on the right, the central atom and the solid lines are understood to be in the plane of the page. Atoms connected to the central atom by dashed lines are behind the plane of the page, and atoms connected to the central atom by wedges are in front of the plane of the page.

In a compound composed of molecules, the individual molecules move around as independent units. For example, a methane molecule is represented in Fig. 2.15 using a **space-filling model.** These models show the relative sizes of the atoms, as well as their relative orientation in the molecule. Figure 2.16 shows other examples. **Ball-and-stick models** are also used to represent molecules. The ball-and-stick model of methane is shown in Fig. 2.17.

A second type of chemical bonding results from attractions among ions. An **ion** is an atom or group of atoms that has a net positive or negative charge. The best-known ionic compound is common table salt, or sodium chloride, which forms when neutral chlorine and sodium react.

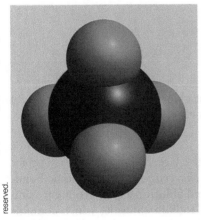

Figure 2.15
Space-filling model of the methane molecule. This type of model shows both the relative sizes of the atoms in the molecule and their spatial relationships.

Figure 2.16
Space-filling models of various molecules.

Figure 2.17
Ball-and-stick model of methane.

To see how ions are formed, consider what happens when an electron is transferred from sodium to chlorine (the neutrons in the nuclei will be ignored):

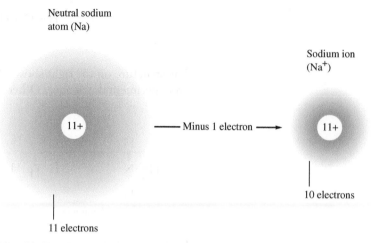

With one electron stripped off, the sodium with its 11 protons and only 10 electrons has become a *positive ion* with a net 1+ charge. A positive ion is called a **cation.** The process can be represented in shorthand form as

$$Na \longrightarrow Na^+ + e^-$$

If an electron is added to chlorine,

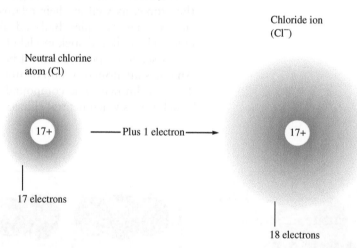

the 18 electrons produce a net 1− charge; the chlorine has become an *ion with a negative charge*—an **anion.** This process is represented as

$$Cl + e^- \longrightarrow Cl^-$$

Because anions and cations have opposite charges, they attract each other. This *force of attraction between oppositely charged ions* is called **ionic bonding.** As shown in Fig. 2.19, sodium metal and chlorine gas (a green gas composed of Cl_2 molecules) react to form solid sodium chloride, which contains many Na^+ and Cl^- ions packed together. The solid forms beautiful, colorless cubic crystals.

A solid consisting of oppositely charged ions is called an *ionic solid,* or (often) a *salt.* Ionic solids can consist of simple ions, as in sodium chloride, or of **polyatomic** (many-atom) **ions,** as in ammonium nitrate (NH_4NO_3), which contains ammonium cations (NH_4^+) and nitrate anions (NO_3^-). The ball-and-stick models of these ions are shown in Fig. 2.18.

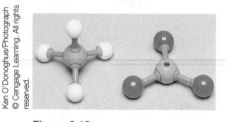

Figure 2.18
Ball-and-stick models of the ammonium ion (NH_4^+) and the nitrate ion (NO_3^-).

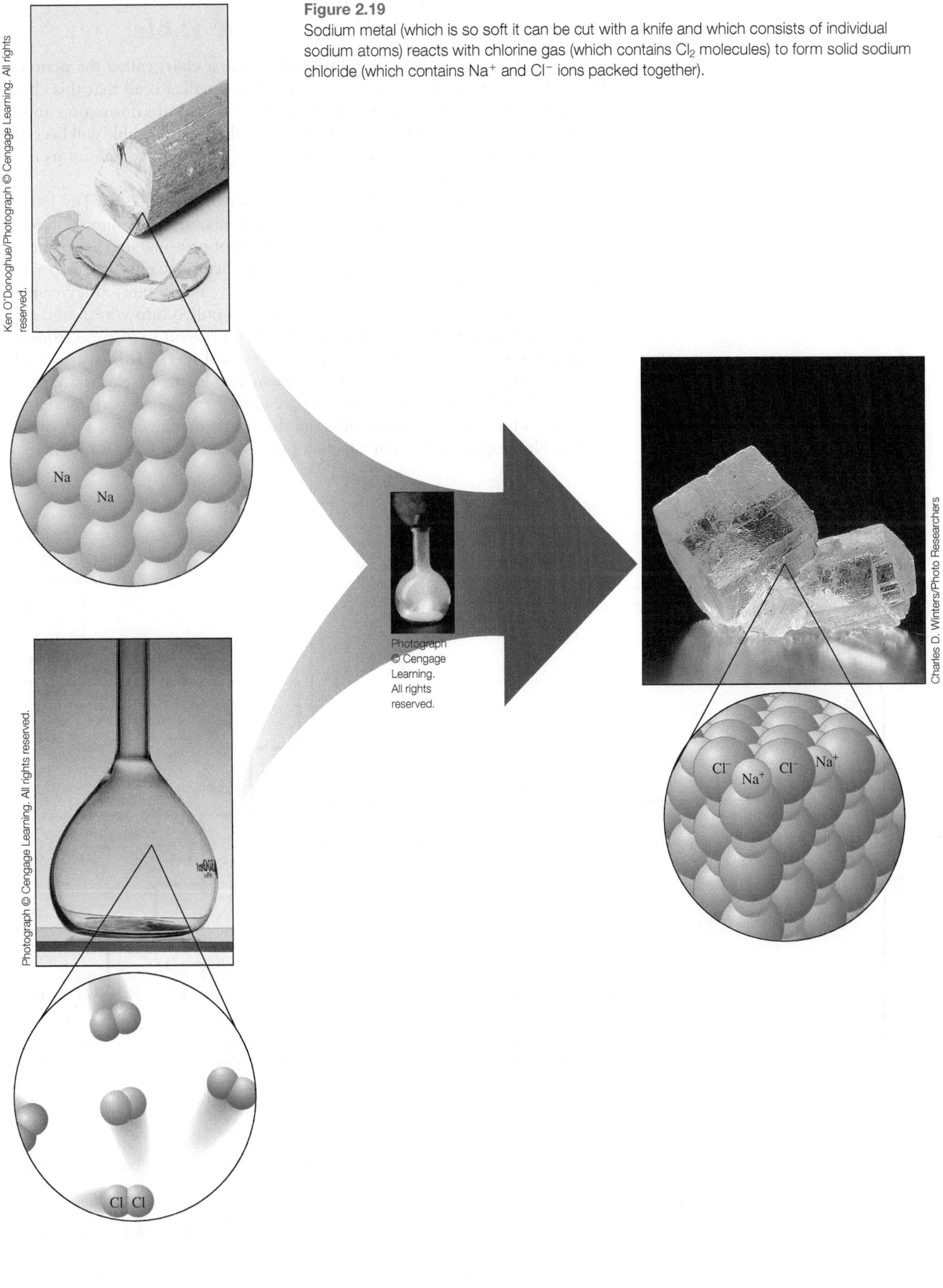

Figure 2.19
Sodium metal (which is so soft it can be cut with a knife and which consists of individual sodium atoms) reacts with chlorine gas (which contains Cl_2 molecules) to form solid sodium chloride (which contains Na^+ and Cl^- ions packed together).

2.8 | An Introduction to the Periodic Table

In a room where chemistry is taught or practiced, a chart called the **periodic table** is almost certain to be found hanging on the wall. Recall that this chart shows all the known elements and provides a good deal of information about each. As your knowledge of chemistry increases, the periodic table will become more and more useful to you. In this section we will remind you about its fundamental aspects.

A simple version of the periodic table is shown in Fig. 2.20. The letters given in the boxes are the symbols for the elements, and the number shown above each symbol is the atomic number (number of protons) for that element. Most of the elements are **metals**. Metals have characteristic physical properties such as efficient conduction of heat and electricity, malleability (they can be hammered into thin sheets), ductility (they can be pulled into wires), and (often) a lustrous appearance. Chemically, metal atoms tend to *lose* electrons to form positive ions. For example, copper is a typical metal. It is lustrous (although it tarnishes readily); it is an excellent conductor of electricity (it is widely used in electrical wires); and it is readily formed into various shapes such as pipes for water systems. Copper is also found in many salts, such as the beautiful blue copper sulfate, in which copper is present as Cu^{2+} ions. Copper

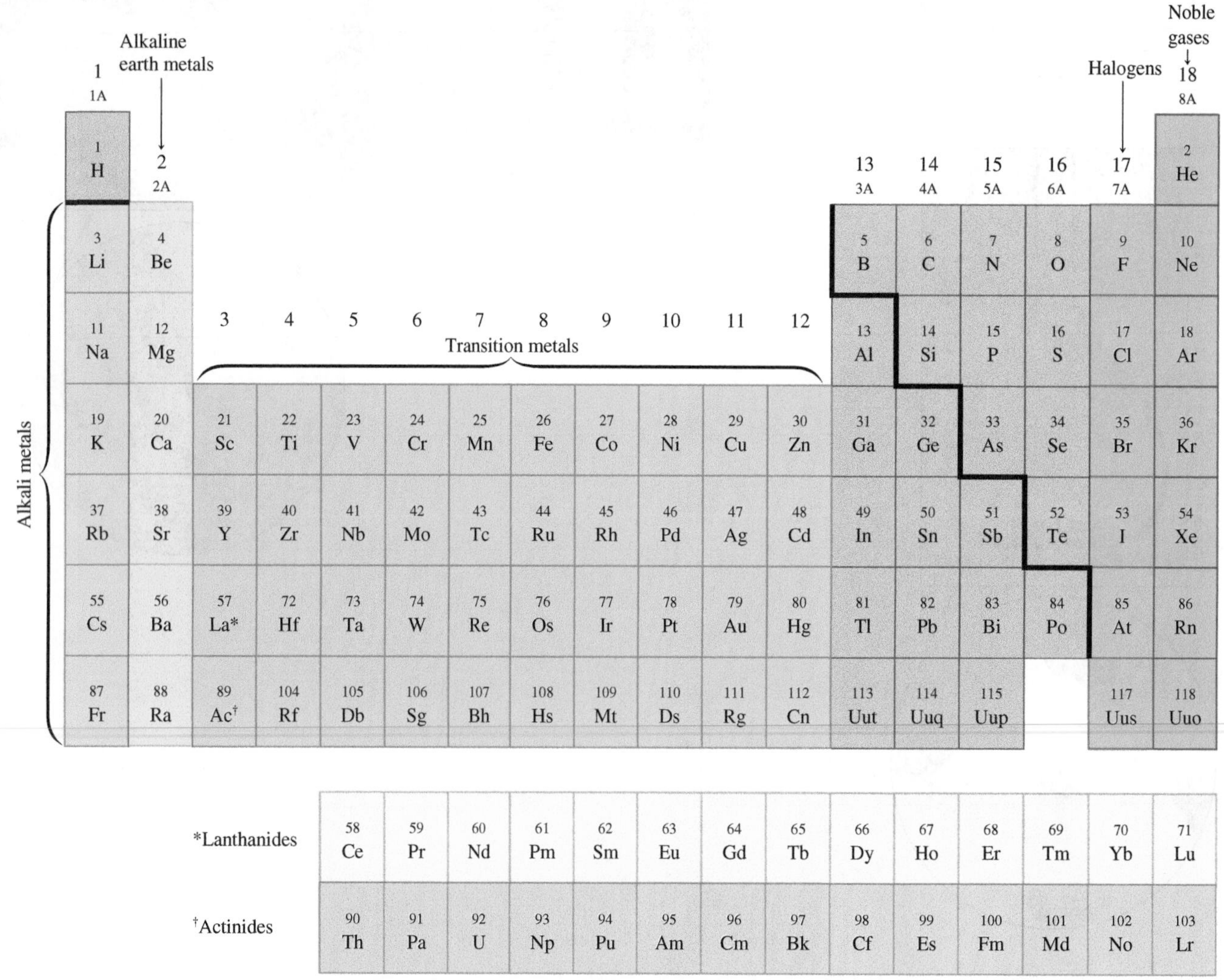

Figure 2.20

The periodic table continues to expand as new elements are synthesized in particle accelerators.

Samples of the alkali metals lithium, sodium, and potassium.

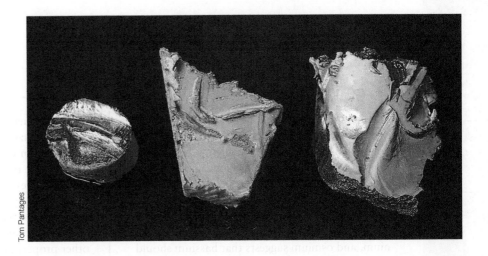

is a member of the transition metals—the metals shown in the center of the periodic table.

The relatively few **nonmetals** appear in the upper right-hand corner of the table (to the right of the heavy line in Fig. 2.20), except hydrogen, a nonmetal that is grouped with the metals. The nonmetals typically lack the physical properties that characterize the metals. Chemically, they tend to *gain* electrons to form anions in reactions with metals. Nonmetals often bond to each other by forming covalent bonds. For example, chlorine is a typical nonmetal. Under normal conditions, it exists as Cl_2 molecules; it reacts with metals to form salts containing Cl^- ions (NaCl, for example); and it forms covalent bonds with nonmetals (for example, hydrogen chloride gas, or HCl).

The periodic table is arranged so that elements in the same vertical columns (called **groups** or **families**) have *similar chemical properties*. For example, all of the **alkali metals,** members of Group 1A—lithium (Li), sodium (Na), potassium (K), rubidium (Rb), cesium (Cs), and francium (Fr)—are very active elements that readily form ions with a 1+ charge when they react with non-metals. The members of Group 2A—beryllium (Be), magnesium (Mg), calcium (Ca), strontium (Sr), barium (Ba), and radium (Ra)—are called the **alkaline earth metals.** They all form ions with a 2+ charge when they react with non-metals. The **halogens,** the members of Group 7A—fluorine (F), chlorine (Cl), bromine (Br), iodine (I), and astatine (At)—all form diatomic molecules. Fluorine, chlorine, bromine, and iodine all react with metals to form salts containing ions with a 1− charge (F^-, Cl^-, Br^-, and I^-). The members of Group 8A—helium (He), neon (Ne), argon (Ar), krypton (Kr), xenon (Xe), and radon (Rn)—are known as the **noble gases.** They all exist under normal conditions as monatomic (single-atom) gases and have little chemical reactivity.

Metals tend to form positive ions; nonmetals tend to form negative ions.

The horizontal rows of elements in the periodic table are called **periods.** Horizontal row one is called the first period (it contains H and He), row two is called the second period (elements Li through Ne), and so on.

We will learn much more about the periodic table as we continue with our study of chemistry. Meanwhile, when an element is introduced in this text, you should always note its position on the periodic table.

Three members of the halogen family: chlorine, bromine, and iodine.

2.9 | Naming Simple Compounds

When chemistry was an infant science, there was no system for naming compounds. Names such as sugar of lead, blue vitriol, quicklime, Epsom salts, milk of magnesia, gypsum, and laughing gas were coined by early chemists. Such names are called *common names*. As chemistry grew, it became clear that using

Chemical Insights Hassium Fits Right In

Hassium, element 108, does not exist in nature but must be made in a particle accelerator. It was first created in 1984 and can be made by shooting magnesium-26 ($^{26}_{12}$Mg) atoms at curium-248 ($^{248}_{96}$Cm) atoms. The collisions between these atoms produce some hassium-265 ($^{265}_{108}$Hs) atoms. The position of hassium in the periodic table (see Fig. 2.20) in the vertical column containing iron, ruthenium, and osmium suggests that hassium should have chemical properties similar to these metals. However, it is not easy to test this prediction— only a few atoms of hassium can be made at a given time and they last for only about 9 seconds. Imagine having to get your next lab experiment done in 9 seconds!

Amazingly, a team of chemists from the Lawrence Berkeley National Laboratory in California,

the Paul Scherrer Institute and the University of Bern in Switzerland, and the Institute of Nuclear Chemistry in Germany have done experiments to characterize the chemical behavior of hassium. For example, they have observed that hassium atoms react with oxygen to form a hassium oxide compound of the type expected from its position on the periodic table. The team has also measured other properties of hassium, including the energy released as it undergoes nuclear decay to another atom.

This work would have surely pleased Dmitri Mendeleev, who originally developed the periodic table and showed its power to predict chemical properties.

common names for compounds would lead to unacceptable chaos. More than 4 million chemical compounds are currently known. Memorizing common names for these compounds would be an impossible task.

The solution, of course, is to adopt a *system* for naming compounds in which the name tells something about the composition of the compound. After learning the system, a chemist given a formula should be able to name the compound, or given a name should be able to construct the compound's formula. In this section we will specify the most important rules for naming compounds other than organic compounds (those based on chains of carbon atoms).

We will begin with the systems for naming inorganic **binary compounds**— compounds composed of two elements—which we classify into various types for easier recognition. We will consider both ionic and covalent compounds.

The systematic naming of organic compounds will be discussed in Chapter 21.

Binary Compounds (Type I; Ionic)

Binary ionic compounds contain a positive ion (cation), always written first in the formula, and a negative ion (anion). In the naming of these compounds, the following rules apply:

1. The cation is always named first and the anion second.

2. A monatomic (meaning from one atom) cation takes its name from the name of the element. For example, Na^+ is called sodium in the names of compounds containing this ion.

A monatomic cation has the same name as its parent element.

3. A monatomic anion is named by taking the first part of the element name and adding *-ide*. Thus the Cl^- ion is called chloride.

Some common monatomic cations and anions and their names are given in Table 2.3.

Table 2.3

Common Monatomic Cations and Anions

Cation	Name	Anion	Name
H^+	Hydrogen	H^-	Hydride
Li^+	Lithium	F^-	Fluoride
Na^+	Sodium	Cl^-	Chloride
K^+	Potassium	Br^-	Bromide
Cs^+	Cesium	I^-	Iodide
Be^{2+}	Beryllium	O^{2-}	Oxide
Mg^{2+}	Magnesium	S^{2-}	Sulfide
Ca^{2+}	Calcium	N^{3-}	Nitride
Ba^{2+}	Barium	P^{3-}	Phosphide
Al^{3+}	Aluminum		
Ag^+	Silver		
Zn^{2+}	Zinc		

In formulas of ionic compounds, simple ions are represented by the element symbol: Cl means Cl^-, Na means Na^+, and so on.

A Type I binary ionic compound contains a metal that forms only one type of cation. The rules for naming Type I compounds are illustrated by the following examples:

Compound	Ions Present	Name
NaCl	Na^+, Cl^-	Sodium chloride
KI	K^+, I^-	Potassium iodide
CaS	Ca^{2+}, S^{2-}	Calcium sulfide
Li_3N	Li^+, N^{3-}	Lithium nitride
CsBr	Cs^+, Br^-	Cesium bromide
MgO	Mg^{2+}, O^{2-}	Magnesium oxide

Binary Compounds (Type II; Ionic)

Type II binary ionic compounds contain a metal that can form more than one type of cation.

In the ionic compounds considered previously (Type I), the metal involved forms only a single type of cation. That is, sodium forms only Na^+, calcium forms only Ca^{2+}, and so on. However, as we will see in more detail later in the text, many metals can form more than one type of positive ion and thus form more than one type of ionic compound with a given anion. For example, the compound $FeCl_2$ contains Fe^{2+} ions, and the compound $FeCl_3$ contains Fe^{3+} ions. In cases such as these, the *charge on the metal ion must be specified*. The systematic names for these two iron compounds are iron(II) chloride and iron(III) chloride, respectively, where the *Roman numeral indicates the charge of the cation*.

A compound containing a metal that forms multiple cations must have a Roman numeral in its name.

Another system for naming these ionic compounds that is seen in the older literature was used for metals that form only two ions. *The ion with the higher charge has a name ending in -ic, and the one with the lower charge has a name ending in -ous.* In this system, for example, Fe^{3+} is called the ferric ion, and Fe^{2+} is called the ferrous ion. The names for $FeCl_3$ and $FeCl_2$ are then ferric chloride and ferrous chloride, respectively.

Table 2.4 gives both names for many common Type II cations. The system that uses Roman numerals will be used exclusively in this text.

Note that the use of a Roman numeral in a systematic name is required only in cases in which more than one ionic compound forms between a given pair of elements. This case most commonly occurs for compounds containing transition metals, which often form more than one cation. *Elements that form only one cation do not need to be identified by a Roman numeral.* Common metals that do not require Roman numerals are the Group 1A elements, which form only 1+ ions; the Group 2A elements, which form only 2+ ions; and

Table 2.4

Common Type II Cations

Ion	Systematic Name	Alternate Name
Fe^{3+}	Iron(III)	Ferric
Fe^{2+}	Iron(II)	Ferrous
Cu^{2+}	Copper(II)	Cupric
Cu^+	Copper(I)	Cuprous
Co^{3+}	Cobalt(III)	Cobaltic
Co^{2+}	Cobalt(II)	Cobaltous
Sn^{4+}	Tin(IV)	Stannic
Sn^{2+}	Tin(II)	Stannous
Pb^{4+}	Lead(IV)	Plumbic
Pb^{2+}	Lead(II)	Plumbous
Hg^{2+}	Mercury(II)	Mercuric
Hg_2^{2+}*	Mercury(I)	Mercurous

*Note that mercury(I) ions always occur bound together to form Hg_2^{2+}.

(top) Copper(I) chloride.
(bottom) Copper(II) chloride.

aluminum, which forms only Al^{3+}. Common transition metals that do not require a Roman numeral (because they form only one ion) are zinc (Zn^{2+}) and silver (Ag^+).

When a metal ion that forms more than one type of cation is present, the charge on the metal ion must be determined by balancing the positive and negative charges of the compound. To make this determination, you must be able to recognize the common cations and anions and know their charges (see Tables 2.3 and 2.5).

The following flowchart is useful when you are naming binary ionic compounds:

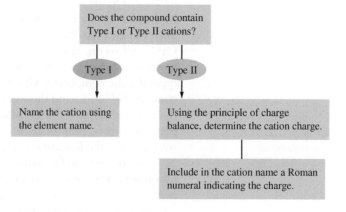

Various chromium compounds dissolved in water. From left to right: $CrCl_2$, $K_2Cr_2O_7$, $Cr(NO_3)_3$, $CrCl_3$, K_2CrO_4.

EXAMPLE 2.2

Give the systematic name of each of the following compounds.

a. $CoBr_2$ **b.** $CaCl_2$ **c.** Al_2O_3 **d.** $CrCl_3$

Solution

Compound	Name	Comment
a. $CoBr_2$	Cobalt(II) bromide	Cobalt is a transition metal that requires a Roman numeral. The two Br^- ions must be balanced by a Co^{2+} cation.

b. $CaCl_2$	Calcium chloride	Calcium, an alkaline earth metal, forms only the Ca^{2+} ion. A Roman numeral is not necessary.	
c. Al_2O_3	Aluminum oxide	Aluminum forms only Al^{3+}. A Roman numeral is not necessary.	
d. $CrCl_3$	Chromium(III) chloride	Chromium is a transition metal that must have a Roman numeral. $CrCl_3$ contains Cr^{3+}.	

Ionic Compounds with Polyatomic Ions

Ionic compounds that contain polyatomic ions are not binary compounds.

We have not yet considered ionic compounds that contain polyatomic ions. For example, the compound ammonium nitrate (NH_4NO_3) contains the polyatomic ions NH_4^+ and NO_3^-. Polyatomic ions are assigned special names that *must be memorized* to name the compounds containing them. The most important polyatomic ions and their names are listed in Table 2.5.

Note in Table 2.5 that several series of anions contain an atom of a given element and different numbers of oxygen atoms. These anions are called **oxyanions**. When there are two members in such a series, the name of the one with the smaller number of oxygen atoms ends in *-ite*, and the name of the one with the larger number ends in *-ate*—for example, sulfite (SO_3^{2-}) and sulfate (SO_4^{2-}). When more than two oxyanions make up a series, *hypo-* (less than) and *per-* (more than) are used as prefixes to name the members of the series with the fewest and the most oxygen atoms, respectively. The best example involves the oxyanions containing chlorine, as shown in Table 2.5.

Binary Compounds
(Type III; Covalent—Contain Two Nonmetals)

In binary covalent compounds, the element names follow the same rules as those for binary ionic compounds.

Binary covalent compounds are formed between *two nonmetals*. Although these compounds do not contain ions, they are named very similarly to binary ionic compounds.

Table 2.5

Common Polyatomic Ions

Ion	Name	Ion	Name
NH_4^+	Ammonium	CO_3^{2-}	Carbonate
NO_2^-	Nitrite	HCO_3^-	Hydrogen carbonate (bicarbonate is a widely used common name)
NO_3^-	Nitrate		
SO_3^{2-}	Sulfite		
SO_4^{2-}	Sulfate	$C_2H_3O_2^-$	Acetate
HSO_4^-	Hydrogen sulfate (bisulfate is a widely used common name)	MnO_4^-	Permanganate
		$Cr_2O_7^{2-}$	Dichromate
		CrO_4^{2-}	Chromate
OH^-	Hydroxide	O_2^{2-}	Peroxide
CN^-	Cyanide		
PO_4^{3-}	Phosphate	ClO^-	Hypochlorite
HPO_4^{2-}	Hydrogen phosphate	ClO_2^-	Chlorite
$H_2PO_4^-$	Dihydrogen phosphate	ClO_3^-	Chlorate
		ClO_4^-	Perchlorate

Table 2.6

Prefixes Used to Indicate Number in Chemical Names

Prefix	Number Indicated
mono-	1
di-	2
tri-	3
tetra-	4
penta-	5
hexa-	6
hepta-	7
octa-	8

In the naming of binary covalent compounds, the following rules apply:

1. The first element in the formula is named first, using the full element name.
2. The second element is named as if it were an anion.
3. Prefixes are used to denote the numbers of atoms present. These prefixes are given in Table 2.6.
4. The prefix *mono-* is never used for naming the first element. For example, CO is called carbon monoxide, *not* monocarbon monoxide.

To see how these rules apply, we will now consider the names of the several covalent compounds formed by nitrogen and oxygen:

Compound	Systematic Name	Common Name
N_2O	Dinitrogen monoxide	Nitrous oxide
NO	Nitrogen monoxide	Nitric oxide
NO_2	Nitrogen dioxide	
N_2O_3	Dinitrogen trioxide	
N_2O_4	Dinitrogen tetroxide	
N_2O_5	Dinitrogen pentoxide	

Notice from the preceding examples that to avoid awkward pronunciations, we often drop the final *o* or *a* of the prefix when the element begins with a vowel. For example, N_2O_4 is called dinitrogen tetroxide, *not* dinitrogen tetra-oxide; and CO is called carbon monoxide, *not* carbon monooxide.

Some compounds are always referred to by their common names. The two best examples are water and ammonia. The systematic names for H_2O and NH_3 are never used.

The rules for naming binary compounds are summarized in Fig. 2.21. Notice that prefixes to indicate the number of atoms are used only in Type III binary compounds (those containing two nonmetals). An overall strategy for naming compounds is summarized in Fig. 2.22.

Figure 2.21
A flowchart for naming binary compounds.

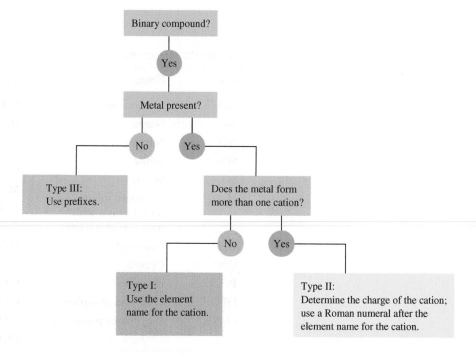

Figure 2.22
Overall strategy for naming chemical compounds.

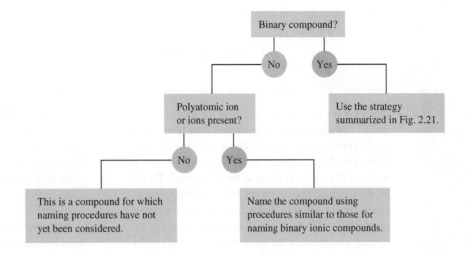

OWL INTERACTIVE EXAMPLE 2.3

Give the systematic name of each of the following compounds.

a. Na_2SO_4 **e.** Na_2SO_3 **i.** $NaOCl$
b. KH_2PO_4 **f.** Na_2CO_3 **j.** Na_2SeO_4
c. $Fe(NO_3)_3$ **g.** $NaHCO_3$ **k.** $KBrO_3$
d. $Mn(OH)_2$ **h.** $CsClO_4$

Solution

Compound	Name	Comment
a. Na_2SO_4	Sodium sulfate	
b. KH_2PO_4	Potassium dihydrogen phosphate	
c. $Fe(NO_3)_3$	Iron(III) nitrate	Transition metal that requires a Roman numeral. Fe^{3+} ion balances three NO_3^- ions.
d. $Mn(OH)_2$	Manganese(II) hydroxide	Transition metal that requires a Roman numeral. Mn^{2+} ion balances two OH^- ions.
e. Na_2SO_3	Sodium sulfite	
f. Na_2CO_3	Sodium carbonate	
g. $NaHCO_3$	Sodium hydrogen carbonate	Often called sodium bicarbonate.
h. $CsClO_4$	Cesium perchlorate	
i. $NaOCl$	Sodium hypochlorite	
j. Na_2SeO_4	Sodium selenate	Atoms in the same group, such as sulfur and selenium, often form similar ions that are named similarly. Thus SeO_4^{2-} is selenate, like SO_4^{2-} (sulfate).
k. $KBrO_3$	Potassium bromate	As above BrO_3^- is bromate, like ClO_3^- (chlorate).

Chemical Insights   Playing Tag

Bombs have become the favorite weapons of terrorists, producing massive destruction from a relatively small, cheap device. Because of the devastation caused by a typical bomb, definitive evidence to solve the crime is often difficult to find. To aid in the forensic investigation of a bombing, law enforcement agencies have suggested that explosive materials be "tagged" so that their source can be readily identified. One method for tagging explosives was developed in the 1970s by Richard Livesag, a research chemist at 3M Corporation. Called Microtaggant, the tagging material consists of irregularly shaped particles approximately 0.1 millimeter in diameter. Examined under a microscope, the tiny specks reveal a laminated structure of 10 layers of melamine plastic, a chemically unreactive substance that is very difficult to destroy. The colored layers of the chips act as a kind of bar code, identifying the manufacturer, the date of production, and the name of the distributor of the explosive. Fluorescent and magnetic materials added to the chips aid in their detection at the scene of an explosion.

Although it seems that the tagging of explosives should be noncontroversial, this has not proved to be the case. Manufacturers of explosive materials and gun owners' associations have opposed the use of taggants, arguing that the added substances produce instabilities in the explosives. Also, manu-

facturers fear that they will be held liable for the damage caused by misuse of their products. Thus, at this stage, only Switzerland routinely uses Microtaggant to label explosives, and the Swiss claim to have solved nearly 600 bombing cases since 1984 using the taggant evidence.

A different tagging method has been pioneered by Isotag of Houston, Texas. Isotag labels explosives by inserting unusual atomic isotopes of the atoms present in the ions or molecules of the explosive substance. The isotopic labeling is done in a way that makes the tagged substances distinctly different from naturally occurring substances. For example, if labeled ammonium nitrate were used in a bomb, residue at the scene could be collected and analyzed with a mass spectrometer to show the unique isotopic patterns present, which could be used to trace the origin of the compound. Although Isotag claims its system to be safe and effective, manufacturers of fertilizers containing ammonium nitrate are reluctant to allow tagging because of fears of liability.

The U.S. Antiterrorism and Effective Death Penalty Act of 1996 authorized a thorough study of taggants. The results of this study and the outcome of the political struggle over taggants will determine whether the United States will follow Switzerland and require taggants for some or all explosive substances.

Formulas from Names

So far we have started with the chemical formula of a compound and decided on its systematic name. The reverse process is also important. For example, given the name calcium hydroxide, we can write the formula as $Ca(OH)_2$, since we know that calcium forms only Ca^{2+} ions and that, since hydroxide is OH^-, two of these anions will be required to give a neutral compound. Similarly, the name iron(II) oxide implies the formula FeO, since the Roman numeral II indicates the presence of Fe^{2+} and the oxide ion is O^{2-}.

⬛WL INTERACTIVE EXAMPLE 2.4

Given the following systematic names, write the formula for each compound.

a. Ammonium sulfate   **c.** Dioxygen difluoride   **e.** Gallium oxide

b. Vanadium(V) fluoride   **d.** Rubidium peroxide

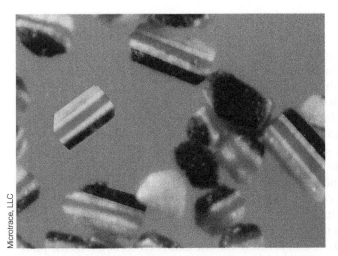

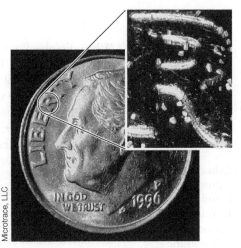

Microtrace, LLC

Microtrace, LLC

The multilayered plastic particles of Microtaggants (left) can produce over 37 million unique codes that can be used to identify substances. The tiny size of the taggants is shown (right) compared with the "R" on a dime.

Although taggants for explosives have proved controversial, approximately 500 consumer items already contain Microtaggants to authenticate brand-name products and discourage counterfeiting. For example, taggants are found in shampoo, paint, and carpet adhesives. The latter application enables business owners to check that a requested brand-name glue has been used to secure carpet rather than cheaper off-brand substitutes. Isotag markets taggants for substances such as gasoline and perfume, in which the plastic Microtaggant chips are impractical. For instance, isotopic tagging of perfumes enables a manufacturer to protect its product against dilution by an unethical distributor who might seek to increase profits by selling a diluted perfume.

So chemical taggants represent an increasing market. However, the question of whether explosives will be tagged remains a technical and political question mark.

Solution

Name	*Chemical Formula*	*Comment*
a. Ammonium sulfate	$(NH_4)_2SO_4$	Two ammonium ions (NH_4^+) are required for each sulfate ion (SO_4^{2-}) to achieve charge balance.
b. Vanadium(V) fluoride	VF_5	The compound contains V^{5+} ions and requires five F^- ions for charge balance.
c. Dioxygen difluoride	O_2F_2	The prefix *di-* indicates two of each atom.
d. Rubidium peroxide	Rb_2O_2	Since rubidium is in Group 1A, it forms only 1+ ions. Thus two Rb^+ ions are needed to balance the 2− charge on the peroxide ion (O_2^{2-}).

Name	Chemical Formula	Comment
e. Gallium oxide	Ga_2O_3	Gallium in Group 3A, like aluminum, forms only 3+ ions. Two Ga^{3+} ions are required to balance the charge on three O^{2-} ions.

Acids

When dissolved in water, certain molecules produce a solution containing free H^+ ions (protons). These substances, acids, will be discussed in detail in Chapters 4. Here we will simply present the rules for naming acids.

An acid can be viewed as a molecule with one or more H^+ ions attached to an anion. The rules for naming acids depend on whether the anion contains oxygen. If the *anion does not contain oxygen,* the acid is named with the prefix *hydro-* and the suffix *-ic.* For example, when gaseous HCl is dissolved in water, it forms hydrochloric acid. Similarly, HCN and H_2S dissolved in water are called hydrocyanic and hydrosulfuric acid, respectively.

When the *anion contains oxygen,* the acid name is formed from the root name of the anion with a suffix of *-ic* or *-ous.* If the anion name ends in *-ate,* the acid name ends with *-ic* (or sometimes *-ric*). For example, H_2SO_4 contains the sulfate anion (SO_4^{2-}) and is called sulfuric acid; H_3PO_4 contains the phosphate anion (PO_4^{3-}) and is called phosphoric acid; and $HC_2H_3O_2$ contains the acetate ion ($C_2H_3O_2^-$) and is called acetic acid. If the anion has an *-ite* ending, the acid name ends with *-ous.* For example, H_2SO_3, which contains sulfite (SO_3^{2-}), is named sulfurous acid; HNO_2, which contains nitrite (NO_2^-), is named nitrous acid. The application of these rules can be seen in the names of the acids of the oxyanions of chlorine:

Acid	Anion	Name
$HClO_4$	Perchlor*ate*	Perchlor*ic* acid
$HClO_3$	Chlor*ate*	Chlor*ic* acid
$HClO_2$	Chlor*ite*	Chlor*ous* acid
$HClO$	Hypochlor*ite*	Hypochlor*ous* acid

The names of the most important acids are given in Tables 2.7 and 2.8. An overall strategy for naming acids is shown in Fig. 2.23.

Table 2.7

Names of Acids That Do Not Contain Oxygen

Acid	Name
HF	Hydrofluoric acid
HCl	Hydrochloric acid
HBr	Hydrobromic acid
HI	Hydroiodic acid
HCN	Hydrocyanic acid
H_2S	Hydrosulfuric acid

Table 2.8

Names of Some Oxygen-Containing Acids

Acid	Name
HNO_3	Nitric acid
HNO_2	Nitrous acid
H_2SO_4	Sulfuric acid
H_2SO_3	Sulfurous acid
H_3PO_4	Phosphoric acid
$HC_2H_3O_2$	Acetic acid

Figure 2.23
A flowchart for naming acids. The acid has one or more H^+ ions attached to an anion.

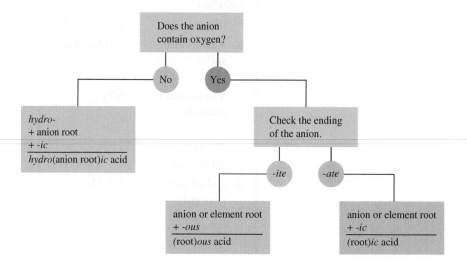

Key Terms

For Review

Section 2.2
law of conservation of mass
law of definite proportion
law of multiple proportions

Section 2.3
atomic masses
Avogadro's hypothesis

Section 2.5
cathode ray
electrons
radioactivity
nuclear atom
nucleus

Section 2.6
protons
neutrons
isotopes
atomic number
mass number

Section 2.7
chemical bonds
covalent bonds
molecule
chemical formula
structural formula
space-filling model
ball-and-stick models
ion
cation
anion
ionic bonding
polyatomic ion

Section 2.8
periodic table
metals
nonmetals
groups (families)
alkali metals
alkaline earth metals
halogens
noble gases
periods

Section 2.9
binary compounds
binary ionic compounds
oxyanions
binary covalent compounds

OWL and **go Chemistry**

Sign in at **www.cengage.com/owl** to:
- View tutorials and simulations, develop problem-solving skills, and complete online homework assigned by your professor.
- Download Go Chemistry mini lecture modules for quick review and exam prep from OWL (or purchase them at **www.cengagebrain.com**)

Fundamental laws
- Conservation of mass
- Definite proportion
- Multiple proportions

Dalton's atomic theory
- All elements are composed of atoms.
- All atoms of a given element are identical.
- Chemical compounds are formed when atoms combine.

Early atomic experiments
- Thomson model: electrons in a diffuse cloud of positive charge
- Millikan experiment: determined mass of electron
- Rutherford experiment: nuclear atom

Atomic structure
- Small dense nucleus contains protons and neutrons.
  - Protons—positive charge
  - Neutrons—no charge
- Electrons reside outside the nucleus in the relatively large remaining atomic volume.
  - Electrons—negative charge, small mass (1/1840 of proton)
- Isotopes have the same atomic number but different mass numbers.

Formation of molecules
- Atoms combine to form molecules by sharing electrons to form covalent bonds.
- Molecules are described by chemical formulas.
- Chemical formulas show number and type of atoms.
  - Structural formula
  - Ball-and-stick model
  - Space-filling model

Formation of ions
- Cation—formed by a loss of an electron, positive charge
- Anion—formed by gain of an electron, negative charge
- Ionic bonds—formed by interaction of cations and anions

Periodic table
- Elements are organized in order of increasing atomic number.
- Elements with similar properties are in columns, or groups.
- Metals are in the majority and tend to form cations.
- Nonmetals tend to form anions.

Naming of compounds
- Binary compounds
  - Type I—contain a metal that always forms the same cation
  - Type II—contain a metal that can form more than one cation
  - Type III—contain two nonmetals
- Compounds containing a polyatomic ion
- Acids

Discussion Questions

These questions are designed to be considered by groups of students in class. Often these questions work well for introducing a particular topic in class.

1. You may have noticed that when water boils, you can see bubbles that rise to the surface of the water. What is inside these bubbles? Explain.
   a. air
   b. hydrogen and oxygen gas
   c. oxygen gas
   d. water vapor
   e. carbon dioxide gas

2. Which of the following is true about an individual atom?
   a. An individual atom should be considered a solid.
   b. An individual atom should be considered a liquid.
   c. An individual atom should be considered a gas.
   d. The state of the atom depends on which element it is.
   e. An individual atom cannot be considered a solid, liquid, or gas.

   Justify your choice, and for those you did not choose, explain why they are incorrect.

3. How would you go about finding the number of "chalk molecules" it takes to write your name on the board? Explain what you would need to do and provide a sample calculation.

4. These questions concern the work of J. J. Thomson:
   a. From what you know of Thomson's work, which particles do you think he would believe are most important in the formation of compounds (chemical changes) and why?
   b. Of the remaining two subatomic particles, which do you place second in importance for forming compounds and why?
   c. Propose three models that explain Thomson's findings and evaluate them. Include Thomson's findings.

5. Heat is applied to an ice cube in a closed container until only steam is present. Draw a representation of this process, assuming you can see it at an extremely high level of magnification. What happens to the size of the molecules? What happens to the total mass of the sample?

6. You have a chemical in a sealed glass container filled with air. The setup is sitting on a balance, as shown. The chemical is ignited by means of a magnifying glass focusing sunlight on the reactant. After the chemical has completely burned, which of the following is true? Explain your answer.
   a. The balance will read less than 250.0 g.
   b. The balance will read 250.0 g.
   c. The balance will read greater than 250.0 g.
   d. Cannot be determined without knowing the identity of the chemical.

7. The vitamin niacin (nicotinic acid, $C_6H_5NO_2$) can be isolated from a variety of natural sources such as liver, yeast, milk, and whole grain. It also can be synthesized from commercially available materials. From a nutritional point of view, which source of nicotinic acid is best for use in a multivitamin tablet? Why?

8. One of the best indications of a useful theory is that it raises more questions for further experimentation than it originally answered. Is this true of Dalton's atomic theory? Give examples.

9. Dalton assumed that all atoms of the same element are identical in all their properties. Explain why this assumption is not valid.

10. How does Dalton's atomic theory account for each of the following?
    a. the law of conservation of mass
    b. the law of definite proportion
    c. the law of multiple proportions

11. What refinements had to be made in Dalton's atomic theory to account for Gay-Lussac's results on the combining volumes of gases?

12. Which (if any) of the following can be determined by knowing the number of protons in a neutral element? Explain your answer.
    a. the number of neutrons in the neutral element
    b. the number of electrons in the neutral element
    c. the name of the element

13. The average mass of a carbon atom is 12.011. Assuming you were able to pick up only one carbon atom, the chance that you would randomly get one with a mass of 12.011 is
    a. 0%.   d. 12.011%.
    b. 0.011%.   e. greater than 50%.
    c. about 12%.   f. None of these is true.
    Explain.

14. Which of the following explain how an ion is formed? Explain your answer.
    a. adding or subtracting protons to/from an atom
    b. adding or subtracting neutrons to/from an atom
    c. adding or subtracting electrons to/from an atom

15. The formula of water is H_2O. Which of the following is indicated by this formula? Explain your answer.
    a. the mass of hydrogen is twice that of oxygen in each molecule
    b. there are two hydrogen atoms and one oxygen atom per water molecule
    c. the mass of oxygen is twice that of hydrogen in each molecule
    d. there are two oxygen atoms and one hydrogen atom per water molecule

16. Why do we call $Ba(NO_3)_2$ barium nitrate, but we call $Fe(NO_3)_2$ iron(II) nitrate?

17. Why is calcium dichloride not the correct systematic name for $CaCl_2$?

Exercises

A blue exercise number indicates that the answer to that exercise appears at the back of this book and a solution appears in the *Solutions Guide*.

Development of the Atomic Theory

18. Explain the law of conservation of mass, the law of definite proportion, and the law of multiple proportions.

19. A reaction of 1 L of chlorine gas (Cl_2) with 5 L of fluorine gas (F_2) yields 2 L of a gaseous product. All gas volumes are at the same temperature and pressure. What is the formula of the gaseous product?

20. When mixtures of gaseous H_2 and gaseous Cl_2 react, a product forms that has the same properties regardless of the relative amounts of H_2 and Cl_2 used.
    a. How is this result interpreted in terms of the law of definite proportion?
    b. When a volume of H_2 reacts with an equal volume of Cl_2 at the same temperature and pressure, what volume of product having the formula HCl is formed?

21. Observations of the reaction between nitrogen gas and hydrogen gas show us that 1 volume of nitrogen reacts with 3 volumes of hydrogen to make 2 volumes of gaseous product, as shown below:

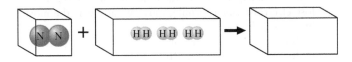

    Determine the formula of the product and justify your answer.

22. The three most stable oxides of carbon are carbon monoxide (CO), carbon dioxide (CO_2), and carbon suboxide (C_3O_2). The molecules can be represented as

    Explain how these molecules illustrate the law of multiple proportions.

23. Hydrazine, ammonia, and hydrogen azide all contain only nitrogen and hydrogen. The mass of hydrogen that combines with 1.00 g of nitrogen for each compound is 1.44×10^{-1} g, 2.16×10^{-1} g, and 2.40×10^{-2} g, respectively. Show how these data illustrate the law of multiple proportions.

24. Consider 100.0-g samples of two different compounds consisting only of carbon and oxygen. One compound contains 27.2 g of carbon, and the other has 42.9 g of carbon. How can these data support the law of multiple proportions if 42.9 is not a multiple of 27.2? Show that these data support the law of multiple proportions.

25. Early tables of atomic weights (masses) were generated by measuring the mass of a substance that reacts with 1.00 g of oxygen. Given the following data and taking the atomic mass of hydrogen as 1.00, generate a table of relative atomic masses for oxygen, sodium, and magnesium.

Element	Mass That Combines with 1.00 g Oxygen	Assumed Formula
Hydrogen	0.126 g	HO
Sodium	2.875 g	NaO
Magnesium	1.500 g	MgO

How do your values compare with those in the periodic table? How do you account for any differences?

The Nature of the Atom

26. What evidence led to the conclusion that cathode rays had a negative charge? Is there a difference between a cathode ray and a β particle?

27. From the information in this chapter on the mass of the proton, the mass of the electron, and the sizes of the nucleus and the atom, calculate the densities of a hydrogen nucleus and a hydrogen atom.

28. A chemistry instructor makes the following claim: "Consider that if the nucleus were the size of a grape, the electrons would be about 1 *mile* away on average." Is this claim reasonably accurate? Provide mathematical support.

29. A chemist in a galaxy far, far away performed the Millikan oil drop experiment and got the following results for the charge on various drops. What is the charge of the electron in zirkombs?

2.56×10^{-12} zirkombs	7.68×10^{-12} zirkombs
3.84×10^{-12} zirkombs	6.40×10^{-13} zirkombs

30. Do the proton and the neutron have exactly the same mass? How do the masses of the proton and the neutron compare with the mass of the electron? Which particles make the greatest contribution to the mass of an atom? Which particles make the greatest contribution to the chemical properties of an atom?

31. Consider Ernest Rutherford's α-particle bombardment experiment illustrated in Fig. 2.11. How did the results of this experiment lead Rutherford away from the plum pudding model of the atom to propose the nuclear model of the atom?

Elements, Ions, and the Periodic Table

32. Distinguish between the following terms.
    a. molecule versus ion
    b. covalent bonding versus ionic bonding
    c. molecule versus compound
    d. anion versus cation

33. What is the distinction between atomic number and mass number? Between mass number and atomic mass?

34. a. Classify the following elements as metals or nonmetals.

Mg	Si	Rn
Ti	Ge	Eu
Au	B	Am
Bi	At	Br

    b. The distinction between metals and nonmetals is really not a clear one. Some elements, called *metalloids*, are intermediate in their properties. Which of these elements would you reclassify as metalloids? What other elements in the periodic table would you expect to be metalloids?

35. a. List the noble gas elements. Which of the noble gases has only radioactive isotopes? (This situation is indicated on most periodic tables by parentheses around the mass of the element. See inside front cover.)
    b. Which lanthanide element and which transition element have only radioactive isotopes?

36. Consider the elements of the carbon family: C, Si, Ge, Sn, and Pb. What is the trend in metallic character as one goes down a group in the periodic table? What is the trend in metallic character going from left to right across a period in the periodic table?

37. Identify the elements that correspond to the following atomic numbers. Label each as either a noble gas, a halogen, an alkali metal, an alkaline earth metal, a transition metal, a lanthanide metal, or an actinide metal.
    a. 17   e. 2
    b. 4   f. 92
    c. 63   g. 55
    d. 72

38. The number of protons in an atom determines the identity of the atom. What does the number and arrangement of the electrons in an atom determine? What does the number of neutrons in an atom determine?

39. For lighter, stable isotopes, the ratio of the mass number to the atomic number is close to a certain value. What is the value? What happens to the value of the mass number to atomic number ratio as stable isotopes become heavier?

40. Write the atomic symbol ($_Z^A X$) for each of the isotopes described below.
    a. number of protons = 27, number of neutrons = 31
    b. the isotope of boron with mass number 10
    c. $Z = 12$, $A = 23$
    d. atomic number 53, number of neutrons = 79
    e. $Z = 9$, number of neutrons = 10
    f. number of protons = 29, mass number 65

41. How many protons, neutrons, and electrons are in each of the following atoms or ions?
    a. $_{12}^{24}Mg$ d. $_{27}^{59}Co^{3+}$ g. $_{34}^{79}Se^{2-}$
    b. $_{12}^{24}Mg^{2+}$ e. $_{27}^{59}Co$ h. $_{28}^{63}Ni$
    c. $_{27}^{59}Co^{2+}$ f. $_{34}^{79}Se$ i. $_{28}^{59}Ni^{2+}$

42. Complete the following table.

Symbol	Number of Protons in Nucleus	Number of Neutrons in Nucleus	Number of Electrons	Net Charge
$_{92}^{238}U$	—	—	—	—
	20	20		2+
	23	28	20	—
$_{39}^{89}Y$	—	—	—	—
	35	44	36	—
	15	16		3−

43. What is the symbol for an ion with 63 protons, 60 electrons, and 88 neutrons? If an ion contains 50 protons, 68 neutrons, and 48 electrons, what is its symbol?

44. What is the symbol of an ion with 16 protons, 18 neutrons, and 18 electrons? What is the symbol for an ion that has 16 protons, 16 neutrons, and 18 electrons?

45. Would you expect each of the following atoms to gain or lose electrons when forming ions? What ion is the most likely in each case?
    a. Ra   c. P   e. Br
    b. In   d. Te   f. Rb

46. For each of the following atomic numbers, use the periodic table to write the formula (including the charge) for the simple *ion* that the element is most likely to form in ionic compounds.
    a. 13   c. 56   e. 87
    b. 34   d. 7   f. 35

Nomenclature

47. The compounds $AlCl_3$, $CrCl_3$, and ICl_3 have similar formulas, yet each follows a different set of rules to name it. Name these compounds, and then compare and contrast the nomenclature rules used in each case.

48. Each of the following compounds has three possible names listed for it. For each compound, what is the correct name and why aren't the other names used?
    a. N_2O: nitrogen oxide, nitrogen(I) oxide, dinitrogen monoxide
    b. Cu_2O: copper oxide, copper(I) oxide, dicopper monoxide
    c. Li_2O: lithium oxide, lithium(I) oxide, dilithium monoxide

49. Name each of the following compounds.

a.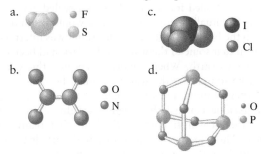
• F
• S

c.
● I
● Cl

b.
● O
● N

d.
● O
● P

50. Name the following compounds.
a. $NaClO_4$
b. $Mg_3(PO_4)_2$
c. $Al_2(SO_4)_3$
d. SF_2
e. SF_6
f. Na_2HPO_4
g. NaH_2PO_4
h. Li_3N
i. $NaOH$
j. $Mg(OH)_2$
k. $Al(OH)_3$
l. Ag_2CrO_4

51. Name each of the following compounds.
a. CuI
b. CuI_2
c. CoI_2
d. Na_2CO_3
e. $NaHCO_3$
f. S_4N_4
g. $SeBr_4$
h. $NaOCl$
i. $BaCrO_4$
j. NH_4NO_3

52. Name the following compounds. Assume the potential acids are dissolved in water.
a. $HC_2H_3O_2$
b. NH_4NO_2
c. Co_2S_3
d. ICl
e. $Pb_3(PO_4)_2$
f. $KClO_3$
g. H_2SO_4
h. Sr_3N_2
i. $Al_2(SO_3)_3$
j. SnO_2
k. Na_2CrO_4
l. $HClO$

53. Write formulas for the following compounds.
a. Sulfur dioxide
b. Sulfur trioxide
c. Sodium sulfite
d. Potassium hydrogen sulfite
e. Lithium nitride
f. Chromium(III) carbonate
g. Chromium(II) acetate
h. Tin(IV) fluoride
i. Ammonium hydrogen sulfate
j. Ammonium hydrogen phosphate
k. Potassium perchlorate
l. Sodium hydride
m. Hypobromous acid
n. Hydrobromic acid

54. Write formulas for the following compounds.
a. Sodium oxide
b. Sodium peroxide
c. Potassium cyanide
d. Copper(II) nitrate
e. Silicon tetrachloride
f. Lead(II) oxide
g. Lead(IV) oxide (common name lead dioxide)
h. Copper(I) chloride
i. Gallium arsenide
j. Cadmium selenide
k. Zinc sulfide
l. Mercury(I) chloride
m. Nitrous acid
n. Diphosphorus pentoxide

55. The common names and formulas for several substances are given below. What are the systematic names for these substances?
a. Sugar of lead $Pb(C_2H_3O_2)_2$
b. Blue vitriol $CuSO_4$
c. Quicklime CaO
d. Epsom salts $MgSO_4$
e. Milk of magnesia $Mg(OH)_2$
f. Gypsum $CaSO_4$
g. Laughing gas N_2O

56. Each of the following compounds is incorrectly named. What is wrong with each name, and what is the correct name for each compound?
a. $FeCl_3$, iron chloride
b. NO_2, nitrogen(IV) oxide
c. CaO, calcium(II) monoxide
d. Al_2S_3, dialuminum trisulfide
e. $Mg(C_2H_3O_2)_2$, manganese diacetate
f. $FePO_4$, iron(II) phosphide
g. P_2S_5, phosphorus sulfide
h. Na_2O_2, sodium oxide
i. HNO_3, nitrate acid
j. H_2S, sulfuric acid

57. Name the following acids.

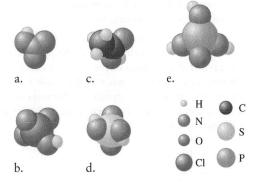

a.   c.   e.

● H   ● C
● N   ● S
● O   ● P
● Cl

b.   d.

Additional Exercises

58. What discoveries were made by J. J. Thomson, Henri Becquerel, and Lord Rutherford? How did Dalton's model of the atom have to be modified to account for these discoveries?

59. Consider the chemical reaction depicted to the right. Label as much as you can using the terms *atom, molecule, element, compound, ionic, gas,* and *solid.*

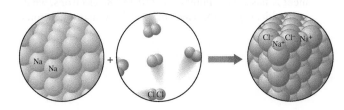

60. Section 2.3 describes the postulates of Dalton's atomic theory. With some modifications, these postulates hold up very well regarding how we view elements, compounds, and chemical reactions today. Answer the following questions concerning Dalton's atomic theory and the modifications made today.
    a. The atom can be broken down into smaller parts. What are the smaller parts?
    b. How are atoms of hydrogen identical to each other, and how can they be different from each other?
    c. How are atoms of hydrogen different from atoms of helium? How can H atoms be similar to He atoms?
    d. How is water different from hydrogen peroxide (H_2O_2) even though both compounds are composed of only hydrogen and oxygen?
    e. What happens in a chemical reaction, and why is mass conserved in a chemical reaction?

61. A sample of chloroform is found to contain 12.0 g of carbon, 106.4 g of chlorine, and 1.01 g of hydrogen. If a second sample of chloroform is found to contain 30.0 g of carbon, what is the total mass of chloroform in the second sample?

62. In a reaction, 34.0 g of chromium(III) oxide reacts with 12.1 g of aluminum to produce chromium and aluminum oxide. If 23.3 g of chromium is produced, what mass of aluminum oxide is produced?

63. The isotope of an unknown element, X, has a mass number of 79. The most stable ion of the isotope has 36 electrons and forms a binary compound with sodium having a formula of Na_2X. Which of the following statements is(are) *true*? Correct the false statements.
    a. The binary compound formed between X and fluorine will be a covalent compound.
    b. The isotope of X contains 38 protons.
    c. The isotope of X contains 41 neutrons.
    d. The identity of X is strontium, Sr.

64. For each of the following ions, indicate the total number of protons and electrons in the ion. For the positive ions in the list, predict the formula of the simplest compound formed between each positive ion and the oxide ion. For the negative ions in the list, predict the formula of the simplest compound formed between each negative ion and the aluminum ion.
    a. Fe^{2+} e. S^{2-}
    b. Fe^{3+} f. P^{3-}
    c. Ba^{2+} g. Br^-
    d. Cs^+ h. N^{3-}

65. An element's most stable ion forms an ionic compound with bromine, having the formula XBr_2. If the ion of element X has a mass number of 230 and 86 electrons, what is the identity of the element, and how many neutrons does it have?

66. The early alchemists used to do an experiment in which water was boiled for several days in a sealed glass container. Eventually, some solid residue would begin to appear in the bottom of the flask. This result was interpreted to mean that some of the water in the flask had been converted into earth. When Lavoisier repeated this experiment, he found that the water weighed the same before and after heating, and the weight of the flask plus the solid residue equaled the original weight of the flask. Were the alchemists correct? Explain what really happened. (This experiment is described in the article by A. F. Scott in *Scientific American*, January 1984.)

67. Elements in the same family often form oxyanions of the same general formula. The anions are named in a similar fashion. What are the names of the oxyanions of selenium and tellurium: SeO_4^{2-}, SeO_3^{2-}, TeO_4^{2-}, TeO_3^{2-}?

68. How would you name $HBrO_4$, KIO_3, $NaBrO_2$, and HIO? Refer to Table 2.5 and the acid nomenclature discussion in the text.

69. Indium oxide contains 4.784 g of indium for every 1.000 g of oxygen. In 1869, when Mendeleev first presented his version of the periodic table, he proposed the formula In_2O_3 for indium oxide. Before that time, it was thought that the formula was InO. What values for the atomic mass of indium are obtained using these two formulas? Assume that oxygen has an atomic mass of 16.00.

70. The designations 1A through 8A used for certain families of the periodic table are helpful for predicting the charges on ions in binary ionic compounds. In these compounds, the metals generally take on a positive charge equal to the family number, and the nonmetals take on a negative charge equal to the family number minus 8. Thus the compound formed from sodium and chlorine contains Na^+ and Cl^- ions and has the formula NaCl. Predict the formula and the name of the binary compound formed from the following pairs of elements.
    a. Ca and N   e. Ba and I
    b. K and O   f. Al and Se
    c. Rb and F   g. Cs and P
    d. Mg and S   h. In and Br

71. A binary ionic compound is known to contain a cation with 51 protons and 48 electrons. The anion contains one-third the number of protons as the cation. The number of electrons in the anion is equal to the number of protons plus 1. What is the formula of this compound? What is the name of this compound?

72. Identify each of the following elements.
    a. a member of the same family as oxygen whose most stable ion contains 54 electrons
    b. a member of the alkali metal family whose most stable ion contains 36 electrons
    c. a noble gas with 18 protons in the nucleus
    d. a halogen with 85 protons and 85 electrons

73. A certain element has only two naturally occurring isotopes: one with 18 neutrons and the other with 20 neutrons. The element forms 1− charged ions when in ionic compounds. Predict the identity of the element. What number of electrons does the 1− charged ion have?

Challenge Problems

74. Reaction of 2.0 L of hydrogen gas with 1.0 L of oxygen gas yields 2.0 L of water vapor. All gases are at the same temperature and pressure. Show how these data support the idea that oxygen gas is a diatomic molecule. Must we consider hydrogen to be a diatomic molecule to explain these results?

75. Each of the statements below is true, but Dalton might have had trouble explaining some of them with his atomic theory. Give explanations for the following statements.
    a. The space-filling models for ethyl alcohol and dimethyl ether are shown below.

    - ● C
    - ● O
    - ● H

    These two compounds have the same composition by mass (52% carbon, 13% hydrogen, and 35% oxygen), yet the two have different melting points, boiling points, and solubilities in water.
    b. Burning wood leaves an ash that is only a small fraction of the mass of the original wood.
    c. Atoms can be broken down into smaller particles.
    d. One sample of lithium hydride is 87.4% lithium by mass, whereas another sample of lithium hydride is 74.9% lithium by mass. However, the two samples have the same properties.

76. You take three compounds, each consisting of two elements (X, Y, and/or Z) and decompose them to their respective elements. To determine the relative masses of X, Y, and Z, you collect and weigh the elements, obtaining the following data:

Elements in Compound	Masses of Elements
1. X and Y	X = 0.4 g, Y = 4.2 g
2. Y and Z	Y = 1.4 g, Z = 1.0 g
3. X and Y	X = 2.0 g, Y = 7.0 g

    a. What are the assumptions needed to solve this problem?
    b. What are the relative masses of X, Y, and Z?

    c. What are the chemical formulas of the three compounds?
    d. If you decompose 21 g of compound XY, how much of each element is present?

77. Two elements, R and Q, combine to form two binary compounds. In the first compound, 14.0 g of R combines with 3.00 g of Q. In the second compound, 7.00 g of R combines with 4.50 g of Q. Show that these data are in accord with the law of multiple proportions. If the formula of the second compound is RQ, what is the formula of the first compound?

78. A single molecule has a mass of 7.31×10^{-23} g. Provide an example of a real molecule that can have this mass.

79. A combustion reaction involves the reaction of a substance with oxygen gas. The complete combustion of any hydrocarbon (binary compound of carbon and hydrogen) produces carbon dioxide and water as the only products. Octane is a hydrocarbon found in gasoline. Complete combustion of octane produces 8 L of carbon dioxide for every 9 L of water vapor (both measured at the same temperature and pressure). What is the ratio of carbon atoms to hydrogen atoms in a molecule of octane?

80. You have two distinct gaseous compounds made from element X and element Y. The mass percents are as follows:

    Compound I: 30.43% X, 69.57% Y

    Compound II: 63.64% X, 36.36% Y

    In their natural standard states, element X and element Y exist as gases. (Monatomic? Diatomic? Triatomic? That is for you to determine.) When you react "gas X" with "gas Y" to make the products, you get the following data (all at standard pressure and temperature):

    1 volume "gas X" + 2 volumes "gas Y" ⟶
    2 volumes compound I

    2 volumes "gas X" + 1 volume "gas Y" ⟶
    2 volumes compound II

    Assume the simplest possible formulas for reactants and products in these chemical equations. Then determine the relative atomic masses of element X and element Y.

Marathon Problem

81. You have gone back in time and are working with Dalton on a table of relative masses. Following are his data:

    0.602 g gas A reacts with 0.295 g gas B

    0.172 g gas B reacts with 0.401 g gas C

    0.320 g gas A reacts with 0.374 g gas C

    a. Assuming simplest formulas (AB, BC, and AC), construct a table of relative masses for Dalton.
    b. Knowing some history of chemistry, you tell Dalton that if he determines the volumes of the gases reacted at constant temperature and pressure, he need not assume simplest formulas. You collect the following data:

    6 volumes gas A + 1 volume gas B $\longrightarrow$ 4 volumes product

    1 volume gas B + 4 volumes gas C $\longrightarrow$ 4 volumes product

    3 volumes gas A + 2 volumes gas C $\longrightarrow$ 6 volumes product

    Write the simplest balanced equations, and find the actual relative masses of the elements. Explain your reasoning.

Quantum Mechanics and Atomic Theory

12

White light passing through two prisms.

Tetra Images/Alamy

In the past 200 years, a great deal of experimental evidence has accumulated to support the atomic model. This theory has proved to be both extremely useful and physically reasonable. When atoms were first suggested by the Greek philosophers Democritus and Leucippus about 400 B.C., the concept was based mostly on intuition. In fact, for the following 20 centuries, no convincing experimental evidence was available to support the existence of atoms. The first real scientific data were gathered by Lavoisier and others from quantitative measurements of chemical reactions. The results of these stoichiometric experiments led John Dalton to propose the first systematic atomic theory. Dalton's theory, although crude, has stood the test of time extremely well.

Once we came to "believe in" atoms, it was logical to ask: What is the nature of an atom? Does an atom have parts, and if so, what are they? In Chapter 2 we considered some of the experiments most important for shedding light on the nature of the atom. Now we will see how the atomic theory has evolved to its present state.

One of the most striking things about the chemistry of the elements is the periodic repetition of properties. There are several groups of elements that show great similarities in chemical behavior. As we saw in Chapter 2, these similarities led to the development of the periodic table of the elements. In this chapter we will see that the modern theory of atomic structure accounts for periodicity in terms of the electron arrangements in atoms.

However, before we examine atomic structure, we must consider the revolution that took place in physics in the first 30 years of the twentieth century. During that time, experiments were carried out, the results of which could not be explained by the theories of classical physics developed by Isaac Newton and many others who followed him. A radical new theory called quantum mechanics was developed to account for the behavior of light and atoms. This "new physics" provides many surprises for people who are used to the macroscopic world, but it seems to account flawlessly (within the bounds of necessary approximations) for the behavior of matter.

As the first step in our exploration of this revolution in science, we will consider the properties of light, more properly called electromagnetic radiation.

12.0 | The Nature of Energy

The total energy content of the universe is constant.

Although the concept of energy is quite familiar, energy is rather difficult to define precisely. We will define **energy** as the *capacity to do work or to produce heat*. In this chapter we will concentrate on the transfer of energy via heat flow that accompanies chemical processes.

One of the most important characteristics of energy is that it is conserved. The **law of conservation of energy** states that *energy can be converted from one form to another but can be neither created nor destroyed*. That is, the energy of the universe is constant. Energy can be classified as either potential energy or kinetic energy. **Potential energy** is energy due to position or composition. For example, water behind a dam has potential energy that can be converted to work when the water flows down through turbines, thereby creating electricity. Attractive and repulsive forces also lead to potential energy. The energy released when gasoline is burned results from differences in the attractive forces between nuclei and electrons in the reactants and products. The **kinetic energy** of an object is due to the motion of the object and depends on the mass of the object (m) and its velocity (v): KE = $\frac{1}{2}mv^2$.

Energy can be converted from one form to another easily. For example, consider the two balls in Fig. 12.0(a). Ball A, because of its higher position, initially has more potential energy than ball B. When A is released, it moves down

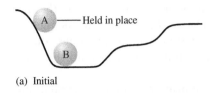

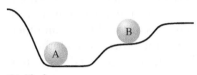

Figure 12.0
(a) In the initial positions, ball A has a higher potential energy than ball B. (b) After A has rolled down the hill, the potential energy lost by A has been converted to random motions of the components of the hill (frictional heating) and to the increase in the potential energy of B.

Heat involves a *transfer* of energy.

Energy is a state function; work and heat are not.

the hill and strikes B. Eventually the arrangement shown in Fig. 12.0(b) is achieved. What has happened in going from the initial to the final arrangement? The potential energy of A has decreased, but since energy is conserved, all the energy lost by A must be accounted for. How is this energy distributed?

Initially, the potential energy of A is changed to kinetic energy as the ball rolls down the hill. Part of this kinetic energy has been transferred to B, causing it to be raised to a higher final position. Thus the potential energy of B has increased. However, since the final position of B is lower than the original position of A, some of the energy is still unaccounted for. Both balls are at rest in their final positions, so the missing energy cannot be due to their motions. What has happened to the remaining energy?

The answer lies in the interaction between the hill's surface and the ball. As A rolls down the hill, some of its kinetic energy is transferred to the surface of the hill as heat. This transfer of energy is called *frictional heating*. The temperature of the hill increases very slightly as the ball rolls down.

At this point it is important to recognize that heat and temperature are decidedly different. Recall that temperature is a property that reflects the random motions of the particles in a particular substance. **Heat,** on the other hand, involves the *transfer* of energy between two objects due to a temperature difference. Heat is not a substance contained in an object, although we often talk of heat as if this were true.

Note that in going from the initial to the final arrangements in Fig. 12.0, ball B gains potential energy because ball A has done work on B. **Work** is defined as *a force acting over a distance*. Work is required to raise B from its original position to a higher one. Part of the original energy stored as potential energy in A has been transferred through work to B, thereby increasing B's potential energy. Thus there are two ways to transfer energy: through work and through heat.

In rolling to the bottom of the hill as shown in Fig. 12.0, ball A always loses the same amount of potential energy. However, the way that this energy transfer is divided between work and heat depends on the specific conditions—the **pathway.** For example, the surface of the hill might be so rough that the energy of A is expended completely through frictional heating; A is moving so slowly when it hits B that it cannot move B to the next level. In this case no work is done. Regardless of the condition of the hill's surface, the *total energy* transferred will be constant. However, the amounts of heat and work will differ. Energy change is independent of the pathway; however, work and heat are both dependent on the pathway.

This brings us to a very important concept: the **state function** or *state property*. A state function refers to a property of the system that depends only on its *present state*. A state function (property) does not depend in any way on the system's past (or future). In other words, the value of a state function does not depend on how the system arrived at the present state; it depends only on the characteristics of the present state.

Stated more precisely, one very important characteristic of a state function is that a change in this function (property) in going from one state to another state is independent of the particular pathway taken between the two states.

Of the functions considered in our present example, energy is a state function, but work and heat are not state functions.

Chemical Energy

The ideas we have just illustrated using mechanical examples also apply to chemical systems. The combustion of methane, for example,

$$CH_4(g) + 2O_2(g) \longrightarrow CO_2(g) + 2H_2O(g) + \text{energy (heat)}$$

is used to heat many homes in the United States. To discuss this reaction, we divide the universe into two parts: the system and the surroundings. The system is the part of the universe on which we wish to focus attention; the **surroundings** include everything else in the universe. In this case we define the system as the reactants and products of the reaction. The surroundings consist of the reaction container, the room, and everything else other than the reactants and products.

When a reaction results in the evolution of heat, it is said to be **exothermic** (*exo-* is a prefix meaning "out of"); that is, energy flows *out of the system*. For example, in the combustion of methane, energy flows out of the system as heat. Reactions that absorb energy from the surroundings are said to be **endothermic**. That is, when the heat flow is *into a system*, the process is endothermic. For example, the formation of nitric oxide from nitrogen and oxygen is endothermic:

$$N_2(g) + O_2(g) + \text{energy (heat)} \longrightarrow 2NO(g)$$

A familiar endothermic physical process is the vaporization of water:

$$H_2O(l) + \text{energy} \longrightarrow H_2O(g)$$

Where does the energy, released as heat, come from in an exothermic reaction? The answer lies in the difference in potential energy between the products and the reactants. In an exothermic reaction, which has lower potential energy, the reactants or the products? We know that total energy is conserved and that energy flows from the system into the surroundings in an exothermic reaction. This means that *the energy gained by the surroundings must be equal to the energy lost by the system.* For methane combustion, the energy content of the system decreases, which means that 1 mole of CO_2 and 2 moles of H_2O molecules (the products) possess less potential energy than do 1 mole of CH_4 and 2 moles of O_2 molecules (the reactants). The heat flow into the surroundings results from a lowering of the potential energy of the reaction system. This always holds true. *In any exothermic reaction, the potential energy stored in the chemical bonds is being converted to thermal energy (random kinetic energy) via heat.*

The energy diagram for the combustion of methane is shown in Fig. 12.0A, where $\Delta(PE)$ represents the *change* in potential energy stored in the bonds of the products as compared with the bonds of the reactants. In other words, this quantity represents the difference between the energy required to break the bonds in the reactants and the energy released when the bonds in the products are formed. In an exothermic process, the bonds in the products are stronger (on average) than those of the reactants. That is, more energy is released in forming the new bonds in the products than is consumed in breaking the bonds in the reactants. The net result is that the quantity of energy $\Delta(PE)$ is transferred to the surroundings through heat.

Figure 12.0A

The combustion of methane releases the quantity of energy $\Delta(PE)$ to the surroundings via heat flow. This is an exothermic process.

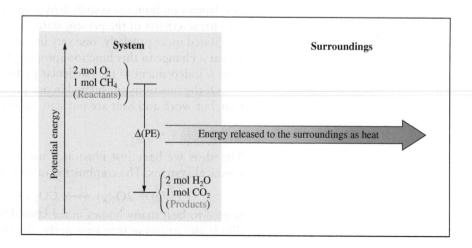

For an endothermic reaction, the situation is reversed, as shown in Fig. 12.0B. Energy that flows into the system as heat is used to increase the potential energy of the system. In this case the products have higher potential energy (weaker bonds on average) than the reactants.

Figure 12.0B
The energy diagram for the reaction of nitrogen and oxygen to form nitric oxide. This is an endothermic process.

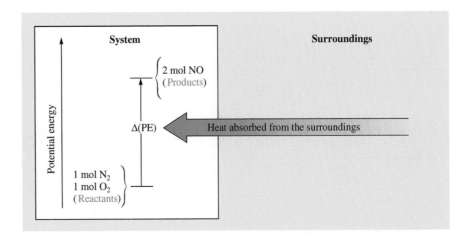

12.1 | Electromagnetic Radiation

One of the ways that energy travels through space is by **electromagnetic radiation**. The light from the sun, the energy used to cook food in a microwave oven, the X rays used by dentists, and the radiowaves used by physicians to make MRI maps of body tissues are all examples of electromagnetic radiation. Although these forms of radiant energy seem quite different, they all exhibit the same type of wavelike behavior and travel at the speed of light in a vacuum. Electromagnetic radiation is so named because it has electrical and magnetic fields that simultaneously oscillate in planes mutually perpendicular to each other and to the direction of propagation through space (Fig. 12.1).

Waves are characterized by wavelength, frequency, and speed. As shown in Fig. 12.2, **wavelength** (symbolized by the Greek letter lambda, λ) is the *distance between two consecutive peaks or troughs in a wave*. The **frequency** (symbolized by the Greek letter nu, ν) is defined as the *number of waves (cycles) per second that pass a given point in space*. Since all types of electromagnetic radiation travel at the speed of light, short-wavelength radiation must have a high frequency. You can see this in Fig. 12.2, where three waves are shown traveling between two points at constant speed. Note that the wave with the shortest wavelength (λ_3) has the highest frequency, and the wave with

Figure 12.1
Electromagnetic radiation has oscillating electric (E) and magnetic (H) fields in planes perpendicular to each other and to the direction of propagation.

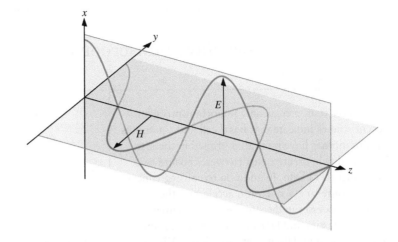

the longest wavelength (λ_1) has the lowest frequency. This implies an inverse relationship between wavelength and frequency; that is, $\lambda \propto 1/\nu$, or

$$\lambda\nu = c$$

Wavelength (λ) and frequency (ν) are inversely related.

In this equation λ is the wavelength in meters, ν is the frequency in cycles per second, and c is the speed of light, a defined quantity with the exact value of 2.99792458×10^8 m/s. In the SI system, *cycles* is understood, and the unit cycles per second becomes 1/s, or s^{-1}, which is called the *hertz* (abbreviated Hz).

Electromagnetic radiation is classified as shown in Fig. 12.3. Radiation provides an important means of energy transfer. For example, the energy from the sun reaches the earth mainly in the forms of visible and ultraviolet radiation, and the glowing coals of a fireplace transmit heat energy by infrared radiation. In a microwave oven, the water molecules in food absorb microwave radiation, which

Figure 12.2
The nature of waves. Note that the radiation with the shortest wavelength has the highest frequency. This diagram can represent the oscillating electric or magnetic field of the wave.

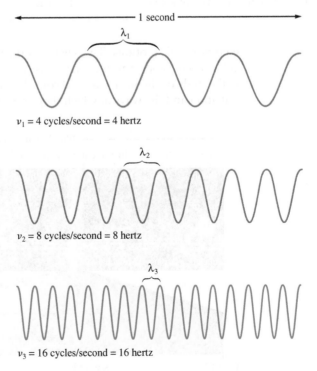

Chemical Insights | New-Wave Sunscreens

Skin cancer is an increasingly important problem. Recent studies indicate that basal cell and squamous cell carcinomas have more than tripled in the last 30 years due in greatest part to overexposure to ultraviolet (UV) light. In addition to causing cancer, overexposure to UV radiation accelerates the "aging" processes in the skin because it damages proteins, elastin, and DNA in the upper and middle layers of the skin. Ultraviolet radiation (UVR) is classified as UVB (wavelengths from 280–320 nm) and UVA (wavelengths from 320–400 nm). Studies show that UVA accounts for over 80% of the detrimental effects of exposure to UVR, including DNA damage and ultimately skin cancer. UVA rays, which penetrate deeper into the skin, can pass through clouds, windows, and even clothing.

Although it's impossible to eliminate UVR exposure to the skin, it can be minimized by wearing protective clothing and by applying sunblocks and sunscreens. Sunblocks, which are physical agents that act as barriers to UVR, often contain zinc oxide (ZnO), titanium(IV) oxide (TiO$_2$), or both, which are highly reflective white powders. Traditional ZnO sunblocks worn by lifeguards are opaque white, but by reducing the particle sizes of the white oxide to about 100 nm, they can be made invisible on the skin while retaining their UV-blocking

Structure of ecamsule

ability. Traditional chemical sunscreens, most of which are based on *p*-aminobenzoic acid, act primarily by binding to skin proteins and absorbing UVB photons. Recently, the Food and Drug Administration (FDA) has approved a sunscreen formula for use in the United States that has long been used abroad. The facial moisturizer Anthelios SX, marketed by L'Oreal, contains ecamsule (trade name Mexoryl SX), a sunscreen ingredient that is particularly effective at blocking short UVA radiation (320–340 nm). The product also contains other ingredients that block longer UVA rays and UVB rays to make it a broad-spectrum sunscreen. Although there are already some sunscreens, such as avobenzene, that offer UVA protection, the advantage of ecamsule is that it does not decompose on exposure to sunlight. A major disadvantage is that ecamsule is water soluble and thus is not useful at the beach.

increases their motions. This energy is then transferred to other types of molecules via collisions, causing an increase in the food's temperature. As we proceed in the study of chemistry, we will consider many of the classes of electromagnetic radiation and the ways in which they affect matter.

Figure 12.3
Classification of electromagnetic radiation.

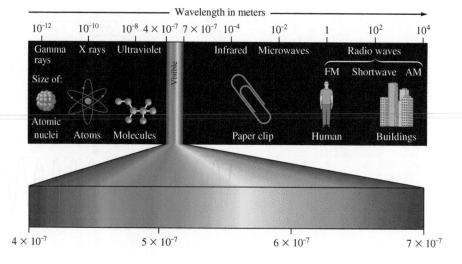

12.2 | The Nature of Matter

It is probably fair to say that at the end of the nineteenth century physicists were feeling rather smug. Available theories could explain phenomena ranging from the motions of the planets to the dispersion of visible light by a prism. Rumor has it that students were being discouraged from pursuing physics as a career because it was believed that all the major problems had been solved or at least described in terms of the current physical theories.

At the end of the nineteenth century, the idea prevailed that matter and energy were distinct. Matter was thought to consist of particles, whereas energy in the form of light (electromagnetic radiation) was described as a wave. Particles were things that had mass and whose positions in space could be specified. Waves were described as massless and delocalized; that is, their positions in space could not be specified. It was also assumed that there was no intermingling of matter and light. Everything known before 1900 seemed to fit neatly into this view.

At the beginning of the twentieth century, however, certain experimental results suggested that this picture was incorrect. The first important advance came in 1901 from German physicist Max Planck, who studied the profile (intensity versus wavelength) of the electromagnetic radiation emitted from a solid body heated to incandescence. (An example is a piece of iron that glows red and then white as it is heated to higher and higher temperatures.) The profiles shown in Fig. 12.4 are for so-called blackbody radiation. This may seem like a contradiction in terms, since a blackbody is an idealized object that absorbs all the radiation incident on it. The term is used in this context to mean radiation that originates from the thermal energy of the body only. It does not include radiation reflected from the object and does not depend on the material composing the object. Blackbody radiation is closely approximated by the radiation emitted through a tiny hole from a cavity inside an object. The main point to be made here is that the radiation profiles shown in Fig. 12.4 are not the ones expected from classical physics. The classical theory of matter, which assumes that matter can absorb or emit any quantity of energy, predicts a radiation profile that has no maximum and goes to infinite intensity at very short wavelengths (an effect often called the **ultraviolet catastrophe**).

Planck found that the observed profiles (with their intensity maxima) could be accounted for by postulating that energy can be gained or lost only in *whole-number multiples* of the quantity $h\nu$, where h is a constant now called **Planck's constant**, determined by experiment to have the value 6.626×10^{-34} J s. That is, the change in energy for a system ΔE can be represented by the equation

$$\Delta E = nh\nu$$

where n is an integer (1, 2, 3, . . .), h is Planck's constant, and ν is the frequency of the electromagnetic radiation absorbed or emitted.

Planck's result was a real surprise. Physicists had always assumed that the energy of matter was continuous, which meant that the transfer of any quantity of energy was possible. Now it seemed clear that energy is in fact **quantized** and can be transferred only in discrete units of size $h\nu$. Each of these small "packets" of energy is called a *quantum*. A system can transfer energy only in whole *quanta*. Thus energy seems to have particulate properties.

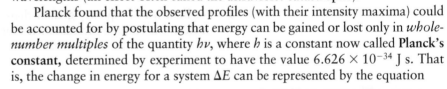

OWL INTERACTIVE EXAMPLE 12.1

The blue color in fireworks is often achieved by heating copper(I) chloride (CuCl) to about 1200°C. The hot compound emits blue light having a wavelength of 450 nm. What is the increment of energy (the quantum) that is emitted at 4.50×10^2 nm by CuCl?

Figure 12.4
The profile of radiation emitted from a blackbody. Note that the maximum shifts to shorter wavelengths as the temperature is increased, in agreement with the observed change from a reddish to a white glow as iron is heated to higher temperatures.

Energy can be gained or lost only in integer multiples of $h\nu$.

Planck's constant = 6.626×10^{-34} J s.

CuCl produces a blue flame when heated in a burner.

G. N. Lewis (see Section 13.10) actually coined the term "photon" in 1926.

Solution The quantum of energy can be calculated from the equation

$$\Delta E = h\nu$$

The frequency ν for this case can be calculated as follows:

$$\nu = \frac{c}{\lambda} = \frac{2.9979 \times 10^8 \text{ m/s}}{4.50 \times 10^{-7}\text{m}} = 6.66 \times 10^{14} \text{ s}^{-1}$$

So

$$\Delta E = h\nu = (6.626 \times 10^{-34} \text{ J s})(6.66 \times 10^{14} \text{ s}^{-1}) = 4.41 \times 10^{-19} \text{ J}$$

A sample of CuCl emitting light at 450 nm can lose energy only in increments of 4.41×10^{-19} J, the size of the quantum in this case.

The next important development in the knowledge of atomic structure came when Albert Einstein (Fig. 12.5) proposed that electromagnetic radiation is itself quantized. Einstein suggested that electromagnetic radiation can be viewed as a stream of "particles" now called **photons.** The energy of each photon is given by the expression

$$E_{\text{photon}} = h\nu = \frac{hc}{\lambda}$$

where h is Planck's constant, ν is the frequency of the radiation, and λ is the wavelength of the radiation.

Einstein arrived at this conclusion through his analysis of the **photoelectric effect** (for which he later was awarded the Nobel Prize). The photoelectric effect refers to the phenomenon in which electrons are emitted from the surface of a metal when light strikes it. The following observations characterize the photoelectric effect.

1. Studies in which the frequency of the light is varied show that no electrons are emitted by a given metal below a specific threshold frequency ν_0.

2. For light with frequency lower than the threshold frequency, no electrons are emitted regardless of the intensity of the light.

3. For light with frequency greater than the threshold frequency, the number of electrons emitted increases with the intensity of the light.

Figure 12.5

Albert Einstein (1879–1955) was born in Germany. Nothing in his early development suggested genius; even at the age of 9 he did not speak clearly, and his parents feared that he might have a handicap. When asked what profession Einstein should follow, his school principal replied, "It doesn't matter; he'll never make a success of anything." When he was 10, Einstein entered the Luitpold Gymnasium (high school), which was typical of German schools of that time in being harshly disciplinarian. There he developed a deep suspicion of authority and a skepticism that encouraged him to question and doubt—valuable qualities in a scientist. In 1905, while a patent clerk in Switzerland, Einstein published a paper explaining the photoelectric effect via the quantum theory. For this revolutionary thinking, he received a Nobel Prize in 1921. Highly regarded by this time, he worked in Germany until 1933, when Hitler's persecution of Jews forced him to come to the United States. He worked at the Institute for Advanced Study at Princeton University until his death in 1955.

Einstein was undoubtedly the greatest physicist of our age. Even if someone else had derived the theory of relativity, his other work would have ensured his ranking as the second greatest physicist of his time. Our concepts of space and time were radically changed by ideas he first proposed when he was 26 years old. From then until the end of his life, he attempted unsuccessfully to find a single unifying theory that would explain all physical events.

4. For light with frequency greater than the threshold frequency, the kinetic energy of the emitted electrons increases linearly with the frequency of the light.

These observations can be explained by assuming that electromagnetic radiation is quantized (consists of photons) and that the threshold frequency represents the minimum energy required to remove the electron from the metal's surface.

$$\text{Minimum energy required to remove an electron} = E_0 = h\nu_0$$

Because a photon with energy less than E_0 ($\nu < \nu_0$) cannot remove an electron, light with a frequency less than the threshold frequency produces no electrons. On the other hand, for light where $\nu > \nu_0$, the energy in excess of that required to remove the electron is given to the electron as kinetic energy (KE):

$$\text{KE}_{\text{electron}} = \tfrac{1}{2}mv^2 = h\nu - h\nu_0$$

Mass of electron	Velocity of electron	Energy of incident photon	Energy required to remove electron from metal's surface

Because in this picture the intensity of light is a measure of the number of photons present in a given part of the beam, a greater intensity means that more photons are available to release electrons (as long as $\nu > \nu_0$ for the radiation).

At about the same time that Einstein was performing his analysis of the photoelectric effect, he was also constructing the theory of special relativity. In connection with this work, Einstein derived the famous equation

$$E = mc^2$$

which he published in 1905. This equation points out the close relationship between energy and mass. In fact, we have learned that mass is a form of energy. When a system loses energy, it also loses mass. This result is more apparent if we rearrange the equation to the following form:

$$m = \frac{E}{c^2} \leftarrow \text{Energy}$$

Mass   Speed of light

Using this form of the equation, we can calculate the mass associated with a given quantity of energy.

If a beam of light can be considered to be a stream of "particles" (photons), do the photons have mass? The answer to this question is "no." Photons do not exhibit mass in the same way as classical particles do. Einstein's equations, however, predict that a photon has momentum, which is best thought of as an intrinsic property of the photon that does not depend separately on mass and velocity, unlike the case for a classical particle. In 1922 American physicist Arthur Compton performed experiments involving collisions of X rays with electrons. These experiments showed that photons do exhibit the momentum calculated from Einstein's equation. Also, photons do seem to be affected by gravity, as Einstein postulated in his general theory of relativity. However, it is important to recognize that the photon is in no sense a typical particle. A photon has mass only in a relativistic sense—it has no rest mass.

We can summarize the important conclusions from the work of Planck and Einstein as follows:

Energy is quantized. It can be transferred only in discrete units called quanta. Electromagnetic radiation, which was previously thought to exhibit only wave properties, seems to show certain characteristics of particulate matter as well. This phenomenon, illustrated in Fig. 12.6, is sometimes referred to as the **dual nature of light.**

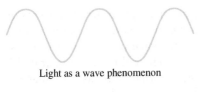

Light as a wave phenomenon

Light as a stream of photons

Figure 12.6
Electromagnetic radiation exhibits wave properties and particulate properties. The energy of each photon of the radiation is related to the wavelength and frequency by the equation $E_{\text{photon}} = h\nu = hc/\lambda$.

Thus light, which was previously thought to be purely wavelike, was found to have certain characteristics of particulate matter. But is the opposite also true? That is, does matter that is normally assumed to be particulate exhibit wave properties? This question was raised in 1923 by a young French physicist named Louis de Broglie (1892–1987), who derived the following relationship for the wavelength of a particle with momentum mv:

Do not confuse ν (frequency) with v (velocity).

$$\lambda = \frac{h}{mv}$$

This equation, called de Broglie's equation, allows us to calculate the wavelength for a particle, as shown in Example 12.2.

ⓌWL INTERACTIVE EXAMPLE 12.2

Compare the wavelength for an electron (mass = 9.11×10^{-31} kg) traveling at a speed of 1.0×10^7 m/s with that for a ball (mass = 0.10 kg) traveling at 35 m/s.

Solution We use the equation $\lambda = h/mv$, where

$$h = 6.626 \times 10^{-34} \text{ J s} \quad \text{or} \quad 6.626 \times 10^{-34} \text{ kg m}^2/\text{s}$$

since

$$1 \text{ J} = 1 \text{ kg m}^2/\text{s}^2$$

For the electron,

$$\lambda_e = \frac{6.626 \times 10^{-34} \dfrac{\text{kg m}^2}{\text{s}}}{(9.11 \times 10^{-31} \text{ kg})(1.0 \times 10^7 \text{ m/s})} = 7.3 \times 10^{-11} \text{ m}$$

For the ball,

$$\lambda_b = \frac{6.626 \times 10^{-34} \dfrac{\text{kg m}^2}{\text{s}}}{(0.10 \text{ kg})(35 \text{ m/s})} = 1.9 \times 10^{-34} \text{ m}$$

Notice from Example 12.2 that the wavelength associated with the ball is incredibly short. On the other hand, the wavelength of the electron, although quite small, happens to be of the same order as the spacing between the atoms in a typical crystal. This is important because, as we will see presently, it provides a means for testing de Broglie's equation.

Diffraction results when light is scattered from a regular array of points or lines. The diffraction of light from a diffraction grating is shown in the accompanying photograph. The colors result because the various wavelengths of visible light are not all scattered in the same way. The colors are "separated," giving the same effect as light passing through a prism. Just as a regular arrangement of ridges and grooves produces diffraction, so does a regular array of atoms or ions in a crystal. For example, when X rays are directed onto a crystal of sodium chloride with its regular array of Na^+ and Cl^- ions, the scattered radiation produces a **diffraction pattern** of bright areas and dark spots on a photographic plate, as shown in Fig. 12.7(a). This pattern occurs because the scattered light can interfere constructively (the peaks and troughs of the beams are in phase) to produce a bright area [Fig. 12.7(b)] or destructively (the peaks and troughs are out of phase) to produce a dark spot [Fig. 12.7(c)].

A diffraction pattern can be explained only in terms of waves. Thus this phenomenon provides a test for the postulate that particles such as electrons

Spectrum obtained by shining a beam of light at an angle to a diffraction grating.

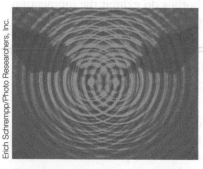

Constructive and destructive interference with water waves.

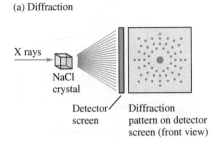

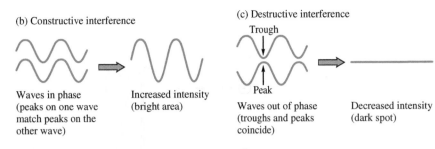

(a) Diffraction

X rays

NaCl crystal

Detector screen

Diffraction pattern on detector screen (front view)

(b) Constructive interference

Waves in phase (peaks on one wave match peaks on the other wave)

Increased intensity (bright area)

(c) Destructive interference

Trough

Peak

Waves out of phase (troughs and peaks coincide)

Decreased intensity (dark spot)

Figure 12.7

(a) Diffraction occurs when electromagnetic radiation is scattered from a regular array of objects, such as the ions in a crystal of sodium chloride. The large spot in the center is from the main incident beam of X rays. (b) Bright areas in the diffraction pattern result from *constructive interference* of waves. The waves are in phase; that is, their peaks match. (c) Dark spots result from *destructive interference* of waves. The waves are out of phase; the peaks of one wave coincide with the troughs of another wave.

have wave properties. As we saw in Example 12.2, an electron with a velocity of 10^7 m/s (easily achieved by acceleration of the electron in an electric field) has a wavelength of about 10^{-10} m, roughly the distance between the components in a typical crystal. This is important because diffraction occurs most efficiently when the spacing between the scattering points is about the same as the wavelength. Thus, if electrons actually do have an associated wavelength, a crystal should diffract electrons. An experiment to test this idea was carried out in 1927 by Davisson and Germer at Bell Laboratories. When they directed a beam of electrons at a nickel crystal, they observed a diffraction pattern similar to that seen from the diffraction of X rays. This result verified de Broglie's relationship, at least for electrons. Larger chunks of matter, such as balls, have wavelengths (Example 12.2) too small to verify experimentally. However, we believe that all matter obeys de Broglie's equation.

Now we have come full circle. Electromagnetic radiation, which at the turn of the twentieth century was thought to be a pure waveform, was found to exhibit particulate properties. Conversely, electrons, which were thought to be particles, were found to have a wavelength associated with them. The significance of these results is that matter and energy are not distinct. Energy is really a form of matter, and all matter shows the same types of properties. That is, *all matter exhibits both particulate and wave properties.* Large "pieces" of matter, such as baseballs, exhibit predominantly particulate properties. The associated wavelength is so small that it is not observed. Very small "pieces" of matter, such as photons, while showing some particulate properties through relativistic effects, exhibit predominantly wave properties. Pieces of matter with intermediate mass, such as electrons, show both the particulate and wave properties of matter.

12.3 | The Atomic Spectrum of Hydrogen

Recall from Chapter 2 that key information about the structure of the atom came from several experiments carried out in the early twentieth century. Particularly important were Thomson's discovery of the electron and Rutherford's discovery of the nucleus. Another important experiment concerned the study of the emission of light by excited hydrogen atoms. When a high-energy discharge is passed through a sample of hydrogen gas, the H_2 molecules absorb energy, causing some of the H—H bonds to break. The resulting hydrogen atoms are *excited;* that is, they contain excess energy, which they release by emitting light of various wavelengths to produce what is called the *emission spectrum* of the hydrogen atom.

To understand the significance of the hydrogen emission spectrum, we must first describe the **continuous spectrum** that results when white light is passed through a prism, as shown in Fig. 12.8(a). This spectrum, like the rainbow produced when sunlight is dispersed by raindrops, contains *all* the wave-

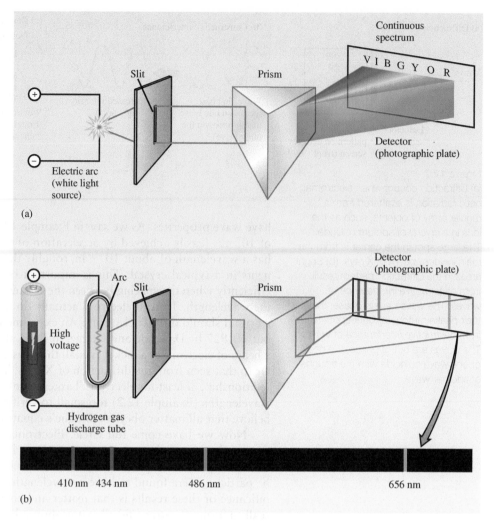

Figure 12.8

(a) A continuous spectrum containing all wavelengths of visible light (indicated by the first letters of the colors of the rainbow). (b) The hydrogen line spectrum contains only a few discrete wavelengths.

The energy of the electron in the hydrogen atom is quantized.

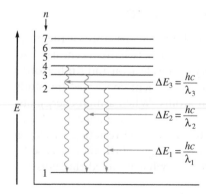

Figure 12.9

A change between two discrete energy levels emits a photon of light.

lengths of visible light. In contrast, when the hydrogen emission spectrum in the visible region is passed through a prism, as shown in Fig. 12.8(b), we see only a few lines, each corresponding to a discrete wavelength. The hydrogen emission spectrum is called a **line spectrum.**

What is the significance of the line spectrum of hydrogen? It indicates that *only certain energies are allowed for the electron in the hydrogen atom.* In other words, the energy of the electron in the hydrogen atom is *quantized.* Changes in energy between discrete energy levels in hydrogen produce only certain wavelengths of emitted light, as shown in Fig. 12.9. For example, a given change in energy from a high to a lower level gives a wavelength of light that can be calculated from Einstein's equation:

$$\Delta E = h\nu = \frac{hc}{\lambda} \leftarrow \text{Wavelength of light emitted}$$

$\uparrow$ Change in energy

$\nwarrow$ Frequency of light emitted

The discrete line spectrum of hydrogen shows that only certain energies are possible; that is, the electron energy levels are quantized. In contrast, if any energy level were allowed, the emission spectrum would be continuous.

12.4 | **The Bohr Model**

In 1913 a Danish physicist named Niels Bohr, aware of most of the experimental results we have just discussed, developed a **quantum model** for the hydrogen atom. Bohr proposed a model that included the idea that the *electron in a hydrogen atom moves around the nucleus only in certain allowed circular orbits.* He calculated the radii for these allowed orbits by using the theories of classical physics and by making some new assumptions.

From classical physics Bohr knew that a particle in motion tends to move in a straight line and can be made to travel in a circle only by application of a force toward the center of the circle. Thus Bohr reasoned that the tendency of the revolving electron to fly off the atom must be exactly balanced by its attraction for the positively charged nucleus. But classical physics also decreed that a charged particle under acceleration should radiate energy. Since an electron revolving around the nucleus constantly changes its direction, it is constantly accelerating. Therefore, the electron should emit light and lose energy and thus be drawn into the nucleus. This conclusion, of course, does not correlate with the existence of stable atoms.

Clearly, an atomic model based solely on the theories of classical physics was untenable. Bohr dealt with the problem of the collapse of the classical atom by simply assuming that the hydrogen electron could exist only in stationary, nonradiating orbits. Ultimately, the correct model had to account for the experimental spectrum of hydrogen, which showed that only certain electron energies were allowed. The experimental data were absolutely clear on this point. Bohr's model fits the experimental results by assuming that the angular momentum of the electron could occur only in certain increments. It wasn't clear why this should be true, but with this assumption Bohr's model gave hydrogen atom energy levels consistent with the hydrogen emission spectrum. The model is represented pictorially in Fig. 12.10.

Although we will not discuss its origins here, the expression for the *energy levels available to the electron in the hydrogen atom is*

$$E = -2.178 \times 10^{-18} \text{ J}\left(\frac{Z^2}{n^2}\right) \qquad (12.1)$$

Niels Bohr at 37 years of age, photographed in 1922 when he received the Nobel Prize for physics.

Angular momentum equals the product of mass, velocity, and orbital radius.

Figure 12.10

Electronic transitions in the Bohr model for the hydrogen atom. (a) An energy-level diagram for electronic transitions. (b) An orbit-transition diagram, which accounts for the experimental spectrum. (Note that the orbits shown are schematic. They are not drawn to scale.) (c) The resulting line spectrum on a photographic plate. Note that the lines in the visible region of the spectrum correspond to transitions from higher levels to the $n = 2$ level.

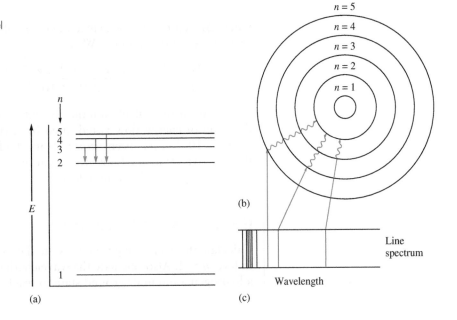

where n is an integer (the larger the value of n, the larger is the orbit radius) and Z is the atomic number ($Z = 1$ for hydrogen). The negative sign in Equation (12.1) simply means that the energy of the electron bound to the nucleus is lower than it would be if the electron were at an infinite distance ($n = \infty$) from the nucleus, where there is no interaction and the energy is zero:

The "J" in Equation (12.1) stands for joules.

$$E = -2.178 \times 10^{-18}\ \text{J}\left(\frac{Z^2}{\infty}\right) = 0$$

The energy of the electron in any orbit is negative relative to this reference state.

Equation (12.1) can be used to calculate the change in energy when the electron changes orbits. For example, suppose the electron in level $n = 6$ of an excited hydrogen atom falls back to level $n = 1$ as the hydrogen atom returns to its lowest possible energy state, its **ground state**. We use Equation (12.1) with $Z = 1$ since the hydrogen nucleus contains a single proton. The energies corresponding to the two states are

Equation (12.1) applies to all one-electron species. In addition to being used to calculate the energy levels in the hydrogen atom, it can also be used for He^+ ($Z = 2$), Li^{2+} ($Z = 3$), Be^{3+} ($Z = 4$), and so on.

For $n = 6$: $E_6 = -2.178 \times 10^{-18}\ \text{J}\left(\frac{1^2}{6^2}\right) = -6.05 \times 10^{-20}\ \text{J}$

For $n = 1$: $E_1 = -2.178 \times 10^{-18}\ \text{J}\left(\frac{1^2}{1^2}\right) = -2.178 \times 10^{-18}\ \text{J}$

Note that for $n = 1$ the electron has a more negative energy than it does for $n = 6$, which means that the electron is more tightly bound in the smallest allowed orbit.

The change in energy ΔE when the electron falls from $n = 6$ to $n = 1$ is

ΔE = energy of final state − energy of initial state

$= E_1 - E_6 = (-2.178 \times 10^{-18}\ \text{J}) - (-6.05 \times 10^{-20}\ \text{J})$

$= -2.118 \times 10^{-18}\ \text{J}$

The negative sign for the *change* in energy indicates that the atom has *lost* energy and is now in a more stable state. The energy is carried away from the atom by the production (emission) of a photon.

The wavelength of the emitted photon can be calculated from the equation

$$\Delta E = h\left(\frac{c}{\lambda}\right) \quad \text{or} \quad \lambda = \frac{hc}{\Delta E}$$

where ΔE represents the change in energy of the atom and thus equals the energy of the emitted photon. We have

$$\lambda = \frac{hc}{\Delta E} = \frac{(6.626 \times 10^{-34}\ \text{J s})(2.9979 \times 10^8\ \text{m/s})}{2.18 \times 10^{-18}\ \text{J}} = 9.379 \times 10^{-8}\ \text{m}$$

Note that for this calculation the absolute value of ΔE is used. In this case the direction of energy flow is indicated by saying that a photon of wavelength 9.379×10^{-8} m has been *emitted* from the hydrogen atom. Simply plugging the negative value of ΔE into the equation would produce a negative value for λ, which is physically meaningless.

⬛WL INTERACTIVE EXAMPLE 12.3

Calculate the energy required to excite the hydrogen electron from level $n = 1$ to level $n = 2$. Also calculate the wavelength of light that must be absorbed by a hydrogen atom in its ground state to reach this excited state.

Solution Using Equation (12.1) with $Z = 1$, we have

$$E_1 = -2.178 \times 10^{-18} \text{ J}\left(\frac{1^2}{1^2}\right) = -2.178 \times 10^{-18} \text{ J}$$

$$E_2 = -2.178 \times 10^{-18} \text{ J}\left(\frac{1^2}{2^2}\right) = -5.445 \times 10^{-19} \text{ J}$$

$$\Delta E = E_2 - E_1 = (-5.445 \times 10^{-19} \text{ J}) - (-2.178 \times 10^{-18} \text{ J})$$

$$= 1.634 \times 10^{-18} \text{ J}$$

The positive value for ΔE indicates that the system has gained energy. The wavelength of light that must be *absorbed* to produce this change is

$$\lambda = \frac{hc}{\Delta E} = \frac{(6.626 \times 10^{-34} \text{ J s})(2.9979 \times 10^8 \text{ m/s})}{1.634 \times 10^{-18} \text{ J}}$$

$$= 1.216 \times 10^{-7} \text{ m}$$

Note from Fig. 12.3 that the light required to produce the transition from the $n = 1$ to $n = 2$ level in hydrogen lies in the ultraviolet region.

At this time we must emphasize two important points about the Bohr model:

1. The model correctly fits the quantized energy levels of the hydrogen atom as inferred from its emission spectrum. These energy levels correspond to certain allowed circular orbits for the electrons.

2. As the electron becomes more tightly bound, its energy becomes more negative relative to the zero-energy reference state (corresponding to the electron being an infinite distance from the nucleus). That is, as the electron is brought closer to the nucleus, energy is released from the system.

Using Equation (12.1), we can derive a general equation for the electron moving from one level (n_{initial}) to another level (n_{final}):

$$\Delta E = \text{energy of level } n_{\text{final}} - \text{energy of level } n_{\text{initial}}$$

$$= E_{\text{final}} - E_{\text{initial}}$$

$$= (-2.178 \times 10^{-18} \text{ J})\left(\frac{1^2}{n_{\text{final}}^2}\right) - (-2.178 \times 10^{-18} \text{ J})\left(\frac{1^2}{n_{\text{initial}}^2}\right)$$

$$= -2.178 \times 10^{-18} \text{ J}\left(\frac{1}{n_{\text{final}}^2} - \frac{1}{n_{\text{initial}}^2}\right) \tag{12.2}$$

EXAMPLE 12.4

Calculate the minimum energy required to remove the electron from a hydrogen atom in its ground state.

Solution

■ What are we trying to solve?

We want to determine the energy needed to remove a ground state electron from a hydrogen atom. We know how to determine the energy required for the electron moving from one level to another. The equation is

$$\Delta E = -2.178 \times 10^{-18} \text{ J}\left(\frac{1}{n_{\text{final}}^2} - \frac{1}{n_{\text{initial}}^2}\right)$$

Since the electron starts in the ground state, $n_{\text{initial}} = 1$. To determine ΔE we only need n_{final}. So what is n_{final} if we are removing an electron? Recall that

Chemical Insights   The New, Improved Atomic Clock

To celebrate the turn of the century, the National Institute of Standards and Technology (NIST) in Boulder, Colorado, gave the world a new precision timepiece—a clock so accurate that it will neither gain nor lose a second in 20 million years! Called NIST F-1, the new cesium atomic clock is classified as a fountain clock because it tosses spheres of cesium atoms upward inside the device.

The timepiece works as follows: Gaseous cesium atoms are introduced into a vacuum chamber where six infrared laser beams are positioned to push the cesium atoms into a spherical arrangement. In this process the cesium atoms are slowed almost to the point of absolute zero. Two vertical lasers then "toss" the sphere upward for about a meter in a microwave-filled cavity. At this point all of the lasers are turned off. The sphere of atoms then falls through the cavity under the influence of gravity, and some of the atoms are excited by the microwaves. At the bottom the cesium atoms, which were excited by the microwaves, are induced (by a laser beam) to emit light (a process called fluorescence). The entire process is repeated many times during which the frequency of the microwave energy in the cavity is adjusted until the maximum fluorescence is achieved. The microwave frequency that produces the greatest fluorescence is the natural resonance frequency for the cesium

atom. This frequency (9.192631770×10^9 cycles per second) is used to define the second. The NIST F-1 clock is much more accurate than its predecessor, NIST-7, which fired heated cesium atoms at high speeds through a horizontal microwave chamber. In NIST F-1 the slower movement of the atoms gives more time for the microwaves to interact with the atoms so that the characteristic frequency can be more precisely determined.

NIST F-1, which is now the official clock in the United States, provides the extremely accurate timekeeping necessary for modern technology-based operations. NIST F-1 is also in the pool of atomic clocks used to define Coordinated Universal Time (known as UTC), the official world time.

However, the reign of the cesium-based superclocks may be over very soon. A team led by physicist John C. Berquist at NIST has developed an atomic clock, called the NIST optical clock, that is based on the interactions between ultraviolet light and a single mercury atom. Studies by the Berquist group show that the new optical clock is 10 times more precise than the cesium clock. This means that the optical clock would have an error of only 0.1 second in 70 million years of continuous operation. The search is now underway for an atom that might provide even more precise time measurements than mercury.

James Bergquist and D. Wineland/National Institute of Standards and Technology

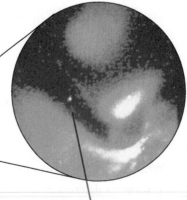

Single Hg$^+$ ion

When installed in an atomic clock, this molybdenum structure (left) traps a mercury ion (right) at its center. The clock uses the ion to keep time with unprecedented precision.

$E = 0$ when there is no interaction between the nucleus and the electron. This is true if the electron were at an infinite distance from the nucleus or $n_{final} = \infty$.

So we have

$$\Delta E = -2.178 \times 10^{-18} \text{ J}\left(\frac{1}{\infty} - \frac{1}{1^2}\right)$$

$$\Delta E = -2.178 \times 10^{-18} \text{ J}(0 - 1) = 2.178 \times 10^{-18} \text{ J}$$

Thus the energy required to remove the electron from a hydrogen atom in its ground state is 2.178×10^{-18} J.

Equation (12.2) can be used to calculate the energy change between *any* two energy levels in a hydrogen atom, as shown in Example 12.4.

At first, Bohr's model appeared to be very promising. The energy levels calculated by Bohr closely agreed with the values obtained from the hydrogen emission spectrum. However, when Bohr's model was applied to atoms other than hydrogen, it did not work at all. Although some attempts were made to adapt the model using elliptical orbits, it was concluded that Bohr's model is fundamentally incorrect. The model is, however, very important historically because it shows that the observed quantization of energy in atoms can be explained by making rather simple assumptions. Bohr's model paved the way for later theories. It is important to realize, however, that the current theory of atomic structure is in no way derived from the Bohr model. Electrons do *not* move around the nucleus in circular orbits, as we will see later in this chapter.

Although Bohr's model fits the energy levels for hydrogen, it is a fundamentally incorrect model for the hydrogen atom.

12.5 | The Quantum Mechanical Description of the Atom

By the mid-1920s it had become apparent that the Bohr model was not a valid one. A totally new approach was needed. Three physicists were at the forefront of this effort: Werner Heisenberg, Louis de Broglie, and Erwin Schrödinger. The approach developed by de Broglie and Schrödinger became known as **wave mechanics** or, more commonly, **quantum mechanics**. As we have already seen, de Broglie originated the idea that the electron, previously considered to be a particle, also shows wave properties. Pursuing this line of reasoning, Schrödinger, an Austrian physicist, decided to attack the problem of atomic structure by giving emphasis to the wave properties of the electron. To Schrödinger and de Broglie, the electron bound to the nucleus seemed similar to a standing wave, and they began research on a wave mechanical description of the atom.

The most familiar example of standing waves occurs in association with musical instruments such as guitars or violins, where a string attached at both ends vibrates to produce the musical tone. The waves are described as standing since they are stationary; the waves do not travel along the length of the string. The motions of the string can be explained as a combination of simple waves of the type shown in Fig. 12.11. The dots in this figure indicate the nodes, or points of zero lateral (sideways) displacement for a given wave. Note that there are limitations on the allowed wavelengths of the standing wave. Since each end of the string is fixed, there is always a node at each end. This means that there must be a whole number of *half*-wavelengths in any of the allowed motions of the string (Fig. 12.11).

The wave model was applied by de Broglie to the Bohr atom by imagining the electron in the hydrogen atom to be a standing wave. As shown in

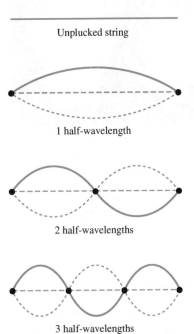

Unplucked string

1 half-wavelength

2 half-wavelengths

3 half-wavelengths

Figure 12.11
The standing wave produced by the vibration of a guitar string fastened at both ends. Each dot represents a node (a point of zero displacement).

Chemical Insights | Fireworks

The art of using mixtures of chemicals to produce explosives is an ancient one. Black powder—a mixture of potassium nitrate, charcoal, and sulfur—was being used in China well before 1000 A.D. and has been used through the centuries in military explosives, in construction blasting, and in fireworks. The DuPont Company, now a major chemical manufacturer, started out as a manufacturer of black powder. In fact, the founder, Eleuthère du Pont, learned the manufacturing technique from none other than Lavoisier.

Before the nineteenth century, fireworks were mainly confined to rockets and loud bangs. Orange and yellow colors came from the presence of charcoal and iron filings. However, with the great advances in chemistry in the nineteenth century, new compounds found their way into fireworks. Salts of copper, strontium, and barium added brilliant colors. Magnesium and aluminum metals gave a dazzling white light. Fireworks, in fact, have changed very little since then.

How do fireworks produce their brilliant colors and loud bangs? Actually, only a handful of different chemicals are responsible for most of the spectacular effects. The noise and flashes are produced by an oxidizer (an oxidizing agent) and a fuel (a reducing agent). A common mixture involves potassium perchlorate ($KClO_4$) as the oxidizer and aluminum and sulfur as the fuel. The perchlorate compound oxidizes the fuel in a very exothermic reaction, which produces a brilliant flash, caused by the aluminum, and a loud report from the rapidly expanding gases produced. For a color effect, an element with a colored emission spectrum is included. Recall that the electrons in atoms can be raised to higher energy levels when the atoms absorb energy. The excited atoms can then release this excess energy by emitting light of specific wavelengths, often in the visible region. In fireworks the energy to excite the electrons comes from the reaction between the oxidizer and fuel.

Yellow colors in fireworks are caused by the 589-nm emission of sodium atoms. Red colors come from strontium salts emitting at 606 nm and

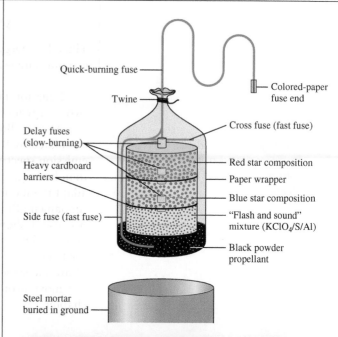

Quick-burning fuse
Twine
Colored-paper fuse end
Delay fuses (slow-burning)
Cross fuse (fast fuse)
Heavy cardboard barriers
Red star composition
Paper wrapper
Blue star composition
Side fuse (fast fuse)
"Flash and sound" mixture ($KClO_4$/S/Al)
Black powder propellant
Steel mortar buried in ground

Courtesy, Pyro Shows of LaFollette, Tennessee

A typical aerial shell used in fireworks displays. Time-delayed fuses cause a shell to explode in stages. In this case a red starburst occurs first, followed by a blue starburst, and finally a flash and loud report. Reprinted with permission from *Chemical and Engineering News*, Vol. 59, Issue 26, June 29, 1981, p. 25. Copyright © 1981 American Chemical Society.

636–688 nm. (This red color may be familiar from highway safety flares.) Barium salts give a green color in fireworks, caused by a series of emission lines between 505 and 535 nm. A really good blue

Chemicals Commonly Used in the Manufacture of Fireworks

Oxidizers	Fuels	Special Effects
Potassium nitrate	Aluminum	Red flame: strontium nitrate, strontium carbonate
Potassium chlorate	Magnesium	Green flame: barium nitrate, barium chlorate
Potassium perchlorate	Titanium	Blue flame: copper carbonate, copper sulfate, copper oxide
Ammonium perchlorate	Charcoal	Yellow flame: sodium oxalate, cryolite (Na_3AlF_6)
Barium nitrate	Sulfur	White flame: magnesium, aluminum
Barium chlorate	Antimony sulfide	Gold sparks: iron filings, charcoal
Strontium nitrate	Dextrin	White sparks: aluminum, magnesium, aluminum–magnesium alloy, titanium
	Red gum	Whistle effect: potassium benzoate or sodium salicylate
	Polyvinyl chloride	White smoke: mixture of potassium nitrate and sulfur
		Colored smoke: mixture of potassium chlorate, sulfur, and an organic dye

color, however, is hard to obtain. Copper salts give a blue color, emitting in the 420–460-nm region. But difficulties occur because another commonly used oxidizing agent, potassium chlorate ($KClO_3$), reacts with copper salts to form copper chlorate, a highly explosive compound that is dangerous to store. Paris green, a copper salt containing arsenic, was once extensively used but is now considered to be too toxic.

A typical aerial shell is shown in the figure. The shell is launched from a mortar (a steel cylinder), using black powder as the propellant. Time-delayed fuses are used to fire the shell in stages. A list of chemicals commonly used in fireworks is given in the table.

Although you might think that the chemistry of fireworks is simple, the achievement of the vivid white flashes and the brilliant colors requires complex combinations of chemicals. For example, because the white flashes produce high flame temperatures, the colors tend to wash out. Thus oxidizers, such as $KClO_4$, are sometimes used with fuels that produce relatively low flame temperatures. An added difficulty, however, is that perchlorates are very prone to accidental ignition and are therefore quite hazardous. Another problem

arises from the use of sodium salts. Because sodium produces an extremely bright yellow emission, sodium salts cannot be used when other colors are desired. Carbon-based fuels also give a yellow flame that masks other colors, therefore limiting the use of organic compounds as fuels. You can see that the manufacture of fireworks that produce the desired effects and are also safe to handle requires careful selection of chemicals. And, of course, there is still the dream of that special deep blue flame.

Carlos E. Santa Maria/Shutterstock.com

Fireworks are a beautiful illustration of chemistry in action.

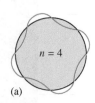

$n = 4$

(a)

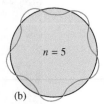

$n = 5$

(b)

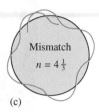

Mismatch
$n = 4\frac{1}{3}$

(c)

Figure 12.12
The hydrogen electron visualized as a standing wave around the nucleus. The circumference of a particular circular orbit has to correspond to a whole number of wavelengths, as shown in (a) and (b), or else destructive interference occurs, as shown in (c). This model is consistent with the fact that only certain electron energies are allowed; the atom is quantized. (Although this idea has encouraged scientists to use a wave theory, it does not mean that the electron really travels in circular orbits.)

Fig. 12.12, only certain circular orbits have a circumference into which a whole number of wavelengths of the standing electron wave will "fit." All other orbits would produce destructive interference of the standing electron wave and are not allowed. This seemed like a possible explanation for the observed quantization of the hydrogen atom. The mathematical formalism that Schrödinger developed in 1925 to describe the hydrogen electron as a wave was heavily based on the classical descriptions of wave phenomena. We will first give an overview of this approach before considering it in more detail.

The form of Schrödinger's equation is

$$\hat{H}\psi = E\psi$$

where ψ, called the **wave function**, is a function of the coordinates (x, y, and z) of the electron's position in three-dimensional space, and where $\hat{H}$ represents a set of mathematical instructions called an *operator*. An operator is a mathematical tool that acts on a function to produce another function. In some special cases, the operator gives back the original function simply multiplied by a constant. Note that the Schrödinger equation corresponds to such a special case. In the Schrödinger equation, the operator $\hat{H}$, called the Hamiltonian, acts to give back the wave function multiplied by the constant E, which represents the total energy of the atom (the sum of the potential energy due to the attraction between the proton and the electron and the kinetic energy of the moving electron). When this equation is analyzed, many solutions are found. Each solution consists of a wave function ψ that is characterized by a particular value of E. A specific wave function for a given electron is often called an **orbital.** It is important to recognize that Schrödinger could not be sure that treating an electron as a wave makes any sense: The test would be whether the model could correctly fit the experimental data for hydrogen and other atoms.

To illustrate the most important ideas of the wave mechanical (quantum mechanical) model of the atom, we will first concentrate on the wave function corresponding to the lowest energy for the hydrogen atom. This wave function is called the 1s orbital. The first point of interest is the meaning of the word *orbital*. One thing is clear: An orbital is *not* a Bohr orbit. The electron in the hydrogen 1s orbital is not moving around the nucleus in a circular orbit. How, then, is the electron moving? The answer is somewhat surprising: *We do not know.* The wave function gives us no information about the movements of the electron. This observation is somewhat disturbing. When we solve problems involving the motions of particles in the macroscopic world, we are able to predict their trajectories. For example, when two billiard balls with known velocities collide, we can predict their motions after the collision. However, we cannot predict the electron's motion using the 1s orbital function. Does this mean that the theory is useless? Not necessarily: We have already learned that an electron does not behave much like a billiard ball, so we must examine the situation closely before we discard the theory.

Werner Heisenberg, who was also involved in the development of the quantum mechanical model for the atom, discovered a very important principle in 1927 that helps us to understand the meaning of orbitals—the **Heisenberg uncertainty principle.** Heisenberg's mathematical analysis led him to a surprising conclusion: *There is a fundamental limitation to just how precisely we can know both the position and the momentum of a particle at a given time.* Stated mathematically, the uncertainty principle is

$$\Delta x \cdot \Delta p \geq \frac{\hbar}{2}$$

where Δx is the uncertainty in a particle's position, Δp is the uncertainty in a particle's momentum, and $\hbar$ is Planck's constant divided by 2π ($\hbar = h/2\pi$).

Thus the minimum uncertainty in the product $\Delta x \cdot \Delta p$ is $h/4\pi$. This relationship means that the more precisely we know a particle's position, the less precisely we can know its momentum, and vice versa. This limitation is so small for large particles such as baseballs or billiard balls that it is unnoticed. However, for a small particle such as the electron, the limitation becomes quite important. Applied to the electron, the uncertainty principle implies that we cannot know the exact path of the electron as it moves around the nucleus. It is therefore not appropriate to assume that the electron is moving around the nucleus in a well-defined orbit as in the Bohr model.

EXAMPLE 12.5

The hydrogen atom has a radius on the order of 0.05 nm. Assuming that we know the position of an electron to an accuracy of 1% of the hydrogen radius, calculate the uncertainty in the velocity of the electron using the Heisenberg uncertainty principle. Then compare this value with the uncertainty in the velocity of a ball of mass 0.2 kg and radius 0.05 m whose position is known to an accuracy of 1% of its radius.

The uncertainty principle is sometimes called the indeterminacy principle.

Solution From Heisenberg's uncertainty principle, the smallest possible uncertainty in the product $\Delta x \cdot \Delta p$ is $\hbar/2$; that is,

$$\Delta x \cdot \Delta p = \frac{\hbar}{2} = \frac{h}{4\pi}$$

For the electron the uncertainty in position (Δx) is 1% of 0.05 nm, or

$$\Delta x = (0.01)(0.05 \text{ nm}) = 5. \times 10^{-4} \text{ nm}$$

Converting to meters gives

$$5 \times 10^{-4} \text{ nm} \times \frac{10^{-9} \text{ m}}{1 \text{ nm}} = 5 \times 10^{-13} \text{ m}$$

The values of the constants are

$$m = \text{mass of the electron} = 9.11 \times 10^{-31} \text{ kg}$$

$$h = 6.626 \times 10^{-34} \text{ J s} = 6.626 \times 10^{-34} \frac{\text{kg m}^2}{\text{s}}$$

$$\pi = 3.14$$

We can now solve for the uncertainty in momentum:

$$\Delta p = \frac{\hbar}{2 \cdot \Delta x} = \frac{h}{4\pi \cdot \Delta x} = \frac{6.626 \times 10^{-34} \frac{\text{kg m}^2}{\text{s}}}{4(3.14)(5 \times 10^{-13} \text{ m})}$$

$$= 1.05 \times 10^{-22} \text{ kg m/s} \quad \text{(keeping extra significant figures)}$$

Recalling that $p = mv$ and assuming that the electron mass is constant (ignoring any relativistic corrections), we have

$$\Delta p = \Delta(mv) = m\Delta v$$

and the uncertainty in velocity is

$$\Delta v = \frac{\Delta p}{m} = \frac{1.05 \times 10^{-22} \text{ kg m/s}}{9.11 \times 10^{-31} \text{ kg}} = 1.15 \times 10^8 \text{ m/s} = 1 \times 10^8 \text{ m/s}$$

Thus, if we know the electron's position with a minimum uncertainty of 5×10^{-13} m, the uncertainty in the electron's velocity is at least 1×10^8 m/s. This is a very large number; in fact, it is the same magnitude as the speed of

Chemical Insights   Electrons as Waves

Although scientists talk about the dual wave and particle properties of electrons, many nonscientists still believe that electrons are only tiny particles. Rooted as we are in the macroscopic world, it can be difficult for some to picture a particle as also being a wave. One look at the accompanying picture, however, should help change that. What looks like ripples surrounding two barely submerged pebbles in a pool of water is really the surface of a copper crystal.

Although they are true believers in the wave nature of electrons, the physicists at the IBM Almaden Research Center in San Jose, California, were genuinely surprised when their scanning tunneling microscope (STM) produced this image of the copper surface. "We looked at the surface with all these waves and thought, 'Is our machine broken?'" says Michael Crommie, one of the IBM physicists. But the researchers soon realized that the waves were produced by electrons confined to the metal's surface that bounced off impurities (the two pits). Because the electrons are waves, they form interference patterns after reflecting off the impurities, producing standing waves.

To further explore this behavior, the IBM scientists constructed a "quantum corral" by using their STM to place 48 iron atoms on a copper surface in a circle approximately 14 nm in diameter. Then using the STM to study electron behavior on the copper surface inside the corral, they observed the standing electron waves shown in the photo on the right. This image provides a unique visual confirmation of what the Schrödinger equation predicts. Electrons are wavelike. Seeing is believing!

(left) The electrons form interference patterns, the ripples shown here, and produce standing waves.
(right) Iron atoms in a circular "corral" cause electron standing waves.

Photos: Research Division, Almaden Research Center/IBM Corporation

light (3×10^8 m/s). At this level of uncertainty, we have virtually no idea of the velocity of the electron.

For the ball, the uncertainty in position (Δx) is 1% of 0.05 m, or 5×10^{-4} m. Thus the minimum uncertainty in velocity is

$$\Delta v = \frac{\Delta p}{m} = \frac{h}{\Delta x \cdot m \cdot 4\pi} = \frac{6.626 \times 10^{-34} \frac{\text{kg m}^2}{\text{s}}}{(5 \times 10^{-4}\ \text{m})(0.2\ \text{kg})(4)(3.14)}$$

$$= 5 \times 10^{-31}\ \text{m/s}$$

This means there is a very small (undetectable) uncertainty in our measurements of the speed of a ball. Note that this uncertainty is not caused by the limitations of measuring instruments; Δv is an *inherent* uncertainty.

Thus the uncertainty principle is negligible in the world of macroscopic objects but is very important for objects with small masses, such as the electron.

12.6 | The Particle in a Box

Overview

The Schrödinger wave equation, $\hat{H}\psi = E\psi$, lies at the heart of the quantum mechanical description of atoms. Recall from the preceding discussion that $\hat{H}$ represents an operator (the Hamiltonian) that "extracts" the total energy E (the sum of the potential and kinetic energies) from the wave function. The wave function ψ depends on the x, y, and z coordinates of the electron's position in space.

Note that the Schrödinger equation requires that when ψ is operated on by $\hat{H}$, the result is ψ multiplied by a constant, E, that represents the total energy of the particular state described by ψ. As we will see, there are many possible solutions to the Schrödinger equation for a given system. For example, for the hydrogen atom there are many functions that satisfy the Schrödinger equation, each one corresponding to a particular energy for hydrogen's electron. Each of these specific wave functions for the hydrogen atom is called an orbital.

Although the detailed solution of the Schrödinger equation for the hydrogen atom is not appropriate in this text, we will illustrate some of the properties of wave mechanics and wave functions by using the wave equation to describe a very simple, hypothetical system commonly called "the particle in a box," a situation in which a particle is trapped in a one-dimensional box that has infinitely high "sides." It is important to recognize that this situation is not an accurate physical model for the hydrogen atom. That is, the hydrogen atom is really not much like this particle in a box. The reasons for treating the particle in a box are that (1) it illustrates the mathematics of wave mechanics, (2) it gives an indication of the characteristics of wave functions, and (3) it shows how energy quantization arises. Thus this treatment of a particle in a box illustrates the "flavor" of the wave mechanical description of the hydrogen atom, but it should not be taken to be an accurate representation of the hydrogen atom itself.

The Particle in a Box as a Model

Consider a particle with mass m that is free to move back and forth along one dimension (we arbitrarily choose x) between the values $x = 0$ and $x = L$ (that is, we are considering a one-dimensional "box" of size L meters). We will assume that the potential energy $V(x)$ of the particle is zero at all points along its path, except at the endpoints $x = 0$ and $x = L$, where $V(x)$ is infinitely large. In effect, we have a repulsive barrier of infinite strength at each end of the box. Thus the particle is trapped in a one-dimensional box with impenetrable walls (Fig. 12.13).

Figure 12.13

A schematic representation of a particle in a one-dimensional box with infinitely high potential walls.

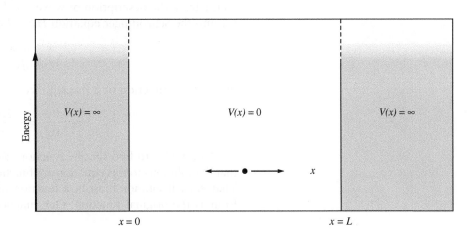

Chemistry Explorers   Charles Sykes Researches Surface Architecture

Charles Sykes, Assistant Professor of Chemistry at Tufts University in Medford, Massachusetts, did his undergraduate work at Oxford University (United Kingdom) and obtained his Ph.D. from Cambridge University (United Kingdom). His interests focus on how atoms and molecules inter-act on surfaces and on building novel, nanoscale surface structures using scanning tunneling microscopy (STM), which enables control of single atoms and molecules. The figure shows a "quantum corral," which is made of approximately 650 gold atoms on a metallic surface. The peaks inside the triangle represent electron density maxima that are caused by constructive interference of the electron waves as they are reflected by the edges of the box. Simple particle-in-a-box calculations can predict these maxima.

Charles Sykes.

Courtesy of M. El Kouedi/Charles Sykes

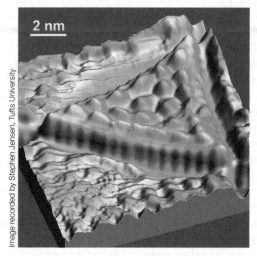

Image recorded by Stephen Jensen, Tufts University

Surface architecture showing electrons forming an interference pattern.

A goal of Professor Sykes's research group is to understand how molecules approaching such a surface will interact with the electron density on the surface and to explore how to tailor surfaces and better assist molecules to self-assemble in new surface architectures. Professor Sykes is also interested in studying the effect of surface structure on the ability of the surface to catalyze various chemical reactions.

As we mentioned before, the Schrödinger equation contains the energy operator $\hat{H}$. In this case, since the potential energy is zero inside the box, the only energy possible is the kinetic energy of the particle as it moves back and forth along the x axis. The operator for this kinetic energy is

$$-\frac{\hbar^2}{2m}\frac{d^2}{dx^2}$$

where $\hbar$ is Planck's constant divided by 2π, m is the mass of the particle, and d^2/dx^2 is the second derivative with respect to x. The form of this operator comes from the description of waves in classical physics. Inserting this operator into the Schrödinger equation $\hat{H}\psi = E\psi$ gives

$$-\frac{\hbar^2}{2m}\frac{d^2\psi}{dx^2} = E\psi$$

where ψ is a function of x {$[\psi(x)]$}. We can rearrange this equation to give

$$\frac{d^2\psi}{dx^2} = -\frac{2mE}{\hbar^2}\psi$$

Our goal is to find specific functions $\psi(x)$ that satisfy this equation. Notice that the solutions to this equation are functions such that $d^2\psi/dx^2 = (\text{constant})\psi$. That is, each solution must be a function whose second derivative has the same form as the original function. One function that behaves this way is the sine function. For example, consider the function $A \sin(kx)$, where A and k are constants. We will now take the second derivative of this function with respect to x:

$$\frac{d^2}{dx^2}(A \sin kx) = A\frac{d}{dx}\left(\frac{d \sin kx}{dx}\right) = A\frac{d}{dx}(k \cos kx)$$

$$= Ak\left(\frac{d \cos kx}{dx}\right) = Ak(-k \sin kx)$$

$$= -Ak^2 \sin kx = -k^2 A \sin kx$$

Thus we have shown that

$$\frac{d^2(A \sin kx)}{dx^2} = -k^2(A \sin kx)$$

This is just the type of function that will satisfy the Schrödinger equation for the particle in a box. In fact, when we compare the general form of the Schrödinger equation

$$\frac{d^2\psi}{dx^2} = -\frac{2mE}{\hbar^2}\psi$$

with

$$\frac{d^2(A \sin kx)}{dx^2} = -k^2(A \sin kx)$$

we see that

$$-k^2 = -\frac{2mE}{\hbar^2}$$

which can be rearranged to give an expression for energy:

$$E = \frac{\hbar^2 k^2}{2m}$$

What does this equation mean? We have simply specified that A and k are constants. What values can these constants have? Note that if they could assume any values, this equation would lead to an infinite number of possible energies—that is, a continuous distribution of energy levels. However, this is not correct. For reasons we will discuss presently, we find that only certain energies are allowed. That is, this system is quantized. In fact, the ability of wave mechanics to account for the observed (but initially unexpected) quantization of energy in nature is one of the most important factors in convincing us that it may be a correct description of the properties of matter.

Quantization enters the wave mechanical description of the particle in a box via the boundary conditions. Boundary conditions arise from the physical requirements of natural systems. That is, we must insist that our descriptions of natural systems make physical sense. For example, assume that in describing an aqueous solution containing an acid we arrive at the expression $[H^+]^2 = 4.0 \times 10^{-8} \ M^2$. The solutions to this expression are

$$[H^+] = 2.0 \times 10^{-4} \ M \quad \text{and} \quad [H^+] = -2.0 \times 10^{-4} \ M$$

In doing such a problem, we automatically reject the second possibility because there is no physical meaning for a negative concentration. What we have done here is apply a type of boundary condition to this situation.

The boundary conditions for the particle in a box enforce the following facts:

1. The particle cannot be outside the box—it is bound inside the box.

2. In a given state the total probability of finding the particle in the box must be 1.

3. The wave function must be continuous.

We have seen that the function $\psi = A \sin(kx)$ satisfies the Schrödinger equation $\hat{H}\psi = E\psi$. We will now define the constants k and A so that this function also satisfies the boundary conditions based on the three constraints listed above. Because the particle must stay inside the box, and because the wave function must be continuous, the value of $\psi(x)$ must be zero at each wall. That is,

$$\psi(0) = 0 \quad \text{and} \quad \psi(L) = 0$$

Recall that the sine function is zero at angles of $0°$, $180°$ (π radians), $360°$ (2π radians), and so on. Thus the function $A \sin(kx)$ is automatically zero when $x = 0$.

The requirement that the wave function must also be zero at the other wall, which can be stated as $\psi(L) = A \sin(kL) = 0$, means that k is limited to the values of $n\pi/L$, where n is an integer $(1, 2, 3, \ldots)$. That is,

$$\psi(x) = A \sin\left(\frac{n\pi}{L}x\right)$$

then

$$\psi(L) = A \sin\left(\frac{n\pi}{L} \cdot L\right) = A \sin(n\pi) = 0$$

To assign the value of the constant A, we need to introduce a new idea. In the application of wave mechanics to the description of matter, scientists have learned to associate the square of the wave function with probability. As we will discuss in more detail below, this means that the square of the wave function evaluated at a given point gives the relative probability of finding a particle near that point. This concept is relevant to the boundary conditions for the particle in a box because the total probability in a given state must be 1. To be more precise, the probability of finding the particle on a segment of the x axis of length dx surrounding point x is $\psi^2(x)\,dx$. Because there is one particle in the box, the sum of all those probabilities along the x axis from $x = 0$ to $x = L$ must be 1. We sum these probabilities over the length of the box (from $x = 0$ to $x = L$) by integration from $x = 0$ to $x = L$:

$$\begin{array}{l}\text{Total probability of finding} \\ \text{the particle in the box}\end{array} = \int_0^L \psi^2(x)\,dx = 1$$

Substituting $\psi(x) = A \sin[(n\pi/L)x]$, we have

$$\int_0^L \psi^2(x)\,dx = \int_0^L A^2 \sin^2\left(\frac{n\pi}{L}x\right)dx = 1$$

or

$$\int_0^L \sin^2\left(\frac{n\pi}{L}x\right)dx = \frac{1}{A^2}$$

The value of the integral is $L/2$, which means that

$$\frac{L}{2} = \frac{1}{A^2} \quad \text{and} \quad A = \sqrt{\frac{2}{L}}$$

Now that we know the allowed values of k and A, we can specify the wave function for the particle in a one-dimensional box as

$$\psi(x) = \sqrt{\frac{2}{L}} \sin\left(\frac{n\pi}{L}x\right)$$

We can also substitute the value of k into the expression for energy:

$$E = \frac{\hbar^2 k^2}{2m} = \frac{\hbar^2(n\pi/L)^2}{2m}$$

Substituting $\hbar = h/2\pi$ gives

$$E = \frac{n^2 h^2}{8mL^2} \qquad \text{where} \qquad n = 1, 2, 3, 4, \ldots$$

Note that this analysis leads to a series of solutions to the Schrödinger equation, where each function corresponds to a given energy state:

n	Function	Energy
1	$\psi_1 = \sqrt{\dfrac{2}{L}} \sin\left(\dfrac{\pi}{L}x\right)$	$E_1 = \dfrac{h^2}{8mL^2}$
2	$\psi_2 = \sqrt{\dfrac{2}{L}} \sin\left(\dfrac{2\pi}{L}x\right)$	$E_2 = \dfrac{4h^2}{8mL^2} = \dfrac{h^2}{2mL^2}$
3	$\psi_3 = \sqrt{\dfrac{2}{L}} \sin\left(\dfrac{3\pi}{L}x\right)$	$E_3 = \dfrac{9h^2}{8mL^2}$
4	$\psi_4 = \sqrt{\dfrac{2}{L}} \sin\left(\dfrac{4\pi}{L}x\right)$	$E_4 = \dfrac{16h^2}{8mL^2} = \dfrac{2h^2}{mL^2}$
$\vdots$	$\vdots$	$\vdots$

Notice something very important about these results. The application of the boundary conditions has led to a series of *quantized* energy levels. That is, only certain energies are allowed for the particle bound in the box. This result fits very nicely with the experimental evidence, such as the hydrogen emission spectrum, that nature does not allow continuous energy levels for *bound* systems, as classical physics had led us to expect. Note that the energies are quantized, because the boundary conditions require that n assume only integer values. Consequently, we call n the quantum number for this system.

We can diagram the solutions to the particle-in-a-box problem conveniently by showing a plot of the wave function that corresponds to each energy level. The energy level, wave function, and probability distribution are shown in Fig. 12.14 for the first three levels.

Figure 12.14
(a) The first three energy levels for a particle in a one-dimensional box in increments of $h^2/(8mL^2)$. (b) The wave functions for the first three levels plotted as a function of x. Note that the maximum value is $\sqrt{2/L}$ in each case. (c) The square of the wave functions for the first three levels plotted as a function of x. Note that the maximum value is $2/L$ in each case.

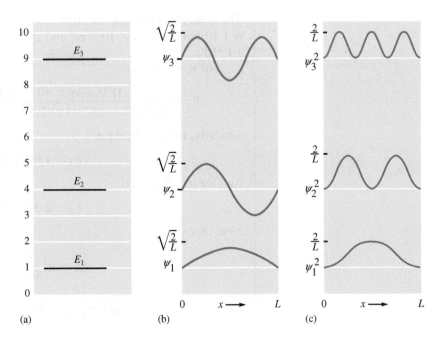

Note that each wave function goes to zero at the edges of the box, as required by the boundary conditions. Another way to say this is that the standing waves that represent the particle must have wavelengths such that an *integral number of half-wavelengths exactly equals the size of the box*. Waves with any other wavelengths could not exist because they would destructively interfere. Also note from Fig. 12.14 that the probability distribution is significantly different for the three levels. For $n = 1$ (the lowest energy or ground state), the particle is most likely to be found near the center of the box. In contrast, for $n = 2$ the particle has zero probability of being found in the center of the box. This zero point is called a node. Notice that the number of nodes increases with n.

Another interesting characteristic of the particle in a box is that the particle cannot have zero energy (that is, n cannot equal zero). For example, if n were equal to zero, ψ_0 would be zero everywhere in the box ($\sin 0 = 0$). This would mean that ψ_0^2 would also be zero. In this case there could be no particle in the box, which contradicts the boundary conditions. This fact that the particle must have a nonzero energy in its ground state is a characteristic of all particles with quantized energies. In addition, for the particle in a box, a value of zero for the energy would mean that the particle was sitting still (zero kinetic energy). This condition would violate the uncertainty principle because we would simultaneously know the exact values of the momentum (zero) and the position of the particle. For similar reasons all quantized particles must possess a minimum energy, often called the *zero-point energy*.

EXAMPLE 12.6

Assume that an electron is confined to a one-dimensional box 1.50 nm in length. Calculate the lowest three energy levels for this electron, and calculate the wavelength of light necessary to promote the electron from the ground state to the first excited state.

Solution To solve this problem, we need to substitute appropriate values into the general expression for energy:

$$E = \frac{n^2 h^2}{8mL^2}$$

The mass of an electron (m) is 9.11×10^{-31} kg; the dimension of the box (L) is 1.50 nm, or 1.50×10^{-9} m; and the value of Planck's constant is 6.626×10^{-34} J s.

For $n = 1$ we get

$$E_1 = \frac{(1)^2(6.626 \times 10^{-34} \text{ J s})^2}{(8)(9.11 \times 10^{-31} \text{ kg})(1.50 \times 10^{-9} \text{ m})^2} = 2.68 \times 10^{-20} \text{ J}$$

Similarly, for $n = 2$ we get

$$E_2 = 1.07 \times 10^{-19} \text{ J}$$

And for $n = 3$ we get

$$E_3 = 2.41 \times 10^{-19} \text{ J}$$

Note that since

$$E_n = n^2 \frac{h^2}{8mL^2} = n^2 E_1$$

then

$$E_2 = (2)^2 \frac{h^2}{8mL^2} = 4E_1 \quad \text{and} \quad E_3 = 9E_1$$

To calculate the wavelength of light necessary to excite the electron from level 1 to level 2 (the first *excited* state), we first need to obtain the energy difference between the two levels:

$$\Delta E = E_2 - E_1 = (n_2{}^2 - n_1{}^2)\frac{h^2}{8mL^2}$$

$$= (3)(2.68 \times 10^{-20}\ \text{J}) = 8.04 \times 10^{-20}\ \text{J}$$

Then we find the wavelength required from the equation

$$\Delta E = \frac{hc}{\lambda}$$

Inserting the appropriate values gives

$$\lambda = \frac{hc}{\Delta E} = \frac{(6.626 \times 10^{-34}\ \text{J s})(2.9979 \times 10^8\ \text{m/s})}{8.04 \times 10^{-20}\ \text{J}}$$

$$= 2.47 \times 10^{-6}\ \text{m} = 2470\ \text{nm}$$

12.7 | The Wave Equation for the Hydrogen Atom

Unlike the particle in a one-dimensional box, the electron of the hydrogen atom moves in three dimensions and has potential energy because of its attraction to the positive nucleus at the atom's center. These differences can be easily accounted for by including the second derivatives with respect to all three of the Cartesian coordinates and by inserting a term that specifies the dependence of the electron's potential energy on its position in space.

Because it is more convenient mathematically, the coordinate system is changed from Cartesian to spherical polar coordinates (Fig. 12.15) before the Schrödinger equation is solved. In the system of spherical polar coordinates, a given point in space, specified by values of the Cartesian coordinates x, y, and z, is described by specific values of r, θ, and ϕ.

In the spherical polar coordinate system, the wave function $\psi(r, \theta, \phi)$ can be written as a product of one function depending on r, one depending on θ, and one depending on ϕ:

$$\psi(r, \theta, \phi) = R(r)\Theta(\theta)\Phi(\phi)$$

This separation of variables allows an exact solution to the Schrödinger equation

$$\hat{H}\psi = E\psi$$

for the hydrogen atom.

In spherical polar coordinates, the potential energy (in cgs units) of the electron is

$$V(r) = -\frac{(Ze)(e)}{r}$$

where Ze represents the nuclear charge ($Z = 1$ for the hydrogen atom). As with the particle in a box, when the Schrödinger equation for the hydrogen atom is solved and the boundary conditions are applied, a series of wave functions is obtained, each function corresponding to a particular energy. In contrast to the particle in a one-dimensional box, where one quantum number emerges from the mathematics, the three-dimensional hydrogen atom gives rise to three quantum numbers.

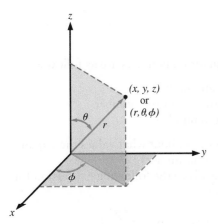

Figure 12.15
The spherical polar coordinate system.

To convert the potential energy from cgs units to SI units (joules), the expression shown must be multiplied by $1/4\pi\epsilon_0$, where ϵ_0 (the permittivity of the vacuum) is $8.854 \times 10^{-12}\ \text{C}^2/\text{J m}$.

Chemical Insights

0.035 Femtometer Is a Big Deal

The long accepted value for the radius of the proton is 0.8768 fm (fm = 10^{-15} m). However, new experiments suggest that this value might be about 4% too large. This doesn't sound like much, but if proved correct it will raise havoc in the scientific community.

The possible problem with the currently accepted value of the proton radius results from work done by Randolf Pohl and his coworkers at the Max Planck Institute of Quantum Optics in Garching, Germany. These scientists created an exotic form of hydrogen in which they replaced the hydrogen electron by a muon. A muon is a particle that has the same charge as an electron but is 200 times more massive than the electron. Because of its greater mass, the muon has orbitals with smaller average radii than those of an electron. The German team attempted to excite the muon to higher energy levels using laser pulses. They set their laser to detect muon transitions assuming the proton radius was in the range from 0.87 to

0.91 femtometers (fm), the value expected from current theories. After years of failing to see the expected energy transitions, the German scientists were within weeks of shutting down the experiment when they decided to assume a smaller value for the proton radius. They saw the expected transition when they tuned their laser at a value corresponding to a proton radius of 0.84184 fm. Although this value doesn't seem too different from 0.8768 fm, it has tremendous implications. A change in the radius of the proton will affect the value of the charge density of the proton, a value that affects the values of all of the fundamental physical constants since all of these constants are interrelated. Thus, more experiments are needed to determine the correct value of the proton radius. If the new, smaller value proves to be correct, it has important implications for the fundamental theory (quantum electrodynamics) of matter. Perhaps this will lead to a better understanding of nature.

The boundary conditions, which differ in some important aspects from those of the particle in the box because of the very different nature of the physical system, will not be discussed here.

The conventional symbols for these quantum numbers are as follows:

n	the principal quantum number
ℓ	the angular momentum quantum number
m_ℓ	the magnetic quantum number

We will have more to say in succeeding sections about what values these quantum numbers can assume and their physical meanings.

The mathematics of wave mechanics leads to the following expression for the allowed energies of hydrogen's electron:

$$E_n = -\frac{Z^2}{n^2}\left(\frac{me^4}{8\epsilon_0^2 h^2}\right) = -2.178 \times 10^{-18} \text{ J}\left(\frac{Z^2}{n^2}\right)$$

where $Z = 1$ for hydrogen and where n can assume only integer values (1, 2, 3, . . .). Several characteristics of this equation are worth emphasizing. First, note that the energy of the electron depends only on the principal quantum number (this is true only for one-electron species). Also note that because n is restricted to integer values, hydrogen's electron can assume only discrete energy values—the energy levels are quantized. Finally, note that this is exactly the same equation for energy as obtained in the Bohr model.

So that you have an idea of what they look like, the first few wave functions for hydrogen are shown in Table 12.1, along with the three quantum numbers n, ℓ, and m_ℓ.

When we solve the Schrödinger equation for the hydrogen atom, some of the solutions contain complex numbers (that is, they contain $i = \sqrt{-1}$). Because it is more convenient physically to deal with orbitals that contain only real numbers, the complex orbitals are usually combined (added and sub-

Table 12.1

Solutions of the Schrödinger Wave Equation for a One-Electron Atom

n	ℓ	m_ℓ	Orbital	Solution
1	0	0	$1s$	$\psi_{1s} = \dfrac{1}{\sqrt{\pi}}\left(\dfrac{Z}{a_0}\right)^{3/2} e^{-\sigma}$
2	0	0	$2s$	$\psi_{2s} = \dfrac{1}{4\sqrt{2\pi}}\left(\dfrac{Z}{a_0}\right)^{3/2}(2-\sigma)e^{-\sigma/2}$
2	1	0	$2p_z$	$\psi_{2p_z} = \dfrac{1}{4\sqrt{2\pi}}\left(\dfrac{Z}{a_0}\right)^{3/2}\sigma e^{-\sigma/2}\cos\theta$
2	1	± 1	$2p_x$	$\psi_{2p_x} = \dfrac{1}{4\sqrt{2\pi}}\left(\dfrac{Z}{a_0}\right)^{3/2}\sigma e^{-\sigma/2}\sin\theta\cos\phi$
			$2p_y$	$\psi_{2p_y} = \dfrac{1}{4\sqrt{2\pi}}\left(\dfrac{Z}{a_0}\right)^{3/2}\sigma e^{-\sigma/2}\sin\theta\sin\phi$
3	0	0	$3s$	$\psi_{3s} = \dfrac{1}{81\sqrt{3\pi}}\left(\dfrac{Z}{a_0}\right)^{3/2}(27-18\sigma+2\sigma^2)e^{-\sigma/3}$
3	1	0	$3p_z$	$\psi_{3p_z} = \dfrac{\sqrt{2}}{81\sqrt{\pi}}\left(\dfrac{Z}{a_0}\right)^{3/2}(6\sigma-\sigma^2)e^{-\sigma/3}\cos\theta$
3	1	± 1	$3p_x$	$\psi_{3p_x} = \dfrac{\sqrt{2}}{81\sqrt{\pi}}\left(\dfrac{Z}{a_0}\right)^{3/2}(6\sigma-\sigma^2)e^{-\sigma/3}\sin\theta\cos\phi$
			$3p_y$	$\psi_{3p_y} = \dfrac{\sqrt{2}}{81\sqrt{\pi}}\left(\dfrac{Z}{a_0}\right)^{3/2}(6\sigma-\sigma^2)e^{-\sigma/3}\sin\theta\sin\phi$
3	2	0	$3d_{z^2}$	$\psi_{3d_{z^2}} = \dfrac{1}{81\sqrt{6\pi}}\left(\dfrac{Z}{a_0}\right)^{3/2}\sigma^2 e^{-\sigma/3}(3\cos^2\theta-1)$
3	2	± 1	$3d_{xz}$	$\psi_{3d_{xz}} = \dfrac{\sqrt{2}}{81\sqrt{\pi}}\left(\dfrac{Z}{a_0}\right)^{3/2}\sigma^2 e^{-\sigma/3}\sin\theta\cos\theta\cos\phi$
			$3d_{yz}$	$\psi_{3d_{yz}} = \dfrac{\sqrt{2}}{81\sqrt{\pi}}\left(\dfrac{Z}{a_0}\right)^{3/2}\sigma^2 e^{-\sigma/3}\sin\theta\cos\theta\sin\phi$
3	2	± 2	$3d_{xy}$	$\psi_{3d_{xy}} = \dfrac{1}{81\sqrt{2\pi}}\left(\dfrac{Z}{a_0}\right)^{3/2}\sigma^2 e^{-\sigma/3}\sin^2\theta\sin 2\phi$
			$3d_{x^2-y^2}$	$\psi_{3d_{x^2-y^2}} = \dfrac{1}{81\sqrt{2\pi}}\left(\dfrac{Z}{a_0}\right)^{3/2}\sigma^2 e^{-\sigma/3}\sin^2\theta\cos 2\phi$

Note: $\sigma = Zr/a_0$, where $Z = 1$ for hydrogen; $a_0 = \epsilon_0 h^2/\pi m e^2 = 5.29 \times 10^{-11}$ m.

tracted) to remove the complex portions. For example, the p_x and p_y orbitals shown in Table 12.1 are combinations of the complex orbitals that correspond to values of m_ℓ of $+1$ and -1. These orbitals are indicated with a brace in Table 12.1. The last four d orbitals listed are also obtained by combination of complex orbitals, as indicated by braces in Table 12.1.

12.8 | The Physical Meaning of a Wave Function

Now that we have examined some of the mathematical details of the quantum mechanical treatment of the hydrogen atom, we need to consider what it all means. What is a wave function, and what does it tell us about the electron to which it applies? First, a warning: There is always danger in taking a mathematical description of nature and using our human experiences to interpret it.

Although our attempts to attach physical significance to mathematical descriptions are quite useful to us as we try to understand how nature operates, they must be viewed with caution. Simple pictorial models of a particular natural phenomenon always oversimplify the phenomenon and should not be taken too literally. With this caveat we will proceed to try to picture what the "quantum mechanical atom" is like.

Recall that the uncertainty principle indicates that there is no way of knowing the detailed movements of the electron in a hydrogen atom. Given this severe limitation, what then is the physical meaning of a wave function for an electron? Although the function itself has no easily visualized meaning, as we mentioned in the treatment of the particle in a box, the square of the wave function does have a physical significance. *The square of the function evaluated at a particular point in space indicates the probability of finding an electron near that point.* For example, suppose we have two positions in space: one defined by the coordinates r_1, θ_1, and ϕ_1 and the other defined by the coordinates r_2, θ_2, and ϕ_2. The relative probability of finding the electron near positions 1 and 2 is determined by substituting the values of r, θ, and ϕ for the two positions into the wave function, squaring the function value, and computing the following ratio:

$$\frac{[\psi(r_1, \theta_1, \phi_1)]^2 \, dv}{[\psi(r_2, \theta_2, \phi_2)]^2 \, dv} = \frac{N_1}{N_2}$$

The quotient N_1/N_2 is the ratio of the probabilities of finding the electron in the infinitesimally small volume elements dv around points 1 and 2. For example, if the value of the ratio N_1/N_2 is 100, the electron is 100 times more likely to be found at position 1 than at position 2. The model gives no information concerning when the electron will be at either position or how it moves between the positions. This vagueness is consistent with the concept of the Heisenberg uncertainty principle.

The square of the wave function is most conveniently represented as a **probability distribution,** in which the intensity of color is used to indicate the probability value at a given point in space. The probability distribution for the hydrogen 1s orbital is shown in Fig. 12.16(a). The best way to think about this diagram is as a three-dimensional time exposure, with the electron as a tiny moving light. The more times the electron visits a particular point, the darker the negative becomes. Thus the darkness (intensity) of a point indicates the probability of finding an electron at that position. This diagram is sometimes known as an *electron density map;* electron density and electron probability mean the same thing.

Another way of representing the electron probability distribution for the 1s orbital is to calculate the probability at points along a line drawn outward in any direction from the nucleus. The result is shown in Fig. 12.16(b), where R^2 (the square of the radial part—the part that depends on r—of the 1s orbital) is plotted versus r. Note that the probability of finding the electron at a particular position is greatest close to the nucleus and that it drops off rapidly as the distance from the nucleus increases.

We are also interested in knowing the *total* probability of finding the electron in the hydrogen atom at a particular *distance* from the nucleus. Imagine that the space around the hydrogen nucleus is made up of a series of thin spherical shells (rather like layers in an onion), as shown in Fig. 12.17(a). When the total probability of finding the electron in each spherical shell is plotted versus the distance from the nucleus, the plot in Fig. 12.17(b) is obtained. This graph is called the **radial probability distribution,** which is a plot of $4\pi r^2 R^2$ versus r, where R represents the radial part of the wave function.

The square of the function here means the square of the magnitude, $|\psi|^2$. This distinction is important when orbitals with complex numbers are being considered: $|\psi|^2 = $ (real part)$^2 + $ (imaginary part)^2.

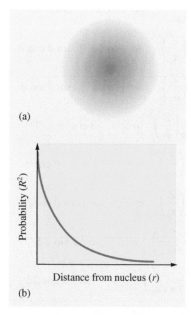

(a)

(b)

y-axis: Probability (R^2)

x-axis: Distance from nucleus (r)

Figure 12.16
(a) The probability distribution for the hydrogen 1s orbital in three-dimensional space. (b) The probability density of the electron at points along a line drawn outward from the nucleus in any direction for the hydrogen 1s orbital.

The maximum in the curve occurs because of two opposing effects. The probability of finding an electron at a particular position is greatest near the nucleus, but the volume of the spherical shell increases with the distance from the nucleus. Therefore, as we move away from the nucleus, the probability of finding the electron at a given position decreases. However, we are summing more positions. Thus the total probability increases to a certain radius and then decreases as the electron probability at each position becomes very small. Mathematically, the maximum occurs because in the function $4\pi r^2 R^2$, r^2 increases with r while R^2 decreases with r [Fig. 12.16(b)]. For the hydrogen 1s orbital, the maximum radial probability (the distance at which the electron is most likely to be found) occurs at a distance of 5.29×10^{-2} nm, or 0.529 Å (angstrom), from the nucleus. Interestingly, this distance is exactly the radius of the innermost orbit in the Bohr model and thus is called the Bohr radius, denoted by a_0. Note that in Bohr's model the electron is assumed to have a circular path and so is *always* found at this distance. In the wave mechanical model the specific electron motions are unknown; therefore, this is the *most probable* distance at which the electron is found.

One more characteristic of the hydrogen 1s orbital that we must consider is its size. As we can see from Fig. 12.16, the size of this orbital cannot be precisely defined, since the probability never becomes zero (although it drops to an extremely small value at large values of r). Therefore, the hydrogen 1s orbital has no distinct size. However, it is useful to have a definition of relative orbital size. *The normally accepted arbitrary definition of the size of the hydrogen 1s orbital is the radius of the sphere that encloses 90% of the total electron probability.* That is, 90% of the time the electron is found inside this sphere. Application of this rule to the hydrogen atom 1s orbital gives a sphere with radius 2.6 a_0, or 1.4×10^{-10} m (140 pm).

So far we have described only the lowest-energy wave function in the hydrogen atom, the 1s orbital. Hydrogen has many other orbitals, which are described in the next section.

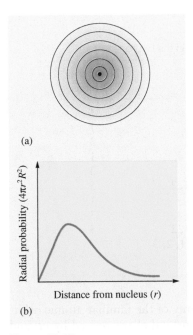

Figure 12.17

(a) Cross section of the hydrogen 1s orbital probability distribution divided into successive thin spherical shells. (b) The radial probability distribution. A plot of the total probability of finding the electron in each thin spherical shell as a function of distance from the nucleus.

1 Å = 10^{-10} m; the angstrom is often used as the unit for atomic radius because of its convenient size. Another convenient unit is the picometer (1 pm = 10^{-12} m).

12.9 | The Characteristics of Hydrogen Orbitals

Quantum Numbers

As we have seen, when we solve the Schrödinger equation for the hydrogen atom, we find many wave functions (orbitals) that satisfy it. Each of these orbitals is characterized by a set of **quantum numbers** that arise when the boundary conditions are applied. Now we will systematically describe these quantum numbers in terms of the values they can assume and their physical meanings.

The **principal quantum number** (n), which can have integral values (1, 2, 3, . . .), is related to the size and energy of the orbital. As n increases, the orbital becomes larger and the electron spends more time farther from the nucleus. An increase in n also means higher energy because the electron is less tightly bound to the nucleus, and the energy is less negative. The **angular momentum quantum number** (ℓ) can have integral values from 0 to $n - 1$ for each value of n. This quantum number relates to the angular momentum of an electron in a given orbital. The dependence of the wave functions on ℓ determines the shapes of the atomic orbitals. The value of ℓ for a particular orbital is commonly assigned a letter: $\ell = 0$ is called s, $\ell = 1$ is called p, $\ell = 2$ is called d, and $\ell = 3$ is called f (Table 12.2). The **magnetic quantum number** (m_ℓ) can have integral values between ℓ and $-\ell$, including zero. The value of m_ℓ relates to the orientation in space of the angular momentum associated

Table 12.2

The Angular Momentum Quantum Numbers and Corresponding Letter Symbols

Value	Letter Used
0	s
1	p
2	d
3	f
4	g

Table 12.3

Quantum Numbers for the First Four Levels of Orbitals in the Hydrogen Atom

n	ℓ	Orbital Designation	m_ℓ	Number of Orbitals
1	0	1s	0	1
2	0	2s	0	1
	1	2p	$-1, 0, +1$	3
3	0	3s	0	1
	1	3p	$-1, 0, 1$	3
	2	3d	$-2, -1, 0, 1, 2$	5
4	0	4s	0	1
	1	4p	$-1, 0, 1$	3
	2	4d	$-2, -1, 0, 1, 2$	5
	3	4f	$-3, -2, -1, 0, 1, 2, 3$	7

$n = 1, 2, 3, \ldots$
$\ell = 0, 1, \ldots, (n-1)$
$m_\ell = -\ell, \ldots, 0, \ldots, +\ell$

The labels s, p, d, and f are used for historical reasons. They originally referred to characteristics of lines observed in the atomic spectra: s (sharp), p (principal), d (diffuse), and f (fundamental). Beyond f the letters become alphabetic: g, h, $\ldots$, skipping j, which is reserved as a symbol for angular momentum.

Number of Orbitals
per Subshell

$s = 1$
$p = 3$
$d = 5$
$f = 7$
$g = 9$

with the orbital. As we mentioned earlier, many of the familiar atomic orbitals are actually a combination of a complex orbital characterized by m_ℓ and one characterized by $-m_\ell$.

◷WL INTERACTIVE EXAMPLE 12.7

For principal quantum level $n = 5$, determine the number of subshells (different values of ℓ) and give the designation of each.

Solution For $n = 5$ the allowed values of ℓ run from 0 to 4 ($n - 1 = 5 - 1$). Thus the subshells and their designations are

$\ell = 0$	$\ell = 1$	$\ell = 2$	$\ell = 3$	$\ell = 4$
5s	5p	5d	5f	5g

The first four levels of orbitals in the hydrogen atom are listed with their quantum numbers in Table 12.3. Note that each set of orbitals with a given value of ℓ (sometimes called a **subshell**) is designated by giving the value of n and the letter for ℓ. Thus an orbital where $n = 2$ and $\ell = 1$ is symbolized as $2p$. There are three $2p$ orbitals, which have different orientations in space. We will describe these orbitals in the next section.

Orbital Shapes and Energies

We have seen that the meaning of an orbital is illustrated most clearly by a probability distribution. Each orbital in the hydrogen atom has a unique probability distribution. We also have seen that another means of representing an orbital is by the surface that surrounds 90% of the total electron probability. These three types of representations for the hydrogen $1s$, $2s$, and $3s$ orbitals are shown in Fig. 12.18. Note the characteristic spherical shape of each of the s orbitals. Note also that the $2s$ and $3s$ orbitals contain areas of high probability separated by areas of zero probability. These latter areas are called **nodal surfaces**, or simply **nodes**. The number of nodes increases as n increases. For s orbitals, the number of nodes is given by $n - 1$. For our purposes, however, we will think of s orbitals only in terms of their overall spherical shape, which becomes larger as the value of n increases.

Two types of representations for the $2p$ orbitals (there are no $1p$ orbitals) are shown in Fig. 12.19. Note that the p orbitals are not spherical, like s orbitals, but have two **lobes** separated by a node at the nucleus. The p orbitals are

n value
↓
$2p_x$ ← orientation in space
↑
ℓ value

Figure 12.18

Three representations of the hydrogen 1s, 2s, and 3s orbitals. (a) The square of the wave function. (b) "Slices" of the three-dimensional electron density. (c) The surfaces that contain 90% of the total electron probability (the "sizes" of the orbitals).

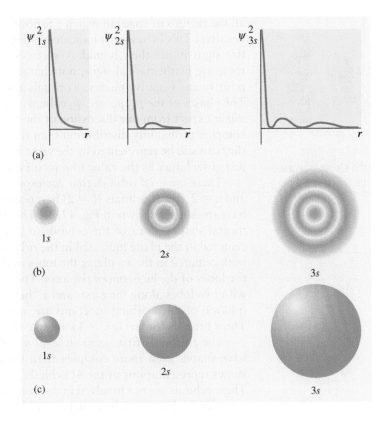

labeled according to the axis of the Cartesian coordinate system along which the lobes lie. For example, the 2p orbital with lobes along the x axis is called the $2p_x$ orbital.

At this point it is useful to remember that mathematical functions have signs. For example, a simple sine wave (Fig. 12.1) oscillates from positive to negative and repeats this pattern. Atomic orbital functions also have signs. The functions for s orbitals are positive everywhere in three-dimensional space. That is, when the s orbital function is evaluated at any point in space, it results in a positive number. In contrast, the p orbital functions have different signs in different regions of space. For example, the p_z orbital has a positive sign in

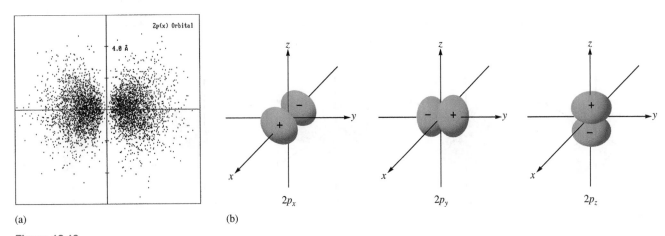

Figure 12.19

Representation of the 2p orbitals. (a) The electron probability distribution for a 2p orbital. Generated from a program by Robert Allendoerfer on Project SERAPHIM disk PC 2402; reprinted with permission. (b) The boundary surface representations of all three 2p orbitals. Note that the signs inside the surface indicate the phases (signs) of the orbital in that region of space.

Figure 12.20

A cross section of the electron probability distribution for a 3p orbital.

all the regions of space in which z is positive and has a negative sign when z is negative. This behavior is indicated in Fig. 12.19(b) by the positive and negative signs inside their boundary surfaces. It is important to understand that these are mathematical signs, not charges. Just as a sine wave has alternating positive and negative phases, p orbitals also have positive and negative phases. The phases of the p_x, p_y, and p_z orbitals are indicated in Fig. 12.19(b). As you might expect from our discussion of the s orbitals, the $3p$ orbitals have a more complex probability distribution than that of the $2p$ orbitals (Fig. 12.20), but they can still be represented by the same boundary surface shapes. The surfaces just grow larger as the value of n increases.

There are no d orbitals that correspond to principal quantum levels $n = 1$ and $n = 2$. The d orbitals ($\ell = 2$) first occur in level $n = 3$. The five $3d$ orbitals have the shapes shown in Fig. 12.21. The d orbitals have two different fundamental shapes. Four of the orbitals (d_{xz}, d_{yz}, d_{xy}, and $d_{x^2-y^2}$) have four lobes centered in the plane indicated in the orbital label. Note that d_{xy} and $d_{x^2-y^2}$ are both centered in the xy plane; the lobes of $d_{x^2-y^2}$ lie *along* the x and y axes, but the lobes of d_{xy} lie *between* the axes. The fifth orbital, d_{z^2}, has a unique shape with two lobes along the z axis and a "belt" centered in the xy plane. The signs (phases) of the d orbital functions are indicated inside the boundary surfaces. The d orbitals for levels $n > 3$ look like the $3d$ orbitals but have larger lobes.

The f orbitals first occur in level $n = 4$, and as might be expected, they have shapes even more complex than those of the d orbitals. Figure 12.22 shows representations of the $4f$ orbitals ($\ell = 3$) along with their designations. These orbitals are not involved in the bonding in any of the compounds we will consider in this text. Their shapes and labels are included here for complete-

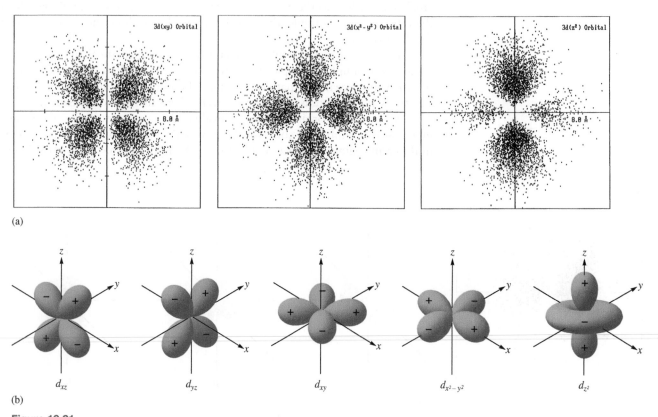

Figure 12.21

Representation of the 3d orbitals. (a) Electron density plots of selected 3d orbitals. Generated from a program by Robert Allendoerfer on Project SERAPHIM disk PC 2402; reprinted with permission. (b) The boundary surfaces of all five 3d orbitals, with the signs (phases) indicated.

Figure 12.22
Representation of the 4*f* orbitals in terms of their boundary surfaces.

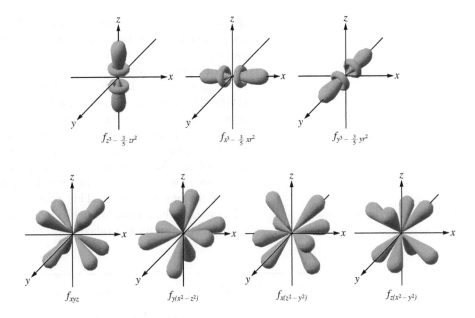

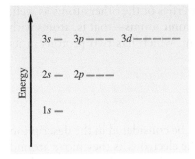

Figure 12.23
Orbital energy levels for the hydrogen atom.

ness. Because of their complexity, the phases of the *f* orbital functions are not represented in this diagram.

So far we have talked about the shapes of the hydrogen atomic orbitals but not about their energies. For the hydrogen atom, the energy of a particular orbital is determined by its value of *n*. Thus *all* orbitals with the same value of *n* have the *same energy*—they are said to be **degenerate**. This feature is illustrated in Fig. 12.23, where the energies for the orbitals in the first three quantum levels for hydrogen are shown.

Hydrogen's single electron can occupy any of its atomic orbitals. However, in the lowest energy state, the ground state, the electron resides in the 1*s* orbital. If energy is put into the atom, the electron can be transferred to a higher-energy orbital, producing an excited state.

The Hydrogen Atom

1. In the quantum mechanical model, the electron is described as a wave. This representation leads to a series of wave functions (orbitals) that describe the possible energies and spatial distributions available to the electron.

2. In agreement with the Heisenberg uncertainty principle, the model cannot specify the detailed electron motions. Instead, the square of the wave function represents the probability distribution of the electron in that orbital. This approach allows us to picture orbitals in terms of probability distributions, or electron density maps.

3. The size of an orbital is arbitrarily defined as the surface that contains 90% of the total electron probability.

4. The hydrogen atom has many types of orbitals. In the ground state, the single electron resides in the 1*s* orbital. The electron can be excited to higher-energy orbitals if the atom absorbs energy.

12.10 | Electron Spin and the Pauli Principle

The electron does not literally spin. The term "spin" is just a name for the intrinsic angular momentum of the electron.

The concept of **electron spin** was developed by Samuel Goudsmit and George Uhlenbeck in 1925 while they were graduate students at the University of Leyden in the Netherlands. They found that a fourth quantum number (in addition to *n*, ℓ, and m_ℓ) was necessary to account for the details of the emission spectra of atoms. The new quantum number adopted to describe this phenomenon, called the **electron spin quantum number** (m_s), can have only one of two values, $+\frac{1}{2}$ and $-\frac{1}{2}$.

For our purposes the main significance of the electron spin quantum number is connected with the postulate of Austrian physicist Wolfgang Pauli (1900–1958), which is often stated as follows: *In a given atom no two electrons can have the same set of four quantum numbers (n, ℓ, m_ℓ, and m_s).* This is called the **Pauli exclusion principle**. Since electrons in the same orbital have the same values of n, ℓ, and m_ℓ, this postulate requires that they have different values of m_s. Since only two values of m_s are allowed, we might paraphrase the Pauli principle as follows: *An orbital can hold only two electrons, and they must have opposite spins.* This principle will have important consequences when we use the atomic model to relate the electron arrangement of an atom to its position in the periodic table.

$m_s = +\frac{1}{2}$ or $-\frac{1}{2}$

Each orbital can hold a maximum of two electrons.

12.11 | Polyelectronic Atoms

The quantum mechanical model provides a description of the hydrogen atom that agrees very well with experimental data. However, the model would not be very useful if it did not account for the properties of the other atoms as well.

To see how the model applies to **polyelectronic atoms**—that is, atoms with more than one electron—let's consider helium, which has two protons in its nucleus and two electrons:

There are three energy contributions that must be considered in the description of the helium atom: (1) the kinetic energy of the electrons as they move around the nucleus, (2) the potential energy of attraction between the nucleus and the electrons, and (3) the potential energy of repulsion between the two electrons.

Although this atom can be readily described in terms of the quantum mechanical model, the Schrödinger equation that results cannot be solved exactly. The difficulty arises in dealing with the repulsion between the electrons. This so-called *electron correlation problem* refers to the fact that we cannot rigorously account for the effect a given electron has on the motions of the other electrons in an atom.

The electron correlation problem occurs with all polyelectronic atoms. To treat these systems using the quantum mechanical model, we must make approximations. The simplest approximation involves treating each electron as if it were moving in a *field of charge that is the net result of the nuclear attraction and the average repulsions of all the other electrons.* To see how this is done, let's compare the neutral helium atom and the He$^+$ ion:

He   He$^+$

What energy is required to remove an electron from each of these species? Experiments show that 2372 kJ of energy is required to remove one electron from all the atoms in a mole of helium. Removing the one electron from each ion in a mole of He$^+$ ions requires 5248 kJ of energy. Thus it takes more than twice as much energy to remove an electron from a He$^+$ ion than from a He atom.

Why is there such a large difference? In both cases the nucleus has a 2+ charge. However, in the helium atom, there are two electrons that repel each other, but in the He$^+$ ion there is only one electron and thus no electron–electron repulsion. That is, the large difference in the energies required to remove one electron must arise from the electron–electron repulsions in the neutral atom. Each electron in the He atom is much less tightly bound to the nucleus than the electron in the He$^+$ ion. In other words, the effectiveness of the positively charged nucleus in binding the electrons has been decreased by the repulsions between the electrons. Thus the *effect of the electron repulsions can be thought of as reducing the nuclear charge* to an apparent value of less than 2+ toward a particular electron, as shown below:

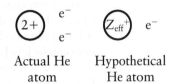

Actual He atom   Hypothetical He atom

The *apparent* nuclear charge, or the **effective nuclear charge**, is designated Z_{eff}. For a helium atom Z_{eff}, the charge "experienced" by each electron, is less than 2. In general,

$$\text{Effective nuclear charge} = Z_{eff} = Z_{actual} - (\text{effect of electron repulsions})$$

$Z_{eff} = Z$ − effect of electron repulsions

where $Z_{actual} = Z$, the atomic number (number of protons).

This simplification allows us to treat each electron individually, where each electron is viewed as moving under the influence of a positive nuclear charge Z_{eff}. This simplified atom has one electron like hydrogen, but with a positive nuclear charge of Z_{eff} instead of 1. We therefore can find the energy and wave function for each helium electron by substituting Z_{eff} in place of $Z = 1$ in the hydrogen wave mechanical equations. When we do this, we find that both helium electrons reside in a modified 1s orbital that is spherical, like that for the hydrogen atom, but smaller because Z_{eff} is greater than 1. The larger nuclear charge draws each of the electrons closer to the nucleus, therefore binding each more tightly than the electron in hydrogen is bound. The increased nuclear charge of the helium atom is more important than the repulsions between the two electrons, so that each of the electrons in helium is bound more tightly than the electron in the hydrogen atom.

The model we have just described so greatly oversimplifies the structure of polyelectronic atoms that, although it produces some qualitatively useful ideas about polyelectronic atoms, it is not satisfactory for the description of quantitative atomic properties. To get an accurate description of polyelectronic atoms, we must take into account the electron–electron interactions in a much more detailed manner than simply assuming that they reduce the nuclear charge.

Nothing we do will allow us to solve the problem exactly, because the electron motions are correlated. That is, because electrons repel each other, the movement of a given electron will affect the movements of all the others. This correlation problem is reflected in the Schrödinger equation for polyelectronic atoms in the following way. Because the equation contains energy terms that simultaneously involve two different electrons, it cannot be separated rigorously into equations that involve only one electron. Thus the Schrödinger equation for polyelectronic atoms cannot be solved exactly.

One approach for dealing with this problem is to solve the equation numerically. That is, a computer is used to find the numerical values of the wave functions at each point in space that produce the lowest overall energy for the atom. Although this approach allows accurate calculation of atomic properties, it suffers from two major disadvantages: It is prohibitively time-consuming for any but the simplest of atoms, and the results are very difficult to interpret physically.

A more practical approach, the **self-consistent field (SCF) method,** is now used almost universally to treat polyelectronic atoms. In this method a given electron is assumed to be moving in a potential energy field that is a result of both the nucleus and the average "electron density" of all the other electrons in the atom (residing in their various orbitals). This approximation allows the many-electron Schrödinger equation to be separated into a set of one-electron equations that can be solved by computers. The orbitals (one-electron functions) that result from this approach have angular properties exactly the same as those of the hydrogen orbitals but have radial characteristics somewhat different from those of the hydrogen orbitals. Although the quantum numbers obtained in the description of the hydrogen atom do not apply exactly to the orbitals obtained from the self-consistent field approach, we still use them as convenient labels for the atomic orbitals in polyelectronic atoms.

We will have more to say later about the self-consistent field approach, but first we will see how the atomic orbitals for polyelectronic atoms can be used to account for the form of the periodic table of the elements.

12.12 | The History of the Periodic Table

The modern periodic table contains a tremendous amount of useful information. In this section we will discuss the origin of this valuable tool; later, we will see how the quantum mechanical model for the atom explains the periodicity of chemical properties. Certainly one of the greatest successes of the quantum mechanical model is its ability to account for the arrangement of the elements on the periodic table.

The periodic table was originally constructed to represent the patterns observed in the chemical properties of the elements. As chemistry progressed during the eighteenth and nineteenth centuries, it became evident that the earth is composed of a great many elements with very different properties. Things are much more complicated than the simple model of earth, air, fire, and water suggested by the ancients. At first, the array of elements and properties was bewildering. Gradually, however, patterns were noticed.

The first chemist to recognize patterns was Johann Dobereiner, who found several groups of three elements with similar properties—for example, chlorine, bromine, and iodine. However, as Dobereiner attempted to expand this model of **triads** (as he called them) to the rest of the known elements, it became clear that this concept was severely limited.

The next notable attempt was made by English chemist John Newlands, who in 1864 suggested that elements should be arranged in **octaves.** He noticed that certain properties seemed to repeat for every eighth element in a way similar to the musical scale, which repeats for every eighth tone. Although this model managed to group several elements with similar properties, it was not generally successful.

The present form of the periodic table was conceived independently by two chemists in 1869: German Julius Lothar Meyer and Russian Dmitri Ivanovich Mendeleev (Fig. 12.24). Usually, Mendeleev is given most of the credit because it was he who showed how useful the table could be in predicting the existence and properties of yet unknown elements. For example, in 1872 when Mendeleev first published his table (Fig. 12.25), the elements gallium, scandium, and germanium were unknown. Mendeleev correctly predicted the existence and properties of these elements from gaps in his periodic table. The data for germanium (which Mendeleev called *ekasilicon*) are shown in Table 12.4. Note the excellent agreement between the actual values and Mendeleev's predictions, which were based on the properties of other members in the group of elements similar to germanium.

Figure 12.24

Dmitri Ivanovich Mendeleev (1834–1907), born in Siberia as the youngest of 17 children, taught chemistry at the University of St. Petersburg. In 1860 Mendeleev heard Italian chemist Cannizzaro lecture on a reliable method for determining the correct atomic masses of the elements. This important development paved the way for Mendeleev's own brilliant contribution to chemistry—the periodic table. In 1861 Mendeleev returned to St. Petersburg, where he wrote a book on organic chemistry. Later Mendeleev also wrote a book on inorganic chemistry, and he was struck by the fact that the systematic approach characterizing organic chemistry was lacking in inorganic chemistry. In attempting to systematize inorganic chemistry, he eventually arranged the elements in the form of the periodic table.

Mendeleev was a versatile genius who was interested in many fields of science. He worked on many problems associated with Russia's natural resources, such as coal, salt, and various metals. Being particularly interested in the petroleum industry, he visited the United States in 1876 to study the Pennsylvania oil fields. His interests also included meteorology and hot-air balloons. In 1887 he made an ascent in a balloon to study a total eclipse of the sun.

Annalen der Chemie und Pharmacia, VIII, Supplementary Volume for 1872

Tabelle II.

Reihen	Gruppe I. — R²O	Gruppe II. — RO	Gruppe III. — R²O³	Gruppe IV. RH⁴ RO²	Gruppe V. RH³ R²O⁵	Gruppe VI. RH² RO³	Gruppe VII. RH R²O⁷	Gruppe VIII. — RO⁴
1	H = 1							
2	Li = 7	Be = 9,4	B = 11	C = 12	N = 14	O = 16	F = 19	
3	Na = 23	Mg = 24	Al = 27,3	Si = 28	P = 31	S = 32	Cl = 35,5	
4	K = 39	Ca = 40	— = 44	Ti = 48	V = 51	Cr = 52	Mn = 55	Fe = 56, Co = 59, Ni = 59, Cu = 63.
5	(Cu = 63)	Zn = 65	— = 68	— = 72	As = 75	Se = 78	Br = 80	
6	Rb = 85	Sr = 87	?Yt = 88	Zr = 90	Nb = 94	Mo = 96	— = 100	Ru = 104, Rh = 104, Pd = 106, Ag = 108.
7	(Ag = 108)	Cd = 112	In = 113	Sn = 118	Sb = 122	Te = 125	J = 127	
8	Cs = 133	Ba = 137	?Di = 138	?Ce = 140	—	—	—	— — — —
9	(—)	—	—	—	—	—	—	
10	—	—	?Er = 178	?La = 180	Ta = 182	W = 184	—	Os = 195, Ir = 197, Pt = 198, Au = 199.
11	(Au = 199)	Hg = 200	Tl = 204	Pb = 207	Bi = 208	—	—	
12	—	—	—	Th = 231	—	U = 240	—	— — — —

Figure 12.25

Mendeleev's early periodic table, published in 1872. Note the spaces left for missing elements with atomic masses 44, 68, 72, and 100. From *Annalen der Chemie und Pharmacia*, VIII, Supplementary Volume for 1872, page 511.

Table 12.4

Comparison of the Properties of Germanium as Predicted by Mendeleev and as Actually Observed

Properties of Germanium	Predicted in 1871	Observed in 1886
Atomic mass	72	72.3
Density	5.5 g/cm³	5.47 g/cm³
Specific heat	0.31 J °C⁻¹ g⁻¹	0.32 J °C⁻¹ g⁻¹
Melting point	Very high	960°C
Oxide formula	RO₂	GeO₂
Oxide density	4.7 g/cm³	4.70 g/cm³
Chloride formula	RCl₄	GeCl₄
Boiling point of chloride	100°C	86°C

Table 12.5

Predicted Properties of Elements 113 and 114

Property	Element 113	Element 114
Chemically like	Thallium	Lead
Atomic mass	297	298
Density	16 g/mL	14 g/mL
Melting point	430°C	70°C
Boiling point	1100°C	150°C

Using his table, Mendeleev was also able to correct several values of atomic masses. For example, the original atomic mass of 76 for indium was based on the assumption that indium oxide had the formula InO. This atomic mass placed indium, which has metallic properties, among the nonmetals. Mendeleev assumed that the atomic mass was probably incorrect and proposed that the formula of indium oxide was really In_2O_3. On the basis of this (correct) formula, indium has an atomic mass of about 113, placing the element among the metals. Mendeleev also corrected the atomic masses of beryllium and uranium.

Because of its obvious usefulness, Mendeleev's periodic table was almost universally adopted, and it remains one of the most valuable tools at the chemist's disposal. For example, it is still used to predict the properties of elements yet to be discovered, as shown in Table 12.5.

A current version of the periodic table is shown inside the front cover of this book. The only fundamental difference between this table and that of Mendeleev is that the current table lists the elements in order of atomic number rather than atomic mass. The reason for this will become clear later in this chapter as we explore the electron arrangements of the atom.

12.13 | The Aufbau Principle and the Periodic Table

We can use the quantum mechanical model of the atom to show how the electron arrangements in the atomic orbitals of the various atoms account for the organization of the periodic table. Our main assumption here is that all atoms have orbitals similar to those that have been described for the hydrogen atom. *As protons are added one by one to the nucleus to build up the elements, electrons are similarly added to these atomic orbitals.* This is called the **aufbau principle.**

Hydrogen has one electron, which occupies the 1s orbital in its ground state. The configuration for hydrogen is written as $1s^1$, which can be represented by the following *orbital diagram:*

Aufbau is German for "building up."

H: $1s^1$ ⇡ (1s) □ (2s) □□□ (2p)

The arrow represents a particular electron spin state.

The next element, *helium*, has two electrons. Since two electrons with opposite spins can occupy an orbital, according to the Pauli exclusion principle, the electrons for helium are in the 1s orbital with opposite spins. This yields a $1s^2$ configuration:

He: $1s^2$ ⇅ (1s) □ (2s) □□□ (2p)

We will see in Section 12.14 why the 2s orbital is lower in energy than the 2p orbital.

Lithium has three electrons, two of which can go into the 1s orbital before the orbital is filled. Since the 1s orbital is the only orbital with $n = 1$, the third

The Chemistry of Copernicium

Although element 112 is not exactly a newborn (it was discovered in 1996), it has just been given a name. The International Union of Pure and Applied Chemistry announced on February 19, 2010, that the official name of 112 is Copernicium (pronounced koh-pur-NEE-see-um) and has the symbol Cn. The name honors Nicolaus Copernicus, who is best known for first recognizing that the planetary system is sun-centered rather than Earth-centered.

Now scientists from the Paul Sherrer Institute in Switzerland and the Joint Institute for Nuclear Research in Russia have studied the properties of Cn. By firing a beam of ^{48}Ca projectiles at a target of ^{242}Pu (doped with Nd_2O_3), these scientists have produced just two atoms of Cn. Given the relatively long lifetime of Cn atoms (a few seconds), the researchers have been able to compare the properties of Cn, Hg, and Ar atoms. When these atoms were injected into a series of gold-covered detectors, it was found that, similar to Hg (and in contrast to Ar), Cn atoms were "mildly" volatile and readily formed bonds with gold. Thus, as predicted by the periodic table, the element Cn, which has an expected electron configuration of $[Rn]7s^26d^{10}$, fits with the Zn, Cd, and Hg group of elements, all of which have the $ns^2(n-1)d^{10}$ configuration.

electron will occupy the lowest-energy orbital with $n = 2$, or the $2s$ orbital, giving a $1s^22s^1$ configuration:

Li: $1s^22s^1$

The next element, *beryllium,* has four electrons, which occupy the $1s$ and $2s$ orbitals:

Be: $1s^22s^2$

Boron has five electrons, four of which occupy the $1s$ and $2s$ orbitals. The fifth electron goes into the second type of orbital with $n = 2$, the $2p$ orbitals:

B: $1s^22s^22p^1$

Since all the $2p$ orbitals are equivalent, it does not matter which $2p$ orbital the electron occupies.

Carbon has six electrons: Two electrons occupy the $1s$ orbital, two occupy the $2s$ orbital, and two occupy $2p$ orbitals. Since there are three equivalent $2p$ orbitals, the electrons will occupy *separate* $2p$ orbitals.

This behavior is summarized by **Hund's rule** (named for German physicist F. H. Hund), which states that *the lowest-energy configuration for an atom is the one having the maximum number of unpaired electrons allowed by the Pauli principle in a particular set of degenerate orbitals.*

The configuration for carbon could be written $1s^22s^22p^12p^1$ to indicate that the electrons occupy separate $2p$ orbitals. However, the configuration is usually given as $1s^22s^22p^2$, and it is understood that the electrons are in different $2p$ orbitals. The orbital diagram for carbon is

C: $1s^22s^22p^2$

Note the unpaired electrons in the $2p$ orbitals, as required by Hund's rule.

For an atom with unfilled subshells, the lowest energy is achieved by electrons occupying separate orbitals, as allowed by the Pauli exclusion principle.

The configuration for *nitrogen,* which has seven electrons, is $1s^2 2s^2 2p^3$. The three electrons in $2p$ orbitals occupy separate orbitals:

		$1s$	$2s$	$2p$
N:	$1s^2 2s^2 2p^3$	↑↓	↑↓	↑ | ↑ | ↑

The configuration for *oxygen,* which has eight electrons, is $1s^2 2s^2 2p^4$. One of the $2p$ orbitals is now occupied by a pair of electrons with opposite spins, as required by the Pauli exclusion principle:

		$1s$	$2s$	$2p$
O:	$1s^2 2s^2 2p^4$	↑↓	↑↓	↑↓ | ↑ | ↑

The orbital diagrams and electron configurations for *fluorine* (nine electrons) and *neon* (ten electrons) are given below:

		$1s$	$2s$	$2p$
F:	$1s^2 2s^2 2p^5$	↑↓	↑↓	↑↓ | ↑↓ | ↑
Ne:	$1s^2 2s^2 2p^6$	↑↓	↑↓	↑↓ | ↑↓ | ↑↓

With neon, the orbitals with $n = 1$ and $n = 2$ are now completely filled.

For *sodium* the first ten electrons occupy the $1s$, $2s$, and $2p$ orbitals, and the eleventh electron must occupy the first orbital with $n = 3$, the $3s$ orbital. The electron configuration for sodium is $1s^2 2s^2 2p^6 3s^1$. To avoid writing the inner-level electrons, we often abbreviate this configuration as [Ne]$3s^1$, where [Ne] represents the electron configuration of neon, $1s^2 2s^2 2p^6$.

[Ne] is shorthand for $1s^2 2s^2 2p^6$.

The next element, *magnesium,* has the configuration $1s^2 2s^2 2p^6 3s^2$, or [Ne]$3s^2$. Then the next six elements, *aluminum* through *argon,* have configurations obtained by filling the $3p$ orbitals one electron at a time. Figure 12.26 summarizes the electron configurations of the first 18 elements by giving the number of electrons in the type of orbital occupied last.

At this point it is useful to introduce the concept of **valence electrons,** *the electrons in the outermost principal quantum level of an atom.* The valence electrons of the nitrogen atom, for example, are the $2s$ and $2p$ electrons. For the sodium atom, the valence electron is the electron in the $3s$ orbital, and so on. Valence electrons are the most important electrons to chemists because they are involved in bonding, as we will see in the next two chapters. The inner electrons are known as **core electrons.**

Note in Fig. 12.26 that a very important pattern is developing: *The elements in the same group (vertical column of the periodic table) have the same valence electron configuration.* Remember that Mendeleev originally placed the elements in groups based on similarities in chemical properties. Now we understand the reason behind these groupings. Elements with the same valence electron configuration often show similar chemical behavior.

The element after argon is *potassium.* Since the $3p$ orbitals are fully occupied in argon, we might expect the next electron to go into a $3d$ orbital (recall

Figure 12.26
The electron configurations in the type of orbital occupied last for the first 18 elements.

H $1s^1$							He $1s^2$
Li $2s^1$	Be $2s^2$	B $2p^1$	C $2p^2$	N $2p^3$	O $2p^4$	F $2p^5$	Ne $2p^6$
Na $3s^1$	Mg $3s^2$	Al $3p^1$	Si $3p^2$	P $3p^3$	S $3p^4$	Cl $3p^5$	Ar $3p^6$

that for $n = 3$ the orbitals are $3s$, $3p$, and $3d$). However, the chemistry of potassium is clearly very similar to that of lithium and sodium, indicating that the last electron in potassium occupies the $4s$ orbital instead of one of the $3d$ orbitals, a conclusion confirmed by many types of experiments. The electron configuration of potassium is

K: $1s^2 2s^2 2p^6 3s^2 3p^6 4s^1$ or $[Ar]4s^1$

The next element is *calcium:*

Ca: $[Ar]4s^2$

The next element, *scandium,* begins a series of ten elements (scandium through zinc) called the **transition metals,** whose configurations are obtained by adding electrons to the five $3d$ orbitals. The configuration of scandium is

Sc: $[Ar]4s^2 3d^1$

That of *titanium* is   Ti: $[Ar]4s^2 3d^2$

And that of *vanadium* is   V: $[Ar]4s^2 3d^3$

Chromium is the next element. The expected configuration is $[Ar]4s^2 3d^4$. However, the observed configuration is

Cr: $[Ar]4s^1 3d^5$

The explanation for this configuration of chromium is beyond the scope of this book. In fact, chemists are still disagreeing over the exact cause of this anomaly.[*] Note, however, that the observed configuration has both the $4s$ and $3d$ orbitals half-filled. This is a good way to remember the correct configuration.

The next four elements, *manganese* through *nickel,* have the expected configurations:

Mn: $[Ar]4s^2 3d^5$ Co: $[Ar]4s^2 3d^7$

Fe: $[Ar]4s^2 3d^6$ Ni: $[Ar]4s^2 3d^8$

The configuration for *copper* is expected to be $[Ar]4s^2 3d^9$. However, the observed configuration is

Cu: $[Ar]4s^1 3d^{10}$

In this case a half-filled $4s$ orbital and a filled set of $3d$ orbitals characterize the actual configuration.

Zinc has the expected configuration:

Zn: $[Ar]4s^2 3d^{10}$

The configurations of the transition metals are shown in Fig. 12.27. The next six elements, *gallium* through *krypton,* have configurations that correspond to filling the $4p$ orbitals (Fig. 12.27).

The entire periodic table is represented in Fig. 12.28 in terms of which orbitals are being filled. The valence electron configurations are given in Fig. 12.29 on page 567.

From these two figures, note the following additional points:

1. The $(n + 1)s$ orbitals always fill before the nd orbitals. For example, the $5s$ orbitals fill in rubidium and strontium before the $4d$ orbitals fill in the second row of transition metals (yttrium through cadmium).

2. After lanthanum, which has the configuration $[Xe]6s^2 5d^1$, a group of 14 elements called the **lanthanide series,** or the lanthanides, occurs. This series

[Ar] is shorthand for $1s^2 2s^2 2p^6 3s^2 3p^6$.

When an electron configuration is given in this text, the orbitals are listed in the order in which they fill.

The $(n + 1)s$ orbitals fill before the nd orbitals.

Lanthanides are elements in which the $4f$ orbitals are being filled.

---

[*]See M. P. Melrose and E. R. Scerri, *J. Chem. Educ.* **73** (1996): 498, for more information.

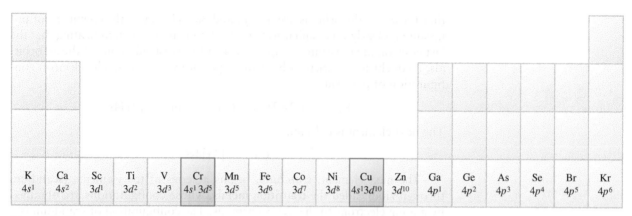

Figure 12.27

Electron configurations for potassium through krypton. The transition metals (scandium through zinc) have the general configuration $[Ar]4s^2 3d^n$, except for chromium and copper.

Actinides are elements in which the $5f$ orbitals are being filled.

The group label tells the total number of valence electrons for that group.

of elements corresponds to the filling of the seven $4f$ orbitals. Note that sometimes one electron occupies a $5d$ instead of a $4f$ orbital. This occurs because the energies of the $4f$ and $5d$ orbitals are very similar.

3. After actinium, which has the configuration $[Rn]7s^2 6d^1$, a group of 14 elements called the **actinide series,** or the actinides, occurs. This series corresponds to the filling of the seven $5f$ orbitals. Note that sometimes one or two electrons occupy the $6d$ orbitals instead of the $5f$ orbitals because these orbitals have very similar energies.

4. The group labels for the Groups 1A, 2A, 3A, 4A, 5A, 6A, 7A, and 8A indicate the *total number* of valence electrons for the atoms in these groups. For example, all the elements in Group 5A have the configuration $ns^2 np^3$. (The d electrons fill one period late and are usually not counted as valence electrons.) The meaning of the group labels for the transition metals is not as clear as for the A group elements, so these will not be used in this text.

5. The groups labeled 1A, 2A, 3A, 4A, 5A, 6A, 7A, and 8A are often called the **main-group,** or **representative, elements.** Remember that every member of these groups has the same valence electron configuration.

Figure 12.28

The orbitals being filled for elements in various parts of the periodic table. Note that when we move along a horizontal row (a period), the $(n + 1)s$ orbital fills before the nd orbital. The group labels indicate the number of valence electrons (ns plus np electrons) for the elements in each group.

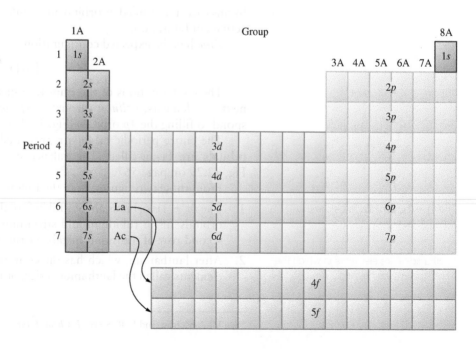

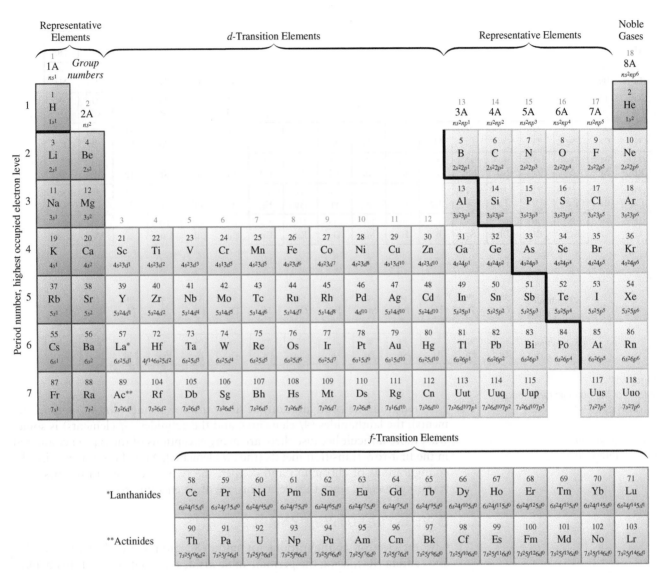

Figure 12.29
The periodic table with atomic symbols, atomic numbers, and partial electron configurations.

In 1985 the International Union of Pure and Applied Chemistry (IUPAC), a body of scientists organized to standardize scientific conventions, recommended a new form for the periodic table, which the American Chemical Society has adopted (Fig. 12.30 on page 568). In this new version, the group number indicates the number of s, p, and d electrons added since the last noble gas. We will not use the new format in this book, but you should be aware that the familiar periodic table may soon be replaced by this or a similar format.

The results considered in this section are very important. We have seen that the wave mechanical model can be used to explain the arrangement of elements in the periodic table. This model allows us to understand that the similar chemistry exhibited by the members of a given group arises from the fact that they all have the same valence electron configuration. Only the principal quantum number of the occupied orbitals changes in going down a particular group.

It is important to be able to give the electron configuration for each of the main-group elements. This is most easily done by using the periodic table. If you understand how the table is organized, it is not necessary to memorize the order in which the orbitals fill. Review Fig. 12.28 and Fig. 12.29 to make sure that you understand the correspondence among the orbitals and the periods and groups.

1																		18
1 H	2											13	14	15	16	17	2 He
3 Li	4 Be												5 B	6 C	7 N	8 O	9 F	10 Ne
11 Na	12 Mg	3	4	5	6	7	8	9	10	11	12	13 Al	14 Si	15 P	16 S	17 Cl	18 Ar
19 K	20 Ca	21 Sc	22 Ti	23 V	24 Cr	25 Mn	26 Fe	27 Co	28 Ni	29 Cu	30 Zn	31 Ga	32 Ge	33 As	34 Se	35 Br	36 Kr
37 Rb	38 Sr	39 Y	40 Zr	41 Nb	42 Mo	43 Tc	44 Ru	45 Rh	46 Pd	47 Ag	48 Cd	49 In	50 Sn	51 Sb	52 Te	53 I	54 Xe
55 Cs	56 Ba	57 La*	72 Hf	73 Ta	74 W	75 Re	76 Os	77 Ir	78 Pt	79 Au	80 Hg	81 Tl	82 Pb	83 Bi	84 Po	85 At	86 Rn
87 Fr	88 Ra	89 Ac**	104 Rf	105 Db	106 Sg	107 Bh	108 Hs	109 Mt	110 Ds	111 Rg	112 Cn	113 Uut	114 Uuq	115 Uup		117 Uus	118 Uuo

*Lanthanide series	58 Ce	59 Pr	60 Nd	61 Pm	62 Sm	63 Eu	64 Gd	65 Tb	66 Dy	67 Ho	68 Er	69 Tm	70 Yb	71 Lu

**Actinide series	90 Th	91 Pa	92 U	93 Np	94 Pu	95 Am	96 Cm	97 Bk	98 Cf	99 Es	100 Fm	101 Md	102 No	103 Lr

Figure 12.30
A form of the periodic table recommended by IUPAC.

Cr: [Ar]$4s^1 3d^5$
Cu: [Ar]$4s^1 3d^{10}$

Predicting the configurations of the transition metals (3d, 4d, and 5d elements), the lanthanides (4f elements), and the actinides (5f elements) is somewhat more difficult because there are many exceptions of the type encountered in the first-row transition metals (the 3d elements). You should memorize the configurations of chromium and copper, the two exceptions in the first-row transition metals, since these elements are often encountered.

◖WL INTERACTIVE EXAMPLE 12.8

Give the electron configurations for sulfur (S), cadmium (Cd), hafnium (Hf), and radium (Ra), using the periodic table inside the front cover of this book.

Solution *Sulfur,* element 16, resides in Period 3, where the 3p orbitals are being filled (Fig. 12.31). Since sulfur is the fourth among the 3p elements, it must have four 3p electrons. Its configuration is

$$\text{S:} \quad 1s^2 2s^2 2p^6 3s^2 3p^4 \quad \text{or} \quad [\text{Ne}]3s^2 3p^4$$

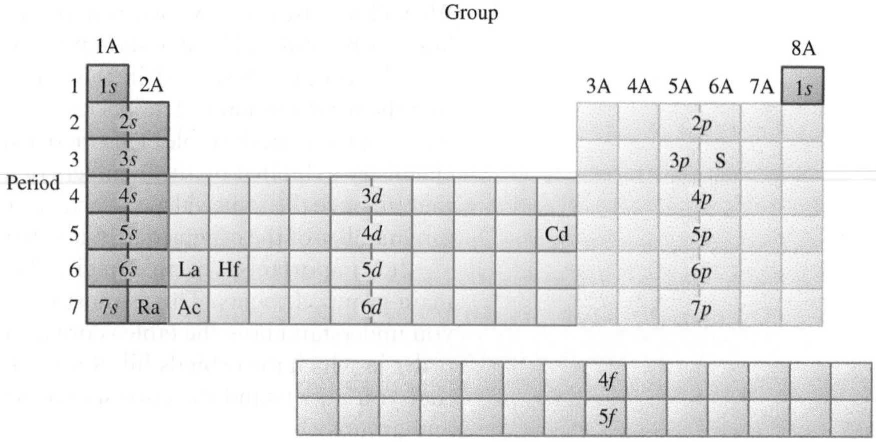

Figure 12.31
The positions of the elements considered in Example 12.8.

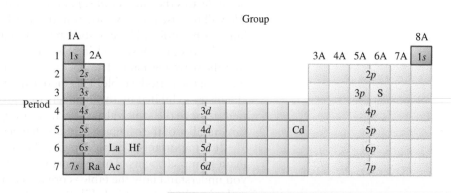

Cadmium, element 48, is located in Period 5 at the end of the 4*d* transition metals, as shown in Fig. 12.31. It is the tenth element in the series and thus has ten electrons in the 4*d* orbitals (in addition to the two electrons in the 5*s* orbital). The configuration is

Cd: $1s^2 2s^2 2p^6 3s^2 3p^6 4s^2 3d^{10} 4p^6 5s^2 4d^{10}$ or $[Kr]5s^2 4d^{10}$

Hafnium, element 72, is found in Period 6, as shown in Fig. 12.31. Note that it occurs just after the lanthanide series. Thus the 4*f* orbitals are already filled. Hafnium is the second member of the 5*d* transition series and has two 5*d* electrons. The configuration is

Hf: $1s^2 2s^2 2p^6 3s^2 3p^6 4s^2 3d^{10} 4p^6 5s^2 4d^{10} 5p^6 6s^2 4f^{14} 5d^2$

or $[Xe]6s^2 4f^{14} 5d^2$

Radium, element 88, is in Period 7 (and Group 2A), as shown in Fig. 12.31. Thus radium has two electrons in the 7*s* orbital, and the configuration is

Ra: $1s^2 2s^2 2p^6 3s^2 3p^6 4s^2 3d^{10} 4p^6 5s^2 4d^{10} 5p^6 6s^2 4f^{14} 5d^{10} 6p^6 7s^2$

or $[Rn]7s^2$

12.14 | Further Development of the Polyelectronic Model

Before we proceed with further discussion of polyelectronic atoms, we should summarize some of the most important things that have been said about the quantum mechanical description of atoms to this point. Most important, there is a fundamental difference between the solution of the Schrödinger equation for the hydrogen atom and the solutions for all polyelectronic atoms. The Schrödinger equation for the hydrogen atom can be solved exactly to yield the now-familiar hydrogen orbitals. These orbitals are characterized by the quantum numbers n, ℓ, m_ℓ, and m_s, and the energy levels corresponding to these orbitals depend only on n (all orbitals with the same value of n are degenerate). Recall that some of the orbitals directly obtained from the solution to the Schrödinger equation are complex (contain $\sqrt{-1}$). For example, of the three orbitals corresponding to $n = 2$ and $\ell = 1$ (2*p* orbitals), the orbital corresponding to $m_\ell = 0$ is real (the $2p_z$ orbital), but the orbitals corresponding to the values of m_ℓ of +1 and −1 are complex. For ease of physical interpretation, these latter two orbitals are combined to produce two real orbitals ($2p_x$ and $2p_y$). These same procedures apply to all the *p* orbitals (corresponding to higher values of n). Similarly, for the 3*d* orbitals ($n = 3$, $\ell = 2$), the orbital corresponding to $m_\ell = 0$ is real (d_{z^2}), whereas the orbitals corresponding to m_ℓ values of ± 1 and ± 2 are complex and are used to construct the familiar real orbitals.

In contrast to the Schrödinger equation for the hydrogen atom, the Schrödinger equation for a polyelectronic atom cannot be solved exactly. For example, although the hydrogen and helium atoms are similar in many respects, the mathematical descriptions of these atoms are fundamentally different. Because electrons repel each other, the motions of the two helium electrons are correlated (coupled), and this fact prevents the exact separation of the Schrödinger equation for helium into independent, solvable equations for each electron. Thus solving the Schrödinger equation for helium (or any other polyelectronic atom) requires approximations. The approach most commonly used, the self-consistent field (SCF) method, was developed by Hartree and is applied as follows: For an atom containing N electrons, a wave function (orbital) is guessed for each electron except electron 1. For example, assume that orbitals are guessed for electrons 2, 3, 4, . . . , N: $\psi_2, \psi_3, \psi_4, \ldots, \psi_N$. The next step involves solving the Schrödinger equation for electron 1, which is moving in a potential field created by the nucleus and the electrons in orbitals $\psi_2, \psi_3, \ldots,$ ψ_N. The repulsions between electron 1 and the other electrons are computed at each point in space from the sum of the average electron densities (probabilities) corresponding to $|\psi_2|^2, |\psi_3|^2, \ldots, |\psi_N|^2$ in volume element dv around that point. With the aid of a computer, the problem is solved to yield the wave function for electron 1, which we will label ψ'_1.

The next step is to do the same type of calculation to obtain a new wave function for electron 2 moving in a field of electrons described by the wave functions $\psi'_1, \psi_3, \psi_4, \ldots, \psi_N$. This step leads to a new function ψ'_2 for electron 2. Now the process is carried out for electron 3 interacting with electrons described by the wave functions $\psi'_1, \psi'_2, \psi_4, \ldots, \psi_N$ to produce a new function ψ'_3. This procedure continues until all electrons have been covered to yield the wave functions $\psi'_1, \psi'_2, \psi'_3, \ldots, \psi'_N$. Then the entire process starts again with electron 1 and continues through electron N to give the new functions $\psi''_1, \psi''_2,$ $\psi''_3, \ldots, \psi''_N$. The procedure is diagramed in Fig. 12.32. When a given cycle produces a set of wave functions that are virtually identical to the previous set, a self-consistent field is achieved and the procedure is terminated.

The orbitals that arise from the SCF method are quite similar to hydrogen orbitals. They have the same angular characteristics (same type of boundary surfaces) as do the orbitals of hydrogen. However, the radial parts of the orbitals are different from those of the hydrogen orbitals. Although the n quantum number from the treatment of hydrogen does not apply exactly to the SCF orbitals, it is still convenient to retain it as a label. It is important to note that the energies of the SCF orbitals for polyelectronic atoms depend on both n and ℓ, not just n, as for hydrogen.

Finally, although it is not precisely correct to assume that the N electrons in an atom occupy N independent one-electron orbitals, this remains a very useful idea for understanding many atomic properties, including the organization of the periodic table. Recall that for us to account for the arrangement of the atoms on the periodic table, the orbitals that correspond to a given value of n must fill in the order ns, then np, then nd, and finally, nf. From this observation we would expect the energies of the one-electron SCF orbitals to vary in the order

$$E_{ns} < E_{np} < E_{nd} < E_{nf}$$

and this ordering is borne out by the calculations.

Figure 12.32
A schematic of the SCF method for obtaining the orbitals of a polyelectronic atom.

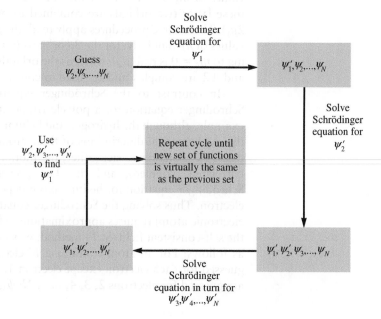

Figure 12.33
The radial distribution of electron probability density for the sodium atom. The shaded area represents the 10 core electrons. The radial distributions of the 3s, 3p, and 3d orbitals are also shown. Note the difference in the penetration effects of an electron in these three orbitals.

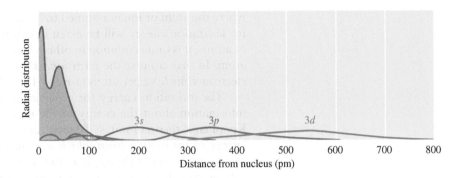

We can understand the observed order of orbital energies in a qualitative sense by considering the so-called **penetration effect**. To get an appreciation for this concept, consider the radial probability plots for the 3s, 3p, and 3d orbitals in a sodium atom, as shown in Fig. 12.33. Note that although an electron in the 3s orbital spends most of its time far from the nucleus and outside the core electrons (the electrons in the 1s, 2s, and 2p orbitals), which **shields** it from the nuclear charge, it has a small but significant probability of being quite close to the nucleus. We say it significantly *penetrates* the shielding core electron "cloud" and thus "feels" more of the nuclear charge. On the other hand, an electron in a 3p orbital does not have a probability maximum close to the nucleus. Thus we can say that an electron in a 3p orbital penetrates the core electrons to a lesser extent than an electron in the 3s orbital. Similarly, an electron in a 3d orbital (Fig. 12.33) shows much less penetration than a 3p electron does. These ideas help us to understand why an electron "prefers" the 3s orbital to the 3p or 3d and why, after the 3s orbital is filled, the next electron occupies the 3p rather than the 3d orbital. That is, the penetration effect helps us to understand qualitatively the order

$$E_{3s} < E_{3p} < E_{3d}$$

The penetration effect also helps to explain why the 4s orbital fills before the 3d orbital. Recall that potassium has the electron configuration $1s^2 2s^2 2p^6 3s^2 3p^6 4s^1$ rather than the expected $1s^2 2s^2 2p^6 3s^2 3p^6 3d^1$. We can explain this result by observing that an electron in a 4s orbital penetrates much more than an electron in a 3d orbital, as shown graphically in Fig. 12.34. Note that although the most probable distance from the nucleus for a 3d electron is less than that for a 4s electron, the 4s electron has a significant probability of penetrating close to the nucleus. This explains why the potassium atom in its lowest-energy state has its last electron in the 4s orbital rather than in the 3d orbital.

Although the rigorous description of polyelectronic atoms is quite complicated, our simple qualitative ideas about electrons in independent orbitals are often very useful when we try to understand why atoms behave the way they do. We will consider some specific atomic properties in the next section.

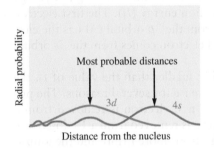

Figure 12.34
Radial probability distributions for the 3d and 4s orbitals. Note that the most probable distance of the electron from the nucleus for the 3d orbital is less than that for the 4s orbital. However, the 4s orbital allows more electron penetration close to the nucleus and thus is preferred over the 3d orbital.

12.15 | Periodic Trends in Atomic Properties

We have developed a fairly complete picture of polyelectronic atoms that is quite successful in accounting for the periodic table of elements. We will next use the model to account for the observed trends in several important atomic properties: ionization energy, electron affinity, and atomic size.

Ionization Energy

Ionization energy is the energy required to remove an electron from a gaseous atom or ion,

$$X(g) \longrightarrow X^+(g) + e^-$$

where the atom or ion is assumed to be in its ground state. Although the values for ionization energy will be given in this text in terms of kilojoules per mole of atoms, it is quite common in other chemical literature to see values given per atom. In that context the term *ionization potential* is used, and the units are electron-volts (eV) per atom (1 eV = 1.602×10^{-19} J).

The ionization energy for a particular electron in an atom is a source of information about the energy of the orbital it occupies in the atom. In fact, Koopmans' theorem states: *The ionization energy of an electron is equal to the energy of the orbital from which it came.* This rule is an approximation because, among other things, it assumes that the electrons left behind in the resulting ion will not reorganize in response to the removal of an electron. However, ionization energies do provide information that is quite useful in testing the orbital model of the atom.

To introduce some of the characteristics of ionization energy, we will consider the energy required to remove several electrons in succession from aluminum atoms in the gaseous state. The ionization energies are

$$Al(g) \longrightarrow Al^+(g) + e^- \qquad I_1 = 580 \text{ kJ/mol}$$

$$Al^+(g) \longrightarrow Al^{2+}(g) + e^- \qquad I_2 = 1815 \text{ kJ/mol}$$

$$Al^{2+}(g) \longrightarrow Al^{3+}(g) + e^- \qquad I_3 = 2740 \text{ kJ/mol}$$

$$Al^{3+}(g) \longrightarrow Al^{4+}(g) + e^- \qquad I_4 = 11,600 \text{ kJ/mol}$$

Several important points can be illustrated from these results. In a stepwise ionization process, it is always the highest-energy electron (the one bound least tightly) that is removed first. The energy required to remove the highest-energy electron of an atom is called the **first ionization energy** (I_1). The first electron removed from the aluminum atom comes from the $3p$ orbital (Al has the electron configuration [Ne]$3s^23p^1$). The second electron comes from the $3s$ orbital (since Al$^+$ has the configuration [Ne]$3s^2$).

Note that the value of I_1 is considerably smaller than the value of I_2, the **second ionization energy**. This result makes sense for several reasons. The primary factor is simply charge. Note that the first electron is removed from a neutral atom (Al), whereas the second electron is removed from a 1+ ion (Al$^+$). The increase in positive charge binds the electrons more firmly and the ionization energy increases. The same trend shows up in the third (I_3) and fourth (I_4) ionization energies, where the electron is removed from the Al^{2+} and Al^{3+} ions, respectively.

The increase in successive ionization energies for an atom also makes sense in terms of relative orbital energies. The increase from I_1 to I_2 is expected because the first electron is removed from a $3p$ orbital that is higher in energy than the $3s$ orbital from which the second electron is removed. The largest jump in ionization energy by far occurs in going from the third ionization energy (I_3) to the fourth (I_4). This large jump occurs because I_4 corresponds to removing a core electron (Al^{3+} has the configuration $1s^22s^22p^6$), and core electrons are bound much more tightly than valence electrons.

Table 12.6 gives the values of ionization energies for all the Period 3 elements. Note the large jump in energy in each case in going from the removal of valence electrons to the removal of core electrons.

The values of the first ionization energy for the elements in the first five periods of the periodic table are graphed in Fig. 12.35. Note that, in general, as we go *across a period from left to right, the first ionization energy increases.* To account for this trend qualitatively, we need to consider more fully the concept of electrons shielding each other from the nuclear charge. Shielding occurs because electrons repel each other. Our simple pictures of the atom lead us to expect that core electrons should be quite effective in shielding outer

Table 12.6

Successive Ionization Energies in Kilojoules per Mole for the Elements in Period 3

Element	I_1	I_2	I_3	I_4	I_5	I_6	I_7
Na	495	4560					
Mg	735	1445	7730	Core electrons*			
Al	580	1815	2740	11,600			
Si	780	1575	3220	4350	16,100		
P	1060	1890	2905	4950	6270	21,200	
S	1005	2260	3375	4565	6950	8490	27,000
Cl	1255	2295	3850	5160	6560	9360	11,000
Ar	1527	2665	3945	5770	7230	8780	12,000

←———————————— General increase ————————————→

General decrease ↑↓

*Note the large jump in ionization energy in going from removal of valence electrons to removal of core electrons.

electrons from the nuclear charge, since the core electrons are between the nucleus and the outer electrons. On the other hand, electrons in the same principal quantum level, which on the average are all at about the same distance from the nucleus, are not expected to shield each other very well. Thus, as we move from left to right in a given period of the periodic table, we do not expect the electrons to completely shield each other from the increasing nuclear charge as the number of protons in the nucleus increases. The electrons are expected to be bound more firmly in going from left to right across a given period, which means that the ionization energy should increase.

On the other hand, *the first ionization energy values decrease in going down a group.* This can be seen most clearly by focusing on the Group 1A elements (the alkali metals) and the Group 8A elements (the noble gases), as shown in Table 12.7. The main reason for the decrease in going down a group

Electrons in the same principal quantum level do not shield each other as well as core electrons shield outer electrons.

First ionization energy increases across a period and decreases down a group.

Table 12.7

First Ionization Energies for the Alkali Metals and Noble Gases

Atom	I_1 (kJ/mol)
Group 1A	
Li	520.
Na	495
K	419
Rb	409
Cs	382
Group 8A	
He	2377
Ne	2088
Ar	1527
Kr	1356
Xe	1176
Rn	1042

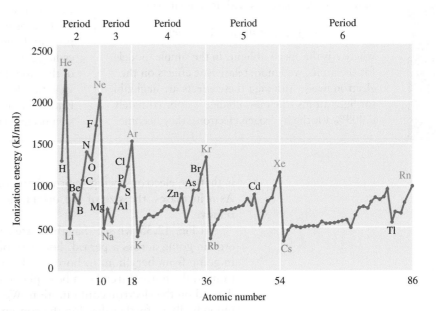

Figure 12.35

The values of first ionization energy for the elements in the first five periods. In general, ionization energy decreases in going down a group. For example, note the decrease in values for Group 1A and Group 8A. In general, ionization energy increases in going from left to right across a period. For example, note the sharp increase going across Period 2 from lithium through neon.

Chemical Insights   Why Is Mercury a Liquid?

The silver liquid called mercury has been known since ancient times. In fact, the symbol for mercury (Hg) comes from its Greek name *Hydrargyrum,* which means "watery silver." Although elements in the liquid state at ambient temperature and pressure are quite rare (Br_2 is another example), the liquid nature of mercury is especially confounding. For example, compare the properties of mercury and gold:

	Mercury	Gold
Melting point	$-39°C$	$1064°C$
Density	13.6 g cm^{-3}	19.3 g cm^{-3}
Energy of fusion	2.30 kJ mol^{-1}	12.8 kJ mol^{-1}
Conductivity	10.4 kS m^{-1}	426 kS m^{-1}

It is quite apparent that these metals, which are neighbors on the periodic table, have strikingly different properties. Why? The answer is not at all straightforward—but very interesting. It seems to hinge on relativity.

Recall that Einstein postulated in his theory of special relativity in 1905 that the mass (m) of a moving object increases with its velocity (v):

$$m_{\text{relativistic}} = m_{\text{rest}}/\sqrt{1 - (v/c)^2}$$

where c is the speed of light. In the simple models for the atom, we ignore relativistic effects on the electron mass. Although these effects are negligible for light atoms (the mass change is approximately 0.003% for the hydrogen electron), they become

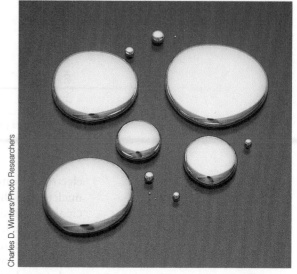

Liquid mercury forms flat drops because of its lack of surface tension.

important for heavy elements such as gold and mercury. For example, the relativistic mass for a $1s$ electron in mercury is approximately 1.23 times its rest mass, and this effect leads to a very significant contraction in the radius of the $1s$ orbital.

It turns out that relativity has an even more profound impact on atomic theory than the preceding calculations suggest. A relativistic treatment of the atom fundamentally changes the way we view the electrons in atoms. In fact, as shown by British physicist Paul Dirac, the concept of electron spin occurs naturally in a relativistic treatment of

is that the electrons being removed are, on average, farther from the nucleus. As n increases, the size of the orbital increases, and the electron is easier to remove.

In Fig. 12.35 we see that there are some discontinuities in ionization energy in going across a period. For example, discontinuities occur in Period 2, in going from beryllium to boron and from nitrogen to oxygen. These exceptions to the normal trend can be explained in terms of how electron repulsions depend on the electron configuration. We will discuss the elements in Period 2 individually to further develop the concept of shielding.

The increase in the ionization energy in going from lithium ($1s^22s^1$) to beryllium ($1s^22s^2$) is expected, since the $2s$ electrons do not shield each other completely. The decrease in the ionization energy in going from beryllium ($1s^22s^2$) to boron ($1s^22s^22p^1$) suggests that the electrons in the $2s$ orbital effectively shield the $2p$ electron. This is sensible in view of the greater penetration

the atom and does not have to be "tacked on" as in the wave mechanical treatment. The point here is not to explain these very complex ideas but to alert you to concepts you will be learning more about in higher-level courses.

How does relativity explain why mercury has a melting point of $-39°C$, whereas that of neighboring gold is $1064°C$? The first step in answering this question involves considering the electron configurations of these atoms:

$$Au: [Xe]4f^{14}5d^{10}6s^1$$

$$Hg: [Xe]4f^{14}5d^{10}6s^2$$

Notice that gold has an unfilled $6s$ subshell, but the $6s$ level is filled in mercury. Because of its configuration, a gold atom can use its half-filled $6s$ orbital to form a bond to another gold atom. In fact, the metal–metal bond in the Au_2 molecule is an astonishingly strong 221 kJ mol^{-1}, a value very close to the bond energy of the Cl_2 molecule (239 kJ mol^{-1}) and greater than the bond energy of I_2 (149 kJ mol^{-1}). In addition, gold has an electron affinity (-220 kJ mol^{-1}) that is higher than that of oxygen and sulfur. Further, gold forms a compound with cesium (CsAu) that exhibits the CsCl crystal structure (see Fig. 16.41 and Section 16.8) in which gold atoms take the place of Cl^- ions. Thus a gold atom seems to behave a lot like a halogen atom.

What causes gold to emulate many properties of the nonmetallic halogens? The apparent answer lies in the dramatic contraction of the gold $6s$ orbital because of relativistic effects. The unexpectedly small radius of the $6s$ orbital of a gold atom results in a much lower energy than is predicted in the absence of relativistic effects. It is this very-low-energy, unfilled $6s$ orbital that causes gold atoms to form very stable Au_2 molecules in the gas phase and to bind strongly to each other in the solid state, producing its high melting point. This same low-energy $6s$ orbital also leads to gold's unexpectedly high electron affinity and to its unusual color. Gold is not the silvery color exhibited by most metals because of the absorption of blue light to transfer an electron between the $5d$ and $6s$ orbitals in gold atoms.

So why are gold and mercury so different? The answer lies in the different electron configurations of the two atoms. Unlike gold, the low-energy $6s$ orbital in mercury is filled, and these two electrons are very tightly bound to the mercury atom. In fact, one can think of Hg as being analogous to He. That is, the low-energy pair of $6s$ electrons on mercury causes it to behave like a noble gas atom—it cannot bond to another mercury atom. This explains why mercury is unique among metals in that it is almost entirely monomeric in its gas phase. In contrast, the species Hg_2^{2+} is extremely stable even in aqueous solution. This fact is not surprising once it is realized that Hg^+ is isoelectronic with Au.

Thus it is the unusually low energy of the $6s$ orbitals apparently caused by relativistic effects that causes gold to behave like a halogen atom and mercury to behave like a noble gas.

by the $2s$ electrons as compared with the $2p$ electron. The $2s$ electrons spend more time closer to the nucleus than the $2p$ electrons, where they provide effective shielding. The steady increase in the ionization energy in going from boron ($1s^2 2s^2 2p^1$) to carbon ($1s^2 2s^2 2p^2$) to nitrogen ($1s^2 2s^2 2p^3$) is expected because the $2p$ electrons are not very effective in shielding each other from the increasing nuclear charge. The drop in the ionization energy in going from nitrogen ($1s^2 2s^2 2p^3$) to oxygen ($1s^2 2s^2 2p^4$) is usually explained as follows: In nitrogen each $2p$ electron is in a separate orbital. When the extra electron for oxygen is added, one $2p$ orbital becomes doubly occupied. The electron repulsions between the electrons in the doubly occupied orbital make either of these electrons easier to remove.* As we move from oxygen ($1s^2 2s^2 2p^4$) to fluorine

---

*This explanation is greatly oversimplified. A more complete explanation involves a detailed analysis of the electron interactions, which is beyond the scope of this text.

($1s^2 2s^2 2p^5$) to neon ($1s^2 2s^2 2p^6$), the ionization energy increases because in each case the electron being considered is in a doubly occupied orbital. Note that the ionization energy values for oxygen, fluorine, and neon are different from those of boron, carbon, and nitrogen by an amount that represents the extra electron repulsions in doubly occupied orbitals, as shown in Fig. 12.35.

EXAMPLE 12.9

The first ionization energy for phosphorus is 1060 kJ/mol, and that for sulfur is 1005 kJ/mol. Why?

Solution Phosphorus and sulfur are neighboring elements in Period 3 of the periodic table and have the following valence electron configurations: Phosphorus is $3s^2 3p^3$, and sulfur is $3s^2 3p^4$.

Ordinarily, the first ionization energy increases as we go across a period, so we might expect sulfur to have a greater ionization energy than phosphorus. However, in this case the fourth p electron in sulfur must be placed in an already occupied orbital. The electron–electron repulsions that result cause this electron to be more easily removed than might be expected.*

OWL INTERACTIVE EXAMPLE 12.10

Consider atoms with the following electron configurations:

$$1s^2 2s^2 2p^6$$
$$1s^2 2s^2 2p^6 3s^1$$
$$1s^2 2s^2 2p^6 3s^2$$

Which atom has the largest first ionization energy, and which has the smallest second ionization energy? Explain your choices.

Solution The atom with the largest value of I_1 is the one with the configuration $1s^2 2s^2 2p^6$ (this is the neon atom) because this element is found at the right end of Period 2. Since the $2p$ electrons do not shield each other very effectively, I_1 will be large. The other configurations given include $3s$ electrons. These electrons are effectively shielded by the core electrons and are farther from the nucleus than the $2p$ electrons in neon. Thus I_1 for these atoms is smaller than I_1 for neon.

The atom with the smallest value of I_2 is the one with the configuration $1s^2 2s^2 2p^6 3s^2$ (the magnesium atom). For magnesium both I_1 and I_2 involve valence electrons. For the atom with the configuration $1s^2 2s^2 2p^6 3s^1$ (sodium), the second electron lost (corresponding to I_2) is a core electron from a $2p$ orbital).

Electron Affinity

Electron affinity *is the energy change associated with the addition of an electron to a gaseous atom:*

$$X(g) + e^- \longrightarrow X^-(g)$$

Because two different conventions have been used, there is a good deal of confusion in the chemical literature about the signs for electron affinity values. Electron affinity has been defined in many textbooks as the energy *released* when an electron is added to a gaseous atom. This convention requires that a positive sign be attached to an exothermic addition of an electron to an atom,

---

*See page 573.

Figure 12.36

The electron affinity values for atoms among the first 20 elements that form stable, isolated X⁻ ions. The lines shown connect adjacent elements. The absence of a line indicates missing elements (He, Be, N, Ne, Mg, and Ar) whose atoms do not add an electron exothermically and thus do not form stable, isolated X⁻ ions.

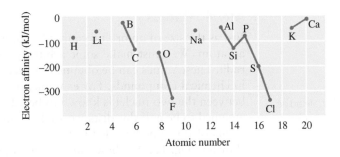

which opposes normal thermodynamic conventions. Therefore, in this book we define electron affinity as a *change* in energy. This means that if the addition of the electron is exothermic, the corresponding value for electron affinity will carry a negative sign.

Figure 12.36 shows the electron affinity values for the atoms among the first 20 elements that form stable, isolated, negative ions—that is, the atoms that undergo the addition of an electron as shown above. As expected, all these elements have negative (exothermic) electron affinities. Note that the *more negative* the energy, the greater is the quantity of energy released. Although electron affinities generally become more negative from left to right across a period, there are several exceptions to this rule in each period. The dependence of electron affinity on atomic number can be explained by considering the changes in electron repulsions as a function of electron configurations. For example, the fact that the nitrogen atom does not form a stable, isolated $N^-(g)$ ion, whereas carbon forms $C^-(g)$, reflects the difference in the electron configurations of these atoms. An electron added to nitrogen $(1s^22s^22p^3)$ to form the $N^-(g)$ ion $(1s^22s^22p^4)$ would have to occupy a $2p$ orbital that already contains one electron. The extra repulsion between the electrons in this doubly occupied orbital causes $N^-(g)$ to be unstable. When an electron is added to carbon $(1s^22s^22p^2)$ to form the $C^-(g)$ ion $(1s^22s^22p^3)$, no such extra repulsions occur.

In contrast to the nitrogen atom, the oxygen atom can add one electron to form the stable $O^-(g)$ ion. Presumably, oxygen's greater nuclear charge, compared with that of nitrogen, is sufficient to overcome the repulsion associated with putting a second electron into an already occupied $2p$ orbital. However, it should be noted that a second electron *cannot* be added to an oxygen atom $[O^-(g) + e^- \not\rightarrow O^{2-}(g)]$ to form an isolated oxide ion. This outcome seems strange in view of the many stable oxide compounds (MgO, Fe_2O_3, and so on) that are known. As we will discuss in detail in Chapter 13, the O^{2-} ion is stabilized in ionic compounds by the large attractions that occur among the positive ions and the oxide ions.

When we go down a group, electron affinity should become more positive (less energy released), since the electron is added at increasing distances from the nucleus. Although this is generally the case, the changes in electron affinity in going down most groups are relatively small, and numerous exceptions occur. This behavior is demonstrated by the electron affinities of the Group 7A elements (the halogens) shown in Table 12.8. Note that the range of values is quite small compared with the changes that typically occur across a period. Also note that although chlorine, bromine, and iodine show the expected trend, the energy released when an electron is added to fluorine is smaller than might be expected. This smaller energy release has been attributed to the small size of the $2p$ orbitals. Because the electrons must be very close together in these orbitals, there are unusually large electron–electron repulsions. In the other halogens with their larger orbitals, the repulsions are not as severe.

Table 12.8

Electron Affinities of the Halogens

Atom	Electron Affinity (kJ/mol)
F	−327.8
Cl	−348.7
Br	−324.5
I	−295.2

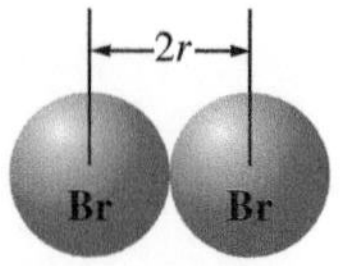

Figure 12.37
The radius of an atom (*r*) is defined as half the distance between the nuclei in a molecule consisting of identical atoms.

Atomic radius decreases across a period and increases down a group.

Atomic Radius

Just as the size of an orbital cannot be specified exactly, neither can the size of an atom. We must make some arbitrary choices to obtain values for **atomic radii**. These values can be obtained by measuring the distances between atoms in chemical compounds. For example, in the bromine molecule, the distance between the two nuclei is known to be 228 pm. The bromine atomic radius is assumed to be half this distance, or 114 pm, as shown in Fig. 12.37. Measurements of this type have led to the values of the atomic radii for the elements shown in Fig. 12.38. These radii are often called *covalent atomic radii* because of the way they are determined. These values are significantly smaller than might be expected from the 90% electron density volumes of isolated atoms because when atoms form bonds, their electron "clouds" interpenetrate. However, these values form a self-consistent data set that can be used to discuss the trends in atomic radii. The radii for metal atoms are obtained by halving the distance between metal atoms in solid metal crystals. Note from Fig. 12.38 that the atomic radius decreases in going from left to right across a period. This decrease can be explained in terms of the increasing effective nuclear charge (decreasing shielding) in going from left to right. This means that the valence electrons are drawn closer to the nucleus, decreasing the size of the atom.

Atomic radius increases down a group because of the increases in the orbital sizes in successive principal quantum levels.

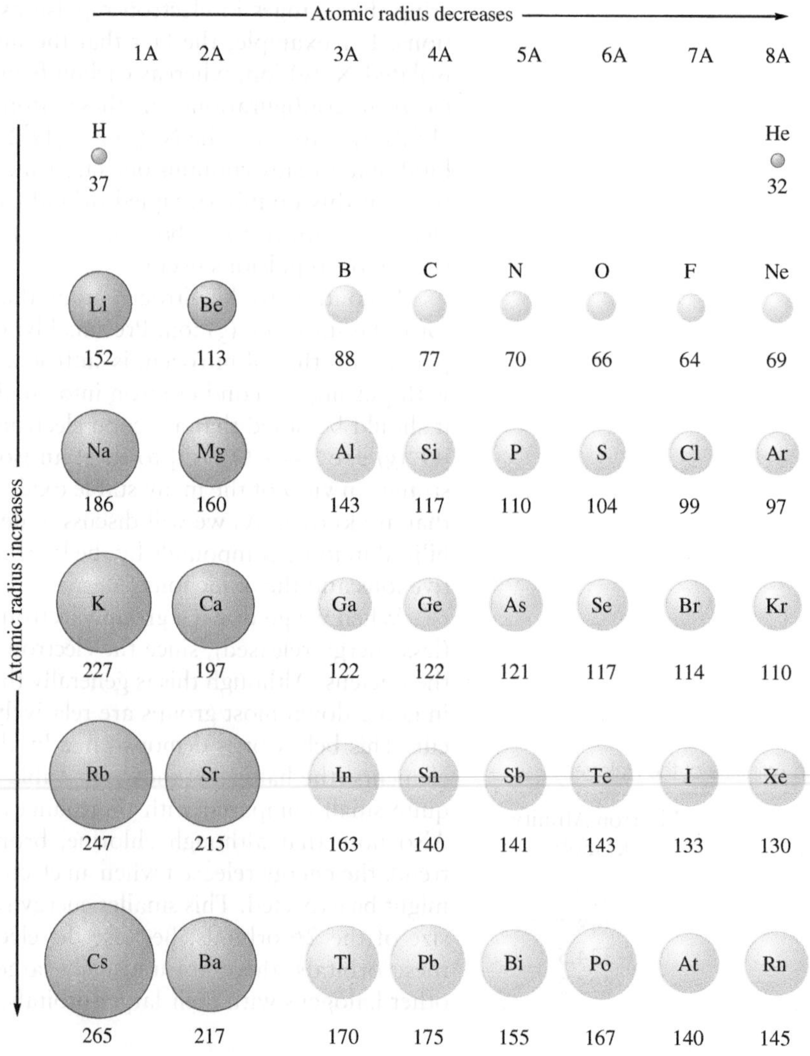

Figure 12.38
Atomic radii (in picometers) for selected atoms. Note that atomic radius decreases going across a period and increases going down a group. The values for the noble gases are estimated because data from bonded atoms are lacking.

Atomic radius decreases →

Atomic radius increases ↓

	1A	2A	3A	4A	5A	6A	7A	8A
	H 37							He 32
	Li 152	Be 113	B 88	C 77	N 70	O 66	F 64	Ne 69
	Na 186	Mg 160	Al 143	Si 117	P 110	S 104	Cl 99	Ar 97
	K 227	Ca 197	Ga 122	Ge 122	As 121	Se 117	Br 114	Kr 110
	Rb 247	Sr 215	In 163	Sn 140	Sb 141	Te 143	I 133	Xe 130
	Cs 265	Ba 217	Tl 170	Pb 175	Bi 155	Po 167	At 140	Rn 145

⚫WL **INTERACTIVE EXAMPLE 12.11**

Predict the trend in radius of the following ions: Be^{2+}, Mg^{2+}, Ca^{2+}, and Sr^{2+}.

Solution All these ions are formed by removing two electrons from an atom of a Group 2A element. In going from beryllium to strontium, we are going down the group, so the sizes increase.

$$Be^{2+} < Mg^{2+} < Ca^{2+} < Sr^{2+}$$

↑ Smallest radius   ↑ Largest radius

12.16 | The Properties of a Group: The Alkali Metals

We have seen that the periodic table originated as a way to portray the systematic properties of the elements. Mendeleev was primarily responsible for first showing its usefulness in correlating and predicting the elemental properties. In this section we will summarize much of the information available from the table. We will also illustrate the usefulness of the table by discussing the properties of a representative group, the alkali metals.

Information Contained in the Periodic Table

1. The essence of the periodic table is that members of each group of representative elements exhibit similar chemical properties that change in a regular way. The quantum mechanical model has allowed us to understand that the similarity of properties of the atoms in a group arises from the identical valence electron configurations shared by group members. *It is the number and type of valence electrons that primarily determine an atom's chemistry.*

2. One of the most valuable types of information available from the periodic table is the electron configuration of any representative element. If you understand the organization of the table, you do not need to memorize electron configurations for the elements. Although the predicted electron configurations for transition metals are sometimes incorrect, this is not a serious problem. You should, however, memorize the configuration of two exceptions, chromium and copper, since these $3d$ transition elements are found in many important compounds.

3. As we mentioned in Chapter 2, certain groups in the periodic table have special names. These names are summarized in Fig. 12.39.

4. The most fundamental classification of the elements is into metals and nonmetals. The essential chemical property of a metal is the tendency to give up electrons to form a positive ion; metals tend to have low ionization energies. The metallic elements are found on the left side of the table, as shown in Fig. 12.39. The most reactive metals are found in the lower left-hand portion of the table where the ionization energies are smallest. The distinctive chemical property of a nonmetal is the ability to gain electrons to form an anion when reacting with a metal. The nonmetals have large ionization energies and most have negative electron affinities. The nonmetals are found on the right side of the table. The most reactive ones are located in the upper right-hand corner, excluding the noble gas elements, which are quite unreactive. The division between metals and nonmetals shown in Fig. 12.39 is only approximate. Many elements along the division line exhibit both metallic and nonmetallic properties under certain circumstances. These elements are called **metalloids**, or **semimetals**.

Figure 12.39

Special names for groups in the periodic table.

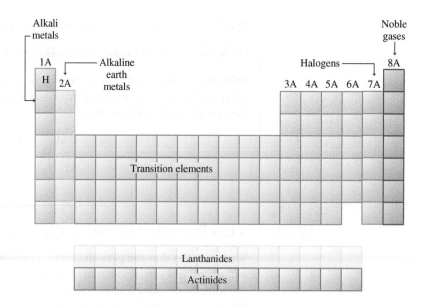

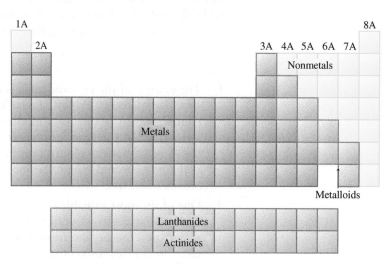

The Alkali Metals

The metals of Group 1A, the alkali metals, illustrate well the relationships among the properties of the elements in a group. Lithium, sodium, potassium, rubidium, cesium, and francium are the most reactive of the metals. We will not discuss francium here since it occurs in nature in only very small quantities. Although hydrogen is found in Group 1A, it behaves as a nonmetal, in contrast to the other members of that group. The fundamental reason for hydrogen's nonmetallic character is its very small size (see Fig. 12.38). The electron in the small 1s orbital is bound very tightly to the nucleus.

Some important properties of the first five alkali metals are shown in Table 12.9. The data in Table 12.9 show that when we move down the group, the first ionization energy decreases and the atomic radius increases. This agrees with the general trends discussed in Section 12.15.

The overall increase in density in going down Group 1A is typical of all groups. It occurs because atomic mass generally increases more rapidly than atomic size.

The smooth decrease in melting point (mp) and boiling point (bp) in going down Group 1A is not typical; in most other groups, more complicated behavior occurs. Note that the melting point of cesium is only 29°C. Cesium can be

Table 12.9

Properties of Five Alkali Metals

Element	Valence Electron Configuration	Density at 25°C (g/cm³)	mp (°C)	bp (°C)	First Ionization Energy (kJ/mol)	Atomic (covalent) Radius (pm)	Ionic (M⁺) Radius (pm)
Li	$2s^1$	0.53	180	1330	520.	152	60
Na	$3s^1$	0.97	98	892	495	186	95
K	$4s^1$	0.86	64	760	419	227	133
Rb	$5s^1$	1.53	39	688	409	247	148
Cs	$6s^1$	1.87	29	690	382	265	169

melted readily from the heat of your hand. Cesium's low melting point is very unusual—metals typically have high melting points. For example, tungsten melts at 3410°C. The only other metals with low melting points are mercury (mp = −39°C) and gallium (mp = 30°C).

Recall that the chemical property most characteristic of a metal is the ability to lose its valence electrons. The Group 1A elements are very reactive. They have low ionization energies and react readily with nonmetals to form ionic solids. A typical example involves the reaction of sodium with chlorine to form sodium chloride:

$$2Na(s) + Cl_2(g) \longrightarrow 2NaCl(s)$$

This is an oxidation–reduction reaction in which chlorine oxidizes sodium to form Na^+ and Cl^- ions. In the reactions between metals and nonmetals, it is typical for the nonmetal to behave as the oxidizing agent and the metal to behave as the reducing agent, as shown by the following reactions:

$$2Na(s) + S(s) \longrightarrow Na_2S(s)$$
Contains Na^+ and S^{2-} ions

$$6Li(s) + N_2(g) \longrightarrow 2Li_3N(s)$$
Contains Li^+ and N^{3-} ions

$$4Na(s) + O_2(g) \longrightarrow 2Na_2O(s)$$
Contains Na^+ and O^{2-} ions

For reactions of this type, the relative reducing powers of the alkali metals can be predicted from the first ionization energies listed in Table 12.9. Since it is much easier to remove an electron from a cesium atom than from a lithium atom, cesium should be the better reducing agent. The expected trend in reducing ability is

$$Cs > Rb > K > Na > Li$$

This order is observed experimentally for direct reactions between the solid alkali metals and nonmetals. However, this order of reducing ability is not observed when the alkali metals react in aqueous solution. For example, the reduction of water by an alkali metal is very vigorous and exothermic:

$$2M(s) + 2H_2O(l) \longrightarrow H_2(g) + 2M^+(aq) + 2OH^-(aq) + energy$$

The order of reducing abilities observed for this reaction (for the first three group members) is

$$Li > K > Na$$

which is not the order expected from the relative ionization energies of these metals.

Chemical Insights | Lithium: Behavior Medicine

More and more people in our society seem to be suffering from the debilitating effects of mania and depression, but the alkali metal lithium can provide help for many. In fact, more than three million prescriptions for lithium carbonate are filled annually by retail pharmacies.

Although the details are not well understood, the lithium ion seems to alleviate mood disorders by affecting the way that brain cells respond to neurotransmitters, a class of molecules that facilitate the transmission of nerve impulses.

Specifically, physiologists think that the lithium ion may interfere with a complex cycle of reactions that relays and amplifies messages carried to the cells by neurotransmitters and hormones. They theorize that exaggerated forms of behavior, such as mania or depression, arise from the overactivity of this cycle. Thus the fact that lithium inhibits this cycle may be responsible for its moderating effect on behavior.

There is a growing collection of evidence that violent behavior may result at least partially from the improper regulation of neurotransmitters and hormones. For example, a study in Finland showed that violent criminals, especially arsonists, often

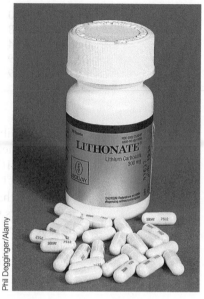

Capsules of lithium carbonate.

had low levels of serotonin, a common neurotransmitter. Studies are now under way to determine whether lithium might also be effective for treating these and other aberrant forms of behavior.

This unexpected order occurs because the formation of the M^+ ions in aqueous solution is strongly influenced by the hydration of these ions by the polar water molecules. The hydration energy of an ion represents the change in energy that occurs when water molecules attach to the M^+ ion. The hydration energies for the Li^+, Na^+, and K^+ ions shown in Table 12.10 indicate that the process is exothermic in each case. However, nearly twice as much energy is released by the hydration of the Li^+ ion as compared with that of the K^+ ion. This difference is caused by size effects; the Li^+ ion is much smaller than the K^+ ion, and thus its *charge density* (charge per unit volume) is much greater. This means that the polar water molecules are more strongly attracted to the small Li^+ ion. Because the Li^+ ion is so strongly hydrated, its formation from the lithium atom occurs more readily than the formation of the K^+ ion from the potassium atom. Although a potassium atom in the gas phase loses its valence electron more readily than a lithium atom in the gas phase, the opposite is true in aqueous solution. This anomaly is an example of the importance of the polarity of the water molecule in aqueous reactions.

There is one more surprise involving the highly exothermic reactions of the alkali metals with water. Experiments show that lithium is the best reducing agent in water, so we might expect lithium to react most violently with water. However, it does not. Sodium and potassium react much more vigorously. Why? The answer lies in the relatively high melting point for lithium. When sodium and potassium react with water, the heat evolved causes them to melt, giving a larger area of contact with water. Lithium, on the other hand, does not

Table 12.10

Hydration Energies for Li^+, Na^+, and K^+ Ions

Ion	Hydration Energy (kJ/mol)
Li^+	−500
Na^+	−400
K^+	−300

melt under these conditions and thus reacts more slowly. This example illustrates the important principle (which we will discuss in detail in Chapter 15) that the energy of a reaction and the rate at which it occurs are not necessarily related.

In this section we have seen that the trends in atomic properties summarized by the periodic table can be a great help in understanding the chemical behavior of the elements. This fact will be emphasized over and over as we proceed in our study of chemistry.

Key Terms

Section 12.1
electromagnetic radiation
wavelength
frequency

Section 12.2
ultraviolet catastrophe
Planck's constant
quantized
photon
photoelectric effect
dual nature of light
diffraction
diffraction pattern

Section 12.3
continuous spectrum
line spectrum

Section 12.4
quantum model
ground state

Section 12.5
wave mechanics (quantum mechanics)
wave function
orbital
Heisenberg uncertainty principle

Section 12.8
probability distribution
radial probability distribution

Section 12.9
quantum numbers
principal quantum number (n)
angular momentum quantum number (l)
magnetic quantum number (m_1)
subshell
nodal surfaces (nodes)
lobe
degenerate orbital

Section 12.10
electron spin
electron spin quantum number
Pauli exclusion principle

Section 12.11
polyelectronic atom
effective nuclear charge
self-consistent field (SCF) method

For Review

OWL and **go Chemistry**

Sign in at **www.cengage.com/owl** to:
• View tutorials and simulations, develop problem-solving skills, and complete online homework assigned by your professor.
• Download Go Chemistry mini lecture modules for quick review and exam prep from OWL (or purchase them at **www.cengagebrain.com**)

Electromagnetic radiation

■ Characterized by its wavelength (λ), frequency (ν), and speed ($c = 2.9979 \times 10^8$ m/s)

$$\lambda \nu = c$$

■ Can be viewed as a stream of "particles" called photons, each with energy $h\nu$, where h is Planck's constant (6.626×10^{-34} J · s)

Photoelectric effect

■ When light strikes a metal surface, electrons are emitted
■ Analysis of the kinetic energy and numbers of the emitted electrons led Einstein to suggest that electromagnetic radiation can be viewed as a stream of photons

Hydrogen spectrum

■ The emission spectrum of hydrogen shows discrete wavelengths
■ Indicates that hydrogen has discrete energy levels

Bohr model of the hydrogen atom

■ Using the data from the hydrogen spectrum and assuming angular momentum to be quantized, Bohr devised a model in which the electron traveled in circular orbits
■ Although an important pioneering effort, this model proved to be entirely incorrect

Wave (quantum) mechanical model

■ An electron is described as a standing wave
■ The square of the wave function (often called an orbital) gives a probability distribution for the electron position
■ The exact position of the electron is never known, which is consistent with the Heisenberg uncertainty principle: it is impossible to know accurately both the position and the momentum of a particle simultaneously
■ Probability maps are used to define orbital shapes
■ Orbitals are characterized by the quantum numbers n, ℓ, and m_ℓ

Particle in a box

■ Not an accurate physical model of the hydrogen atom
■ Illustrates the mathematics of wave mechanics
■ $E = \dfrac{n^2 h^2}{8mL^2}$

Section 12.12
triads
octaves

Section 12.13
aufbau principle
Hund's rule
valence electron
core electron
transition metals
lanthanide series
actinide series
main-group (representative)
  elements

Section 12.14
penetration effect
shielding

Section 12.15
ionization energy
first ionization energy
second ionization energy
electron affinity
atomic radii

Section 12.16
metalloids (semimetals)

Electron spin
- Described by the spin quantum number m_s, which can have values of $\pm\frac{1}{2}$
- Pauli exclusion principle: no two electrons in a given atom can have the same set of quantum numbers n, ℓ, m_ℓ, and m_s
- Only two electrons with opposite spins can occupy a given orbital

Periodic table
- By populating the orbitals from the wave mechanical model (the aufbau principle), the form of the periodic table can be explained
- According to the wave mechanical model, atoms in a given group have the same valence (outer) electron configuration
- The trends in properties such as ionization energies and atomic radii can be explained in terms of the concepts of nuclear attraction, electron repulsions, shielding, and penetration

Discussion Questions

These questions are designed to be considered by groups of students in class. Often these questions work well for introducing a particular topic in class.

1. Explain what it means for something to have wavelike properties; for something to have particulate properties. Electromagnetic radiation can be discussed in terms of both particles and waves. Explain the experimental verification for each of these views.

2. Defend and criticize Bohr's model. Why was it reasonable that such a model was proposed, and what evidence was there that it "works"? Why do we no longer "believe" in it?

3. The first ionization energy for magnesium is 735 kJ/mol. Which electron is this for? Estimate Z_{eff} for this electron, and explain your reasoning. Calculate Z_{eff} for this electron, and compare it to your estimate.

4. The first four ionization energies for elements X and Y are shown below. The units are not kJ/mol.

	X	Y
First	170	200
Second	350	400
Third	1800	3500
Fourth	2500	5000

Identify the elements X and Y. There may be more than one answer, so explain completely.

5. Compare the first ionization energy of helium with its second ionization energy, remembering that both electrons come from the 1s orbital. Explain the difference without using actual numbers from the text.

6. Which has a larger second ionization energy, lithium or beryllium? Why?

7. Explain why a graph of ionization energy versus atomic number (across a row) is not linear. Where are the exceptions? Explain why they occur.

8. Without referring to your text, predict the trend of second ionization energies for the elements sodium through argon. Compare your answer with the data in Table 12.6. Explain any differences.

9. Account for the fact that the line that separates the metals from the nonmetals on the periodic table is diagonal downward to the right instead of horizontal or vertical.

10. Explain the term *electron* from a quantum mechanical perspective, including a discussion of atomic radii, probabilities, and orbitals.

11. Choose the best response for the following. The ionization energy for the chlorine atom is equal in magnitude to the electron affinity for
   a. the Cl atom   d. the F atom
   b. the Cl⁻ ion   e. none of these
   c. the Cl⁺ ion

   Explain.

12. Consider the following statement: "The ionization energy for the potassium atom is negative because when K loses an electron to become K^+ it achieves a noble gas electron configuration." Indicate what is incorrect. Explain.

13. What is the difference between Z_{eff} and Z? When are they the same? Explain.

14. In going across a row of the periodic table, electrons are added and ionization energy generally increases. In going down a column of the periodic table, electrons are also being added but ionization energy generally decreases. Explain.

15. Explain the difference between the probability density distribution for an orbital and its radial probability.

16. How does the energy of a hydrogen 1s orbital compare with that of a lithium 1s orbital? Why? What is meant by the term *energy of the orbital*? What is its sign? Why? What is meant by the term *lower in energy*?

17. Which is larger, the hydrogen 1s orbital or the lithium 1s orbital? Why? Which has the larger radius, the hydrogen atom or the lithium atom? Why?

18. Is the following statement true or false: The hydrogen atom has a 3s orbital. Explain.

19. Which is higher in energy: the 2s or 2p orbital in hydrogen? Is this also true for helium? Explain.

20. Prove mathematically that it is more energetically favorable for a fluorine atom to take an electron from a sodium atom than for a fluorine atom to take an electron from another fluorine atom.

Exercises

OWL Interactive versions of these problems may be assigned in OWL.

A blue exercise number indicates that the answer to that exercise appears at the end of this book and a solution appears in the *Solutions Guide*.

Light and Matter

21. Microwave radiation has a wavelength on the order of 1.0 cm. Calculate the frequency and the energy of a single photon of this radiation. Calculate the energy of an Avogadro's number of photons (called an einstein) of this electromagnetic radiation.

22. Consider the following waves representing electromagnetic radiation:

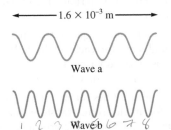

Which wave has the longer wavelength? Calculate the wavelength. Which wave has the higher frequency and larger photon energy? Calculate these values. Which wave has the greater velocity? What type of electromagnetic radiation does each wave represent?

23. One type of electromagnetic radiation has a frequency of 107.1 MHz, another type has a wavelength of 2.12×10^{-10} m, and another type of electromagnetic radiation has photons with energy equal to 3.97×10^{-19} J/photon. Identify each type of electromagnetic radiation, and place them in order of increasing photon energy and increasing frequency.

24. Carbon absorbs energy at a wavelength of 150. nm. The total amount of energy emitted by a carbon sample is 1.98×10^5 J. Calculate the number of carbon atoms present in the sample, assuming that each atom emits one photon.

25. A carbon–oxygen double bond in a certain organic molecule absorbs radiation that has a frequency of 6.0×10^{13} s^{-1}.
   a. What is the wavelength of this radiation?
   b. To what region of the spectrum does this radiation belong?
   c. What is the energy of this radiation per photon? Per mole of photons?
   d. A carbon–oxygen bond in a different molecule absorbs radiation with frequency equal to 5.4×10^{13} s^{-1}. Is this radiation more or less energetic?

26. X rays have wavelengths on the order of 1×10^{-10} m. Calculate the energy of 1.0×10^{-10} m X rays in units of kilojoules per mole of X rays. AM radio waves have wavelengths on the order of 1×10^4 m. Calculate the energy of 1.0×10^4 m radio waves in units of kilojoules per mole of radio waves. Consider that the bond energy of a carbon–carbon single bond found in organic compounds is 347 kJ/mol. Would X rays and/or radio waves be able to disrupt organic compounds by breaking carbon–carbon single bonds?

27. The work function of an element is the energy required to remove an electron from the surface of the solid. The work function for lithium is 279.7 kJ/mol (that is, it takes 279.7 kJ of energy to remove 1 mole of electrons from 1 mole of Li atoms on the surface of Li metal). What is the maximum wavelength of light that can remove an electron from an atom in lithium metal?

28. Ionization energy is the energy required to remove an electron from an atom in the gas phase. The ionization energy of gold is 890.1 kJ/mol. Is light with a wavelength of 225 nm capable of ionizing a gold atom (removing an electron) in the gas phase?

29. It takes 208.4 kJ of energy to remove 1 mole of electrons from the atoms on the surface of rubidium metal. If rubidium metal is irradiated with 254-nm light, what is the maximum kinetic energy the released electrons can have?

30. What experimental evidence supports the quantum theory of light? Explain the wave–particle duality of all matter. For what size particle must one consider both the wave and the particle properties?

31. Explain the photoelectric effect.

32. Calculate the de Broglie wavelength for each of the following.
    a. an electron with a velocity 10.% of the speed of light
    b. a tennis ball (55 g) served at 35 m/s (~80 mi/h)

33. Neutron diffraction is used in determining the structures of molecules.
    a. Calculate the de Broglie wavelength of a neutron moving at 1.00% of the speed of light.
    b. Calculate the velocity of a neutron with a wavelength of 75 pm (1 pm = 10^{-12} m).

34. Calculate the velocities of electrons with de Broglie wavelengths of 1.0×10^2 nm and 1.0 nm, respectively.

35. An atom of a particular element is traveling at 1% of the speed of light. The de Broglie wavelength is found to be 3.31×10^{-3} pm. Which element is this?

Hydrogen Atom: The Bohr Model

36. Characterize the Bohr model of the atom. In the Bohr model, what do we mean when we say something is quantized? How does the Bohr model of the hydrogen atom explain the hydrogen emission spectrum? Why is the Bohr model fundamentally incorrect?

37. The following is an energy-level diagram illustrating three different electronic transitions in the Bohr hydrogen atom.

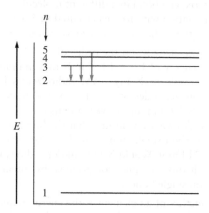

    a. Explain why the energy levels get closer together as they increase. Provide mathematical support for this.
    b. Verify that the colors given in the diagram are correct. Provide mathematical support.

38. Calculate the wavelength of light emitted when each of the following transitions occur in the hydrogen atom. What type of electromagnetic radiation is emitted in each transition?
    a. $n = 4 \rightarrow n = 3$
    b. $n = 5 \rightarrow n = 4$
    c. $n = 5 \rightarrow n = 3$

39. Assume that a hydrogen atom's electron has been excited to the $n = 5$ level. How many different wavelengths of light can be emitted as this excited atom loses energy?

40. What is the maximum wavelength of light capable of removing an electron from a hydrogen atom in the energy states characterized by $n = 1$ and $n = 3$?

41. An electron is excited from the ground state to the $n = 3$ state in a hydrogen atom. Which of the following statements are true? Correct any false statements.
    a. It takes more energy to ionize (remove) the electron from $n = 3$ than from the ground state.
    b. The electron is farther from the nucleus on average in the $n = 3$ state than in the ground state.
    c. The wavelength of light emitted if the electron drops from $n = 3$ to $n = 2$ is shorter than the wavelength of light emitted if the electron falls from $n = 3$ to $n = 1$.
    d. The wavelength of light emitted when the electron returns to the ground state from $n = 3$ is the same as the wavelength of light absorbed to go from $n = 1$ to $n = 3$.
    e. The first excited state corresponds to $n = 3$.

42. Does a photon of visible light ($\lambda = 400–700$ nm) have sufficient energy to excite an electron in a hydrogen atom from the $n = 1$ to the $n = 5$ energy state? From the $n = 2$ to the $n = 6$ energy state?

43. An excited hydrogen atom emits light with a wavelength of 397.2 nm to reach the energy level for which $n = 2$. In which principal quantum level did the electron begin?

44. An excited hydrogen atom with an electron in the $n = 5$ state emits light having a frequency of 6.90×10^{14} s^{-1}. Determine the principal quantum level for the final state in this electronic transition.

45. Consider an electron for a hydrogen atom in an excited state. The maximum wavelength of electromagnetic radiation that can completely remove (ionize) the electron from the H atom is 1460 nm. Determine the initial excited state for the electron ($n = ?$).

46. Calculate the energy (in kJ/mol) required to remove the electron in the ground state for each of the following one-electron species using the Bohr model.
    a. H   b. He$^+$ c. Li^{2+} d. C^{5+} e. Fe^{25+}

47. One of the emission spectral lines for Be^{3+} has a wavelength of 253.4 nm for an electronic transition that begins in the state with $n = 5$. What is the principal quantum number of the lower-energy state corresponding to this emission?

Wave Mechanics and Particle in a Box

48. The Heisenberg uncertainty principle can be expressed in the form

$$\Delta E \cdot \Delta t \geq \frac{\hbar}{2}$$

where E represents energy and t represents time. Show that the units for this form are the same as the units for the form used in this chapter:

$$\Delta x \cdot \Delta p \geq \frac{\hbar}{2}$$

49. Using the Heisenberg uncertainty principle, calculate Δx for each of the following.
    a. an electron with $\Delta v = 0.100$ m/s
    b. a baseball (mass = 145 g) with $\Delta v = 0.100$ m/s
    How does the answer in part a compare with the size of a hydrogen atom? How does the answer in part b correspond to the size of a baseball?

50. We can represent both probability and radial probability versus distance from the nucleus for a hydrogen $1s$ orbital as depicted below.

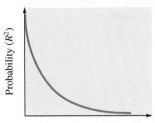
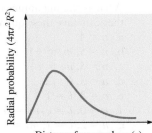

    What does each graph tell us about the electron in a hydrogen $1s$ orbital? Describe the significance of the radial probability distribution.

51. Discuss why a function of the type $A \cos(Lx)$ is not an appropriate solution for the particle in a one-dimensional box.

52. Calculate the wavelength of the electromagnetic radiation required to excite an electron from the ground state to the level with $n = 5$ in a one-dimensional box 40.0 pm in length.

53. An electron in a one-dimensional box requires a wavelength of 8080 nm to excite an electron from the $n = 2$ to the $n = 3$ energy level. Calculate the length of this box.

54. An electron in a 10.0-nm one-dimensional box is excited from the ground state into a higher-energy state by absorbing a photon of electromagnetic radiation with a wavelength of 1.374×10^{-5} m. Determine the final energy state for this transition.

55. Discuss what happens to the energy levels for an electron trapped in a one-dimensional box as the length of the box increases.

56. What is the total probability of finding a particle in a one-dimensional box in level $n = 3$ between $x = 0$ and $x = L/6$?

57. Which has the lowest (ground-state) energy, an electron trapped in a one-dimensional box of length 10^{-6} m or one with length 10^{-10} m?

Orbitals and Quantum Numbers

58. What are quantum numbers? What information do we get from the quantum numbers n, ℓ, and m_ℓ? We define a spin quantum number (m_s), but do we know that an electron literally spins?

59. How do $2p$ orbitals differ from each other? How do $2p$ and $3p$ orbitals differ from each other? What is a nodal surface in an atomic orbital?

60. Identify each of the following orbitals, and determine the n and l quantum numbers. Explain your answers.

    a.

    b. Node   c.

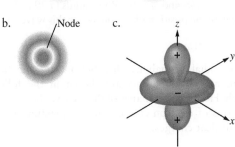

61. Which of the following orbital designations are incorrect: $1s$, $1p$, $7d$, $9s$, $3f$, $4f$, $2d$?

62. Which of the following sets of quantum numbers are not allowed in the hydrogen atom? For the sets of quantum numbers that are incorrect, state what is wrong in each set.
    a. $n = 3$, $\ell = 2$, $m_\ell = 2$
    b. $n = 4$, $\ell = 3$, $m_\ell = 4$
    c. $n = 0$, $\ell = 0$, $m_\ell = 0$
    d. $n = 2$, $\ell = -1$, $m_\ell = 1$

63. Which of the following sets of quantum numbers are not allowed? For each incorrect set, state why it is incorrect.
    a. $n = 3$, $\ell = 3$, $m_\ell = 0$, $m_s = -\frac{1}{2}$
    b. $n = 4$, $\ell = 3$, $m_\ell = 2$, $m_s = -\frac{1}{2}$
    c. $n = 4$, $\ell = 1$, $m_\ell = 1$, $m_s = +\frac{1}{2}$
    d. $n = 2$, $\ell = 1$, $m_\ell = -1$, $m_s = -1$
    e. $n = 5$, $\ell = -4$, $m_\ell = 2$, $m_s = +\frac{1}{2}$
    f. $n = 3$, $\ell = 1$, $m_\ell = 2$, $m_s = -\frac{1}{2}$

64. How many orbitals can have the designation $5p$, $3d_{z^2}$, $4d$, $n = 5$, and $n = 4$?

65. How many electrons in an atom can have the designation $1p$, $6d_{x^2-y^2}$, $4f$, $7p_y$, $2s$, and $n = 3$?

66. What is the physical significance of the value of ψ^2 at a particular point in an atomic orbital?

67. In defining the sizes of orbitals, why must we use an arbitrary value, such as 90% of the probability of finding an electron in that region?

68. From the diagrams of $2p$ and $3p$ orbitals in Fig. 12.19 and Fig. 12.20, respectively, draw a rough graph of the square of the wave function for these orbitals in the direction of one of the lobes.

69. The wave function for the $2p_z$ orbital in the hydrogen atom is

$$\psi_{2p_z} = \frac{1}{4\sqrt{2\pi}} \left(\frac{Z}{a_0} \right)^{3/2} \sigma e^{-\sigma/2} \cos \theta$$

where a_0 is the value for the radius of the first Bohr orbit in meters (5.29×10^{-11}), σ is Zr/a_0, r is the value for the distance from the nucleus in meters, and θ is an angle. Calculate the value of $\psi_{2p_z}^2$ at $r = a_0$ for $\theta = 0$ (z axis) and for $\theta = 90°$ (xy plane).

70. For hydrogen atoms, the wave function for the state $n = 3$, $\ell = 0$, and $m_\ell = 0$ is

$$\psi_{300} = \frac{1}{81\sqrt{3\pi}}\left(\frac{1}{a_0}\right)^{3/2} (27 - 18\sigma + 2\sigma^2)e^{-\sigma/3}$$

where $\sigma = r/a_0$ and a_0 is the Bohr radius (5.29×10^{-11} m). Calculate the position of the nodes for this wave function.

Polyelectronic Atoms

71. Total radial probability distributions for the helium, neon, and argon atoms are shown in the following graph. How can the shapes of these curves be interpreted in terms of electron configurations, quantum numbers, and nuclear charges?

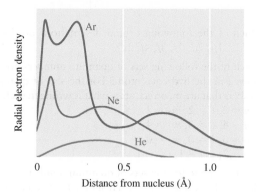

72. The relative orbital levels for the hydrogen atom can be represented as

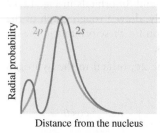

Draw the relative orbital energy levels for atoms with more than one electron, and explain your answer. Also explain how the following radial probability distributions support your answer.

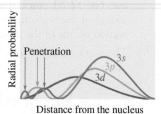

73. What is the difference between core electrons and valence electrons? Why do we emphasize the valence electrons in an atom when discussing atomic properties? What is the relationship between valence electrons and elements in the same group of the periodic table?

74. The periodic table consists of four blocks of elements that correspond to s, p, d, and f orbitals being filled. After f orbitals come g and h orbitals. In theory, if a g block and an h block of elements existed, how long would the rows of g and h elements be in this theoretical periodic table?

75. What is the maximum number of electrons in an atom that can have these quantum numbers?
   a. $n = 4$
   b. $n = 5, m_\ell = +1$
   c. $n = 5, m_s = +\frac{1}{2}$
   d. $n = 3, \ell = 2$
   e. $n = 2, \ell = 1$
   f. $n = 0, \ell = 0, m_\ell = 0$
   g. $n = 2, \ell = 1, m_\ell = -1, m_s = -\frac{1}{2}$
   h. $n = 3, m_s = +\frac{1}{2}$
   i. $n = 2, \ell = 2$
   j. $n = 1, \ell = 0, m_\ell = 0$

76. The elements of Si, Ga, As, Ge, Al, Cd, S, and Se are all used in the manufacture of various semiconductor devices. Write the expected electron configurations for these atoms.

77. Write the expected electron configurations for the following atoms: Sc, Fe, P, Cs, Eu, Pt, Xe, and Br.

78. Write the expected electron configurations for each of the following atoms: Cl, As, Sr, W, Pb, and Cf.

79. Using Fig. 12.29, list elements (ignore the lanthanides and actinides) that have ground-state electron configurations that differ from those we would expect from their positions in the periodic table.

80. Write the expected ground-state electron configuration for the following.
   a. the element with one unpaired $5p$ electron that forms a covalent compound with fluorine
   b. the (as yet undiscovered) alkaline earth metal after radium
   c. the noble gas with electrons occupying $4f$ orbitals
   d. the first-row transition metal with the most unpaired electrons

81. For elements 1–36, there are two exceptions to the filling order as predicted from the periodic table. Draw the atomic orbital diagrams for the two exceptions, and indicate how many unpaired electrons are present.

82. Given the valence electron orbital level diagram and the description, identify the element or ion.
   a. A ground state atom

   b. An atom in an excited state (assume two electrons occupy the $1s$ orbital)

c. A ground state ion with a charge of -1

$$4s \qquad 4p$$

$$\boxed{\uparrow\downarrow} \qquad \boxed{\uparrow\downarrow}\,\boxed{\uparrow\downarrow}\,\boxed{\uparrow}$$

83. How many valence electrons do each of the following elements have, and what are the specific valence electrons for each element?
    a. Ca
    b. O
    c. element 117
    d. In
    e. Ar
    f. Bi

84. In the ground state of mercury (Hg),
    a. how many electrons occupy atomic orbitals with $n = 3$?
    b. how many electrons occupy d atomic orbitals?
    c. how many electrons occupy p_z atomic orbitals?
    d. how many electrons have spin "up" ($m_s = +\frac{1}{2}$)?

85. In the ground state of element 115, Uup,
    a. how many electrons have $n = 5$ as one of their quantum numbers?
    b. how many electrons have $\ell = 3$ as one of their quantum numbers?
    c. how many electrons have $m_\ell = 1$ as one of their quantum numbers?
    d. how many electrons have $m_s = -\frac{1}{2}$ as one of their quantum numbers?

86. Give possible values for the quantum numbers of the valence electrons in an atom of titanium (Ti).

87. One bit of evidence that the quantum mechanical model is "correct" lies in the magnetic properties of matter. Atoms with unpaired electrons are attracted by magnetic fields and thus are said to exhibit *paramagnetism*. The degree to which this effect is observed is directly related to the number of unpaired electrons present in the atom. Consider the ground-state electron configurations for Li, N, Ni, Te, Ba, and Hg. Which of these atoms would be expected to be paramagnetic, and how many unpaired electrons are present in each paramagnetic atom?

88. Which of elements 1–36 have two unpaired electrons in the ground state?

89. Which of elements 1–36 have one unpaired electron in the ground state?

90. A certain oxygen atom has the electron configuration $1s^2 2s^2 2p_x^2 2p_y^2$. How many unpaired electrons are present? Is this an excited state for oxygen? In going from this state to the ground state, would energy be released or absorbed?

91. How many unpaired electrons are present in each of the following in the ground state: O, O$^+$, O$^-$, Os, Zr, S, F, Ar?

92. Which of the following electron configurations correspond to an excited state? Identify the atoms, and write the ground-state electron configuration where appropriate.
    a. $1s^2 2s^2 3p^1$
    b. $1s^2 2s^2 2p^6$
    c. $1s^2 2s^2 2p^4 3s^1$
    d. $[Ar]4s^2 3d^5 4p^1$

The Periodic Table and Periodic Properties

93. Using the element phosphorus as an example, write equations for the processes in which the energy change

will correspond to the ionization energy and to the electron affinity.

94. Explain why the first ionization energy tends to increase as one proceeds from left to right across a period. Why is the first ionization energy of aluminum lower than that of magnesium and the first ionization energy of sulfur lower than that of phosphorus?

95. Why do the successive ionization energies of an atom always increase? Note the successive ionization energies for silicon given in Table 12.6. Would you expect to see any large jumps between successive ionization energies of silicon as you removed all the electrons, one by one, beyond those shown in the table?

96. The radius trend and the ionization energy trend are exact opposites. Does this make sense? Define electron affinity. Electron affinity values are both exothermic (negative) and endothermic (positive). However, ionization energy values are always endothermic (positive). Explain.

97. Arrange the following groups of atoms in order of increasing size.
    a. Te, S, Se
    b. K, Br, Ni
    c. Ba, Si, F
    d. Rb, Na, Be
    e. Sr, Se, Ne
    f. Fe, P, O

98. Arrange the atoms in Exercise 97 in order of increasing first ionization energy.

99. In each of the following sets, which atom or ion has the smallest ionization energy?
    a. Ca, Sr, Ba
    b. K, Mn, Ga
    c. N, O, F
    d. S^{2-}, S, S^{2+}
    e. Cs, Ge, Ar

100. In each of the following sets, which atom or ion has the smallest radius?
    a. H, He
    b. Cl, In, Se
    c. element 120, element 119, element 117
    d. Nb, Zn, Si
    e. Na$^-$, Na, Na$^+$

101. The first ionization energies of As and Se are 0.947 MJ/mol and 0.941 MJ/mol, respectively. Rationalize these values in terms of electron configurations.

102. Rank the elements Be, B, C, N, and O in order of increasing first ionization energy. Explain your reasoning.

103. We expect the atomic radius to increase down a group in the periodic table. Can you suggest why the atomic radius of hafnium breaks this rule? (See the following data.)

Element	Atomic Radius (Å)	Element	Atomic Radius (Å)
Sc	1.57	Ti	1.477
Y	1.693	Zr	1.593
La	1.915	Hf	1.476

104. Three elements have the electron configurations $1s^2 2s^2 2p^6 3s^2 3p^6$, $1s^2 2s^2 2p^6 3s^2$, and $1s^2 2s^2 2p^6 3s^2 3p^6 4s^1$. The first ionization energies of these elements (not in the same order) are 0.419, 0.735, and 1.527 MJ/mol. The atomic radii are 1.60, 0.98, and 2.35 Å. Identify the

three elements, and match the appropriate values of ionization energy and atomic radius to each configuration.

105. Predict some of the properties of element 117 (symbol Uus following conventions proposed by the International Union of Pure and Applied Chemistry [IUPAC]).
    a. What will be its electron configuration?
    b. What element will it most resemble chemically?
    c. What will be the formulas of the neutral binary compounds it forms with sodium, magnesium, carbon, and oxygen?
    d. What oxyanions would you expect Uus to form?

106. Order each of the following sets from the least exothermic electron affinity to the most.
    a. F, Cl, Br, I   b. N, O, F

107. In the second row of the periodic table, Be, N, and Ne all have endothermic (unfavorable) electron affinities, whereas the other second-row elements have exothermic (favorable) electron affinities. Rationalize why Be, N, and Ne have unfavorable electron affinities.

108. Which has the more negative electron affinity, the oxygen atom or the O^- ion? Explain your answer.

109. The electron affinity for sulfur is more exothermic than that for oxygen. How do you account for this?

110. The electron affinities of the elements from aluminum to chlorine are -44 kJ/mol, -120 kJ/mol, -74 kJ/mol, -200.4 kJ/mol, and -348.7 kJ/mol, respectively. Rationalize the trend in these values.

111. Use data in this chapter to determine the following.
    a. the electron affinity of Mg^{2+}
    b. the electron affinity of Al^+
    c. the ionization energy of Cl^-
    d. the ionization energy of Cl
    e. the electron affinity of Cl^+

112. For each of the following pairs of elements,

    (C and N)   (Ar and Br)   (Mg and K)   (F and Cl)

pick the one with
    a. the more favorable (exothermic) electron affinity
    b. the higher ionization energy
    c. the larger size

The Alkali Metals

113. Does the information on alkali metals in Table 12.9 of the text confirm the general periodic trends in ionization energy and atomic radius? Explain.

114. An ionic compound of potassium and oxygen has the empirical formula KO. Would you expect this compound to be potassium(II) oxide or potassium peroxide? Explain.

115. Complete and balance the equations for the following reactions.
    a. $Li(s) + N_2(g) \longrightarrow$ c. $Cs(s) + H_2O(l) \longrightarrow$
    b. $Rb(s) + S(s) \longrightarrow$ d. $Na(s) + Cl_2(g) \longrightarrow$

116. Cesium was discovered in natural mineral waters in 1860 by R. W. Bunsen and G. R. Kirchhoff, using the spectroscope they invented in 1859. The name comes from the Latin word *caesius*, meaning "sky blue," which describes the prominent blue line observed for this element at 455.5 nm. Calculate the frequency and energy of a photon of this light.

117. The bright yellow light emitted by a sodium vapor lamp consists of two emission lines at 589.0 nm and 589.6 nm. What are the frequency and the energy of a photon of light at each of these wavelengths? What are the energies in kJ/mol?

118. Give the name and formula of the binary compound formed by each of the following pairs of elements.
    a. Li and N   d. Li and P
    b. Na and Br   e. Rb and H
    c. K and S   f. Na and H

119. Predict the atomic number of the next alkali metal after francium, and give its ground-state electron configuration.

Additional Exercises

120. Spectroscopists use emission spectra to confirm the presence of an element in materials of unknown composition. How is this possible?

121. On which quantum number(s) does the energy of an electron depend in each of the following?
    a. a one-electron atom or ion
    b. an atom or ion with more than one electron

122. Elements with very large ionization energies also tend to have highly exothermic electron affinities. Explain. Which group of elements would you expect to be an exception to this statement?

123. Diagonal relationships in the periodic table exist as well as vertical relationships. For example, Be and Al are similar in some of their properties, as are B and Si. Rationalize why these diagonal relationships hold for properties such as size, ionization energy, and electron affinity.

124. A certain microwave oven delivers 750. watts (J/s) of power to a coffee cup containing 50.0 g of water at 25.0°C. If the wavelength of microwaves in the oven is 9.75 cm, how long does it take, and how many photons must be absorbed, to make the water boil? The specific heat capacity of water is 4.18 J °C^{-1} g^{-1}. Assume that only the water absorbs the energy of the microwaves.

125. Mars is roughly 60 million km from earth. How long does it take for a radio signal originating from earth to reach Mars?

126. Photogray lenses incorporate small amounts of silver chloride in the glass of the lens. When light hits the AgCl particles, the following reaction occurs:

$$AgCl \xrightarrow{h\nu} Ag + Cl$$

The silver metal formed causes the lenses to darken. The energy change for this reaction is 3.10×10^2 kJ/mol. Assuming that all this energy must be supplied by light, what is the maximum wavelength of light that can cause this reaction?

127. Consider the following approximate visible light spectrum:

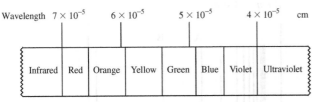

Barium emits light in the visible region of the spectrum. If each photon of light emitted from barium has an energy of 3.59×10^{-19} J, what color of visible light is emitted?

128. One of the visible lines in the hydrogen emission spectrum corresponds to the $n = 6$ to $n = 2$ electronic transition. What color light is this transition? See Exercise 127.

129. Consider the representations of the p and d atomic orbitals in Figs. 12.19 and 12.21. What do the $+$ and $-$ signs indicate?

130. The following graph plots the first, second, and third ionization energies for Mg, Al, and Si. Without referencing the text, which plot corresponds to which element? In one of the plots, there is a huge jump in energy between I_2 and I_3, unlike in the other two plots. Explain this phenomenon.

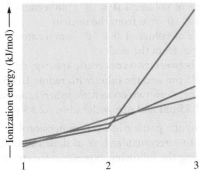

Number of electrons removed

131. Using data from this chapter, calculate the change in energy expected for each of the following processes.
    a. $Na(g) + Cl(g) \longrightarrow Na^+(g) + Cl^-(g)$
    b. $Mg(g) + F(g) \longrightarrow Mg^+(g) + F^-(g)$
    c. $Mg^+(g) + F(g) \longrightarrow Mg^{2+}(g) + F^-(g)$
    d. $Mg(g) + 2F(g) \longrightarrow Mg^{2+}(g) + 2F^-(g)$

132. Write equations corresponding to the following energy terms.
    a. the fourth ionization energy of Se
    b. the electron affinity of S^-
    c. the electron affinity of Fe^{3+}
    d. the ionization energy of Mg
    e. the work function of Mg (see Exercise 27)

133. The successive ionization energies for an unknown element are

$$I_1 = 896 \text{ kJ/mol}$$
$$I_2 = 1752 \text{ kJ/mol}$$
$$I_3 = 14,807 \text{ kJ/mol}$$
$$I_4 = 17,948 \text{ kJ/mol}$$

To which family in the periodic table does the unknown element most likely belong?

134. An unknown element is a nonmetal and has a valence electron configuration of ns^2np^4.
    a. How many valence electrons does this element have?
    b. What are some possible identities for this element?
    c. What is the formula of the compound this element would form with potassium?
    d. Would this element have a larger or smaller radius than barium?
    e. Would this element have a greater or smaller ionization energy than fluorine?

135. An ion having a 4+ charge and a mass of 49.9 amu has two electrons with $n = 1$, eight electrons with $n = 2$, and ten electrons with $n = 3$. Supply the following properties for the ion. (*Hint:* In forming ions, the $4s$ electrons are lost before the $3d$ electrons.)
    a. the atomic number
    b. total number of s electrons
    c. total number of p electrons
    d. total number of d electrons
    e. the number of neutrons in the nucleus
    f. the mass of 3.01×10^{23} atoms
    g. the ground-state electron configuration of the neutral atom

136. Consider the following ionization energies for aluminum.

$$Al(g) \longrightarrow Al^+(g) + e^- \qquad I_1 = 580 \text{ kJ/mol}$$
$$Al^+(g) \longrightarrow Al^{2+}(g) + e^- \qquad I_2 = 1815 \text{ kJ/mol}$$
$$Al^{2+}(g) \longrightarrow Al^{3+}(g) + e^- \qquad I_3 = 2740 \text{ kJ/mol}$$
$$Al^{3+}(g) \longrightarrow Al^{4+}(g) + e^- \qquad I_4 = 11,600 \text{ kJ/mol}$$

    a. Account for the increasing trend in the values of the ionization energies.
    b. Explain the large increase between I_3 and I_4.
    c. Which one of the four ions has the greatest electron affinity? Explain.
    d. List the four aluminum ions given in the preceding reactions in order of increasing size, and explain your ordering. (*Hint:* Remember that most of the size of an atom or ion is due to its electrons.)

137. Answer the following questions, assuming that m_s has four values rather than two and that the normal rules apply for n, ℓ, and m_ℓ.
    a. How many electrons could an orbital hold?
    b. How many elements would be contained in the first and second periods of the periodic table?
    c. How many elements would be contained in the first transition metal series?
    d. How many electrons would the set of $4f$ orbitals be able to hold?

138. Although Mendeleev predicted the existence of several undiscovered elements, he did not predict the existence of the noble gases, the lanthanides, or the actinides. Propose reasons why Mendeleev was not able to predict the existence of the noble gases.

139. Human color vision is "produced" by the nervous system based on how three different cone receptors interact with photons of light in the eye. These three different types of cones interact with photons of different frequency light, as indicated in the following chart:

Cone Type	Range of Light Frequency Detected
S	$6.00–7.49 \times 10^{14}$ s^{-1}
M	$4.76–6.62 \times 10^{14}$ s^{-1}
L	$4.28–6.00 \times 10^{14}$ s^{-1}

What wavelength ranges (and corresponding colors) do the three types of cones detect?

140. Assume that four electrons are confined to a one-dimensional box 5.64×10^{-10} m in length. If two electrons can occupy each allowed energy level, calculate the wavelength of electromagnetic radiation necessary to promote the highest-energy electron into the first excited state.

141. The figure below represents part of the emission spectrum for a one-electron ion in the gas phase. All the lines result from electronic transitions from excited states to the $n = 3$ state.

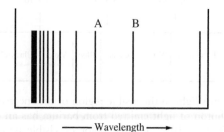

a. What electronic transitions correspond to lines A and B?
b. If the wavelength of line B is 142.5 nm, calculate the wavelength of line A.

Challenge Problems

142. An atom moving at its root mean square velocity at 100.°C has a wavelength of 2.31×10^{-11} m. Which atom is it?

143. The ground state ionization energy for the one electron ion X^{m+} is 4.72×10^4 kJ/mol. Identify X and m.

144. When the excited electron in a hydrogen atom falls from $n = 5$ to $n = 2$, a photon of blue light is emitted. If an excited electron in He$^+$ falls from $n = 4$, which energy level must it fall to so that a similar blue light (as with hydrogen) is emitted? Prove it.

145. The treatment of a particle in a one-dimensional box can be extended to a two-dimensional box of dimensions L_x and L_y yielding the following expression for energy:

$$E = \frac{h^2}{8m}\left(\frac{n_x^2}{L_x^2} + \frac{n_y^2}{L_y^2}\right)$$

The two quantum numbers independently can assume only integer values. Consider an electron confined to a two-dimensional box that is 8.00 nm in the x direction and 5.00 nm in the y direction.
a. What are the quantum numbers for the first three allowed energy levels?
b. Calculate the wavelength of light necessary to promote an electron from the first excited state to the second excited state.

146. The following numbers are the ratios of second ionization energy to first ionization energy:

Na: 9.2   P: 1.8

Mg: 2.0   S: 2.3

Al: 3.1   Cl: 1.8

Si: 2.0   Ar: 1.8

Explain these relative numbers.

147. For a hydrogen atom in its ground state, calculate the relative probability of finding the electron in the area described.
a. in a sphere of volume 1.0×10^{-3} pm^3 centered at the nucleus
b. in a sphere of volume 1.0×10^{-3} pm^3 centered on a point 1.0×10^{-11} m from the nucleus
c. in a sphere of volume 1.0×10^{-3} pm^3 centered on a point 53 pm from the nucleus
d. in a shell between two concentric spheres, one with radius 9.95 pm and the other with radius 10.05 pm
e. in a shell between two concentric spheres, one with radius 52.85 pm and one with radius 52.95 pm

148. The treatment of a particle in a one-dimensional box can be extended to a rectangular box of dimensions L_x, L_y, and L_z, yielding the following expression for energy:

$$E = \frac{h^2}{8m}\left(\frac{n_x^2}{L_x^2} + \frac{n_y^2}{L_y^2} + \frac{n_z^2}{L_z^2}\right)$$

The three quantum numbers n_x, n_y, and n_z independently can assume only integer values.
a. Determine the energies of the three lowest levels, assuming that the box is cubic.
b. Describe the degeneracies of all the levels that correspond to quantum numbers having values of 1 or 2. How will these degeneracies change in a box where $L_x \neq L_y \neq L_z$?

149. Assume that eight electrons are placed into the allowed energy levels of a cubic box where two electrons can occupy each allowed energy level. (See Exercise 148 for the appropriate energy equation.) Calculate the wavelength of light necessary to promote the highest-energy ground-state electron into the lowest-energy excited state assum-

ing a cubic box with dimensions 1.50 nm × 1.50 nm × 1.50 nm.

150. Assume that we are in another universe with different physical laws. Electrons in this universe are described by four quantum numbers with meanings similar to those we use. We will call these quantum numbers p, q, r, and s. The rules for these quantum numbers are as follows:

$p = 1, 2, 3, 4, 5, \ldots$.

q takes on positive odd integer values and $q \leq p$.

r takes on all even integer values from $-q$ to $+q$.

(Zero is considered an even number.)

$s = +\frac{1}{2}$ or $-\frac{1}{2}$

a. Sketch what the first four periods of the periodic table will look like in this universe.

b. What are the atomic numbers of the first four elements you would expect to be least reactive?

c. Give an example, using elements in the first four rows, of ionic compounds with the formulas XY, XY_2, X_2Y, XY_3, and X_2Y_3.

d. How many electrons can have $p = 3$?

e. How many electrons can have $p = 4$, $q = 3$, $r = 2$?

f. How many electrons can have $p = 4$, $q = 3$?

g. How many electrons can have $p = 3$, $q = 0$, $r = 0$?

h. What are the possible values of q and r for $p = 5$?

i. How many electrons can have $p = 6$?

151. The ionization energy for a 1s electron in a silver atom is 2.462×10^6 kJ/mol.

a. Determine an approximate value for Z_{eff} for the Ag 1s electron. You will first have to derive an equation that relates Z_{eff} to ionization energy.

b. How does Z_{eff} from part a compare to Z for Ag? Rationalize the relative numbers.

152. Without looking at data in the text, sketch a qualitative graph of the third ionization energy versus atomic number for the elements Na through Ar, and explain your graph.

Marathon Problem*

153. From the information below, identify element X.

a. The wavelength of the radiowaves sent by an FM station broadcasting at 97.1 MHz is 30 million (3.00×10^7) times greater than the wavelength corresponding to the energy difference between a particular excited state of the hydrogen atom and the ground state.

b. Let V represent the principal quantum number for the valence shell of element X. If an electron in the hydrogen atom falls from shell V to the inner shell corresponding to the excited state mentioned in part a, the wavelength of light emitted is the same as the wavelength of an electron moving at a speed of 570. m/s.

c. The number of unpaired electrons for element X in the ground state is the same as the maximum number of electrons in an atom that can have the quantum number designations $n = 2$, $m_\ell = -1$, and $m_s = -\frac{1}{2}$.

d. Let A represent the principal quantum number for the electron in an excited He^+ ion in which the single electron has the same energy as the electron in the ground state of a hydrogen atom. This value of A also represents the angular momentum quantum number for the subshell containing the unpaired electron(s) for element X.

*From James H. Burness, "The Use of "Marathon" Problems as Effective Vehicles for the Presentation of General Chemistry Lectures," Journal of Chemical Education, 68(11). Copyright © 1991 American Chemical Society. Reprinted by permission.

Bonding: General Concepts

13

chapter

Model of a buckyball with potassium ion.

Kenneth Eward/Science Photo Library/Photo Researchers

(top) Quartz grows in beautiful, regular crystals. (bottom) Two forms of carbon: graphite and diamond.

The world around us is composed almost entirely of compounds and mixtures of compounds: Rocks, coal, soil, petroleum, trees, and human bodies are all complex mixtures of chemical compounds in which different kinds of atoms are bound together. Substances composed of unbound atoms do exist in nature, but they are very rare. Examples are the argon in the atmosphere and the helium mixed with natural gas reserves.

The manner in which atoms are bound together in a given substance has a profound effect on its chemical and physical properties. For example, graphite is a soft, slippery material used as a lubricant in locks, and diamond is one of the hardest materials known, valuable both as a gemstone and in industrial cutting tools. Why do these materials, both composed solely of carbon atoms, have such different properties? The answer, as we will see, lies in the bonding within these substances.

Silicon and carbon are next to each other in Group 4A on the periodic table. From our knowledge of periodic trends, we might expect SiO_2 and CO_2 to be very similar. But SiO_2 is the empirical formula of silica, which is found in sand and quartz, whereas carbon dioxide is a gas, a product of respiration. Why are they so different? We will be able to answer this question after we have developed models for bonding.

Bonding and structure play a central role in determining the course of all chemical reactions, many of which are vital to our survival. Later in this book we will demonstrate the importance of bonding and structure by showing how enzymes facilitate complex chemical reactions, how genetic characteristics are transferred, and how hemoglobin in the blood carries oxygen throughout the body. All these fundamental biological reactions hinge on the geometric structures of molecules, sometimes depending on very subtle differences in molecular shape to channel the chemical reaction one way rather than another.

Many of the world's current problems require fundamentally chemical answers: disease and pollution control, the search for new energy sources, the development of new fertilizers to increase crop yields, the improvement of the protein content in various staple grains, and many more. To understand the behavior of natural materials, we must understand the nature of chemical bonding and the factors that control the structures of compounds. In this chapter we will present various classes of compounds that illustrate the different types of bonds and then develop models to describe the structure and bonding that characterize materials found in nature. Later these models will prove useful in understanding chemical reactions.

13.1 | Types of Chemical Bonds

What is a chemical bond? There is no simple and yet complete answer to this question. In Chapter 2 we defined bonds as forces that hold groups of atoms together and make the atoms function as a unit.

There are many types of experiments we can perform to determine the fundamental nature of materials. For example, we can study physical properties such as melting point, hardness, and electrical and thermal conductivity. We can also study solubility characteristics and the properties of the resulting solutions. To determine the charge distribution in a molecule, we can study its behavior in an electric field. We can obtain information about the strength of a bonding interaction by measuring the energy required to break the bond, the **bond energy**. Spectroscopy, the study of the interactions of electromagnetic radiation with matter, gives a wealth of information about molecular structure and energy level spacings.

There are several ways atoms can interact with one another to form aggregates. We will consider several specific examples to illustrate the various types of chemical bonds.

When solid sodium chloride is melted, it conducts electricity, a fact that convinces us that sodium chloride contains Na^+ and Cl^- ions. Thus, when sodium and chlorine react to form sodium chloride, electrons must be transferred from the sodium atoms to the chlorine atoms to form Na^+ and Cl^- ions, which then aggregate to form solid sodium chloride. Why does this happen? The best simple answer is that *the system can achieve the lowest possible energy by behaving in this way.* Part of the favorable energy change results from the attraction of a chlorine atom for an extra electron. Even more important are the very strong attractions between the oppositely charged ions. The resulting solid sodium chloride is a very sturdy material; it has a melting point of about 800°C. The bonding forces that produce this great thermal stability result from the electrostatic attractions of the closely packed, oppositely charged ions. This is an example of *ionic bonding.* Ionic substances are formed when an atom that loses electrons relatively easily reacts with an atom that has a high affinity for electrons. That is, an **ionic compound** results when a metal reacts with a nonmetal.

The energy of interaction between a pair of ions can be calculated by using **Coulomb's law:**

$$V = \frac{Q_1 Q_2}{4\pi\epsilon_0 r} = 2.31 \times 10^{-19} \text{ J nm}\left(\frac{Q_1 Q_2}{r}\right)$$

where V has units of joules, r is the distance between the ion centers in nanometers, Q_1 and Q_2 are the numerical ion charges, and ϵ_0 is the permittivity of the vacuum. For example, in solid sodium chloride, where the distance between the centers of the Na^+ and Cl^- ions is 276 picometers (0.276 nm), the ionic energy per pair of ions is

$$V = 2.31 \times 10^{-19} \text{ J nm}\left[\frac{(+1)(-1)}{0.276 \text{ nm}}\right] = -8.37 \times 10^{-19} \text{ J}$$

The negative sign indicates an attractive force. That is, *the ion pair has lower energy than the separated ions.* For a mole of pairs of Na^+ and Cl^- ions, the energy of interaction is

$$V = \left(-8.37 \times 10^{-19} \frac{\text{J}}{\text{ion pair}}\right)\left(6.022 \times 10^{23} \frac{\text{ion pair}}{\text{mol}}\right)$$

$$= -504 \text{ kJ/mol}$$

Note that this energy refers to a mole of $Na^+ \cdot \cdot \, Cl^-$ ion pairs in the gas phase where a given pair is far from any other pair. In solid sodium chloride, which contains a large array of closely packed Na^+ and Cl^- ions, where a given ion is close to many oppositely charged ions, the energy associated with ionic bonding is much greater than 504 kJ/mol because of the larger numbers of interacting ions.

Coulomb's law can also be used to calculate the repulsive energy when two like-charged ions are brought together. In this case the calculated energy value will have a positive sign.

We have seen that a bonding force develops when two very different atoms react to form oppositely charged ions. But how does a bonding force develop between two identical atoms? Let's explore this situation from a very simple point of view by considering the energy terms that result when two hydrogen atoms are brought close together, as shown in Fig. 13.1(a). For two closely spaced hydrogen atoms, there are two unfavorable energy terms, proton–proton

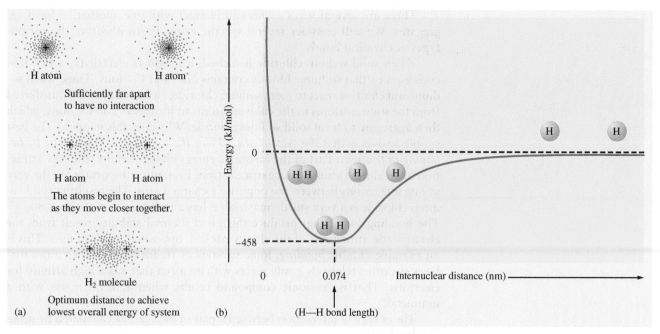

Figure 13.1
(a) The interaction of two hydrogen atoms. (b) Energy profile as a function of the distance between the nuclei of the hydrogen atoms. As the atoms approach each other, the energy decreases until the distance reaches 0.074 nm (0.74 Å) and then begins to increase again because of repulsions.

Bonding occurs if the energy of the aggregate is lower than that of the separated atoms.

The atoms in H_2 (and all other molecules) actually vibrate back and forth around the equilibrium internuclear distance.

repulsion and electron–electron repulsion, and one favorable term, proton–electron attraction. Under what conditions will the H_2 molecule be favored over the separated hydrogen atoms? That is, what conditions will favor bond formation? The answer lies in nature's strong tendency to achieve the lowest possible energy. A bond will form—that is, the two hydrogen atoms will exist as a molecular unit—if the system can lower its total energy in the process.

Therefore, the hydrogen atoms will assume the positions that give the lowest possible energy; the system will act to minimize the sum of the positive (repulsive) energy terms and the negative (attractive) energy terms. The distance at which the energy is minimum is called the equilibrium internuclear distance or, more commonly, the **bond length**. The total energy of this system as a function of distance between the hydrogen nuclei is shown in Fig. 13.1(b). Note four important features of this diagram:

1. The energy terms involved are the potential energy that results from the attractions and repulsions among the charged particles and the kinetic energy caused by the motions of the electrons.

2. The zero reference point for energy is defined for the atoms at infinite separation.

3. At very short distances the energy rises steeply because of the great importance of the internuclear repulsive forces at these distances.

4. The bond length is the distance at which the system has minimum energy, and the bond energy corresponds to the depth of the "well" at this distance.

In the H_2 molecule the electrons reside primarily in the space between the two nuclei, where they are attracted simultaneously by both protons. This positioning is precisely what leads to the stability of the H_2 molecule relative to two separated hydrogen atoms. The potential energy of each electron is lowered because of the increased attractive forces in this area. Although it is not usually discussed in connection with simple models of bonding, we should note that the kinetic energy of the electrons also changes when the individual atoms form the molecule. Thus the energy plotted in Fig. 13.1(b) is the total energy of the system, not just the potential energy. When we say that a bond is formed between the hydrogen atoms, we mean that the H_2 molecule is more stable

No Lead Pencils

Did you ever wonder why the part of a pencil that makes the mark is called the "lead"? Pencils have no lead in them now—and they never have. Apparently the association between writing and the element lead arose during the Roman Empire, when lead rods were used as writing utensils because they leave a gray mark on paper. Many centuries later, in 1564, a deposit of a black substance found to be very useful for writing was discovered in Borrowdale, England. This substance, originally called "black lead," was shown in 1879 by Swedish chemist Carl Sheele to be a form of carbon and was subsequently named graphite (after the Greek *graphein*, meaning "to write").

Originally, chunks of graphite from Borrowdale, called "marking stones," were used as writing instruments. Later, sticks of graphite were used. Because graphite is brittle, the sticks needed reinforcement. At first they were wrapped in string, which was unwound as the core wore down. Eventually, graphite rods were tied between two wooden slats or inserted into hollowed-out wooden sticks to form the first crude pencils.

Although Borrowdale graphite was pure enough to use directly, most graphite must be mixed with other materials to be useful for writing instruments. In 1795, French chemist Nicolas-Jaques Conté invented a process in which graphite is mixed with clay and water to produce pencil "lead," a recipe that is still used today. In modern pencil manufacture, graphite and clay are mixed and crushed into a fine powder to which water is added. After the gray sludge is blended for several days, it is dried, ground up again, and mixed with more water to give a gray paste. The paste is extruded through a metal tube to form thin rods, which are then cut into pencil-length pieces called

"leads." These leads are heated in an oven to 1000°C until they are smooth and hard. The ratio of clay to graphite is adjusted to vary the hardness of the lead—the more clay in the mix, the harder the lead and the lighter the line it makes.

Pencils are made from a slat of wood with several grooves cut in it to hold the leads. A similar grooved slat is then placed on top and glued to form a "sandwich" from which individual pencils are cut, sanded smooth, and painted. Although many types of wood have been used over the years to make pencils, the current favorite is incense cedar from the Sierra Nevada Mountains of California.

Modern pencils are simple but amazing instruments. The average pencil can write approximately 45,000 words, which is equivalent to a line 35 miles long. The graphite in a pencil is easily transferred to paper because graphite contains layers of carbon atoms bound together in a "chicken-wire" structure. Although the bonding *within* each layer is very strong, the bonding *between* layers is weak, giving graphite its slippery, soft nature. In this way, graphite is much different from diamond, the other common elemental form of carbon. In diamond the carbon atoms are bound tightly in all three dimensions, making it extremely hard—the hardest natural substance.

Pencils are very useful—especially for doing chemistry problems—because we can erase our mistakes. Most pencils used in the United States have erasers (first attached to pencils in 1858), although most European pencils do not. Laid end to end, the number of pencils made in the United States each year would circle the earth about 15 times. Pencils illustrate how useful a simple substance like graphite can be.

than two separated hydrogen atoms by a certain quantity of energy (the bond energy).

We can also think of a bond in terms of forces. The simultaneous attraction for each electron by the two protons generates a force that pulls the protons toward each other. This attractive force just balances the proton–proton and electron–electron repulsive forces at the distance corresponding to the bond length.

The type of bonding we encounter in the hydrogen molecule and in many other molecules in which *electrons are shared by nuclei* is called **covalent bonding.**

Figure 13.2

The effect of an electric field on hydrogen fluoride molecules. (a) When no electric field is present, the molecules are randomly oriented. (b) When the field is turned on, the molecules tend to line up with their negative ends toward the positive pole and their positive ends toward the negative pole. (This illustration exaggerates the effect. Actually, only a small fraction of the molecules are lined up with the field at a given instant.)

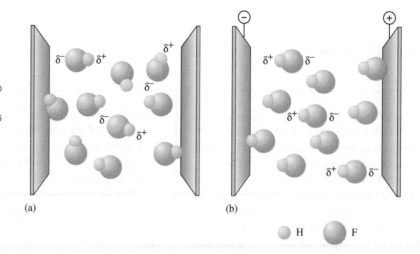

So far we have considered two extreme types of bonding. In ionic bonding the participating atoms are so different that one or more electrons are transferred to form oppositely charged ions. The bonding results from electrostatic interactions among the resulting ions. In covalent bonding two identical atoms share electrons equally. The bonding results from the mutual attraction of the two nuclei for the shared electrons. Between these extremes lie intermediate cases in which the atoms are not so different that electrons are completely transferred but are different enough so that unequal sharing results. These are called **polar covalent bonds.** An example of this type of bond occurs in the hydrogen fluoride (HF) molecule. When a sample of hydrogen fluoride gas is placed in an electric field, the molecules tend to orient themselves as shown in Fig. 13.2, with the fluoride end closest to the positive pole and the hydrogen end closest to the negative pole. This result implies that the HF molecule has the following charge distribution:

$$H\!-\!F$$
$$\delta+ \quad \delta-$$

where δ (delta) is used to indicate a fractional charge. This same effect was noted in Chapter 4, where many of water's unusual properties were attributed to the polar O—H bonds in the H_2O molecule.

The most logical explanation for the development of the partial positive and negative charges on the atoms (bond polarity) in such molecules as HF and H_2O is that the electrons in the bonds are not shared equally. For example, we can account for the polarity of the HF molecule by assuming that the fluorine atom has a stronger attraction for the shared electrons than the hydrogen atom. Similarly, in the H_2O molecule the oxygen atom appears to attract the shared electrons more strongly than the hydrogen atoms. Because bond polarity has important chemical implications, we find it useful to quantify the ability of an atom to attract shared electrons. In the next section we show how this is done.

13.2 | Electronegativity

The different affinities of atoms for the electrons in a bond are described by a property called **electronegativity:** *the ability of an atom in a molecule to attract shared electrons to itself.*

The most widely accepted method for determining electronegativity values is that of Linus Pauling (1901–1995), an American scientist who won Nobel Prizes for both chemistry and peace. To understand Pauling's model, consider a hypothetical molecule HX. The relative electronegativities of the H and X atoms are determined by comparing the measured H—X bond energy with the

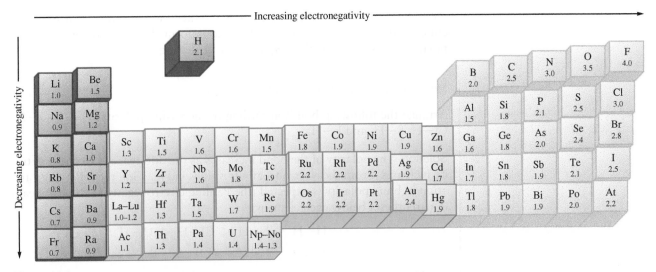

Figure 13.3

The Pauling electronegativity values. Electronegativity generally increases across a period and decreases down a group.

"expected" H—X bond energy. The expected bond energy is an "average" (actually the geometric mean) of the H—H and X—X bond energies:

Expected H—X bond energy
$$= [(\text{H—H bond energy})(\text{X—X bond energy})]^{1/2}$$

The difference (Δ) between the actual (measured) and expected bond energies is

$$\Delta = (\text{H—X})_{\text{act}} - (\text{H—X})_{\text{exp}}$$

If H and X have identical electronegativities, $(\text{H—X})_{\text{act}}$ and $(\text{H—X})_{\text{exp}}$ are the same and Δ is 0. On the other hand, if X has a greater electronegativity than H, the shared electron(s) will tend to be closer to the X atom. The molecule will be polar, with the following charge distribution:

$$\underset{\delta+ \quad \delta-}{\text{H—X}}$$

Note that this bond can be viewed as having an ionic as well as a covalent component. The electrostatic attraction between the partially charged H and X atoms will lead to a greater bond strength. Thus $(\text{H—X})_{\text{act}}$ will be larger than $(\text{H—X})_{\text{exp}}$. The greater the difference in the electronegativities of the atoms, the greater is the ionic component of the bond and the greater is the value of Δ. Thus the relative electronegativities of H and X can be assigned from the Δ values.

The actual formula Pauling used to calculate electronegativity (EN) differences is

$$\text{EN(X)} - \text{EN(H)} = 0.102\sqrt{\Delta}$$

The factor of 0.102 is a conversion factor between kJ and eV (the units originally used by Pauling).

where all bond energies are in units of kJ/mol. Pauling then obtained absolute electronegativity values for the elements by assigning a value of 4.0 to fluorine (the element with the highest electronegativity).

Electronegativity values have been determined by this process for virtually all the elements; the results are given in Fig. 13.3. Note that for the representative elements, electronegativity generally increases from left to right across a period and decreases down a group. The range of electronegativity values is from 4.0 for fluorine to 0.7 for francium.

The relationship between electronegativity and bond type is shown in Table 13.1. For identical atoms (electronegativity difference of zero), the electrons in the bond are shared equally and no polarity occurs. When two atoms

Table 13.1

The Relationship Between Electronegativity and Bond Type

Electronegativity Difference in the Bonding Atoms	Bond Type
Zero	Covalent
↓	↓
Intermediate	Polar covalent
↓	↓
Large	Ionic

with widely differing electronegativities interact, electron transfer usually occurs, producing ions—an ionic substance is formed. Intermediate cases give polar covalent bonds with unequal electron sharing.

⚙WL INTERACTIVE EXAMPLE 13.1

Arrange the following bonds according to increasing polarity: H—H, O—H, Cl—H, S—H, and F—H.

Solution The polarity of the bond increases as the difference in electronegativity increases. From the electronegativity values in Fig. 13.3, the following variation in bond polarity is expected (the Pauling electronegativity value appears in parentheses below each element):

$$H—H < S—H < Cl—H < O—H < F—H$$

$$(2.2)(2.2) \quad (2.6)(2.2) \quad (3.2)(2.2) \quad (3.4)(2.2) \quad (4.0)(2.2)$$

| Electronegativity difference | 0 | 0.4 | 1.1 | 1.2 | 1.8 |

Covalent bond $\xrightarrow[\text{Polarity increases}]{}$ polar covalent bond

Table 13.2

A Comparison of Pauling's and Allen's Electronegativity Values for Selected Representative Elements

Atom	Pauling	Allen
H	2.20	2.300
Li	0.98	0.912
Be	1.57	1.576
B	2.04	2.051
C	2.55	2.544
N	3.04	3.066
O	3.44	3.610
F	3.98	4.193
Ne	—	4.787
Cl	3.16	2.869
Br	2.96	2.685
I	2.66	2.359

Although Pauling's electronegativity values are the ones most commonly found in textbooks, several other systems for obtaining electronegativity values have been proposed. Recently, Leland C. Allen of Princeton University has pioneered an electronegativity scale based on the average ionization energies of the valence electrons for a given atom. Allen's system allows calculation of an electronegativity value for an atom that is independent of its bonding environment. In this system electronegativity becomes a property of the isolated atom. This approach is fundamentally different from Pauling's system, which is derived from the bond energies of atoms attached to one another.

Although we will not consider the details of Allen's quantum mechanical analysis, it is useful to compare Allen's and Pauling's values for some of the more important representative elements (Table 13.2). While many values are similar, some significant differences appear.

Allen has made a strong case that his system for obtaining electronegativities is more meaningful than that created by Pauling. Allen's values are now becoming accepted by the chemical community.

13.3 | Bond Polarity and Dipole Moments

We have seen that when hydrogen fluoride is placed in an electric field, the molecules have a preferential orientation (Fig. 13.2). This follows from the charge distribution in the HF molecule, which has a positive end and a negative end. A molecule such as HF that has a center of positive charge and a center of negative charge is said to be *dipolar*, or to have a **dipole moment**. A molecule that has a positive center of charge of magnitude Q and a negative center of charge of magnitude Q separated by a distance R has a dipole moment given by the expression

$$\text{Dipole moment} = \mu = QR$$

The debye is named after Peter Debye, who pioneered in the measurement of dipole moments.

which has SI units of coulomb meter (C m) but is most often given in units of debye [1 debye (D) = 3.336×10^{-30} C m]. The dipolar character of a molecule is often represented by an arrow pointing to the negative charge center, with the tail of the arrow indicating the positive center of charge:

$$\overset{\longrightarrow}{\underset{\delta+ \qquad \delta-}{\vdash}}$$

The dipole moment of a molecule gives useful information about its bonding and electron distribution. For example, the observed dipole moment for HF is 1.83 D. If HF were totally ionic (H^+F^-), the expected dipole moment (symbolized by μ) would be

$$\mu = (\underset{\substack{\text{Electron} \\ \text{charge}}}{1.60 \times 10^{-19} \text{ C}})(\underset{\substack{\text{H—F bond} \\ \text{distance}}}{9.17 \times 10^{-11} \text{ m}})$$

$$= 1.47 \times 10^{-29} \text{ C m} = 4.40 \text{ D}$$

This calculation shows that HF is not fully ionic, since the measured dipole moment is much less than 4.40 D. We can estimate the ionic character of HF by assuming that the hydrogen has a charge $\delta+$ and the fluorine has a charge $\delta-$. Using the measured dipole moment, we have

$$1.83 \text{ D} = (\delta)(9.17 \times 10^{-11} \text{ m}) \times \frac{1 \text{ D}}{3.336 \times 10^{-30} \text{ C m}}$$

Solving for δ gives 6.66×10^{-20} C. Since the charge on an electron is 1.60×10^{-19} C, each atom in HF has a fractional charge of

$$\frac{6.66 \times 10^{-20} \text{ C}}{1.60 \times 10^{-19} \text{ C}} = 0.416$$

From this argument we might say that HF has 42% ionic bonding. Although this analysis is somewhat oversimplified (it assumes that charge distributions can be represented as point charges, for example), it does provide useful information about bonding. Recall that the dipolar character of a molecule is often represented by an arrow pointing to the negative charge center with the tail of the arrow indicating the positive center of charge:

$\delta+$ $\qquad\qquad$ $\delta-$

Another way to represent the charge distribution in HF is by an electrostatic potential diagram (Fig. 13.4). For this representation the colors of visible light are used to show the variation in charge distribution. Red indicates the most electron-rich region of the molecule, and blue indicates the most electron-poor region.

From what has been said so far, we would expect any diatomic molecule with a polar bond (between atoms with different electronegativities) to exhibit a dipole moment. Although this is generally true, the observed dipole moments of diatomic molecules are sometimes smaller than expected. For example, the carbon monoxide molecule CO has a dipole moment of only 0.11 D, much smaller than expected from the polarity of the CO bond. This discrepancy is most likely caused by the lone pairs of electrons on the atoms, which make large contributions to the dipole moment in opposition to that from the bond polarity. We will not explore the details of this situation here. The dipole moments of some representative diatomic molecules are listed in Table 13.3.

Figure 13.4
An electrostatic potential diagram of HF. Red indicates the most electron-rich area (the fluorine atom) and blue indicates the most electron-poor region (the hydrogen atom).

Table 13.3

The Dipole Moments of Some Diatomic Molecules (gas phase)

Molecule	Dipole Moment (D)
CO	0.112
HF	1.83
HCl	1.11
HBr	0.78
HI	0.38
NaCl	9.00
LiF	6.33
KF	8.60
KBr	10.41

Figure 13.5
(a) The charge distribution in the water molecule. (b) The water molecule in an electric field. (c) The electrostatic potential diagram of the water molecule.

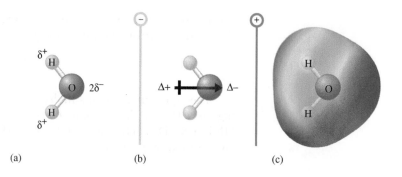

(a)   (b)   (c)

Figure 13.6
(a) The structure and charge distribution of the ammonia molecule. The polarity of the N—H bonds occurs because nitrogen has a greater electronegativity than hydrogen. (b) The dipole moment of the ammonia molecule oriented in an electric field. (c) The electrostatic potential diagram for ammonia.

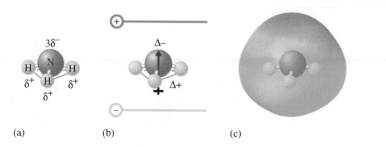

(a)   (b)   (c)

Figure 13.7
(a) The carbon dioxide molecule.
(b) The opposed bond polarities cancel out, and the carbon dioxide molecule has no dipole moment. (c) The electrostatic potential diagram for carbon dioxide.

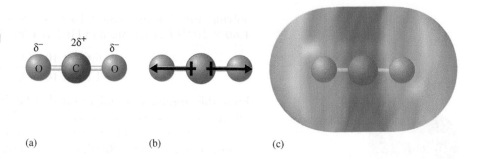

(a)   (b)   (c)

Polyatomic molecules can also exhibit dipolar behavior. For example, because the oxygen atom in the water molecule has a greater electronegativity than the hydrogen atoms, the molecular charge distribution is that shown in Fig. 13.5(a). This charge distribution causes the water molecule to behave in an electric field as if it had two centers of charge—one positive and one negative—as shown in Fig. 13.5(b). Thus the water molecule has a dipole moment. Similar behavior is observed for the NH_3 molecule (Fig. 13.6). Some molecules have polar bonds but do not have a dipole moment. This occurs when the individual bond polarities are arranged in such a way that they cancel. An example is the CO_2 molecule, a linear molecule that has the charge distribution shown in Fig. 13.7. In this case, since the opposing bond polarities cancel, the carbon dioxide molecule does not have a dipole moment. There is no preferential way for this molecule to line up in an electric field. (Try to find a preferred orientation.)

There are many cases where the bond polarities in molecules oppose and exactly cancel each other. Some common types of molecules with polar bonds but without dipole moments are shown in Table 13.4.

EXAMPLE 13.2

For each of the following molecules, show the direction of the bond polarities. Also indicate which ones have dipole moments: HCl, Cl_2, SO_3 (planar), CH_4 (tetrahedral), and H_2S (V-shaped).

Table 13.4

Types of Molecules with Polar Bonds but No Resulting Dipole Moment

Type		Cancellation of Polar Bonds	Example	Ball-and-Stick Model
Linear molecules with two identical bonds	B—A—B	←— + —→	CO_2	
Planar molecules with three identical bonds 120 degrees apart			SO_3	
Tetrahedral molecules with four identical bonds 109.5 degrees apart			CCl_4	

Solution The HCl molecule: Because the electronegativity of chlorine (3.2) is greater than that of hydrogen (2.2), the chlorine is partially negative, and the hydrogen is partially positive. The HCl molecule has a dipole moment oriented as follows:

$\delta+$ $\delta-$

The Cl₂ molecule: Because the two chlorine atoms share the electrons equally, no bond polarity occurs. The Cl₂ molecule has no dipole moment.

The SO₃ molecule: Because the electronegativity of oxygen (3.4) is greater than that of sulfur (2.6), each oxygen has a partial negative charge, and the sulfur has a partial positive charge:

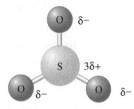

However, the bond polarities cancel, and the molecule has no dipole moment.

The CH₄ molecule: Carbon has a slightly higher electronegativity (2.6) than hydrogen (2.2). This leads to small partial positive charges on the hydrogen atoms and a small partial negative charge on the carbon:

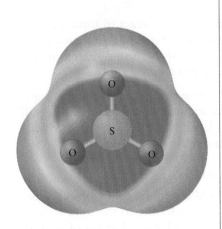

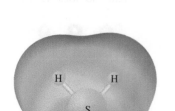

This case is similar to the third type in Table 13.4. Since the bond polarities cancel, the molecule has no dipole moment.

The H₂S molecule: Since the electronegativity of sulfur (2.6) is greater than that of hydrogen (2.2), the sulfur has a partial negative charge, and the hydrogen atoms have a partial positive charge, which can be represented as follows:

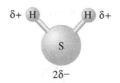

This case is analogous to the water molecule. The polar bonds result in a dipole moment oriented as shown.

13.4 | Ions: Electron Configurations and Sizes

The description of the electron arrangements in atoms that emerged from the quantum mechanical model has helped a great deal in our understanding of what constitutes a stable compound. For example, in a very large number of stable compounds, the atoms have noble gas arrangements of electrons. Nonmetallic elements achieve a noble gas electron configuration either by sharing electrons with other nonmetals to form covalent bonds or by taking electrons from metals to form ions. In the latter case the nonmetals form anions and the metals form cations. The following generalizations can be applied to the electron configurations in most stable compounds:

Atoms in stable compounds usually have a noble gas electron configuration.

■ When *two nonmetals* react to form a covalent bond, they share electrons in a way that completes the valence electron configurations of both atoms. That is, both nonmetals attain noble gas electron configurations.

As we will see later, there are exceptions to these rules, but they remain a useful place to start.

■ When *a nonmetal and a representative group metal* react to form a binary ionic compound, the ions form so that the valence electron configuration of the nonmetal is completed and the valence orbitals of the metal are emptied. In this way both ions achieve noble gas electron configurations.

Although there are some important exceptions, these generalizations apply to the vast majority of compounds and are important to remember. We will deal with covalent bonds more thoroughly later. Next, we will consider what implications these rules hold for ionic compounds.

Predicting Formulas of Ionic Compounds

In the solid state of an ionic compound, the ions are relatively close together, and many ions are simultaneously interacting:

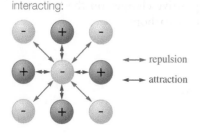

At the beginning of this discussion, we should emphasize that when chemists use the term *ionic compound,* they are usually referring to the solid state of that compound. Solid ionic compounds contain a large collection of positive and negative ions packed together in a way that minimizes the ⊖ · · ⊖ and ⊕ · · ⊕ repulsions and maximizes the ⊕ · · ⊖ attractions. This situation is in contrast to the gas phase of an ionic substance, where discrete ion pairs exist. Thus, when we speak in this text of the stability of an ionic compound, we are referring to the solid state, where the large attractive forces present among the oppositely charged ions tend to stabilize (favor the formation of) the ions. For example, as we mentioned in the previous chapter, the O^{2-} ion is not stable as

In the gas phase of an ionic substance, the ions would be relatively far apart and would not contain large groups of ions:

an isolated gas-phase species but, of course, is very stable in many solid ionic compounds. That is, MgO(*s*), which contains Mg^{2+} and O^{2-} ions, is very stable, but the isolated gas-phase ion pair $Mg^{2+} \cdot \cdot O^{2-}$ is not energetically favorable in comparison with the separate neutral gaseous atoms. Thus you should keep in mind that in this section, and in most other cases in which we are describing the nature of ionic compounds, the discussion usually refers to the solid state, in which many ions are simultaneously interacting.

To illustrate the principles of electron configurations in stable, solid ionic compounds, we will consider the formation of an ionic compound from calcium and oxygen. We can predict what compound will form by considering the valence electron configurations of the two atoms:

$$Ca: \quad [Ar]4s^2$$

$$O: \quad [He]2s^22p^4$$

From Fig. 13.3 we see that the electronegativity of oxygen (3.4) is much greater than that of calcium (1.0). Because of this large difference, electrons will be transferred from calcium to oxygen to form oxygen anions and calcium cations in the compound. How many electrons are transferred? We can base our prediction on the observation that noble gas configurations are generally the most stable. Note that oxygen needs two electrons to fill its 2*s* and 2*p* valence orbitals and to achieve the configuration of neon ($1s^22s^22p^6$). And by losing two electrons, calcium can achieve the configuration of argon. Two electrons are therefore transferred:

$$Ca + O \longrightarrow Ca^{2+} + O^{2-}$$
$$\underset{2e^-}{\overbrace{}}$$

To predict the formula of the ionic compound, we simply recognize that chemical compounds are always electrically neutral—they have the same quantities of positive and negative charges. In this case we must have equal numbers of Ca^{2+} and O^{2-} ions, and the empirical formula of the compound is CaO.

The same principles can be applied to many other cases. For example, consider the compound formed between aluminum and oxygen. Because aluminum has the configuration $[Ne]3s^23p^1$, it must lose three electrons to form the Al^{3+} ion and thus achieve the neon configuration. Therefore, the Al^{3+} and O^{2-} ions form in this case. Since the compound must be electrically neutral, there must be three O^{2-} ions for every two Al^{3+} ions, and the compound has the empirical formula Al_2O_3.

Table 13.5 shows common elements that form ions with noble gas electron configurations in ionic compounds. In losing electrons to form cations, metals in Group 1A lose one electron, those in Group 2A lose two electrons, and those in Group 3A lose three electrons. In gaining electrons to form anions, nonmetals in Group 7A (the halogens) gain one electron, and those in Group 6A gain

Table 13.5

Common Ions with Noble Gas Electron Configurations in Ionic Compounds

Group 1A	Group 2A	Group 3A	Group 6A	Group 7A	Electron Configuration
H^-, Li^+	Be^{2+}				[He]
Na^+	Mg^{2+}	Al^{3+}	O^{2-}	F^-	[Ne]
K^+	Ca^{2+}		S^{2-}	Cl^-	[Ar]
Rb^+	Sr^{2+}		Se^{2-}	Br^-	[Kr]
Cs^+	Ba^{2+}		Te^{2-}	I^-	[Xe]

two electrons. Hydrogen typically behaves as a nonmetal and can gain one electron to form the hydride ion (H^-), which has the electron configuration of helium.

There are some important exceptions to the rules discussed here. For example, tin forms both Sn^{2+} and Sn^{4+} ions, and lead forms both Pb^{2+} and Pb^{4+} ions. Also, bismuth forms Bi^{3+} and Bi^{5+} ions, and thallium forms Tl^+ and Tl^{3+} ions. There are no simple explanations for the behavior of these ions. For now, just note them as exceptions to the very useful rule that ions generally adopt noble gas electron configurations in ionic compounds. Our discussion here refers to representative metals.

Sizes of Ions

Ion size plays an important role in determining the structure and stability of ionic solids, the properties of ions in aqueous solution, and the biological effects of ions. As with atoms, it is impossible to define precisely the sizes of ions. Most often, ionic radii are determined from the measured distances between ion centers in ionic compounds. This method, of course, involves an assumption about how the distance should be divided up between the two ions. Thus you will note considerable disagreement among ionic sizes given in various sources. Here we are mainly interested in trends and will be less concerned with absolute ion sizes.

Various factors influence ionic size. We will first consider the relative sizes of an ion and its parent atom. Since a positive ion is formed by removing electrons from a neutral atom, the resulting cation is smaller than its parent atom. The opposite is true for negative ions; the addition of electrons to a neutral atom produces an anion significantly larger than its parent atom.

It is also important to know how the sizes of ions vary depending on the positions of the parent elements in the periodic table. Figure 13.8 shows the sizes of the most important ions (each with a noble gas configuration) and their position in the periodic table. Note that ion size increases down a group. The changes that occur horizontally are complicated because of the change from predominantly metals on the left-hand side of the periodic table to nonmetals on the right-hand side. A given period thus contains both elements that give up electrons to form cations and ones that accept electrons to form anions.

One trend worth noting involves the relative sizes of a set of **isoelectronic ions**—*ions containing the same number of electrons*. Consider the ions O^{2-}, F^-, Na^+, Mg^{2+}, and Al^{3+}. Each of these ions has the neon electron configuration. How do the sizes of these ions vary? In general, there are two important facts to consider in predicting the relative sizes of ions: the number of electrons and the number of protons. Since these ions are isoelectronic, the number of electrons is 10 in each case. Electron repulsions should therefore be about the same in all cases. However, the number of protons increases from 8 to 13 as we go from the O^{2-} ion to the Al^{3+} ion. Thus, in going from O^{2-} to Al^{3+}, the 10 electrons experience a greater attraction as the positive charge on the nucleus increases. This causes the ions to become smaller. You can confirm this by looking at Fig. 13.8. In general, for a series of isoelectronic ions, the size decreases as the nuclear charge (Z) increases.

For isoelectronic ions, size generally decreases as Z increases.

ⓦL INTERACTIVE EXAMPLE 13.3

Arrange the ions Se^{2-}, Br^-, Rb^+, and Sr^{2+} in order of decreasing size.

Solution This is an isoelectronic series of ions with the krypton electron configuration. Since these ions all have the same number of electrons, their sizes

Figure 13.8
Sizes of ions related to positions of elements in the periodic table. Note that size generally increases down a group. Also note that in a series of isoelectronic ions, size decreases with increasing atomic number. The ionic radii are given in units of picometers.

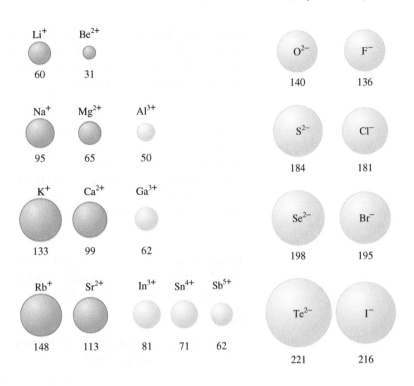

will depend on nuclear charge. The Z values are 34 for Se^{2-}, 35 for Br^-, 37 for Rb^+, and 38 for Sr^{2+}. Since the nuclear charge is greatest for Sr^{2+}, it is the smallest of these ions. The Se^{2-} ion is largest.

$$Se^{2-} > Br^- > Rb^+ > Sr^{2+}$$
$$\uparrow \qquad\qquad\qquad \uparrow$$
Largest   Smallest

◉WL INTERACTIVE EXAMPLE 13.4

Choose the largest ion in each of the following groups.

a. Li^+, Na^+, K^+, Rb^+, Cs^+ **b.** Ba^{2+}, Cs^+, I^-, Te^{2-}

Solution

a. The ions are all from Group 1A elements. Since size increases down a group (the ion with the greatest number of electrons is the largest), Cs^+ is the largest ion.

b. This is an isoelectronic series of ions, all of which have the xenon electron configuration. The ion with the smallest nuclear charge is the largest ion.

$$Te^{2-} > I^- > Cs^+ > Ba^{2+}$$
$$Z = 52 \quad Z = 53 \quad Z = 55 \quad Z = 56$$

Ion size generally increases down a group.

13.5 | Formation of Binary Ionic Compounds

In this section we will introduce the factors that influence the stability and the structures of solid binary ionic compounds. We know that metals and nonmetals react by transferring electrons to form cations and anions that are mutually attractive. The resulting ionic solid forms because the aggregated oppositely charged ions have a lower energy than the original elements. Just how strongly the ions attract each other in the solid state is indicated by the **lattice energy**—*the change in energy that takes place when separated gaseous ions are packed together to form an ionic solid:*

$$M^+(g) + X^-(g) \longrightarrow MX(s)$$

The lattice energy is often defined as the energy *released* when an ionic solid forms from its ions. However, in this book the sign of an energy term is always determined from the system's point of view: negative if the process is exothermic; positive if endothermic. Thus lattice energy has a negative sign.

We can illustrate the energy changes involved in the formation of an ionic solid by considering the formation of solid lithium fluoride from its elements:

$$Li(s) + \tfrac{1}{2}F_2(g) \longrightarrow LiF(s)$$

To see the energy terms associated with this process, we take advantage of the fact that energy is a state function and break this reaction into steps, the sum of which gives the overall reaction.

Step 1

Sublimation of solid lithium. Sublimation involves taking a substance from the solid state to the gaseous state:

$$Li(s) \longrightarrow Li(g)$$

The energy of sublimation for $Li(s)$ is 161 kJ/mol.

Step 2

Ionization of lithium atoms to form Li^+ ions in the gas phase:

$$Li(g) \longrightarrow Li^+(g) + e^-$$

This process corresponds to the first ionization energy for lithium, which is 520 kJ/mol.

Step 3

Dissociation of fluorine molecules. We need to form 1 mole of fluorine atoms by breaking the F—F bonds in 0.5 mole of F_2 molecules:

$$\tfrac{1}{2}F_2(g) \longrightarrow F(g)$$

The energy required to break this bond is 154 kJ/mol. In this case we are breaking the bonds in a half mole of fluorine, so the energy required for this step is 154 kJ/2, or 77 kJ.

Step 4

Formation of F^- ions from fluorine atoms in the gas phase:

$$F(g) + e^- \longrightarrow F^-(g)$$

The energy change for this process corresponds to the electron affinity of fluorine, which is −328 kJ/mol.

Step 5

Formation of solid lithium fluoride from the gaseous Li^+ and F^- ions:

$$Li^+(g) + F^-(g) \longrightarrow LiF(s)$$

This corresponds to the lattice energy for LiF, which is −1047 kJ/mol.

Figure 13.9
The energy changes involved in the formation of solid lithium fluoride from its elements. The numbers in parentheses refer to the reaction steps discussed in the text.

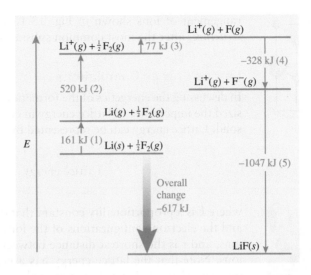

Since the sum of these five processes yields the desired overall reaction, the sum of the individual energy changes gives the overall energy change:

Process	Energy Change (kJ)
$Li(s) \rightarrow Li(g)$	161
$Li(g) \rightarrow Li^+(g) + e^-$	520
$\frac{1}{2}F_2(g) \rightarrow F(g)$	77
$F(g) + e^- \rightarrow F^-(g)$	−328
$Li^+(g) + F^-(g) \rightarrow LiF(s)$	−1047
Overall: $Li(s) + \frac{1}{2}F_2(g) \rightarrow LiF(s)$	−617 kJ (per mole of LiF)

In doing this calculation, we have ignored the small difference between ΔE_{sub} and ΔE_{sub}.

This process is summarized by the energy diagram in Fig. 13.9. Note that the formation of solid lithium fluoride from its elements is highly exothermic mainly because of the very large negative lattice energy. A great deal of energy is released when the ions combine to form the solid. In fact, note that the energy released when an electron is added to a fluorine atom to form the F^- ion (328 kJ/mol) is not enough to remove an electron from lithium (520 kJ/mol). That is, when a metallic lithium atom reacts with a nonmetallic fluorine atom to form *separated* ions,

$$Li(g) + F(g) \longrightarrow Li^+(g) + F^-(g)$$

the process is endothermic and thus unfavorable. Clearly, then, the main impetus for the formation of the ionic compound rather than a covalent compound results from the strong mutual attractions among the Li^+ and F^- ions in the solid. The lattice energy is the dominant energy term.

The structure of the solid lithium fluoride is represented in Fig. 13.10. Note the alternating arrangement of the Li^+ and F^- ions. Also note that each Li^+ is surrounded by six F^- ions and each F^- ion is surrounded by six Li^+ ions. This structure can be rationalized by assuming that the ions behave as hard spheres that pack together in a way that both maximizes the attractions among the oppositely charged ions and minimizes the repulsions among the identically charged ions.

All the binary ionic compounds formed by an alkali metal and a halogen have the structure shown in Fig. 13.10, except for the cesium salts. The ar-

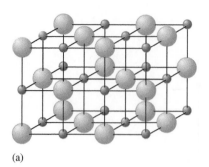

(a)

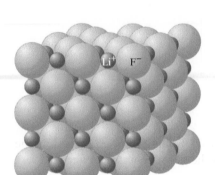

(b)

Figure 13.10
The structure of lithium fluoride.
(a) Represented by a ball-and-stick model. Note that each Li^+ ion is surrounded by six F^- ions, and each F^- ion is surrounded by six Li^+ ions.
(b) Represented with the ions shown as spheres. The structure is determined by packing the spherical ions in a way that both maximizes the ionic attractions and minimizes the ionic repulsions.

Since the equation for lattice energy contains the product Q_1Q_2, the lattice energy for a solid with 2+ and 2− ions should be four times that for a solid with 1+ and 1− ions. That is,

$$\frac{(+2)(-2)}{(+1)(-1)} = 4$$

For MgO and NaF, the observed ratio of lattice energies (Fig. 13.11) is

$$\frac{-3916 \text{ kJ}}{-923 \text{ kJ}} = 4.24$$

rangement of ions shown in Fig. 13.10 is often called the *sodium chloride structure,* after the most common substance that possesses it.

Lattice Energy Calculations

In discussing the energetics of the formation of solid lithium fluoride, we emphasized the importance of lattice energy in contributing to the stability of the ionic solid. Lattice energy can be represented by a modified form of Coulomb's law,

$$\text{Lattice energy} = k\left(\frac{Q_1Q_2}{r}\right)$$

where k is a proportionality constant that depends on the structure of the solid and the electron configurations of the ions, Q_1 and Q_2 are the charges on the ions, and r is the shortest distance between the centers of the cations and anions. Note that the lattice energy has a negative sign when Q_1 and Q_2 have opposite signs. This result is expected, since bringing cations and anions together is an exothermic process. Also note that the process becomes more exothermic as the ionic charges increase and as the distances between the ions in the solid decrease.

The importance of the charges in ionic solids can be illustrated by comparing the energies involved in the formation of $NaF(s)$ and $MgO(s)$. These solids contain the isoelectric ions Na^+, F^-, Mg^{2+}, and O^{2-}. The energy diagram for the formation of the two solids is given in Fig. 13.11. Note several important features:

The energy released when the gaseous Mg^{2+} and O^{2-} ions combine to form solid MgO is much greater (more than four times greater) than that released when the gaseous Na^+ and F^- ions combine to form solid NaF.

The energy required to remove two electrons from the magnesium atom (735 kJ/mol for the first and 1445 kJ/mol for the second, yielding a total of 2180 kJ/mol) is much greater than the energy required to remove an electron from a sodium atom (495 kJ/mol).

Energy (737 kJ/mol) is required to add two electrons to the oxygen atom in the gas phase. Addition of the first electron is exothermic (-141 kJ/mol), but addition of the second electron is quite endothermic (878 kJ/mol). This latter energy must be obtained indirectly, since the $O^{2-}(g)$ is not stable.

Because twice as much energy is required to remove the second electron from magnesium as to remove the first, and because addition of an electron to the gaseous O^- ion is quite endothermic, it seems puzzling that magnesium oxide contains Mg^{2+} and O^{2-} ions rather than Mg^+ and O^- ions. The answer lies in the lattice energy. Note that the lattice energy for combining gaseous Mg^{2+} and O^{2-} ions to form $MgO(s)$ is 3000 kJ/mol more negative than that for combining gaseous Na^+ and F^- ions to form $NaF(s)$. Thus the energy released in forming a solid containing Mg^{2+} and O^{2-} ions rather than Mg^+ and O^- ions more than compensates for the energies required for the processes that produce the Mg^{2+} and O^{2-} ions.

If there is so much lattice energy to be gained in going from singly charged to doubly charged ions in the case of magnesium oxide, why then does solid sodium fluoride contain Na^+ and F^- ions rather than Na^{2+} and F^{2-} ions? We can answer this question by recognizing that both Na^+ and F^- ions have the neon electron configuration. Removal of an electron from Na^+ requires an extremely large quantity of energy (4560 kJ/mol) because a $2p$ electron must be removed. Conversely, the addition of an electron to F^- would require use of the relatively high-energy $3s$ orbital, which is also an unfavorable process. Thus we

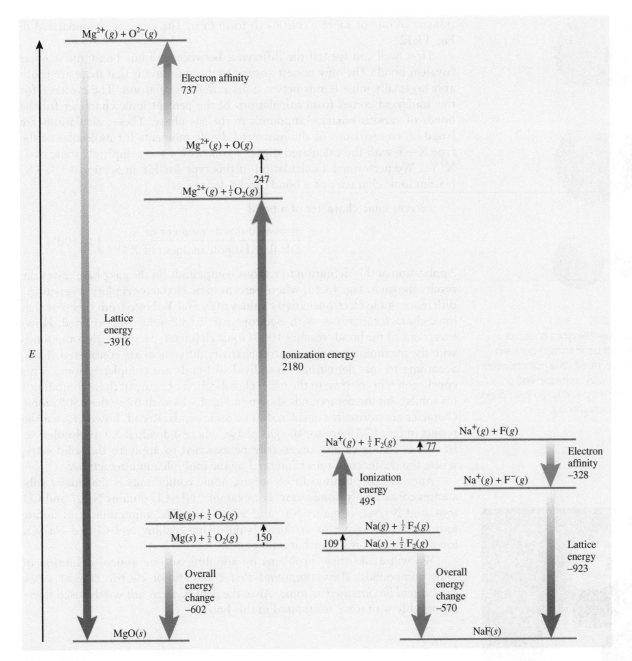

Figure 13.11

Comparison of the energy changes involved in the formation of solid sodium fluoride and solid magnesium oxide. Note the large lattice energy for magnesium oxide (where doubly charged ions are combining) compared with that for sodium fluoride (where singly charged ions are combining).

can say that for sodium fluoride the extra energy required to form the doubly charged ions is greater than the gain in lattice energy that would result.

This discussion of the energies involved in the formation of solid ionic compounds illustrates that a variety of factors operate to determine the composition and structure of these compounds. The most important of these factors involve the balancing of the energies required to form highly charged ions and the energy released when highly charged ions combine to form the solid.

13.6 | Partial Ionic Character of Covalent Bonds

Recall that when atoms with different electronegativities react to form molecules, the electrons are not shared equally. The possible result is a polar covalent bond or, in the case of a large electronegativity difference, a complete

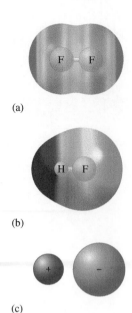

(a)

(b)

(c)

Figure 13.12
The three possible types of bonds:
(a) a covalent bond formed between
identical F atoms; (b) the polar covalent
bond of HF, with both ionic and covalent components; and (c) an ionic bond
with no electron sharing.

transfer of one or more electrons to form ions. The cases are summarized in
Fig. 13.12.

How well can we tell the difference between an ionic bond and a polar
covalent bond? The only honest answer to this question is that there are probably no totally ionic bonds between *discrete pairs of atoms*. The evidence for
this statement comes from calculations of the percent ionic character for the
bonds of various binary compounds in the gas phase. These calculations are
based on comparisons of the measured dipole moments for molecules of the
type X—Y with the calculated dipole moments for the completely ionic case,
X^+Y^-. We performed a calculation of this type for HF in Section 13.3. The
percent ionic character of a bond can be defined as

Percent ionic character of a bond

$$= \left(\frac{\text{measured dipole moment of X—Y}}{\text{calculated dipole moment of } X^+Y^-} \right) \times 100\%$$

Application of this definition to various compounds (in the gas phase) gives the
results shown in Fig. 13.13, where percent ionic character is plotted versus the
difference in the electronegativity values of X and Y. Note from this plot that
ionic character increases with electronegativity difference, as expected. However, none of the bonds reaches 100% ionic character, even though compounds
with the maximum possible electronegativity differences are considered. Thus,
according to this definition, no individual bonds are completely ionic. This
conclusion is in contrast to the usual classification of many of these compounds
(as solids). All the compounds shown in Fig. 13.13 with more than 50% ionic
character are normally considered to be ionic solids. Recall, however, that the
results in Fig. 13.13 are for the gas phase, where individual XY molecules exist. These results cannot necessarily be assumed to apply to the solid state,
where the existence of ions is favored by the multiple ion interactions.

Another complication in identifying ionic compounds is that many substances contain polyatomic ions. For example, NH_4Cl contains NH_4^+ and Cl^-
ions, and Na_2SO_4 contains Na^+ and SO_4^{2-} ions. The ammonium and sulfate
ions are held together by covalent bonds. Thus, calling NH_4Cl and Na_2SO_4
ionic compounds is somewhat ambiguous.

We will avoid these problems by adopting an operational definition of
ionic compounds: *Any compound that conducts an electric current when
melted will be classified as ionic.* Also, the generic term *salt* will be used interchangeably with *ionic compound* in this book.

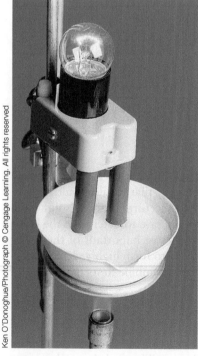

Molten NaCl conducts an electric
current, indicating the presence of
mobile Na^+ and Cl^- ions.

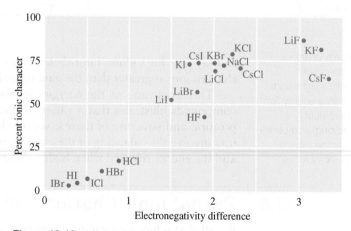

Figure 13.13
The relationship between the ionic character of a covalent bond and the electronegativity
difference of the bonded atoms. The compounds normally considered to be ionic in the
solid phase are shown in red.

13.7 | The Covalent Chemical Bond: A Model

Before we develop specific models for covalent chemical bonding, it will be helpful to summarize some of the concepts introduced in this chapter.

What is a chemical bond? Chemical bonds can be viewed as forces that cause a group of atoms to behave as a unit.

Why do chemical bonds occur? There is no principle of nature that states that bonds are favored or disfavored. Bonds are neither inherently "good" nor inherently "bad" as far as nature is concerned; they result from the tendency of a system to seek its lowest possible energy. From a simplistic point of view, bonds occur when collections of atoms are more stable (lower in energy) than the separate atoms. For example, about 1652 kJ of energy is required to break a mole of methane (CH_4) molecules into separate C and H atoms. Or, taking the opposite view, 1652 kJ of energy is released when 1 mole of methane is formed from 1 mole of gaseous C atoms and 4 moles of gaseous H atoms. Thus we can say that 1 mole of CH_4 molecules in the gas phase is 1652 kJ lower in energy than 1 mole of carbon atoms plus 4 moles of hydrogen atoms. Methane is therefore a stable molecule relative to its separated atoms.

We find it useful to interpret molecular stability in terms of a model called a chemical bond. To help understand why this model was invented, let's continue with methane, which consists of four hydrogen atoms arranged at the corners of a tetrahedron around a carbon atom:

A tetrahedron has four equal triangular faces.

Given this structure, it is natural to envision four individual C—H interactions (we call them bonds). The energy of stabilization of CH_4 is divided equally among the four bonds to give an average C—H bond energy per mole of C—H bonds:

$$\frac{1652 \text{ kJ}}{4} = 413 \text{ kJ}$$

Next, consider methyl chloride, which consists of CH_3Cl molecules having the structure

Experiments have shown that about 1578 kJ of energy is required to break down 1 mole of gaseous CH_3Cl molecules into gaseous carbon, chlorine, and hydrogen atoms. The reverse process can be represented as

$$C(g) + Cl(g) + 3H(g) \longrightarrow CH_3Cl(g) + 1578 \text{ kJ/mol}$$

A mole of gaseous methyl chloride is lower in energy by 1578 kJ than its separate gaseous atoms. Thus a mole of methyl chloride is held together by 1578 kJ of energy. Again, it is very useful to divide this energy into individual bonds. Methyl chloride can be visualized as containing one C—Cl bond and three C—H bonds. If we assume arbitrarily that a C—H interaction represents the same quantity of energy in any situation (that is, the strength of a

C—H bond is independent of its molecular environment), we can do the following bookkeeping:

$$1 \text{ mol of C—Cl bonds plus 3 mol of C—H bonds} = 1578 \text{ kJ}$$

$$\text{C—Cl bond energy} + 3(\text{average C—H bond energy}) = 1578 \text{ kJ}$$

$$\text{C—Cl bond energy} + 3(413 \text{ kJ/mol}) = 1578 \text{ kJ}$$

$$\text{C—Cl bond energy} = 1578 - 1239 = 339 \text{ kJ/mol}$$

These assumptions allow us to associate given quantities of energy with C—H and C—Cl bonds.

It is important to note that the bond concept is a human invention. Bonds provide a method for dividing up the energy evolved when a stable molecule is formed from its component atoms. Thus in this context *a bond represents a quantity of energy* obtained from the molecular energy of stabilization in a rather arbitrary way. This is not to say that the concept of individual bonds is a bad idea. In fact, the modern concept of the chemical bond, conceived by American chemists G. N. Lewis and Linus Pauling, is one of the most useful ideas chemists have ever developed.

Models: An Overview

The framework of chemistry, like that of any science, consists of models—attempts to explain how nature operates on the microscopic level based on experiences in the macroscopic world. To understand chemistry, one must understand its models and how they are used. We will use the concept of bonding to reemphasize the important characteristics of models, including their origin, structure, and uses.

Models originate from our observations of the properties of nature. For example, the concept of bonds arose from the observations that most chemical processes involve collections of atoms and that chemical reactions involve rearrangements of the ways in which the atoms are grouped. So to understand reactions, we must understand the forces that bind atoms together.

In natural processes there is a tendency toward lower energy. Collections of atoms therefore occur because the aggregated state has lower energy than

Bonding is a model proposed to explain molecular stability.

The concept of individual bonds makes it much easier to deal with complex molecules such as DNA. A small segment of a DNA molecule is shown here.

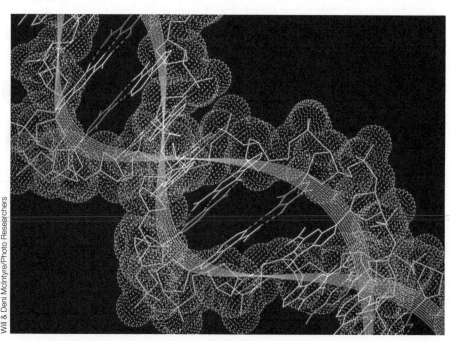

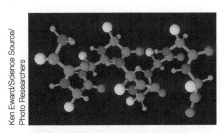

A ball-and-stick model of a protein segment illustrating the alpha helix.

the separated atoms. Why? As we have seen earlier in this chapter, the best explanations for the energy change involve atoms sharing electrons or atoms transferring electrons to become ions. In the case of electron sharing, we find it convenient to assume that individual bonds occur between pairs of atoms. Let's explore the validity of this assumption and see how it is useful.

In a diatomic molecule such as H_2, it is natural to assume that a bond exists between the atoms, holding them together. It is also useful to assume that individual bonds are present in polyatomic molecules such as CH_4. So instead of thinking of CH_4 as a unit with a stabilization energy of 1652 kJ per mole, we choose to think of CH_4 as containing four C—H bonds, each worth 413 kJ of energy per mole of bonds. Without this concept of individual bonds in molecules, chemistry would be hopelessly complicated. There are millions of different chemical compounds, and if each of these compounds had to be considered as an entirely new entity, the task of understanding chemical behavior would be overwhelming.

The bonding model provides a framework to systematize chemical behavior by enabling us to think of molecules as collections of common fundamental components. For example, a typical biomolecule, such as a protein, contains hundreds of atoms and might seem discouragingly complex. However, if we think of a protein as constructed of individual bonds, C—C, C—H, C—N, C—O, N—H, and so on, it helps tremendously in predicting and understanding the protein's behavior. The essential idea is that we expect a given bond to behave about the same in any molecular environment. Used in this way, the model of the chemical bond has helped chemists to systematize the reactions of the millions of existing compounds.

Fundamental Properties of Models

1. Models are human inventions, always based on an incomplete understanding of how nature works. *A model does not equal reality.*

2. Models are often wrong. This property derives from the first property. Models are based on speculation and are always oversimplifications.

3. Models tend to become more complicated as they age. As flaws are discovered in our models, we "patch" them and thus add more detail.

4. It is very important to understand the assumptions that are inherent in a particular model before you use it to interpret observations or to make predictions. Simple methods usually involve very restrictive assumptions and can be expected to yield only qualitative information. Asking for a sophisticated explanation from a simple model is like expecting to get an accurate mass for a diamond by using a bathroom scale.

   For a model to be used effectively, we must understand its strengths and weaknesses and ask only appropriate questions. An illustration of this point is the simple aufbau principle used to explain the electron configurations of the elements. Although this model correctly predicts the configuration for most atoms, chromium and copper do not agree with the predictions. Detailed studies show that the configurations of chromium and copper result from complex electron interactions that are not taken into account in the simple model. However, this does not mean that we should discard the simple model that is so useful for most atoms. Instead, we must apply it with caution and not expect it to be correct in every case.

5. When a model is wrong, we often learn much more than when it is right. If a model makes a wrong prediction, it usually means we do not understand some fundamental characteristics of nature. We often learn by making mistakes. (Try to remember that when you get back your next chemistry test.)

In addition to being very useful, the bonding model is physically sensible. It makes sense that atoms can form stable groups by sharing electrons; shared electrons give a lower energy state because they are simultaneously attracted by two nuclei.

Also, as we will see in the next section, bond energy data support the existence of discrete bonds that are relatively independent of the molecular environment. It is very important to remember, however, that the chemical bond is only a model. Although our concept of discrete bonds in molecules agrees with many of our observations, some molecular properties require that we think of a molecule as a whole, with the electrons free to move through the entire molecule. This is called *delocalization* of the electrons, a concept that will be discussed more completely in the next chapter.

13.8 │ Covalent Bond Energies and Chemical Reactions

In this section we will consider the energies associated with various types of bonds and see how the bonding concept is useful in dealing with the energies of chemical reactions. One important consideration is to establish the sensitivity of a particular type of bond to its molecular environment. For example, consider the stepwise decomposition of methane:

Process	Energy Required (kJ/mol)
$CH_4(g) \rightarrow CH_3(g) + H(g)$	435
$CH_3(g) \rightarrow CH_2(g) + H(g)$	453
$CH_2(g) \rightarrow CH(g) + H(g)$	425
$CH(g) \rightarrow C(g) + H(g)$	339
	Total = 1652

$$\text{Average} = \frac{1652}{4} = 413$$

Although a C—H bond is broken in each case, the energy required varies in a nonsystematic way. This example shows that the C—H bond is somewhat sensitive to its environment. We use the *average* of these individual bond dissociation energies even though this quantity only approximates the energy associated with a C—H bond in a particular molecule. The degree of sensitivity of a bond to its environment also can be seen from experimental measurements of the energy required to break the C—H bond in the following molecules:

Molecule	Measured C—H Bond Energy (kJ/mol)
$HCBr_3$	380
$HCCl_3$	380
HCF_3	430
C_2H_6	410

Table 13.6 | Average Bond Energies (kJ/mol)

	Single Bonds						Multiple Bonds	
H—H	432	N—H	391	I—I	149	C≡C	614	
H—F	565	N—N	160	I—Cl	208	C≡C	839	
H—Cl	427	N—F	272	I—Br	175	O≡O	495	
H—Br	363	N—Cl	200			C≡O*	745	
H—I	295	N—Br	243	S—H	347	C≡O	1072	
		N—O	201	S—F	327	N≡O	607	
C—H	413	O—H	467	S—Cl	253	N≡N	418	
C—C	347	O—O	146	S—Br	218	N≡N	941	
C—N	305	O—F	190	S—S	266	C≡N	891	
C—O	358	O—Cl	203			C≡N	615	
C—F	485	O—I	234					
C—Cl	339			Si—Si	340			
C—Br	276	F—F	154	Si—H	393			
C—I	240	F—Cl	253	Si—C	360			
C—S	259	F—Br	237	Si—O	452			
		Cl—Cl	239					
		Cl—Br	218					
		Br—Br	193					

*C═O(in CO_2) = 799

These data show that the C—H bond strength varies significantly with its environment, but the concept of an average C—H bond strength remains useful to chemists. The average values of bond energies for various types of bonds are listed in Table 13.6.

So far we have discussed bonds in which one pair of electrons is shared. This type of bond is called a **single bond**. As we will see in more detail later, atoms sometimes share two pairs of electrons, forming a **double bond**, or share three pairs of electrons, forming a **triple bond**. Notice that the bond energy of a double bond is not twice the bond energy of a single bond. Similarly, the bond energy of a triple bond is not three times the single bond energy. The bond energies for these *multiple bonds* are also given in Table 13.6.

A relationship also exists between the number of shared electron pairs and the bond length. As the number of shared electrons increases, the bond length shortens. This relationship is shown for selected bonds in Table 13.7.

Table 13.7 | Bond Lengths for Selected Bonds

Bond	Bond Type	Bond Length (pm)	Bond Dissociation Energy (kJ/mol)
C—C	Single	154	347
C═C	Double	134	614
C≡C	Triple	120	839
C—O	Single	143	358
C═O	Double	123	745
C—N	Single	143	305
C═N	Double	138	615
C≡N	Triple	116	891

Bond Energies

Bond energy values can be used to calculate approximate energies for reactions. To illustrate how this is done, we will calculate the change in energy that accompanies the following reaction:

$$H_2(g) + F_2(g) \longrightarrow 2HF(g)$$

This reaction involves breaking one H—H and one F—F bond and forming two H—F bonds. For bonds to be broken, energy must be *added* to the system—a positive ΔE. Consequently, the energy terms associated with bond breaking have *positive* signs. The formation of a bond *releases* energy, so the energy terms associated with bond making carry a *negative* sign. We can write the energy change for a reaction as follows:

$\Delta E =$ sum of the energies required to break old bonds (positive signs) plus the sum of the energies released in the formation of new bonds (negative signs)

This leads to the expression

$$\Delta E = \underbrace{\Sigma n \times D \text{ (bonds broken)}}_{\text{Energy required}} - \underbrace{\Sigma n \times D \text{ (bonds formed)}}_{\text{Energy released}}$$

where Σ represents the sum of terms, D represents the bond dissociation energy per mole of bonds (D *always* has a positive sign), and n represents the moles of a particular type of bond.

In the case of the formation of HF,

$$\Delta E = D_{H-H} + D_{F-F} - 2D_{H-F}$$

$$= 1 \text{ mol} \times \frac{432 \text{ kJ}}{\text{mol}} + 1 \text{ mol} \times \frac{154 \text{ kJ}}{\text{mol}} - 2 \text{ mol} \times \frac{565 \text{ kJ}}{\text{mol}}$$

$$= -544 \text{ kJ}$$

Thus, when 1 mole of $H_2(g)$ and 1 mole of $F_2(g)$ react to form 2 moles of HF(g), 544 kJ of energy should be released.

INTERACTIVE EXAMPLE 13.5

ΔE from Bond Energies

Using the bond energies listed in Table 13.6, calculate ΔE for the reaction of methane with chlorine and fluorine to give Freon-12 (CF_2Cl_2).

$$CH_4(g) + 2Cl_2(g) + 2F_2(g) \longrightarrow CF_2Cl_2(g) + 2HF(g) + 2HCl(g)$$

Solution

The idea here is to break the bonds in the gaseous reactants to give individual atoms and then assemble these atoms into the gaseous products by forming new bonds:

$$\text{Reactants} \xrightarrow[\text{required}]{\text{Energy}} \text{atoms} \xrightarrow[\text{released}]{\text{Energy}} \text{products}$$

We then combine the energy changes to calculate ΔE:

$\Delta E =$ energy required to break bonds $-$ energy released when bonds form

where the minus sign gives the correct sign to the energy terms for the exothermic processes.

Reactant Bonds Broken:

$$CH_4: \quad 4 \text{ mol } C-H \qquad 4 \text{ mol} \times \frac{413 \text{ kJ}}{\text{mol}} = 1652 \text{ kJ}$$

$$2Cl_2: \quad 2 \text{ mol } Cl-Cl \qquad 2 \text{ mol} \times \frac{239 \text{ kJ}}{\text{mol}} = 478 \text{ kJ}$$

$$2F_2: \quad 2 \text{ mol } F-F \qquad 2 \text{ mol} \times \frac{154 \text{ kJ}}{\text{mol}} = 308 \text{ kJ}$$

$$\text{Total energy required} = 2438 \text{ kJ}$$

Product Bonds Formed:

$$CF_2Cl_2: \quad 2 \text{ mol } C-F \qquad 2 \text{ mol} \times \frac{485 \text{ kJ}}{\text{mol}} = 970 \text{ kJ}$$

and

$$2 \text{ mol } C-Cl \qquad 2 \text{ mol} \times \frac{339 \text{ kJ}}{\text{mol}} = 678 \text{ kJ}$$

$$HF: \quad 2 \text{ mol } H-F \qquad 2 \text{ mol} \times \frac{565 \text{ kJ}}{\text{mol}} = 1130 \text{ kJ}$$

$$HCl: \quad 2 \text{ mol } H-Cl \qquad 2 \text{ mol} \times \frac{427 \text{ kJ}}{\text{mol}} = 854 \text{ kJ}$$

$$\text{Total energy released} = 3632 \text{ kJ}$$

We now can calculate ΔE:

$$\Delta E = \text{energy required to break bonds} - \text{energy released when bonds form}$$
$$= 2438 \text{ kJ} - 3632 \text{ kJ}$$
$$= -1194 \text{ kJ}$$

Since the sign of the value for the energy change is negative, this means that 1194 kJ of energy is released per mole of CF_2Cl_2 formed.

13.9 | The Localized Electron Bonding Model

So far we have discussed the general characteristics of the chemical bonding model and have seen that properties such as bond strength and polarity can be assigned to individual bonds. In this section we introduce a specific model used to describe covalent bonds. We need a simple model that can be easily applied even to very complicated molecules and that can be used routinely by chemists to interpret and organize the wide variety of chemical phenomena. The model that serves this purpose is often called the **localized electron (LE) model.** This model assumes that *a molecule is composed of atoms that are bound together by using atomic orbitals to share electron pairs.* The electron pairs in the molecule are assumed to be localized on a particular atom or in the space between two atoms. Those pairs of electrons localized on an atom are called **lone pairs,** and those found in the space between the atoms are called **bonding pairs.**

As we will apply it, the LE model has three parts:

1. Description of the valence electron arrangement in the molecule using Lewis structures (will be discussed in the next section).

2. Prediction of the geometry of the molecule, using the valence shell electron-pair repulsion (VSEPR) model (will be discussed in Section 13.13).

3. Description of the types of atomic orbitals used by the atoms to share electrons or hold lone pairs (will be discussed in Chapter 14).

13.10 | Lewis Structures

The **Lewis structure** of a molecule represents the arrangement of valence electrons among the atoms in the molecule. These representations are named after G. N. Lewis (Fig. 13.14). The rules for writing Lewis structures are based on the observations of thousands of molecules, which show that *in most stable compounds the atoms achieve noble gas electron configurations*. Although this is not always the case, it is so common that it provides a very useful place to start.

We have already seen that when metals and nonmetals react to form solid binary ionic compounds, electrons are transferred, and the resulting ions typically have noble gas electron configurations. An example is the formation of KBr, where the K^+ ion has the [Ar] electron configuration and the Br^- ion has the [Kr] electron configuration. In writing Lewis structures, the rule is that *only the valence electrons are included*. Using dots to represent electrons, the Lewis structure for KBr is

K   : Br :

1+   1−
charge   charge

No dots are shown in the K^+ ion since it has no valence electrons. The Br^- ion is shown with eight electrons since it has a filled valence shell.

Lewis structures show only valence electrons.

Figure 13.14
G. N. Lewis (above) conceived the octet rule while lecturing to a class of general chemistry students in 1902. He was also one of the two authors of a now classic work on thermodynamics, Lewis and Randall, *Thermodynamics and the Free Energy of Chemical Substances* (1923). (right) This is his original sketch. From G. N. Lewis, *Valence*, Dover Publications, Inc., New York, 1966.

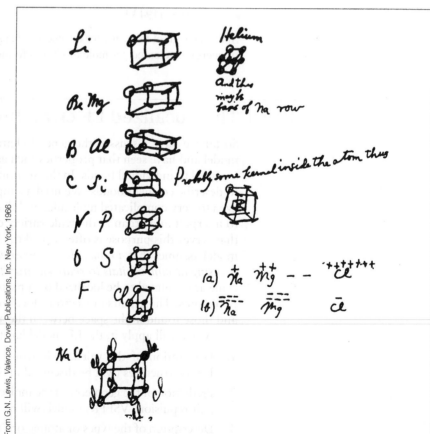

From G.N. Lewis, *Valence*, Dover Publications, Inc. New York, 1966.

The Bancroft Library

Next, we will consider Lewis structures for molecules with covalent bonds involving elements in the first and second periods. The principle of achieving a noble gas electron configuration applies to these elements as follows:

Hydrogen forms stable molecules where it shares two electrons. That is, it follows a **duet rule.** For example, when two hydrogen atoms, each with one electron, combine to form the H_2 molecule, we have

$$H\cdot \qquad \cdot H$$
$$\searrow \; H\!:\!H \; \swarrow$$

By sharing electrons, each hydrogen in H_2 has two electrons. This gives each hydrogen a filled valence shell.

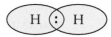

Helium does not form bonds because its valence orbitals are already filled; it is a noble gas. Helium has the electron configuration $1s^2$ and can be represented by the Lewis structure

$$He\!:$$

Carbon, nitrogen, oxygen, and fluorine almost always obey the octet rule in stable molecules.

The second-row nonmetals (carbon through fluorine) form stable molecules when they are surrounded by enough electrons to fill the valence orbitals—the $2s$ and the three $2p$ orbitals. Since eight electrons are required to fill the $2s$ and $2p$ orbitals, these elements typically obey the **octet rule;** they are surrounded by eight electrons. An example is the F_2 molecule, which has the following Lewis structure:

$$:\!\ddot{F}\!\cdot \quad \longrightarrow \quad :\!\ddot{F}\!:\!\ddot{F}\!: \quad \longleftarrow \quad \cdot\ddot{F}\!:$$

F atom with seven F_2 F atom with seven
valence electrons   molecule   valence electrons

Note that each fluorine atom in F_2 is, in effect, surrounded by eight electrons, two of which are shared with the other atom. Recall that the shared pair of electrons is called a *bonding pair.* Each fluorine atom also has three pairs of electrons not involved in bonding. These are the *lone pairs.*

Neon does not form bonds since it already has an octet of valence electrons (it is a noble gas). The Lewis structure is

$$:\!\ddot{Ne}\!:$$

Note that only the valence electrons of the neon atom ($2s^2 2p^6$) are represented by the Lewis structure. The $1s^2$ electrons are core electrons and take no part in chemical reactions.

From the discussion above, we can formulate the following rules for writing Lewis structures of molecules containing atoms from the first two periods.

STEPS	**Writing Lewis Structures**

1 Sum the valence electrons from all the atoms. Do not worry about keeping track of which electrons come from which atoms. It is the *total* number of electrons that is important.

2 Use a pair of electrons to form a bond between each pair of bound atoms.

3 Arrange the remaining electrons to satisfy the duet rule for hydrogen and the octet rule for the second-row elements.

To see how these rules are applied, we will construct the Lewis structures for a few molecules. We will first consider the water molecule and follow the rules above.

Step 1

We sum the *valence* electrons for H_2O as shown:

$$1 + 1 + 6 = 8 \text{ valence electrons}$$
$$\nearrow \quad \nearrow \quad \nearrow$$
$$\text{H} \quad \text{H} \quad \text{O}$$

Step 2

Using one pair of electrons per bond, we draw in the two O—H single bonds:

$$\text{H—O—H}$$

Note that *a line instead of a pair of dots is used to indicate each pair of bonding electrons*. This is the standard notation.

Step 3

We distribute the remaining electrons around the atoms to achieve a noble gas electron configuration for each atom. Since four electrons have been used in forming the two bonds, four electrons (8 − 4) remain to be distributed. Hydrogen is satisfied with two electrons (duet rule), but oxygen needs eight electrons to achieve a noble gas configuration. Thus the remaining four electrons are added to oxygen as two lone pairs. Dots are used to represent the lone pairs:

$$\text{H—Ö̤—H} \qquad \text{Lone pairs}$$

This is the correct Lewis structure for the water molecule. Each hydrogen has two electrons and the oxygen has eight:

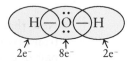

$$\underset{2e^-}{\uparrow} \qquad \underset{8e^-}{\uparrow} \qquad \underset{2e^-}{\uparrow}$$

As a second example, we will write the Lewis structure for carbon dioxide. Summing the valence electrons gives

$$4 + 6 + 6 = 16$$
$$\nearrow \quad \nearrow \quad \nearrow$$
$$\text{C} \quad \text{O} \quad \text{O}$$

After forming a bond between the carbon and each oxygen,

$$\text{O—C—O}$$

the remaining electrons are distributed to achieve noble gas configurations on each atom. In this case we have 12 electrons (16 − 4) remaining after the bonds are drawn. The distribution of these electrons is determined by a trial-and-error process. We have six pairs of electrons to distribute. Suppose we try three pairs on each oxygen to give

$$:\!\ddot{\text{O}}\!\text{—C—}\!\ddot{\text{O}}\!:$$

To see if this structure is correct, we need to check two things:

1. The total number of electrons. There are 16 valence electrons in this structure, which is the correct number.

2. The octet rule for each atom. Each oxygen has eight electrons, but the carbon has only four. This cannot be the correct Lewis structure.

H—O—H represents H:O:H

How can we arrange the 16 available electrons to achieve an octet for each atom? Suppose that there are two shared pairs between the carbon and each oxygen:

 represents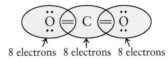

8 electrons 8 electrons 8 electrons

Now each atom is surrounded by 8 electrons, and the total number of electrons is 16, as required. Thus the correct Lewis structure for carbon dioxide has two double bonds.

Finally, let's consider the Lewis structure of the CN^- (cyanide) ion. Summing the valence electrons, we have

$$\begin{array}{ccc} C & N & ^- \\ \uparrow & \uparrow & \uparrow \\ \end{array}$$
$$4 + 5 + 1 = 10$$

Note that the negative charge requires that an extra electron be added. After drawing a single bond (C—N), we distribute the remaining electrons to achieve a noble gas configuration for each atom. Eight electrons remain to be distributed. We can try various possibilities, for example:

$$\ddot{C}\text{—}\ddot{N}$$

This structure is incorrect because C and N have only six electrons each instead of eight. The correct arrangement is

$$[:C\equiv N:]^-$$

(Satisfy yourself that both carbon and nitrogen have eight electrons.)

⚙WL INTERACTIVE EXAMPLE 13.6

Give the Lewis structure for each of the following.

a. HF **b.** N_2 **c.** NH_3 **d.** CH_4 **e.** CF_4 **f.** NO^+

Solution In each case we apply the three rules for writing Lewis structures. Recall that lines are used to indicate shared electron pairs and that dots are used to indicate nonbonding pairs (lone pairs). We have the following tabulated results:

	Total Valence Electrons	Draw Single Bonds	Calculate Number of Electrons Remaining	Use Remaining Electrons to Achieve Noble Gas Configurations
a. HF	$1 + 7 = 8$	H—F	6	H—$\ddot{\underset{\cdot\cdot}{F}}$:
b. N_2	$5 + 5 = 10$	N—N	8	:N≡N:
c. NH_3	$5 + 3(1) = 8$	H—N—H ‎ | ‎ H	2	H—$\ddot{N}$—H ‎ | ‎ H
d. CH_4	$4 + 4(1) = 8$	‎ H ‎ | H—C—H ‎ | ‎ H	0	‎ H ‎ | H—C—H ‎ | ‎ H

(continued)

	Total Valence Electrons	Draw Single Bonds	Calculate Number of Electrons Remaining	Use Remaining Electrons to Achieve Noble Gas Configurations
e. CF_4	$4 + 4(7) = 32$	F—C—F with F above and F below	24	structure with $:\ddot{F}:$ and $:\ddot{F}-C-\ddot{F}:$ and $:\ddot{F}:$
f. NO^+	$5 + 6 - 1 = 10$	N—O	8	$[:N\equiv O:]^+$

When writing Lewis structures, don't worry about which electrons came from which atoms. The best way to look at a molecule is to regard it as a new entity that uses all of the available valence electrons of the atoms to achieve the lowest possible energy.* The valence electrons belong to the molecule rather than to the individual atoms. Simply distribute all valence electrons so that the various rules are satisfied, without regard to the origin of each particular electron.

13.11 | Resonance

A valid Lewis structure is one that obeys the rules we have outlined.

Sometimes more than one valid Lewis structure is possible for a given molecule. For example, consider the Lewis structure for the nitrate ion (NO_3^-), which has 24 valence electrons. So that an octet of electrons surrounds each atom, a structure like the following is required:

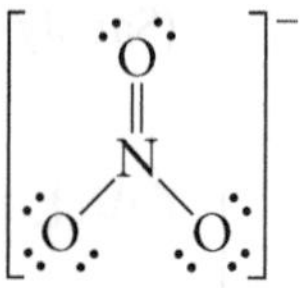

If this structure accurately represents the bonding in NO_3^-, there should be two types of N—O bonds observed in the molecule: one shorter bond (the double bond) and two identical longer ones (the two single bonds). However, experiments clearly show that NO_3^- exhibits only *one* type of N—O bond with a length and strength between those expected for a single bond and a double bond. Thus, although the structure we have shown above is a valid Lewis structure, it does *not* correctly represent the bonding in NO_3^-. This is a serious problem, and it means that the model must be modified.

Look again at the proposed Lewis structure for NO_3^-. Because there is no reason for choosing a particular oxygen atom to have the double bond, there are really three valid Lewis structures:

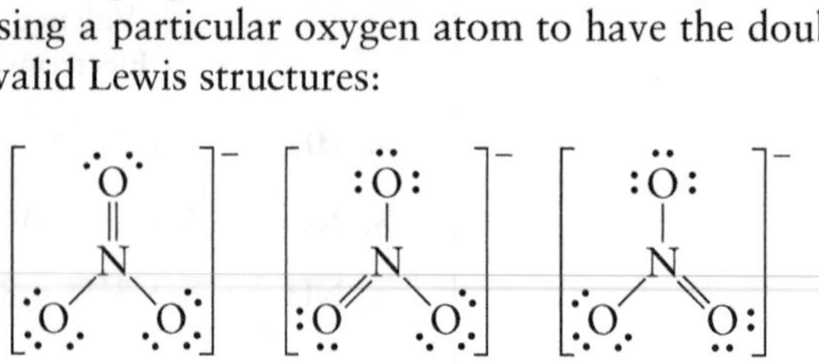

Is any of these structures a correct description of the bonding in NO_3^-? No, because NO_3^- does not have one double and two single bonds—it has three

---

*In a sense this approach corrects for the fact that the LE model overemphasizes the point that a molecule is simply a sum of its parts—that is, that the atoms retain their individual identities in the molecule.

equivalent bonds. We can solve this problem by making the following assumption: The correct description of NO_3^- is *not given by any one* of the three Lewis structures individually but is given only by the *superposition of all three.*

The nitrate ion does not exist as any of the three extreme forms indicated by the individual Lewis structures but instead exists as an average of all three. **Resonance** *is invoked when more than one valid Lewis structure can be written for a particular molecule.* The resulting electron structure of the molecule is given by the average of these **resonance structures.** This situation is usually represented by double-headed arrows as follows:

Note that in all these resonance structures the arrangement of the nuclei is the same. Only the placement of the electrons differs. The arrows do not indicate that the molecule "flips" from one resonance structure to another. They simply show that the *actual structure is an average of the three resonance structures.*

The concept of resonance is necessary because the LE model postulates that electrons are localized between a given pair of atoms. However, nature doesn't really operate this way. Electrons are actually delocalized—they can move around the entire molecule. The valence electrons in the NO_3^- molecule distribute themselves to provide equivalent N—O bonds. Resonance is necessary to compensate for this defective assumption of the LE model. However, because this model is so useful, we retain the concept of localized electrons and add resonance to accommodate species like NO_3^-.

EXAMPLE 13.7

Describe the electron arrangement in the nitrite anion (NO_2^-) using the LE model.

Solution We will follow the usual procedure for obtaining the Lewis structure for the NO_2^- ion.

In NO_2^- there are $5 + 2(6) + 1 = 18$ valence electrons. Indicating the single bonds gives the structure

$$O—N—O$$

The remaining 14 electrons $(18 - 4)$ can be distributed to produce these structures:

This is a resonance situation. Two equivalent Lewis structures can be drawn. *The electronic structure of the molecule is not correctly represented by either resonance structure but by the average of the two.* There are two equivalent N—O bonds, each one intermediate between a single and a double bond.

Equivalent Lewis structures contain the same numbers of single and multiple bonds. For example, the resonance structures for O_3,

and

are equivalent Lewis structures. They are equally important in describing the bonding in O_3. Nonequivalent Lewis structures contain different numbers of single and multiple bonds.

13.12 | Exceptions to the Octet Rule

The LE model is a simple but very successful model, and the rules we have used for Lewis structures apply to most molecules. To implement this model, we have relied heavily on the octet rule. So far we have treated molecules for which this rule is easily applied. However, inevitably, cases arise where the importance of an octet of electrons is called into question. Boron, for example, tends to form compounds in which the boron atom has fewer than eight electrons around it—it does not have a complete octet. Boron trifluoride (BF_3), a gas at normal temperatures and pressures, reacts very energetically with molecules such as water and ammonia that have available lone pairs. The violent reactivity of BF_3 with electron-rich molecules occurs because the boron atom is electron-deficient. Boron trifluoride has 24 valence electrons. The Lewis structure that seems most consistent with the properties of BF_3 is

$$\begin{array}{c} :\ddot{F}: \\ | \\ B \\ \diagup \quad \diagdown \\ :\ddot{F} \qquad \ddot{F}: \end{array}$$

Note that in this structure boron has only six electrons around it. The octet rule for boron can be satisfied by drawing a structure with a double bond, such as

$$\begin{array}{c} \ddot{F}: \\ \| \\ B \\ \diagup \quad \diagdown \\ :\ddot{F} \qquad \ddot{F}: \end{array}$$

and there are some theoretical studies that support such a structure for BF_3. However, since fluorine is so much more electronegative than boron, this structure seems questionable. In fact, some experiments indicate that each B—F bond is probably best described by the first Lewis structure, which is also consistent with the reactivity of BF_3 toward electron-rich molecules such as NH_3 with which it reacts to form H_3NBF_3:

$$\begin{array}{cc} \begin{array}{c} H \\ \diagdown \\ H-N: \\ \diagup \\ H \end{array} + \begin{array}{c} \ddot{F}: \\ \diagup \\ B-\ddot{F}: \\ \diagdown \\ \ddot{F}: \end{array} & \longrightarrow \begin{array}{c} H \qquad \ddot{F}: \\ \diagdown \quad \diagup \\ H-N-B-\ddot{F}: \\ \diagup \quad \diagdown \\ H \qquad \ddot{F}: \end{array} \end{array}$$

In this stable compound, boron has an octet of electrons.

It is characteristic of boron to form molecules in which the boron atom is electron-deficient. On the other hand, carbon, nitrogen, oxygen, and fluorine do obey the octet rule.

Some atoms appear to exceed the octet rule. This behavior is observed only for those elements in Period 3 of the periodic table and beyond. To see how this arises, we will consider the Lewis structure for sulfur hexafluoride (SF_6). The sum of the valence electrons for SF_6 is

$$6 + 6(7) = 48 \text{ electrons}$$

Indicating the single bonds gives the structure on the left below:

$$\begin{array}{cc} \begin{array}{c} F \\ F\diagdown | \diagup F \\ S \\ F\diagup | \diagdown F \\ F \end{array} & \begin{array}{c} :\ddot{F}: \\ :\ddot{F}\diagdown | \diagup \ddot{F}: \\ S \\ :\ddot{F}\diagup | \diagdown \ddot{F}: \\ :\ddot{F}: \end{array} \end{array}$$

We have used 12 electrons to form the S—F bonds, which leaves 36 electrons. Since fluorine always follows the octet rule, we complete the six fluorine octets

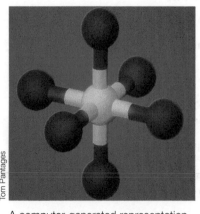

A computer-generated representation of sulfur hexafluoride.

to give the structure on the right above. This structure uses all 48 valence electrons for SF_6, but sulfur has 12 electrons around it; that is, sulfur *exceeds* the octet rule. How can this happen? There are several ways to approach this situation. The classical explanation for molecules like SF_6 involves using the empty $3d$ orbitals on the third-period elements. Recall that the second-row elements have only $2s$ and $2p$ valence orbitals, whereas the third-row elements have $3s$, $3p$, and $3d$ orbitals. The $3s$ and $3p$ orbitals fill with electrons in going from sodium to argon, but the $3d$ orbitals remain empty. For example, the valence-orbital diagram for a sulfur atom is

Thus one way to account for the electronic structure of SF_6 is to assume that the empty $3d$ orbitals on sulfur can be used to accommodate extra electrons: The sulfur atom can have 12 electrons around it by using the $3s$ and $3p$ orbitals to hold 8 electrons, with the extra 4 electrons in the formerly empty $3d$ orbitals.

Lewis Structures and the Octet Rule

1. The second-row elements C, N, O, and F should always be assumed to obey the octet rule.

2. The second-row elements B and Be often have fewer than eight electrons around them in their compounds. These electron-deficient compounds are very reactive.

3. The second-row elements never exceed the octet rule, since their valence orbitals ($2s$ and $2p$) can accommodate only eight electrons.

4. Third-row and heavier elements often satisfy the octet rule but are assumed in the simplest model to exceed the octet rule by using their empty valence d orbitals.

5. When writing the Lewis structure for a molecule, first draw single bonds between all bonded atoms, and then satisfy the octet rule for all the atoms. If electrons remain after the octet rule has been satisfied, place them on the elements having available d orbitals (elements in the third period or beyond).

⚙WL INTERACTIVE EXAMPLE 13.8

Write the Lewis structure for PCl_5.

Solution We can follow the same stepwise procedure we used previously for sulfur hexafluoride.

Step 1

Sum the valence electrons.

$$5 + 5(7) = 40 \text{ electrons}$$
$$\uparrow \qquad \uparrow$$
$$\text{P} \qquad \text{Cl}$$

Step 2

Indicate single bonds between bound atoms.

Step 3

Distribute the remaining electrons. In this case, 30 electrons (40 − 10) remain. These are used to satisfy the octet rule for each chlorine atom. The final Lewis structure is

$$\begin{array}{c}
: \ddot{\text{Cl}} : \\
\vert \quad \swarrow \text{Cl} : \\
: \ddot{\text{Cl}} - \text{P} \\
\vert \quad \nwarrow \ddot{\text{Cl}} : \\
: \ddot{\text{Cl}} :
\end{array}$$

Note that phosphorus, a third-row element, exceeds the octet rule by two electrons.

In the PCl_5 and SF_6 molecules, the third-row central atoms (P and S, respectively) are assigned the extra electrons. However, in molecules having more than one atom that can exceed the octet rule, it is not always clear which atom should have the extra electrons. Consider the Lewis structure for the triiodide ion (I_3^-), which has

$$3(7) + 1 = 22 \text{ valence electrons}$$
$$\uparrow \qquad \uparrow$$
$$\text{I} \qquad -1 \text{ charge}$$

Indicating the single bonds gives I—I—I. At this point 18 electrons (22 − 4) remain. Trial and error will convince you that one of the iodine atoms must exceed the octet rule, but *which* one?

The rule we will follow is that *when it is necessary to exceed the octet rule for one of several third-row (or higher) elements, assume that the extra electrons are placed on the central atom.*

Thus for I_3^- the Lewis structure is

$$\left[: \ddot{\text{I}} - \dot{\ddot{\text{I}}} - \ddot{\text{I}} : \right]^-$$

where the central iodine exceeds the octet rule. This structure agrees with known properties of I_3^-.

EXAMPLE 13.9

Write the Lewis structure for each molecule or ion.

a. ClF_3 **b.** XeO_3 **c.** $RnCl_2$ **d.** $BeCl_2$ **e.** ICl_4^-

Solution

a. The chlorine atom (third row) accepts the extra electrons.

$$\begin{array}{c}
\ddot{\text{F}} : \\
\diagup \\
: \ddot{\text{Cl}} - \ddot{\text{F}} : \\
\diagdown \\
\ddot{\text{F}} :
\end{array}$$

b. All atoms obey the octet rule.

$$\begin{array}{c}
\ddot{\text{O}} : \\
\diagup \\
: \ddot{\text{Xe}} - \ddot{\text{O}} : \\
\diagdown \\
\ddot{\text{O}} :
\end{array}$$

c. Radon, a noble gas in Period 6, accepts the extra electrons.

$$: \ddot{\underset{..}{Cl}} - \dot{\underset{..}{Rn}} - \ddot{\underset{..}{Cl}} :$$

d. Beryllium is electron-deficient.

$$: \ddot{\underset{..}{Cl}} - Be - \ddot{\underset{..}{Cl}} :$$

e. Iodine exceeds the octet rule.

So far we have assumed that third-row and heavier atoms can exceed the octet rule by using their valence *d* orbitals to accommodate the extra electrons. However, recent calculations* indicate that because the 3*d* orbitals are so much higher in energy than the 3*s* and 3*p* orbitals for a given atom, it is not feasible to use them. Researchers argue that satisfying the octet rule is a high priority for molecules and that there are ways to describe the bonding in molecules like SF_6 and PCl_5 without formally exceeding the octet rule. One such explanation depends on a concept called *hyperconjugation,* which is explained in the special feature "Hyperconjugation—The Octet Rules" on p. 632.

The main point that should be made here is that chemists disagree on the best way to explain molecules such as SF_6 and PCl_5. Researchers continue to try to find the best answers.

Odd-Electron Molecules

In addition to the question about the use of *d* orbitals in third-row and heavier atoms, another problem for the simple LE model involves molecules with odd numbers of electrons. Although relatively few molecules formed from nonmetals contain odd numbers of electrons, there are some notable examples. One such molecule is nitric oxide (NO), which is formed when nitrogen and oxygen gases react at the high temperatures present in automobile engines. Nitric oxide is emitted into the air, where it reacts with oxygen to form gaseous nitrogen dioxide (NO_2), another odd-electron molecule.

Since the LE model is based on pairs of electrons, it does not handle odd-electron cases in a natural way, although Lewis structures are sometimes written for these species. To treat odd-electron molecules accurately, we need a more sophisticated model.

Formal Charge

Molecules or polyatomic ions often have many nonequivalent Lewis structures, all which obey the rules for writing Lewis structures. For example, as we will see in detail, the sulfate ion has a Lewis structure with all single bonds and several Lewis structures that contain double bonds. How do we decide which of the many possible Lewis structures best describes the actual bonding in sulfate? One method involves estimating the charge on each atom in the various possible Lewis structures and using these charges to select the most appropriate structure(s). We will see below how this is done, but first we must decide on a method to assign atomic charges in molecules.

*L. Suidan, J. K. Bodenhopp, E. D. Glendening, and F. Weinhold, *J. Chem. Ed.* **72** (1995): 583.

Chemical Insights Hyperconjugation—The Octet Rules

All our observations tell us that molecules such as SF_6 and PCl_5 are very stable, but what is the bonding like in these molecules? There are two extreme points of view: (1) The S and P atoms in these molecules exceed the octet rule, placing the extra electrons in $3d$ orbitals, and (2) the S and P atoms in these molecules obey the octet rule, resorting to hyperconjugation. *Hyperconjugation* involves binding n atoms to a central atom using fewer than n electron pairs around the central atom. To illustrate this model, consider SF_6. We know that there are six fluorine atoms around the central sulfur atom in this molecule. Can we explain the bonding without exceeding the octet rule? The answer is yes, by using Lewis structures such as the following:

Note that in each of these resonance structures (and the many other similar ones that can be drawn) the sulfur atom always has an octet of electrons around it. The "true" structure is a composite of these equivalent resonance structures. The overall bonding is described as a combination of covalent and ionic contributions. The covalent contribution to the bonding involves four electron pairs "spread out" over the six sulfur–fluorine bonds. The ionic contribution to the bonding arises as follows. Note that for each Lewis structure two of the fluorines have -1 formal charges and the sulfur has a $+2$ formal charge,

leading to ionic attractive forces. It is important to recall at this point that the description of the bonding in SF_6 by this model involves *all* the resonance structures similar to the one shown. Thus the F atoms are bound to the S atom by a combination of covalent bonding,

$$\frac{\text{4 electron-pair bonds}}{\text{6 S—F interactions}}$$

$$= \tfrac{2}{3} \text{ covalent bond per S—F interaction}$$

plus the ionic bonding described above.

A similar treatment can be given for PCl_5, using the following resonance structures,

each of which satisfies the octet rule.

Thus the use of hyperconjugation preserves the octet rule and does not require the central atom to use d orbitals, which this model's proponents argue are too high in energy to participate in the bonding of these types of molecules.

So honest disagreements exist among chemists as to the best Lewis structures for molecules that, at least at first glance, appear to exceed the octet rule. This uncertainty shows the limitations of the Lewis model with its localized electron pairs. Note, however, that even with its limitations, it is still very useful because of its simplicity. The ability to obtain a reasonable bonding picture with a "back-of-the-envelope" model has led to the enduring influence of the Lewis model.

Equivalent Lewis structures contain the same numbers of single and multiple bonds. For example, the resonance structures for O_3

$$\ddot{O} \qquad and \qquad \ddot{O}$$

are equivalent Lewis structures. These are equally important in describing the bonding in O_3. Non-equivalent Lewis structures contain different numbers of single and multiple bonds.

We will now consider a concept called *formal charge* for estimating the charge of an individual atom in a molecule. We will use the formal charges of atoms to evaluate Lewis structures. As we will see below, the **formal charge** of an atom in a molecule is *the difference between the number of valence electrons on the free atom and the number of valence electrons assigned to the atom in the molecule.*

Therefore, to determine the formal charge of a given atom in a molecule, we need to know two things:

1. the number of valence electrons on the free neutral atom (which has a charge of zero because the number of electrons equals the number of protons) and

2. the number of valence electrons "belonging" to a given atom in a molecule.

If an atom in a molecule has the same number of valence electrons as it does in the free state, the positive and negative charges just balance, and the atom has a formal charge of 0. If an atom has one more valence electron in a molecule than it has on a free atom, it has a formal charge of -1, and so on. Thus the formal charge on an atom in a molecule is defined as

$$Formal\ charge = \begin{pmatrix} number\ of\ valence \\ electrons\ on\ a\ free\ atom \end{pmatrix} - \begin{pmatrix} number\ of\ valence\ electrons \\ assigned\ to\ the\ atom\ in\ the \\ molecule \end{pmatrix}$$

To compute the formal charge of an atom in a molecule, we assign the valence electrons to the various atoms by making the following assumptions:

1. Lone pair electrons belong entirely to the atom in question.

2. Shared electrons are *divided equally* between the two sharing atoms.

Thus the number of valence electrons assigned to a given atom is calculated as follows:

$$(Valence\ electrons)_{assigned} = \begin{pmatrix} number\ of\ lone \\ pair\ electrons \end{pmatrix} + \tfrac{1}{2}\begin{pmatrix} number\ of \\ shared\ electrons \end{pmatrix}$$

We will illustrate the procedures for calculating formal charges by considering two of the possible Lewis structures for the sulfate ion, which has 32 valence electrons. For the Lewis structure

$$\left[\begin{array}{c} :\!\ddot{O}\!: \\ | \\ :\!\ddot{O}\!-\!S\!-\!\ddot{O}\!: \\ | \\ :\!\ddot{O}\!: \end{array} \right]^{2-}$$

each oxygen atom has six lone pair electrons and shares two electrons with the sulfur atom. Thus, according to the preceding assumptions, each oxygen is assigned seven valence electrons:

$$Valence\ electrons\ assigned\ to\ each\ oxygen = 6\ plus\ \tfrac{1}{2}(2) = 7$$

Lone pair electrons   Shared electrons

$$\text{Formal charge on oxygen} = 6 - 7 = -1$$

Valence
electrons on
a free O atom

Valence electrons
assigned to each O
in SO_4^{2-}

The formal charge on each oxygen is -1.

For the sulfur atom, there are no lone pair electrons, and eight electrons are shared with the oxygen atoms. Thus for sulfur,

$$\text{Valence electrons assigned to sulfur} = 0 + \tfrac{1}{2}(8) = 4$$

Lone
pair
electrons

Shared
electrons

$$\text{Formal charge on sulfur} = 6 - 4 = 2$$

Valence
electrons on
free S atom

Valence
electrons
assigned to S
in SO_4^{2-}

A second possible Lewis structure is

$$\left[\begin{array}{c} \ddot{\text{O}} \\ \| \\ :\ddot{\text{O}}-\text{S}-\ddot{\text{O}}: \\ \| \\ .\ddot{\text{O}}. \end{array} \right]^{2-}$$

In this case the formal charges are as calculated below.

For oxygen atoms with single bonds:

$$\text{Valence electrons assigned} = 6 + \tfrac{1}{2}(2) = 7$$

$$\text{Formal charge} = 6 - 7 = -1$$

For oxygen atoms with double bonds:

$$\text{Valence electrons assigned} = 4 + \tfrac{1}{2}(4) = 6$$

Each double bond
has 4 electrons

$$\text{Formal charge} = 6 - 6 = 0$$

For the sulfur atom:

$$\text{Valence electrons assigned} = 0 + \tfrac{1}{2}(12) = 6$$

$$\text{Formal charge} = 6 - 6 = 0$$

Now, having determined the formal charges for the various Lewis structures of the sulfate ion, can we use them to identify which of the resonance structures is closest to the actual electronic structure of the ion? There are two schools of thought on this issue. One position assumes that the atoms in a molecule or ion will try to achieve minimum formal charges. In other words, the assumption is that electrons will naturally flow from negatively charged parts of the molecule to positively charged parts, thus minimizing the charges on the atoms. From this point of view, the resonance structures of SO_4^{2-} with two double bonds (and minimum formal charges)

$$
\begin{bmatrix}
& \overset{\cdot\cdot}{\underset{(0)}{O}} & \\
& \overset{(0)}{\|} & \\
:\overset{\cdot\cdot}{\underset{(-1)}{O}}\!-\!\overset{|}{\underset{\underset{(0)}{\cdot\cdot}}{S}}\!=\!\overset{\cdot\cdot}{\underset{(-1)}{O}}: & \\
\end{bmatrix}^{2-}
\longleftrightarrow
\begin{bmatrix}
& \overset{\cdot\cdot}{\underset{(-1)}{O}}: & \\
& | & \\
:\overset{\cdot\cdot}{\underset{(0)}{O}}\!=\!\overset{(0)}{S}\!=\!\overset{\cdot\cdot}{\underset{(0)}{O}}: & \\
& \overset{|}{\underset{(-1)}{O}}: & \\
\end{bmatrix}^{2-}
$$

would be favored. Note that these structures exceed the octet rule, thus requiring the sulfur to use its $3d$ orbitals to hold electrons.

The other school of thought argues for the primacy of the octet rule and against the use of $3d$ orbitals. This position favors the single-bonded resonance structure of SO_4^{2-}

$$
\begin{bmatrix}
& \overset{\cdot\cdot}{\underset{(-1)}{O}}: & \\
& | & \\
:\overset{\cdot\cdot}{\underset{(-1)}{O}}\!-\!\overset{|}{\underset{(+2)}{S}}\!-\!\overset{\cdot\cdot}{\underset{(-1)}{O}}: & \\
& \overset{|}{\underset{(-1)}{O}}: & \\
\end{bmatrix}^{2-}
$$

with its octet of electrons around the sulfur and its high formal charges.

Which point of view is correct? What do we know about the sulfate ion that might help us decide? One pertinent fact is that the sulfur–oxygen bonds in SO_4^{2-} are known by experiment to be shorter than expected for normal single bonds. This would seem to favor the resonance structures with double bonds. However, one can also argue that the high formal charges on the atoms in the single-bonded structure cause ionic attractions that pull the atoms closer together. Thus both schools of thought can adequately explain the short sulfur–oxygen bond lengths.

At this point the dispute continues about which position is correct. For second-row elements where the octet rule is never exceeded, it seems clear that the "best" Lewis structures conform to the following rules:

1. Atoms in molecules try to achieve formal charges as close to zero as possible.

2. Any negative formal charges are expected to reside on the most electronegative atoms.

However, for molecules or ions containing third-row or heavier atoms, the situation is still unclear.

Rules Governing Formal Charge

1. To calculate the formal charge on an atom:
   - Take the sum of the lone pair electrons and one-half of the shared electrons. This is the number of valence electrons assigned to a given atom in the molecule.
   - Subtract the number of assigned electrons from the number of valence electrons on the free, neutral atom to obtain the formal charge.

2. The sum of the formal charges of all atoms in a given molecule or ion must equal the overall charge on that species.

3. If nonequivalent Lewis structures exist for a species containing second-row atoms, those with formal charges closest to zero and with any negative formal charges on the most electronegative atoms are considered to best describe the bonding in the molecule or ion.

EXAMPLE 13.10

Give possible Lewis structures for XeO_3, an explosive compound of xenon. Determine the formal charges of each atom in the various Lewis structures.

Solution For XeO_3 (26 valence electrons) we can draw the following possible Lewis structures (formal charges are indicated in parentheses):

The concept of formal charge is most often used to evaluate the importance of various Lewis structures for molecules that exhibit resonance. However, formal charge arguments also can be helpful in predicting which, among a given group of atoms, is the central atom in a simple molecule. For example, why is carbon dioxide O—C—O rather than C—O—O? Although this question can be pursued at many different levels of sophistication, the simplest approach involves considering the formal charges in the two possible structures. Note that in the Lewis structure given previously for carbon dioxide,

$$\ddot{\text{O}}=\text{C}=\ddot{\text{O}}$$

all atoms have formal charges of 0. However, if the atoms are arranged as follows,

$$\text{C—O—O}$$

all the Lewis structures give unreasonable formal charges. Consider the following possibilities, where the formal charges are listed below each atom:

$$:\text{C}\equiv\text{O}-\ddot{\text{O}}: \qquad :\ddot{\text{C}}=\text{O}=\ddot{\text{O}}: \qquad :\ddot{\text{C}}-\text{O}\equiv\text{O}:$$
$$-1 \quad +2 \quad -1 \qquad -2 \quad +2 \quad 0 \qquad -3 \quad +2 \quad +1$$

None of these Lewis structures (with their resulting formal charges) agrees with our observation that oxygen has a significantly greater electronegativity than carbon. That is, it doesn't make sense that a compound would contain a negatively charged carbon atom next to a positively charged oxygen atom.

As a final note, there are several cautions about formal charge to keep in mind. First, although formal charges are closer to actual atomic charges in molecules than are oxidation states, formal charges still are only estimates of charge—they should not be taken as actual atomic charges. Second, the evaluation of Lewis structures using formal charge ideas can lead to erroneous predictions.

In this same vein, note the difference between a "correct," or valid, Lewis structure and an electronic structure that accurately accounts for a molecule's observed properties. A valid Lewis structure is one that obeys the rules we have established for Lewis structures. However, this Lewis structure may or may not give an accurate picture of the molecule and its properties. Experiments must be carried out to make the final decisions on the correct description of the bonding in a molecule or polyatomic ion.*

---

*For a discussion of this issue, see Gordon H. Purser, *J. Chem. Ed.* **76** (1999): 1013.

13.13 | Molecular Structure: The VSEPR Model

The structures of molecules play a very important role in determining their chemical properties. As we will see later, structure is particularly important for biological molecules; a slight change in the structure of a large biomolecule can completely destroy its usefulness to a cell or may even change the cell from normal to cancerous.

Many accurate methods now exist for determining **molecular structure,** the three-dimensional arrangement of the atoms in a molecule. These methods must be used if precise information about structure is required. However, it is often useful to predict the approximate molecular structure of a molecule. In this section we consider a simple model that allows us to do this. This model, called the **valence shell electron-pair repulsion (VSEPR) model,** is useful in predicting the geometries of molecules formed from nonmetals. The main postulate of this model is that *the structure around a given atom is determined principally by minimizing electron-pair repulsions.* The idea is that the bonding and nonbonding pairs around a given atom should be positioned as far apart as possible. To see how this model works, we will first consider the molecule $BeCl_2$, which has the Lewis structure

$$:\overset{..}{Cl}-Be-\overset{..}{Cl}:$$

Note that there are two pairs of electrons around the beryllium atom. What arrangement of these electron pairs allows them to be as far apart as possible to minimize the repulsions? Clearly, the best arrangement places the pairs on opposite sides of the beryllium atom at 180 degrees:

This is the maximum possible separation for two electron pairs. Once we have determined the optimal arrangement of the electron pairs around the central atom, we can specify the molecular structure of $BeCl_2$ — that is, the positions of the atoms. Since each electron pair on beryllium is shared with a chlorine atom, the molecule has a **linear structure** with a bond angle of 180 degrees:

Cl—Be—Cl
180°

Next, let's consider BF_3, which has the Lewis structure

$$:\overset{..}{\underset{..}{F}}-\overset{\overset{..}{F}:}{\underset{|}{B}}-\overset{..}{\underset{..}{F}}:$$

Here the boron atom is surrounded by three pairs of electrons. What arrangement will minimize the repulsions? The electron pairs are farthest apart at angles of 120 degrees:

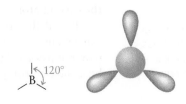

The origin of the "repulsions" among electron pairs probably results more from the operation of the Pauli exclusion principle than from electrostatic effects, but we will not be concerned with that in this text.

Since each electron pair is shared with a fluorine atom, the molecular structure is

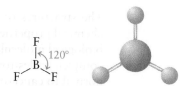

This is a planar (flat) and triangular molecule, which is commonly described as **trigonal planar.**

Next, let's consider the methane molecule, which has the Lewis structure

$$H-\underset{\underset{H}{|}}{\overset{\overset{H}{|}}{C}}-H$$

There are four pairs of electrons around the central carbon atom. What arrangement of these electron pairs best minimizes the repulsions? First, let's try a square planar arrangement:

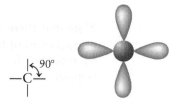

The carbon atom and the electron pairs are centered in the plane of the paper, and the angles between the pairs are all 90 degrees.

Is there another arrangement with angles greater than 90 degrees that would put the electron pairs even farther away from each other? The answer is yes. The **tetrahedral arrangement** has angles of 109.5 degrees:

It can be shown that this is the maximum possible separation of four pairs around a given atom. This means that *whenever four pairs of electrons are present around an atom, they should always be arranged tetrahedrally.*

Now that we have obtained the electron-pair arrangement that gives the least repulsions, we can determine the positions of the atoms and thus the molecular structure of CH_4. In methane each of the four electron pairs is shared between the carbon atom and a hydrogen atom. Thus the hydrogen atoms are placed as shown in Fig. 13.15, giving the molecule a tetrahedral structure with the carbon atom at the center.

Recall that the fundamental idea of the VSEPR model is to find the arrangement of electron pairs around the central atom that minimizes the electron repulsions. Then we can determine the molecular structure from knowing how the electron pairs are shared with the peripheral atoms.

When four uniform balloons are tied together, they naturally form a tetrahedral shape.

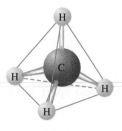

Figure 13.15
The molecular structure of methane. The tetrahedral arrangement of electron pairs produces a tetrahedral arrangement of hydrogen atoms.

Steps for Using the VSEPR Model

1 Draw the Lewis structure for the molecule.

2 Count the electron pairs around the central atom, and arrange them in the way that minimizes repulsions (that is, put the pairs as far apart as possible).

3 Determine the positions of the atoms from the ways the electron pairs are shared.

4 Name the molecular structure from the positions of the *atoms*.

We will now predict the structure of ammonia (NH_3) using this approach.

■ **Draw the Lewis structure.**

$$H-\overset{\displaystyle ..}{N}-H$$
$$|$$
$$H$$

■ **Count the pairs of electrons, and arrange them to minimize repulsions.**

The NH_3 molecule has four pairs of electrons: three bonding pairs and one nonbonding pair. From the discussion of the methane molecule, we know that the best arrangement of four electron pairs is a tetrahedral array, as shown in Fig. 13.16(a).

■ **Determine the positions of the atoms.**

The three H atoms share electron pairs, as shown in Fig. 13.16(b).

■ **Name the molecular structure.**

It is very important to recognize that the *name* of the molecular structure is always based on the *positions of the atoms*. The placement of the electron pairs determines the structure, but the name is based on the positions of the atoms. Thus it is incorrect to say that the NH_3 molecule is tetrahedral. It has a tetrahedral arrangement of electron pairs but not a tetrahedral arrangement of atoms. The molecular structure of ammonia is a **trigonal pyramid** (one triangular side is different from the other three), rather than a tetrahedron, as shown in Fig. 13.16(c).

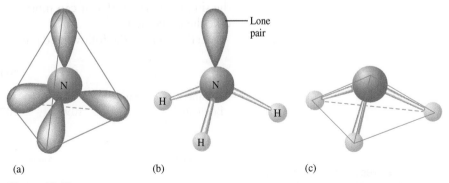

(a)   (b)   (c)

Figure 13.16
(a) The tetrahedral arrangement of electron pairs around the nitrogen atom in the ammonia molecule. (b) Three of the electron pairs around nitrogen are shared with hydrogen atoms, as shown, and the fourth is a lone pair. Although the arrangement of *electron pairs* is tetrahedral, as in the methane molecule, the hydrogen atoms in the ammonia molecule occupy only three corners of the tetrahedron. A lone pair occupies the fourth corner. (c) Note that molecular geometry is trigonal pyramidal, not tetrahedral.

Figure 13.17
(a) The tetrahedral arrangement of the four electron pairs around oxygen in the water molecule. (b) Two of the electron pairs are shared between oxygen and the hydrogen atoms, and two are lone pairs. (c) The V-shaped molecular structure of the water molecule.

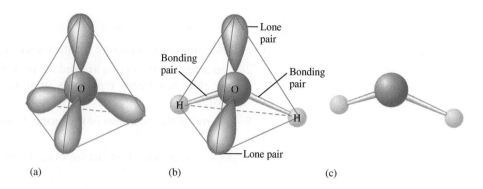

(a)　　　　(b)　　　　(c)

EXAMPLE 13.11

Describe the molecular structure of the water molecule.

Solution The Lewis structure for water is

$$H—\overset{..}{\underset{..}{O}}—H$$

There are four pairs of electrons: two bonding pairs and two nonbonding pairs. To minimize repulsions, these are best arranged in a tetrahedral array, as shown in Fig. 13.17(a). Although H_2O has a tetrahedral arrangement of electron pairs, it is not a tetrahedral molecule. The atoms in the H_2O molecule form a V-shape, as shown in Fig. 13.17(b) and (c).

From Example 13.11 we see that the H_2O molecule is V-shaped, or bent, because of the presence of the lone pairs. If no lone pairs were present, the molecule would be linear, the polar bonds would cancel, and the molecule would have no dipole moment. This would make water very different from the polar substance so familiar to us.

From the previous discussion, we would predict that the H—X—H bond angle (where X is the central atom) in CH_4, NH_3, and H_2O should be the tetrahedral angle (109.5 degrees). Experiments, however, show that the actual bond angles are those given in Fig. 13.18. What significance do these results have for the VSEPR model? One possible point of view is that the observed angles are close enough to the tetrahedral angle to be satisfactory. The opposite view is that the deviations are significant enough to require modification of the simple model so that it can more accurately handle similar cases. We will take the latter view.

Let's examine the following data:

	CH_4	NH_3	H_2O
Number of lone pairs	0	1	2
Bond angle	109.5°	107°	104.5°

Figure 13.18
The bond angles in the CH_4, NH_3, and H_2O molecules. Note that the bond angle between bonding pairs decreases as the number of lone pairs increases.

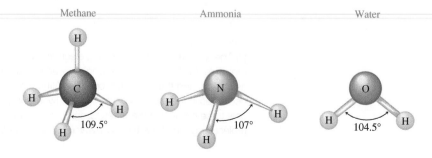

Methane　　　　Ammonia　　　　Water

109.5°　　　　107°　　　　104.5°

(a)

(b)

Figure 13.19
(a) In a bonding pair of electrons, the electrons are shared by two nuclei.
(b) In a lone pair, since both electrons must be close to a single nucleus, they tend to take up more of the space around that atom.

One interpretation of the trend observed here is that lone pairs require more space than bonding pairs; in other words, as the number of lone pairs increases, the bonding pairs are increasingly squeezed together.

This interpretation seems to make physical sense if we think in the following terms: A bonding pair is shared between two nuclei, and the electrons can be close to either nucleus. Therefore they are relatively confined between the two nuclei. A lone pair is localized on only one nucleus, so both electrons are close to that nucleus only, as shown schematically in Fig. 13.19. These pictures help us to understand why a lone pair may require more space near an atom than a bonding pair.

As a result of these observations, we make the following addition to the original postulate of the VSEPR model: *Lone pairs require more room than bonding pairs and tend to compress the angles between the bonding pairs.*

So far we have considered cases with two, three, and four electron pairs around the central atom. These are summarized in Table 13.8. Table 13.9 summarizes the structures possible for molecules in which there are four electron pairs around the central atom with various numbers of atoms bonded to it. Note that molecules with four pairs of electrons around the central atom can be tetrahedral (AB$_4$), trigonal pyramidal (AB$_3$), and V-shaped (AB$_2$). For five pairs

Table 13.8

Arrangements of Electron Pairs Around an Atom Yielding Minimum Repulsion

Number of Electron Pairs	Arrangement of Electron Pairs		Example
2	Linear	180°	
3	Trigonal planar	120°	
4	Tetrahedral	109.5°	
5	Trigonal bipyramidal	90° 120°	
6	Octahedral	90° 90°	

Table 13.9

Structures of Molecules That Have Four Electron Pairs Around the Central Atom

Electron-Pair Arrangement	Molecular Structure
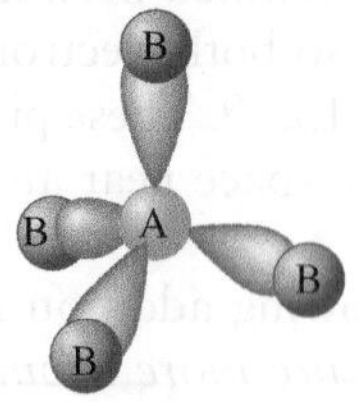	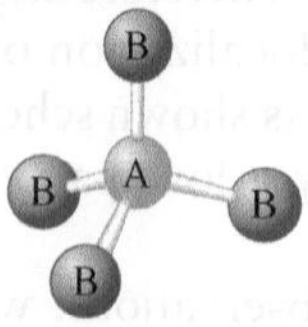 Tetrahedral
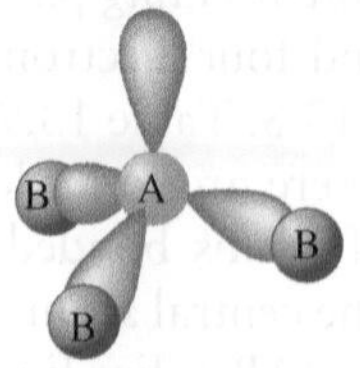	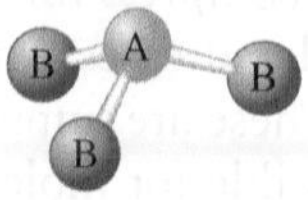 Trigonal pyramid
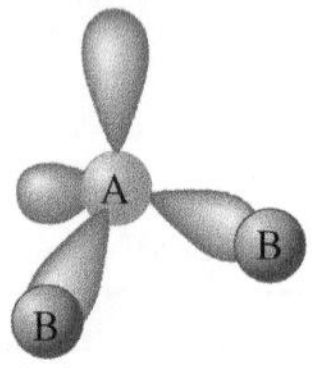	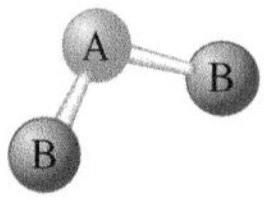 V-shaped (bent)

Table 13.10

Structures of Molecules with Five Electron Pairs Around the Central Atom

Electron-Pair Arrangement	Molecular Structure
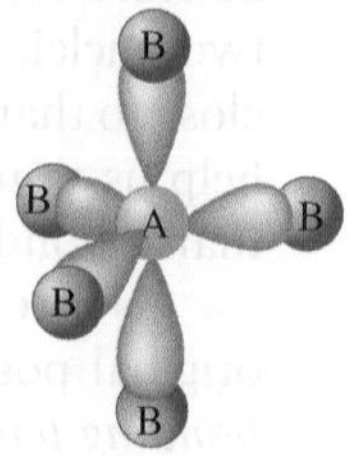	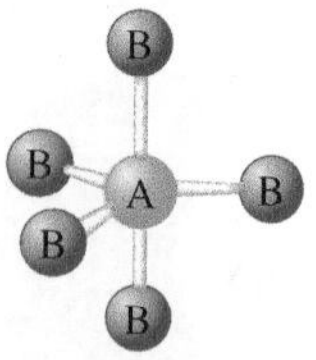 Trigonal bipyramidal
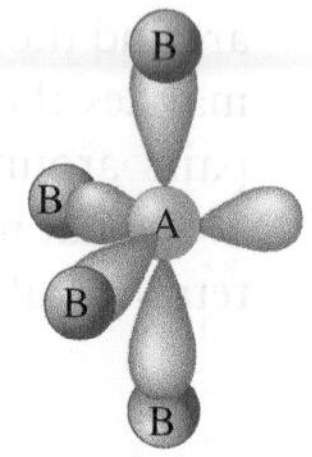	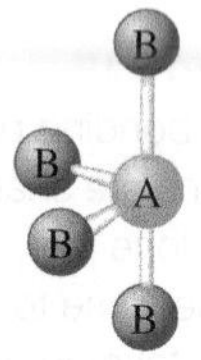 See-saw
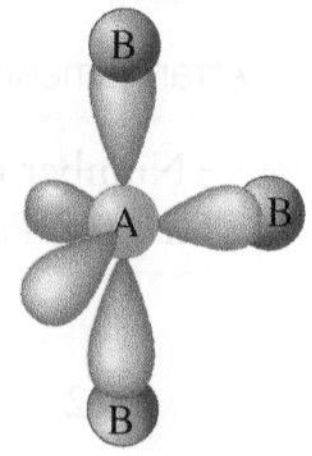	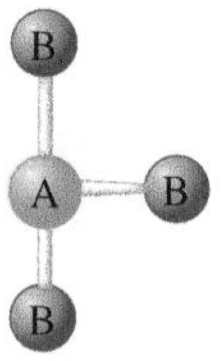 T-shaped
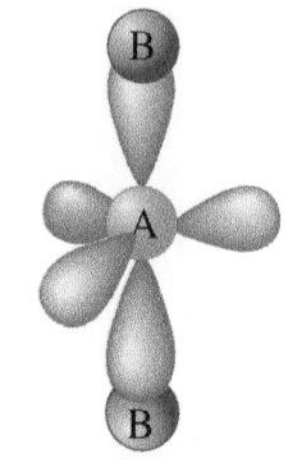	 Linear

of electrons, there are several possible electron-pair arrangements. The one that produces minimum repulsion is a **trigonal bipyramid.** Note from Table 13.8 that this arrangement has two different angles, 90 degrees and 120 degrees. As the name suggests, the structure formed by this arrangement of pairs consists of two trigonal-based pyramids that share a common base. Table 13.10 summarizes the structures possible for molecules in which there are five electron pairs around the central atom with various numbers of atoms bonded to it. Note that molecules with five pairs of electrons around the central atom can be trigonal bipyramidal (AB_5), see-saw (AB_4), T-shaped (AB_3), and linear (AB_2). Six pairs of electrons can best be arranged around a given atom to form an **octahedral structure** with 90-degree angles, as shown in Table 13.8.

To use the VSEPR model to determine the geometric structures of molecules, you should memorize the relationships between the number of electron pairs and their best arrangement.

When phosphorus reacts with excess chlorine gas, the compound phosphorus pentachloride (PCl_5) is formed. In the gaseous and liquid states, this substance consists of PCl_5 molecules, but in the solid state, it consists of a 1:1 mixture of PCl_4^+ and PCl_6^- ions. Predict the geometric structures of PCl_5, PCl_4^+, and PCl_6^-.

Solution The traditional Lewis structure for PCl_5 is shown in the margin. Five pairs of electrons around the phosphorus atom require a trigonal bipyramidal arrangement (see Table 13.8). When the chlorine atoms are included, a trigonal bipyramidal molecule results.

Lewis structure for PCl_5

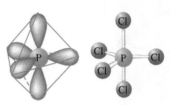

The Lewis structure for the PCl_4^+ ion [$5 + 4(7) - 1 = 32$ valence electrons] is shown in the margin. There are four pairs of electrons surrounding the phosphorus atom in the PCl_4^+ ion. This requires a tetrahedral arrangement of the pairs, as shown in the figure in the margin. Since each pair is shared with a chlorine atom, a tetrahedral PCl_4^+ cation results.

The traditional Lewis structure for PCl_6^- [$5 + 6(7) + 1 = 48$ valence electrons] is

Lewis structure for PCl_4^+

Since phosphorus is surrounded by six pairs of electrons, an octahedral arrangement is required to minimize repulsions, as shown below on the left. Since each electron pair is shared with a chlorine atom, an octahedral PCl_6^- anion is predicted.

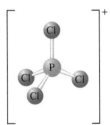

Tetrahedral PCl_4^+ cation

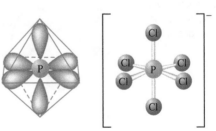

Because the noble gases have filled *s* and *p* valence orbitals, they are not expected to be chemically reactive. In fact, for many years these elements were called *inert gases* because of this supposed inability to form any compounds. However, in the early 1960s, several compounds of krypton, xenon, and radon were synthesized. For example, a team at the Argonne National Laboratory produced the stable colorless compound xenon tetrafluoride (XeF_4). Predict its structure and determine whether it has a dipole moment.

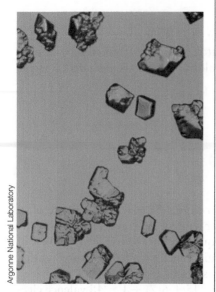

Xenon tetrafluoride crystals.

Solution   The traditional Lewis structure for XeF_4 is

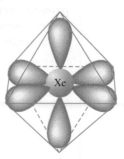

The xenon atom in this molecule is surrounded by six pairs of electrons, requiring an octahedral arrangement:

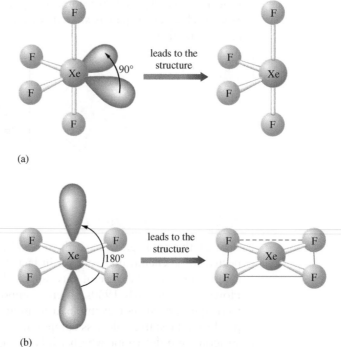

The structure predicted for this molecule depends on how the lone pairs and bonding pairs are arranged. Consider the two possibilities shown in Fig. 13.20. The bonding pairs are indicated by the presence of fluorine atoms. Since the structure predicted differs in the two cases, we must decide which of these arrangements is preferable. The key is to look at the lone pairs. In the structure in part (a), the lone pair–lone pair angle is 90 degrees; in the structure in part (b), the lone pairs are separated by 180 degrees. Since lone pairs require more room than bonding pairs, a structure with two lone pairs at 90 degrees is unfavorable. Thus the arrangement in Fig. 13.20(b) is preferred, and the molecular structure is predicted to be square planar. Note that this molecule is *not* described as being octahedral. There is an *octahedral arrangement of electron pairs,* but the *atoms* form a **square planar** structure.

Figure 13.20
Possible electron-pair arrangement for XeF_4. Since arrangement (a) has lone pairs 90 degrees apart, it is less favorable than arrangement (b), where the lone pairs are 180 degrees apart.

Although each Xe—F bond is polar (fluorine has a greater electronegativity than xenon), the square planar arrangement of these bonds causes the polarities to cancel.

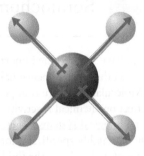

Thus XeF_4 has no dipole moment.

We can further illustrate the use of the VSEPR model for molecules or ions with lone pairs by considering the triiodide ion (I_3^-). The Lewis structure for I_3^- is

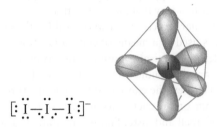

The central iodine atom has five pairs around it, requiring a trigonal bipyramidal arrangement. Several possible arrangements of the lone pairs are shown in Fig. 13.21. Note that structures (a) and (b) have lone pairs at 90 degrees, whereas in (c) all lone pairs are at 120 degrees. Thus structure (c) is preferred. The resulting molecular structure for I_3^- is linear.

$$[I—I—I]^-$$

The VSEPR Model and Multiple Bonds

So far in our treatment of the VSEPR model, we have not considered any molecules with multiple bonds. To see how these molecules are handled by this model, let's consider the NO_3^- ion, which requires three resonance structures to describe its electronic structure:

Figure 13.21

Three possible arrangements of the electron pairs in the I_3^- ion. Arrangement (c) is preferred because there are no 90-degree lone pair–lone pair interactions.

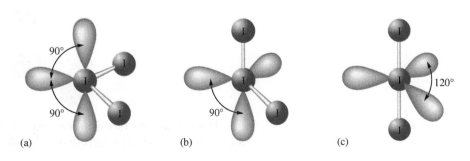

(a)   (b)   (c)

Chemical Insights

Chemical Structure and Communication: Semiochemicals

In this chapter we have stressed the importance of being able to predict the three-dimensional structure of a molecule. Molecular structure is important because of its effect on chemical reactivity. This is especially true in biological systems, where reactions must be efficient and highly specific. Among the hundreds of types of molecules in the fluids of a typical biological system, the appropriate reactants must find and react only with each other—they must be very discriminating. This specificity depends primarily on structure. The molecules are constructed so that only the appropriate partners can approach each other in a way that allows reaction.

Molecular structure is also central for those molecules used as a means of communication. Examples of chemical communication occurring in humans are the conduction of nerve impulses across synapses, the control of the manufacture and storage of key chemicals in cells, and the senses of smell and taste. Plants and animals also use chemical communication. For example, ants lay down a chemical trail so that other ants can find a certain food supply. Ants also warn their fellow workers of approaching danger by emitting certain chemicals.

Molecules convey messages by fitting into appropriate receptor sites in a very specific way, which is determined by their structure. When a molecule occupies a receptor site, chemical processes that produce the appropriate response are stimulated. Sometimes receptors can be fooled, as in the use of artificial sweeteners—molecules fit the sites on the taste buds that stimulate a "sweet" response in the brain, but they are not metabolized in the same way as natural sugars. Similar decep-

tion is useful in insect control. If an area is sprayed with synthetic female sex attractant molecules, the males of that species become so confused that mating does not occur.

A *semiochemical* is a molecule that delivers a message between members of the same or different species of plant or animal. There are three groups of these chemical messengers: allomones, kairomones, and pheromones. Each is of great ecological importance.

An *allomone* is defined as a chemical that gives adaptive advantage to the producer. For example, leaves of the black walnut tree contain an herbicide, juglone, that appears after the leaves fall to the ground. Juglone is not toxic to grass or certain grains, but it is effective against plants such as apple trees that would compete for the available water and food supplies.

Antibiotics are also allomones, since the microorganisms produce them to inhibit other species from growing near them.

Many plants produce bad-tasting chemicals to protect themselves from plant-eating insects and animals. The familiar compound nicotine deters animals from eating the tobacco plant. The millipede sends an unmistakable "back off" message by squirting a predator with benzaldehyde and hydrogen cyanide.

Defense is not the only use of allomones, however. Flowers use scent to attract pollinating insects. Honeybees, for instance, are guided to alfalfa flowers by a series of sweet-scented compounds.

Kairomones are chemical messengers that bring advantageous news to the receiver. For example,

The NO_3^- ion is known to be planar with 120-degree bond angles:

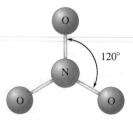

This planar structure is the one expected for three pairs of electrons around a central atom, which means that *a double bond should be counted as one ef-*

the floral scents are kairomones from the honey-bees' viewpoint. Many predators are guided by kairomones emitted by their food. For example, apple skins exude a chemical that attracts the codling moth larva. In some cases kairomones help the underdog. Certain marine mollusks can pick up the "scent" of their predators, the sea stars, and make their escape.

Pheromones are chemicals that affect receptors of the same species as the donor. That is, they are specific within a species. *Releaser pheromones* cause an immediate reaction in the receptor, whereas *primer pheromones* cause long-term effects. Examples of releaser pheromones are the sex attractants of insects, generated in some species by the males and in others by the females. Sex pheromones have also been found in plants and mammals.

Alarm pheromones are highly volatile compounds (ones easily changed to a gas) released to warn of danger. Honeybees produce isoamyl acetate ($C_7H_{14}O_2$) in their sting glands. Because of its high volatility, this compound does not linger after the state of alert is over. Social behavior in insects is characterized by the use of *trail pheromones,* which are used to indicate a food source. Social insects such as bees, ants, wasps, and termites use these substances. Since trail pheromones are less volatile compounds, the indicators persist for some time.

Primer pheromones, which cause long-term behavioral changes, are harder to isolate and identify. One example, however, is the "queen substance" produced by queen honeybees. All the eggs in a colony are laid by one queen bee. If she is

Scott Camazine/Photo Researchers

Honeybees are attracted to these alfalfa flowers by sweet-scented compounds the flowers emit.

removed from the hive or dies, the worker bees are activated by the absence of the queen substance and begin to feed royal jelly to bee larvae to raise a new queen. The queen substance also prevents the development of the workers' ovaries so that only the queen herself can produce eggs.

Many studies of insect pheromones are now under way in the hope that they will provide a method of controlling insects that is more efficient and safer than the current chemical pesticides.

fective pair in using the VSEPR model. This makes sense because the two pairs of electrons involved in the double bond are *not* independent pairs. Both of the electron pairs must be in the space between the nuclei of the two atoms to form the double bond. In other words, the double bond acts as one center of electron density to repel the other pairs of electrons. The same holds true for triple bonds. This leads us to another general rule: *For the VSEPR model, multiple bonds count as one effective electron pair.*

The molecular structure of nitrate also illustrates one more important point: *When a molecule exhibits resonance, any one of the resonance structures can be used to predict the molecular structure using the VSEPR model.* These rules are illustrated in Example 13.14.

Chemical Insights   Smelling and Tasting Electronically

The human nose and tongue are excellent quality-control sensors. For example, we can tell whether food is spoiled by its disagreeable odor and taste. Because it's impractical to use humans as sensors in industrial settings, several companies are now developing electronic noses.

Cyrano Sciences has developed a hand-held electronic nose (called a Cyranose) that can identify specific odors by the "smell print" they create in the 32 sensors of the instrument. Each sensor is composed of conductive carbon black combined with a nonconducting polymer. In the presence of the chemicals associated with an odor, the polymer swells, thereby disrupting the conductive pathways and increasing the resistance. The device is "trained" to detect particular odors by subjecting it to known sources of those odors and storing the electrical signals in the machine's database. When the "nose" is then exposed to an odor in an industrial setting, it identifies the odor by comparing the input signals with its database. The Cyranose is used in the food and beverage industries to monitor the condition of raw materials and the quality of the finished product. In the chemical industry, it is used to pinpoint leaks and to identify manufacturing odors.

Other artificial noses are now being developed that can furnish early detection of diseases. Various researchers are now developing "noses" that can detect different types of bacteria and can provide early diagnosis of lung cancer.

A company called Alpha M.O.S. has recently introduced what it calls the "world's first commercial electronic tongue," a device used to identify various tastes associated with liquids. Like the Cyranose, the electronic tongue must first be "trained" by exposing its probe to known liquid characteristics to record their "fingerprints." Once programmed, the "tongue" can recognize tastes such as sweetness, sourness, bitterness, and salti-

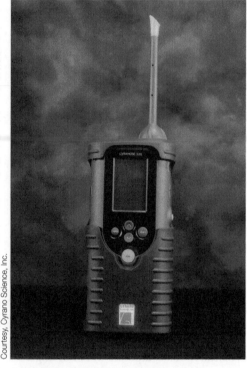

Courtesy, Cyrano Science, Inc.

A Cyranose sensor (an "electronic nose").

ness and can detect rancidity and various types of contamination. The electronic tongue is of particular interest to the pharmaceutical industry, where it is hoped it can reduce the need for human tasting panels.

Artificial tasters are also being developed for sensing diseases. For example, Eric V. Anslyn and his coworkers at the University of Texas at Austin have reported a system that can recognize the "taste of heart disease" by analyzing the "taste" of blood samples.

Humans and animals are still the best "smellers" and tasters, but computers are rapidly catching up.

⊙WL INTERACTIVE EXAMPLE 13.14

Predict the molecular structure of the sulfur dioxide molecule. Is this molecule expected to have a dipole moment?

Solution First, we must determine the Lewis structure for the SO_2 molecule, which has 18 valence electrons. The expected resonance structures are

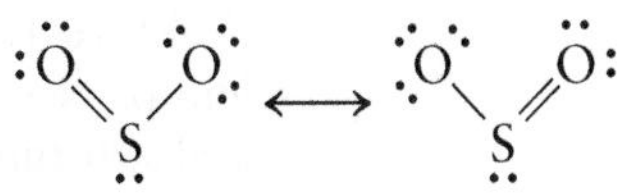

To determine the molecular structure, we must count the electron pairs around the sulfur atom. In each resonance structure, the sulfur has one lone pair, one pair in a single bond, and one double bond. Counting the double bond as one pair yields three effective pairs around the sulfur. According to Table 13.8, a trigonal planar arrangement is required, yielding a V-shaped molecule:

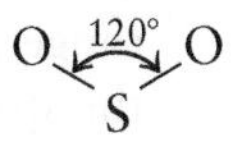

Thus the structure of the SO_2 molecule is expected to be V-shaped with a 120-degree bond angle. The molecule has a dipole moment directed as shown:

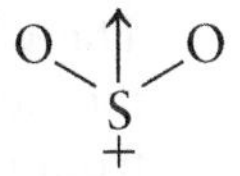

Since the molecule is V-shaped, the polar bonds do not cancel.

It should be noted at this point that lone pairs oriented at least 120 degrees from other pairs do not produce significant distortions of bond angles. For example, the angle in the SO_2 molecule is actually quite close to 120 degrees. We will follow the general principle that *an angle of 120 degrees provides lone pairs with enough space so that distortions do not occur. Angles less than 120 degrees are distorted when lone pairs are present.*

Molecules Containing No Single Central Atom

So far we have considered molecules consisting of one central atom surrounded by other atoms. The VSEPR model can be readily extended to more complicated molecules, such as methanol (CH_3OH). This molecule is represented by the following Lewis structure:

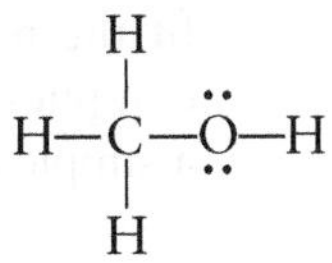

The VSEPR Model

The following rules are helpful in using the VSEPR model to predict molecular structure.

1. Determine the Lewis structure(s) for the molecule.
2. For molecules with resonance structures, use any of the structures to predict the molecular structure.
3. Sum the electron pairs around the central atom.

(continued)

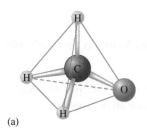

(a)

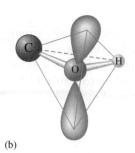

(b)

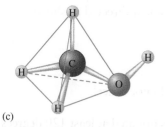

(c)

Figure 13.22
The molecular structure of methanol.
(a) The arrangement of electron pairs and atoms around the carbon atom.
(b) The arrangement of bonding and lone pairs around the oxygen atom.
(c) The molecular structure.

The VSEPR Model (Continued)

4. When counting pairs, count each multiple bond as a single effective pair.

5. Determine the arrangement of the pairs that minimizes electron-pair repulsions. These arrangements are shown in Table 13.8.

6. Lone pairs require more space than bonding pairs. Choose an arrangement that gives the lone pairs as much room as possible, although it appears that an angle of at least 120 degrees between lone pairs provides enough space. Recognize that lone pairs at angles less than 120 degrees may produce distortions from the idealized structure.

The molecular structure can be predicted from the arrangement of pairs around the carbon and oxygen atoms. Note that there are four pairs of electrons around the carbon, which calls for a tetrahedral arrangement, as shown in Fig. 13.22(a). The oxygen also has four pairs, requiring a tetrahedral arrangement. However, in this case the tetrahedron will be slightly distorted by the space requirements of the lone pairs [Fig. 13.22(b)]. The overall geometric arrangement for the molecule is shown in Fig. 13.22(c).

The VSEPR Model—How Well Does It Work?

The VSEPR model is very simple. There are only a few rules to remember, yet the model correctly predicts the molecular structures of most molecules formed from nonmetallic elements. Molecules of any size can be treated by applying the VSEPR model to each appropriate atom (those bonded to at least two other atoms) in the molecule. Thus we can use this model to predict the structures of molecules with hundreds of atoms. It does, however, fail in a few instances. For example, phosphine (PH_3), which has a Lewis structure analogous to that of ammonia,

$$H\!-\!\overset{\cdot\cdot}{P}\!-\!H \qquad H\!-\!\overset{\cdot\cdot}{N}\!-\!H$$
$$\quad\ \ | \qquad\qquad\quad |$$
$$\quad\ \ H \qquad\qquad\quad H$$

would be predicted to have a molecular structure similar to that for NH_3 with bond angles of about 107 degrees. However, the bond angles of phosphine are actually 94 degrees. There are ways of explaining this structure, but more rules have to be added to the model.

This example again illustrates the point that simple models will certainly have exceptions. In introductory chemistry we want to use simple models that fit the majority of cases; we are willing to accept a few failures rather than complicate the model. The amazing thing about the VSEPR model is that such a simple model correctly predicts the structures of so many molecules.

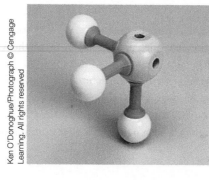

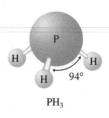

PH_3

Key Terms

Section 13.1
bond energy
ionic compound
Coulomb's law
bond length
covalent bonding
polar covalent bond

Section 13.2
electronegativity

Section 13.3
dipole moment

Section 13.4
isoelectronic ions

Section 13.5
lattice energy

Section 13.8
single bond
double bond
triple bond

Section 13.9
localized electron (LE) model
lone pair
bonding pair

Section 13.10
Lewis structure
duet rule
octet rule

Section 13.11
resonance
resonance structure

Section 13.12
formal charge

Section 13.13
molecular structure
valence shell electron-pair
   repulsion (VSEPR) model
linear structure
trigonal planar
tetrahedral arrangement
trigonal pyramid
trigonal bipyramid
octahedral structure
square planar

For Review

⊌WL and 𝗀ₒ Chemistry

Sign in at **www.cengage.com/owl** to:
- View tutorials and simulations, develop problem-solving skills, and complete online homework assigned by your professor.
- Download Go Chemistry mini lecture modules for quick review and exam prep from OWL (or purchase them at **www.cengagebrain.com**)

Chemical bonds
- Hold groups of atoms together
- Occur when a group of atoms can lower its total energy by aggregating
- Types of chemical bonds
  - Ionic: electrons are transferred to form ions
  - Covalent: equal sharing of electrons
  - Polar covalent: unequal electron sharing
- Percent ionic character of a bond X—Y

$$\frac{\text{Measured dipole moment of X—Y}}{\text{Calculated dipole moment for X}^+ \text{ Y}^-} \times 100\%$$

- Electronegativity: the relative ability of an atom to attract shared electrons
  - The polarity of a bond depends on the electronegativity difference of the bonded atoms
- The spatial arrangement of polar bonds in a molecule determines whether the molecule has a dipole moment

Ionic bonding
- An ion has a different size than its parent atom
  - An anion is larger than its parent ion
  - A cation is smaller than its parent atom
- Lattice energy: the change in energy when ions are packed together to form an ionic solid

Bond energy
- The energy necessary to break a covalent bond
- Increases as the number of shared pairs increases
- Can be used to estimate the energy change for a chemical reaction

Lewis structures
- Show how the valence electron pairs are arranged among the atoms in a molecule or polyatomic ion
- Stable molecules usually contain atoms that have their valence orbitals filled
  - Leads to a duet rule for hydrogen
  - Leads to an octet rule for second-row elements
  - The atoms of elements in the third row and beyond can exceed the octet rule
- Several equivalent Lewis structures can be drawn for some molecules, a concept called resonance
- When several nonequivalent Lewis structures can be drawn for a molecule, formal charge is often used to choose the most appropriate structure(s)

VSEPR model
- Based on the idea that electron pairs will be arranged around a central atom in a way that minimizes the electron repulsions
- Can be used to predict the geometric structure of most molecules

Discussion Questions

These questions are designed to be considered by groups of students in class. Often these questions work well for introducing a particular topic in class.

1. Explain the electronegativity trends across a row and down a column of the periodic table. Compare these trends with those of ionization energy and atomic radii. How are they all related?

2. The ionic compound AB is formed. The charges on the ions may be +1, −1; +2, −2; +3, −3; or even larger. What are the factors that determine the charge for an ion in an ionic compound?

3. Using only the periodic table, predict the most stable ion for Na, Mg, Al, S, Cl, K, Ca, and Ga. Arrange these from largest to smallest radius, and explain why the radius varies as it does. Compare your predictions with Fig. 13.8.

4. The bond energy for the C—H bond is about 413 kJ/mol in CH_4 but 380 kJ/mol in $CHBr_3$. Although these values are relatively close in magnitude, they are different. Explain why they are different. Does the fact that the C—H bond energy in $CHBr_3$ is lower make any sense? Why?

5. Consider the following statement: "Because oxygen seems to prefer a negative two charge, the second electron affinity is more negative than the first." Indicate everything that is correct in this statement. Indicate everything that is incorrect. Correct the incorrect information, and explain.

6. Which has the greater bond lengths: NO_2^- or NO_3^-? Explain.

7. The following ions are best described with resonance structures. Draw the resonance structures, and using formal charge arguments, predict the "best" Lewis structure for each ion.
   a. NCO^-
   b. CNO^-

8. Would you expect the electronegativity of titanium to be the same in the species Ti, Ti^{2+}, Ti^{3+}, and Ti^{4+}? Explain.

9. The second electron affinity values for both oxygen and sulfur are unfavorable (endothermic). Explain.

10. Arrange the following molecules from most to least polar, and explain your order: CH_4, CF_2Cl_2, CF_2H_2, CCl_4, and CCl_2H_2.

Exercises

OWL Interactive versions of these problems may be assigned in OWL.

A blue exercise number indicates that the answer to that exercise appears at the back of this book and a solution appears in the *Solutions Guide*.

Chemical Bonds and Electronegativity

11. Distinguish between the terms *electronegativity* and *electron affinity*, *covalent bond* and *ionic bond*, and *pure covalent bond* and *polar covalent bond*. Characterize the types of bonds in terms of electronegativity difference. Energetically, why do ionic and covalent bonds form?

12. The following electrostatic potential diagrams represent H_2, HCl, or NaCl. Label each, and explain your choices.

(a)

(c)

(b)

13. An alternative definition of electronegativity is

$$\text{Electronegativity} = \text{constant (I.E.} - \text{E.A.)}$$

where I.E. is the ionization energy and E.A. is the electron affinity using the sign conventions of this book. Use data in Chapter 12 to calculate the (I.E. − E.A.) term for F, Cl, Br, and I. Do these values show the same trend as the electronegativity values given in this chapter? The first ionization energies of the halogens are 1678, 1255, 1138, and 1007 kJ/mol, respectively. (*Hint:* Choose a constant so that the electronegativity of fluorine equals 4.0. Using this constant, calculate relative electronegativities for the other halogens and compare to values given in the text.)

14. Use Coulomb's law,

$$V = \frac{Q_1 Q_2}{4\pi\epsilon_0 r} = 2.31 \times 10^{-19} \text{ J nm}\left(\frac{Q_1 Q_2}{r}\right)$$

to calculate the energy of interaction for the following two arrangements of charges, each having a magnitude equal to the electron charge.

a. 1×10^{-10} m 1×10^{-10} m
   ⊕ ⟷ ⊖ ← ∞ → ⊕ ⟷ ⊖
   (+1)   (−1)   (+1)   (−1)

b. 1×10^{-10} m   (−1) 1×10^{-10} m

   (+1)   (+1)

   1×10^{-10} m   (−1) 1×10^{-10} m

15. Without using Fig. 13.3, predict the order of increasing electronegativity in each of the following groups of elements.
    a. C, N, O
    b. S, Se, Cl
    c. Si, Ge, Sn
    d. Tl, S, Ge
    e. Na, K, Rb
    f. B, O, Ga

16. Without using Fig. 13.3, predict which bond in each of the following groups is the most polar.
    a. C—F, Si—F, Ge—F
    b. P—Cl, S—Cl
    c. S—F, S—Cl, S—Br
    d. Ti—Cl, Si—Cl, Ge—Cl
    e. C—H, Si—H, Sn—H
    f. Al—Br, Ga—Br, In—Br, Tl—Br

17. Repeat Exercises 15 and 16. This time use the values of the electronegativities of the elements given in Fig. 13.3. Are there any differences among your answers?

18. Hydrogen has an electronegativity value between boron and carbon and identical to phosphorus. With this in mind, rank the following bonds in order of decreasing polarity: P—H, O—H, N—H, F—H, C—H.

19. Rank the following bonds in order of increasing ionic character: N—O, Ca—O, C—F, Br—Br, K—F.

20. List all the possible bonds that can occur between the elements P, Cs, O, and H. Predict the type of bond (ionic, covalent, or polar covalent) one would expect to form for each bond.

21. Some plant fertilizer compounds are $(NH_4)_2SO_4$, $Ca_3(PO_4)_2$, K_2O, P_2O_5, and KCl. Which of these compounds contain both ionic and covalent bonds?

22. The following electrostatic potential diagrams represent CH_4, NH_3, or H_2O. Label each, and explain your choices.

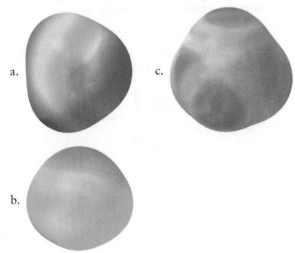

a.
b.
c.

Ions and Ionic Compounds

23. When an element forms an anion, what happens to the radius? When an element forms a cation, what happens to the radius? Why? Define the term *isoelectronic*. When comparing sizes of ions, which ion has the largest radius, and which ion has the smallest radius in an isoelectronic series? Why?

24. Consider the ions Sc^{3+}, Cl^-, K^+, Ca^{2+}, and S^{2-}. Match these ions to the following pictures that represent the relative sizes of the ions.

25. For each of the following groups, place the atoms and ions in order of decreasing size.
    a. Cu, Cu^+, Cu^{2+}
    b. Ni^{2+}, Pd^{2+}, Pt^{2+}
    c. O, O^-, O^{2-}
    d. La^{3+}, Eu^{3+}, Gd^{3+}, Yb^{3+}
    e. Te^{2-}, I^-, Cs^+, Ba^{2+}, La^{3+}

26. Write electron configurations for each of the following.
    a. the cations: Mg^{2+}, Sn^{2+}, K^+, Al^{3+}, Tl^+, As^{3+}
    b. the anions: N^{3-}, O^{2-}, F^-, Te^{2-}

27. Write electron configurations for the most stable ion formed by each of the elements Rb, Ba, Se, and I (when in stable ionic compounds).

28. Give an example of an ionic compound where both the anion and the cation are isoelectronic with each of the following noble gases.
    a. Ne
    b. Ar
    d. Kr
    e. Xe

29. What noble gas has the same electron configuration as each of the ions in the following compounds?
    a. cesium sulfide
    b. strontium fluoride
    c. calcium nitride
    d. aluminum bromide

30. Which of the following ions have noble gas electron configurations?
    a. Fe^{2+}, Fe^{3+}, Sc^{3+}, Co^{3+}
    b. Tl^+, Te^{2-}, Cr^{3+}
    c. Pu^{4+}, Ce^{4+}, Ti^{4+}
    d. Ba^{2+}, Pt^{2+}, Mn^{2+}

31. Give three ions that are isoelectronic with krypton. Place these ions in order of increasing size.

32. Which compound in each of the following pairs of ionic substances has the most exothermic lattice energy? Justify your answers.
    a. LiF, CsF
    b. NaBr, NaI
    c. $BaCl_2$, BaO
    d. Na_2SO_4, $CaSO_4$
    e. KF, K_2O
    f. Li_2O, Na_2S

33. Predict the empirical formulas of the ionic compounds formed from the following pairs of elements. Name each compound.
    a. Al and S
    b. K and N
    c. Mg and Cl
    d. Cs and Br

34. Following are some important properties of ionic compounds:
    i. low electrical conductivity as solids, and high conductivity in solution or when molten
    ii. relatively high melting and boiling points
    iii. brittleness

    How does the concept of ionic bonding discussed in this chapter account for these properties?

35. Use the following data to estimate ΔE for the formation of potassium chloride.

$$K(s) + \tfrac{1}{2}Cl_2(g) \longrightarrow KCl(s)$$

Lattice energy	−690. kJ/mol
Ionization energy for K	419 kJ/mol
Electron affinity of Cl	−349 kJ/mol
Bond energy of Cl_2	239 kJ/mol
Energy of sublimation for K	90. kJ/mol

36. Use the following data to estimate ΔE for the formation of magnesium fluoride.

$$Mg(s) + F_2(g) \longrightarrow MgF_2(s)$$

Lattice energy	−2913 kJ/mol
First ionization energy of Mg	735 kJ/mol
Second ionization energy of Mg	1445 kJ/mol
Electron affinity of F	−328 kJ/mol
Bond energy of F_2	154 kJ/mol
Energy of sublimation of Mg	150. kJ/mol

37. Consider the following: $Li(s) + \tfrac{1}{2}I_2(g) \rightarrow LiI(s)$ $\Delta E = -292$ kJ. $LiI(s)$ has a lattice energy of −753 kJ/mol. The ionization energy of $Li(g)$ is 520. kJ/mol, the bond energy of $I_2(g)$ is 151 kJ/mol, and the electron affinity of $I(g)$ is −295 kJ/mol. Use these data to determine the heat of sublimation of $Li(s)$.

38. In general, the higher the charge on the ions in an ionic compound, the more favorable is the lattice energy. Why do some stable ionic compounds have +1 charged ions even though +4, +5, and +6 charged ions would have a more favorable lattice energy?

39. Consider the following energy changes:

	ΔE (kJ/mol)
$Mg(g) \longrightarrow Mg^+(g) + e^-$	735
$Mg^+(g) \longrightarrow Mg^{2+}(g) + e^-$	1445
$O(g) + e^- \longrightarrow O^-(g)$	−141
$O^-(g) + e^- \longrightarrow O^{2-}(g)$	878

a. Magnesium oxide exists as $Mg^{2+}O^{2-}$, not as Mg^+O^-. Explain.

b. What experiment could be done to confirm that magnesium oxide does not exist as Mg^+O^-?

40. Use the following data (in kJ/mol) to estimate ΔE for the reaction $S^-(g) + e^- \rightarrow S^{2-}(g)$. Include an estimate of uncertainty.

	ΔE_f°	Lattice Energy	IE of M	ΔE_{sub} of M
Na_2S	−365	−2203	495	109
K_2S	−381	−2052	419	90.
Rb_2S	−361	−1949	409	82
Cs_2S	−360.	−1850.	382	78

$$S(s) \longrightarrow S(g) \qquad \Delta E = 277 \text{ kJ/mol}$$

$$S(g) + e^- \longrightarrow S^-(g) \qquad \Delta E = -200. \text{ kJ/mol}$$

41. Rationalize the following lattice energy values:

Compound	Lattice Energy (kJ/mol)
CaSe	−2862
Na_2Se	−2130
CaTe	−2721
Na_2Te	−2095

42. The lattice energies of $FeCl_3$, $FeCl_2$, and Fe_2O_3 are (in no particular order) −2631 kJ/mol, −5339 kJ/mol, and −14,774 kJ/mol. Match the appropriate formula to each lattice energy.

Bond Energies

43. Use bond energy values in Table 13.6 to estimate ΔE for each of the following reactions in the gas phase.

a. $H_2(g) + Cl_2(g) \rightarrow 2HCl(g)$

b. $N\equiv N(g) + 3H_2(g) \rightarrow 2NH_3(g)$

c. $H-C\equiv N(g) + 2H_2(g) \longrightarrow$ H–C–N with H, H, H, H substituents (g)

d. $H_2N-NH_2(g) + 2F_2(g) \longrightarrow N\equiv N(g) + 4HF(g)$

44. Compare your answers from parts a and b of Exercise 43 with ΔE values calculated for each reaction using standard enthalpies of formation in Appendix 4. Do energy changes calculated from bond energies give a reasonable estimate of the actual values?

45. Use bond energies to predict ΔE for the isomerization of methyl isocyanide to acetonitrile.

$$CH_3N\equiv C(g) \longrightarrow CH_3C\equiv N(g)$$

46. Use data from Table 13.6 to estimate ΔE for the combustion of methane (CH_4), as shown below:

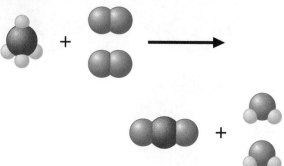

47. Use bond energies to estimate ΔE for the combustion of 1 mole of acetylene:

$$C_2H_2(g) + \tfrac{5}{2}O_2(g) \longrightarrow 2CO_2(g) + H_2O(g)$$

48. Consider the following reaction:

$$A_2 + B_2 \longrightarrow 2AB \qquad \Delta E = -285 \text{ kJ}$$

The bond energy for A_2 is one-half the amount of the AB bond energy. The bond energy of $B_2 = 432$ kJ/mol. What is the bond energy of A_2?

49. The space shuttle orbiter uses the oxidation of methyl hydrazine by dinitrogen tetroxide for propulsion:

$$5N_2O_4(g) + 4N_2H_3CH_3(g)$$
$$\longrightarrow 12H_2O(g) + 9N_2(g) + 4CO_2(g)$$

Use bond energies to estimate ΔE for this reaction. The structures for the reactants are

50. Following are three processes that have been used for the industrial manufacture of acrylonitrile—an important chemical used in the manufacture of plastics, synthetic rubber, and fibers. Use bond energy values (Tables 13.6 and 13.7) to estimate ΔE for each of the reactions.

b. $4CH_2{=}CHCH_3 + 6NO \xrightarrow[\text{Ag}]{700°C}$
$$4CH_2{=}CHCN + 6H_2O + N_2$$

The nitrogen–oxygen bond energy in nitric oxide (NO) is 630. kJ/mol.

c. $2CH_2{=}CHCH_3 + 2NH_3 + 3O_2 \xrightarrow[425{-}510°C]{\text{Catalyst}}$
$$2CH_2{=}CHCN + 6H_2O$$

51. Is the elevated temperature noted in parts b and c of Exercise 50 needed to provide energy to endothermic reactions?

52. Acetic acid is responsible for the sour taste of vinegar. It can be manufactured using the following reaction:

Use tabulated values of bond energies (Table 13.6) to estimate ΔE for this reaction. Compare this result to the ΔE value calculated using standard enthalpies of formation in Appendix 4. Explain any discrepancies.

53. Use bond energies (Table 13.6), values of electron affinities (Table 12.8), and the ionization energy of hydrogen (1312 kJ/mol) to estimate ΔE for each of the following reactions.
   a. $HF(g) \longrightarrow H^+(g) + F^-(g)$
   b. $HCl(g) \longrightarrow H^+(g) + Cl^-(g)$
   c. $HI(g) \longrightarrow H^+(g) + I^-(g)$
   d. $H_2O(g) \longrightarrow H^+(g) + OH^-(g)$
      (Electron affinity of $OH(g) = -180.$ kJ/mol.)

54. The standard enthalpies of formation of $S(g)$, $F(g)$, $SF_4(g)$, and $SF_6(g)$ are $+278.8$ kJ/mol, $+79.0$ kJ/mol, -775 kJ/mol, and -1209 kJ/mol, respectively.
   a. Use these data to estimate the energy of an S—F bond.
   b. Compare the value that you calculated in part a with the value given in Table 13.6. What conclusions can you draw?
   c. Why are the ΔE values for the formation of $S(g)$ and $F(g)$ not equal to zero, even though sulfur and fluorine are elements?

55. Use the following standard enthalpies of formation to estimate the N—H bond energy in ammonia. Compare this with the value in Table 13.6.

$N(g)$	472.7 kJ/mol
$H(g)$	216.0 kJ/mol
$NH_3(g)$	-46.1 kJ/mol

56. The standard energy of formation for $NO(g)$ is 90. kJ/mol. Use this and the values for the $O{=}O$ and $N{\equiv}N$ bond energies to estimate the bond strength in NO.

Lewis Structures and Resonance

57. Write Lewis structures that obey the octet rule for each of the following. Except for HCN and H_2CO, the first atom listed is the central atom. For HCN and H_2CO, carbon is the central atom.
   a. HCN   d. NH_4^+ g. CO_2
   b. PH_3 e. H_2CO h. O_2
   c. $CHCl_3$ f. SeF_2 i. HBr

58. Draw a Lewis structure that obeys the octet rule for each of the following molecules and ions. In each case the first atom listed is the central atom.
   a. $POCl_3$, SO_4^{2-}, XeO_4, PO_4^{3-}, ClO_4^-
   b. NF_3, SO_3^{2-}, PO_3^{3-}, ClO_3^-
   c. ClO_2^-, SCl_2, PCl_2^-

59. Considering your answers to Exercise 58, what conclusions can you draw concerning the structures of species containing the same number of atoms and the same number of valence electrons?

60. Draw Lewis structures for the following. Show all resonance structures, where applicable. Carbon is the central atom in OCN^- and SCN^-.
   a. NO_2^-, NO_3^-, N_2O_4(N_2O_4 exists as $O_2N{-}NO_2$.)
   b. OCN^-, SCN^-, N_3^-

61. Some of the pollutants in the atmosphere are ozone, sulfur dioxide, and sulfur trioxide. Draw Lewis structures for these three molecules. Show all resonance structures.

62. Peroxyacetyl nitrate, or PAN, is present in photochemical smog. Draw Lewis structures (including resonance forms) for PAN. The skeletal arrangement is

63. A toxic cloud covered Bhopal, India, in December 1984 when water leaked into a tank of methyl isocyanate, and the product escaped into the atmosphere. Methyl isocya-

nate is used in the production of many pesticides. Draw the Lewis structures for methyl isocyanate, CH_3NCO, including resonance forms.

64. Explain the terms *resonance* and *delocalized electrons*. When a substance exhibits resonance, we say that none of the individual Lewis structures accurately portrays the bonding in the substance. Why do we draw resonance structures?

65. Benzene (C_6H_6) consists of a six-membered ring of carbon atoms with one hydrogen bonded to each carbon. Draw Lewis structures for benzene, including resonance structures.

66. An important observation supporting the need for resonance in the LE model is that there are only three different structures of dichlorobenzene ($C_6H_4Cl_2$). How does this fact support the need for the concept of resonance?

67. Borazine ($B_3N_3H_6$) has often been called "inorganic" benzene. Draw Lewis structures for borazine. Borazine is a six-membered ring of alternating boron and nitrogen atoms.

68. Draw all the possible Lewis structures for dimethylborazine [$(CH_3)_2B_3N_3H_4$]. (See Exercise 67.) Would there be a different number of structures if there was no resonance?

69. Which of the following statements is(are) true? Correct the false statements.
    a. It is impossible to satisfy the octet rule for all atoms in XeF_2.
    b. Because SF_4 exists, OF_4 should also exist because oxygen is in the same family as sulfur.
    c. The bond in NO^+ should be stronger than the bond in NO^-.
    d. As predicted from the two Lewis structures for ozone, one oxygen–oxygen bond is stronger than the other oxygen–oxygen bond.

70. Lewis structures can be used to understand why some molecules react in certain ways. Write the Lewis structures for the reactants and products in the reactions described below.
    a. Nitrogen dioxide dimerizes to produce dinitrogen tetroxide.
    b. Boron trihydride accepts a pair of electrons from ammonia, forming BH_3NH_3.

    Give a possible explanation for why these two reactions occur.

71. The most common type of exception to the octet rule are compounds or ions with central atoms having more than eight electrons around them. PF_5, SF_4, ClF_3, and Br_3^- are examples of this type of exception. Draw the Lewis structures for these compounds or ions. Which elements, when they have to, can have more than eight electrons around them? How is this rationalized?

72. SF_6, ClF_5, and XeF_4 are three compounds whose central atoms do not follow the octet rule. Draw Lewis structures for these compounds.

73. Consider the following bond lengths:

    $C-O$ 1.43 Å $C=O$ 1.23 Å $C\equiv O$ 1.09 Å

    In the CO_3^{2-} ion, all three C—O bonds have identical bond lengths of 1.36 Å. Why?

74. Order the following species with respect to the carbon–oxygen bond length (longest to shortest):

    $$CO, CO_2, CO_3^{2-}, CH_3OH$$

    What is the order from the weakest to the strongest carbon–oxygen bond?

75. Place the species below in order of the shortest to the longest nitrogen–oxygen bond.

    $$H_2NOH, \quad N_2O, \quad NO^+, \quad NO_2^-, \quad NO_3^-$$

    (H_2NOH exists as H_2N-OH.)

Formal Charge

76. Use the formal charge arguments to rationalize why BF_3 would not follow the octet rule.

77. Use formal charge arguments to explain why CO has a much smaller dipole moment than would be expected on the basis of electronegativity.

78. Nitrous oxide (N_2O) has three possible Lewis structures:

    $$:N=N=\overset{..}{\overset{..}{O}}: \longleftrightarrow :N\equiv N-\overset{..}{\underset{..}{O}}: \longleftrightarrow :\overset{..}{N}-N\equiv O:$$

    Given the following bond lengths,

N—N	167 pm	N=O	115 pm
N=N	120 pm	N—O	147 pm
N≡N	110 pm		

    rationalize the observations that the N—N bond length in N_2O is 112 pm and that the N—O bond length is 119 pm. Assign formal charges to the resonance structures for N_2O. Can you eliminate any of the resonance structures on the basis of formal charges? Is this consistent with observation?

79. Draw Lewis structures that obey the octet rule for the following species. Assign the formal charge to each central atom.
    a. $POCl_3$ c. ClO_4^- e. SO_2Cl_2 g. ClO_3^-
    b. SO_4^{2-} d. PO_4^{3-} f. XeO_4 h. NO_4^{3-}

80. Draw the Lewis structures that involve minimum formal charges for the species in Exercise 79.

81. When molten sulfur reacts with chlorine gas, a vile-smelling orange liquid forms that has an empirical formula of SCl. The structure of this compound has a formal charge of zero on all elements in the compound. Draw the Lewis structure for the vile-smelling orange liquid.

82. Oxidation of the cyanide ion produces the stable cyanate ion (OCN^-). The fulminate ion (CNO^-), on the other hand, is very unstable. Fulminate salts explode when struck; $Hg(CNO)_2$ is used in blasting caps. Write the Lewis structures and assign formal charges for the cyanate and fulminate ions. Why is the fulminate ion so unstable? (C is the central atom in OCN^-, and N is the central atom in CNO^-.)

83. Write the Lewis Structure for O_2F_2 (O_2F_2 exists as F—O—O—F). Assign oxidation states and formal charges to the atoms in O_2F_2. This compound is a vigorous and

potent oxidizing and fluorinating agent. Are oxidation states or formal charges more useful in accounting for these properties of O_2F_2?

84. Benzoic acid is a food preservative. The space-filling model for benzoic acid is shown below.

- C
- H
- O

Benzoic acid
($C_6H_5CO_2H$)

Draw the Lewis structure for benzoic acid, including all resonance structures in which all atoms have a formal charge of zero.

Molecular Structure and Polarity

85. Write the name of each of the following molecular structures.

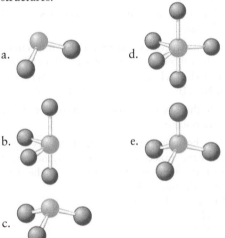

a.

b.

c.

d.

e.

86. State whether or not each of the following has a permanent dipole moment.

a.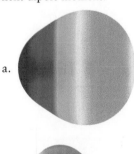

b.

c.

d.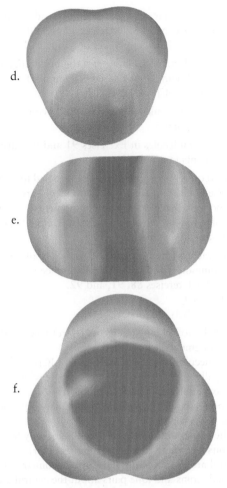

e.

f.

87. Predict the molecular structure and the bond angles for each molecule or ion in Exercises 57, 58, and 60.

88. Predict the molecular structure and the bond angles for each of the following.
a. SeO_3 b. SeO_2 c. PCl_3 d. SCl_2 e. SiF_4

89. There are several molecular structures based on the trigonal bipyramid geometry. Three such structures are

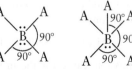

Linear   T-shaped   See-saw

Which of the compounds or ions in Exercises 71 and 72 have these molecular structures?

90. Two variations of the octahedral geometry are illustrated below.

Square planar   Square pyramid

Which of the compounds or ions in Exercises 71 and 72 have these molecular structures?

91. Predict the molecular structure and the bond angles for each of the following. (See Exercises 89 and 90.)
    a. $XeCl_2$ b. ICl_3 c. TeF_4 d. PCl_5

92. Predict the molecular structure and the bond angles for each of the following. (See Exercises 89 and 90.)
    a. ICl_5 b. $XeCl_4$ c. $SeCl_6$

93. Which of the molecules in Exercise 88 have net dipole moments (are polar)?

94. Which of the molecules in Exercises 91 and 92 have net dipole moments (are polar)?

95. Give two requirements that should be satisfied for a molecule to be polar. Explain why CF_4 and XeF_4 are nonpolar compounds (have no net dipole moments), whereas SF_4 is polar (has a net dipole moment). Is CO_2 polar? What about COS? Explain.

96. What do each of the following sets of compounds/ions have in common with each other? Reference your Lewis structures for Exercises 88, 91, and 92.
    a. $XeCl_4$, $XeCl_2$
    b. ICl_5, TeF_4, ICl_3, PCl_3, SCl_2, SeO_2

97. Which of the following statements is(are) true? Correct the false statements.
    a. The molecules SeS_3, SeS_2, PCl_5, $TeCl_4$, ICl_3, and $XeCl_2$ all exhibit at least one bond angle which is approximately 120 degrees.
    b. The bond angle in SO_2 should be similar to the bond angle in CS_2 or SCl_2.
    c. Of the compounds CF_4, KrF_4, and SeF_4, only SeF_4 exhibits an overall dipole moment (is polar).
    d. Central atoms in a molecule adopt a geometry of the bonded atoms and lone pairs about the central atom in order to maximize electron repulsions.

98. Consider the following Lewis structure, where E is an unknown element:

$$\left[\ddot{\underset{\displaystyle ..}{O}}-\underset{\displaystyle \underset{..}{\overset{|}{O}}:}{E}-\ddot{\underset{\displaystyle ..}{O}}: \right]^-$$

What are some possible identities for element E? Predict the molecular structure (including bond angles) for this ion.

99. Consider the following Lewis structure, where E is an unknown element:

$$\left[:\ddot{F}-\underset{\underset{\displaystyle \ddot{F}:}{|}}{E}\overset{\displaystyle \ddot{O}:}{\diagdown} \right]^{2-}$$

What are some possible identities for element E? Predict the molecular structure (including bond angles) for this ion. (See Exercises 89 and 90.)

100. Although the VSEPR model is correct in predicting that CH_4 is tetrahedral, NH_3 is pyramidal, and H_2O is bent, the model in its simplest form does not account for the fact that these molecules do not have exactly the same bond angles (< HCH is 109.5 degrees, as expected for a tetrahedron, but < HNH is 107.3 degrees and < HOH is 104.5 degrees). Explain these deviations from the tetrahedral angle.

101. Draw Lewis structures and predict the molecular structures of the following. (See Exercises 89 and 90.)
     a. OCl_2, KrF_2, BeH_2, SO_2 c. CF_4, SeF_4, KrF_4
     b. SO_3, NF_3, IF_3 d. IF_5, AsF_5

     Which of the above compounds have net dipole moments (are polar)?

102. Which of the following molecules have net dipole moments? For the molecules that are polar, indicate the polarity of each bond and the direction of the net dipole moment of the molecule.
     a. CH_2Cl_2, $CHCl_3$, CCl_4
     b. CO_2, N_2O
     c. PH_3, NH_3

103. The molecules BF_3, CF_4, CO_2, PF_5, and SF_6 are all nonpolar, even though they contain polar bonds. Why?

Additional Exercises

104. Although both the Br_3^- and I_3^- ions are known, the F_3^- ion does not exist. Explain.

105. Write Lewis structures for CO_3^{2-}, HCO_3^-, and H_2CO_3. When acid is added to an aqueous solution containing carbonate or bicarbonate ions, carbon dioxide gas is formed. We generally say that carbonic acid (H_2CO_3) is unstable. Use bond energies to estimate ΔE for the reaction (in the gas phase):

$$H_2CO_3 \longrightarrow CO_2 + H_2O$$

Specify a possible cause for the instability of carbonic acid.

106. The structure of TeF_5^- is

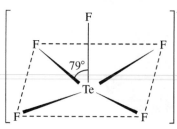

Draw a complete Lewis structure for TeF_5^-, and explain the distortion from the ideal square pyramidal structure. (See Exercise 90.)

107. The compound NF_3 is quite stable, but NCl_3 is very unstable (NCl_3 was first synthesized in 1811 by P. L. Dulong, who lost three fingers and an eye studying its properties). The compounds NBr_3 and NI_3 are unknown, although the explosive compound $NI_3 \cdot NH_3$ is known. Account for the instability of these halides of nitrogen.

108. There are two possible structures of XeF_2Cl_2, where Xe is the central atom. Draw them, and describe how measurements of dipole moments might be used to distinguish among them.

109. Which member of the following pairs would you expect to be more energetically stable? Justify each choice.
   a. NaBr or $NaBr_2$
   b. ClO_4 or ClO_4^-
   c. SO_4 or XeO_4
   d. OF_4 or SeF_4

110. Many times, extra stability is characteristic of a molecule or ion in which resonance is possible. How could this feature be used to explain the acidities of the following compounds? (The acidic hydrogen is marked by an asterisk.) Part c shows resonance in the phenyl ring (C_6H_5).

   a.
   $$\begin{array}{c} O \\ \| \\ H-C-OH^* \end{array}$$

   b.
   $$\begin{array}{c} O \qquad OH^* \\ \| \qquad | \\ CH_3-C-CH=C-CH_3 \end{array}$$

   c.
   $$OH^*$$

111. Arrange the following in order of increasing radius and increasing ionization energy.
   a. N^+, N, N^-
   b. Se, Se^-, Cl, Cl^+
   c. Br^-, Rb^+, Sr^{2+}

112. Draw a Lewis structure for the *N,N*-dimethylformamide molecule. The skeletal structure is

   $$\begin{array}{c} O \\ | \\ H-C-N-CH_3 \\ | \\ CH_3 \end{array}$$

Various types of evidence lead to the conclusion that there is some double-bond character to one of the C—N bonds. Draw one or more resonance structures that support this observation.

113. A compound, XF_5, is 42.81% fluorine by mass. Identify the element X. What is the molecular structure of XF_5?

114. The study of carbon-containing compounds and their properties is called organic chemistry. Besides carbon atoms, *organic compounds* also can contain hydrogen, oxygen, and nitrogen atoms (as well as other types of atoms). A common trait of simple organic compounds is to have Lewis structures in which all atoms have a formal charge of zero. Consider the following incomplete Lewis structure for an organic compound called *histidine* (one of the amino acids, which are the building blocks of proteins found in human bodies):

   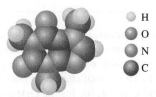

   Draw a complete Lewis structure for histidine in which all atoms have a formal charge of zero. What are the approximate bond angles about the carbon atom labeled 1 and the nitrogen atom labeled 2?

115. Do the Lewis structures obtained in Exercises 79 and 80 predict the same molecular structure for each case?

116. Predict the molecular structure for each of the following. (See Exercises 89 and 90.)
   a. $BrFI_2$
   b. XeO_2F_2
   c. $TeF_2Cl_3^-$

   For each formula, there are at least two different structures that can be drawn using the same central atom. Draw the possible structures for each formula.

Challenge Problems

117. Predict the molecular structure of KrF_2. Using hyperconjugation, draw the Lewis structures for KrF_2 that obey the octet rule. Show all resonance forms.

118. Consider the following computer-generated model of caffeine.

○	H
●	O
●	N
●	C

   Draw a Lewis structure for caffeine in which all atoms have a formal charge of zero.

119. Given the following information:

   Heat of sublimation of Li(s) = 166 kJ/mol
   Bond energy of HCl = 427 kJ/mol
   Ionization energy of Li(g) = 520. kJ/mol
   Electron affinity of Cl(g) = −349 kJ/mol
   Lattice energy of LiCl(s) = −829 kJ/mol
   Bond energy of H_2 = 432 kJ/mol

   Calculate the net change in energy for the following reaction:

   $$2Li(s) + 2HCl(g) \longrightarrow 2LiCl(s) + H_2(g)$$

120. Use data in this chapter and Chapter 12 to discuss why MgO is an ionic compound but CO is not an ionic compound.

121. A promising new material with great potential as a fuel in solid rocket motors is ammonium dinitramide [$NH_4N(NO_2)_2$].
    a. Draw Lewis structures (including resonance forms) for the dinitramide ion [$N(NO_2)_2^-$].
    b. Predict the bond angles around each nitrogen in the dinitramide ion.
    c. Ammonium dinitramide can decompose explosively to nitrogen, water, and oxygen. Write a balanced equation for this reaction, and use bond energies to estimate ΔE for the explosive decomposition of this compound.
    d. To estimate ΔE from bond energies, you made several assumptions. What are some of your assumptions?

122. Think of forming an ionic compound as three steps (this is a simplification, as with all models): (1) removing an electron from the metal, (2) adding an electron to the nonmetal, and (3) allowing the metal cation and non-metal anion to come together.
    a. What is the sign of the energy change for each of these three processes?
    b. In general, what is the sign of the sum of the first two processes? Use examples to support your answer.
    c. What must be the sign of the sum of the three processes?
    d. Given your answer to part c, why do ionic bonds occur?
    e. Given your explanations to part d, why is NaCl stable but not Na_2Cl_2 and $NaCl_2$? What about MgO compared to MgO_2 and Mg_2O?

123. The compound hexaazaisowurtzitane is one of the highest-energy explosives known (*C & E News*, p. 26, Jan. 17, 1994). The compound, also known as CL-20, was first synthesized in 1987. The method of synthesis and detailed performance data are still classified information because of CL-20's potential military application in rocket boosters and in warheads of "smart" weapons. The structure of CL-20 is

In such shorthand structures, each point where lines meet represents a carbon atom. In addition, the hydrogens attached to the carbon atoms are omitted. Each of the six carbon atoms has one hydrogen atom attached. Three possible reactions for the explosive decomposition of CL-20 are

i. $C_6H_6N_{12}O_{12}(s) \longrightarrow$
$$6CO(g) + 6N_2(g) + 3H_2O(g) + \tfrac{3}{2}O_2(g)$$
ii. $C_6H_6N_{12}O_{12}(s) \longrightarrow$
$$3CO(g) + 3CO_2(g) + 6N_2(g) + 3H_2O(g)$$
iii. $C_6H_6N_{12}O_{12}(s) \longrightarrow$
$$6CO_2(g) + 6N_2(g) + 3H_2(g)$$

a. Use bond energies to estimate ΔE for these three reactions.
b. Which of the above reactions releases the largest amount of energy per kilogram of CL-20?

124. In molecules of the type X—O—H, as the electronegativity of X increases, the acid strength increases. In addition, if the electronegativity of X is a very small value, the molecule acts like a base. Explain these observations and provide examples.

125. Calculate the standard heat of formation of the compound ICl(g) at 25°C. (*Hint*: Use Table 13.6 and Appendix 4 data.)

126. An ionic compound made from the metal M and the diatomic gas X_2 has the formula M_aX_b, in which $a = 1$ or 2 and $b = 1$ or 2. Use the data provided to determine the most likely values for a and b, along with the most likely charges for each of the ions in the ionic compound.

Data (in units of kJ/mol)

Successive ionization energies of M: 480., 4750.

Successive electron affinity values for X: -175, 920.

Energy of sublimation for $M(s) \rightarrow M(g)$: 110.

Bond energy of X_2: 250.

Lattice energy for MX (M^+ and X^-): $-1200.$ kJ/mol

Lattice energy for MX_2 (M^{2+} and X^-): $-3500.$ kJ/mol

Lattice energy for M_2X (M^+ and X^{2-}): $-3600.$ kJ/mol

Lattice energy for MX (M^{2+} and X^{2-}): $-4800.$ kJ/mol

Marathon Problem

127. Identify the following five compounds of H, N, and O. For each compound, write a Lewis structure that is consistent with the information given.
    a. All the compounds are electrolytes, although not all are strong electrolytes. Compounds C and D are ionic and compound B is covalent.
    b. Nitrogen occurs in its highest possible oxidation state in compounds A and C; nitrogen occurs in its lowest possible oxidation state in compounds C, D, and E. The formal charge on both nitrogens in compound C is +1; the formal charge on the only nitrogen in compound B is 0.

c. Compounds A and E exist in solution. Both solutions give off gases. Commercially available concentrated solutions of compound A are normally 16 *M*. The commercial, concentrated solution of compound E is 15 *M*.

d. Commercial solutions of compound E are labeled with a misnomer that implies that a binary, gaseous compound of nitrogen and hydrogen has reacted with water to produce ammonium ions and hydroxide ions. Actually, this reaction occurs to only a slight extent.

e. Compound D is 43.7% N and 50.0% O by mass. If compound D were a gas at STP, it would have a density of 2.86 g/L.

f. A formula unit of compound C has one more oxygen than a formula unit of compound D. Compounds C and A have one ion in common when compound A is acting as a strong electrolyte.

g. Solutions of compound C are weakly acidic; solutions of compound A are strongly acidic; solutions of compounds B and E are basic. The titration of 0.726 g of compound B requires 21.98 mL of 1.000 *M* HCl for complete neutralization.

Stoichiometry

3

chapter

Massive eruption of the Kileuea volcano in Hawaii.

Jim Sugar/Science Faction

Chemical reactions have a profound effect on our lives. There are many examples: Food is converted to energy in the human body; nitrogen and hydrogen are combined to form ammonia, which is used as a fertilizer; fuels and plastics are produced from petroleum; the starch in plants is synthesized from carbon dioxide and water using energy from sunlight; human insulin is produced in laboratories by bacteria; cancer is induced in humans by substances from our environment; and so on, in a seemingly endless list. The central activity of chemistry is to understand chemical changes such as these, and the study of reactions occupies a central place in this text. We will examine why reactions occur, how fast they occur, and the specific pathways they follow.

In this chapter we will consider the quantities of materials consumed and produced in chemical reactions. This area of study is called **chemical stoichiometry.** To understand chemical stoichiometry, you must first understand the concept of relative atomic masses.

3.1 | Atomic Masses

As we saw in Chapter 2, the first quantitative information about atomic masses came from the work of Dalton, Gay-Lussac, Lavoisier, Avogadro, Cannizzaro, and Berzelius. By observing the proportions in which elements combine to form various compounds, nineteenth-century chemists calculated relative atomic masses. The modern system of atomic masses, instituted in 1961, is based on ^{12}C (carbon-12) as the standard. In this system ^{12}C *is assigned a mass of exactly 12 atomic mass units* (amu), and the masses of all other atoms are given relative to this standard.

The most accurate method currently available for comparing the masses of atoms involves the use of the **mass spectrometer.** In this instrument, diagrammed in Fig. 3.1, atoms or molecules are passed into a beam of high-speed electrons. The high-speed electrons knock electrons off the atoms or molecules being analyzed and change them to positive ions. An applied electric field then accelerates these ions through a magnetic field, which deflects the paths of the ions. The amount of path deflection for each ion depends on its mass—the most massive ions are deflected the smallest amount—and this deflection causes the ions to separate, as shown in Fig. 3.1. A comparison of the positions where the ions hit the detector plate gives very accurate values of their relative masses. For example, when ^{12}C and ^{13}C are analyzed in a mass spectrometer, the ratio of their masses is found to be

$$\frac{\text{Mass } ^{13}C}{\text{Mass } ^{12}C} = 1.0836129$$

Chemist using a mass spectrometer to analyze for copper in blood plasma.

Figure 3.1
Schematic diagram of a mass spectrometer.

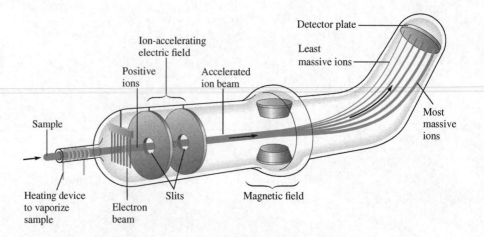

Elemental Analysis Catches Elephant Poachers

In an effort to combat the poaching of elephants by controlling illegal exports of ivory, scientists are now using the isotopic composition of ivory trinkets and elephant tusks to identify the region of Africa where the elephant lived. Using a mass spectrometer, scientists analyze the ivory for the relative amounts of ^{12}C, ^{13}C, ^{14}N, ^{15}N, ^{86}Sr, and ^{87}Sr to determine the diet of the elephant and thus its place of origin. For example, because grasses use a different photosynthetic pathway to produce glucose than do trees, grasses have a slightly different $^{13}C/^{12}C$ ratio than trees. They have different ratios because each time a carbon is added in going from simpler to more complex compounds, the more massive ^{13}C is disfavored relative to ^{12}C since it reacts more slowly. Because trees use more steps to build up glucose, they end up with a smaller $^{13}C/^{12}C$ ratio in their leaves relative to grasses, and this difference is then reflected in the tissues of elephants. Thus scientists can tell whether a particular tusk came from a savanna-dwelling (grass-eating) elephant or from a tree-browsing elephant.

Similarly, because the ratios of $^{15}N/^{14}N$ and $^{87}Sr/^{86}Sr$ in elephant tusks also vary depending on the region of Africa the elephant inhabited, they can be used to trace the elephant's origin. In fact,

A herd of savanna-dwelling elephants.

using these techniques, scientists have reported being able to discriminate between elephants living only about 100 miles apart.

There is now international concern about the dwindling elephant populations in parts of Africa, where their numbers have decreased dramatically over the past several decades. This concern has led to bans on the export of ivory from many countries in Africa. However, a few nations still allow ivory to be exported. Thus, to enforce the trade restrictions, the origin of a given piece of ivory must be established. It is hoped that the "isotope signature" of the ivory can be used for this purpose.

Most elements occur in nature as mixtures of isotopes; thus atomic masses are generally reported as average values. It turns out the average mass for a given atom varies at different geographical locations, and the new values are given as intervals to reflect this. Carbon, for example, now has an official mass of [12.0096; 12.0116]. This is not due to uncertainty but takes into account variations in atomic masses based on location. This new system has recently been adopted for 10 elements (hydrogen, lithium, boron, carbon, nitrogen, oxygen, silicon, sulfur, chlorine, and thallium). In the text we will continue with the standard method of average atomic masses for these elements.

Since the atomic mass unit is defined such that the mass of ^{12}C is *exactly* 12 atomic mass units, then on this same scale,

$$\text{Mass of } ^{13}C = (1.0836129)(12 \text{ amu}) = 13.003355 \text{ amu}$$

↑
Exact number,
by definition

The masses of other atoms can be determined in a similar manner.

The mass for each element is given in the table inside the front cover of this book. This value, even though it is actually a mass, is sometimes called (for historical reasons) the atomic weight for each element.

Look at the value of the atomic mass of carbon given in the table. You might expect to see 12 since we said the system of atomic masses is based on ^{12}C. However, the number given for carbon is 12.01 because the carbon found on earth (natural carbon) is a mixture of the isotopes ^{12}C, ^{13}C, and ^{14}C. All three isotopes have six protons, but they have six, seven, and eight neutrons, respectively. Because natural carbon is a mixture of isotopes, the atomic mass we use for carbon is an *average value* based on its isotopic composition.

The average atomic mass for carbon is computed as follows. Chemists know that natural carbon is composed of 98.89% ^{12}C atoms and 1.11% ^{13}C atoms. The amount of ^{14}C is negligibly small at this level of precision. Using

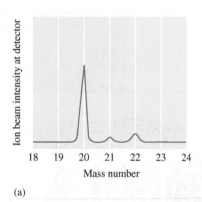

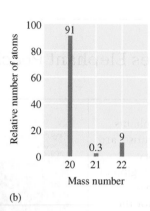

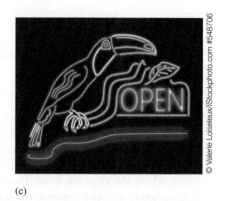

Figure 3.2

The relative intensities of the signals recorded when natural neon is injected into a mass spectrometer, represented in terms of (a) "peaks" and (b) a bar graph. The relative areas of the peaks are 0.9092 (^{20}Ne), 0.00257 (^{21}Ne), and 0.0882 (^{22}Ne); natural neon is therefore 90.92% ^{20}Ne, 0.257% ^{21}Ne, and 8.82% ^{22}Ne. (c) A neon sign.

the masses of ^{12}C (exactly 12 amu) and ^{13}C (13.003355 amu), the average atomic mass for natural carbon can be calculated.

98.89% of 12 amu + 1.11% of 13.0034 amu
$$= (0.9889)(12 \text{ amu}) + (0.0111)(13.0034 \text{ amu}) = 12.01 \text{ amu}$$

See Appendix A1.5 for a discussion of significant figures.

This average mass is often called the atomic weight of carbon.

Even though natural carbon does not contain a single atom with mass 12.01, for stoichiometric purposes we consider carbon to be composed of only one type of atom with a mass of 12.01. We do this so that we can count atoms of natural carbon by weighing a sample of carbon. Let's consider a nonchemical example. It is much easier to weigh out 3000 grams of jelly beans (with an average mass of 3 grams per jelly bean) than to count out 1000 of them. Note that none of the jelly beans has to have a mass of 3 grams for this method to work; only the *average* mass must be 3 grams. We extend this same principle to counting atoms. For natural carbon with an average mass of 12.01 atomic mass units, to obtain 1000 atoms would require weighing out 12,010 atomic mass units of natural carbon (a mixture of ^{12}C and ^{13}C).

As in the case of carbon, the mass for each element given in the table inside the front cover of this book is an average value based on the isotopic composition of the naturally occurring element. For instance, the mass listed for hydrogen (1.008) is the average mass for natural hydrogen, which is a mixture of ^{1}H and ^{2}H (deuterium). *No* atom of hydrogen actually has the mass 1.008.

In addition to being used for determining accurate mass values for individual atoms, the mass spectrometer is used to determine the isotopic composition of a natural element. For example, when a sample of natural neon is injected into a mass spectrometer, the results shown in Fig. 3.2 are obtained. The areas of the "peaks" or the heights of the bars indicate the relative numbers of $^{22}_{10}$Ne, $^{22}_{10}$Ne, and $^{22}_{10}$Ne atoms.

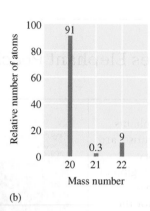

Figure 3.3
Mass spectrum of natural copper.

EXAMPLE 3.1

Copper is a very important metal used for water pipes, electrical wiring, roof coverings, and other materials. When a sample of natural copper is vaporized and injected into a mass spectrometer, the results shown in Fig. 3.3 are obtained. Use these data to compute the average mass of natural copper. (The mass values for ^{63}Cu and ^{65}Cu are 62.93 amu and 64.93 amu, respectively.)

Solution As shown by the graph, of every 100 atoms of natural copper, on average 69.09 are ^{63}Cu and 30.91 are ^{65}Cu. Thus the average mass of 100 atoms of natural copper is

$$(69.09 \text{ atoms}) \left(62.93 \frac{\text{amu}}{\text{atom}}\right) + (30.9 \text{ atoms}) \left(64.93 \frac{\text{amu}}{\text{atom}}\right) = 6355 \text{ amu}$$

The average mass per atom is

$$\frac{6355 \text{ amu}}{100 \text{ atoms}} = 63.55 \text{ amu/atom}$$

This mass value is used in calculations involving the reactions of copper and is the value given in the table inside the front cover of this book.

3.2 | The Mole

Because samples of matter typically contain so many atoms, a unit of measure called the mole has been established for use in counting atoms. For our purposes it is most convenient to define the **mole** (abbreviated mol) as *the number equal to the number of carbon atoms in exactly 12 grams of pure ^{12}C*. Modern techniques that allow us to count atoms very precisely have been used to determine this number as 6.022137×10^{23} (6.022×10^{23} will be sufficient for our purposes). This number is called **Avogadro's number** to honor his contributions to chemistry. *One mole of something consists of 6.022×10^{23} units of that substance.* Just as a dozen eggs is 12 eggs, a mole of eggs is 6.022×10^{23} eggs.

The magnitude of the number 6.022×10^{23} is very difficult to imagine. To give you some idea, 1 mole of seconds represents a span of time 4 million times as long as the earth has already existed, and 1 mole of marbles is enough to cover the entire earth to a depth of 50 miles! However, since atoms are so tiny, a mole of atoms or molecules is a perfectly manageable quantity to use in a reaction (see Fig. 3.4).

How do we use the mole in chemical calculations? Recall that Avogadro's number is defined as the number of atoms in exactly 12 grams of ^{12}C. Thus 12 grams of ^{12}C contains 6.022×10^{23} atoms. Also, a 12.01-gram sample of natural carbon contains 6.022×10^{23} atoms (a mixture of ^{12}C, ^{13}C, and ^{14}C atoms, with an average mass of 12.01). Since the ratio of the masses of the samples (12 g/12.01 g) is the same as the ratio of the masses of the individual components (12 amu/12.01 amu), the two samples contain the *same number* of components.

To be sure this point is clear, think of oranges with an average mass of 0.5 pound each and grapefruit with an average mass of 1.0 pound each. Any two sacks for which the sack of grapefruit weighs twice as much as the sack of oranges will contain the same number of pieces of fruit. The same idea extends to atoms. Compare natural carbon (average mass of 12.01) and natural helium (average mass of 4.003). A sample of 12.01 grams of natural carbon contains the same number of atoms as 4.003 grams of natural helium. Both samples contain 1 mole of atoms (6.022×10^{23}). Table 3.1 gives more examples that illustrate this basic idea.

Thus the mole is defined such that a sample of a natural element with a mass equal to the element's atomic mass expressed in grams contains 1 mole of atoms. This definition also fixes the relationship between the atomic mass unit

The SI definition of the mole is the amount of a substance that contains as many entities as there are in exactly 0.012 kg (12 g) of carbon-12.

Figure 3.4
Proceeding clockwise from the top, samples containing 1 mole each of copper, aluminum, iron, sulfur, iodine, and (in the center) mercury.

The mass of 1 mole of an element is equal to its atomic mass in grams.

Table 3.1

Comparison of 1-Mole Samples of Various Elements

Element	Number of Atoms	Mass of Sample (g)
Aluminum	6.022×10^{23}	26.98
Gold	6.022×10^{23}	196.97
Iron	6.022×10^{23}	55.85
Sulfur	6.022×10^{23}	32.07
Boron	6.022×10^{23}	10.81
Xenon	6.022×10^{23}	131.30

and the gram. Since 6.022×10^{23} atoms of carbon (each with a mass of 12 amu) have a mass of 12 grams, then

$$(6.022 \times 10^{23} \text{ atoms}) \left(\frac{12 \text{ amu}}{\text{atom}} \right) = 12 \text{ g}$$

and
$$6.022 \times 10^{23} \text{ amu} = 1 \text{ g}$$
$$\uparrow$$
$$\text{Exact}$$
$$\text{number}$$

⊙WL INTERACTIVE EXAMPLE 3.2

Americium is an element that does not occur naturally. It can be made in very small amounts in a device called a particle accelerator. Compute the mass in grams of a sample of americium containing six atoms.

Solution From the table inside the front cover of this book, note that one americium atom has a mass of 243 amu. Thus the mass of six atoms is

$$6 \text{ atoms} \times 243 \frac{\text{amu}}{\text{atom}} = 1.46 \times 10^3 \text{ amu}$$

From the relationship 6.022×10^{23} amu = 1 g, the mass of six americium atoms in grams is

$$1.46 \times 10^3 \text{ amu} \times \frac{1 \text{ g}}{6.022 \times 10^{23} \text{ amu}} = 2.42 \times 10^{-21} \text{ g}$$

Refer to Appendix 2 for a discussion of units and the conversion from one unit to another.

This relationship can be used to derive the factor needed to convert between atomic mass units and grams.

To perform chemical calculations, you must understand what the mole means and how to determine the number of moles in a given mass of a substance. These procedures are illustrated in Example 3.3.

⊙WL INTERACTIVE EXAMPLE 3.3

A silicon chip used in an integrated circuit of a microcomputer has a mass of 5.68 mg. How many silicon (Si) atoms are present in this chip?

Solution The strategy for doing this problem is to convert from milligrams of silicon to grams of silicon, then to moles of silicon, and finally to atoms of silicon:

$$5.68 \text{ mg Si} \times \frac{1 \text{ g Si}}{1000 \text{ mg Si}} = 5.68 \times 10^{-3} \text{ g Si}$$

$$5.68 \times 10^{-3} \text{ g Si} \times \frac{1 \text{ mol Si}}{28.09 \text{ g Si}} = 2.02 \times 10^{-4} \text{ mol Si}$$

$$2.02 \times 10^{-4} \text{ mol Si} \times \frac{6.022 \times 10^{23} \text{ atoms}}{1 \text{ mol Si}} = 1.22 \times 10^{20} \text{ atoms}$$

It always makes sense to think about orders of magnitude as you do a calculation. In Example 3.3, the 5.68-milligram sample of silicon is clearly much less than 1 mole of silicon (which has a mass of 28.09 grams), so the final answer of 1.22×10^{20} atoms (compared with 6.022×10^{23} atoms) is at least in the right direction. Paying careful attention to units and making sure the answer is sensible can help you detect an inverted conversion factor or a number that was incorrectly entered in your calculator.

Always check to see if your answer is sensible.

3.3 | Molar Mass

A chemical compound is, ultimately, a collection of atoms. For example, methane (the major component of natural gas) consists of molecules that each contain one carbon atom and four hydrogen atoms (CH_4). How can we calculate the mass of 1 mole of methane; that is, what is the mass of 6.022×10^{23} CH_4 molecules? Since each CH_4 molecule contains one carbon atom and four hydrogen atoms, 1 mole of CH_4 molecules consists of 1 mole of carbon atoms and 4 moles of hydrogen atoms. The mass of 1 mole of methane can be found by summing the masses of carbon and hydrogen present:

The average atomic mass for carbon to five significant digits is 12.011.

$$
\begin{aligned}
\text{Mass of 1 mol of C} \quad &= \quad 12.011 \text{ g} \\
\text{Mass of 4 mol of H} \quad &= 4 \times 1.008 \text{ g} \\
\hline
\text{Mass of 1 mol of } CH_4 \quad &= \quad 16.043 \text{ g}
\end{aligned}
$$

⬥WL INTERACTIVE EXAMPLE 3.4

Isopentyl acetate ($C_7H_{14}O_2$), the compound responsible for the scent of bananas, can be produced commercially. Interestingly, bees release about 1 μg (1×10^{-6} g) of this compound when they sting to attract other bees to join the attack. How many molecules of isopentyl acetate are released in a typical bee sting? How many atoms of carbon are present?

Solution Since we are given a mass of isopentyl acetate and want the number of molecules, we must first compute the molar mass.

The average atomic mass for hydrogen to five significant digits is 1.0079 and that for oxygen is 15.999.

$$7 \text{ mol C} \times 12.011 \frac{\text{g}}{\text{mol}} \ = \ 84.077 \text{ g C}$$

$$14 \text{ mol H} \times 1.0079 \frac{\text{g}}{\text{mol}} \ = \ 14.111 \text{ g H}$$

$$2 \text{ mol O} \times 15.999 \frac{\text{g}}{\text{mol}} \ = \ \underline{31.998 \text{ g O}}$$

$$\text{Mass of 1 mol of } C_7H_{14}O_2 = 130.186 \text{ g}$$

Thus 1 mole of isopentyl acetate (6.022×10^{23} molecules) has a mass of 130.186 g.

To find the number of molecules released in a sting, we must first determine the number of moles of isopentyl acetate in 1×10^6 g:

$$1 \times 10^{-6} \text{ g } C_7H_{14}O_2 \times \frac{1 \text{ mol } C_7H_{14}O_2}{130.186 \text{ g } C_7H_{14}O_2} = 8 \times 10^{-9} \text{ mol } C_7H_{14}O_2$$

Since 1 mol is 6.022×10^{23} units, we can determine the number of molecules:

$$8 \times 10^{-9} \text{ mol } C_7H_{14}O_2 \times \frac{6.022 \times 10^{23} \text{ molecules}}{1 \text{ mol } C_7H_{14}O_2} = 5 \times 10^{15} \text{ molecules}$$

Chemical Insights

Measuring the Masses of Large Molecules or Making Elephants Fly

When a chemist produces a new molecule, one crucial property for making a positive identification is the molecule's mass. There are many ways to determine the molar mass of a compound, but one of the fastest and most accurate methods involves mass spectrometry. This method requires that the substance be put into the gas phase and ionized. The deflection that the resulting ion exhibits as it is accelerated through a magnetic field can be used to obtain a very precise value of its mass. One drawback of this method is that it is difficult to use with large molecules because they are difficult to vaporize. That is, substances that contain large molecules typically have very high boiling points, and these molecules are often damaged when they are vaporized at such high temperatures. A case in point involves proteins, an extremely important class of large biologic molecules that are quite fragile at high temperatures. Typical methods used to obtain the masses of protein molecules are slow and tedious.

Mass spectrometry has not previously been used to obtain protein masses because proteins decompose at the temperatures necessary to vaporize them. However, a relatively new technique called matrix-assisted laser desorption has been developed that allows mass spectrometric determination of protein molar masses. In this technique, the large "target" molecule is embedded in a matrix of smaller molecules. The matrix is then placed in a mass spectrometer and blasted with a laser beam, which causes its disintegration. Disintegration of the matrix frees the large target molecule, which is then swept into the mass spectrometer. One researcher involved in this project likened this method to an elephant on top of a tall building: "The elephant must fly if the building suddenly turns into fine grains of sand."

This technique allows scientists to determine the masses of huge molecules. So far, researchers have measured proteins with masses up to 350,000 daltons (1 dalton is equal to 1 atomic mass unit). This method probably will be extended to even larger molecules such as DNA and could be a revolutionary development in the characterization of biomolecules.

To determine the number of carbon atoms present, we must multiply the number of molecules by 7 (each molecule of isopentyl acetate contains seven carbon atoms):

$$5 \times 10^{15} \text{ molecules} \times \frac{7 \text{ carbon atoms}}{\text{molecule}} = 4 \times 10^{16} \text{ carbon atoms}$$

Note: In keeping with our practice of always showing the correct number of significant figures, we have rounded off after each step. However, if extra digits are carried throughout this problem, the final answer rounds to 3×10^{16}.

To show the correct number of significant figures in each calculation, we round off after each step. In your calculations, always carry extra significant figures through to the end; then round off.

Since the number 16.043 represents the mass of 1 mole of methane molecules, it makes sense to call it the *molar mass* for methane. However, traditionally, the term *molecular weight* has been used to describe the mass of 1 mole of a substance. Thus the terms **molar mass** and **molecular weight** mean exactly the same thing: *the mass in grams of 1 mole of a compound*. The molar mass of a known substance is obtained by summing the masses of the component atoms, as we did for methane.

A substance's molar mass (molecular weight) is the mass in grams of 1 mole of the substance.

Some substances exist as a collection of ions rather than as separate molecules. An example is ordinary table salt, sodium chloride (NaCl), which is composed of an array of Na^+ and Cl^- ions. There are no NaCl molecules present. However, in this text, for convenience, we will apply the term *molar mass* to both ionic and molecular substances. Thus we will refer to 58.44

(22.99 + 35.45) as the molar mass for NaCl. In some texts the term *formula weight* is used for ionic compounds instead of the terms *molar mass* and *molecular weight*.

3.4 | Conceptual Problem Solving

One of the great rewards of studying chemistry is to become a good problem solver. Being able to solve complex problems is a talent that will serve you well in all walks of life. It is our purpose in this text to help you learn to solve problems in a flexible, creative way based on understanding the fundamental ideas of chemistry. We call this approach **conceptual problem solving.**

The ultimate goal is to be able to solve new problems (that is, problems you have not seen before) on your own. In this text we will provide problems and offer solutions by explaining how to think about the problems. Although the answers to these problems are important, it is perhaps even more important to understand the process—the thinking necessary to get the answer. While studying the solution, it is crucial that you interactively think through the problem with us. Do not skip the discussion and jump to the answer. Make sure that you understand each step in the process.

A main goal in conceptual problem solving is to get the "big picture"—a real understanding of the situation. This approach to problem solving looks within the problem for a solution. In essence, we ask a series of questions as we proceed and use our knowledge of fundamental principles to answer these questions; we then let the problem (and our questions) guide us as we solve it.

The following organizing principles will be useful to us as we proceed to solve a problem:

- First, we need to read the problem and decide on the final goal. Then we sort through the facts given, focusing on the key words and, when appropriate, drawing a diagram of the problem. In this part of the analysis we need to state the problem as simply as possible. The questions we ask at first are general and similar regardless of the problem. They are basically of the type "What are we trying to solve?" and "What does this mean?"

- We need to work backward from the final goal to decide where to start. Our questions become more specific depending on the given problem, such as, "What are the reactants and products?" "What is the balanced equation?" "What do we mean by molar mass?" and so on. Our understanding of the fundamental principles of chemistry will enable us to answer each of these questions and will eventually lead us to the final solution.

- After getting an answer we should check to see whether it is reasonable. The extent to which we can do this varies with the type of problem. If we are computing mass percents of elements in a compound, do they add up to 100%? Do we get a negative answer for a mass? Sometimes it is more difficult to judge if an answer is reasonable. However, once we get the solution of the problem, we should ask, "Does it make sense?"

In summary, instead of looking outside the problem using a memorized scheme, we will look inside the problem and let the problem help us as we proceed to a solution. Learning this approach requires some patience, but the reward for learning to solve problems this way is that you become an effective solver of any new problem that confronts you in daily life or in your work in any field. You will no longer panic when you see a problem that is different in some ways from those you have solved in the past. Although you might be frustrated at times as you learn this method, we guarantee that it will pay dividends later and should make your experience with chemistry a positive one that will prepare you for any career you choose.

We will model this approach with the examples in this text, beginning with Example 3.5. We will continue this approach throughout the examples in Chapters 3 and 4. We will not, however, discuss all example problems throughout the text to this extent because we expect you to take an increasingly active role in this process. As the problems become more complicated, the method of conceptual problem solving becomes more important, and it is crucial that you work through these on your own before reading the solution.

3.5 | Percent Composition of Compounds

So far we have discussed the composition of a compound in terms of the numbers of its constituent atoms. It is often useful to know a compound's composition in terms of the masses of its elements. We can obtain this information from the formula of the compound by comparing the mass of each element present in 1 mole of the compound with the total mass of 1 mole of the compound.

For example, consider ethanol, which has the formula C_2H_5OH. The mass of each element present and the molar mass are obtained through the following procedure:

$$\text{Mass of C} = 2 \text{ mol} \times 12.011 \frac{g}{mol} = 24.022 \text{ g}$$

$$\text{Mass of H} = 6 \text{ mol} \times 1.008 \frac{g}{mol} = 6.048 \text{ g}$$

$$\text{Mass of O} = 1 \text{ mol} \times 15.999 \frac{g}{mol} = 15.999 \text{ g}$$

$$\text{Mass of 1 mol of } C_2H_5OH = 46.069 \text{ g}$$

The **mass percent** (often called the weight percent) of carbon in ethanol can be computed by comparing the mass of carbon in 1 mole of ethanol with the total mass of 1 mole of ethanol and multiplying the result by 100%:

$$\text{Mass percent of C} = \frac{\text{mass of C in 1 mol } C_2H_5OH}{\text{mass of 1 mol } C_2H_5OH} \times 100\%$$

$$= \frac{24.022 \text{ g}}{46.069 \text{ g}} \times 100\%$$

$$= 52.144\%$$

The mass percents of hydrogen and oxygen in ethanol are obtained in a similar manner:

$$\text{Mass percent of H} = \frac{\text{mass of H in 1 mol } C_2H_5OH}{\text{mass of 1 mol } C_2H_5OH} \times 100\%$$

$$= \frac{6.048 \text{ g}}{46.069 \text{ g}} \times 100\%$$

$$= 13.13\%$$

$$\text{Mass percent of O} = \frac{\text{mass of O in 1 mol } C_2H_5OH}{\text{mass of 1 mol } C_2H_5OH} \times 100\%$$

$$= \frac{15.999 \text{ g}}{46.069 \text{ g}} \times 100\%$$

$$= 34.728\%$$

Notice that the percentages add to 100% if rounded to two decimal places; this is the check of the calculations.

❂WL INTERACTIVE EXAMPLE 3.5

Penicillin, the first of a now large number of antibiotics (antibacterial agents), was discovered accidentally by the Scottish bacteriologist Alexander Fleming in 1928, but he was never able to isolate it as a pure compound. This and similar antibiotics have saved millions of lives that might have been lost to infections. Penicillin F has the formula $C_{14}H_{20}N_2SO_4$. Compute the mass percent of each element.

Solution As we discussed in Section 3.4, your solution to a problem should begin with questions, the first of which is:

■ What is the problem asking us to solve?

In this case you are asked to determine the mass percent of each element in penicillin F. This leads directly to the next question:

■ What does this mean?

The mass percent for a given element in a compound is the mass of the element in the compound as a percentage of the mass of the compound. We know the formula for penicillin F is $C_{14}H_{20}N_2SO_4$. The mass percent of carbon, for example, is

$$\text{Mass percent of carbon} = \frac{\text{Mass of carbon in 1 mole of } C_{14}H_{20}N_2SO_4}{\text{Mass of 1 mole of } C_{14}H_{20}N_2SO_4} \times 100\%$$

Notice how we are letting the problem guide us. The original problem was to find the mass percent of each element in a compound. By using the definition of mass percent, we see that we will solve for each element individually. We also have changed the problem to two new and more specific questions:

1. What is the mass of carbon in 1 mole of penicillin F? (the numerator above)
2. What is the mass of 1 mole of penicillin F? (the denominator above)

From the discussion in Section 3.3, we see that the second question is asking for the molar mass of penicillin F. This shows us that although allowing the problem to guide us is important, we also need knowledge of fundamental principles. The molar mass of penicillin F is computed as follows:

$$\text{C:} \quad 14 \text{ mol} \times 12.011 \frac{g}{\text{mol}} = 168.15 \text{ g}$$

$$\text{H:} \quad 20 \text{ mol} \times 1.008 \frac{g}{\text{mol}} = 20.16 \text{ g}$$

$$\text{N:} \quad 2 \text{ mol} \times 14.007 \frac{g}{\text{mol}} = 28.014 \text{ g}$$

$$\text{S:} \quad 1 \text{ mol} \times 32.07 \frac{g}{\text{mol}} = 32.07 \text{ g}$$

$$\text{O:} \quad 4 \text{ mol} \times 15.999 \frac{g}{\text{mol}} = 63.996 \text{ g}$$

$$\text{Mass of 1 mol of } C_{14}H_{20}N_2SO_4 = 312.39 \text{ g}$$

Notice that in solving for the molar mass of penicillin F, we also solved for the mass of each element in 1 mole of the compound. With these masses we can determine the mass percent of each element:

$$\text{Mass percent of C} = \frac{168.15 \text{ g C}}{312.39 \text{ g } C_{14}H_{20}N_2SO_4} \times 100\% = 53.827\%$$

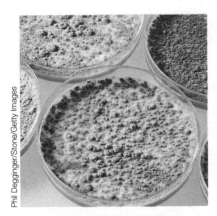

Penicillin is isolated from a mold.

Dorothy Hodgkin (1910–1994) was born in Cairo, Egypt. She became interested in chemistry and in crystals at about the age of 10, and on her 16th birthday she received a book by the Nobel Prize–winning physicist William Bragg. The subject of the book was how to use X rays to analyze crystals, and from that point on, her career path was set.

Dr. Hodgkin used X-ray analysis for three important discoveries. In 1945 she determined the structure of penicillin, which helped manufacturers create penicillin. In 1954 she determined the structure of vitamin B_{12}, which led to her winning the Nobel Prize in Chemistry in 1964. Although both of these are important and useful discoveries, Dr. Hodgkin considered her greatest scientific achievement to be the discovery of insulin (1969), now used in the treatment of diabetes.

$$\text{Mass percent of H} = \frac{20.16 \text{ g H}}{312.39 \text{ g C}_{14}\text{H}_{20}\text{N}_2\text{SO}_4} \times 100\% = 6.453\%$$

$$\text{Mass percent of N} = \frac{28.014 \text{ g N}}{312.39 \text{ g C}_{14}\text{H}_{20}\text{N}_2\text{SO}_4} \times 100\% = 8.968\%$$

$$\text{Mass percent of S} = \frac{32.07 \text{ g S}}{312.39 \text{ g C}_{14}\text{H}_{20}\text{N}_2\text{SO}_4} \times 100\% = 10.27\%$$

$$\text{Mass percent of O} = \frac{63.996 \text{ g O}}{312.39 \text{ g C}_{14}\text{H}_{20}\text{N}_2\text{SO}_4} \times 100\% = 20.486\%$$

Finally, we can check that the answer is reasonable because the percentages add up to 100%.

Let's summarize the approach:

1. We started with the general question, "What are we trying to solve?"

2. Once we decided on the answer to question 1, we explained what this meant, in this case with a formula.

3. We let the answers guide us to new questions, which were more specific to the problem (such as, "What is the mass of 1 mole of $C_{14}H_{20}N_2SO_4$?").

4. We answered these specific questions using knowledge of fundamental principles.

5. We came to the solution.

This approach will guide you in solving problems throughout the textbook. No matter how complicated the problems become, you should always know specifically what you are trying to solve and then ask (and answer) questions to get to the solution. Your knowledge is important as well, and in chemistry this knowledge builds. Solving this particular problem, for example, would not have been possible without knowing what a chemical formula means and without an understanding of molar mass.

3.6 | Determining the Formula of a Compound

When a new compound is prepared, one of the first items of interest is its formula. The formula is often determined by taking a weighed sample of the compound and either decomposing it into its component elements or reacting it with oxygen to produce substances such as CO_2, H_2O, and N_2, which are then collected and weighed. A device for doing this type of analysis is shown in Fig. 3.5. The results of such analyses provide the mass of each type of element in the compound, which can be used to determine the mass percent of each element present.

We will see how information of this type can be used to compute the formula of a compound. Suppose a substance has been prepared that is composed of carbon, hydrogen, and nitrogen. When 0.1156 gram of this compound is reacted with oxygen, 0.1638 gram of carbon dioxide (CO_2) and 0.1676 gram of water (H_2O) are collected. Assuming that all of the carbon in the compound

Figure 3.5
A schematic diagram of the combustion device used to analyze substances for carbon and hydrogen. The sample is burned in the presence of excess oxygen, which converts all of its carbon to carbon dioxide and all of its hydrogen to water. These compounds are collected by absorption using appropriate materials, and their amounts are determined by measuring the increase in weights of the absorbents.

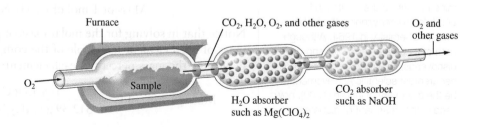

Furnace CO_2, H_2O, O_2, and other gases O_2 and other gases

O_2 Sample H_2O absorber such as $Mg(ClO_4)_2$ CO_2 absorber such as NaOH

is converted to CO_2, we can determine the mass of carbon originally present in the 0.1156-gram sample. To do so, we must use the fraction (by mass) of carbon in CO_2. The molar mass of CO_2 is 12.011 g/mol plus 2(15.999) g/mol, or 44.009 g/mol. The fraction of carbon present by mass (12.011 grams C/44.009 grams CO_2) can now be used to determine the mass of carbon in 0.1638 gram of CO_2:

$$0.1638 \text{ g } CO_2 \times \frac{12.011 \text{ g C}}{44.009 \text{ g } CO_2} = 0.04470 \text{ g C}$$

Remember that this carbon originally came from the 0.1156-gram sample of the unknown compound. Thus the mass percent of carbon in this compound is

$$\frac{0.04470 \text{ g C}}{0.1156 \text{ g compound}} \times 100\% = 38.67\% \text{ C}$$

The same procedure can be used to find the mass percent of hydrogen in the unknown compound. We assume that all of the hydrogen present in the original 0.1156 gram of compound was converted to H_2O. The molar mass of H_2O is 18.015 grams, and the fraction of hydrogen by mass in H_2O is 2.016 grams H/18.015 grams H_2O. Therefore, the mass of hydrogen in 0.1676 gram of H_2O is

$$0.1676 \text{ g } H_2O \times \frac{2.016 \text{ g H}}{18.015 \text{ g } H_2O} = 0.01876 \text{ g H}$$

And the mass percent of hydrogen in the compound is

$$\frac{0.01876 \text{ g H}}{0.1156 \text{ g compound}} \times 100\% = 16.23\% \text{ H}$$

The unknown compound contains only carbon, hydrogen, and nitrogen. So far, we have determined that it is 38.67% carbon and 16.23% hydrogen. The remainder must be nitrogen:

$$100.00\% - (38.67\% + 16.23\%) = 45.10\% \text{ N}$$
$$\uparrow \qquad\quad \uparrow$$
$$\% \text{ C} \qquad \% \text{ H}$$

We have determined that the compound contains 38.67% carbon, 16.23% hydrogen, and 45.10% nitrogen. Next, we use these data to obtain the formula.

Since the formula of a compound indicates the *numbers* of atoms in the compound, we must convert the masses of the elements to numbers of atoms. The easiest way to do this is to work with 100.00 grams of the compound. In the present case 38.67% carbon by mass means 38.67 grams of carbon per 100.00 grams of compound; 16.23% hydrogen means 16.23 grams of hydrogen per 100.00 grams of compound; and so on. To determine the formula, we must calculate the number of carbon atoms in 38.67 grams of carbon, the number of hydrogen atoms in 16.23 grams of hydrogen, and the number of nitrogen atoms in 45.10 grams of nitrogen. We can do this as follows:

$$38.67 \text{ g C} \times \frac{1 \text{ mol C}}{12.011 \text{ g C}} = 3.220 \text{ mol C}$$

$$16.23 \text{ g H} \times \frac{1 \text{ mol H}}{1.008 \text{ g H}} = 16.10 \text{ mol H}$$

$$45.10 \text{ g N} \times \frac{1 \text{ mol N}}{14.007 \text{ g N}} = 3.220 \text{ mol N}$$

Thus 100.00 grams of this compound contains 3.220 moles of carbon atoms, 16.10 moles of hydrogen atoms, and 3.220 moles of nitrogen atoms.

Figure 3.6
Examples of substances whose empirical and molecular formulas differ. Notice that molecular formula = (empirical formula)$_x$, where x is an integer.

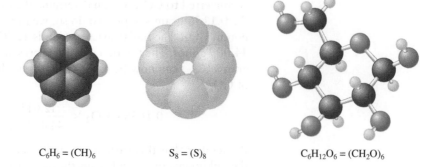

$C_6H_6 = (CH)_6$ $\qquad$ $S_8 = (S)_8$ $\qquad$ $C_6H_{12}O_6 = (CH_2O)_6$

We can find the smallest *whole-number ratio* of atoms in this compound by dividing each of the mole values above by the smallest of the three:

$$C: \qquad \frac{3.220}{3.220} = 1$$

$$H: \qquad \frac{16.10}{3.220} = 5$$

$$N: \qquad \frac{3.220}{3.220} = 1$$

Thus the formula of this compound can be written CH_5N. This formula is called the **empirical formula**. It represents the *simplest whole-number ratio of the various types of atoms in a compound.*

If this compound is molecular, then the formula might well be CH_5N. It might also be $C_2H_{10}N_2$, or $C_3H_{15}N_3$, and so on—that is, some multiple of the simplest whole-number ratio. Each of these alternatives also has the correct relative numbers of atoms. Any molecule that can be represented as $(CH_5N)_x$, where x is an integer, has the empirical formula CH_5N. To be able to specify the exact formula of the molecule involved, the **molecular formula,** we must know the molar mass.

Suppose we know that this compound with empirical formula CH_5N has a molar mass of 31.06. How do we determine which of the possible choices represents the molecular formula? Since the molecular formula is always a whole-number multiple of the empirical formula, we must first find the empirical formula mass for CH_5N:

$$1\ C: \qquad 1 \times 12.011\ g = 12.011\ g$$

$$5\ H: \qquad 5 \times \ 1.008\ g = \ 5.040\ g$$

$$1\ N: \qquad 1 \times 14.007\ g = \underline{14.007\ g}$$

Formula mass of CH_5N = 31.058 g

This value is the same as the known molar mass of the compound. Thus, in this case, the empirical formula and the molecular formula are the same; this substance consists of molecules with the formula CH_5N. It is quite common for the empirical and molecular formulas to be different; some examples in which this is the case are shown in Fig. 3.6.

Molecular formula = (empirical formula)$_x$, where x is an integer.

ⓦWL INTERACTIVE EXAMPLE 3.6

A white powder is analyzed and found to contain 43.64% phosphorus and 56.36% oxygen by mass. The compound has a molar mass of 283.88 g. What are the compound's empirical and molecular formulas?

Solution

■ What are we trying to solve?

In this problem we are asked to solve for the empirical and molecular formulas for a compound.

■ What does this mean?

The empirical formula is the simplest whole-number ratio of the atoms in the compound, and the molecular formula is the actual formula for the compound. In both cases the formula will look like P_xO_y, and we are trying to solve for x and y.

We know x and y represent numbers of atoms (or relative moles of atoms), but we are given mass percents of the elements in the compound. So now we have a new question:

■ How can we convert a mass percent of an element to the moles of atoms?

We know we can convert mass to moles of atoms using atomic masses. So, we must convert a mass percent to a mass, and a mass to a number.

One way—although not the only way—is to realize that mass percents have the same value as masses if we assume 100.00 g of the sample. Thus, in 100.00 g of this compound, there are 43.64 g of phosphorus and 56.36 g of oxygen. If we convert these masses to moles, the ratio of the numbers of moles of each element represents the ratio of x to y in the formula. In terms of moles, in 100.00 g of compound we have

$$43.64 \text{ g P} \times \frac{1 \text{ mol P}}{30.97 \text{ g P}} = 1.409 \text{ mol P}$$

$$56.36 \text{ g O} \times \frac{1 \text{ mol O}}{15.999 \text{ g O}} = 3.523 \text{ mol O}$$

These numbers give us a ratio of moles of atoms of P/O, but the empirical formula is the *simplest whole-number ratio* of these atoms. Dividing both mole values by the smaller one gives

$$\frac{1.409}{1.409} = 1 \text{ P} \quad \text{and} \quad \frac{3.523}{1.409} = 2.5 \text{ O}$$

This yields the formula $PO_{2.5}$. Since compounds must contain whole numbers of atoms, the empirical formula should contain only whole numbers. To obtain the simplest set of whole numbers, we multiply both numbers by 2 to give the empirical formula P_2O_5.

To obtain the molecular formula, we must compare the empirical formula mass with the molar mass. The empirical formula mass for P_2O_5 is 141.94.

$$\frac{\text{Molar mass}}{\text{Empirical formula mass}} = \frac{283.88}{141.94} = 2$$

The molecular formula is $(P_2O_5)_2$, or P_4O_{10}.

■ Does the answer make sense?

The molar mass of the compound is a whole-number multiple of the empirical molar mass, which should make us more confident about the answer. The structural formula of this interesting compound is given in Fig. 3.7.

In Example 3.6 we found the molecular formula by comparing the empirical formula mass with the molar mass. There is an alternative way to obtain the molecular formula. The molar mass and the percentages (by mass) of each element present can be used to compute the moles of each element

Figure 3.7
The structural formula of P_4O_{10}. Note that some of the oxygen atoms act as "bridges" between the phosphorus atoms. This compound has a great affinity for water and is often used as a desiccant, or drying agent.

present in one mole of compound. These numbers of moles then represent directly the subscripts in the molecular formula. This procedure is illustrated in Example 3.7.

⍟WL INTERACTIVE EXAMPLE 3.7

Caffeine, a stimulant found in coffee, tea, chocolate, and some medications, contains 49.48% carbon, 5.15% hydrogen, 28.87% nitrogen, and 16.49% oxygen by mass and has a molar mass of 194.2. Determine the molecular formula of caffeine.

Solution

▪ What are we trying to solve?

In this problem we are asked to solve for the molecular formula for caffeine.

▪ What does this mean?

The molecular formula will look like $C_aH_bN_cO_d$, where a, b, c, and d are whole numbers. We need to solve for a, b, c, and d.

This problem is similar to Example 3.6, but in this case, we are going to determine the molecular formula without the empirical formula.

▪ How can we use percent by mass data of an element and the molar mass?

By multiplying the molar mass of the compound by the individual percents by mass of each element, we can determine the mass of each element in 1 mole (194.2 g) of caffeine:

$$\frac{49.48 \text{ g C}}{100.0 \text{ g caffeine}} \times \frac{194.2 \text{ g}}{\text{mol}} = \frac{96.09 \text{ g C}}{\text{mol caffeine}}$$

$$\frac{5.15 \text{ g H}}{100.0 \text{ g caffeine}} \times \frac{194.2 \text{ g}}{\text{mol}} = \frac{10.0 \text{ g H}}{\text{mol caffeine}}$$

$$\frac{28.87 \text{ g N}}{100.0 \text{ g caffeine}} \times \frac{194.2 \text{ g}}{\text{mol}} = \frac{56.07 \text{ g N}}{\text{mol caffeine}}$$

$$\frac{16.49 \text{ g O}}{100.0 \text{ g caffeine}} \times \frac{194.2 \text{ g}}{\text{mol}} = \frac{32.02 \text{ g O}}{\text{mol caffeine}}$$

We have masses and we need moles, which we can compute using atomic masses.

$$\text{C:} \quad \frac{96.09 \text{ g C}}{\text{mol caffeine}} \times \frac{1 \text{ mol C}}{12.011 \text{ g C}} = \frac{8.000 \text{ mol C}}{\text{mol caffeine}}$$

$$\text{H:} \quad \frac{10.0 \text{ g H}}{\text{mol caffeine}} \times \frac{1 \text{ mol H}}{1.008 \text{ g H}} = \frac{9.92 \text{ mol H}}{\text{mol caffeine}}$$

$$\text{N:} \quad \frac{56.07 \text{ g N}}{\text{mol caffeine}} \times \frac{1 \text{ mol N}}{14.01 \text{ g N}} = \frac{4.002 \text{ mol N}}{\text{mol caffeine}}$$

$$\text{O:} \quad \frac{32.02 \text{ g O}}{\text{mol caffeine}} \times \frac{1 \text{ mol O}}{16.00 \text{ g O}} = \frac{2.001 \text{ mol O}}{\text{mol caffeine}}$$

Rounding the numbers to integers gives the molecular formula for caffeine: $C_8H_{10}N_4O_2$.

▪ Does the answer make sense?

The answers to the number of moles should be whole numbers, because, unlike the first part of the solution to Example 3.6, we are solving for the actual number of moles of each element in 1 mole of the compound. There is not much rounding needed to get whole numbers for the subscripts. This is a good sign.

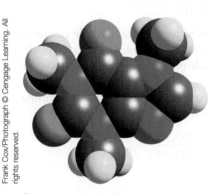

Computer-generated molecule of caffeine.

The methods for obtaining empirical and molecular formulas are summarized below.

Numbers very close to whole numbers, such as 9.92 and 1.08, should be rounded to whole numbers. Numbers such as 2.25, 4.33, and 2.72 should not be rounded to whole numbers.

STEPS | **Determination of the Empirical Formula**

1 Since mass percent gives the number of grams of a particular element per 100 grams of compound, base the calculation on 100 grams of compound. Each percent will then represent the mass in grams of that element present in the compound.

2 Determine the number of moles of each element present in 100 grams of compound using the atomic weights (masses) of the elements present.

3 Divide each value of the number of moles by the smallest of the values. If each resulting number is a whole number (after appropriate rounding), these numbers represent the subscripts of the elements in the empirical formula.

4 If the numbers obtained in the previous step are not whole numbers, multiply each number by an integer so that the results are all whole numbers.

STEPS | **Determination of the Molecular Formula**

Method 1

1 Obtain the empirical formula.

2 Compute the empirical formula mass.

3 Calculate the ratio:

$$\frac{\text{Molar mass}}{\text{Empirical formula mass}}$$

4 The integer from the previous step represents the number of empirical formula units in one molecule. When the empirical formula subscripts are multiplied by this integer, we obtain the molecular formula.

Method 2

1 Using the mass percents and the molar mass, determine the mass of each element present in 1 mole of compound.

2 Determine the number of moles of each element present in 1 mole of compound.

3 The integers from the previous step represent the subscripts in the molecular formula.

3.7 | Chemical Equations

Chemical Reactions

A chemical change involves reorganization of the atoms in one or more substances. For example, when the methane (CH_4) in natural gas combines with oxygen (O_2) in the air and burns, carbon dioxide (CO_2) and water (H_2O) are formed. This process is represented by a **chemical equation** with the **reactants** (here methane and oxygen) on the left side of an arrow and the **products** (carbon dioxide and water) on the right side:

$$CH_4 + O_2 \longrightarrow CO_2 + H_2O$$

Reactants   Products

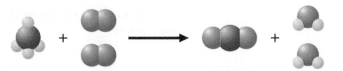

Figure 3.8
The reaction between methane and oxygen to give water and carbon dioxide. Note that no atoms have been gained or lost in the reaction. The reaction simply reorganizes the atoms.

A flare in a natural gas field is an example of a chemical reaction.

Notice that the atoms have been reorganized. *Bonds have been broken and new ones formed.* Remember that *in a chemical reaction, atoms are neither created nor destroyed. All atoms present in the reactants must be accounted for among the products.* In other words, there must be the same number of each type of atom on the product side as there is on the reactant side of the arrow. Making sure that this rule is followed is called **balancing a chemical equation** for a reaction. The equation just shown for the reaction between CH_4 and O_2 is not balanced. As we will see in the next section, the equation can be balanced to produce

$$CH_4 + 2O_2 \longrightarrow CO_2 + 2H_2O$$

This reaction is shown graphically in Fig. 3.8. We can check whether the equation is balanced by comparing the number of each type of atom on both sides:

$$CH_4 + 2O_2 \longrightarrow CO_2 + 2H_2O$$

$$1\,C \quad 4\,H \qquad \qquad 1\,C \qquad 4\,H$$
$$4\,O \qquad \qquad 2\,O \qquad 2\,O$$

The Meaning of a Chemical Equation

The chemical equation for a reaction provides two important types of information: the nature of the reactants and products and the relative numbers of each. The reactants and products in a specific reaction must be identified by experiment. Besides specifying the compounds involved in the reaction, the equation often includes the *physical states* of the reactants and products:

State	Symbol
Solid	(*s*)
Liquid	(*l*)
Gas	(*g*)
Dissolved in water (in aqueous solution)	(*aq*)

For example, when hydrochloric acid in aqueous solution is added to solid sodium hydrogen carbonate, the products carbon dioxide gas, liquid water, and sodium chloride (which dissolves in the water) are formed:

$$HCl(aq) + NaHCO_3(s) \longrightarrow CO_2(g) + H_2O(l) + NaCl(aq)$$

The relative numbers of reactants and products in a reaction are indicated by the *coefficients* in the balanced equation. (The coefficients can be determined since we know that the same number of each type of atom must occur on both sides of the equation.) For example, the balanced equation

$$CH_4(g) + 2O_2(g) \longrightarrow CO_2(g) + 2H_2O(g)$$

can be interpreted in several equivalent ways, as shown in Table 3.2. Note that the total mass is 80 grams for both reactants and products. We should expect this result, since chemical reactions involve only a rearrangement of atoms. Atoms, and therefore mass, are conserved in a chemical reaction.

Table 3.2

Information Conveyed by the Balanced Equation for the Combustion of Methane

Reactants	$\longrightarrow$	Products
$CH_4(g) + 2O_2(g)$	$\longrightarrow$	$CO_2(g) + 2H_2O(g)$
1 molecule CH_4 + 2 molecules O_2	$\longrightarrow$	1 molecule CO_2 + 2 molecules H_2O
1 mole of CH_4 molecules + 2 moles of O_2 molecules	$\longrightarrow$	1 mole of CO_2 molecules + 2 moles of H_2O molecules
6.022×10^{23} CH_4 molecules + $2(6.022 \times 10^{23})$ O_2 molecules	$\longrightarrow$	6.022×10^{23} CO_2 molecules + $2(6.022 \times 10^{23})$ H_2O molecules
16 g CH_4 + 2(32 g) O_2	$\longrightarrow$	44 g CO_2 + 2(18 g) H_2O
80 g reactants	$\longrightarrow$	80 g products

From this discussion you can see that a balanced chemical equation gives you a great deal of information.

3.8 | Balancing Chemical Equations

An unbalanced chemical equation is of limited use. Whenever you see an equation, you should ask yourself whether it is balanced. The principle that lies at the heart of the balancing process is that atoms are conserved in a chemical reaction. The same number of each type of atom must be found among the reactants and products. Also, remember that the identities of the reactants and products of a reaction are determined by experimental observation. For example, when liquid ethanol is burned in the presence of sufficient oxygen gas, the products will always be carbon dioxide and water. When the equation for this reaction is balanced, the *identities* of the reactants and products must not be changed. *The formulas of the compounds must never be changed when balancing a chemical equation.* That is, the subscripts in a formula cannot be changed, nor can atoms be added or subtracted from a formula.

In balancing equations, start with the most complicated molecule.

Most chemical equations can be balanced by inspection—that is, by trial and error. It is always best to start with the most complicated molecules (those containing the greatest number of atoms). For example, consider the reaction of ethanol with oxygen, given by the unbalanced equation

$$C_2H_5OH(l) + O_2(g) \longrightarrow CO_2(g) + H_2O(g)$$

The most complicated molecule here is C_2H_5OH. We will begin by balancing the products that contain the atoms in C_2H_5OH. Since C_2H_5OH contains two carbon atoms, we place a 2 before the CO_2 to balance the carbon atoms:

$$C_2H_5OH(l) + O_2(g) \longrightarrow 2CO_2(g) + H_2O(g)$$
2 C atoms   2 C atoms

Since C_2H_5OH contains six hydrogen atoms, the hydrogen atoms can be balanced by placing a 3 before the H_2O:

$$C_2H_5OH(l) + O_2(g) \longrightarrow 2CO_2(g) + 3H_2O(g)$$
(5 + 1) H   (3 × 2) H

Last, we balance the oxygen atoms. Note that the right side of the preceding equation contains seven oxygen atoms, whereas the left side has only three.

We can correct this by putting a 3 before the O_2 to produce the balanced equation:

$$C_2H_5OH(l) + 3O_2(g) \longrightarrow 2CO_2(g) + 3H_2O(g)$$

1 O   6 O   (2 × 2) O   3 O

Now we check:

$$C_2H_5OH(l) + 3O_2(g) \longrightarrow 2CO_2(g) + 3H_2O(g)$$

2 C atoms   2 C atoms
6 H atoms   6 H atoms
7 O atoms   7 O atoms

The balanced equation can be represented by space-filling models as follows:

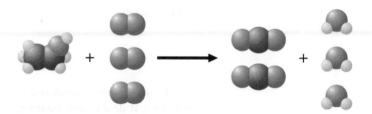

STEPS	**Writing and Balancing the Equation for a Chemical Reaction**

1 Determine what reaction is occurring. What are the reactants, the products, and the states involved?

2 Write the *unbalanced* equation that summarizes the preceding information.

3 Balance the equation by inspection, starting with the most complicated molecule(s). Determine what coefficients are necessary to ensure that the same number of each type of atom appears on both reactant and product sides. Do not change the identities (formulas) of any of the reactants or products.

ⓦWL INTERACTIVE EXAMPLE 3.8

Chromate and dichromate compounds are suspected carcinogens (cancer-inducing agents) and should be handled carefully.

Chromium compounds exhibit a variety of bright colors. When solid ammonium dichromate, $(NH_4)_2Cr_2O_7$, a vivid orange compound, is ignited, a spectacular reaction occurs, as shown in the two photographs on the next page. Although the reaction is somewhat more complex, let's assume here that the products are solid chromium(III) oxide, nitrogen gas (consisting of N_2 molecules), and water vapor. Balance the equation for this reaction.

Solution From the description given, the reactant is solid ammonium dichromate, $(NH_4)_2Cr_2O_7(s)$, and the products are nitrogen gas, $N_2(g)$; water vapor, $H_2O(g)$; and solid chromium(III) oxide, $Cr_2O_3(s)$. The formula for chromium (III) oxide can be determined by recognizing that the Roman numeral III means that Cr^{3+} ions are present. For a neutral compound the formula must then be Cr_2O_3, since each oxide ion is O^{2-}.

The unbalanced equation is

$$(NH_4)_2Cr_2O_7(s) \longrightarrow Cr_2O_3(s) + N_2(g) + H_2O(g)$$

Note that nitrogen and chromium are balanced (two nitrogen atoms and two chromium atoms on each side), but hydrogen and oxygen are not. A coefficient of 4 for H_2O balances the hydrogen atoms:

$$(NH_4)_2Cr_2O_7(s) \longrightarrow Cr_2O_3(s) + N_2(g) + 4H_2O(g)$$
$$(4 \times 2) \text{ H} \qquad\qquad\qquad\qquad\qquad\qquad\qquad (4 \times 2) \text{ H}$$

Note that in balancing the hydrogen, we have also balanced the oxygen since there are seven oxygen atoms in the reactants and in the products.

Check: $\quad$ 2 N, 8 H, 2 Cr, 7 O $\longrightarrow$ 2 N, 8 H, 2 Cr, 7 O

$\qquad\qquad\qquad$ Reactant atoms $\qquad\qquad\qquad$ Product atoms

The equation is balanced.

3.9 | # Stoichiometric Calculations: Amounts of Reactants and Products

Recall that the coefficients in chemical equations represent *numbers* of molecules, not masses of molecules. However, in the laboratory or chemical plant, when a reaction is to be run, the amounts of substances needed cannot be determined by counting molecules directly. Counting is always done by weighing. In this section we will see how chemical equations can be used to deal with *masses* of reacting chemicals.

To develop the principles involved in dealing with the stoichiometry of reactions, we will consider the combustion of propane (C_3H_8), a hydrocarbon used for gas barbecue grills and often used as a fuel in rural areas where natural gas pipelines are not available. Propane reacts with oxygen to produce carbon dioxide and water. We will consider the question, "What mass of oxygen will react with 96.1 grams of propane?" The first thing that must always be done when performing calculations involving chemical reactions is to *write the balanced chemical equation* for the reaction. In this case the balanced equation is

$$C_3H_8(g) + 5O_2(g) \longrightarrow 3CO_2(g) + 4H_2O(g)$$

Recall that this equation means that 1 mole of C_3H_8 will react with 5 moles of O_2 to produce 3 moles of CO_2 and 4 moles of H_2O. To use this equation to find the masses of reactants and products, we must be able to convert between masses and moles of substances. Thus we must first ask, "How many moles of propane are present in 96.1 grams of propane?" The molar mass of propane to three significant figures is 44.1 g/mol. The moles of propane can be calculated as follows:

$$96.1 \text{ g } C_3H_8 \times \frac{1 \text{ mol } C_3H_8}{44.1 \text{ g } C_3H_8} = 2.18 \text{ mol } C_3H_8$$

Next, we must take into account that each mole of propane reacts with 5 moles of oxygen. The best way to do this is to use the balanced equation to construct a **mole ratio**. In this case we want to convert from moles of propane to moles of oxygen. From the balanced equation we see that 5 moles of O_2 is required for each mole of C_3H_8, so the appropriate ratio is

$$\frac{5 \text{ mol } O_2}{1 \text{ mol } C_3H_8}$$

which can be used to calculate the number of moles of O_2 required:

$$2.18 \text{ mol } C_3H_8 \times \frac{5 \text{ mol } O_2}{1 \text{ mol } C_3H_8} = 10.9 \text{ mol } O_2$$

Before doing any calculations involving a chemical reaction, be sure the equation for the reaction is balanced.

Decomposition of ammonium dichromate.

Chemical Insights

High Mountains—Low Octane

The next time you visit a gas station, take a moment to note the octane rating that accompanies the grade of gasoline that you are purchasing. The gasoline is priced according to its octane rating—a measure of the fuel's antiknock properties. In a conventional internal combustion engine, gasoline vapors and air are drawn into the combustion cylinder on the downward stroke of the piston. This air–fuel mixture is compressed on the upward piston stroke (compression stroke), and a spark from the sparkplug ignites the mix. The rhythmic combustion of the air–fuel mix occurring sequentially in several cylinders furnishes the power to propel the vehicle down the road. Excessive heat and pressure (or poor-quality fuel) within the cylinder may cause the premature combustion of the mixture—commonly known as engine "knock" or "ping." Over time, this engine knock can damage the engine, resulting in inefficient performance and costly repairs.

A consumer typically is faced with three choices of gasoline, with octane ratings of 87 (regular), 89 (midgrade), and 93 (premium). But if you happen to travel or live in the higher eleva-

tions of the Rocky Mountain states, you might be surprised to find different octane ratings at the gasoline pumps. The reason for this provides a lesson in stoichiometry. At higher elevations the air is less dense—the volume of oxygen per unit volume of air is smaller. Most engines are designed to achieve a 14:1 oxygen-to-fuel ratio in the cylinder prior to combustion. If less oxygen is available, then less fuel is required to achieve this optimal ratio. In turn, the lower volumes of oxygen and fuel result in a lower pressure in the cylinder. Because high pressure tends to promote knocking, the lower pressure within engine cylinders at higher elevations promotes a more controlled combustion of the air–fuel mixture, and therefore, octane requirements are lower. Although consumers in the Rocky Mountain states can purchase three grades of gasoline, the octane ratings of these fuel blends are different from those in the rest of the United States. In Denver, Colorado, regular gasoline is 85 octane, midgrade is 87 octane, and premium is 91 octane—2 points lower than gasoline sold in most of the rest of the country.

Since the original question asked for the mass of oxygen needed to react with 96.1 grams of propane, the 10.9 moles of O_2 must be converted to *grams*, using the molar mass of O_2:

$$10.9 \text{ mol } O_2 \times \frac{32.0 \text{ g } O_2}{1 \text{ mol } O_2} = 349 \text{ g } O_2$$

Therefore, 349 grams of oxygen is required to burn 96.1 grams of propane.

This example can be extended by asking, "What mass of carbon dioxide is produced when 96.1 grams of propane is combusted with oxygen?" In this case we must convert between moles of propane and moles of carbon dioxide. This conversion can be done by inspecting the balanced equation, which shows that 3 moles of CO_2 is produced for each mole of C_3H_8 reacted:

$$2.18 \text{ mol } C_3H_8 \times \frac{3 \text{ mol } CO_2}{1 \text{ mol } C_3H_8} = 6.54 \text{ mol } CO_2$$

Then we use the molar mass of CO_2 (44.0 g/mol) to calculate the mass of CO_2 produced:

$$6.54 \text{ mol } CO_2 \times \frac{44.0 \text{ g } CO_2}{1 \text{ mol } CO_2} = 288 \text{ g } CO_2$$

The process for finding the mass of carbon dioxide produced from 96.1 grams of propane is summarized here:

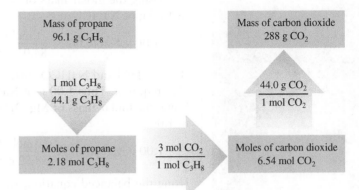

Calculation of Masses of Reactants and Products in Chemical Reactions

1 Balance the equation for the reaction.
2 Convert the known masses of the substances to moles.
3 Use the balanced equation to set up the appropriate mole ratios.
4 Use the appropriate mole ratios to calculate the number of moles of the desired reactant or product.
5 Convert from moles back to grams if required by the problem.

✪WL INTERACTIVE EXAMPLE 3.9

Baking soda ($NaHCO_3$) is often used as an antacid. It neutralizes excess hydrochloric acid secreted by the stomach:

$$NaHCO_3(s) + HCl(aq) \longrightarrow NaCl(aq) + H_2O(l) + CO_2(aq)$$

Milk of magnesia, which is an aqueous suspension of magnesium hydroxide, is also used as an antacid:

$$Mg(OH)_2(s) + 2HCl(aq) \longrightarrow 2H_2O(l) + MgCl_2(aq)$$

Which is the more effective antacid per gram, $NaHCO_3$ or $Mg(OH)_2$?

Solution

■ What are we trying to solve?

In this problem we are asked to determine which antacid is more effective.

■ What does this mean?

The more effective antacid will react with (neutralize) more acid. So to answer this question, we must answer the following:

1. How much HCl is neutralized per gram of $NaHCO_3$?

2. How much HCl is neutralized per gram of $Mg(OH)_2$?

We will then compare the answers and choose the more effective antacid.

■ How can we determine the amount of base (antacid) that reacts with an amount of acid?

We have balanced chemical equations, which give us the mole ratios of $NaHCO_3$/HCl and $Mg(OH)_2$/HCl. Thus we must convert 1.00 g of each

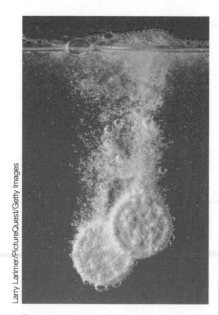

Two antacid tablets containing HCO_3^- dissolve to produce CO_2 gas.

antacid to moles of antacid and then to moles of HCl. The antacid that reacts with the greater number of moles of HCl is the more effective one.

Using the molar mass of $NaHCO_3$, we determine the moles of $NaHCO_3$ in 1.00 g of $NaHCO_3$:

$$1.00 \text{ g NaHCO}_3 \times \frac{1 \text{ mol NaHCO}_3}{84.01 \text{ g NaHCO}_3} = 1.19 \times 10^{-2} \text{ mol NaHCO}_3$$

Because HCl and $NaHCO_3$ react 1:1, this answer also represents the moles of HCl required. Thus 1.00 g of $NaHCO_3$ will neutralize 1.19×10^{-2} mol HCl. Using the molar mass of $Mg(OH)_2$, we next determine the moles of $Mg(OH)_2$ in 1.00 g:

$$1.00 \text{ g Mg(OH)}_2 \times \frac{1 \text{ mol Mg(OH)}_2}{58.32 \text{ g Mg(OH)}_2} = 1.71 \times 10^{-2} \text{ mol Mg(OH)}_2$$

Using the balanced equation, we determine the moles of HCl that will react with this amount of $Mg(OH)_2$:

$$1.71 \times 10^{-2} \text{ mol Mg(OH)}_2 \times \frac{2 \text{ mol HCl}}{1 \text{ mol Mg(OH)}_2} = 3.42 \times 10^{-2} \text{ mol HCl}$$

Thus 1.00 g of $Mg(OH)_2$ will neutralize 3.42×10^{-2} mol HCl. It is a better antacid per gram than $NaHCO_3$.

3.10 | Calculations Involving a Limiting Reactant

When chemicals are mixed together to undergo a reaction, they are often mixed in **stoichiometric quantities**—that is, in exactly the correct amounts so that all reactants "run out" (are used up) at the same time. To clarify this concept, let's consider the production of hydrogen for use in the manufacture of ammonia by the Haber process. Ammonia, a very important fertilizer itself and a starting material for other fertilizers, is made by combining nitrogen from the air with hydrogen according to the equation

$$N_2(g) + 3H_2(g) \longrightarrow 2NH_3(g)$$

The hydrogen for this process is produced from the reaction of methane with water:

$$CH_4(g) + H_2O(g) \longrightarrow 3H_2(g) + CO(g)$$

Now consider the following question: What mass of water is required to react with *exactly* 2.50×10^3 kilograms of methane? That is, how much water will just use up all of the 2.50×10^3 kilograms of methane, leaving no methane or water remaining? Using the principles developed in the preceding section, we can calculate that if 2.50×10^3 kilograms of methane is mixed with 2.81×10^3 kilograms of water, both reactants will run out at the same time. The reactants have been mixed in stoichiometric quantities.

If, however, 2.50×10^3 kilograms of methane is mixed with 3.00×10^3 kilograms of water, the methane will be consumed before the water runs out. The water will be in *excess*. In this case the quantity of products formed will be determined by the quantity of methane present. Once the methane is consumed, no more products can be formed, even though some water still remains. In this situation, because the amount of methane *limits* the amount of products that can be formed, it is called the **limiting reactant,** or **limiting reagent**. In any stoichiometry problem it is essential to determine which reactant is the limiting one to calculate correctly the amounts of products that will be formed.

Figure 3.9

Hydrogen and nitrogen react to form ammonia according to the equation $N_2 + 3H_2 \longrightarrow 2NH_3$.

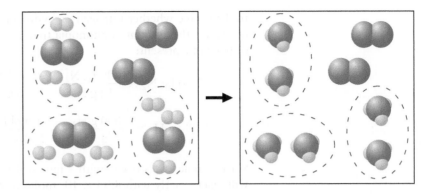

To further explore the idea of a limiting reactant, consider the ammonia synthesis reaction:

$$N_2(g) + 3H_2(g) \longrightarrow 2NH_3(g)$$

Assume that 5 N_2 molecules and 9 H_2 molecules are placed in a flask. Is this a stoichiometric mixture of reactants, or will one of them be consumed before the other runs out? From the balanced equation we know that each N_2 molecule requires 3 H_2 molecules for the reaction to occur:

Thus the required H_2/N_2 ratio is $3H_2/1N_2$. In our experiment, we have 9 H_2 and 5 N_2, or a ratio of $9H_2/5N_2 = 1.8H_2/1N_2$.

Since the actual ratio (1.8:1) of H_2/N_2 is less than the ratio required by the balanced equation (3:1), there is not enough hydrogen to react with all the nitrogen. That is, the hydrogen will run out first, leaving some unreacted N_2 molecules. We can visualize this as shown in Fig. 3.9, which shows that 3 of the N_2 molecules react with the 9 H_2 molecules to produce 6 NH_3 molecules:

$$3N_2 + 9H_2 \longrightarrow 6NH_3$$

This leaves 2 N_2 molecules unreacted—the nitrogen is in excess.

What we have shown here is that in this experiment the hydrogen is the limiting reactant. The amount of H_2 initially present determines the amount of NH_3 that can form. The reaction was not able to use up all the N_2 molecules because the H_2 molecules were all consumed by the first 3 N_2 molecules to react.

In the laboratory or chemical plant we work with much larger quantities than the few molecules of the preceding example. Therefore we must use moles to deal with limiting reactants. The ideas are exactly the same, except that we are using moles of molecules instead of individual molecules. For example, suppose 25.0 kilograms of nitrogen and 5.00 kilograms of hydrogen are mixed and reacted to form ammonia. How do we calculate the mass of ammonia produced when this reaction is run to completion (until one of the reactants is completely consumed)?

As in the preceding example, we must use the balanced equation

$$N_2(g) + 3H_2(g) \longrightarrow 2NH_3(g)$$

to determine whether nitrogen or hydrogen is a limiting reactant and then to determine the amount of ammonia that is formed. We first calculate the moles of reactants present:

$$25.0 \text{ kg N}_2 \times \frac{1000 \text{ g N}_2}{1 \text{ kg N}_2} \times \frac{1 \text{ mol N}_2}{28.0 \text{ g N}_2} = 8.93 \times 10^2 \text{ mol N}_2$$

$$5.00 \text{ kg H}_2 \times \frac{1000 \text{ g H}_2}{1 \text{ kg H}_2} \times \frac{1 \text{ mol H}_2}{2.016 \text{ g H}_2} = 2.48 \times 10^3 \text{ mol H}_2$$

Since 1 mole of N_2 reacts with 3 moles of H_2, the number of moles of H_2 that will react exactly with 8.93×10^2 moles of N_2 is

$$8.93 \times 10^2 \text{ mol N}_2 \times \frac{3 \text{ mol H}_2}{1 \text{ mol N}_2} = 2.68 \times 10^3 \text{ mol H}_2$$

Thus 8.93×10^2 moles of N_2 requires 2.68×10^3 moles of H_2 to react completely. However, in this case only 2.48×10^3 moles of H_2 is present. Thus the hydrogen will be consumed before the nitrogen. Therefore, hydrogen is the *limiting reactant* in this particular situation, and we must use the amount of hydrogen to compute the quantity of ammonia formed:

Always check to see which reactant is limiting.

$$2.48 \times 10^3 \text{ mol H}_2 \times \frac{2 \text{ mol NH}_3}{3 \text{ mol H}_2} = 1.65 \times 10^3 \text{ mol NH}_3$$

$$1.65 \times 10^3 \text{ mol NH}_3 \times \frac{17.0 \text{ g NH}_3}{1 \text{ mol NH}_3} = 2.80 \times 10^4 \text{ g NH}_3 = 28.0 \text{ kg NH}_3$$

Note that to determine the limiting reactant, we could have started instead with the given amount of hydrogen and calculated the moles of nitrogen required:

$$2.48 \times 10^3 \text{ mol H}_2 \times \frac{1 \text{ mol N}_2}{3 \text{ mol H}_2} = 8.27 \times 10^2 \text{ mol N}_2$$

Thus 2.48×10^3 moles of H_2 requires 8.27×10^2 moles of N_2. Since 8.93×10^2 moles of N_2 is actually present, the nitrogen is in excess. The hydrogen will run out first, and thus again we find that hydrogen limits the amount of ammonia formed.

A related but simpler way to determine which reactant is limiting is to compare the mole ratio of the substances required by the balanced equation with the mole ratio of reactants actually present. For example, in this case the mole ratio of H_2 to N_2 required by the balanced equation is

$$\frac{3 \text{ mol H}_2}{1 \text{ mol N}_2}$$

That is,

$$\frac{\text{mol H}_2}{\text{mol N}_2} \text{ (required)} = \frac{3}{1} = 3$$

In this experiment we have 2.48×10^3 moles of H_2 and 8.93×10^2 moles of N_2. Thus the ratio

$$\frac{\text{mol H}_2}{\text{mol N}_2} \text{ (actual)} = \frac{2.48 \times 10^3}{8.93 \times 10^2} = 2.78$$

Since 2.78 is less than 3, the actual mole ratio of H_2 to N_2 is too small, and H_2 must be limiting. If the actual H_2/N_2 mole ratio had been greater than 3, then the H_2 would have been in excess and the N_2 would have been limiting.

Nitrogen gas can be prepared by passing gaseous ammonia over solid copper(II) oxide at high temperatures. The other products of the reaction are solid copper and water vapor. If 18.1 g of NH_3 is reacted with 90.4 g of CuO, which is the limiting reactant? How many grams of N_2 will be formed?

Solution

■ What are we trying to solve?

In this example we are asked to solve two problems: to determine the limiting reactant and to determine the mass of N_2 that will be formed from a given amount of reactants.

 We first need to answer the following two questions: What is meant by the term limiting reactant? and What do we need to do to solve for an amount of N_2?

■ What is meant by the term limiting reactant?

It is the reactant that is completely used up in the reaction. Since a chemical equation gives us the mole ratio of the reactants, we can determine how many moles of a given reactant we need to have compared with what we actually have. To do this we need to have a balanced equation, which we can get from the description of the problem.

$$2NH_3(g) + 3CuO(s) \longrightarrow N_2(g) + 3Cu(s) + 3H_2O(g)$$

To use this equation we have to compare the amounts of reactants in moles to the balanced equation, so we must compute the moles of NH_3 and CuO:

$$18.1 \text{ g } NH_3 \times \frac{1 \text{ mol } NH_3}{17.0 \text{ g } NH_3} = 1.06 \text{ mol } NH_3$$

$$90.4 \text{ g CuO} \times \frac{1 \text{ mol CuO}}{79.5 \text{ g CuO}} = 1.14 \text{ mol CuO}$$

We can now use either one of these to determine the number of moles of the other reactant that would be required to react completely. For example, if all of the NH_3 reacts, what number of moles of CuO is required?

$$1.06 \text{ mol } NH_3 \times \frac{3 \text{ mol CuO}}{2 \text{ mol } NH_3} = 1.59 \text{ mol CuO}$$

Thus 1.59 moles of CuO is required to react with 1.06 moles of NH_3. Since only 1.14 moles of CuO is actually present, the amount of CuO is limiting.

 We can verify this conclusion by comparing the mole ratio of CuO to NH_3 required by the balanced equation,

$$\frac{\text{mol CuO}}{\text{mol } NH_3} \text{ (required)} = \frac{3}{2} = 1.5$$

with the mole ratio actually present,

$$\frac{\text{mol CuO}}{\text{mol } NH_3} \text{ (actual)} = \frac{1.14}{1.06} = 1.08$$

Since the actual ratio is too small (smaller than 1.5), CuO is the limiting reactant.

■ What do we need to do to solve for an amount of N_2?

To determine this we need to use the limiting reactant to calculate the moles, then mass, of N_2.

Because CuO is the limiting reactant, we must use the amount of CuO to calculate the amount of N_2 formed:

$$1.14 \text{ mol CuO} \times \frac{1 \text{ mol N}_2}{3 \text{ mol CuO}} = 0.380 \text{ mol N}_2$$

Using the molar mass of N_2, we can calculate the mass of N_2 produced:

$$0.380 \text{ mol N}_2 \times \frac{28.0 \text{ g N}_2}{1 \text{ mol N}_2} = 10.6 \text{ g N}_2$$

Note: As with most problems, there is more than one way to solve this. We could have answered, "What is meant by the term limiting reactant?" with: the reactant that limits the amount of product. So, another way to solve this is to solve for the number of moles of N_2 produced assuming all of the NH_3 reacts and solve again for moles of N_2 produced assuming all of the CuO reacts. The reactant that results in the smaller amount of product limits the reaction. Once we know the limiting reactant, we can solve for the mass of N_2 produced. We leave this up to you to try.

The amount of a given product formed when the limiting reactant is completely consumed is called the **theoretical yield** of that product. In Example 3.10, 10.6 grams of nitrogen is the theoretical yield. This is the *maximum amount* of nitrogen that can be produced from the quantities of reactants used. Actually, the amount of product predicted by the theoretical yield is seldom obtained because of side reactions (other reactions that involve one or more of the reactants or products) and other complications. The *actual yield* of product is often given as a percentage of the theoretical yield. This value is called the **percent yield**:

Percent yield is important as an indicator of the efficiency of a particular laboratory or industrial reaction.

$$\frac{\text{Actual yield}}{\text{Theoretical yield}} \times 100\% = \text{percent yield}$$

For example, if the reaction considered in Example 3.10 actually produced 6.63 grams of nitrogen instead of the predicted 10.6 grams, the percent yield of nitrogen would be

$$\frac{6.63 \text{ g N}_2}{10.6 \text{ g N}_2} \times 100\% = 62.5\%$$

STEPS

Solving a Stoichiometry Problem Involving Masses of Reactants and Products

1 Write and balance the equation for the reaction.
2 Convert the known masses of substances to moles.
3 By comparing the mole ratio of reactants required by the balanced equation with the mole ratio of reactants actually present, determine which reactant is limiting.
4 Using the amount of the limiting reactant and the appropriate mole ratios, compute the number of moles of the desired product.
5 Convert from moles to grams using the molar mass.

♥WL INTERACTIVE EXAMPLE 3.11

Potassium chromate, a bright yellow solid, is produced by the reaction of solid chromite ore ($FeCr_2O_4$) with solid potassium carbonate and gaseous oxygen at high temperatures. The other products of the reaction are solid iron(III) oxide and gaseous carbon dioxide. In a particular experiment, 169 kg of chromite ore, 298 kg of potassium carbonate, and 75.0 kg of oxygen were sealed in a reaction vessel and reacted at a high temperature. The amount of potassium chromate obtained was 194 kg. Calculate the percent yield of potassium chromate.

Solution

■ What are we trying to solve?

This problem asks us to determine percent yield.

■ What does this mean?

$$\text{Percent yield} = \frac{\text{actual yield}}{\text{theoretical yield}} \times 100\%$$

We are given the actual yield of potassium chromate as 194 kg; thus we have

$$\text{Percent yield} = \frac{194 \text{ kg}}{\text{theoretical yield}} \times 100\%$$

So we have now changed the problem to, What is the theoretical yield? Once we have this, we can solve for percent yield. This leads us to:

■ What do we mean by theoretical yield?

The theoretical yield is the amount of product we can expect if the reaction is allowed to run to completion. It is the amount of product that we have been calculating using the ideas in Sections 3.8 and 3.9.

We are given the masses (and names) of the three reactants and are told the names of the products. First, we will need a balanced chemical equation.

The unbalanced equation, which can be written from the preceding description of the reaction, is

$$FeCr_2O_4(s) + K_2CO_3(s) + O_2(g) \longrightarrow K_2CrO_4(s) + Fe_2O_3(s) + CO_2(g)$$

The balanced equation is

$$4FeCr_2O_4(s) + 8K_2CO_3(s) + 7O_2(g) \longrightarrow 8K_2CrO_4(s) + 2Fe_2O_3(s) + 8CO_2(g)$$

To determine the theoretical yield, we have to decide on which reactant is limiting and then use this reactant to compute the mass of the product formed. To determine the limiting reactant, we will compare the mole ratios of the reactants required by the balanced equation with the actual mole ratios. The numbers of moles of the various reactants are obtained as follows:

$$169 \text{ kg FeCr}_2O_4 \times \frac{1000 \text{ g FeCr}_2O_4}{1 \text{ kg FeCr}_2O_4} \times \frac{1 \text{ mol FeCr}_2O_4}{223.84 \text{ g FeCr}_2O_4}$$
$$= 7.55 \times 10^2 \text{ mol FeCr}_2O_4$$

$$298 \text{ kg K}_2CO_3 \times \frac{1000 \text{ g K}_2CO_3}{1 \text{ kg K}_2CO_3} \times \frac{1 \text{ mol K}_2CO_3}{138.21 \text{ g K}_2CO_3}$$
$$= 2.16 \times 10^3 \text{ mol K}_2CO_3$$

$$75.0 \text{ kg O}_2 \times \frac{1000 \text{ g O}_2}{1 \text{ kg O}_2} \times \frac{1 \text{ mol O}_2}{32.00 \text{ g O}_2} = 2.34 \times 10^3 \text{ mol O}_2$$

Now we must determine which of the three reactants is limiting. For the reactants K_2CO_3 and $FeCr_2O_4$ the required mole ratio is

$$\frac{\text{mol K}_2CO_3}{\text{mol FeCr}_2O_4} \text{ (required)} = \frac{8}{4} = 2$$

The actual mole ratio is

$$\frac{\text{mol K}_2\text{CO}_3}{\text{mol FeCr}_2\text{O}_4} \text{ (actual)} = \frac{2.16 \times 10^3}{7.55 \times 10^2} = 2.86$$

Since the actual mole ratio is greater than that required, the K_2CO_3 is in excess compared with $FeCr_2O_4$. Thus either $FeCr_2O_4$ or O_2 must be limiting. To determine which of these will limit the amounts of products, we compare the required mole ratio,

$$\frac{\text{mol O}_2}{\text{mol FeCr}_2\text{O}_4} \text{ (required)} = \frac{7}{4} = 1.75$$

with the actual mole ratio,

$$\frac{\text{mol O}_2}{\text{mol FeCr}_2\text{O}_4} \text{ (actual)} = \frac{2.34 \times 10^3}{7.55 \times 10^2} = 3.10$$

Thus more K_2CO_3 and O_2 are present than required. These reactants are in excess, so $FeCr_2O_4$ is the limiting reactant.

We must use the amount of $FeCr_2O_4$ to calculate the maximum amount of K_2CrO_4 that can be formed:

$$7.55 \times 10^2 \text{ mol FeCr}_2\text{O}_4 \times \frac{8 \text{ mol K}_2\text{CrO}_4}{4 \text{ mol FeCr}_2\text{O}_4} = 1.51 \times 10^3 \text{ mol K}_2\text{CrO}_4$$

Using the molar mass of K_2CrO_4, we can determine the mass:

$$1.51 \times 10^3 \text{ mol K}_2\text{CrO}_4 \times \frac{194.19 \text{ g K}_2\text{CrO}_4}{1 \text{ mol K}_2\text{CrO}_4} = 2.93 \times 10^5 \text{ g K}_2\text{CrO}_4$$

This value represents the theoretical yield of K_2CrO_4. The actual yield was 194 kg, or 1.94×10^5 g. Thus the percent yield is

$$\frac{1.94 \times 10^5 \text{ g K}_2\text{CrO}_4}{2.93 \times 10^5 \text{ g K}_2\text{CrO}_4} \times 100\% = 66.2\%$$

Key Terms

chemical stoichiometry

Section 3.1
mass spectrometer

Section 3.2
mole
Avogadro's number

Section 3.3
molar mass

Section 3.4
conceptual problem solving

Section 3.5
molecular weight
mass percent

Section 3.6
empirical formula
molecular formula

Section 3.7
chemical equation
reactants
products
balancing a chemical equation

For Review

Sign in at **www.cengage.com/owl** to:
• View tutorials and simulations, develop problem-solving skills, and complete online homework assigned by your professor.
• Download Go Chemistry mini lecture modules for quick review and exam prep from OWL (or purchase them at **www.cengagebrain.com**)

Stoichiometry
■ Deals with the amounts of substances consumed and/or produced in a chemical reaction.
■ We count atoms by measuring the mass of the sample.
■ To relate mass and the number of atoms, the average atomic mass is required.

Mole
■ The number of carbon atoms in exactly 12 g of pure ^{12}C
■ 6.022×10^{23} units of a substance
■ The mass of 1 mole of an element = the atomic mass in grams

Molar mass
■ Mass (g) of 1 mole of a compound or element
■ Obtained for a compound by finding the sum of the average masses of its constituents

Section 3.9
mole ratio

Section 3.10
stoichiometric quantities
Haber process
limiting reactant (reagent)
theoretical yield
percent yield

Percent composition
- The mass percent on each element in a compound
- $\text{Mass percent} = \dfrac{\text{mass of element in 1 mole of substance}}{\text{mass of 1 mole of substance}} \times 100\%$

Empirical formula
- The simplest whole-number ratio of the various types of atoms in a compound
- Can be obtained from the mass percent of elements in a compound

Molecular formula
- For molecular substance:
  - The formula of the constituent molecules
  - Always an integer multiple of an empirical formula
- For ionic substances:
  - The same as the empirical formula

Chemical reactions
- Reactants are turned into products.
- Atoms are neither created nor destroyed.
- All of the atoms present in the reactants must also be present in the products.

Characteristics of a chemical equation
- Represents a chemical reaction
- Reactants on the left side of the arrow; products on the right side
- When balanced, gives the relative numbers of reactant and product molecules or ions

Stoichiometry calculations
- Amounts of reactants consumed and products formed can be determined from the balanced chemical equation.
- The limiting reactant is the one consumed first, thus limiting the amount of product that can form.

Yield
- The theoretical yield is the maximum amount that can be produced from a given amount of the limiting reactant.
- The actual yield, the amount of product actually obtained, is always less than the theoretical yield.
- $\text{Percent yield} = \dfrac{\text{actual yield (g)}}{\text{theoretical yield (g)}} \times 100\%$

Discussion Questions

These questions are designed to be considered by groups of students in class. Often these questions work well for introducing a particular topic in class.

1. The following are actual student responses to the question: Why is it necessary to balance chemical equations?
   a. The chemicals will not react until you have added the correct mole ratios.
   b. The correct products will not be formed unless the right amount of reactants have been added.
   c. A certain number of products cannot be formed without a certain number of reactants.
   d. The balanced equation tells you how much reactant you need and allows you to predict how much product you will make.

   e. A mole-to-mole ratio must be established for the reaction to occur as written.

   What is the best choice? For those you did not choose, explain why they are incorrect. State the fundamental reason why an equation for a reaction must be balanced.

2. Consider the equation $A + 2B \rightarrow AB_2$. Imagine that 10 moles of A is reacted with 26 moles of B. Use a scale from 0 to 10 to express your level of agreement with each of the following statements. Justify and discuss your responses.
   a. There will be some As left over.
   b. There will be some Bs left over.
   c. Because of leftover As, some A_2 molecules will be formed.
   d. Because of leftover Bs, some B_2 molecules will be formed.

e. Even if A is not limiting, A_2 molecules will be formed.

f. Even if B is not limiting, B_2 molecules will be formed.

g. Along with the molecule AB_2, molecules with the formula A_xB_y (other than AB_2) will be formed.

3. What information do we get from a formula? From an equation?

4. A sample of liquid heptane (C_7H_{16}) weighing 11.50 g is reacted with 1.300 moles of oxygen gas. The heptane is burned completely (heptane reacts with oxygen to form both carbon monoxide and water and carbon dioxide and water). After the reaction is complete, the amount of gas present is 1.050 moles (assume that all of the water formed is liquid).

   a. How many moles of CO are produced?

   b. How many moles of CO_2 are produced?

   c. How many moles of O_2 are left over?

5. Nitrogen (N_2) and hydrogen (H_2) react to form ammonia (NH_3). Consider the mixture of N_2(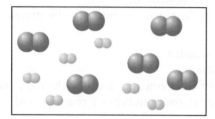) and H_2( ) in a closed container as illustrated:

Assuming that the reaction goes to completion, draw a representation of the product mixture. Explain how you arrived at this representation.

6. For the preceding question, which of the following equations best represents the reaction?

   a. $6N_2 + 6H_2 \rightarrow 4NH_3 + 4N_2$

   b. $N_2 + H_2 \rightarrow NH_3$

   c. $N + 3H \rightarrow NH_3$

   d. $N_2 + 3H_2 \rightarrow 2NH_3$

   e. $2N_2 + 6H_2 \rightarrow 4NH_3$

   Justify your choice. For those you did not choose, explain why they are incorrect.

7. You know that chemical A reacts with chemical B. You react 10.0 g A with 10.0 g B. What information do you need to have to determine the amount of product that will be produced? Explain.

8. A kerosene lamp has a mass of 1.5 kg. You put 0.5 kg of kerosene in the lamp. You burn all the kerosene until the lamp has a mass of 1.5 kg. What is the mass of the gases that are given off? Explain.

9. Consider an iron bar on a balance as shown.

As the iron bar rusts, which of the following is true? Explain your answer.

   a. The balance will read less than 75.0 g.

   b. The balance will read 75.0 g.

   c. The balance will read greater than 75.0 g.

   d. The balance will read greater than 75.0 g, but if the bar is removed, the rust scraped off, and the bar replaced, the balance will read 75.0 g.

10. You may have noticed that water sometimes drips from an exhaust pipe of a car as it is running. Is this evidence that there is at least a small amount of water originally present in the gasoline? Explain.

Questions 11 and 12 deal with the following situation: You react chemical A with chemical B to make one product. It takes 100 g of A to react completely with 20 g B.

11. What is the mass of the product?

   a. less than 20 g   d. exactly 120 g

   b. between 20 and 100 g   e. more than 120 g

   c. between 100 and 120 g

12. What is true about the chemical properties of the product?

   a. The properties are more like those of chemical A.

   b. The properties are more like those of chemical B.

   c. The properties are an average of those of chemical A and chemical B.

   d. The properties are not necessarily like those of either chemical A or chemical B.

   Justify your choice. For those you did not choose, explain why they are incorrect.

13. What is the difference between the empirical and molecular formulas of a compound? Can they ever be the same? Explain.

14. Atoms of three different elements are represented by O, □, and Δ. Which compound is left over when three molecules of OΔ and three molecules of □□Δ react to form O□Δ and OΔΔ?

15. One way of determining the empirical formula is to burn a compound in air and weigh the amounts of carbon dioxide and water given off. For what types of compounds does this work? Explain the assumptions that are made. Why is the formula an empirical formula and not necessarily a molecular formula?

16. In chemistry, what is meant by the term *mole*? What is the importance of the mole concept?

17. Which (if any) of the following is true regarding the limiting reactant in a chemical reaction?

   a. The limiting reactant has the lowest coefficient in a balanced equation.

   b. The limiting reactant is the reactant for which you have the fewest number of moles.

   c. The limiting reactant has the lowest ratio of moles available/coefficient in the balanced equation.

   d. The limiting reactant has the lowest ratio of coefficient in the balanced equation/moles available.

   Justify your choice. For those you did not choose, explain why they are incorrect.

18. Consider the equation $3A + B \rightarrow C + D$. You react 4 moles of A with 2 moles of B. Which of the following is true?

   a. The limiting reactant is the one with the higher molar mass.

   b. A is the limiting reactant because you need 6 moles of A and have 4 moles.

c. B is the limiting reactant because you have fewer moles of B than A.

d. B is the limiting reactant because three A molecules react with each B molecule.

e. Neither reactant is limiting.

Justify your choice. For those you did not choose, explain why they are incorrect.

19. Chlorine exists mainly as two isotopes, ^{37}Cl and ^{35}Cl. Which is more abundant? How do you know?

20. According to the law of conservation of mass, mass cannot be gained or destroyed in a chemical reaction. Why can't you simply add the masses of two reactants to determine the total mass of product?

21. The atomic mass of boron (B) is given in the periodic table as 10.81, yet no single atom of boron has a mass of 10.81 amu. Explain.

22. Why is the actual yield of a reaction often less than the theoretical yield?

Exercises

OWL Interactive versions of these problems may be assigned in OWL.

A blue exercise number indicates that the answer to that exercise appears at the back of this book and a solution appears in the *Solutions Guide*.

Atomic Masses and the Mass Spectrometer

23. An element X has five major isotopes, which are listed below along with their abundances. Calculate the average atomic mass, and identify the element.

Isotope	Percent Natural Abundance	Mass (amu)
^{46}X	8.00	45.95269
^{47}X	7.30	46.951764
^{48}X	73.80	47.947947
^{49}X	5.50	48.947841
^{50}X	5.40	49.944792

24. The stable isotopes of iron are ^{54}Fe, ^{56}Fe, ^{57}Fe, and ^{58}Fe. The mass spectrum of iron looks like the following:

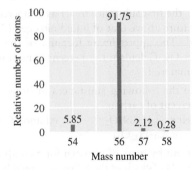

Use the data on the mass spectrum to estimate the average atomic mass of iron and compare it with the value given in the table inside the front cover of this book.

25. The element silver (Ag) has two naturally occurring isotopes: ^{109}Ag and ^{107}Ag with a mass of 106.905 amu. Silver consists of 51.82% ^{107}Ag and has an average atomic mass of 107.868 amu. Calculate the mass of ^{109}Ag.

26. The element europium exists in nature as two isotopes: ^{151}Eu has a mass of 150.9196 amu, and ^{153}Eu has a mass of 152.9209 amu. The average atomic mass of europium is 151.96 amu. Calculate the relative abundance of the two europium isotopes.

27. The element rhenium (Re) has two naturally occurring isotopes, ^{185}Re and ^{187}Re, with an average atomic mass of 186.207 amu. Rhenium is 62.60% ^{187}Re, and the atomic mass of ^{187}Re is 186.956 amu. Calculate the mass of ^{185}Re.

28. An element consists of 1.40% of an isotope with mass 203.973 amu, 24.10% of an isotope with mass 205.9745 amu, 22.10% of an isotope with mass 206.9759 amu, and 52.40% of an isotope with mass 207.9766 amu. Calculate the average atomic mass and identify the element.

29. The mass spectrum of bromine (Br_2) consists of three peaks with the following relative sizes:

Mass (amu)	Relative Size
157.84	0.2534
159.84	0.5000
161.84	0.2466

How do you interpret these data?

30. Naturally occurring tellurium (Te) has the following isotopic abundances:

Isotope	Abundance	Mass (amu)
^{120}Te	0.09%	119.90
^{122}Te	2.46%	121.90
^{123}Te	0.87%	122.90
^{124}Te	4.61%	123.90
^{125}Te	6.99%	124.90
^{126}Te	18.71%	125.90
^{128}Te	31.79%	127.90
^{130}Te	34.48%	129.91

Draw the mass spectrum of H_2Te, assuming that the only hydrogen isotope present is ^1H (mass 1.008).

31. Gallium arsenide (GaAs) has gained widespread use in semiconductor devices that interconvert light and electrical signals in fiber-optic communications systems. Gallium

consists of 60.% ^{69}Ga and 40.% ^{71}Ga. Arsenic has only one naturally occurring isotope, ^{75}As. Gallium arsenide is a polymeric material, but its mass spectrum shows fragments with formulas GaAs and Ga_2As_2. What would the distribution of peaks look like for these two fragments?

Moles and Molar Masses

32. Ascorbic acid, or vitamin C ($C_6H_8O_6$), is an essential vitamin. It cannot be stored by the body and must be present in the diet. What is the molar mass of ascorbic acid? Vitamin C tablets are taken as a dietary supplement. If a typical tablet contains 500.0 mg vitamin C, what amount (moles) and what number of molecules of vitamin C does it contain?

33. The molecular formula of acetylsalicylic acid (aspirin), one of the most commonly used pain relievers, is $C_9H_8O_4$.
    a. Calculate the molar mass of aspirin.
    b. A typical aspirin tablet contains 500. mg $C_9H_8O_4$. What amount (moles) of $C_9H_8O_4$ molecules and what number of molecules of acetylsalicylic acid are in a 500.-mg tablet?

34. Complete the following table.

Mass of Sample	Moles of Sample	Molecules in Sample	Total Atoms in Sample
4.24 g C_6H_6	___	___	___
___	0.224 mol H_2O	___	___
___	___	2.71×10^{22} molecules CO_2	___
___	___	___	3.35×10^{22} total atoms in CH_3OH sample

35. What amount (moles) is represented by each of these samples?
    a. 20.0 mg caffeine, $C_8H_{10}N_4O_2$
    b. 2.72×10^{21} molecules of ethanol, C_2H_5OH
    c. 1.50 g of dry ice, CO_2

36. How many atoms of nitrogen are present in 5.00 g of each of the following?
    a. glycine, $C_2H_5O_2N$ c. calcium nitrate
    b. magnesium nitride   d. dinitrogen tetroxide

37. Consider the following gas samples: 4.0 g of hydrogen gas, 4.0 g of helium gas, 1.0 mole of fluorine gas, 44.0 g of carbon dioxide gas, and 146 g of sulfur hexafluoride gas. Arrange the gas samples in order of increasing number of total atoms present.

38. Aspartame is an artificial sweetener that is 160 times sweeter than sucrose (table sugar) when dissolved in water. It is marketed as NutraSweet. The molecular formula of aspartame is $C_{14}H_{18}N_2O_5$.
    a. Calculate the molar mass of aspartame.
    b. How many moles of molecules are in 10.0 g of aspartame?
    c. What is the mass in grams of 1.56 moles of aspartame?

d. How many molecules are in 5.0 mg of aspartame?
e. How many atoms of nitrogen are in 1.2 g of aspartame?
f. What is the mass in grams of 1.0×10^9 molecules of aspartame?
g. What is the mass in grams of one molecule of aspartame?

39. Chloral hydrate ($C_2H_3Cl_3O_2$) is a drug formerly used as a sedative and hypnotic. It is the compound used to make "Mickey Finns" in detective stories.
    a. Calculate the molar mass of chloral hydrate.
    b. How many moles of $C_2H_3Cl_3O_2$ molecules are in 500.0 g of chloral hydrate?
    c. What is the mass in grams of 2.0×10^{-2} mol chloral hydrate?
    d. How many chlorine atoms are in 5.0 g chloral hydrate?
    e. What mass of chloral hydrate would contain 1.0 g Cl?
    f. What is the mass of exactly 500 molecules of chloral hydrate?

40. In the spring of 1984, concern arose over the presence of ethylene dibromide, or EDB, in grains and cereals. EDB has the molecular formula $C_2H_4Br_2$ and until 1984 was commonly used as a plant fumigant. The federal limit for EDB in finished cereal products is 30.0 parts per billion (ppb), where 1.0 ppb = 1.0×10^{-9} g of EDB for every 1.0 g of sample. How many molecules of EDB are in 1.0 lb of flour if 30.0 ppb of EDB is present?

Percent Composition

41. Anabolic steroids are performance enhancement drugs whose use has been banned from most major sporting activities. One anabolic steroid is fluoxymesterone ($C_{20}H_{29}FO_3$). Calculate the percent composition by mass of fluoxymesterone.

42. Calculate the percent composition by mass of the following compounds that are important starting materials for synthetic polymers:
    a. $C_3H_4O_2$ (acrylic acid, from which acrylic plastics are made)
    b. $C_4H_6O_2$ (methyl acrylate, from which Plexiglas is made)
    c. C_3H_3N (acrylonitrile, from which Orlon is made)

43. In 1987 the first substance to act as a superconductor at a temperature above that of liquid nitrogen (77 K) was discovered. The approximate formula of this substance is $YBa_2Cu_3O_7$. Calculate the percent composition by mass of this material.

44. Arrange the following substances in order of increasing mass percent of carbon.
    a. caffeine, $C_8H_{10}N_4O_2$ c. ethanol, C_2H_5OH
    b. sucrose, $C_{12}H_{22}O_{11}$

45. The percent by mass of nitrogen for a compound is found to be 46.7%. Which of the following could be this species?

46. Vitamin B_{12}, cyanocobalamin, is essential for human nutrition. It is concentrated in animal tissue but not in higher plants. Although nutritional requirements for the vitamin are quite low, people who abstain completely from animal

products may develop a deficiency anemia. Cyanocobalamin is the form used in vitamin supplements. It contains 4.34% cobalt by mass. Calculate the molar mass of cyanocobalamin, assuming that there is one atom of cobalt in every molecule of cyanocobalamin.

47. Fungal laccase, a blue protein found in wood-rotting fungi, is 0.390% Cu by mass. If a fungal laccase molecule contains four copper atoms, what is the molar mass of fungal laccase?

48. Portland cement acts as the binding agent in concrete. A typical Portland cement has the following composition:

Formula	Name	Mass Percent
Ca_3SiO_5	Tricalcium silicate	50.
Ca_2SiO_4	Dicalcium silicate	25
$Ca_3Al_2O_6$	Tricalcium aluminate	12
Ca_2AlFeO_5	Calcium aluminoferrite	8.0
$CaSO_4 \cdot 2H_2O$	Calcium sulfate dihydrate	3.5
Other substances, mostly MgO		1.5

Assuming that the impurities contain no Ca, Al, or Fe, calculate the mass percent of these elements in this Portland cement.

Empirical and Molecular Formulas

49. Express the composition of each of the following compounds as the mass percent of its elements.
   a. formaldehyde, CH_2O c. acetic acid, $HC_2H_3O_2$
   b. glucose, $C_6H_{12}O_6$

   Considering your answers, which type of formula—empirical or molecular—can be obtained from elemental analysis that gives mass percent composition? Explain.

50. Give the empirical formula of each of these compounds.

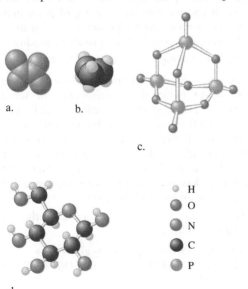

a.   b.

c.

	H
	O
	N
	C
	P

d.

51. Determine the molecular formulas to which the following empirical formulas and molar masses pertain.
   a. SNH (188.35 g/mol)
   b. $NPCl_2$ (347.64 g/mol)
   c. CoC_4O_4 (341.94 g/mol)
   d. SN (184.32 g/mol)

52. A sample of urea contains 1.121 g N, 0.161 g H, 0.480 g C, and 0.640 g O. What is the empirical formula of urea?

53. There are two binary compounds of mercury and oxygen. Heating either of them results in the decomposition of the compound, with oxygen gas escaping into the atmosphere while leaving a residue of pure mercury. Heating 0.6498 g of one of the compounds leaves a residue of 0.6018 g. Heating 0.4172 g of the other compound results in a mass loss of 0.016 g. Determine the empirical formula of each compound.

54. The compound adrenaline contains 56.79% C, 6.56% H, 28.37% O, and 8.28% N by mass. What is the empirical formula of adrenaline?

55. A compound contains only carbon, hydrogen, nitrogen, and oxygen. Combustion of 0.157 g of the compound produced 0.213 g of CO_2 and 0.0310 g of H_2O. In another experiment, 0.103 g of the compound produced 0.0230 g of NH_3. What is the empirical formula of the compound? *Hint:* Combustion involves reacting with excess O_2. Assume that all the carbon ends up in CO_2 and all the hydrogen ends up in H_2O. Also assume that all the nitrogen ends up in the NH_3 in the second experiment.

56. Maleic acid is an organic compound composed of 41.39% C, 3.47% H, and the rest oxygen. If 0.129 mole of maleic acid has a mass of 15.0 g, what are the empirical and molecular formulas of maleic acid?

57. Determine the molecular formula of a compound that contains 26.7% P, 12.1% N, and 61.2% Cl, and has a molar mass of 580 g/mol.

58. Terephthalic acid is an important chemical used in the manufacture of polyesters and plasticizers. It contains only C, H, and O. Combustion of 19.81 mg terephthalic acid produces 41.98 mg CO_2 and 6.45 mg H_2O. If 0.250 mole of terephthalic acid has a mass of 41.5 g, determine the molecular formula of terephthalic acid.

59. A compound contains only carbon, hydrogen, and oxygen. Combustion of 10.68 mg of the compound yields 16.01 mg CO_2 and 4.37 mg H_2O. The molar mass of the compound is 176.1 g/mol. What are the empirical and molecular formulas of the compound?

60. ABS plastic is a tough, hard plastic used in applications requiring shock resistance. (See Chapter 21.) The polymer consists of three monomer units: acrylonitrile (C_3H_3N), butadiene (C_4H_6), and styrene (C_8H_8).
   a. A sample of ABS plastic contains 8.80% N by mass. It took 0.605 g of Br_2 to react completely with a 1.20-g sample of ABS plastic. Bromine reacts 1:1 (by moles) with the butadiene molecules in the polymer and

nothing else. What is the percent by mass of acrylonitrile and butadiene in this polymer?

b. What are the relative numbers of each of the monomer units in this polymer?

Balancing Chemical Equations

61. The reaction of an element X with element Y is represented in the following diagram. Which of the equations best describes this reaction?

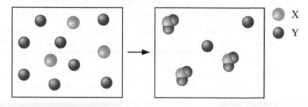

X
Y

a. $3X + 8Y \rightarrow X_3Y_8$
b. $3X + 6Y \rightarrow X_3Y_6$
c. $X + 2Y \rightarrow XY_2$
d. $3X + 8Y \rightarrow 3XY_2 + 2Y$

62. Silicon is produced for the chemical and electronics industries by the following reactions. Give the balanced equation for each reaction.

a. $SiO_2(s) + C(s) \xrightarrow[\text{arc furnace}]{\text{Electric}} Si_2(s) + CO(g)$

b. Silicon tetrachloride is reacted with very pure magnesium, producing silicon and magnesium chloride.

c. $Na_2SiF_6(s) + Na(s) \longrightarrow Si(s) + NaF(s)$

63. Give the balanced equation for each of the following chemical reactions.

a. Glucose ($C_6H_{12}O_6$) reacts with oxygen gas to produce gaseous carbon dioxide and water vapor.

b. Solid iron(III) sulfide reacts with gaseous hydrogen chloride to form solid iron(III) chloride and hydrogen sulfide gas.

c. Carbon disulfide liquid reacts with ammonia gas to produce hydrogen sulfide gas and solid ammonium thiocyanate (NH_4SCN).

64. Give the balanced equation for each of the following.

a. The combustion of ethanol (C_2H_5OH) forms carbon dioxide and water vapor. A combustion reaction refers to a reaction of a substance with oxygen gas.

b. Aqueous solutions of lead(II) nitrate and sodium phosphate are mixed, resulting in the precipitate formation of lead(II) phosphate with aqueous sodium nitrate as the other product.

65. Balance the following equations.

a. $Cr(s) + S_8(s) \longrightarrow Cr_2S_3(s)$

b. $NaHCO_3(s) \xrightarrow{\text{Heat}} Na_2CO_3(s) + CO_2(g) + H_2O(g)$

c. $KClO_3(s) \xrightarrow{\text{Heat}} KCl(s) + O_2(g)$

d. $Eu(s) + HF(g) \longrightarrow EuF_3(s) + H_2(g)$

e. $C_6H_6(l) + O_2(g) \longrightarrow CO_2(g) + H_2O(g)$

66. Balance each of the following chemical equations.

a. $KO_2(s) + H_2O(l) \rightarrow KOH(aq) + O_2(g) + H_2O_2(aq)$

b. $Fe_2O_3(s) + HNO_3(aq) \rightarrow Fe(NO_3)_3(aq) + H_2O(l)$

c. $NH_3(g) + O_2(g) \rightarrow NO(g) + H_2O(g)$

d. $PCl_5(l) + H_2O(l) \rightarrow H_3PO_4(aq) + HCl(g)$

e. $CaO(s) + C(s) \rightarrow CaC_2(s) + CO_2(g)$

f. $MoS_2(s) + O_2(g) \rightarrow MoO_3(s) + SO_2(g)$

g. $FeCO_3(s) + H_2CO_3(aq) \rightarrow Fe(HCO_3)_2(aq)$

Reaction Stoichiometry

67. The reusable booster rockets of the U.S. space shuttle use a mixture of aluminum and ammonium perchlorate for fuel. A possible equation for this reaction is

$3Al(s) + 3NH_4ClO_4(s)$
$\longrightarrow Al_2O_3(s) + AlCl_3(s) + 3NO(g) + 6H_2O(g)$

What mass of NH_4ClO_4 should be used in the fuel mixture for every kilogram of Al?

68. Nitric acid is produced commercially by the Ostwald process. The three steps of the Ostwald process are shown in the following equations:

$4NH_3(g) + 5O_2(g) \longrightarrow 4NO(g) + 6H_2O(g)$

$2NO(g) + O_2(g) \longrightarrow 2NO_2(g)$

$3NO_2(g) + H_2O(l) \longrightarrow 2HNO_3(aq) + NO(g)$

What mass of NH_3 must be used to produce 1.0×10^6 kg of HNO_3 by the Ostwald process, assuming 100% yield in each reaction and assuming the NO produced in the third stage is not recycled?

69. Over the years, the thermite reaction has been used for welding railroad rails, in incendiary bombs, and to ignite solid-fuel rocket motors. The reaction is

$Fe_2O_3(s) + 2Al(s) \longrightarrow 2Fe(l) + Al_2O_3(s)$

What masses of iron(III) oxide and aluminum must be used to produce 15.0 g of iron? What is the maximum mass of aluminum oxide that could be produced?

70. The reaction between potassium chlorate and red phosphorus takes place when you strike a match on a matchbox. If you were to react 52.9 g of potassium chlorate ($KClO_3$) with excess red phosphorus, what mass of tetraphosphorus decoxide (P_4O_{10}) could be produced?

$KClO_3(s) + P_4(s) \longrightarrow P_4O_{10}(s) + KCl(s)$ (unbalanced)

71. The space shuttle environmental control system handles excess CO_2 (which the astronauts breathe out; it is 4.0% by mass of exhaled air) by reacting it with lithium hydroxide (LiOH) pellets to form lithium carbonate (Li_2CO_3) and water. If there are seven astronauts on board the shuttle, and each exhales 20. L of air per minute, how long could clean air be generated if there were 25,000 g of LiOH pellets available for each shuttle mission? Assume the density of air is 0.0010 g/mL.

72. Bacterial digestion is an economical method of sewage treatment. The reaction

$5CO_2(g) + 55NH_4^+(aq) + 76O_2(g) \xrightarrow{\text{Bacteria}}$
$C_5H_7O_2N(s) + 54NO_2^-(aq) + 52H_2O(l) + 109H^+(aq)$
Bacterial tissue

is an intermediate step in the conversion of the nitrogen in organic compounds into nitrate ions. How much bacterial tissue is produced in a treatment plant for every 1.0×10^4 kg of wastewater containing 3.0% NH_4^+ ions by mass? Assume that 95% of the ammonium ions are consumed by the bacteria.

73. Phosphorus can be prepared from calcium phosphate by the following reaction:

$$2Ca_3(PO_4)_2(s) + 6SiO_2(s) + 10C(s)$$
$$\longrightarrow 6CaSiO_3(s) + P_4(s) + 10CO(g)$$

Phosphorite is a mineral that contains $Ca_3(PO_4)_2$ plus other non-phosphorus-containing compounds. What is the maximum amount of P_4 that can be produced from 1.0 kg of phosphorite if the phosphorite sample is 75% $Ca_3(PO_4)_2$ by mass? Assume an excess of the other reactants.

74. In the production of printed circuit boards for the electronics industry, a 0.60-mm layer of copper is laminated onto an insulating plastic board. Next, a circuit pattern made of a chemically resistant polymer is printed on the board. The unwanted copper is removed by chemical etching and the protective polymer is finally removed by solvents. One etching reaction is

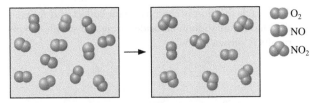

A plant needs to manufacture 10,000 printed circuit boards, each 8.0×16.0 cm in area. An average of 80.% of the copper is removed from each board (density of copper = 8.96 g/cm^3). What masses of $Cu(NH_3)_4Cl_2$ and NH_3 are needed to do this? Assume 100% yield.

Limiting Reactants and Percent Yield

75. Consider the reaction between $NO(g)$ and $O_2(g)$ represented below.

What is the balanced equation for this reaction and what is the limiting reactant?

76. Consider the following reaction:

$$4NH_3(g) + 5O_2(g) \longrightarrow 4NO(g) + 6H_2O(g)$$

If a container were to have 10 molecules of O_2 and 10 molecules of NH_3 initially, how many total molecules (reactants plus products) would be present in the container after this reaction goes to completion?

77. Hydrogen peroxide is used as a cleaning agent in the treatment of cuts and abrasions for several reasons. It is an oxidizing agent that can directly kill many microorganisms; it decomposes upon contact with blood, releasing elemental oxygen gas (which inhibits the growth of anaerobic microorganisms); and it foams upon contact with blood, which provides a cleansing action. In the laboratory, small quantities of hydrogen peroxide can be pre-

pared by the action of an acid on an alkaline earth metal peroxide, such as barium peroxide:

$$BaO_2(s) + 2HCl(aq) \longrightarrow H_2O_2(aq) + BaCl_2(aq)$$

What amount of hydrogen peroxide should result when 1.50 g of barium peroxide is treated with 25.0 mL of hydrochloric acid solution containing 0.0272 g of HCl per mL? What mass of which reagent is left unreacted?

78. Silver sulfadiazine burn-treating cream creates a barrier against bacterial invasion and releases antimicrobial agents directly into the wound. If 25.0 g of Ag_2O is reacted with 50.0 g of $C_{10}H_{10}N_4SO_2$, what mass of silver sulfadiazine ($AgC_{10}H_9N_4SO_2$) can be produced, assuming 100% yield?

$$Ag_2O(s) + 2C_{10}H_{10}N_4SO_2(s) \longrightarrow 2AgC_{10}H_9N_4SO_2(s) + H_2O(l)$$

79. Bornite (Cu_3FeS_3) is a copper ore used in the production of copper. When heated, the following reaction occurs:

$$2Cu_3FeS_3(s) + 7O_2(g) \longrightarrow 6Cu(s) + 2FeO(s) + 6SO_2(g)$$

If 2.50 metric tons of bornite is reacted with excess O_2 and the process has an 86.3% yield of copper, how much copper is produced?

80. DDT, an insecticide harmful to fish, birds, and humans, is produced by the following reaction:

$$2C_6H_5Cl + C_2HOCl_3 \longrightarrow C_{14}H_9Cl_5 + H_2O$$
Chlorobenzene   Chloral   DDT

In a government lab, 1142 g of chlorobenzene is reacted with 485 g of chloral.
a. What mass of DDT is formed, assuming 100% yield?
b. Which reactant is limiting? Which is in excess?
c. What mass of the excess reactant is left over?
d. If the actual yield of DDT is 200.0 g, what is the percent yield?

81. Hydrogen cyanide is produced industrially from the reaction of gaseous ammonia, oxygen, and methane:

$$2NH_3(g) + 3O_2(g) + 2CH_4(g) \longrightarrow 2HCN(g) + 6H_2O(g)$$

If 5.00×10^3 kg each of NH_3, O_2, and CH_4 are reacted, what mass of HCN and of H_2O will be produced, assuming 100% yield?

82. The production capacity for acrylonitrile (C_3H_3N) in the United States exceeds 2 million pounds per year. Acrylonitrile, the building block for polyacrylonitrile fibers and a variety of plastics, is produced from gaseous propylene, ammonia, and oxygen:

$$2C_3H_6(g) + 2NH_3(g) + 3O_2(g)$$
$$\longrightarrow 2C_3H_3N(g) + 6H_2O(g)$$

a. What mass of acrylonitrile can be produced from a mixture of 1.00 kg of propylene (C_3H_6), 1.50 kg of ammonia, and 2.00 kg of oxygen, assuming 100% yield?
b. What mass of water is produced, and what masses of which starting materials are left in excess?

83. Consider the following unbalanced reaction:

$$P_4(s) + F_2(g) \longrightarrow PF_3(g)$$

How many grams of F_2 are needed to produce 120. g of PF_3 if the reaction has a 78.1% yield?

84. The aspirin substitute acetaminophen ($C_8H_9O_2N$) is produced by the following three-step synthesis:

    I. $C_6H_5O_3N(s) + 3H_2(g) + HCl(aq)$
       $\longrightarrow C_6H_8ONCl(s) + 2H_2O(l)$

    II. $C_6H_8ONCl(s) + NaOH(aq)$
        $\longrightarrow C_6H_7ON(s) + H_2O(l) + NaCl(aq)$

    III. $C_6H_7ON(s) + C_4H_6O_3(l)$
         $\longrightarrow C_8H_9O_2N(s) + HC_2H_3O_2(l)$

The first two reactions have percent yields of 87% and 98% by mass, respectively. The overall reaction yields 3 moles of acetaminophen product for every 4 moles of $C_6H_5O_3N$ reacted.

a. What is the percent yield by mass for the overall process?

b. What is the percent yield by mass of step III?

Additional Exercises

85. A sample of a hydrocarbon (a compound consisting of only carbon and hydrogen) contains 2.59×10^{23} atoms of hydrogen and is 17.3% hydrogen by mass. If the molar mass of the hydrocarbon is between 55 and 65 g/mol, how many moles of compound are present, and what is the mass of the sample?

86. A binary compound created by the reaction of an unknown element E and hydrogen contains 91.27% E and 8.73% H by mass. If the formula of the compound is E_3H_8, calculate the atomic mass of E.

87. An ionic compound MX_3 is prepared according to the following unbalanced chemical equation:

    $$M + X_2 \longrightarrow MX_3$$

    A 0.105-g sample of X_2 contains 8.92×10^{20} molecules. The compound MX_3 consists of 54.47% X by mass. What are the identities of M and X, and what is the correct name for MX_3? Starting with 1.00 g each of M and X_2, what mass of MX_3 can be prepared?

88. The empirical formula of styrene is CH; the molar mass of styrene is 104.14 g/mol. How many H atoms are present in a 2.00-g sample of styrene?

89. A 0.755-g sample of hydrated copper(II) sulfate ($CuSO_4 \cdot xH_2O$) was heated carefully until it had changed completely to anhydrous copper(II) sulfate ($CuSO_4$) with a mass of 0.483 g. Determine the value of x. [This number is called the "number of waters of hydration" of copper(II) sulfate. It specifies the number of water molecules per formula unit of $CuSO_4$ in the hydrated crystal.]

90. Many cereals are made with high moisture content so that the cereal can be formed into various shapes before it is dried. A cereal product containing 58% H_2O by mass is produced at the rate of 1000. kg/h. How much water must be evaporated per hour if the final product contains only 20.% water?

91. When aluminum metal is heated with an element from Group 6A of the periodic table, an ionic compound forms. When the experiment is performed with an unknown Group 6A element, the product is 18.56% Al by mass. What is the formula of the compound?

92. A salt contains only barium and one of the halide ions. A 0.158-g sample of the salt was dissolved in water, and an excess of sulfuric acid was added to form barium sulfate ($BaSO_4$), which was filtered, dried, and weighed. Its mass was found to be 0.124 g. What is the formula of the barium halide?

93. A sample of LSD (D-lysergic acid diethylamide, $C_{24}H_{30}N_3O$) is added to some table salt (sodium chloride) to form a mixture. Given that a 1.00-g sample of the mixture undergoes combustion to produce 1.20 g of CO_2, what is the mass percentage of LSD in the mixture?

94. Consider the following unbalanced equation:

    $$Ca_3(PO_4)_2(s) + H_2SO_4(aq) \longrightarrow CaSO_4(s) + H_3PO_4(aq)$$

    What masses of calcium sulfate and phosphoric acid can be produced from the reaction of 1.0 kg of calcium phosphate with 1.0 kg of concentrated sulfuric acid (98% H_2SO_4 by mass)?

95. A 0.4230-g sample of impure sodium nitrate was heated, converting all the sodium nitrate to 0.2864 g of sodium nitrite and oxygen gas. Determine the percent of sodium nitrate in the original sample.

96. You have seven closed containers, each with equal masses of chlorine gas (Cl_2). You add 10.0 g of sodium to the first sample, 20.0 g of sodium to the second sample, and so on (adding 70.0 g of sodium to the seventh sample). Sodium and chlorine react to form sodium chloride according to the equation

    $$2Na(s) + Cl_2(g) \longrightarrow 2NaCl(s)$$

    After each reaction is complete, you collect and measure the amount of sodium chloride formed. A graph of your results is shown below.

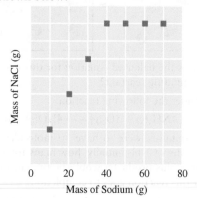

Anwer the following questions:

a. Explain the shape of the graph.

b. Calculate the mass of NaCl formed when 20.0 g of sodium is used.

c. Calculate the mass of Cl_2 in each container.

d. Calculate the mass of NaCl formed when 50.0 g of sodium is used.

e. Identify the leftover reactant and determine its mass for parts b and d.

97. An iron ore sample contains Fe_2O_3 plus other impurities. A 752-g sample of impure iron ore is heated with excess carbon, producing 453 g of pure iron by the following reaction:

$$Fe_2O_3(s) + 3C(s) \longrightarrow 2Fe(s) + 3CO(g)$$

What is the mass percent of Fe_2O_3 in the impure iron ore sample? Assume that Fe_2O_3 is the only source of iron and that the reaction is 100% efficient.

98. In using a mass spectrometer, a chemist sees a peak at a mass of 30.0106. Of the choices $^{12}C_2{}^1H_6$, $^{12}C^1H_2{}^{16}O$, and $^{14}N^{16}O$, which is responsible for this peak? Pertinent masses are ^1H, 1.007825; ^{16}O, 15.994915; and ^{14}N, 14.003074.

99. Natural rubidium has the average mass 85.4678 amu and is composed of isotopes ^{85}Rb (mass = 84.9117 amu) and ^{87}Rb. The ratio of atoms $^{85}Rb/^{87}Rb$ in natural rubidium is 2.591. Calculate the mass of ^{87}Rb.

100. Tetrodotoxin is a toxic chemical found in fugu pufferfish, a popular but rare delicacy in Japan. This compound has an LD_{50} (the amount of substance that is lethal to 50.% of a population sample) of 10. μg per kg of body mass. Tetrodotoxin is 41.38% carbon by mass, 13.16% nitrogen by mass, and 5.37% hydrogen by mass, with the remaining amount consisting of oxygen. What is the empirical formula of tetrodotoxin? If three molecules of tetrodotoxin have a mass of 1.59×10^{-21} g, what is the molecular formula of tetrodotoxin? What number of molecules of tetrodotoxin would be the LD_{50} dosage for a person weighing 165 lb?

101. Consider the following data for three binary compounds of hydrogen and nitrogen:

	% H (by Mass)	% N (by Mass)
I	17.75	82.25
II	12.58	87.42
III	2.34	97.66

When 1.00 L of each gaseous compound is decomposed to its elements, the following volumes of $H_2(g)$ and $N_2(g)$ are obtained:

	H_2 (L)	N_2 (L)
I	1.50	0.50
II	2.00	1.00
III	0.50	1.50

Use these data to determine the molecular formulas of compounds I, II, and III and to determine the relative values for the atomic masses of hydrogen and nitrogen.

102. A 0.200-g sample of protactinium(IV) oxide is converted to another oxide of protactinium by heating in the presence of oxygen to give 0.2081 g of the new oxide, Pa_xO_y. Determine the values of x and y.

103. A 1.000-g sample of XI_2 is dissolved in water, and excess silver nitrate is added to precipitate all of the iodide as AgI. The mass of the dry AgI is found to be 1.375 g. Calculate the atomic weight (mass) of X.

104. A substance X_2Z has the composition (by mass) of 40.0% X and 60.0% Z. What is the composition (by mass) of the compound XZ_2?

105. Vitamin A has a molar mass of 286.4 g and has a general molecular formula of C_xH_yE, where E is an unknown element. If vitamin A is 83.86% C and 10.56% H by mass, what is the molecular formula of vitamin A?

106. Boron consists of two isotopes, ^{10}B and ^{11}B. Chlorine also has two isotopes, ^{35}Cl and ^{37}Cl. Consider the mass spectrum of BCl_3. How many peaks would be present, and what approximate mass would each peak correspond to in the BCl_3 mass spectrum?

Challenge Problems

107. In a mass spectrometer, positive ions are produced when a gaseous mixture is ionized by electron bombardment produced by an electric discharge. When the electric-discharge voltage is low, singly positive ions are produced and the following peaks are observed in the mass spectrum:

Mass (amu)	Relative Intensity
32	0.3743
34	0.0015
40	1.0000

When the electric discharge is increased, still only singly charged ions are produced, but now the peaks observed in the mass spectrum are

Mass (amu)	Relative Intensity
16	0.7500
18	0.0015
40	1.0000

What does the gas mixture consist of, and what is the percent composition by isotope of the mixture?

108. When the supply of oxygen is limited, iron metal reacts with oxygen to produce a mixture of FeO and Fe_2O_3. In a certain experiment, 20.00 g of iron metal was reacted with 11.20 g of oxygen gas. After the experiment, the iron was totally consumed and 3.24 g of oxygen gas remained. Calculate the amounts of FeO and Fe_2O_3 formed in this experiment.

109. Element X forms both a dichloride (XCl_2) and a tetrachloride (XCl_4). Treatment of 10.00 g of XCl_2 with excess chlorine forms 12.55 g of XCl_4. Calculate the atomic weight (mass) of X and identify X.

110. Zinc and magnesium metal each react with hydrochloric acid to make chloride salts of the respective metals and hydrogen gas. A 10.00-g mixture of zinc and magnesium produces 0.5171 g of hydrogen gas upon being mixed with an excess of hydrochloric acid. Determine the percent magnesium by mass in the original mixture.

111. An unknown binary compound containing hydrogen (XH_n) has a density as a gas that is 2.393 times that of oxygen gas under the same conditions. When 2.23×10^{-2} mole of this compound reacts with excess oxygen gas, 0.803 g of water is produced. Identify the element X in this compound.

112. A 2.25-g sample of scandium metal is reacted with excess hydrochloric acid to produce 0.1502 g hydrogen gas. What is the formula of the scandium chloride produced in the reaction?

113. When $M_2S_3(s)$ is heated in air, it is converted to $MO_2(s)$. A 4.000-g sample of $M_2S_3(s)$ shows a decrease in mass of 0.277 g when it is heated in air. What is the average atomic mass of M?

114. Consider a gaseous binary compound with a molar mass of 62.09 g/mol. When 1.39 g of this compound is completely burned in excess oxygen, 1.21 g of water is formed. Determine the formula of the compound.

115. Pure carbon was burned in an excess of oxygen. The gaseous products were

CO_2	72.0 mol%
CO	16.0 mol%
O_2	12.0 mol%

How many moles of O_2 were present in the initial reaction mixture for every mole of carbon?

116. You take 1.00 g of an aspirin tablet (a compound consisting solely of carbon, hydrogen, and oxygen), burn it in air, and collect 2.20 g CO_2 and 0.400 g H_2O. You

know that the molar mass of aspirin is between 170 and 190 g/mol. Reacting 1 mole of salicylic acid with 1 mole of acetic anhydride ($C_4H_6O_3$) gives you 1 mole of aspirin and 1 mole of acetic acid ($C_2H_4O_2$). Use this information to determine the molecular formula of salicylic acid.

117. Lanthanum was reacted with hydrogen in a given experiment to produce the nonstoichiometric compound $LaH_{2.90}$. Assuming that the compound contains H^-, La^{2+}, and La^{3+}, calculate the fraction of La^{2+} and La^{3+} present.

118. A 9.780-g gaseous mixture contains ethane (C_2H_6) and propane (C_3H_8). Complete combustion to form carbon dioxide and water requires 1.120 moles of oxygen gas. Calculate the mass percent of ethane in the original mixture.

119. Consider a mixture of potassium chloride and potassium nitrate that is 43.2% potassium by mass. What is the percent KCl by mass of the original mixture?

120. A 2.077-g sample of an element, which has an atomic mass between 40 and 55, reacts with oxygen to form 3.708 g of an oxide. Determine the formula of the oxide and identify the element.

121. Ammonia reacts with O_2 to form either $NO(g)$ or $NO_2(g)$ according to these unbalanced equations:

$$NH_3(g) + O_2(g) \longrightarrow NO(g) + H_2O(g)$$
$$NH_3(g) + O_2(g) \longrightarrow NO_2(g) + H_2O(g)$$

In a certain experiment, 2.00 moles of $NH_3(g)$ and 10.00 moles of $O_2(g)$ are contained in a closed flask. After the reaction is complete, 6.75 moles of $O_2(g)$ remains. Calculate the number of moles of $NO(g)$ in the product mixture. (*Hint:* You cannot do this problem by adding the balanced equations, because you cannot assume that the two reactions will occur with equal probability.)

122. A gas contains a mixture of $NH_3(g)$ and $N_2H_4(g)$, both of which react with $O_2(g)$ to form $NO_2(g)$ and $H_2O(g)$. The gaseous mixture (with an initial mass of 61.00 g) is reacted with 10.00 moles O_2, and after the reaction is complete, 4.062 moles of O_2 remains. Calculate the mass percent of $N_2H_4(g)$ in the original gaseous mixture.

Marathon Problems*

123. From the information that follows, determine the mass of substance C that will be formed if 45.0 g of substance A reacts with 23.0 g of substance B. (Assume that the reaction between A and B goes to completion.)
    a. Substance A is a gray solid that consists of an alkaline earth metal and carbon (37.5% by mass). It reacts with substance B to produce substances C and D. Forty million trillion formula units of A have a mass of 4.26 mg.

    b. 47.9 g of substance B contains 5.36 g of hydrogen and 42.5 g of oxygen.
    c. When 10.0 g of substance C is burned in excess oxygen, 33.8 g of carbon dioxide and 6.92 g of water are produced. A mass spectrum of substance C shows a parent molecular ion with a mass-to-charge ratio of 26.
    d. Substance D is the hydroxide of the metal in substance A.

124. Consider the following balanced chemical equation:

$$A + 5B \longrightarrow 3C + 4D$$

---

*From James H. Burness, "The Use of "Marathon" Problems as Effective Vehicles for the Presentation of General Chemistry Lectures," Journal of Chemical Education, 68(11). Copyright © 1991 American Chemical Society. Reprinted by permission.

a. Equal masses of A and B are reacted. Complete each of the following with either "A is the limiting reactant because _____"; "B is the limiting reactant because _____"; or "We cannot determine the limiting reactant because _____."

   i. If the molar mass of A is greater than the molar mass of B, then

   ii. If the molar mass of B is greater than the molar mass of A, then

b. The products of the reaction are carbon dioxide (C) and water (D). Compound A has a similar molar mass to carbon dioxide. Compound B is a diatomic molecule. Identify compound B and support your answer.

c. Compound A is a hydrocarbon that is 81.71% carbon by mass. Determine its empirical and molecular formulas.

4

chapter

Types of Chemical Reactions and Solution Stoichiometry

When zinc reacts with iodine, the heat produces a cloud of excess iodine.

Much of the chemistry that affects each of us occurs among substances dissolved in water. For example, virtually all of the chemistry that makes life possible occurs in an aqueous environment. Also, various tests for illnesses involve aqueous reactions. Modern medical practice depends heavily on analyses of blood and other body fluids. In addition to the common tests for sugar, cholesterol, and iron, analyses for specific chemical markers allow detection of many diseases before more obvious symptoms occur.

Aqueous chemistry is also important in our environment. In recent years contamination of the groundwater by substances such as chloroform and nitrates has been widely publicized. Water is essential for life, and the maintenance of an ample supply of clean water is crucial to all civilization.

To understand the chemistry that occurs in such diverse places as the human body, the groundwater, the oceans, the local water treatment plant, your hair as you shampoo it, and so on, we must understand how substances dissolved in water react with one another.

However, before we can understand solution reactions, we need to discuss the nature of solutions in which water is the dissolving medium, or *solvent*. These solutions are called **aqueous solutions.** In this chapter we will study the nature of materials after they are dissolved in water and various types of reactions that occur among these substances. You will see that the procedures developed in Chapter 3 to deal with chemical reactions work very well for reactions that take place in aqueous solutions. To understand the types of reactions that occur in aqueous solutions, we must first explore the types of species present. This requires an understanding of the nature of water.

4.1 | Water, the Common Solvent

Water is one of the most important substances on earth. It is, of course, crucial for sustaining the reactions that keep us alive, but it also affects our lives in many indirect ways. Water helps moderate the earth's temperature; it cools automobile engines, nuclear power plants, and many industrial processes; it provides a means of transportation on the earth's surface and a medium for the growth of a myriad of creatures we use as food; and much more.

One of the most valuable functions of water involves its ability to dissolve many different substances. For example, salt "disappears" when you sprinkle it into the water used to cook vegetables, as does sugar when you add it to your iced tea. In each case the disappearing substance is obviously still present—you can taste it. What happens when a solid dissolves? To understand this process, we need to consider the nature of water. Liquid water consists of a collection of H_2O molecules. An individual H_2O molecule is "bent" or V-shaped, with an H—O—H angle of about 105°:

$$\underset{O}{\overset{H \underset{\curvearrowright}{\overset{105°}{}} H}{}}$$

The O—H bonds in the water molecule are covalent bonds formed by electron sharing between the oxygen and hydrogen atoms. However, the electrons of the bond are not shared equally between these atoms. For reasons we will discuss in later chapters, oxygen has a greater attraction for electrons than does hydrogen. If the electrons were shared equally between the two atoms, both would be electrically neutral because, on average, the number of electrons around each would equal the number of protons in that nucleus. However, because the oxygen atom has a greater attraction for electrons, the shared electrons tend to spend more time close to the oxygen than to either of the hydro-

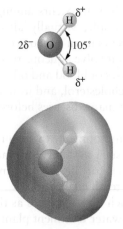

Figure 4.1
(top) The water molecule is polar. (bottom) The electrons in the water molecule are not shared equally between hydrogen and oxygen. This can be represented with a colored map of electrostatic potential. Red areas indicate high electron density, and blue areas represent low electron density. The colors in between indicate varying degrees of electron density.

gens. Thus the oxygen atom gains a slight excess of negative charge, and the hydrogen atoms become slightly positive. This is shown in Fig. 4.1, where δ (delta) indicates a *partial* charge *(less than one unit of charge)*. Because of this unequal charge distribution, water is said to be a **polar molecule.** It is this polarity that gives water its great ability to dissolve compounds.

A schematic of an ionic solid dissolving in water is shown in Fig. 4.2. Note that the "positive ends" of the water molecules are attracted to the negatively charged anions and that the "negative ends" are attracted to the positively charged cations. This process is called **hydration.** The hydration of its ions tends to cause a salt to "fall apart" in the water, or to dissolve. The strong forces present among the positive and negative ions of the solid are replaced by strong water–ion interactions.

It is very important to recognize that when ionic substances (salts) dissolve in water, they break up into the *individual* cations and anions. For instance, when ammonium nitrate (NH_4NO_3) dissolves in water, the resulting solution contains NH_4^+ and NO_3^- ions floating around independently. This process can be represented as

$$NH_4NO_3(s) \xrightarrow{\text{H}_2\text{O}(l)} NH_4^+(aq) + NO_3^-(aq)$$

where *(aq)* indicates that the ions are hydrated by unspecified numbers of water molecules.

The solubility of ionic substances in water varies greatly. For example, sodium chloride is quite soluble in water, whereas silver chloride (contains Ag^+ and Cl^- ions) is only very slightly soluble. The differences in the solubilities of ionic compounds in water typically depend on the relative affinities of the ions for each other (these forces hold the solid together) and the affinities of the ions for water molecules [which cause the solid to disperse (dissolve) in water]. The most important thing to remember at this point is that when an ionic solid does dissolve in water, the ions are dispersed and are assumed to move around independently.

Figure 4.2
Polar water molecules interact with the positive and negative ions of a salt, assisting with the dissolving process.

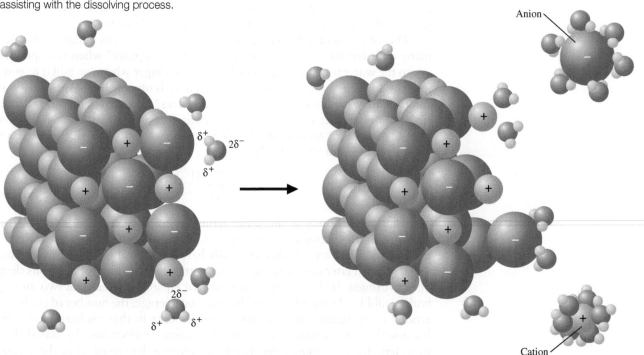

Figure 4.3

(a) The ethanol molecule contains a polar O—H bond similar to those in the water molecule. (b) The polar water molecule interacts strongly with the polar O—H bond in ethanol. This is a case of "like dissolving like."

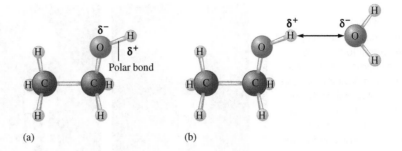

(a)   (b)

Water also dissolves many nonionic substances. Ethanol (C_2H_5OH), for example, is very soluble in water. Wine, beer, and mixed drinks are aqueous solutions of alcohol and other substances. Why is ethanol so soluble in water? The answer lies in the structure of the alcohol molecule, which is shown in Fig. 4.3(a). The molecule contains a polar O—H bond like those in water, which makes it very compatible with water. The interaction of water with ethanol is represented in Fig. 4.3(b).

Many substances do not dissolve in water. Pure water will not, for example, dissolve animal fat because fat molecules are nonpolar and do not interact effectively with polar water molecules. In general, polar and ionic substances are expected to be more soluble in water than nonpolar substances. "Like dissolves like" is a useful rule for predicting solubility.

4.2 | The Nature of Aqueous Solutions: Strong and Weak Electrolytes

Recall that a solution is a homogeneous mixture. It is the same throughout (the first sip of a cup of coffee is the same as the last), but its composition can be varied by changing the amount of dissolved substances (one can make weak or strong coffee). In this section we will consider what happens when a substance, the **solute,** is dissolved in liquid water, the **solvent.**

One useful property for characterizing a solution is its **electrical conductivity,** its ability to conduct an electric current. This characteristic can be checked conveniently by using an apparatus like the one shown in Fig. 4.4. If the solution in the container conducts electricity, the bulb lights. Some solutions conduct current very efficiently, and the bulb shines very brightly; these solutions contain **strong electrolytes.** Other solutions conduct only a small current, and the bulb glows dimly; these solutions contain **weak electrolytes.** Some solutions permit no current to flow, and the bulb remains unlit; these solutions contain **nonelectrolytes.**

The basis for the conductivity properties of solutions was first correctly identified by Svante Arrhenius, then a Swedish graduate student in physics, who carried out research on the nature of solutions at the University of Uppsala in the early 1880s. Arrhenius came to believe that the conductivity of solutions arose from the presence of ions, an idea that was at first scorned by the majority of the scientific establishment. However, in the late 1890s when atoms were found to contain charged particles, the ionic theory suddenly made sense and became widely accepted.

As Arrhenius postulated, the extent to which a solution can conduct an electric current depends directly on the number of ions present. Some materials, such as sodium chloride, readily produce ions in aqueous solution and are thus strong electrolytes. Other substances, such as acetic acid, produce relatively few ions when dissolved in water and are weak electrolytes. A third class

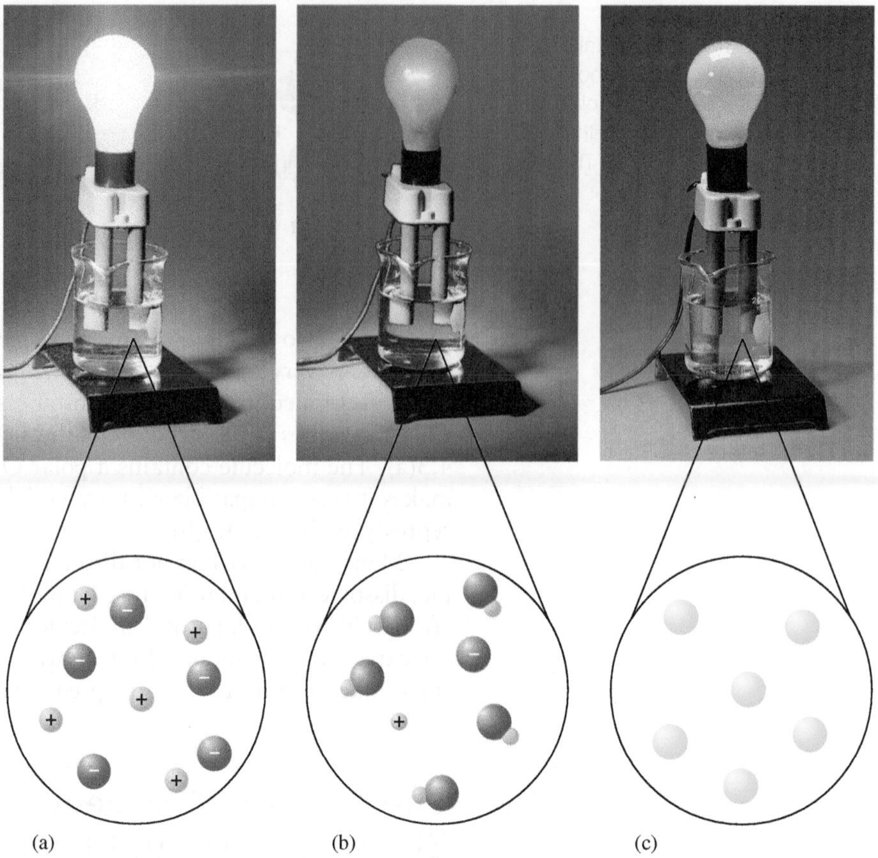

Figure 4.4
Electrical conductivity of aqueous solutions. The circuit will be completed and will allow current to flow only when there are charge carriers (ions) in the solution. *Note:* Water molecules are present but not shown in these pictures. (a) A hydrochloric acid solution, which is a strong electrolyte, contains ions that readily conduct the current and give a brightly lit bulb. (b) An acetic acid solution, which is a weak electrolyte, contains only a few ions and does not conduct as much current as a strong electrolyte. The bulb is only dimly lit. (c) A sucrose solution, which is a nonelectrolyte, contains no ions and does not conduct a current. The bulb remains unlit.

(a)   (b)   (c)

of materials, such as sugar, form virtually no ions when dissolved in water and are nonelectrolytes.

Strong Electrolytes

We will consider several classes of strong electrolytes: (1) soluble salts, (2) strong acids, and (3) strong bases.

As shown in Fig. 4.2, a salt consists of an array of cations and anions that separate and become hydrated when the salt dissolves. **Solubility** is usually measured in terms of the mass (grams) of solute that dissolves per given volume of solvent *or* in terms of the number of moles of solute that dissolve in a given volume of solution. Some salts, such as NaCl, KCl, and NH_4Cl, are very soluble in water. For example, approximately 357 grams of NaCl will dissolve in a liter of water at 25°C. On the other hand, many salts are only very slightly soluble in water; for example, silver chloride (AgCl) dissolves in water only to a slight extent (approximately 2×10^{-3} g/L at 25°C). We will consider only soluble salts at this point.

One of Arrhenius's most important discoveries concerned the nature of **acids.** Acidic behavior was first associated with the sour taste of citrus fruits. In fact, the word *acid* comes directly from the Latin word *acidus,* meaning "sour." The *mineral acids* sulfuric acid (H_2SO_4) and nitric acid (HNO_3), so named because they were originally obtained by the treatment of minerals, were discovered around 1300.

Acids were known to exist for hundreds of years before the time of Arrhenius, but no one had recognized their essential nature. In his studies of solutions, Arrhenius found that when the substances HCl, HNO_3, and H_2SO_4 were dissolved in water, they behaved as strong electrolytes. He postulated that this was the result of ionization reactions in water, for example:

$$HCl \xrightarrow{H_2O} H^+(aq) + Cl^-(aq)$$

$$HNO_3 \xrightarrow{H_2O} H^+(aq) + NO_3^-(aq)$$

$$H_2SO_4 \xrightarrow{H_2O} H^+(aq) + HSO_4^-(aq)$$

Thus Arrhenius proposed that an *acid is a substance that produces H⁺ ions (protons) when it is dissolved in water.*

Studies of conductivity show that when HCl, HNO_3, and H_2SO_4 are placed in water, *virtually every molecule* dissociates to give ions. These substances are strong electrolytes and are thus called **strong acids.** All three are very important chemicals, and much more will be said about them as we proceed. However, at this point the following facts are important:

Hydrochloric acid, nitric acid, and sulfuric acid are aqueous solutions and should be written in chemical equations as $HCl(aq)$, $HNO_3(aq)$, and $H_2SO_4(aq)$, respectively, although they often appear without the *(aq)* symbol.

A strong acid is one that completely dissociates into its ions. Thus, if 100 molecules of HCl are dissolved in water, 100 H⁺ ions and 100 Cl⁻ ions are produced. Virtually no HCl molecules exist in aqueous solution (see Fig. 4.5).

Sulfuric acid is a special case. The formula H_2SO_4 indicates that this acid can produce two H⁺ ions per molecule when dissolved in water. However, only the first H⁺ ion is completely dissociated. The second H⁺ ion can be pulled off under certain conditions, which we will discuss later. Thus a solution of H_2SO_4 dissolved in water contains mostly H⁺ ions and HSO_4^- ions.

Another important class of strong electrolytes is the **strong bases,** soluble compounds containing the *hydroxide ion* (OH⁻) that completely dissociate when dissolved in water. Solutions containing bases have a bitter taste and a slippery feel. The most common basic solutions are those produced when solid sodium hydroxide (NaOH) or potassium hydroxide (KOH) is dissolved in water to produce ions, as follows (Fig. 4.6):

$$NaOH(s) \xrightarrow{H_2O} Na^+(aq) + OH^-(aq)$$

$$KOH(s) \xrightarrow{H_2O} K^+(aq) + OH^-(aq)$$

Weak Electrolytes

Weak electrolytes are substances that produce relatively few ions when dissolved in water, as shown in Fig. 4.4(b). The most common weak electrolytes are weak acids and weak bases.

The main acidic component of vinegar is acetic acid ($HC_2H_3O_2$). The formula is written to indicate that acetic acid has two chemically distinct types of hydrogen atoms. Formulas for acids are often written with the acidic hydrogen atom or atoms (any that will produce H⁺ ions in solution) listed first. If any nonacidic hydrogens are present, they are written later in the formula. Thus the formula $HC_2H_3O_2$ indicates one acidic and three nonacidic hydrogen atoms. The dissociation reaction for acetic acid in water can be written as follows:

$$HC_2H_3O_2(aq) \xrightarrow{H_2O} H^+(aq) + C_2H_3O_2^-(aq)$$

Acetic acid is very different from the strong acids in that only about 1% of its molecules dissociate in aqueous solution (Fig. 4.7). Thus, when 100 molecules

The Arrhenius definition of an acid: a substance that produces H⁺ ions in solution.

Perchloric acid, $HClO_4(aq)$, is another strong acid.

Figure 4.5
HCl(*aq*) is completely ionized.

Strong electrolytes dissociate completely in aqueous solution.

Figure 4.6
An aqueous solution of sodium hydroxide.

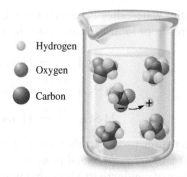

Figure 4.7
Acetic acid ($HC_2H_3O_2$) exists in water mostly as undissociated molecules. Only a small percentage of the molecules are ionized.

Figure 4.8
The reaction of NH_3 in water. The NH_4^+ and OH^- ions are formed by reaction of an NH_3 molecule with an H_2O molecule.

Weak electrolytes dissociate only to a small extent in aqueous solution.

of $HC_2H_3O_2$ are dissolved in water, approximately 99 molecules of $HC_2H_3O_2$ remain intact, and only one H^+ ion and one $C_2H_3O_2^-$ ion are produced.

Because acetic acid is a weak electrolyte, it is called a **weak acid.** Any acid, such as acetic acid, that *dissociates only to a slight extent in aqueous solution is called a weak acid.* We will explore weak acids in detail in Chapter 7.

The most common **weak base** is ammonia (NH_3). When ammonia is dissolved in water, it reacts as follows:

$$NH_3(aq) + H_2O(l) \longrightarrow NH_4^+(aq) + OH^-(aq)$$

The solution is *basic* since OH^- ions are produced. Ammonia is called a **weak base** because *the resulting solution is a weak electrolyte*—very few ions are present (Fig. 4.8). In fact, for every 100 molecules of NH_3 that are dissolved, only one NH_4^+ ion and one OH^- ion are produced; 99 molecules of NH_3 remain unreacted.

Nonelectrolytes

Nonelectrolytes are substances that dissolve in water but do not produce any ions [Fig. 4.4(c)]. An example of a nonelectrolyte is ethanol (see Fig. 4.3 for the structural formula). When ethanol dissolves, entire C_2H_5OH molecules are dispersed in the water. Since the molecules do not break up into ions, the resulting solution does not conduct an electric current. Another common nonelectrolyte is table sugar (sucrose, $C_{12}H_{22}O_{11}$), which is very soluble in water but produces no ions when it dissolves.

4.3 | The Composition of Solutions

Chemical reactions often take place when two solutions are mixed. To perform stoichiometric calculations in such cases, we must know two things: (1) the *nature of the reaction*, which depends on the exact forms the chemicals take when dissolved, and (2) the *amounts of chemicals* present in the solutions, that is, the composition of each solution.

The composition of a solution can be described in many different ways. At this point we will consider only the most commonly used expression of concentration, **molarity** (*M*), which is defined as *moles of solute per volume of solution (expressed in liters):*

$$M = \text{molarity} = \frac{\text{moles of solute}}{\text{liters of solution}}$$

A solution that is 1.0 molar (written as 1.0 *M*) contains 1.0 mole of solute per liter of solution.

⊙WL INTERACTIVE EXAMPLE 4.1

Calculate the molarity of a solution prepared by bubbling 1.56 g of gaseous HCl into enough water to make 26.8 mL of solution.

Solution

■ What are we trying to solve?

We are asked to solve for the concentration of a solution in units of molarity.

■ What does this mean?

$$\text{Molarity} = \frac{\text{moles of solute}}{\text{liters of solution}}$$

We are given the volume of the solution in milliliters, and we can convert this to liters:

$$26.8 \text{ mL} \times \frac{1 \text{ L}}{1000 \text{ mL}} = 2.68 \times 10^{-2} \text{ L}$$

Thus we have

$$\text{Molarity} = \frac{\text{moles of solute}}{2.68 \times 10^{-2} \text{ L}}$$

To calculate the molarity, we need to determine the moles of solute, so we change the original question to *"How many moles of HCl are in 1.56 g?"* Recall from Chapter 3 that to do this we use the molar mass as follows:

$$1.56 \text{ g HCl} \times \frac{1 \text{ mol HCl}}{36.5 \text{ g HCl}} = 4.27 \times 10^{-2} \text{ mol HCl}$$

We can now determine the concentration as follows:

$$\text{Molarity} = \frac{4.27 \times 10^{-2} \text{ mol HCl}}{2.68 \times 10^{-2} \text{ L solution}} = 1.59 \text{ } M \text{ HCl}$$

Note that the description of a solution's composition may not accurately reflect the true chemical nature of the solution. Solution concentration is always given in terms of the form of the solute *before* it dissolves. For example, consider 1.0 liter of a solution labeled as 1.0 *M* NaCl. This solution was prepared by dissolving 1.0 mole of solid NaCl in enough water to make 1.0 liter of solution. The label 1.0 *M* does not mean that the solution contains 1.0 mole of NaCl units. Actually, the solution contains 1.0 mole of Na^+ ions and 1.0 mole of Cl^- ions.

Often we need to determine the number of moles of solute present in a given volume of a solution of known molarity. The procedure for doing so is easily derived from the definition of molarity:

$$M = \frac{\text{moles of solute}}{\text{liters of solution}}$$

$$\text{Liters of solution} \times \text{molarity} = \text{liters of solution} \times \frac{\text{moles of solute}}{\text{liters of solution}}$$

$$= \text{moles of solute}$$

ⓦWL INTERACTIVE EXAMPLE 4.2

Calculate the number of moles of Cl^- ions in 1.75 L of 1.0×10^{-3} M $AlCl_3$.

Solution

■ What are we trying to solve?

We are looking for the number of moles of Cl^- ions, and we are given the volume of the solution and the concentration in molarity, along with the formula for the ionic compound.

We know that molarity is a ratio of moles of solute to liters of solution, or

$$M = \frac{\text{moles of solute}}{\text{liters of solution}}$$

Thus

$$\text{Moles} = M \times \text{volume}$$

This would give us the moles of $AlCl_3$ that would dissolve, but we are looking for the moles of Cl^- ions in solution.

When solid $AlCl_3$ dissolves, it produces ions as follows:

$$AlCl_3(s) \xrightarrow{H_2O} Al^{3+}(aq) + 3Cl^-(aq)$$

Thus a 1.0×10^{-3} M $AlCl_3$ solution contains 1.0×10^{-3} M Al^{3+} ions and 3.0×10^{-3} M Cl^- ions.

To calculate the moles of Cl^- ions in 1.75 L of the 1.0×10^{-3} M $AlCl_3$ solution, we must multiply the volume by the molarity:

$$1.75 \text{ L solution} \times 3.0 \times 10^{-3} \text{ M } Cl^-$$

$$= 1.75 \text{ L solution} \times \frac{3.0 \times 10^{-3} \text{ mol } Cl^-}{\text{L solution}}$$

$$= 5.3 \times 10^{-3} \text{ mol } Cl^-$$

ⓦWL INTERACTIVE EXAMPLE 4.3

Typical blood serum is about 0.14 M $NaCl$. What volume of blood contains 1.0 mg of $NaCl$?

Solution

■ What are we trying to solve?

We want to determine the volume of blood containing 1.0 mg of $NaCl$, and we know the concentration of $NaCl$ in molarity. Thus we are looking for a conversion between volume and mass.

We know that molarity is a ratio of moles of solute to liters of solution, so we have a conversion between volume and moles:

$$M = \frac{\text{moles of solute}}{\text{liters of solution}}$$

Thus

$$\text{Volume} = \frac{\text{moles of solute}}{M}$$

We also have a conversion between mass and moles (molar mass). Thus we can convert mass to moles (using molar mass) and moles to volume (using molarity):

We must first determine the number of moles represented by 1.0 mg of NaCl:

$$1.0 \text{ mg NaCl} \times \frac{1 \text{ g NaCl}}{1000 \text{ mg NaCl}} \times \frac{1 \text{ mol NaCl}}{58.45 \text{ g NaCl}} = 1.7 \times 10^{-5} \text{ mol NaCl}$$

Next, we must determine what volume of 0.14 M NaCl solution contains 1.7×10^{-5} mole of NaCl. There is some volume (V) that when multiplied by the molarity of this solution yields 1.7×10^{-5} mole of NaCl. That is,

$$V \times \frac{0.14 \text{ mol NaCl}}{\text{L solution}} = 1.7 \times 10^{-5} \text{ mol NaCl}$$

Solving for the volume gives

$$V = \frac{1.7 \times 10^{-5} \text{ mol NaCl}}{\dfrac{0.14 \text{ mol NaCl}}{\text{L solution}}} = 1.2 \times 10^{-4} \text{ L solution}$$

Thus 0.12 mL of blood contains 1.7×10^{-5} mole of NaCl, or 1.0 mg of NaCl.

A **standard solution** is a solution *whose concentration is accurately known.* Standard solutions, often used in chemical analysis, can be prepared as shown in Fig. 4.9 and in Example 4.4.

ⓌWL INTERACTIVE EXAMPLE 4.4

To analyze the alcohol content of a certain wine, a chemist needs 1.00 L of an aqueous 0.200 M $K_2Cr_2O_7$ (potassium dichromate) solution. How much solid $K_2Cr_2O_7$ must be weighed out to make this solution?

Solution

■ What are we trying to solve?

We are asked to determine the mass of K_2CrO_7 solute required to make 1.00 L of a 0.200 M solution. Knowing that molarity is a ratio of moles of solute to

Figure 4.9

Steps involved in the preparation of a standard aqueous solution. (a) Put a weighed amount of a substance (the solute) into the volumetric flask, and add a small quantity of water. (b) Dissolve the solid in the water by gently swirling the flask *(with the stopper in place).* (c) Add more water (with gentle swirling) until the level of the solution just reaches the mark etched on the neck of the flask. Then mix the solution thoroughly by inverting the flask several times.

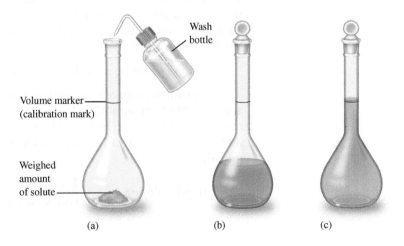

liters of solution, we can use molarity and volume to determine the moles of solute.

$$M = \frac{\text{moles of solute}}{\text{liters of solution}}$$

Thus

$$\text{Moles} = M \times \text{volume}$$

However, we are asked for mass, so we will need to convert the moles to a mass, and we can do this using the molar mass of the solute.

First, determine the moles of $K_2Cr_2O_7$ required:

$$1.00 \text{ L solution} \times \frac{0.200 \text{ mol } K_2Cr_2O_7}{\text{L solution}} = 0.200 \text{ mol } K_2Cr_2O_7$$

This amount can be converted to grams by using the molar mass of $K_2Cr_2O_7$:

$$0.200 \text{ mol } K_2Cr_2O_7 \times \frac{294.2 \text{ g } K_2Cr_2O_7}{\text{mol } K_2Cr_2O_7} = 58.8 \text{ g } K_2Cr_2O_7$$

Thus, to make 1.00 L of 0.200 M $K_2Cr_2O_7$, the chemist must weigh out 58.8 g of $K_2Cr_2O_7$, put it in a 1.00-L volumetric flask, and add water up to the mark on the flask.

Note: In looking back at the solutions to Examples 4.1 through 4.4, you should notice that the problems are solved similarly. For example, in all cases we need to know what molarity means and how to manipulate the formula for concentration. The problems vary in the details. In Examples 4.1, 4.3, and 4.4, we need to use molar mass = mass/mol. In Example 4.2, we need to understand how an ionic solid dissolves. As discussed in Section 3.4, we need to ask questions that allow the problem to guide us, but we also need a bank of knowledge to draw from.

Dilution

To save time and space in the laboratory, routinely used solutions are often purchased or prepared in concentrated form (these are called *stock solutions*). In a process called **dilution,** water is then added to achieve the molarity desired for a particular solution. For example, the common acids are purchased as concentrated solutions and diluted as needed. A typical dilution calculation involves determining how much water must be added to an amount of stock solution to achieve a solution of the desired concentration. The key to doing these calculations is to remember that since only water is added in the dilution, all of the solute in the final dilute solution must come from the concentrated stock solution. That is,

Moles of solute after dilution = moles of solute before dilution

For example, suppose we need to prepare 500. milliliters of 1.00 M acetic acid ($HC_2H_3O_2$) from a 17.5 M stock solution of acetic acid. What volume of the stock solution is required? The first step is to determine the number of moles of acetic acid in the final solution by multiplying the volume by the molarity:

$$500. \text{ mL solution} \times \frac{1 \text{ L solution}}{1000 \text{ mL solution}} \times \frac{1.00 \text{ mol } HC_2H_3O_2}{\text{L solution}}$$

$$= 0.500 \text{ mol } HC_2H_3O_2$$

Dilution with water doesn't alter the number of moles of solute present.

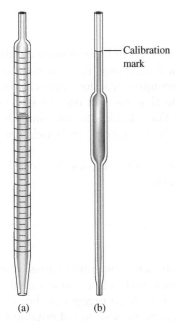

Thus we need to use a volume of 17.5 *M* acetic acid that contains 0.500 mole of $HC_2H_3O_2$. That is,

$$V \times \frac{17.5 \text{ mol } HC_2H_3O_2}{L \text{ solution}} = 0.500 \text{ mol } HC_2H_3O_2$$

Solving for *V* gives

$$V = \frac{0.500 \text{ mol } HC_2H_3O_2}{\dfrac{17.5 \text{ mol } HC_2H_3O_2}{L \text{ solution}}} = 0.0286 \text{ L, or } 28.6 \text{ mL solution}$$

Thus, to make 500. milliliters of a 1.00 *M* acetic acid solution, we can take 28.6 milliliters of 17.5 *M* acetic acid and dilute it to a total volume of 500. milliliters.

A dilution procedure typically involves two types of glassware: a pipet and a volumetric flask. A pipet is a device for accurately measuring and transferring a given volume of solution. There are two common types of pipets: *measuring pipets* and *volumetric pipets*, as shown in Fig. 4.10. Measuring pipets are used to measure out volumes for which a volumetric pipet is not available. For example, we would use a measuring pipet as shown in Fig. 4.11 to deliver 28.6 milliliters of 17.5 *M* acetic acid into a 500-milliliter volumetric flask and then add water to the mark to perform the dilution described above.

Figure 4.10

(a) A measuring pipet is graduated and can be used to measure various volumes of liquid accurately. (b) A volumetric pipet is designed to measure *one* volume accurately. When filled to the calibration mark, it delivers the volume indicated on the pipet.

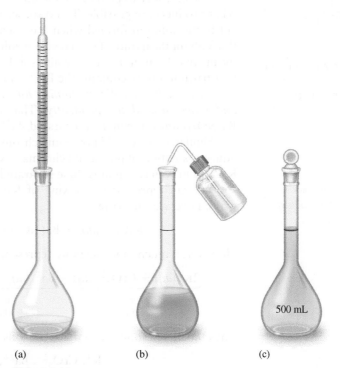

(a)   (b)   (c)

Figure 4.11

(a) A measuring pipet is used to transfer 28.7 mL of 17.4 *M* acetic acid solution to a volumetric flask. (b) Water is added to the flask to the calibration mark. (c) The resulting solution is 1.00 *M* acetic acid.

4.4 | Types of Chemical Reactions

Although we have considered many reactions so far, we have examined only a tiny fraction of the millions of possible chemical reactions. To make sense of all these reactions, we need some system for grouping reactions into classes. Although there are many different ways to do this, we will use the system most commonly used by practicing chemists. They divide reactions into the following groups: *precipitation reactions, acid–base reactions,* and *oxidation–reduction reactions.*

Virtually all reactions can be placed into one of these classes. We will define and illustrate each type in the following sections.

Types of Solution Reactions

Precipitation reactions
Acid–base reactions
Oxidation–reduction reactions

4.5 | Precipitation Reactions

When two solutions are mixed, an insoluble substance sometimes forms; that is, a solid forms and separates from the solution. Such a reaction is called a **precipitation reaction,** and the solid that forms is called a **precipitate.** For example, a precipitation reaction occurs when an aqueous solution of potassium chromate [$K_2CrO_4(aq)$], which is yellow, is mixed with a colorless aqueous solution containing barium nitrate [$Ba(NO_3)_2(aq)$]. As shown in Fig. 4.12, when these solutions are mixed, a yellow solid forms. What is the equation that describes this chemical change? To write the equation, we must know the identities of the reactants and products. The reactants have already been described: $K_2CrO_4(aq)$ and $Ba(NO_3)_2(aq)$. Is there some way we can predict the identities of the products? In particular, what is the yellow solid?

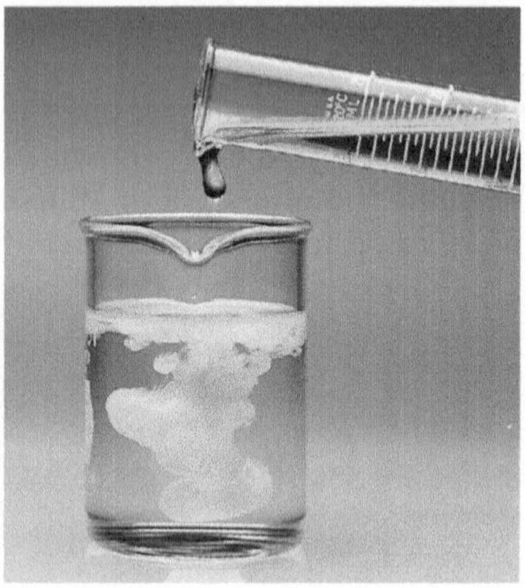

The best way to predict the identity of this solid is to think carefully about what products are possible. To do so, we need to know what species are present in the solution formed when the reactant solutions are mixed. First, let's think about the nature of each reactant solution. The designation $Ba(NO_3)_2(aq)$ means that barium nitrate (a white solid) has been dissolved in water. Notice that barium nitrate contains the Ba^{2+} and NO_3^- ions. *Remember: In virtually every case, when a solid containing ions dissolves in water, the ions separate and move around independently.* That is, $Ba(NO_3)_2(aq)$ does not contain $Ba(NO_3)_2$ units; it contains separated Ba^{2+} and NO_3^- ions (Fig. 4.13).

Similarly, since solid potassium chromate contains K^+ and CrO_4^{2-} ions, an aqueous solution of potassium chromate (which is prepared by dissolving solid K_2CrO_4 in water) contains these separated ions (Fig. 4.13).

We can represent the mixing of $K_2CrO_4(aq)$ and $Ba(NO_3)_2(aq)$ in two ways. First, we can write

$$K_2CrO_4(aq) + Ba(NO_3)_2(aq) \longrightarrow \text{products}$$

However, a much more accurate representation is

$$\underbrace{2K^+(aq) + CrO_4^{2-}(aq)}_{\substack{\text{The ions in} \\ K_2CrO_4(aq)}} + \underbrace{Ba^{2+}(aq) + 2NO_3^-(aq)}_{\substack{\text{The ions in} \\ Ba(NO_3)_2(aq)}} \longrightarrow \text{products}$$

Thus the mixed solution contains the ions

$$K^+, CrO_4^{2-}, Ba^{2+}, \text{ and } NO_3^-$$

How can some or all of these ions combine to form the yellow solid observed when the original solutions are mixed? This is not an easy question to answer. In fact, predicting the products of a chemical reaction is one of the hardest things a beginning chemistry student is asked to do. Even an experi-

Figure 4.12
When yellow aqueous potassium chromate is added to a colorless barium nitrate solution, yellow barium chromate precipitates.

When ionic compounds dissolve in water, the *resulting solution contains the separated ions.*

Figure 4.13
Reactant solutions: (a) Ba(NO₃)₂(aq) and (b) K₂CrO₄(aq).

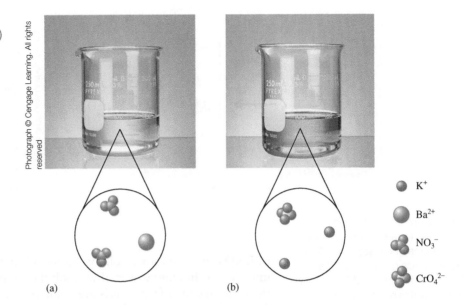

(a)   (b)

K^+

Ba^{2+}

NO_3^-

CrO_4^{2-}

enced chemist, when confronted with a new reaction, is often not sure what will happen. The chemist tries to think of the various possibilities, considers the likelihood of each possibility, and then makes a prediction (an educated guess). Only after identifying each product *experimentally* is the chemist sure what reaction has taken place. However, an educated guess is useful because it provides a place to start. It tells us what kinds of products we are most likely to find.

We already know some things that will help us predict the products:

1. When ions form a solid compound, the compound must have a zero net charge. Thus the products of this reaction must contain *both anions and cations.* For example, K^+ and Ba^{2+} could not combine to form the solid, nor could CrO_4^{2-} and NO_3^-.

2. Most ionic materials contain only two types of ions: one type of cation and one type of anion (for example, NaCl, KOH, Na_2SO_4, K_2CrO_4, $Co(NO_3)_2$, NH_4Cl, and Na_2CO_3).

The possible combinations of a given cation and a given anion from the list of ions K^+, CrO_4^{2-}, Ba^{2+}, and NO_3^- are

$$K_2CrO_4, \quad KNO_3, \quad BaCrO_4, \quad \text{and} \quad Ba(NO_3)_2$$

Which of these possibilities is most likely to represent the yellow solid? We know it's not K_2CrO_4 or $Ba(NO_3)_2$. They are the reactants. They were present (dissolved) in the separate solutions that were mixed. The only real possibilities for the solid that formed are

$$KNO_3 \quad \text{and} \quad BaCrO_4$$

To decide which of these possibilities most likely represents the yellow solid, we need more facts. An experienced chemist knows that the K^+ ion and the NO_3^- ion are both colorless. Thus, if the solid is KNO_3, it should be white, not yellow. On the other hand, the CrO_4^{2-} ion is yellow [note in Fig. 4.12 that $K_2CrO_4(aq)$ is yellow]. Thus the yellow solid is almost certainly $BaCrO_4$. Further tests show that this is the case.

So far we have determined that one product of the reaction between $K_2CrO_4(aq)$ and $Ba(NO_3)_2(aq)$ is $BaCrO_4(s)$, but what happened to the K^+ and NO_3^- ions? The answer is that these ions are left dissolved in the solution. That

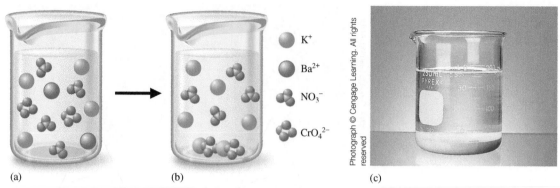

(a)   (b)   (c)

Figure 4.14

The reaction of $K_2CrO_4(aq)$ and $Ba(NO_3)_2(aq)$. (a) The molecular-level "picture" of the mixed solution before any reaction has occurred. (b) The molecular-level "picture" of the solution after the reaction has occurred to form $BaCrO_4(s)$. (c) A photo of the solution after the reaction has occurred, showing the solid $BaCrO_4$ on the bottom.

Doing chemistry requires both understanding ideas and remembering facts.

is, KNO_3 does not form a solid when the K^+ and NO_3^- ions are present in this much water. In other words, if we took the white solid, $KNO_3(s)$, and put it in the same quantity of water as is present in the mixed solution, it would dissolve. Thus, when we mix $K_2CrO_4(aq)$ and $Ba(NO_3)_2(aq)$, $BaCrO_4(s)$ forms, but KNO_3 is left behind in solution [we write it as $KNO_3(aq)$]. This reaction is illustrated in Fig. 4.14. Therefore, the equation for this precipitation reaction is

$$K_2CrO_4(aq) + Ba(NO_3)_2(aq) \longrightarrow BaCrO_4(s) + 2KNO_3(aq)$$

If we removed the solid $BaCrO_4$ by filtration and then evaporated the water, the white solid, KNO_3, would be obtained.

Now let's consider another example. When an aqueous solution of silver nitrate is added to an aqueous solution of potassium chloride, a white precipitate forms. We can represent what we know so far as

$$AgNO_3(aq) + KCl(aq) \longrightarrow \text{unknown white solid}$$

Remembering that when ionic substances dissolve in water, the ions separate, we can write

$$\underbrace{Ag^+, NO_3^-}_{\substack{\text{In silver} \\ \text{nitrate} \\ \text{solution}}} + \underbrace{K^+, Cl^-}_{\substack{\text{In potassium} \\ \text{chloride} \\ \text{solution}}} \longrightarrow \underbrace{Ag^+, NO_3^-, K^+, Cl^-}_{\substack{\text{Combined solution,} \\ \text{before reaction}}} \longrightarrow \text{white solid}$$

Since we know that the white solid must contain both positive and negative ions, the possible compounds that can be assembled from this collection of ions are

$$AgNO_3, KCl, AgCl, \text{ and } KNO_3$$

Since $AgNO_3$ and KCl are the substances dissolved in the reactant solutions, we know that they do not represent the white solid product. The only real possibilities are

$$AgCl \quad \text{and} \quad KNO_3$$

From the example considered above, we know that KNO_3 is quite soluble in water. Thus solid KNO_3 will not form when the reactant solutions are mixed. The product must be $AgCl(s)$ (which can be proved by experiment). The equation for the reaction now can be written

$$AgNO_3(aq) + KCl(aq) \longrightarrow AgCl(s) + KNO_3(aq)$$

Figure 4.15 shows the result of mixing aqueous solutions of $AgNO_3$ and KCl. Figure 4.16 provides a visualization of the reaction.

Figure 4.15

Precipitation of silver chloride by mixing solutions of silver nitrate and potassium chloride. The K^+ and NO_3^- ions remain in solution.

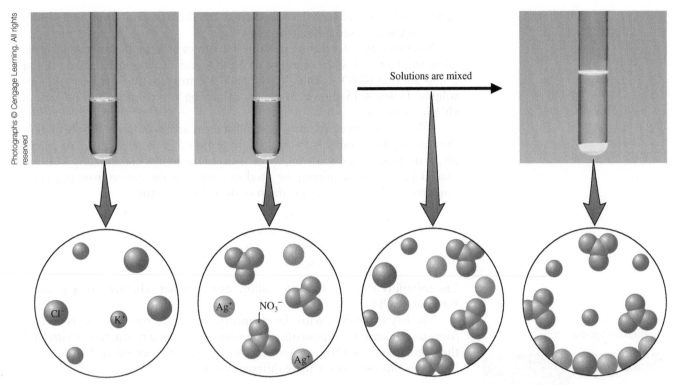

Solutions are mixed

Figure 4.16

Photos and accompanying molecular-level representations illustrating the reaction of KCl(*aq*) with AgNO$_3$(*aq*) to form AgCl(*s*). Note that it is not possible to have a photo of the mixed solution before the reaction occurs because it is an imaginary step that we use to help visualize the reaction. Actually, the reaction occurs immediately when the two solutions are mixed.

Notice that to do these two examples, we had to know both concepts (solids always have a zero net charge) and facts (KNO$_3$ is very soluble in water, the CrO$_4{}^{2-}$ is yellow, and so on).

Predicting the identity of the solid product in a precipitation reaction requires knowledge of the solubilities of common ionic substances. As an aid in predicting the products of precipitation reactions, some simple solubility rules are given in Table 4.1. You should memorize these rules.

The phrase "slightly soluble" used in the solubility rules in Table 4.1 means that the tiny amount of solid that dissolves is not noticeable. The solid

Table 4.1

Simple Rules for Solubility of Salts in Water

1. Most nitrate (NO$_3{}^-$) salts are soluble.
2. Most salts of Na$^+$, K$^+$, and NH$_4{}^+$ are soluble.
3. Most chloride salts are soluble. Notable exceptions are AgCl, PbCl$_2$, and Hg$_2$Cl$_2$.
4. Most sulfate salts are soluble. Notable exceptions are BaSO$_4$, PbSO$_4$, and CaSO$_4$.
5. Most hydroxide salts are only slightly soluble. The important soluble hydroxides are NaOH, KOH, and Ca(OH)$_2$ (marginally soluble).
6. Most sulfide (S^{2-}), carbonate (CO$_3{}^{2-}$), and phosphate (PO$_4{}^{3-}$) salts are only slightly soluble.

appears to be insoluble to the naked eye. Thus the terms *insoluble* and *slightly soluble* are often used interchangeably.

Note that the information in Table 4.1 allows us to predict that AgCl is the white solid formed when solutions of $AgNO_3$ and KCl are mixed; Rules 1 and 2 indicate that KNO_3 is soluble, and Rule 3 states that AgCl is (virtually) insoluble. Figure 4.15 shows the results of mixing silver nitrate and potassium chloride solutions.

When solutions containing ionic substances are mixed, it will be helpful in determining the products if you think in terms of *ion interchange*. For example, in the preceding discussion, we considered the results of mixing $AgNO_3(aq)$ and $KCl(aq)$. In determining the products, we took the cation from one reactant and combined it with the anion of the other reactant:

$$Ag^+ \quad + \quad NO_3^- \quad + \quad K^+ \quad + \quad Cl^- \quad \longrightarrow$$

$$\text{Possible}$$
$$\text{solid}$$
$$\text{products}$$

The solubility rules in Table 4.1 allow us to predict whether either product forms as a solid.

The key to dealing with the chemistry of an aqueous solution is to first *focus on the actual components of the solution before any reaction occurs* and then figure out how those components will react with each other. Example 4.5 illustrates this process for three different reactions.

⬤WL INTERACTIVE EXAMPLE 4.5

Using the solubility rules in Table 4.1, predict what will happen when the following pairs of solutions are mixed.

a. $KNO_3(aq)$ and $BaCl_2(aq)$

b. $Na_2SO_4(aq)$ and $Pb(NO_3)_2(aq)$

c. $KOH(aq)$ and $Fe(NO_3)_3(aq)$

Solution

a. $KNO_3(aq)$ stands for an aqueous solution obtained by dissolving solid KNO_3 in water to form a solution containing the hydrated ions $K^+(aq)$ and $NO_3^-(aq)$. Likewise, $BaCl_2(aq)$ is a solution formed by dissolving solid $BaCl_2$ in water to produce $Ba^{2+}(aq)$ and $Cl^-(aq)$. When these two solutions are mixed, the resulting solution contains the ions K^+, NO_3^-, Ba^{2+}, and Cl^-. All will be hydrated, but (aq) is omitted for simplicity. To look for possible solid products, combine the cation from one reactant with the anion from the other:

$$K^+ \quad + \quad NO_3^- \quad + \quad Ba^{2+} \quad + \quad Cl^- \quad \longrightarrow$$

$$\text{Possible}$$
$$\text{solid}$$
$$\text{products}$$

Note from Table 4.1 that the rules predict that both KCl and $Ba(NO_3)_2$ are soluble in water. Thus no precipitate will form when $KNO_3(aq)$ and $BaCl_2(aq)$ are mixed. All the ions will remain dissolved in the solution. No reaction occurs.

b. Using the same procedures as in part a, we find that the ions present in the combined solution before any reaction occurs are Na^+, SO_4^{2-}, Pb^{2+}, and NO_3^-. The possible salts that could form precipitates are

$$Na^+ \quad + \quad SO_4^{2-} \quad + \quad Pb^{2+} \quad + \quad NO_3^- \quad \longrightarrow$$

Focus on the ions in solution before any reaction occurs.

The precipitation of lead(II) sulfate by mixing solutions of lead(II) nitrate and sodium sulfate.

Solid $Fe(OH)_3$ forms when aqueous KOH and $Fe(NO_3)_3$ are mixed.

The compound $NaNO_3$ is soluble, but $PbSO_4$ is insoluble (see Rule 4 in Table 4.1). When these solutions are mixed, $PbSO_4$ will precipitate from the solution. The balanced equation is

$$Na_2SO_4(aq) + Pb(NO_3)_2(aq) \longrightarrow PbSO_4(s) + 2NaNO_3(aq)$$

c. The combined solution (before any reaction occurs) contains the ions K^+, OH^-, Fe^{3+}, and NO_3^-. The salts that might precipitate are KNO_3 and $Fe(OH)_3$. The solubility rules in Table 4.1 indicate that both K^+ and NO_3^- salts are soluble. However, $Fe(OH)_3$ is only slightly soluble (Rule 5) and hence will precipitate. The balanced equation is

$$3KOH(aq) + Fe(NO_3)_3(aq) \longrightarrow Fe(OH)_3(s) + 3KNO_3(aq)$$

4.6 | Describing Reactions in Solution

In this section we will consider the types of equations used to represent reactions in solution. For example, when we mix aqueous potassium chromate with aqueous barium nitrate, a reaction occurs to form a precipitate ($BaCrO_4$) and dissolved potassium nitrate. So far we have written the **molecular equation** for this reaction:

$$K_2CrO_4(aq) + Ba(NO_3)_2(aq) \longrightarrow BaCrO_4(s) + 2KNO_3(aq)$$

Although this equation shows the reactants and products of the reaction, it does not give a very clear picture of what actually occurs in solution. As we have seen, aqueous solutions of potassium chromate, barium nitrate, and potassium nitrate contain the individual ions, not molecules, as is implied by the molecular equation. Thus the **complete ionic equation**

$$2K^+(aq) + CrO_4^{2-}(aq) + Ba^{2+}(aq) + 2NO_3^-(aq)$$
$$\longrightarrow BaCrO_4(s) + 2K^+(aq) + 2NO_3^-(aq)$$

A strong electrolyte is a substance that completely breaks apart into ions when dissolved in water.

better represents the actual forms of the reactants and products in solution. *In a complete ionic equation, all substances that are strong electrolytes are represented as ions.*

The complete ionic equation reveals that only some of the ions participate in the reaction. The K^+ and NO_3^- ions are present in solution both before and after the reaction. Ions such as these that do not participate directly in a reaction in solution are called **spectator ions.** The ions that participate in this reaction are the Ba^{2+} and CrO_4^{2-} ions, which combine to form solid $BaCrO_4$:

$$Ba^{2+}(aq) + CrO_4^{2-}(aq) \longrightarrow BaCrO_4(s)$$

Net ionic equations include only those components that undergo changes in the reaction.

This equation, called the **net ionic equation,** includes only those solution components directly involved in the reaction. Chemists usually write the net ionic equation for a reaction in solution because it gives the actual forms of the reactants and products and includes only the species that undergo a change.

EXAMPLE 4.6

For each of the following reactions, write the molecular equation, the complete ionic equation, and the net ionic equation.

a. Aqueous potassium chloride is added to aqueous silver nitrate to form a silver chloride precipitate plus aqueous potassium nitrate.

b. Aqueous potassium hydroxide is mixed with aqueous iron(III) nitrate to form a precipitate of iron(III) hydroxide and aqueous potassium nitrate.

Solution

a. *Molecular:*

$$KCl(aq) + AgNO_3(aq) \longrightarrow AgCl(s) + KNO_3(aq)$$

Complete ionic (remember that any ionic compound dissolved in water will be present as the separated ions):

$$K^+(aq) + Cl^-(aq) + Ag^+(aq) + NO_3^-(aq) \longrightarrow$$

    ↑   ↑

  Spectator   Spectator
  ion   ion

$$AgCl(s) + K^+(aq) + NO_3^-(aq)$$

    ↑   ↑   ↑

  Solid,   Spectator   Spectator
  not   ion   ion
  written
  as separate ions

Net ionic: Canceling the spectator ions,

$$\cancel{K^+}(aq) + Cl^-(aq) + Ag^+(aq) + \cancel{NO_3^-}(aq)$$
$$\longrightarrow AgCl(s) + \cancel{K^+}(aq) + \cancel{NO_3^-}(aq)$$

gives the following net ionic equation:

$$Cl^-(aq) + Ag^+(aq) \longrightarrow AgCl(s)$$

b. *Molecular:*

$$3KOH(aq) + Fe(NO_3)_3(aq) \longrightarrow Fe(OH)_3(s) + 3KNO_3(aq)$$

Complete ionic:

$$3K^+(aq) + 3OH^-(aq) + Fe^{3+}(aq) + 3NO_3^-(aq)$$
$$\longrightarrow Fe(OH)_3(s) + 3K^+(aq) + 3NO_3^-(aq)$$

Net ionic:

$$3OH^-(aq) + Fe^{3+}(aq) \longrightarrow Fe(OH)_3(s)$$

Three Types of Equations Used to Describe Reactions in Solution

1. The *molecular equation* gives the overall reaction stoichiometry but not necessarily the actual forms of the reactants and products in solution.
2. The *complete ionic equation* represents as ions all reactants and products that are strong electrolytes.
3. The *net ionic equation* includes only those solution components undergoing a change. Spectator ions are not included.

4.7 | Selective Precipitation

We can use the fact that salts have different solubilities to separate mixtures of ions. For example, suppose we have an aqueous solution containing the cations Ag^+, Ba^{2+}, and Fe^{3+}, and the anion NO_3^-. We want to separate the cations by precipitating them one at a time, a process called **selective precipitation**.

How can the separation of these cations be accomplished? We can perform some preliminary tests and observe the reactivity of each cation toward the anions Cl^-, SO_4^{2-}, and OH^-. For example, to test the reactivity of Ag^+ toward Cl^-, we can mix the $AgNO_3$ solution with aqueous KCl or NaCl. As we have

Chemical Analysis of Cockroaches

Cockroaches can be a big problem. Not only are these hardy pests unpleasant to live with, but they also consume significant quantities of the world's precious food and grain supplies. Because the many different species of cockroaches require different control measures, determining which species is causing a particular problem is important. Careful examination of a cockroach can reveal its species, but this process is very time-consuming. However, a new method of cockroach identification, based on gas chromatography, has been developed at the U.S. Department of Agriculture by D. A. Carlson and R. J. Brenner. In gas chromatography, the compounds to be separated are dispersed in a carrier gas that passes through a porous solid. Because different substances have differing tendencies to adhere to the solid, the components of the mixture travel at different rates through the system, causing them to spread out so that they can be separated and identified.

In the cockroach identification study, Carlson and Brenner found that the composition of the outer, waxy layer of a roach is distinct to the particular species. Thus, by dissolving this waxy coating and injecting it into the gas stream of a gas chromatograph, scientists can identify the cockroach unambiguously in less than half an hour. This technique is particularly useful for identifying hybrid Asian–German cockroaches, which have become a major problem for the food industry.

Although biologists might argue that the gas chromatographic method takes the fun and the challenge out of identifying cockroaches, this technique should lead to significant advances in the control of these insects.

seen, this produces a precipitate. When we carry out tests of this type using all the possible combinations, we obtain the results in Table 4.2.

After studying these results, we might proceed to separate the cations as follows:

Step 1

Add an aqueous solution of NaCl to the solution containing the Ag^+, Ba^{2+}, and Fe^{3+} ions. Solid AgCl will form and can be removed, leaving Ba^{2+} and Fe^{3+} ions in solution.

Table 4.2

Testing the Reactivity of the Cations Ag^+, Ba^{2+}, and Fe^{3+} with the Anions Cl^-, SO_4^{2-}, and OH^-

	Test Solution (anion)		
Cation	NaCl(aq) (Cl^-)	Na$_2$SO$_4$(aq) (SO_4^{2-})	NaOH(aq) (OH^-)
Ag^+	White precipitate (AgCl)	No reaction	White precipitate that turns brown $\left(\begin{array}{c} AgOH \longrightarrow Ag_2O \\ \text{White} \qquad \text{Brown} \end{array}\right)$
Ba^{2+}	No reaction	White precipitate ($BaSO_4$)	No reaction
Fe^{3+}	Yellow color but no solid	No reaction	Reddish brown precipitate [$Fe(OH)_3$]

Figure 4.17
Selective precipitation of Ag^+, Ba^{2+}, and Fe^{3+} ions. In this schematic representation, a double line means that a solid forms, and a single line designates a solution.

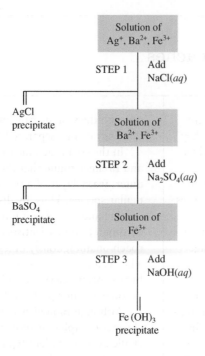

Step 2

Add an aqueous solution of Na_2SO_4 to the solution containing the Ba^{2+} and Fe^{3+} ions. Solid $BaSO_4$ will form and can be removed, leaving only Fe^{3+} ions in solution.

Step 3

Add an aqueous solution of NaOH to the solution containing the Fe^{3+} ions. Solid $Fe(OH)_3$ will form and can be removed.

Steps 1 through 3 are represented schematically in Fig. 4.17.

Note that adding the anions in this order precipitates the cations one at a time and thus separates them. The process whereby mixtures of ions are separated and identified is called **qualitative analysis.** In this example the qualitative analysis was carried out by selective precipitation, but it can also be accomplished by using other separation techniques that will not be discussed here.

4.8 | Stoichiometry of Precipitation Reactions

In Chapter 3 we covered the principles of chemical stoichiometry: the procedures for calculating quantities of reactants and products involved in a chemical reaction. Recall that in performing these calculations, we first convert all quantities to moles and then use the coefficients of the balanced equation to assemble the appropriate molar ratios. In cases in which reactants are mixed, we must determine which reactant is limiting, since the reactant that is consumed first will limit the amounts of products formed. *These same principles apply to reactions that take place in solutions.* However, two points about solution reactions need special emphasis. The first is that it is sometimes difficult to tell immediately which reaction will occur when two solutions are mixed. Usually we must think about the various possibilities and then decide what will happen. The first step in this process *always* should be to write down the species that are actually present in the solution, as we did in Section 4.5.

The second special point about solution reactions is that to obtain the moles of reactants, we must use the volume of a particular solution and its molarity. This procedure was covered in Section 4.3.

We will introduce stoichiometric calculations for reactions in solution in Example 4.7.

⬡WL INTERACTIVE EXAMPLE 4.7

Calculate the mass of solid NaCl that must be added to 1.50 L of a 0.100 M $AgNO_3$ solution to precipitate all the Ag^+ ions in the form of AgCl.

Solution

■ What are we trying to solve?

We want to determine the mass of NaCl to add to a given amount of $AgNO_3(aq)$ to precipitate all of the Ag^+ ions and form AgCl.

■ What does this mean?

We need to recognize that a reaction occurs to form AgCl; thus we will need a balanced equation. First, we must consider what happens chemically.

When added to the $AgNO_3$ solution (which contains Ag^+ and NO_3^- ions), the solid NaCl dissolves to yield Na^+ and Cl^- ions. Thus the mixed solution contains the ions

$$Ag^+, NO_3^-, Na^+, \text{ and } Cl^-$$

$NaNO_3$ is soluble and AgCl is insoluble (Table 4.1), so solid AgCl forms according to the following net ionic reaction:

$$Ag^+(aq) + Cl^-(aq) \longrightarrow AgCl(s)$$

In this case enough Cl^- ions must be added to react with all the Ag^+ ions present. Thus we must calculate the moles of Ag^+ ions present in 1.50 L of a 0.100 M $AgNO_3$ solution (remember that a 0.100 M $AgNO_3$ solution contains 0.100 M Ag^+ ions and 0.100 M NO_3^- ions):

$$1.50 \text{ L} \times \frac{0.100 \text{ mol } Ag^+}{L} = 0.150 \text{ mol } Ag^+$$

Since Ag^+ and Cl^- react in a 1:1 ratio, 0.150 mole of Cl^- ions and thus 0.150 mole of NaCl are required. We calculate the mass of NaCl required as follows:

$$0.150 \text{ mol NaCl} \times \frac{58.4 \text{ g NaCl}}{\text{mol NaCl}} = 8.76 \text{ g NaCl}$$

Notice from Example 4.7 that the procedures for doing stoichiometric calculations for solution reactions are very similar to those for other types of reactions. It is useful to think in terms of the following steps for reactions in solution.

When a solution of NaCl(aq) is added to a solution of $AgNO_3$, the white solid AgCl forms.

Species present
↓ Write the reaction
Balanced net ionic equation
↓ Determine moles of reactants
Identify limiting reactant
↓ Determine moles of products
Check units of products

STEPS

Solving a Stoichiometry Problem Involving Reactions in Solution

1 Identify the species present in the combined solution and determine which reaction occurs.
2 Write the balanced equation for the reaction.
3 Calculate the moles of reactants.
4 Determine which reactant is limiting.
5 Calculate the moles of product or products, as required.
6 Convert to grams or other units, as required.

⊍WL INTERACTIVE EXAMPLE 4.8

When aqueous solutions of Na_2SO_4 and $Pb(NO_3)_2$ are mixed, $PbSO_4$ precipitates. Calculate the mass of $PbSO_4$ formed when 1.25 L of 0.0500 M $Pb(NO_3)_2$ and 2.00 L of 0.0250 M Na_2SO_4 are mixed.

Solution

■ What are we trying to solve?

We are asked to determine the mass of the precipitant given the amounts of the reactants.

This problem is complex in the sense that it incorporates much of what we have learned in Chapters 3 and 4. The list of what we need to know/do is extensive:

■ We need to know what the solutions "look like" at a molecular level.

■ We need to be able to write a net ionic equation.

■ We must use volume and molarity to determine the number of moles of each reactant.

■ Since we are given amounts of both reactants, we will have to determine which reactant is limiting.

■ We need to convert moles to mass using molar mass.

However, by now each step of this solution should be familiar to you. Thus, although there are many parts to the solution to this problem, taking it one step at a time makes it less daunting.

When the aqueous solutions of Na_2SO_4 (containing Na^+ and SO_4^{2-} ions) and $Pb(NO_3)_2$ (containing Pb^{2+} and NO_3^- ions) are mixed, the mixed solution contains the ions Na^+, SO_4^{2-}, Pb^{2+}, and NO_3^-. Since $NaNO_3$ is soluble and $PbSO_4$ is insoluble (Table 4.1), solid $PbSO_4$ will form.

The net ionic equation is

$$Pb^{2+}(aq) + SO_4^{2-}(aq) \longrightarrow PbSO_4(s)$$

Since 0.0500 M $Pb(NO_3)_2$ contains 0.0500 M Pb^{2+} ions, we can calculate the moles of Pb^{2+} ions in 1.25 L of this solution as follows:

$$1.25 \text{ L} \times \frac{0.0500 \text{ mol } Pb^{2+}}{\text{L}} = 0.0625 \text{ mol } Pb^{2+}$$

The 0.0250 M Na_2SO_4 solution contains 0.0250 M SO_4^{2-} ions, and the number of moles of SO_4^{2-} ions in 2.00 L of this solution is

$$2.00 \text{ L} \times \frac{0.0250 \text{ mol } SO_4^{2-}}{\text{L}} = 0.0500 \text{ mol } SO_4^{2-}$$

Because Pb^{2+} and SO_4^{2-} react in a 1:1 ratio, the amount of SO_4^{2-} will be limiting.

Since the Pb^{2+} ions are present in excess, only 0.0500 mole of solid $PbSO_4$ will be formed. The mass of $PbSO_4$ formed can be calculated by using the molar mass of $PbSO_4$ (303.3):

$$0.0500 \text{ mol } PbSO_4 \times \frac{303.3 \text{ g } PbSO_4}{1 \text{ mol } PbSO_4} = 15.2 \text{ g } PbSO_4$$

One method for determining the amount of a given substance present in a solution is to form a precipitate that includes the substance. The precipitate is then filtered, dried, and weighed. This process, called gravimetric analysis, is illustrated in Example 4.9.

Phosphate rock is used in the manufacture of fertilizer.

EXAMPLE 4.9

Phosphorite, also called *phosphate rock,* is a mineral containing PO_4^{3-} and OH^- anions and Ca^{2+} cations. It is treated with sulfuric acid in the manufacture of phosphate fertilizers (see Chapter 3). A chemist finds the calcium content in an impure sample of phosphate rock by weighing out a 0.4367-g sample, dissolving it in water, and precipitating the Ca^{2+} ions as the insoluble hydrated salt* $CaC_2O_4 \cdot H_2O$ ($C_2O_4^{2-}$ is called the oxalate ion). After being filtered and dried (at a temperature of about 100°C so that the extraneous water is driven off but not the water of hydration), the $CaC_2O_4 \cdot H_2O$ precipitate weighed 0.2920 g. Calculate the mass percent of calcium in the sample of phosphate rock.

Solution

■ What are we trying to solve?

We are asked to determine the mass percent of calcium in a sample of phosphate rock.

■ What does this mean?

$$\text{Mass percent of calcium in the rock} = \frac{\text{mass of calcium}}{\text{mass of rock sample}} \times 100\%$$

We know that the sample of rock has a mass of 0.4367 g, so to determine the mass percent of calcium we change the question to *"What is the mass of calcium?"*

The gravimetric procedure can be summarized as follows:

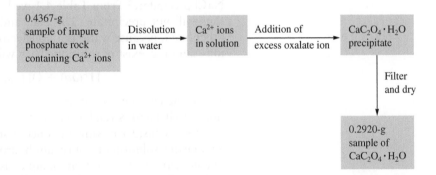

In this analysis, excess $C_2O_4^{2-}$ ions are added to ensure that all Ca^{2+} ions are precipitated. Thus the number of moles of Ca^{2+} ions in the original sample determines the number of moles of $CaC_2O_4 \cdot H_2O$ formed. Using the molar mass of $CaC_2O_4 \cdot H_2O$, we can calculate the moles of $CaC_2O_4 \cdot H_2O$:

$$0.2920 \text{ g } CaC_2O_4 \cdot H_2O \times \frac{1 \text{ mol } CaC_2O_4 \cdot H_2O}{146.12 \text{ g } CaC_2O_4 \cdot H_2O}$$

$$= 1.998 \times 10^{-3} \text{ mol } CaC_2O_4 \cdot H_2O$$

Thus the original sample of impure phosphate rock contained 1.998×10^{-3} mole of Ca^{2+} ions, which we convert to grams:

$$1.998 \times 10^{-3} \text{ mol } Ca^{2+} \times \frac{40.08 \text{ g } Ca^{2+}}{1 \text{ mol } Ca^{2+}} = 8.009 \times 10^{-2} \text{ g } Ca^{2+}$$

---

*Hydrated salts contain one or more H_2O molecules per formula unit in addition to the cations and anions. A dot is used in the formula of these salts.

The mass percent of calcium in the original sample is then

$$\frac{8.009 \times 10^{-2}\ \text{g}}{0.4367\ \text{g}} \times 100\% = 18.34\%$$

4.9 | Acid–Base Reactions

Earlier in this chapter we considered Arrhenius's concept of acids and bases: An acid is a substance that produces H^+ ions when dissolved in water, and a base is a substance that produces OH^- ions. Although these ideas are fundamentally correct, it is convenient to have a more general definition of a base, which covers substances that do not produce OH^- ions. Such a definition was provided by Brønsted and Lowry, who defined acids and bases as follows:

An acid is a proton donor.
A base is a proton acceptor.

How do we recognize acid–base reactions? One of the most difficult tasks for someone inexperienced in chemistry is to predict which reaction might occur when two solutions are mixed. With precipitation reactions, we found that the best way to deal with this problem is to focus on the species actually present in the mixed solution. This also applies to acid–base reactions. For example, when an aqueous solution of hydrogen chloride (HCl) is mixed with an aqueous solution of sodium hydroxide (NaOH), the combined solution contains the ions H^+, Cl^-, Na^+, and OH^-, since HCl is a strong acid and NaOH is a strong base. How can we predict what reaction occurs, if any? First, will NaCl precipitate? From Table 4.1 we know that NaCl is soluble in water and thus will not precipitate. The Na^+ and Cl^- ions are spectator ions. On the other hand, because water is a nonelectrolyte, large quantities of H^+ and OH^- ions cannot coexist in solution. They will react to form H_2O molecules:

$$H^+(aq) + OH^-(aq) \longrightarrow H_2O(l)$$

This is the net ionic equation for the reaction that occurs when aqueous solutions of HCl and NaOH are mixed.

Next, consider mixing an aqueous solution of acetic acid ($HC_2H_3O_2$) with an aqueous solution of potassium hydroxide (KOH). In our earlier discussion of conductivity, we said that an aqueous solution of acetic acid is a weak electrolyte. Thus acetic acid does not dissociate into ions to any great extent. In fact, in aqueous solution 99% of the $HC_2H_3O_2$ molecules remain undissociated. However, when solid KOH is dissolved in water, it dissociates completely to produce K^+ and OH^- ions. So, in the solution formed by mixing aqueous solutions of $HC_2H_3O_2$ and KOH, *before any reaction occurs* the principal species are H_2O, $HC_2H_3O_2$, K^+, and OH^-. Which reaction will occur? A possible precipitation reaction involves K^+ and OH^-, but we know that KOH is soluble. Another possibility is a reaction involving the hydroxide ion and a proton donor. Is there a source of protons in the solution? The answer is yes—the $HC_2H_3O_2$ molecules. The OH^- ion has such a strong affinity for protons that it can strip them from the $HC_2H_3O_2$ molecules. Thus the net ionic equation for the reaction is

$$OH^-(aq) + HC_2H_3O_2(aq) \longrightarrow H_2O(l) + C_2H_3O_2^-(aq)$$

This reaction illustrates a very important general principle: *The hydroxide ion is such a strong base that for purposes of stoichiometry it is assumed to react completely with any weak acid dissolved in water.* Of course, OH^- ions also react completely with the H^+ ions in the solutions of strong acids.

We will now deal with the stoichiometry of acid–base reactions in aqueous solutions. The procedure is fundamentally the same as that used previously.

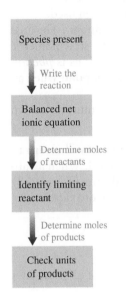

Species present

↓ Write the reaction

Balanced net ionic equation

↓ Determine moles of reactants

Identify limiting reactant

↓ Determine moles of products

Check units of products

STEPS Calculations for Acid–Base Reactions

1 List the species present in the combined solution *before reaction,* and decide which reaction will occur.
2 Write the balanced net ionic equation for this reaction.
3 Change the given quantities of reactants to moles. For reactions in solution, use the volumes of the original solutions and their molarities.
4 Determine the limiting reactant where appropriate.
5 Calculate the moles of the required reactant or product.
6 Convert to grams or a volume of solution, as required by the problem.

An acid–base reaction is often called a **neutralization reaction.** When just enough base is added to react exactly with all of the acid in a solution, we say the acid has been *neutralized.*

Acid–Base Titrations

Acid–base **titrations** are an example of **volumetric analysis,** a technique in which one solution is used to analyze another. The solution used to carry out the analysis is called the **titrant** and is delivered from a device called a buret, which measures the volume accurately. The point in the titration at which enough titrant has been added to react exactly with the substance being determined is called the **equivalence point,** or the **stoichiometric point.** This point is often marked by the change in color of a chemical called an **indicator.** The titration procedure is illustrated in Fig. 4.18.

The following requirements must be met for a titration to be successful:

The concentration of the titrant must be known. Such a titrant is called a *standard solution.*

Figure 4.18
The titration of an acid with a base. (a) The titrant (the base) is in the buret, and the beaker contains the acid solution along with a small amount of indicator. (b) As base is added drop by drop to the acidic solution in the beaker during the titration, the indicator changes color, but the color disappears on mixing. (c) The stoichiometric (equivalence) point is marked by a permanent indicator color change. The volume of the base added is the difference between the final and initial buret readings.

(a) (b) (c)

The exact reaction between titrant and substance being analyzed must be known.

The stoichiometric (equivalence) point must be known. An indicator that changes color at, or very near, the stoichiometric point is often used.

The point at which the indicator changes color is called the **endpoint.** The goal is to choose an indicator whose endpoint coincides with the stoichiometric point. An indicator very commonly used by acid–base titrations is *phenolphthalein,* which is colorless in acid and turns pink at the endpoint when an acid is titrated with a base.

The volume of titrant required to reach the stoichiometric point must be known as accurately as possible.

We will deal with acid–base titrations only briefly here but will return to the topic of titrations and indicators in more detail in Chapter 8. When a substance being analyzed contains an acid, the amount of acid present is usually determined by titration with a standard solution containing hydroxide ions.

> Ideally, the endpoint and stoichiometric point should coincide.

⬛WL INTERACTIVE EXAMPLE 4.10

What volume of a 0.100 M HCl solution is needed to neutralize 25.0 mL of a 0.350 M NaOH solution?

Solution

■ What are we trying to solve?

We are asked to determine the volume of a solution of HCl required to neutralize a given volume of a solution of NaOH.

■ What does this mean?

The HCl and NaOH react with each other, so we need to use a balanced equation to determine the mole ratio between the two reactants. Since we have volumes and molarities of both, we can determine the moles of each reactant. To do this, we must think about the components in the reactant solutions.

The species present in the mixed solutions before any reaction occurs are

$$\underbrace{H^+, Cl^-,}_{\text{From HCl}(aq)} \quad \underbrace{Na^+, OH^-,}_{\text{From NaOH}(aq)} \quad \text{and} \quad H_2O$$

Which reaction will occur? The two possibilities are

$$Na^+(aq) + Cl^-(aq) \longrightarrow NaCl(s)$$
$$H^+(aq) + OH^-(aq) \longrightarrow H_2O(l)$$

Since NaCl is soluble, the first reaction does not take place (Na^+ and Cl^- are spectator ions). However, as we have seen before, the reaction of H^+ and OH^- ions to form H_2O does occur.

The balanced net ionic equation for the reaction is

$$H^+(aq) + OH^-(aq) \longrightarrow H_2O(l)$$

Next, we calculate the number of moles of OH^- ions in the 25.0-mL sample of 0.350 M NaOH:

$$25.0 \text{ mL NaOH} \times \frac{1 \text{ L}}{1000 \text{ mL}} \times \frac{0.350 \text{ mol } OH^-}{\text{L NaOH}} = 8.75 \times 10^{-3} \text{ mol } OH^-$$

This problem requires the addition of just enough H^+ ions to react exactly with the OH^- ions present. Thus we need not be concerned with determining a limiting reactant.

A Hazmat (hazardous materials) team neutralizes a hydrochloric acid (HCl) spill.

Since H^+ and OH^- ions react in a 1:1 ratio, 8.75×10^{-3} mole of H^+ ions is required to neutralize the OH^- ions present.

The volume (V) of 0.100 M HCl required to furnish this amount of H^+ ions can be calculated as follows:

$$V \times \frac{0.100 \text{ mol H}^+}{\text{L}} = 8.75 \times 10^{-3} \text{ mol H}^+$$

Solving for V gives

$$V = 8.75 \times 10^{-2} \text{ L}$$

Thus 8.75×10^{-2} L (87.5 mL) of 0.100 M HCl is required to neutralize 25.0 mL of 0.350 M NaOH.

■ Is the answer reasonable?

The mole ratio between the reactants is 1:1. The NaOH is more concentrated than the HCl, so it makes sense that the volume of HCl is larger than the volume of NaOH.

⬦WL INTERACTIVE EXAMPLE 4.11

In a certain experiment, 28.0 mL of 0.250 M HNO_3 and 53.0 mL of 0.320 M KOH are mixed. Calculate the amount of water formed in the resulting reaction. What is the concentration of H^+ or OH^- ions in excess after the reaction goes to completion?

Solution

■ What are we trying to solve?

We are asked to determine the amount of water formed and the amount of excess reactant when an acid and base react.

■ What does this mean?

The acid and base react with each other, so we need to use a balanced equation to determine the mole ratio between the two reactants. Since we have volumes and molarities of both, we can determine the moles of each reactant. To do this, we must think about the components in the reactant solutions.
The species available for reaction are

$$\underbrace{H^+, NO_3^-,}_{\substack{\text{From HNO}_3 \\ \text{solution}}} \quad \underbrace{K^+, OH^-,}_{\substack{\text{From KOH} \\ \text{solution}}} \quad \text{and} \quad H_2O$$

Since KNO_3 is soluble, K^+ and NO_3^- are spectator ions, so the net ionic equation is

$$H^+(aq) + OH^-(aq) \longrightarrow H_2O(l)$$

We next compute the amounts of H^+ and OH^- ions present.

$$28.0 \text{ mL HNO}_3 \times \frac{1 \text{ L}}{1000 \text{ mL}} \times \frac{0.250 \text{ mol H}^+}{\text{L}} = 7.00 \times 10^{-3} \text{ mol H}^+$$

$$53.0 \text{ mL KOH} \times \frac{1 \text{ L}}{1000 \text{ mL}} \times \frac{0.320 \text{ mol OH}^-}{\text{L}} = 1.70 \times 10^{-2} \text{ mol OH}^-$$

Since H^+ and OH^- react in a 1:1 ratio, the limiting reactant is H^+. Thus 7.00×10^{-3} mole of H^+ ions will react with 7.00×10^{-3} mole of OH^- ions to form 7.00×10^{-3} mole of H_2O.

The amount of OH^- ions in excess is obtained from the following difference:

$$\text{Original amount} - \text{amount consumed} = \text{amount in excess}$$

$$1.70 \times 10^{-2} \text{ mol } OH^- - 7.00 \times 10^{-3} \text{ mol } OH^- = 1.00 \times 10^{-2} \text{ mol } OH^-$$

The volume of the combined solution is the sum of the individual volumes:

$$\text{Original volume of } HNO_3 + \text{original volume of KOH} = \text{total volume}$$

$$28.0 \text{ mL} + 53.0 \text{ mL} = 81.0 \text{ mL} = 8.10 \times 10^{-2} \text{ L}$$

Thus the molarity of OH^- ions in excess is

$$M = \frac{\text{mol } OH^-}{\text{L solution}}$$

$$= \frac{1.00 \times 10^{-2} \text{ mol } OH^-}{8.10 \times 10^{-2} \text{ L}}$$

$$= 0.123 \ M \ OH^-$$

■ Is the answer reasonable?

The mole ratio between the reactants is 1:1. The KOH is more concentrated than the HNO_3, and a greater volume of KOH is used. It makes sense that the OH^- is in excess.

EXAMPLE 4.12

An environmental chemist analyzed the effluent (the released waste material) from an industrial process known to produce the compounds carbon tetrachloride (CCl_4) and benzoic acid ($HC_7H_5O_2$), a weak acid that has one acidic hydrogen atom per molecule. A sample of this effluent weighing 0.3518 g was placed in water and shaken vigorously to dissolve the benzoic acid. The resulting aqueous solution required 10.59 mL of 0.1546 M NaOH for neutralization. Calculate the mass percent of $HC_7H_5O_2$ in the original sample.

Solution

■ What are we trying to solve?

We are asked to determine the mass percent of an acid in a mixture (effluent).

■ What does this mean?

$$\text{Mass percent of benzoic acid} = \frac{\text{mass of benzoic acid}}{\text{mass of mixture}} \times 100\%$$

We know the mass of the mixture is 0.3518 g, so we change the question to "*What is the mass of benzoic acid in the mixture?*"

In this case the sample was a mixture containing CCl_4 and $HC_7H_5O_2$, and it was titrated with OH^- ions. Clearly, CCl_4 is not an acid (it contains no hydrogen atoms), so we can assume it does not react with OH^- ions. However, $HC_7H_5O_2$ is an acid. It donates one H^+ ion per molecule to react with an OH^- ion as follows:

$$HC_7H_5O_2(aq) + OH^-(aq) \longrightarrow H_2O(l) + C_7H_5O_2^-(aq)$$

Although $HC_7H_5O_2$ is a weak acid, the OH^- ion is such a strong base that we can assume that each OH^- ion added will react with a $HC_7H_5O_2$ molecule until all the benzoic acid is consumed.

We must first determine the number of moles of OH^- ions required to react with all of the $HC_7H_5O_2$:

$$10.59 \text{ mL NaOH} \times \frac{1 \text{ L}}{1000 \text{ mL}} \times \frac{0.1546 \text{ mol OH}^-}{\text{L NaOH}}$$

$$= 1.637 \times 10^{-3} \text{ mol OH}^-$$

This number is also the number of moles of $HC_7H_5O_2$ present. The number of grams of the acid is calculated by using its molar mass:

$$1.637 \times 10^{-3} \text{ mol HC}_7\text{H}_5\text{O}_2 \times \frac{122.125 \text{ g HC}_7\text{H}_5\text{O}_2}{1 \text{ mol HC}_7\text{H}_5\text{O}_2} = 0.1999 \text{ g HC}_7\text{H}_5\text{O}_2$$

The mass percent of $HC_7H_5O_2$ in the original sample is

$$\frac{0.1999 \text{ g}}{0.3518 \text{ g}} \times 100\% = 56.82\%$$

The first step in the analysis of a complex solution is to write down the components present and to focus on the chemistry of each one.

Chemical systems often seem difficult to deal with simply because there are many components. Solving a problem involving a solution in which several components are present is simplified if you *think* about the *chemistry* involved. *The key to success is to write down all the components in the solution and to focus on the chemistry of each one.* We have been emphasizing this approach in dealing with the reactions between ions in solution. Make it a habit to write down the components of solutions before trying to decide which reaction(s) might take place.

4.10 | Oxidation–Reduction Reactions

As we have seen, many important substances are ionic. Sodium chloride, for example, can be formed by the reaction of elemental sodium and chlorine:

$$2Na(s) + Cl_2(g) \longrightarrow 2NaCl(s)$$

In this reaction, solid sodium, which contains neutral sodium atoms, reacts with chlorine gas, which contains diatomic Cl_2 molecules, to form the ionic solid NaCl, which contains Na^+ and Cl^- ions. This process is represented in Fig. 4.19. *Reactions like this one, in which one or more electrons are transferred, are called* **oxidation–reduction reactions** *or* **redox reactions.**

Many important chemical reactions involve oxidation and reduction. In fact, most reactions used for energy production are redox reactions. In humans the oxidation of sugars, fats, and proteins provides the energy necessary for life. Combustion reactions, which provide most of the energy to power our civilization, also involve oxidation and reduction. An example is the reaction of methane with oxygen:

$$CH_4(g) + 2O_2(g) \longrightarrow CO_2(g) + 2H_2O(g) + \text{energy}$$

Even though none of the reactants or products in this reaction is ionic, the reaction is still assumed to involve a transfer of electrons from carbon to oxygen. To explain this, we must introduce the concept of oxidation states.

Oxidation States

The concept of **oxidation states** (also called **oxidation numbers**) provides a way to keep track of electrons in oxidation–reduction reactions. Oxidation states are defined by a set of rules, most of which describe how to divide up the

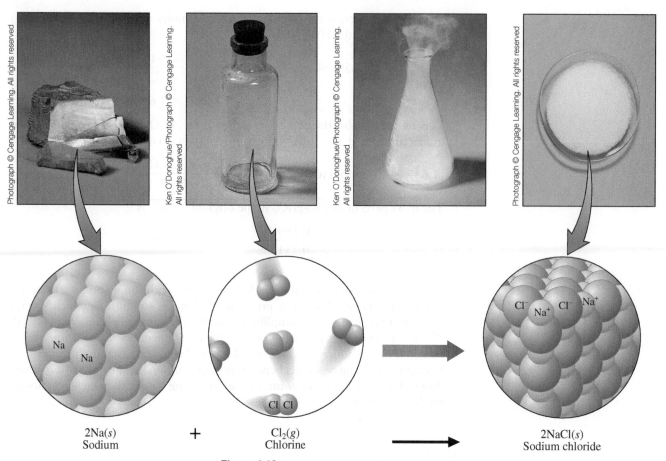

$$2Na(s) \qquad + \qquad Cl_2(g) \qquad \longrightarrow \qquad 2NaCl(s)$$
Sodium   Chlorine   Sodium chloride

Figure 4.19

The reaction of solid sodium and gaseous chlorine to form solid sodium chloride.

Oxidation of copper metal by nitric acid. The copper atoms lose two electrons to form Cu^{2+} ions, which give a deep green color that becomes turquoise when diluted with water. The brown gas NO_2 is also evolved.

shared electrons in compounds containing covalent bonds. However, before we discuss these rules, we need to discuss the distribution of electrons in a bond.

Recall from the discussion of the water molecule in Section 4.1 that oxygen has a greater attraction for electrons than does hydrogen, causing the O—H bonds in the water molecule to be polar. This phenomenon occurs in other bonds as well, and we will discuss the topic of polarity in detail in Chapter 13. For now we will be satisfied with some general guidelines to help us keep track of electrons in oxidation–reduction reactions. The nonmetals with the highest attraction for shared electrons are in the upper right-hand corner of the periodic table. They are fluorine, oxygen, nitrogen, and chlorine. The relative ability of these atoms to attract shared electrons is

$$F > O > N \approx Cl$$

Greatest attraction for electrons   Least attraction for electrons

That is, fluorine attracts shared electrons to the greatest extent, followed by oxygen, then nitrogen and chlorine.

The rules for assigning oxidation states are given in Table 4.3. Application of these rules allows the assignment of oxidation states in most compounds. The principles are illustrated in Example 4.13.

State-of-the-Art Analysis

The real world of chemical analysis is often quite different from what students do in the typical university laboratory. In the real world, chemical analysis must be done quickly, accurately, economically, and often outside the laboratory setting. Analytical accuracy is crucial. A career can hinge on accuracy when a drug test is involved, and sometimes accuracy is truly a life-or-death matter, as in the screening of air travelers' luggage for explosives.

Chemical analysis can turn up in unexpected places. Modern engines in automobiles have been made much more fuel-efficient and less polluting by the inclusion of a sensor to analyze the oxygen (O_2) concentration in the exhaust gases. The signal from this sensor is sent to the computer that controls engine function so that instantaneous adjustments can be made in spark timing and air–fuel mixtures.

The automated screening of luggage for explosives is a very difficult and important analysis problem. One method being developed for luggage screening is called thermal neutron analysis (TNA), in which the substance to be analyzed is bombarded with neutrons. When nuclei in the sample absorb neutrons, they release gamma rays that are characteristic of a specific nucleus. For example, after the nucleus of a nitrogen atom absorbs a neutron, it emits a gamma ray that is unique to nitrogen, whereas an oxygen atom would produce a different gamma ray unique to oxygen, and so on. Thus, when a sample is bombarded by neutrons and the resulting gamma rays are analyzed by a detector connected to a computer, the atoms present in the sample can be specified. In an airport the luggage would pass through the TNA instrument on a conveyor belt and be bombarded by neutrons from californium-252. The detector is set up to look for unusually large quantities of nitrogen because most chemical explosives are based on nitrogen compounds. Although this system is still under development, the Federal Aviation Administration is optimistic that it will work.

Analytical chemists have always admired the supersensitive natural detection devices built into organisms as part of elaborate control systems

A Hawaiian red swimming crab.

used to regulate the levels of various crucial chemicals, such as enzymes, hormones, and neurotransmitters. Because these "biosensors" are so sensitive, chemists are now attaching them to their instruments. For example, the sensory hairs from Hawaiian red swimming crabs can be connected to electrical analyzers and used to detect hormones at concentrations lower than 10^{-12} M. Also, slices from the tissues of pineapple cores can be used to detect hydrogen peroxide at levels of $\approx 10^{-6}$ M.

Another state-of-the-art detection system contains a surface acoustic wave (SAW) device, which is based on a piezoelectric crystal whose resonant frequency is sensitive to tiny changes in its mass—it can sense a change of 10^{-10} g/cm. In one use of this device as a detector, it was coated with a thin film of zeolite, a silicate mineral. Zeolite has intricate passages of a very uniform size. Thus, it can act as a "molecular sieve," allowing only molecules of a certain size to pass through onto the detector, where their accumulation changes the mass and therefore alters the detector frequency. This sensor has been used to detect amounts of methyl alcohol (CH_3OH) as low as 10^{-9} g.

The face of chemical analysis is changing rapidly. In fact, although wet chemical analyses (titrations, for example) are still quite important in the chemical industry, increasingly these routine analyses are done by robots, which not only perform the analyses automatically but also send the results to a computer for interpretation.

Table 4.3

Rules for Assigning Oxidation States

1. The oxidation state of an atom in an element is 0. For example, the oxidation state of each atom in the substances $Na(s)$, $O_2(g)$, $O_3(g)$, and $Hg(l)$ is 0.
2. The oxidation state of a monatomic ion is the same as its charge. For example, the oxidation state of the Na^+ ion is +1.
3. In its covalent compounds with nonmetals, hydrogen is assigned an oxidation state of +1. For example, in the compounds HCl, NH_3, H_2O, and CH_4, hydrogen is assigned an oxidation state of +1.
4. Oxygen is assigned an oxidation state of −2 in its covalent compounds, such as CO, CO_2, SO_2, and SO_3. The exception to this rule occurs in peroxides (compounds containing the O_2^{2-} group), where each oxygen is assigned an oxidation state of −1. The best-known example of a peroxide is hydrogen peroxide (H_2O_2).
5. In binary compounds, the element with the greater attraction for the electrons in the bond is assigned a negative oxidation state equal to its charge in its ionic compounds. For example, fluorine is always assigned an oxidation state of −1. That is, for purposes of counting electrons, fluorine is assumed to be F^-. Nitrogen is usually assigned −3. For example, in NH_3, nitrogen is assigned an oxidation state of −3; in H_2S, sulfur is assigned an oxidation state of −2; in HI, iodine is assigned an oxidation state of −1; and so on.
6. The sum of the oxidation states must be zero for an electrically neutral compound and must be equal to the overall charge for an ionic species. For example, the sum of the oxidation states for the hydrogen and oxygen atoms in water is 0; the sum of the oxidation states for the carbon and oxygen atoms in CO_3^{2-} is −2; and the sum of oxidation states for the nitrogen and hydrogen atoms in NH_4^+ is +1.

⭐WL INTERACTIVE EXAMPLE 4.13

Assign oxidation states to all of the following atoms.

a. CO_2 **b.** SF_6 **c.** NO_3^-

Solution

a. The rule that takes precedence here is that oxygen is assigned an oxidation state of −2. The oxidation state for carbon can be determined by recognizing that since CO_2 has no charge, the sum of the oxidation states for oxygen and carbon must be 0. Since each oxygen is −2 and there are two oxygen atoms, the carbon atom must be assigned an oxidation state of +4:

$$CO_2$$
$$\nearrow \quad \nwarrow$$
$$+4 \quad -2 \text{ for each oxygen}$$

b. Since fluorine has the greater attraction for the shared electrons, we assign its oxidation state first. Because its charge in ionic compounds is 1−, we assign −1 as the oxidation state of each fluorine atom. The sulfur must then be assigned an oxidation state of +6 to balance the total of −6 from the fluorine atoms:

$$SF_6$$
$$\nearrow \quad \nwarrow$$
$$+6 \quad -1 \text{ for each fluorine}$$

c. Since oxygen has a greater attraction than does nitrogen for the shared electrons, we assign its oxidation state of −2 first. Because the sum of the oxidation states of the three oxygens is -6 and the net charge on the NO_3^- ion is $1-$, the nitrogen must have an oxidation state of $+5$:

$$NO_3^-$$
$$\nearrow \quad \nwarrow$$
$$+5 \quad -2 \text{ for each oxygen}$$

Next, let's consider the oxidation states of the atoms in Fe_3O_4, which is the main component in magnetite, an iron ore that accounts for the reddish color of many types of rocks and soils. We assign each oxygen atom its usual oxidation state of -2. The three iron atoms must yield a total of $+8$ to balance the total of -8 from the four oxygens. Thus each iron atom has an oxidation state of $+\frac{8}{3}$. A noninteger value for an oxidation state may seem strange since charge is expressed in whole numbers. However, although they are rare, noninteger oxidation states do occur because of the rather arbitrary way that the electrons are divided up by the rules in Table 4.3. In the compound Fe_3O_4, for example, the rules assume that all of the iron atoms are equal when in fact this compound can best be viewed as containing four O^{2-} ions, two Fe^{3+} ions, and one Fe^{2+} per formula unit. (Note that the "average" charge on iron works out to be $\frac{8}{3}+$, which is equal to the oxidation state we determined above.) Noninteger oxidation states should not intimidate you. They serve the same purpose as integer oxidation states—for keeping track of electrons.

The Characteristics of Oxidation–Reduction Reactions

Oxidation–reduction reactions are characterized by a transfer of electrons. In some cases the transfer occurs in a literal sense to form ions, such as in this reaction:

$$2Na(s) + Cl_2(g) \longrightarrow 2NaCl(s)$$

However, sometimes the transfer occurs in a more formal sense, such as in the combustion of methane (the oxidation state for each atom is given):

$$CH_4(g) + 2O_2(g) \longrightarrow CO_2(g) + 2H_2O(g)$$

Oxidation
state: -4 $+1$ 0 $+4$ -2 $+1$ -2
              (each H)   (each O) (each H)

Note that the oxidation state of oxygen in O_2 is 0 because it is in elemental form. In this reaction there are no ionic compounds, but we can still describe the process in terms of a transfer of electrons. Note that carbon undergoes a change in oxidation state from -4 in CH_4 to $+4$ in CO_2. Such a change can be accounted for by a loss of eight electrons (the symbol e^- stands for an electron):

$$CH_4 \longrightarrow CO_2 + 8e^-$$
$$\uparrow \qquad \uparrow$$
$$-4 \qquad +4$$

On the other hand, each oxygen changes from an oxidation state of 0 in O_2 to -2 in H_2O and CO_2, signifying a gain of two electrons per atom. Since four oxygen atoms are involved, this is a gain of eight electrons:

$$2O_2 + 8e^- \longrightarrow CO_2 + 2H_2O$$
$$\uparrow \qquad\qquad \nwarrow \quad \nearrow$$
$$0 \qquad\qquad 4(-2) = -8$$

No change occurs in the oxidation state of hydrogen, so it is not formally involved in the electron transfer process.

Actual charges are given as $n-$ or $n+$. Oxidation states *(not actual charges)* are given as $-n$ or $+n$. For example, for NO_3^-, the overall charge is $1-$; the oxidation state for N is $+5$ and for O is -2.

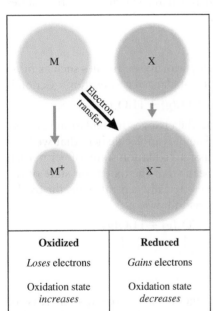

Figure 4.20
A summary of an oxidation–reduction process, in which M is oxidized and X is reduced.

With this background, we can now define some important terms. **Oxidation** is an *increase* in oxidation state (a loss of electrons). **Reduction** is a *decrease* in oxidation state (a gain of electrons). Thus in the reaction

$$2Na(s) + Cl_2(g) \longrightarrow 2NaCl(s)$$
$$0 0 +1 -1$$

sodium is oxidized and chlorine is reduced. In addition, Cl_2 is called the **oxidizing agent** (electron acceptor), and Na is called the **reducing agent** (electron donor). These concepts are summarized in Fig. 4.20.

Concerning the reaction

$$CH_4(g) + 2O_2(g) \longrightarrow CO_2(g) + 2H_2O(g)$$
$$-4 +1 0 +4 -2 +1 -2$$

we can say the following:

Carbon is oxidized because there is an increase in its oxidation state (carbon has formally lost electrons).

Oxygen is reduced as shown by the decrease in its oxidation state (oxygen has formally gained electrons).

CH_4 is the reducing agent.

O_2 is the oxidizing agent.

Note that when the oxidizing or reducing agent is named, the *whole compound* is specified, not just the element that undergoes the change in oxidation state.

Oxidation is an increase in oxidation state. Reduction is a decrease in oxidation state.

A helpful mnemonic device is OIL RIG (Oxidation Involves Loss; Reduction Involves Gain).

An oxidizing agent is reduced and a reducing agent is oxidized in a redox reaction.

4.11 Balancing Oxidation–Reduction Equations

Oxidation–reduction reactions are often complicated, which means that it can be difficult to balance their equations by simple inspection. Two methods for balancing redox reactions will be considered here: (1) the oxidation states method and (2) the half-reaction method.

The Oxidation States Method

Methanol (CH_3OH) is used as a fuel in high-performance engines such as those in the race cars in the Indianapolis 500. The unbalanced combustion reaction is

$$CH_3OH(l) + O_2(g) \longrightarrow CO_2(g) + H_2O(g)$$

We want to balance this equation by using the changes in oxidation state, so we must first specify all oxidation states. The only molecule here that we have not previously considered is CH_3OH. We assign oxidation states of $+1$ to each hydrogen and -2 to the oxygen, which means that the oxidation state of the carbon must be -2, since the compound is electrically neutral. Thus the oxidation states for the reaction participants are as follows:

$$CH_3OH(l) + O_2(g) \longrightarrow CO_2(g) + H_2O(g)$$
$$-2 | -2 +1 0 +4 | | -2$$
$$+1 -2 +1$$
$$\text{(each H)} \text{(each O)} \text{(each H)}$$

Note that the oxidation state of carbon changes from -2 to $+4$, an increase of 6. On the other hand, the oxidation state of oxygen changes from 0 to -2, a decrease of 2. This means that three oxygen atoms are needed to balance the increase in the oxidation state of the single carbon atom. We can write this relationship as follows:

$$CH_3OH(l) + \tfrac{3}{2}O_2(g) \longrightarrow \text{products}$$
$$\text{1 carbon atom} \text{3 oxygen atoms}$$

The rest of the equation can be balanced by inspection:

$$CH_3OH(l) + \tfrac{3}{2}O_2(g) \longrightarrow CO_2(g) + 2H_2O(g)$$

We then write it in conventional format (multiply through by 2):

$$2CH_3OH(l) + 3O_2(g) \longrightarrow 2CO_2(g) + 4H_2O(g)$$

In using the oxidation states method to balance an oxidation–reduction equation, we find the coefficients for the reactants that will make the total increase in oxidation state balance the total decrease. The remainder of the equation is then balanced by inspection.

EXAMPLE 4.14

Because metals are so reactive, very few are found in pure form in nature. Metallurgy involves reducing the metal ions in ores to the elemental form. The production of manganese from the ore pyrolusite, which contains MnO_2, uses aluminum as the reducing agent. Using oxidation states, balance the equation for this process.

$$MnO_2(s) + Al(s) \longrightarrow Mn(s) + Al_2O_3(s)$$

Solution First, we assign oxidation states:

$$MnO_2(s) + Al(s) \longrightarrow Mn(s) + Al_2O_3(s)$$

$$\begin{array}{cccccc} +4 & -2 & 0 & 0 & +3 & -2 \\ & \text{(each O)} & & & \text{(each Al)} & \text{(each O)} \end{array}$$

Each Mn atom undergoes a decrease in oxidation state of 4 (from +4 to 0), whereas each Al atom undergoes an increase of 3 (from 0 to +3).

Thus we need three Mn atoms for every four Al atoms to balance the increase and decrease in oxidation states:

$$\text{Increase} = 4(3) = \text{decrease} = 3(4)$$

$$3MnO_2(s) + 4Al(s) \longrightarrow \text{products}$$

We balance the rest of the equation by inspection:

$$3MnO_2(s) + 4Al(s) \longrightarrow 3Mn(s) + 2Al_2O_3(s)$$

The procedures for balancing an oxidation–reduction equation by the oxidation states method are summarized below.

STEPS

Balancing an Oxidation–Reduction Equation by the Oxidation States Method

1 Assign the oxidation states of all atoms.
2 Decide which element is oxidized, and determine the increase in oxidation state.
3 Decide which element is reduced, and determine the decrease in oxidation state.
4 Choose coefficients for the species containing the atom oxidized and the atom reduced such that the total increase in oxidation state equals the total decrease in oxidation state.
5 Balance the remainder of the equation by inspection.

The Half-Reaction Method

For oxidation–reduction reactions that occur in aqueous solution, it is often useful to separate the reaction into two **half-reactions:** one involving oxidation and the other involving reduction. For example, consider the unbalanced equation for the oxidation–reduction reaction between cerium(IV) ion and tin(II) ion:

$$Ce^{4+}(aq) + Sn^{2+}(aq) \longrightarrow Ce^{3+}(aq) + Sn^{4+}(aq)$$

This reaction can be separated into a half-reaction involving the substance being *reduced,*

$$Ce^{4+}(aq) \longrightarrow Ce^{3+}(aq)$$

and one involving the substance being *oxidized,*

$$Sn^{2+}(aq) \longrightarrow Sn^{4+}(aq)$$

The general procedure is to balance the equations for the half-reactions separately and then to add them to obtain the overall balanced equation. The half-reaction method for balancing oxidation–reduction equations differs slightly depending on whether the reaction takes place in acidic or basic solution.

STEPS | **Balancing Oxidation–Reduction Equations Occurring in Acidic Solution by the Half-Reaction Method**

1 Write the equations for the oxidation and reduction half-reactions.
2 For each half-reaction:
  • Balance all the elements except hydrogen and oxygen.
  • Balance oxygen using H_2O.
  • Balance hydrogen using H^+.
  • Balance the charge using electrons.
3 If necessary, multiply one or both balanced half-reactions by integers to equalize the number of electrons transferred in the two half-reactions.
4 Add the half-reactions, and cancel identical species.
5 Check to be sure that the elements and charges balance.

These steps are summarized by the following flowchart:

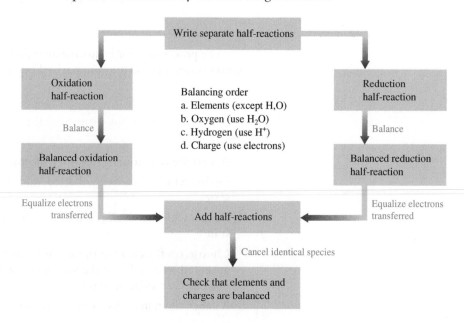

We will illustrate this method by balancing the equation for the reaction between permanganate and iron(II) ions in acidic solution:

$$MnO_4^-(aq) + Fe^{2+}(aq) \xrightarrow{\text{Acidic}} Fe^{3+}(aq) + Mn^{2+}(aq)$$

This reaction is used to analyze iron ore for its iron content.

1. **Identify and write equations for the half-reactions.**

   The oxidation states for the half-reaction involving the permanganate ion show that manganese is reduced:

$$MnO_4^- \longrightarrow Mn^{2+}$$

   $\uparrow$ $\uparrow$ $\qquad\qquad$ $\uparrow$
   +7 -2 (each O)   +2

   This is the *reduction half-reaction*. The other half-reaction involves the oxidation of iron(II) to iron(III) ion and is the *oxidation half-reaction*:

$$Fe^{2+} \longrightarrow Fe^{3+}$$

   $\uparrow$ $\qquad\qquad$ $\uparrow$
   +2 $\qquad\qquad$ +3

2. **Balance each half-reaction.**

   For the reduction reaction, we have

$$MnO_4^-(aq) \longrightarrow Mn^{2+}(aq)$$

   a. The manganese is balanced.

   b. We balance oxygen by adding $4H_2O$ to the right side of the equation:

$$MnO_4^-(aq) \longrightarrow Mn^{2+}(aq) + 4H_2O(l)$$

   c. Next, we balance hydrogen by adding $8H^+$ to the left side:

$$8H^+(aq) + MnO_4^-(aq) \longrightarrow Mn^{2+}(aq) + 4H_2O(l)$$

   d. All the elements have been balanced, but we need to balance the charge by using electrons. At this point we have the following charges for reactants and products in the reduction half-reaction:

$$8H^+(aq) + MnO_4^-(aq) \longrightarrow Mn^{2+}(aq) + 4H_2O(l)$$

   $\underbrace{ \qquad + \qquad 1-}_{7+}$ $\qquad\qquad$ $\underbrace{2+ \qquad + \qquad 0}_{2+}$

   We can equalize the charges by adding five electrons to the left side:

$$\underbrace{5e^- + 8H^+(aq) + MnO_4^-(aq)}_{2+} \longrightarrow \underbrace{Mn^{2+}(aq) + 4H_2O(l)}_{2+}$$

   Both the *elements* and the *charges* are now balanced, so this represents the balanced reduction half-reaction. The fact that five electrons appear on the reactant side of the equation makes sense, since five electrons are required to reduce MnO_4^- (in which Mn has an oxidation state of +7) to Mn^{2+} (in which Mn has an oxidation state of +2).

   For the oxidation reaction,

$$Fe^{2+}(aq) \longrightarrow Fe^{3+}(aq)$$

   the elements are balanced, and we must simply balance the charge:

$$\underbrace{Fe^{2+}(aq)}_{2+} \longrightarrow \underbrace{Fe^{3+}(aq)}_{3+}$$

One electron is needed on the right side to give a net 2+ charge on both sides:

$$\underbrace{Fe^{2+}(aq)}_{2+} \longrightarrow \underbrace{Fe^{3+}(aq) + e^-}_{2+}$$

The number of electrons gained in the reduction half-reaction must equal the number of electrons lost in the oxidation half-reaction.

3. **Equalize the electron transfer in the two half-reactions.**

Since the reduction half-reaction involves a transfer of five electrons and the oxidation half-reaction involves a transfer of only one electron, the oxidation half-reaction must be multiplied by 5:

$$5Fe^{2+}(aq) \longrightarrow 5Fe^{3+}(aq) + 5e^-$$

4. **Add the half-reactions.**

The half-reactions are added to give

$$5e^- + 5Fe^{2+}(aq) + MnO_4^-(aq) + 8H^+(aq)$$
$$\longrightarrow 5Fe^{3+}(aq) + Mn^{2+}(aq) + 4H_2O(l) + 5e^-$$

Note that the electrons cancel (as they must) to give the final balanced equation:

$$5Fe^{2+}(aq) + MnO_4^-(aq) + 8H^+(aq)$$
$$\longrightarrow 5Fe^{3+}(aq) + Mn^{2+}(aq) + 4H_2O(l)$$

5. **Check that the elements and charges balance.**

Elements balance: 5 Fe, 1 Mn, 4 O, 8 H $\longrightarrow$ 5 Fe, 1 Mn, 4 O, 8 H
Charges balance: $5(2+) + (1-) + 8(1+) = 17+$
$$\longrightarrow 5(3+) + (2+) + 0 = 17+$$

The equation is balanced.

Oxidation–reduction reactions can occur in basic as well as in acidic solutions. The half-reaction method for balancing equations is slightly different in such cases.

STEPS	**Balancing Oxidation–Reduction Equations Occurring in Basic Solution by the Half-Reaction Method**

1 Use the half-reaction method as specified for acidic solutions to obtain the final balanced equation *as if H^+ ions were present.*

2 To both sides of the equation obtained by the procedure in Step 1, add the number of OH^- ions that is equal to the number of H^+ ions. (We want to eliminate H^+ by forming H_2O.)

3 Form H_2O on the side containing both H^+ and OH^- ions, and eliminate the number of H_2O molecules that appear on both sides of the equation.

4 Check that the elements and charges balance.

This method is summarized by the following flowchart:

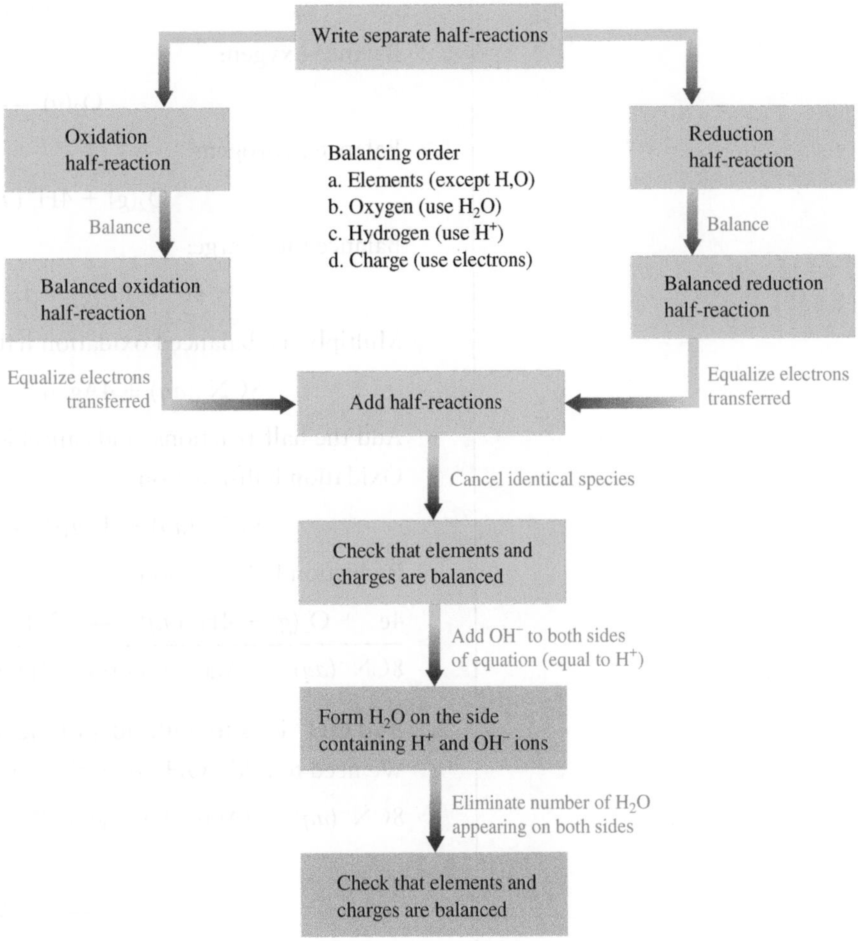

INTERACTIVE EXAMPLE 4.15

Silver is sometimes found in nature as large nuggets; more often it is found mixed with other metals and their ores. Cyanide ion is often used to extract the silver by the following reaction that occurs in basic solution:

$$Ag(s) + CN^-(aq) + O_2(g) \xrightarrow{\text{Basic}} Ag(CN)_2^-(aq)$$

Balance this equation by using the half-reaction method.

Solution

1. **Balance the equation as if H^+ ions were present.**

   Balance the oxidation half-reaction:

   $$CN^-(aq) + Ag(s) \longrightarrow Ag(CN)_2^-(aq)$$

   Balance carbon and nitrogen:

   $$2CN^-(aq) + Ag(s) \longrightarrow Ag(CN)_2^-(aq)$$

   Balance the charge:

   $$2CN^-(aq) + Ag(s) \longrightarrow Ag(CN)_2^-(aq) + e^-$$

Balance the reduction half-reaction:

$$O_2(g) \longrightarrow$$

Balance oxygen:

$$O_2(g) \longrightarrow 2H_2O(l)$$

Balance hydrogen:

$$O_2(g) + 4H^+(aq) \longrightarrow 2H_2O(l)$$

Balance the charge:

$$4e^- + O_2(g) + 4H^+(aq) \longrightarrow 2H_2O(l)$$

Multiply the balanced oxidation half-reaction by 4:

$$8CN^-(aq) + 4Ag(s) \longrightarrow 4Ag(CN)_2^-(aq) + 4e^-$$

Add the half-reactions, and cancel identical species:

Oxidation half-reaction:

$$8CN^-(aq) + 4Ag(s) \longrightarrow 4Ag(CN)_2^-(aq) + 4e^-$$

Reduction half-reaction:

$$4e^- + O_2(g) + 4H^+(aq) \longrightarrow 2H_2O(l)$$

$$8CN^-(aq) + 4Ag(s) + O_2(g) + 4H^+(aq) \longrightarrow 4Ag(CN)_2^-(aq) + 2H_2O(l)$$

2. **Add OH^- ions to both sides of the balanced equation.**

We need to add $4OH^-$ to each side:

$$8CN^-(aq) + 4Ag(s) + O_2(g) + \underbrace{4H^+(aq) + 4OH^-(aq)}_{4H_2O(l)}$$

$$\longrightarrow 4Ag(CN)_2^-(aq) + 2H_2O(l) + 4OH^-(aq)$$

3. **Eliminate as many H_2O molecules as possible.**

$$8CN^-(aq) + 4Ag(s) + O_2(g) + 2H_2O(l) \longrightarrow 4Ag(CN)_2^-(aq) + 4OH^-(aq)$$

4. **Check that elements and charges balance.**

OWL INTERACTIVE EXAMPLE 4.16

Cerium(IV) ion is a strong oxidizing agent that accepts one electron to produce cerium(III) ion:

$$Ce^{4+}(aq) + e^- \longrightarrow Ce^{3+}(aq)$$

A solution containing an unknown concentration of Sn^{2+} ions was titrated with a solution containing Ce^{4+} ions, which oxidize the Sn^{2+} ions to Sn^{4+} ions. In one titration, 1.00 L of the unknown solution required 46.45 mL of a 0.1050 *M* Ce^{4+} solution to reach the stoichiometric point. Calculate the concentration of Sn^{2+} ions in the unknown solution.

Solution

- What are we trying to solve?

We are asked to determine the concentration of 1.00 L of a solution of Sn^{2+} required to react with a given volume and molarity of a Ce^{4+} solution.

■ What does this mean?

The Sn^{2+} and Ce^{4+} react with each other, so we need to use a balanced equation to determine the mole ratio between the two reactants. From the volume and molarity of the Ce^{4+} solution, we can determine the number of moles that, using the balanced equation, can be converted to moles of the Sn^{2+} solution. With moles and volume of Sn^{2+}, we can compute the concentration in terms of molarity.

The unbalanced equation for the titration reaction is

$$Ce^{4+}(aq) + Sn^{2+}(aq) \longrightarrow Ce^{3+}(aq) + Sn^{4+}(aq)$$

The balanced equation is

$$2Ce^{4+}(aq) + Sn^{2+}(aq) \longrightarrow 2Ce^{3+}(aq) + Sn^{4+}(aq)$$

We can obtain the number of moles of Ce^{4+} ions from the volume and molarity of the Ce^{4+} solution used as the titrant:

$$46.45 \text{ mL} \times \frac{1 \text{ L}}{1000 \text{ mL}} \times \frac{0.1050 \text{ mol Ce}^{4+}}{\text{L}} = 4.877 \times 10^{-3} \text{ mol Ce}^{4+}$$

The number of moles of Sn^{2+} ions can be obtained by applying the appropriate mole ratio from the balanced equation:

$$4.877 \times 10^{-3} \text{ mol Ce}^{4+} \times \frac{1 \text{ mol Sn}^{2+}}{2 \text{ mol Ce}^{4+}} = 2.439 \times 10^{-3} \text{ mol Sn}^{2+}$$

This value represents the quantity of Sn^{2+} ions in 1.00 L of solution. Thus the concentration of Sn^{2+} in the unknown solution is

$$\text{Molarity} = \frac{\text{mol Sn}^{2+}}{\text{L solution}} = \frac{2.439 \times 10^{-3} \text{ mol Sn}^{2+}}{1.00 \text{ L}} = 2.44 \times 10^{-3} \text{ M}$$

■ Is the answer reasonable?

The volume of the Sn^{2+} solution is much greater (factor of ~20) than the volume of the Ce^{4+} solution. It makes sense that the concentration of the Sn^{2+} solution is much lower than the concentration of the Ce^{4+} solution.

4.12 | Simple Oxidation–Reduction Titrations

Oxidation–reduction reactions are commonly used as a basis for volumetric analytical procedures. For example, a reducing substance can be titrated with a solution of a strong oxidizing agent, or vice versa. Three of the most frequently used oxidizing agents are aqueous solutions of *potassium permanganate* ($KMnO_4$), *potassium dichromate* ($K_2Cr_2O_7$), and *cerium hydrogen sulfate* [$Ce(HSO_4)_4$].

The strong oxidizing agent, the permanganate ion (MnO_4^-), can undergo several different reactions. The reaction that occurs in acidic solution is the one most commonly used:

$$MnO_4^-(aq) + 8H^+(aq) + 5e^- \longrightarrow Mn^{2+}(aq) + 4H_2O(l)$$

Permanganate has the advantage of being its own indicator—the MnO_4^- ion is intensely purple, and the Mn^{2+} ion is almost colorless. As long as some reducing agent remains in the solution being titrated, the solution remains colorless (assuming all other species present are colorless), since the purple MnO_4^- ion being added is converted to the essentially colorless Mn^{2+} ion. However, when all the reducing agent has been consumed, the next drop of permanganate titrant will turn the solution being titrated light purple (pink). Thus the endpoint (where the color change indicates the titration should stop) occurs approximately one drop beyond the stoichiometric point (the actual point at which all the reducing agent has been consumed).

Example 4.17 describes a typical volumetric analysis using permanganate.

EXAMPLE 4.17

Iron ores often involve a mixture of oxides and contain both Fe^{2+} and Fe^{3+} ions. Such an ore can be analyzed for its iron content by dissolving it in acidic solution, reducing all the iron to Fe^{2+} ions, and then titrating with a standard solution of potassium permanganate. In the resulting solution, MnO_4^- is reduced to Mn^{2+}, and Fe^{2+} is oxidized to Fe^{3+}. A sample of iron ore weighing 0.3500 g was dissolved in acidic solution, and all the iron was reduced to Fe^{2+}. Then the solution was titrated with a 1.621×10^{-2} M $KMnO_4$ solution. The titration required 41.56 mL of the permanganate solution to reach the light purple (pink) endpoint. Determine the mass percent of iron in the iron ore.

Solution

■ What are we trying to solve?

We are asked to determine the mass percent of iron in an iron ore.

■ What does this mean?

$$\text{Mass percent of iron} = \frac{\text{mass of iron}}{\text{mass of iron ore}} \times 100\%$$

We know that the mass of the mixture is 0.3500 g, so we change the question to "*What is the mass of the iron?*"

All of the iron metal is converted to Fe^{2+}, which is reacted with a known volume and molarity of MnO_4^-. From volume and molarity we can get moles, and by using the mole ratio in a balanced equation, we can determine the moles of iron. We convert from moles to mass using the atomic mass of iron.

From the problem it is obvious that this is a redox reaction, so we will need to balance the equation accordingly.

First, we write the unbalanced equation for the reaction:

$$H^+(aq) + MnO_4^-(aq) + Fe^{2+}(aq) \longrightarrow Fe^{3+}(aq) + Mn^{2+}(aq) + H_2O(l)$$

Using the half-reaction method, we balance the equation:

$$8H^+(aq) + MnO_4^-(aq) + 5Fe^{2+}(aq) \longrightarrow 5Fe^{3+}(aq) + Mn^{2+}(aq) + 4H_2O(l)$$

The number of moles of MnO_4^- ion required in the titration is found from the volume and concentration of permanganate solution used:

$$41.56 \text{ mL} \times \frac{1 \text{ L}}{1000 \text{ mL}} \times \frac{1.621 \times 10^{-2} \text{ mol MnO}_4^-}{\text{L}}$$
$$= 6.737 \times 10^{-4} \text{ mol MnO}_4^-$$

The balanced equation shows that five times as much Fe^{2+} as MnO_4^- is required:

$$6.737 \times 10^{-4} \text{ mol MnO}_4^- \times \frac{5 \text{ mol Fe}^{2+}}{1 \text{ mol MnO}_4^-} = 3.368 \times 10^{-3} \text{ mol Fe}^{2+}$$

Thus the 0.3500-g sample of iron ore contained 3.368×10^{-3} mol of iron. The mass of iron present is

$$3.368 \times 10^{-3} \text{ mol Fe} \times \frac{55.85 \text{ g Fe}}{1 \text{ mol Fe}} = 0.1881 \text{ g Fe}$$

The mass percent of iron in the iron ore is

$$\frac{0.1881 \text{ g}}{0.3500 \text{ g}} \times 100\% = 53.74\%$$

Key Terms

aqueous solutions

Section 4.1
polar molecule
hydration

Section 4.2
solute
solvent
electrical conductivity
strong electrolyte
weak electrolyte
nonelectrolyte
solubility
acid
strong acid
strong base
weak acid
weak base

Section 4.3
molarity
standard solution
dilution

Section 4.5
precipitation reaction
precipitate

Section 4.6
molecular equation
complete ionic equation
spectator ion
net ionic equation

Section 4.7
selective precipitation
qualitative analysis

Section 4.9
neutralization reaction
volumetric analysis
titrant
equivalence (stoichiometric)
 point
indicator, endpoint

Section 4.10
oxidation-reduction (redox)
 reaction
oxidation state (oxidation
 number)
oxidation
reduction
oxidizing agent (electron
 acceptor)
reducing agent (electron donor)

Section 4.11
half-reaction

For Review

◗WL and **go Chemistry**
Sign in at **www.cengage.com/owl** to:
• View tutorials and simulations, develop problem-solving skills, and complete online homework
  assigned by your professor.
• Download Go Chemistry mini lecture modules for quick review and exam prep from OWL
  (or purchase them at **www.cengagebrain.com**)

Chemical reactions in solution are very important in everyday life.

Water is a polar solvent that dissolves many ionic and polar substances.
■ Many ionic substances dissolve in water, although solubility varies greatly.
■ Many polar substances dissolve in water.

Electrolytes
■ Strong electrolyte: 100% dissociated to produce separate ions; strongly
  conducts an electric current
■ Weak electrolyte: Only a small percentage of dissolved molecules produce ions; weakly conducts an electric current
■ Nonelectrolyte: Dissolved substance produces no ions; does not conduct an electric current

Acids and bases
■ Arrhenius model
  ■ Acid: produces H^+
  ■ Base: produces OH^-
■ Brønsted–Lowry model
  ■ Acid: proton donor
  ■ Base: proton acceptor
■ Strong acid: completely dissociates into separated H^+ and anions
■ Strong base: completely dissociates into separated OH^- and cation
■ Weak acid: dissociates to a slight extent
■ Weak base: results in a solution that is a weak electrolyte and contains
  OH^- ions

Molarity
■ One way to describe solution composition
■ Molarity $(M) = \dfrac{\text{moles of solute}}{\text{volume of solution (L)}}$
■ Standard solution: Molarity is accurately known.

Dilution
■ Solvent is added to reduce the molarity.
■ Moles of solute after dilution = moles of solute before dilution
■ $M_1 V_1 = M_2 V_2$

Types of equations that describe solution reactions
■ Molecular equation: All reactants and products are written as complete formulas.
■ Complete ionic equation: All reactants and products that are strong
  electrolytes are written as separate ions.
■ Net ionic equation: Only those compounds that undergo a change are
  written; spectator ions are not included.

Solubility rules
■ Based on experiment observation
■ Help predict the outcomes of precipitation reactions

Qualitative analysis
■ A mixture of ions can be separated by selective precipitation

Important types of solution reactions
- Acid–base reactions: involve a transfer of H^+ ions
- Precipitation reactions: formation of a solid occurs
- Oxidation–reduction reactions: involve electron transfer

Titrations
- Measures the volume of a standard solution (titrant) needed to react with a substance in solution
- Stoichiometric (equivalence) point: the point at which the required amount of titrant has been added to exactly react with the substance being analyzed
- Endpoint: the point at which a chemical indicator changes color

Oxidation–reduction reactions
- Oxidation states are assigned using a set of rules to keep track of electron flow
- Oxidation: increase in oxidation state (a loss of electrons)
- Reduction: decrease in oxidation state (a gain of electrons)
- Oxidizing agent: gains electrons (is reduced)
- Reducing agent: loses electrons (is oxidized)
- Balancing oxidation–reduction reactions:
  - Oxidation state method
  - Half-reaction method
    - In acidic solutions
    - In basic solutions
- Can be used for volumetric analytical procedures
  - Titrations

Discussion Questions

These questions are designed to be considered by groups of students in class. Often these questions work well for introducing a particular topic in class.

1. Assume you have a highly magnified view of a solution of HCl that allows you to "see" the HCl. Draw this magnified view. If you dropped in a piece of magnesium, the magnesium would disappear, and hydrogen gas would be released. Represent this change using symbols for the elements, and write out the balanced equation.

2. You have a solution of table salt in water. What happens to the salt concentration (increases, decreases, or stays the same) as the solution boils? Draw pictures to explain your answer.

3. You have a sugar solution (solution A) with concentration x. You pour one-third of this solution into a beaker and add an equivalent volume of water (solution B).
   a. What is the ratio of sugar in solutions A and B?
   b. Compare the volumes of solutions A and B.
   c. What is the ratio of the concentrations of sugar in solutions A and B?

4. You add an aqueous solution of lead nitrate to an aqueous solution of potassium iodide. Draw highly magnified views of each solution individually and the mixed solution, including any product that forms. Write the balanced equation for the reaction.

5. You need to make 150.0 mL of a 0.10 *M* NaCl solution. You have solid NaCl and your lab partner has a 2.5 *M* NaCl solution. Explain how you each make the 0.10 *M* NaCl solution.

6. The exposed electrodes of a light bulb are placed in a solution of H_2SO_4 in an electrical circuit such that the light bulb is glowing. You add a dilute salt solution, and the bulb dims. Which of the following could be the salt in the solution?
   a. $Ba(NO_3)_2$ c. K_2SO_4
   b. $NaNO_3$ d. $Ca(NO_3)_2$

   Justify your choices. For those you did not choose, explain why they are incorrect.

7. You have two solutions of chemical A. To determine which has the highest concentration of A (molarity), which of the following must you know (there may be more than one answer)?
   a. the mass in grams of A in each solution
   b. the molar mass of A
   c. the volume of water added to each solution
   d. the total volume of the solution

   Explain.

8. Which of the following must be known to calculate the molarity of a salt solution (there may be more than one answer)?
   a. the mass of salt added
   b. the molar mass of the salt
   c. the volume of water added
   d. the total volume of the solution

   Explain.

9. Consider separate aqueous solutions of HCl and H_2SO_4, each with the same molar concentration. An aqueous solution of NaOH is added to each solution to neutralize the acid. Which acid solution requires the largest volume of NaOH solution to react completely with the acid present? Explain.

Exercises

OWL Interactive versions of these problems may be assigned in OWL.

A blue exercise number indicates that the answer to that exercise appears at the back of this book and a solution appears in the *Solutions Guide*.

Aqueous Solutions: Strong and Weak Electrolytes

10. Characterize strong electrolytes versus weak electrolytes versus nonelectrolytes. Give examples of each. How do you experimentally determine whether a soluble substance is a strong electrolyte, weak electrolyte, or nonelectrolyte.

11. The figures below are molecular-level representations of four aqueous solutions of the same solute. Arrange the solutions from most to least concentrated.

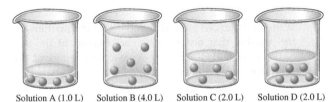

Solution A (1.0 L)   Solution B (4.0 L)   Solution C (2.0 L)   Solution D (2.0 L)

12. Which of the following statements is (are) true? Correct the false statements.
    a. A concentrated solution in water will always contain a strong or weak electrolyte.
    b. A strong electrolyte will break up into ions when dissolved in water.
    c. An acid is a strong electrolyte.
    d. All ionic compounds are strong electrolytes in water.

13. Differentiate between what happens when the following are dissolved in water.
    a. polar solute versus nonpolar solute
    b. KF versus $C_6H_{12}O_6$
    c. RbCl versus AgCl
    d. HNO_3 versus CO

14. Commercial cold packs and hot packs are available for treating athletic injuries. Both types contain a pouch of water and a dry chemical. When the pack is struck, the pouch of water breaks, dissolving the chemical, and the solution becomes either hot or cold. Many hot packs use magnesium sulfate, and many cold packs use ammonium nitrate. Write reaction equations to show how these strong electrolytes break apart in water.

15. Match each name below with the following microscopic pictures of that compound in aqueous solution.

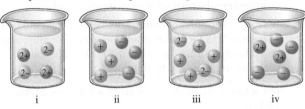

i   ii   iii   iv

   a. barium nitrate   c. potassium carbonate
   b. sodium chloride   d. magnesium sulfate

Solution Concentration: Molarity

16. A solution of ethanol (C_2H_5OH) in water is prepared by dissolving 75.0 mL of ethanol (density = 0.79 g/cm³) in enough water to make 250.0 mL of solution. What is the molarity of the ethanol in this solution?

17. Describe how you would prepare 2.00 L of each of the following solutions.
    a. 0.250 *M* NaOH from solid NaOH
    b. 0.250 *M* NaOH from 1.00 *M* NaOH stock solution
    c. 0.100 *M* K_2CrO_4 from solid K_2CrO_4
    d. 0.100 *M* K_2CrO_4 from 1.75 *M* K_2CrO_4 stock solution

18. How would you prepare 1.00 L of a 0.50 *M* solution of each of the following?
    a. H_2SO_4 from "concentrated" (18 *M*) sulfuric acid
    b. HCl from "concentrated" (12 *M*) reagent
    c. $NiCl_2$ from the salt $NiCl_2 \cdot 6H_2O$
    d. HNO_3 from "concentrated" (16 *M*) reagent
    e. Sodium carbonate from the pure solid

19. What mass of NaOH is contained in 250.0 mL of a 0.400 *M* sodium hydroxide solution?

20. If 10. g of $AgNO_3$ is available, what volume of 0.25 *M* $AgNO_3$ solution can be prepared?

21. Which of the following solutions of strong electrolytes contains the largest number of moles of chloride ions: 100.0 mL of 0.30 *M* $AlCl_3$, 50.0 mL of 0.60 *M* $MgCl_2$, or 200.0 mL of 0.40 *M* NaCl?

22. Calculate the concentration of all ions present in each of the following solutions of strong electrolytes.
    a. 0.100 mole of $Ca(NO_3)_2$ in 100.0 mL of solution
    b. 2.5 moles of Na_2SO_4 in 1.25 L of solution
    c. 5.00 g of NH_4Cl in 500.0 mL of solution
    d. 1.00 g of K_3PO_4 in 250.0 mL of solution

23. Calculate the sodium ion concentration when 70.0 mL of 3.0 M sodium carbonate is added to 30.0 mL of 1.0 M sodium bicarbonate.

24. A solution is prepared by dissolving 25.0 g of ammonium sulfate in enough water to make 100.0 mL of stock solution. A 10.00-mL sample of this stock solution is added to 50.00 mL of water. Calculate the concentration of ammonium ions and sulfate ions in the final solution.

25. A standard solution is prepared for the analysis of fluoxymesterone ($C_{20}H_{29}FO_3$), an anabolic steroid. A stock solution is first prepared by dissolving 10.0 mg of fluoxymesterone in enough water to give a total volume of 500.0 mL. A 100.0-μL aliquot (portion) of this solution is diluted to a final volume of 100.0 mL. Calculate the concentration of the final solution in terms of molarity.

26. A stock solution containing Mn^{2+} ions is prepared by dissolving 1.584 g of pure manganese metal in nitric acid and diluting to a final volume of 1.000 L. The following solutions are prepared by dilution.

   For solution A, 50.00 mL of stock solution is diluted to 1000.0 mL.

   For solution B, 10.00 mL of A is diluted to 250.0 mL.

   For solution C, 10.00 mL of B is diluted to 500.0 mL.

   Calculate the molar concentrations of the stock solution and solutions A, B, and C.

27. The units of parts per million (ppm) and parts per billion (ppb) are commonly used by environmental chemists. In general, 1 ppm means 1 part of solute for every 10^6 parts of solution. (Both solute and solution are measured using the same units.) Mathematically, by mass:

$$\text{ppm} = \frac{\mu\text{g solute}}{\text{g solution}} = \frac{\text{mg solute}}{\text{kg solution}}$$

   In the case of very dilute aqueous solutions, a concentration of 1.0 ppm is equal to 1.0 μg of solute per 1.0 mL of solution, which equals 1.0 g of solution. Parts per billion is defined in a similar fashion. Calculate the molarity of each of the following aqueous solutions.
   a. 5.0 ppb Hg in H_2O
   b. 1.0 ppb $CHCl_3$ in H_2O
   c. 10.0 ppm As in H_2O
   d. 0.10 ppm DDT ($C_{14}H_9Cl_5$) in H_2O

28. In the spectroscopic analysis of many substances, a series of standard solutions of known concentration are measured to generate a calibration curve. How would you prepare standard solutions containing 10.0, 25.0, 50.0, 75.0, and 100. ppm of copper from a commercially produced 1000.0-ppm solution? Assume each solution has a final volume of 100.0 mL. (See Exercise 27 for definitions.)

Precipitation Reactions

29. List the formulas of three soluble bromide salts and three insoluble bromide salts. Do the same exercise for sulfate salts, hydroxide salts, and phosphate salts (list three soluble salts and three insoluble salts). List the formulas for six insoluble Pb^{2+} salts and one soluble Pb^{2+} salt.

30. When 1.0 mole of solid lead nitrate is added to 2.0 moles of aqueous potassium iodide, a yellow precipitate forms. After the precipitate settles to the bottom, does the solution above the precipitate conduct electricity? Explain. Write the complete ionic equation to help you answer this question.

31. When the following solutions are mixed together, what precipitate (if any) will form?
   a. $Hg_2(NO_3)_2(aq) + CuSO_4(aq)$
   b. $Ni(NO_3)_2(aq) + CaCl_2(aq)$
   c. $K_2CO_3(aq) + MgI_2(aq)$
   d. $Na_2CrO_4(aq) + AlBr_3(aq)$

32. For the reactions in Exercise 31, write the balanced molecular equation, complete ionic equation, and net ionic equation. If no precipitate forms, write "No reaction."

33. Write the balanced molecular, complete, and net ionic equations for the reaction, if any, that occurs when aqueous solutions of the following are mixed.
   a. ammonium sulfate and barium nitrate
   b. lead(II) nitrate and sodium chloride
   c. sodium phosphate and potassium nitrate
   d. sodium bromide and rubidium chloride
   e. copper(II) chloride and sodium hydroxide

34. How would you separate the following ions in aqueous solution by selective precipitation?
   a. Ag^+, Ba^{2+}, and Cr^{3+}
   b. Ag^+, Pb^{2+}, and Cu^{2+}
   c. Hg_2^{2+} and Ni^{2+}

35. Write the balanced molecular and net ionic equations for the reaction that occurs when the contents of the two beakers are added together. What colors represent the spectator ions in each reaction?

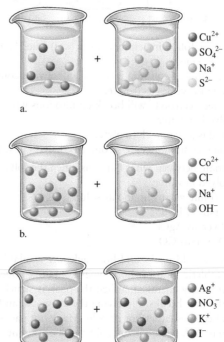

36. Give an example of how each of the following insoluble ionic compounds could be produced using a precipitation reaction. Write the balanced molecular equation for each reaction.
    a. $Fe(OH)_3(s)$ c. $PbSO_4(s)$
    b. $Hg_2Cl_2(s)$ d. $BaCrO_4(s)$

37. Separate samples of a solution of an unknown soluble ionic compound are treated with KCl, Na_2SO_4, and $NaOH$. A precipitate forms only when Na_2SO_4 is added. Which cations could be present in the unknown soluble ionic compound?

38. What volume of $0.100\ M\ Na_3PO_4$ is required to precipitate all of the lead(II) ions from 150.0 mL of $0.250\ M$ $Pb(NO_3)_2$?

39. How many grams of silver chloride can be prepared by the reaction of 100.0 mL of $0.20\ M$ silver nitrate with 100.0 mL of $0.15\ M$ calcium chloride? Calculate the concentrations of each ion remaining in solution after precipitation is complete.

40. The following drawings represent aqueous solutions. Solution A is 2.00 L of a $2.00\ M$ aqueous solution of copper(II) nitrate. Solution B is 2.00 L of a $3.00\ M$ aqueous solution of potassium hydroxide.

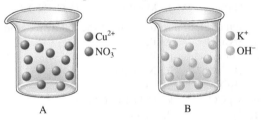

    a. Draw a picture of the solution made by mixing solutions A and B together after the precipitation reaction takes place. Make sure this picture shows the correct relative volume compared with solutions A and B and the correct relative number of ions, along with the correct relative amount of solid formed.
    b. Determine the concentrations (in M) of all ions left in solution (from part a) and the mass of solid formed.

41. What mass of Na_2CrO_4 is required to precipitate all of the silver ions from 75.0 mL of a $0.100\ M$ solution of $AgNO_3$?

42. A 1.00-g sample of an alkaline earth metal chloride is treated with excess silver nitrate. All of the chloride is recovered as 1.38 g of silver chloride. Identify the metal.

43. A mixture contains only $NaCl$ and $Al_2(SO_4)_3$. A 1.45-g sample of the mixture is dissolved in water, and an excess of $NaOH$ is added, producing a precipitate of $Al(OH)_3$. The precipitate is filtered, dried, and weighed. The mass of the precipitate is 0.107 g. What is the mass percent of $Al_2(SO_4)_3$ in the sample?

44. The thallium (present as Tl_2SO_4) in a 9.486-g pesticide sample was precipitated as thallium(I) iodide. Calculate the mass percent of Tl_2SO_4 in the sample if 0.1824 g of TlI was recovered.

45. Saccharin $(C_7H_5NO_3S)$ is sometimes dispensed in tablet form. Ten tablets with a total mass of 0.5894 g were dissolved in water. This solution was then oxidized to convert all the sulfur to sulfate ion, which was precipitated by adding an excess of barium chloride solution. The mass of $BaSO_4$ obtained was 0.5032 g. What is the average mass of saccharin per tablet? What is the average mass percent of saccharin in the tablets?

46. Douglasite is a mineral with the formula $2KCl \cdot FeCl_2 \cdot 2H_2O$. Calculate the mass percent of douglasite in a 455.0-mg sample if it took 37.20 mL of a $0.1000\ M$ $AgNO_3$ solution to precipitate all the Cl^- as $AgCl$. Assume the douglasite is the only source of chloride ion.

47. A 1.42-g sample of a pure compound with formula M_2SO_4 was dissolved in water and treated with an excess of aqueous calcium chloride, resulting in the precipitation of all the sulfate ions as calcium sulfate. The precipitate was collected, dried, and found to weigh 1.36 g. Determine the atomic mass of M and identify M.

Acid–Base Reactions

48. Write balanced equations (all three types) for the reactions that occur when the following aqueous solutions are mixed.
    a. ammonia (aqueous) and nitric acid
    b. barium hydroxide (aqueous) and hydrochloric acid
    c. perchloric acid $[HClO_4(aq)]$ and solid iron(III) hydroxide
    d. solid silver hydroxide and hydrobromic acid

49. What acid and what base would react in aqueous solution so that the following salts appear as products in the molecular equation? Write the balanced molecular equation for each reaction.
    a. potassium perchlorate
    b. cesium nitrate
    c. calcium iodide

50. Carminic acid, a naturally occurring red pigment extracted from the cochineal insect, contains only carbon, hydrogen, and oxygen. It was commonly used as a dye in the first half of the nineteenth century. It is 53.66% C and 4.09% H by mass. A titration required 18.02 mL of $0.0406\ M\ NaOH$ to neutralize 0.3602 g of carminic acid. Assuming that there is only one acidic hydrogen per molecule, what is the molecular formula of carminic acid?

51. What volume of each of the following acids will react completely with 50.00 mL of $0.100\ M\ NaOH$?
    a. $0.100\ M\ HCl$
    b. $0.100\ M\ H_2SO_3$ (two acidic hydrogens)
    c. $0.200\ M\ H_3PO_4$ (three acidic hydrogens)
    d. $0.150\ M\ HNO_3$
    e. $0.200\ M\ HC_2H_3O_2$ (one acidic hydrogen)
    f. $0.300\ M\ H_2SO_4$ (two acidic hydrogens)

52. A 30.0-mL sample of an unknown strong base is neutralized after the addition of 12.0 mL of a $0.150\ M\ HNO_3$ solution. If the unknown base concentration is $0.0300\ M$, give some possible identities for the unknown base.

53. A student had 1.00 L of a 1.00 M acid solution. Much to the surprise of the student, it took 2.00 L of 1.00 M NaOH solution to react completely with the acid. Explain why it took twice as much NaOH to react with all of the acid.

    In a different experiment, a student had 10.0 mL of 0.020 M HCl. Again, much to the surprise of the student, it took only 5.00 mL of 0.020 M strong base to react completely with the HCl. Explain why it took only half as much strong base to react with all of the HCl.

54. Sodium hydroxide solution is usually standardized by titrating a pure sample of potassium hydrogen phthalate (KHC$_8$H$_4$O$_4$, often abbreviated KHP), an acid with one acidic hydrogen and a molar mass of 204.22 g/mol. It takes 34.67 mL of a sodium hydroxide solution to titrate a 0.1082-g sample of KHP. What is the molarity of the sodium hydroxide?

55. A 0.500-L sample of H$_2$SO$_4$ solution was analyzed by taking a 100.0-mL aliquot and adding 50.0 mL of 0.213 M NaOH. After the reaction occurred, an excess of OH$^-$ ions remained in the solution. The excess base required 13.21 mL of 0.103 M HCl for neutralization. Calculate the molarity of the original sample of H$_2$SO$_4$. (Sulfuric acid has two acidic hydrogens.)

56. What volume of 0.0521 M Ba(OH)$_2$ is required to neutralize exactly 14.20 mL of 0.141 M H$_3$PO$_4$? Phosphoric acid contains three acidic hydrogens.

57. A 10.00-mL sample of vinegar, an aqueous solution of acetic acid (HC$_2$H$_3$O$_2$), is titrated with 0.5062 M NaOH, and 16.58 mL is required to reach the endpoint.
    a. What is the molarity of the acetic acid?
    b. If the density of the vinegar is 1.006 g/cm^3, what is the mass percent of acetic acid in the vinegar?

58. A student titrates an unknown amount of potassium hydrogen phthalate (KHP) with 20.46 mL of a 0.1000 M NaOH solution. KHP (molar mass = 204.22 g/mol) has one acidic hydrogen. How many grams of KHP were titrated (reacted completely) by the sodium hydroxide solution?

59. A student mixes four reagents together, thinking that the solutions will neutralize each other. The solutions mixed together are 50.0 mL of 0.100 M hydrochloric acid, 100.0 mL of 0.200 M of nitric acid, 500.0 mL of 0.0100 M calcium hydroxide, and 200.0 mL of 0.100 M rubidium hydroxide. Is the resulting solution neutral? If not, calculate the concentration of excess H$^+$ or OH$^-$ ions left in solution.

60. A 50.00-mL sample of an ammonia solution is analyzed by titration with HCl. The reaction is

$$\text{NH}_3(aq) + \text{H}^+(aq) \longrightarrow \text{NH}_4^+(aq)$$

    It took 39.47 mL of 0.0984 M HCl to titrate (react completely with) the ammonia. What is the concentration of the original ammonia solution?

61. Hydrochloric acid (75.0 mL of 0.250 M) is added to 225.0 mL of 0.0550 M Ba(OH)$_2$ solution. What is the concentration of the excess H$^+$ or OH$^-$ left in this solution?

62. A 2.20-g sample of an unknown acid (empirical formula = C$_3$H$_4$O$_3$) is dissolved in 1.0 L of water. A titration required 25.0 mL of 0.500 M NaOH to react completely with all the acid present. Assuming that the unknown acid has one acidic proton per molecule, what is the molecular formula of the unknown acid?

Oxidation–Reduction Reactions

63. Differentiate between the following terms.
    a. species reduced versus the reducing agent
    b. species oxidized versus the oxidizing agent
    c. oxidation state versus actual charge

64. How do you balance redox reactions by the oxidation states method?

65. Assign oxidation states to all atoms in each compound.
    a. KMnO$_4$ f. Fe$_3$O$_4$
    b. NiO$_2$ g. XeOF$_4$
    c. K$_4$Fe(CN)$_6$ (Fe only)   h. SF$_4$
    d. (NH$_4$)$_2$HPO$_4$ i. CO
    e. P$_4$O$_6$ j. C$_6$H$_{12}$O$_6$

66. Assign oxidation states to all of the following atoms.
    a. UO$_2$$^{2+}$ d. As$_4$ g. Na$_2$S$_2$O$_3$
    b. As$_2$O$_3$ e. HAsO$_2$ h. Hg$_2$Cl$_2$
    c. NaBiO$_3$ f. Mg$_2$P$_2$O$_7$ i. Ca(NO$_3$)$_2$

67. Assign oxidation states to all of the following atoms.
    a. SrCr$_2$O$_7$ g. PbSO$_3$
    b. CuCl$_2$ h. PbO$_2$
    c. O$_2$ i. Na$_2$C$_2$O$_4$
    d. H$_2$O$_2$ j. CO$_2$
    e. MgCO$_3$ k. (NH$_4$)$_2$Ce(SO$_4$)$_3$
    f. Ag   l. Cr$_2$O$_3$

68. Tell which of the following are oxidation–reduction reactions. For those that are, identify the oxidizing agent, the reducing agent, the substance being oxidized, and the substance being reduced.
    a. CH$_4$(g) + 2O$_2$(g) $\longrightarrow$ CO$_2$(g) + 2H$_2$O(g)
    b. Zn(s) + 2HCl(aq) $\longrightarrow$ ZnCl$_2$(aq) + H$_2$(g)
    c. Cr$_2$O$_7$$^{2-}$($aq$) + 2OH$^-$($aq$)
    $\longrightarrow$ 2CrO$_4$$^{2-}$($aq$) + H$_2$O($l$)
    d. O$_3$(g) + NO(g) $\longrightarrow$ O$_2$(g) + NO$_2$(g)
    e. 2H$_2$O$_2$(l) $\longrightarrow$ 2H$_2$O(l) + O$_2$(g)
    f. 2CuCl(aq) $\longrightarrow$ CuCl$_2$(aq) + Cu(s)
    g. HCl(g) + NH$_3$(g) $\longrightarrow$ NH$_4$Cl(s)
    h. SiCl$_4$(l) + 2H$_2$O(l) $\longrightarrow$ 4HCl(aq) + SiO$_2$(s)
    i. SiCl$_4$(l) + 2Mg(s) $\longrightarrow$ 2MgCl$_2$(s) + Si(s)

69. Many oxidation–reduction reactions can be balanced by inspection. Try to balance the following reactions by inspection. In each reaction, identify the substance reduced and the substance oxidized.
    a. Al(s) + HCl(aq) $\longrightarrow$ AlCl$_3$(aq) + H$_2$(g)
    b. CH$_4$(g) + S(s) $\longrightarrow$ CS$_2$(l) + H$_2$S(g)
    c. C$_3$H$_8$(g) + O$_2$(g) $\longrightarrow$ CO$_2$(g) + H$_2$O(l)
    d. Cu(s) + Ag$^+$(aq) $\longrightarrow$ Ag(s) + Cu^{2+}(aq)

70. Balance each of the following oxidation–reduction reactions by using the oxidation states method.
    a. C$_2$H$_6$(g) + O$_2$(g) $\longrightarrow$ CO$_2$(g) + H$_2$O(g)
    b. Mg(s) + HCl(aq) $\longrightarrow$ Mg^{2+}(aq) + Cl$^-$(aq) + H$_2$(g)
    c. Cu(s) + Ag$^+$(aq) $\longrightarrow$ Cu^{2+}(aq) + Ag(s)
    d. Zn(s) + H$_2$SO$_4$(aq) $\longrightarrow$ ZnSO$_4$(aq) + H$_2$(g)

71. Balance the following oxidation–reduction reactions, which occur in acidic solution, using the half-reaction method.
    a. $Cu(s) + NO_3^-(aq) \longrightarrow Cu^{2+}(aq) + NO(g)$
    b. $Cr_2O_7^{2-}(aq) + Cl^-(aq) \longrightarrow Cr^{3+}(aq) + Cl_2(g)$
    c. $Pb(s) + PbO_2(s) + H_2SO_4(aq) \longrightarrow PbSO_4(s)$
    d. $Mn^{2+}(aq) + NaBiO_3(s) \longrightarrow Bi^{3+}(aq) + MnO_4^-(aq)$
    e. $H_3AsO_4(aq) + Zn(s) \longrightarrow AsH_3(g) + Zn^{2+}(aq)$
    f. $As_2O_3(s) + NO_3^-(aq) \longrightarrow H_3AsO_4(aq) + NO(g)$
    g. $Br^-(aq) + MnO_4^-(aq) \longrightarrow Br_2(l) + Mn^{2+}(aq)$
    h. $CH_3OH(aq) + Cr_2O_7^{2-}(aq)$
    $$\longrightarrow CH_2O(aq) + Cr^{3+}(aq)$$

72. Balance the following oxidation–reduction reactions, which occur in basic solution, using the half-reaction method.
    a. $Al(s) + MnO_4^-(aq) \longrightarrow MnO_2(s) + Al(OH)_4^-(aq)$
    b. $Cl_2(g) \longrightarrow Cl^-(aq) + ClO^-(aq)$
    c. $NO_2^-(aq) + Al(s) \longrightarrow NH_3(g) + AlO_2^-(aq)$
    d. $MnO_4^-(aq) + S^{2-}(aq) \longrightarrow MnS(s) + S(s)$
    e. $CN^-(aq) + MnO_4^-(aq) \longrightarrow CNO^-(aq) + MnO_2(s)$

73. Balance the following equations by the half-reaction method.
    a. $Fe(s) + HCl(aq) \longrightarrow HFeCl_4(aq) + H_2(g)$
    b. $IO_3^-(aq) + I^-(aq) \xrightarrow{\text{Acidic}} I_3^-(aq)$
    c. $Cr(NCS)_6^{4-}(aq) + Ce^{4+}(aq)$
    $$\xrightarrow{\text{Acidic}} Cr^{3+}(aq) + Ce^{3+}(aq) + NO_3^-(aq) + CO_2(g) + SO_4^{2-}(aq)$$
    d. $CrI_3(s) + Cl_2(g)$
    $$\xrightarrow{\text{Basic}} CrO_4^{2-}(aq) + IO_4^-(aq) + Cl^-(aq)$$
    e. $Fe(CN)_6^{4-}(aq) + Ce^{4+}(aq)$
    $$\xrightarrow{\text{Basic}} Ce(OH)_3(s) + Fe(OH)_3(s) + CO_3^{2-}(aq) + NO_3^-(aq)$$

74. One of the classic methods for the determination of the manganese content in steel involves converting all the manganese to the deeply colored permanganate ion and then measuring the absorption of light. The steel is first dissolved in nitric acid, producing the manganese(II) ion and nitrogen dioxide gas. This solution is then reacted with an acidic solution containing periodate ion; the products are the permanganate and iodate ions. Write balanced chemical equations for both of these steps.

75. A solution of permanganate is standardized by titration with oxalic acid ($H_2C_2O_4$). It required 28.97 mL of the permanganate solution to react completely with 0.1058 g of oxalic acid. The unbalanced equation for the reaction is
    $$MnO_4^-(aq) + H_2C_2O_4(aq) \xrightarrow{\text{Acidic}} Mn^{2+}(aq) + CO_2(g)$$
    What is the molarity of the permanganate solution?

76. A 50.00-mL sample of solution containing Fe^{2+} ions is titrated with a 0.0216 M KMnO$_4$ solution. It required 20.62 mL of KMnO$_4$ solution to oxidize all the Fe^{2+} ions to Fe^{3+} ions by the reaction
    $$MnO_4^-(aq) + Fe^{2+}(aq) \xrightarrow{\text{Acidic}} Mn^{2+}(aq) + Fe^{3+}(aq)$$
    (Unbalanced)
    a. What was the concentration of Fe^{2+} ions in the sample solution?
    b. What volume of 0.0150 M K$_2$Cr$_2$O$_7$ solution would it take to do the same titration? The reaction is
    $$Cr_2O_7^{2-}(aq) + Fe^{2+}(aq) \xrightarrow{\text{Acidic}} Cr^{3+}(aq) + Fe^{3+}(aq)$$
    (Unbalanced)

77. The iron content of iron ore can be determined by titration with a standard KMnO$_4$ solution. The iron ore is dissolved in HCl, and all the iron is reduced to Fe^{2+} ions. This solution is then titrated with KMnO$_4$ solution, producing Fe^{3+} and Mn^{2+} ions in acidic solution. If it required 38.37 mL of 0.0198 M KMnO$_4$ to titrate a solution made from 0.6128 g of iron ore, what is the mass percent of iron in the iron ore?

78. The vanadium in a sample of ore is converted to VO^{2+}. The VO^{2+} ion is subsequently titrated with MnO_4^- in acidic solution to form $V(OH)_4^+$ and manganese(II) ion. To titrate the solution, 26.45 mL of 0.02250 M MnO$_4^-$ was required. If the mass percent of vanadium in the ore was 58.1%, what was the mass of the ore sample?

79. When hydrochloric acid reacts with magnesium metal, hydrogen gas and aqueous magnesium chloride are produced. What volume of 5.0 M HCl is required to react completely with 3.00 g of magnesium?

80. Triiodide ions are generated in solution by the following (unbalanced) reaction in acidic solution:
    $$IO_3^-(aq) + I^-(aq) \longrightarrow I_3^-(aq)$$
    Triiodide ion is determined by titration with a sodium thiosulfate (Na$_2$S$_2$O$_3$) solution. The products are iodide ion and tetrathionate ion (S$_4$O$_6^{2-}$).
    a. Balance the equation for the reaction of IO_3^- with I^- ions.
    b. A sample of 0.6013 g of potassium iodate was dissolved in water. Hydrochloric acid and solid potassium iodide were then added in excess. What is the minimum mass of solid KI and the minimum volume of 3.00 M HCl required to convert all of the IO_3^- ions to I_3^- ions?
    c. Write and balance the equation for the reaction of $S_2O_3^{2-}$ with I_3^- in acidic solution.
    d. A 25.00-mL sample of a 0.0100 M solution of KIO$_3$ is reacted with an excess of KI. It requires 32.04 mL of Na$_2$S$_2$O$_3$ solution to titrate the I_3^- ions present. What is the molarity of the Na$_2$S$_2$O$_3$ solution?
    e. How would you prepare 500.0 mL of the KIO$_3$ solution in part d, using pure, dry KIO$_3$?

Additional Exercises

81. A 230.-mL sample of a 0.275 M $CaCl_2$ solution is left on a hot plate overnight; the following morning, the solution is 1.10 M. What volume of water evaporated from the 0.275 M $CaCl_2$ solution?

82. Using the general solubility rules given in Table 4.1, name three reagents that would form precipitates with each of the following ions in aqueous solution. Write the net ionic equation for each of your suggestions.
    a. chloride ion   d. sulfate ion
    b. calcium ion   e. mercury(I) ion, Hg_2^{2+}
    c. iron(III) ion   f. silver ion

83. Consider a 1.50-g mixture of magnesium nitrate and magnesium chloride. After dissolving this mixture in water, 0.500 M silver nitrate is added dropwise until precipitate formation is complete. This mass of the white precipitate formed is 0.641 g.
    a. Calculate the mass percent of magnesium chloride in the mixture.
    b. Determine the minimum volume of silver nitrate that must have been added to ensure complete formation of the precipitate.

84. What mass of solid aluminum hydroxide can be produced when 50.0 mL of 0.200 M $Al(NO_3)_3$ is added to 200.0 mL of 0.100 M KOH?

85. In most of its ionic compounds, cobalt is either Co(II) or Co(III). One such compound, containing chloride ion and waters of hydration, was analyzed, and the following results were obtained. A 0.256-g sample of the compound was dissolved in water, and excess silver nitrate was added. The silver chloride was filtered, dried, and weighed, and it had a mass of 0.308 g. A second sample of 0.416 g of the compound was dissolved in water, and an excess of sodium hydroxide was added. The hydroxide salt was filtered and heated in a flame, forming cobalt(III) oxide. The mass of the cobalt(III) oxide formed was 0.145 g.
    a. What is the percent composition, by mass, of the compound?
    b. Assuming the compound contains one cobalt ion per formula unit, what is the formula?
    c. Write balanced equations for the three reactions described.

86. A mixture contains only NaCl and $Fe(NO_3)_3$. A 0.456-g sample of the mixture is dissolved in water, and an excess of NaOH is added, producing a precipitate of $Fe(OH)_3$. The precipitate is filtered, dried, and weighed. Its mass is 0.107 g. Calculate the following.
    a. the mass of iron in the sample
    b. the mass of $Fe(NO_3)_3$ in the sample
    c. the mass percent of $Fe(NO_3)_3$ in the sample

87. A mixture contains only sodium chloride and potassium chloride. A 0.1586-g sample of the mixture was dissolved in water. It took 22.90 mL of 0.1000 M $AgNO_3$ to completely precipitate all the chloride present. What is the composition (by mass percent) of the mixture?

88. Tris(pentafluorophenyl)borane, commonly known by its acronym BARF, is frequently used to initiate polymerization of ethylene or propylene in the presence of a catalytic transition metal compound. It is composed solely of C, F, and B; it is 42.23% C and 55.66% F by mass.
    a. What is the empirical formula of BARF?
    b. A 2.251-g sample of BARF dissolved in 347.0 mL of solution produces a 0.01267 M solution. What is the molecular formula of BARF?

89. A student added 50.0 mL of an NaOH solution to 100.0 mL of 0.400 M HCl. The solution was then treated with an excess of aqueous chromium(III) nitrate, resulting in formation of 2.06 g of precipitate. Determine the concentration of the NaOH solution.

90. In a 1-L beaker, 203 mL of 0.307 M ammonium chromate was mixed with 137 mL of 0.269 M chromium(III) nitrite to produce ammonium nitrite and chromium(III) chromate. Write the balanced chemical equation for the reaction occurring here. If the percent yield of the reaction was 88.0%, how much chromium(III) chromate was isolated?

91. It took 25.06 ± 0.05 mL of a sodium hydroxide solution to titrate a 0.4016-g sample of KHP (see Exercise 54). Calculate the concentration and uncertainty in the concentration of the sodium hydroxide solution. (See Appendix Section A1.5.) Neglect any uncertainty in the mass.

92. You wish to prepare 1 L of a 0.02 M potassium iodate solution. You require that the final concentration be within 1% of 0.02 M and that the concentration must be known accurately to the fourth decimal place. How would you prepare this solution? Specify the glassware you would use, the accuracy needed for the balance, and the ranges of acceptable masses of KIO_3 that can be used.

93. Citric acid, which can be obtained from lemon juice, has the molecular formula $C_6H_8O_7$. A 0.250-g sample of citric acid dissolved in 25.0 mL of water requires 37.2 mL of 0.105 M NaOH for complete neutralization. How many acidic hydrogens per molecule does citric acid have?

94. Acetylsalicylic acid is the active ingredient in aspirin. It took 35.17 mL of 0.5065 M sodium hydroxide to react completely with 3.210 g of acetylsalicylic acid. Acetylsalicylic acid has one acidic hydrogen. What is the molar mass of acetylsalicylic acid?

95. When organic compounds containing sulfur are burned, sulfur dioxide is produced. The amount of SO_2 formed can be determined by reaction with hydrogen peroxide:

$$H_2O_2(aq) + SO_2(g) \longrightarrow H_2SO_4(aq)$$

The resulting sulfuric acid is then titrated with a standard NaOH solution. A 1.325-g sample of coal is burned and the SO_2 collected in a solution of hydrogen peroxide. It took 28.44 mL of 0.1000 M NaOH to neutralize the resulting sulfuric acid. Calculate the mass percent of sulfur in the coal sample. Sulfuric acid has two acidic hydrogens.

Challenge Problems

96. The blood alcohol (C_2H_5OH) level can be determined by titrating a sample of blood plasma with an acidic potassium dichromate solution, resulting in the production of $Cr^{3+}(aq)$ and carbon dioxide. The reaction can be monitored because the dichromate ion ($Cr_2O_7^{2-}$) is orange in solution, and the Cr^{3+} ion is green. The unbalanced redox equation is

$$Cr_2O_7^{2-}(aq) + C_2H_5OH(aq) \longrightarrow Cr^{3+}(aq) + CO_2(g)$$

If 31.05 mL of 0.0600 M potassium dichromate solution is required to titrate 30.0 g of blood plasma, determine the mass percent of alcohol in the blood.

97. Zinc and magnesium metal each react with hydrochloric acid according to the following equations:

$$Zn(s) + 2HCl(aq) \longrightarrow ZnCl_2(aq) + H_2(g)$$
$$Mg(s) + 2HCl(aq) \longrightarrow MgCl_2(aq) + H_2(g)$$

A 10.00-g mixture of zinc and magnesium is reacted with the stoichiometric amount of hydrochloric acid. The reaction mixture is then reacted with 156 mL of 3.00 M silver nitrate to produce the maximum possible amount of silver chloride.
a. Determine the percent magnesium by mass in the original mixture.
b. If 78.0 mL of HCl was added, what was the concentration of the HCl?

98. A 10.00-g sample consisting of a mixture of sodium chloride and potassium sulfate is dissolved in water. This aqueous mixture then reacts with excess aqueous lead(II) nitrate to form 21.75 g of solid. Determine the mass percent of sodium chloride in the original mixture.

99. Consider the reaction of 19.0 g of zinc with excess silver nitrite to produce silver metal and zinc nitrite. The reaction is stopped before all the zinc metal has reacted and 29.0 g of solid metal is present. Calculate the mass of each metal in the 29.0-g mixture.

100. Consider an experiment in which two burets, Y and Z, are simultaneously draining into a beaker that initially contained 275.0 mL of 0.300 M HCl. Buret Y contains 0.150 M NaOH and buret Z contains 0.250 M KOH. The stoichiometric point in the titration is reached 60.65 minutes after Y and Z were started simultaneously. The total volume in the beaker at the stoichiometric point is 655 mL. Calculate the flow rates of burets Y and Z. Assume the flow rates remain constant during the experiment.

101. A sample is a mixture of KCl and KBr. When 0.1024 g of the sample is dissolved in water and reacted with excess silver nitrate, 0.1889 g of solid is obtained. What is the composition by mass percent of the mixture?

102. You made 100.0 mL of a lead(II) nitrate solution for lab but forgot to cap it. The next lab session you noticed that there was only 80.0 mL left (the rest had evaporated). In addition, you forgot the initial concentration of the solution. You decide to take 2.00 mL of the solution and add an excess of a concentrated sodium chloride solution. You obtain a solid with a mass of 3.407 g. What was the concentration of the original lead(II) nitrate solution?

103. Polychlorinated biphenyls (PCBs) have been used extensively as dielectric materials in electrical transformers. Because PCBs have been shown to be potentially harmful, analysis for their presence in the environment has become very important. PCBs are manufactured according to the following generic reaction:

$$C_{12}H_{10} + nCl_2 \xrightarrow[\text{catalyst}]{Fe} C_{12}H_{10-n}Cl_n + nHCl$$

This reaction results in a mixture of PCB products. The mixture is analyzed by decomposing the PCBs and then precipitating the resulting Cl^- as AgCl.
a. Develop a general equation that relates the average value of n to the mass of a given mixture of PCBs and the mass of AgCl produced.
b. A 0.1947-g sample of a commercial PCB yielded 0.4971 g of AgCl. What is the average value of n for this sample?

104. Consider reacting copper(II) sulfate with iron. Two possible reactions can occur, as represented by the following equations.

copper(II) sulfate(aq) + iron(s) $\longrightarrow$
copper(s) + iron(II) sulfate(aq)

copper(II) sulfate(aq) + iron(s) $\longrightarrow$
copper(s) + iron(III) sulfate(aq)

You place 87.7 mL of a 0.500 M solution of copper(II) sulfate in a beaker. You then add 2.00 g of iron filings to the copper(II) sulfate solution. After the reaction occurs, you isolate 2.27 g of copper. Which equation above describes the reaction that occurred? Support your answer.

105. A stream flows at a rate of 5.00×10^4 liters per second (L/s) upstream of a manufacturing plant. The plant discharges 3.50×10^3 L/s of water that contains 65.0 ppm HCl into the stream. (See Exercise 27 for definitions.)
a. Calculate the stream's total flow rate downstream from this plant.
b. Calculate the concentration of HCl in ppm downstream from this plant.
c. Further downstream, another manufacturing plant diverts 1.80×10^4 L/s of water from the stream for its own use. This plant must first neutralize the acid and does so by adding lime:

$$CaO(s) + 2H^+(aq) \longrightarrow Ca^{2+}(aq) + H_2O(l)$$

What mass of CaO is consumed in an 8.00-h work day by this plant?
d. The original stream water contained 10.2 ppm Ca^{2+}. Although no calcium was in the waste water from the first plant, the waste water of the second plant contains Ca^{2+} from the neutralization process. If 90.0% of the water used by the second plant is returned to the stream, calculate the concentration of Ca^{2+} in ppm downstream of the second plant.

106. Chromium has been investigated as a coating for steel cans. The thickness of the chromium film is determined by dissolving a sample of a can in acid and oxidizing the resulting Cr^{3+} to $Cr_2O_7^{2-}$ with the peroxydisulfate ion:

$$S_2O_8^{2-}(aq) + Cr^{3+}(aq) + H_2O(l) \longrightarrow Cr_2O_7^{2-}(aq) \\ + SO_4^{2-}(aq) + H^+(aq) \text{ (Unbalanced)}$$

After removal of unreacted $S_2O_8^{2-}$, an excess of ferrous ammonium sulfate $[Fe(NH_4)_2(SO_4)_2 \cdot 6H_2O]$ is added, reacting with $Cr_2O_7^{2-}$ produced from the first reaction. The unreacted Fe^{2+} from the excess ferrous ammonium sulfate is titrated with a separate $K_2Cr_2O_7$ solution. The reaction is:

$$H^+(aq) + Fe^{2+}(aq) + Cr_2O_7^{2-}(aq) \longrightarrow Fe^{3+}(aq) \\ + Cr^{3+}(aq) + H_2O(l) \text{ (Unbalanced)}$$

a. Write balanced chemical equations for the two reactions.
b. In one analysis, a 40.0-cm² sample of a chromium-plated can was treated according to this procedure. After dissolution and removal of excess $S_2O_8^{2-}$, 3.000 g of $Fe(NH_4)_2(SO_4)_2 \cdot 6H_2O$ was added. It took 8.58 mL of 0.0520 M $K_2Cr_2O_7$ solution to completely react with the excess Fe^{2+}. Calculate the thickness of the chromium film on the can. (The density of chromium is 7.19 g/cm³.)

107. One high-temperature superconductor has the general formula $YBa_2Cu_3O_x$. The copper is a mixture of Cu(II) and Cu(III) oxidation states. This mixture of oxidation states appears vital for high-temperature superconductivity to occur. A simple method for determining the average copper oxidation state has been reported [D. C. Harris, M. E. Hillis, and T. A. Hewston, *J. Chem. Educ.* 64, 847(1987)]. The described analysis takes place in two steps:

i. One superconductor sample is treated directly with I^-:

$$Cu^{2+}(aq) + I^-(aq) \longrightarrow CuI(s) + I_3^-(aq) \text{ (Unbalanced)}$$

$$Cu^{3+}(aq) + I^-(aq) \longrightarrow CuI(s) + I_3^-(aq) \text{ (Unbalanced)}$$

ii. A second superconductor sample is dissolved in acid, converting all copper to Cu(II). This solution is then treated with I^-:

$$Cu^{2+}(aq) + I^-(aq) \longrightarrow CuI(s) + I_3^-(aq) \text{ (Unbalanced)}$$

In both steps the I_3^- is determined by titrating with a standard sodium thiosulfate ($Na_2S_2O_3$) solution:

$$I_3^-(aq) + S_2O_3^{2-}(aq) \longrightarrow S_4O_6^{2-}(aq) + I^-(aq) \\ \text{(Unbalanced)}$$

a. Calculate the average copper oxidation states for materials with the formulas $YBa_2Cu_3O_{6.5}$, $YBa_2Cu_3O_7$, and $YBa_2Cu_3O_8$. Interpret your results in terms of a mixture of Cu(II) and Cu(III) ions, assuming that only Y^{3+}, Ba^{2+}, and O^{2-} are present in addition to the copper ions.
b. Balance the equations involved in the copper analysis.
c. A superconductor sample was analyzed by the above procedure. In step i, it took 37.77 mL of 0.1000 M $Na_2S_2O_3$ to react completely with the I_3^- generated from a 562.5-mg sample. In step ii, it took 22.57 mL of 0.1000 M $Na_2S_2O_3$ to react with the I_3^- generated by a 504.2-mg sample. Determine the formula of this superconductor sample (that is, find the value of x in $YBa_2Cu_3O_x$). Calculate the average oxidation state of copper in this material.

108. You are given a solid that is a mixture of Na_2SO_4 and K_2SO_4. A 0.205-g sample of the mixture is dissolved in water. An excess of an aqueous solution of $BaCl_2$ is added. The $BaSO_4$ that is formed is filtered, dried, and weighed. Its mass is 0.298 g. What mass of SO_4^{2-} ion is in the sample? What is the mass percent of SO_4^{2-} ion in the sample? What are the percent compositions by mass of Na_2SO_4 and K_2SO_4 in the sample?

109. A sample is a mixture of $AgNO_3$, $CuCl_2$, and $FeCl_3$. When a 1.0000-g sample of the mixture is dissolved in water and reacted with excess silver nitrate, 1.7809 g of precipitate forms. When a separate 1.0000-g sample of the mixture is treated with a reducing agent, all the metal ions in the mixture are reduced to pure metals. The total mass of pure metals produced is 0.4684 g. Calculate the mass percent of $AgNO_3$, $CuCl_2$, and $FeCl_3$ in the original mixture.

110. Three students were asked to find the identity of the metal in a particular sulfate salt. They dissolved a 0.1472-g sample of the salt in water and treated it with excess barium chloride, resulting in the precipitation of barium sulfate. After the precipitate had been filtered and dried, it weighed 0.2327 g.

Each student analyzed the data independently and came to different conclusions. Pat decided that the metal was titanium. Chris thought it was sodium. Randy reported that it was gallium. What formula did each student assign to the sulfate salt?

Look for information on the sulfates of gallium, sodium, and titanium in this text and reference books such as the *CRC Handbook of Chemistry and Physics*. What further tests would you suggest to determine which student is most likely correct?

Marathon Problems*

111. The formate ion, CHO_2^-, forms ionic compounds with many metal ions. Assume that 9.7416 g $M(CHO_2)_2$ (where M represents the atomic symbol for a particular metal) is dissolved in water. When a solution of 0.200 M sodium sulfate is added, a white precipitate forms. The sodium sulfate solution is added until no more precipitate forms; then a few milliliters are added in excess. The precipitate is filtered, dried, and weighed. It has a mass of 9.9392 g. The filtrate is saved for further use.

A potassium permanganate solution is standardized by dissolving 0.9234 g sodium oxalate in dilute sulfuric acid and then titrating with the potassium permanganate solution. The principal products of the reaction are manganese(II) ion and carbon dioxide gas. The titration requires 18.55 mL of the potassium permanganate solution to reach the endpoint, which is indicated by the first permanent, but barely perceptible, pink color of the permanganate ion.

The filtrate from the original reaction is diluted by pouring it into a 250-mL volumetric flask, diluting to the mark with water, and then mixing thoroughly. An aliquot consisting of 10.00 mL of this diluted solution is pipetted into a 125-mL Erlenmeyer flask, approximately 25 mL of water is added, and the solution is made basic. What volume of the standard permanganate solution will be needed to titrate this solution to the equivalence point? The principal products of the reaction are carbonate ion and manganese(IV) oxide. Identify M.

112. You have two 500.0-mL aqueous solutions. Solution A is a solution of a metal nitrate that is 8.246% nitrogen by mass. The ionic compound in solution B consists of potassium, chromium, and oxygen; chromium has an oxidation state of +6, and there are 2 potassiums and 1 chromium in the formula. The masses of the solutes in each of the solutions are the same. When the solutions are added together, a blood-red precipitate forms. After the reaction has gone to completion, you dry the solid and find that it has a mass of 331.8 g.

    a. Identify the ionic compounds in solution A and solution B.
    b. Identify the blood-red precipitate.
    c. Calculate the concentration (molarity) of all ions in the original solutions.
    d. Calculate the concentration (molarity) of all ions in the final solution.

*From James H. Burness, "The Use of "Marathon" Problems as Effective Vehicles for the Presentation of General Chemistry Lectures," Journal of Chemical Education, 68(11). Copyright © 1991 American Chemical Society. Reprinted by permission.

Chemical Kinetics

15 chapter

Soccer goalie catching a ball.

Mike Powell/Allsports Concepts/Getty Images

The applications of chemistry focus primarily on chemical reactions, and the commercial use of a reaction requires knowledge of several of its characteristics. A reaction is defined by its reactants and products, whose identities must be learned by experiment. Once the reactants and products are known, the equation for the reaction can be written and balanced, and stoichiometric calculations can be carried out. Another very important characteristic of a reaction is its spontaneity. Spontaneity refers to the *inherent tendency* for the process to occur; however, it implies nothing about speed. *Spontaneous does not mean fast.* There are many spontaneous reactions that are so slow that no apparent reaction occurs over a period of weeks or years at normal temperatures. For example, there is a strong inherent tendency for gaseous hydrogen and oxygen to combine to form water,

$$2H_2(g) + O_2(g) \longrightarrow 2H_2O(l)$$

but in fact the two gases can coexist indefinitely at 25°C. Similarly, the gaseous reactions

$$H_2(g) + Cl_2(g) \longrightarrow 2HCl(g)$$

$$N_2(g) + 3H_2(g) \longrightarrow 2NH_3(g)$$

are both highly likely to occur from a thermodynamic standpoint, but we observe no product formation under normal conditions. In addition, the process of changing diamond to graphite is spontaneous but is so slow that it is not detectable.

To be useful, reactions must occur at a reasonable rate. To produce the 20 million tons of ammonia needed each year for fertilizer, we cannot simply mix nitrogen and hydrogen gases at 25°C and wait for them to react. It is not enough to understand the stoichiometry and thermodynamics of a reaction; we must also understand the factors that govern the rate of the reaction. The area of chemistry that concerns reaction rates is called **chemical kinetics.**

One of the main goals of chemical kinetics is to understand the steps by which a reaction takes place. This series of steps is called the *reaction mechanism.* Understanding the mechanism allows us to find ways to facilitate the reaction. For example, the Haber process for the production of ammonia requires high temperatures to achieve commercially feasible reaction rates. However, even higher temperatures (and more cost) would be required without the use of iron oxide, which speeds up the reaction.

In this chapter we will consider the fundamental ideas of chemical kinetics. We will explore rate laws, reaction mechanisms, and simple models for chemical reactions.

15.1 | Reaction Rates

The kinetics of air pollution is discussed in Section 15.9.

To introduce the concept of reaction rate, we will consider the decomposition of nitrogen dioxide, a gas that causes air pollution. Nitrogen dioxide decomposes to nitric oxide and oxygen as follows:

$$2NO_2(g) \longrightarrow 2NO(g) + O_2(g)$$

Suppose in a particular experiment we start with a flask of nitrogen dioxide at room temperature, where it is stable indefinitely, and quickly heat it to 300°C, where it decomposes according to the preceding equation. We then measure the concentrations of nitrogen dioxide, nitric oxide, and oxygen over time as the nitrogen dioxide decomposes. The results of this experiment are summarized in Table 15.1, and the data are plotted in Fig. 15.1.

Table 15.1

Concentrations of Reactant and Products as a Function of Time for the Reaction $2NO_2(g) \longrightarrow 2NO(g) + O_2(g)$ (at 300°C)

Time (±1 s)	Concentration (mol/L)		
	NO_2	NO	O_2
0	0.0100	0	0
50	0.0079	0.0021	0.0011
100	0.0065	0.0035	0.0018
150	0.0055	0.0045	0.0023
200	0.0048	0.0052	0.0026
250	0.0043	0.0057	0.0029
300	0.0038	0.0062	0.0031
350	0.0034	0.0066	0.0033
400	0.0031	0.0069	0.0035

Figure 15.1
Starting with pure nitrogen dioxide at 300°C, the concentrations of nitrogen dioxide, nitric oxide, and oxygen are plotted versus time.

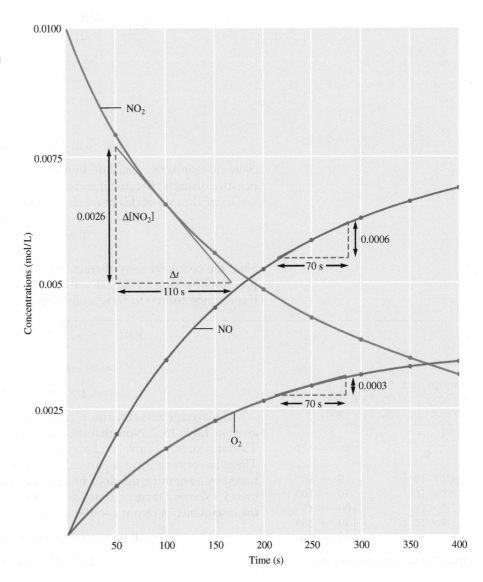

This definition of reaction rate assumes that the volume remains constant. A more general definition of reaction rate is the change in the number of moles per unit of volume per unit of time.

Note from these results that the concentration of the reactant (NO_2) decreases with time and that the concentrations of the products (NO and O_2) increase with time. Chemical kinetics deals with the speed at which these changes occur. The speed, or *rate*, of a process is defined as the change in a given quantity over a specific period of time. For chemical reactions the quantity that changes is the amount or concentration of a reactant or product. So the **reaction rate** of a chemical reaction is defined as the *change in concentration of a reactant or product per unit time:*

$$Rate = \frac{\text{concentration of A at time } t_2 - \text{concentration of A at time } t_1}{t_2 - t_1}$$

$$= \frac{\Delta[A]}{\Delta t}$$

where A represents a specific reactant or product and the square brackets indicate concentration in mol/L. As usual, the symbol Δ indicates a *change* in a given quantity.

Now let's calculate the average rate at which the concentration of NO_2 changes over the first 50 seconds of the reaction, using the data given in Table 15.1.

$$Rate = \frac{\Delta[NO_2]}{\Delta t}$$

$$= \frac{[NO_2]_{t=50} - [NO_2]_{t=0}}{50 \text{ s} - 0 \text{ s}}$$

$$= \frac{0.0079 \text{ mol/L} - 0.0100 \text{ mol/L}}{50 \text{ s}}$$

$$= -4.2 \times 10^{-5} \text{ mol L}^{-1} \text{ s}^{-1}$$

Note that since the concentration of NO_2 decreases with time, $\Delta[NO_2]$ is a negative quantity. Because it is customary to work with *positive* reaction rates, we define the rate of this particular reaction as

$$Rate = -\frac{\Delta[NO_2]}{\Delta t}$$

Since the concentrations of reactants always decrease with time, any rate expression involving a reactant will include a negative sign. The average rate of this reaction from 0 to 50 seconds is then

$$Rate = -\frac{\Delta[NO_2]}{\Delta t}$$

$$= -(-4.2 \times 10^{-5} \text{ mol L}^{-1} \text{ s}^{-1})$$

$$= 4.2 \times 10^{-5} \text{ mol L}^{-1} \text{ s}^{-1}$$

The average rates for this reaction during several other time intervals are given in Table 15.2. Note that the rate is not constant but decreases with time. The rates given in Table 15.2 are *average* rates over 50-second time intervals. The value of the rate at a particular time (the **instantaneous rate**) can be obtained by computing the slope of a line tangent to the curve at that point. Figure 15.1 shows a tangent drawn at $t = 100$ seconds. The *slope* of this line gives the instantaneous rate at $t = 100$ seconds:

$$Rate = -(\text{slope of the tangent line})$$

$$= 2.4 \times 10^{-5} \text{ mol L}^{-1} \text{ s}^{-1}$$

Table 15.2

Average Rate (in mol L^{-1} s^{-1}) of Decomposition of Nitrogen Dioxide as a Function of Time

$-\dfrac{\Delta[NO_2]}{\Delta t}$	Time Period (s)
4.2×10^{-5}	$0 \rightarrow 50$
2.8×10^{-5}	$50 \rightarrow 100$
2.0×10^{-5}	$100 \rightarrow 150$
1.4×10^{-5}	$150 \rightarrow 200$
1.0×10^{-5}	$200 \rightarrow 250$

Note: The *rate* decreases with time.

Femtochemistry

Some reactions occur very slowly, such as when a nail rusts. Others occur very rapidly, such as when methane is combusted in a Bunsen burner. Studying very fast reactions requires very special techniques, usually involving lasers—devices that produce high-energy bursts of light with very precise frequencies. The study of very fast reactions is one of the most important areas of chemical research, as demonstrated by the fact that the 1999 Nobel Prize in chemistry was awarded to Ahmed H. Zewail of the California Institute of Technology in Pasadena, California. Zewail's studies involve reactions that occur on the femtosecond (10^{-15} s) time scale—the time scale for molecular vibrations.

In Zewail's laboratory a strong laser flash of a few femtoseconds' duration shines on beams of molecules streaming into a vacuum chamber. The laser beam is tuned to excite all of the molecules to the same state, where they are vibrating in unison. Subsequent, weaker laser pulses monitor the concentrations of the reactants, intermediates, and products as the reaction occurs.

One reaction studied by Zewail is the decomposition of cyclobutane to two ethylene molecules:

A laser spectroscopy laboratory at the California Institute of Technology.

Zewail has shown that the reaction mechanism involves the breaking of one of the carbon–carbon bonds in cyclobutane to produce a tetramethylene intermediate:

Unpaired electrons

The intermediate exists for approximately 700 fs (700×10^{-15} s) and then decomposes into two ethylene molecules. Techniques similar to Zewail's approach (commonly called femtochemistry) are now widely used in chemical research and are being applied to problems such as elucidating the mechanism for energy conversion in chlorophyll (photosynthesis) and understanding the way human eyes detect light.

So far we have discussed the rate of this reaction only in terms of the reactant. The rate can also be defined in terms of the products. However, in doing so, we must take into account the coefficients in the balanced equation for the reaction because the stoichiometry determines the relative rates of the consumption of reactants and the generation of products. For example, in the reaction

$$2NO_2(g) \longrightarrow 2NO(g) + O_2(g)$$

both NO_2 and NO have a coefficient of 2, so NO is produced at the same rate as NO_2 is consumed. We can verify this from Fig. 15.1. Note that the curve for NO is the same shape as the curve for NO_2 except that it is inverted. This means that at any point in time the slope of the tangent to the curve for NO will be the negative of the slope to the curve for NO_2. (Verify this at the point $t = 100$ seconds on both curves.) In contrast, O_2 has a coefficient of 1, which means it is produced half as fast as NO, which has a coefficient of 2. That is, the rate of NO production is twice the rate of O_2 production.

We can also verify this fact from Fig. 15.1. For example, at $t = 250$ seconds,

Slope of the tangent to the NO curve = 8.6×10^{-6} mol L^{-1} s^{-1}

Slope of the tangent to the O$_2$ curve = 4.3×10^{-6} mol L^{-1} s^{-1}

The slope at $t = 250$ seconds on the NO curve is twice the slope of that point on the O_2 curve, showing that the rate of production of NO is twice that of O_2. The rate information can be summarized as follows:

$$\boxed{\begin{array}{c}\text{Rate of consumption}\\\text{of NO}_2\end{array}} = \boxed{\begin{array}{c}\text{rate of production}\\\text{of NO}\end{array}} = \boxed{2(\text{rate of production of O}_2)}$$

Because the reaction rate changes with time, and because the rate may be different for the various reactants and products (by factors that depend on the coefficients in the balanced equation), we must be very specific when we describe a rate for a chemical reaction.

15.2 | Rate Laws: An Introduction

Note that the term *reversible* has different meanings in kinetics and thermodynamics.

Chemical reactions are *reversible*. In our discussion of the decomposition of nitrogen dioxide, we have so far considered only the forward reaction:

$$2NO_2(g) \longrightarrow 2NO(g) + O_2(g)$$

However, the reverse reaction can also occur. As NO and O_2 accumulate, they can react to re-form NO_2:

$$O_2(g) + 2NO(g) \longrightarrow 2NO_2(g)$$

When gaseous NO_2 is placed in an otherwise empty container, the dominant reaction initially is

$$2NO_2(g) \longrightarrow 2NO(g) + O_2(g)$$

and the change in the concentration of NO_2 ($\Delta[NO_2]$) depends only on the forward reaction. However, after a period of time, enough products accumulate so that the reverse reaction becomes important. Now $\Delta[NO_2]$ depends on the *difference in the rates of the forward and reverse reactions*. This complication can be avoided if we study the rate of a reaction under conditions where the reverse reaction makes only a negligible contribution. Typically, this means that we study a reaction at a point soon after the reactants are mixed, before the products have had time to build up to significant levels.

Under conditions such that the reverse reaction can be neglected, the *reaction rate depends only on the concentrations of the reactants*. For the decomposition of nitrogen dioxide, we can write

$$\text{Rate} = k[NO_2]^n \tag{15.1}$$

Such an expression, which shows how the rate depends on the concentrations of reactants, is called a **rate law**. The proportionality constant k, called the **rate constant**, and n, called the **order** of the reactant, must both be determined by experiment. The order of a reactant can be positive or negative and can be an integer or a fraction. For the relatively simple reactions we will consider in this book, the orders will generally be positive integers.

Note two important points about Equation (15.1):

1. The concentrations of the products do not appear in the rate law because the reaction rate is being studied under conditions where the reverse reaction does not contribute to the overall rate.

2. The value of the exponent n must be determined by experiment; it cannot be written from the balanced equation.

Before we go further, we must define exactly what we mean by the term *rate* in Equation (15.1). In Section 15.1 we saw that reaction rate means a change in concentration per unit time. However, which reactant or product concentration do we choose in defining the rate? For example, for the decomposition of NO_2 to produce O_2 and NO considered in Section 15.1, we could define the rate in terms of any of these three species. However, since O_2 is produced only half as fast as NO_2, we must be careful to specify which species we are talking about in a given case. For instance, we might choose to define the reaction rate in terms of the consumption of NO_2:

$$\text{Rate} = -\frac{\Delta[NO_2]}{\Delta t} = -\frac{d[NO_2]}{dt} = k[NO_2]^n$$

where d indicates an infinitesimally small change. On the other hand, we could define the rate in terms of the production of O_2:

$$\text{Rate}' = \frac{d[O_2]}{dt} = k'[NO_2]^n$$

Note that because $2NO_2$ molecules are consumed for every O_2 molecule produced,

$$\text{Rate} = 2 \times \text{rate}'$$

or

$$k[NO_2]^n = 2k'[NO_2]^n$$

and

$$k = 2 \times k'$$

Thus the value of the rate constant depends on how the rate is defined.

In this text we will always be careful to define exactly what is meant by the rate for a given reaction so that there will be no confusion about which specific rate constant is being used.

Types of Rate Laws

Notice that the rate law we have used to this point expresses rate as a function of concentration. For example, for the decomposition of NO_2 we have defined the rate as

$$\text{Rate} = -\frac{d[NO_2]}{dt} = k[NO_2]^n$$

The terms *differential rate law* and *rate law* will be used interchangeably in this text.

which tells us (once we have determined the value of n) exactly how the rate depends on the concentration of the reactant NO_2. A rate law that expresses how the *rate depends on concentration* is called the **differential rate law,** but it is often simply called the **rate law.** Thus, when we use the term *rate law* in this text, we mean the expression that gives the rate as a function of concentration.

A second kind of rate law, the **integrated rate law,** will also be important in our study of kinetics. The integrated rate law expresses how the *concentrations depend on time.* As we will see, a given differential rate law is always related to a certain type of integrated rate law, and vice versa. That is, if we determine the differential rate law for a given reaction, we automatically know the form of the integrated rate law for the reaction. This means that once we determine either type of rate law for a reaction, we also know the other one.

Which rate law we choose to determine by experiment often depends on what types of data are easiest to collect. If we can conveniently measure how the rate changes as the concentrations are changed, we can readily determine the differential (rate/concentration) rate law. On the other hand, if it is more convenient to measure the concentration as a function of time, we can determine the form of the integrated (concentration/time) rate law. We will discuss how rate laws are actually determined in the next several sections.

Why are we interested in determining the rate law for a reaction? How does it help us? It helps us because we can work backward from the rate law to find the steps by which the reaction occurs. Most chemical reactions do not take place in a single step but result from a series of sequential steps. To understand a chemical reaction, we must learn what these steps are. For example, a chemist who is designing an insecticide may study the reactions involved in the process of insect growth to see what type of molecule may interrupt this series of reactions. Or an industrial chemist may be trying to make a reaction occur faster, using less expensive conditions. To accomplish this, he or she must know which step is slowest because it is that step that must be speeded up. Thus a chemist is usually not interested in a rate law for its own sake but for what it tells about the steps by which a reaction occurs. We will develop a process for finding the reaction steps later in this chapter.

Rate Laws

1. There are two types of rate laws:
   - The differential rate law (often called simply the rate law) shows how the rate of a reaction depends on concentrations.
   - The integrated rate law shows how the concentrations of species in the reaction depend on time.

2. Because we will typically consider reactions under conditions where the reverse reaction is unimportant, our rate laws will involve concentrations of reactants.

3. Because the differential and integrated rate laws for a given reaction are related in a well-defined way, the experimental determination of *either* of the rate laws is sufficient.

4. Experimental convenience usually dictates which type of rate law is determined experimentally.

5. Knowing the rate law for a reaction is important mainly because we can usually infer the individual steps involved in the reaction from the specific form of the rate law.

15.3 | Determining the Form of the Rate Law

Table 15.3

Concentration/Time Data for the Reaction $2N_2O_5(soln) \longrightarrow 4NO_2(soln) + O_2(g)$ (at 45°C)

$[N_2O_5]$ (mol/L)	Time (s)
1.00	0
0.88	200
0.78	400
0.69	600
0.61	800
0.54	1000
0.48	1200
0.43	1400
0.38	1600
0.34	1800
0.30	2000

The first step in understanding how a given chemical reaction occurs is to determine the *form* of the rate law. In this section we will explore ways to obtain the differential rate law for a reaction. First, we will consider the decomposition of dinitrogen pentoxide in carbon tetrachloride solution:

$$2N_2O_5(soln) \longrightarrow 4NO_2(soln) + O_2(g)$$

Data for this reaction at 45°C are listed in Table 15.3 and plotted in Fig. 15.2. In this reaction the oxygen gas escapes from the solution and thus does not react with the nitrogen dioxide, so we do not have to be concerned about the effects of the reverse reaction at any time over the life of the reaction. In other words, the reverse reaction is negligible at all times over the course of this reaction.

Evaluation of the reaction rates at N_2O_5 concentrations of 0.90 *M* and 0.45 *M*, by taking the slopes of the tangents to the curve at these points (Fig. 15.2), yields the following data:

$[N_2O_5]$	Rate (mol L^{-1} s^{-1})
0.90 *M*	5.4×10^{-4}
0.45 *M*	2.7×10^{-4}

Note that when $[N_2O_5]$ is halved, the rate is also halved. This means that the rate of this reaction depends on the concentration of N_2O_5 to the *first power*. In other words, the (differential) rate law for this reaction is

$$\text{Rate} = -\frac{d[N_2O_5]}{dt} = k[N_2O_5]$$

First order: Rate = *k*[A]. Doubling the concentration of A doubles the reaction rate.

Thus the reaction is *first order* in N_2O_5. Note that for this reaction the order is *not* the same as the coefficient of N_2O_5 in the balanced equation for the reaction. This reemphasizes the fact that the order of a particular reactant must be obtained by *observing* how the reaction rate depends on the concentration of that reactant.

We have seen that determining the instantaneous rate at two different reactant concentrations gives the following rate law for the decomposition of N_2O_5:

$$\text{Rate} = -\frac{d[A]}{dt} = k[A]$$

where A represents N_2O_5.

Figure 15.2

A plot of the concentration of N_2O_5 as a function of time for the reaction $2N_2O_5(soln) \longrightarrow 4NO_2(soln) + O_2(g)$ (at 45°C). Note that the reaction rate at $[N_2O_5] = 0.90$ *M* is twice that at $[N_2O_5] = 0.45$ *M*.

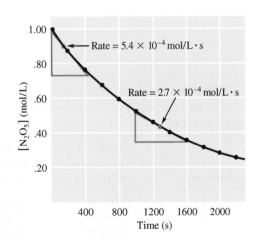

The value of the initial rate is determined for each experiment at the same value of t as close to $t = 0$ as possible.

Method of Initial Rates

The most common method for directly determining the form of the differential rate law for a reaction is the **method of initial rates.** The **initial rate** of a reaction is the instantaneous rate determined just after the reaction begins (just after $t = 0$). The idea is to determine the instantaneous rate before the initial concentrations of reactants have changed significantly. Several experiments are carried out using different initial concentrations, and the initial rate is determined for each run. The results are then compared to see how the initial rate depends on the initial concentrations. This procedure allows the form of the rate law to be determined. We will illustrate the method of initial rates by using the following reaction:

$$\text{NH}_4^+(aq) + \text{NO}_2^-(aq) \longrightarrow \text{N}_2(g) + 2\text{H}_2\text{O}(l)$$

Table 15.4 gives initial rates obtained from three experiments involving different initial concentrations of reactants.

The general form of the rate law for this reaction is

$$\text{Rate} = -\frac{d[\text{NH}_4^+]}{dt} = k[\text{NH}_4^+]^n[\text{NO}_2^-]^m$$

We can determine the values of n and m by observing how the initial rate depends on the initial concentrations of NH_4^+ and NO_2^-. In Experiments 1 and 2, where the initial concentration of NH_4^+ remains the same but where the initial concentration of NO_2^- doubles, the observed initial rate also doubles. Since

$$\text{Rate} = k[\text{NH}_4^+]^n[\text{NO}_2^-]^m$$

we have, for Experiment 1,

$$\text{Rate} = 1.35 \times 10^{-7}\ \text{mol L}^{-1}\ \text{s}^{-1} = k(0.100\ \text{mol/L})^n(0.0050\ \text{mol/L})^m$$

and for Experiment 2,

$$\text{Rate} = 2.70 \times 10^{-7}\ \text{mol L}^{-1}\ \text{s}^{-1} = k(0.100\ \text{mol/L})^n(0.010\ \text{mol/L})^m$$

Rates 1, 2, and 3 were determined at the same value of t (very close to $t = 0$).

The ratio of these rates is

$$\underbrace{\frac{\text{Rate 2}}{\text{Rate 1}} = \frac{2.70 \times 10^{-7}\ \text{mol L}^{-1}\ \text{s}^{-1}}{1.35 \times 10^{-7}\ \text{mol L}^{-1}\ \text{s}^{-1}}}_{2.00} = \frac{k(\cancel{0.100\ \text{mol/L}})^n(0.010\ \text{mol/L})^m}{k(\cancel{0.100\ \text{mol/L}})^n(0.0050\ \text{mol/L})^m}$$

$$= \underbrace{\frac{(0.010\ \text{mol/L})^m}{(0.0050\ \text{mol/L})^m}}_{(2.0)^m}$$

Table 15.4

Initial Rates from Three Experiments for the Reaction $\text{NH}_4^+(aq) + \text{NO}_2^-(aq) \longrightarrow \text{N}_2(g) + 2\text{H}_2\text{O}(l)$

Experiment	Initial Concentration of NH_4^+	Initial Concentration of NO_2^-	Initial Rate (mol L^{-1} s^{-1})
1	0.100 M	0.0050 M	1.35×10^{-7}
2	0.100 M	0.010 M	2.70×10^{-7}
3	0.200 M	0.010 M	5.40×10^{-7}

Thus $\qquad \dfrac{\text{Rate 2}}{\text{Rate 1}} = 2.00 = (2.0)^m$

which means the value of m is 1. The rate law for this reaction is first order in the reactant NO_2^-.

A similar analysis of the results for Experiments 2 and 3 yields the following ratio:

$$\frac{\text{Rate 3}}{\text{Rate 2}} = \frac{5.40 \times 10^{-7} \text{ mol L}^{-1}\text{ s}^{-1}}{2.70 \times 10^{-7} \text{ mol L}^{-1}\text{ s}^{-1}} = \frac{(0.200 \text{ mol/L})^n}{(0.100 \text{ mol/L})^n}$$

$$= 2.00 = \left(\frac{0.200}{1.100}\right)^n = (2.00)^n$$

The value of n is also 1.

We have shown that the values of n and m are both 1. Therefore, the rate law is

$$\text{Rate} = k[NH_4^+][NO_2^-]$$

This rate law is first order in both NO_2^- and NH_4^+. Note that it is merely a coincidence that n and m have the same values as the coefficients of NH_4^+ and NO_2^- in the balanced equation for the reaction.

The **overall reaction order** is the sum of n and m. For this reaction, $n + m = 2$. The reaction is second order overall.

The value of the rate constant (k) can now be calculated by using the results of *any* of the three experiments shown in Table 15.4. From the data for Experiment 1, we know that

$$\text{Rate} = k[NH_4^+][NO_2^-]$$

$$1.35 \times 10^{-7} \text{ mol L}^{-1}\text{ s}^{-1} = k(0.100 \text{ mol/L})(0.0050 \text{ mol/L})$$

Then

$$k = \frac{1.35 \times 10^{-7} \text{ mol L}^{-1}\text{ s}^{-1}}{(0.100 \text{ mol/L})(0.0050 \text{ mol/L})} = 2.7 \times 10^{-4} \text{ L mol}^{-1}\text{ s}^{-1}$$

Overall reaction order is the sum of the orders for each reactant. For a discussion of how this term can be misleading, see John C. Reeve, "Some Provocative Opinions on the Terminology of Chemical Kinetics," *J. Chem. Ed.* 68 (1991): 278.

EXAMPLE 15.1

The reaction between bromate ions and bromide ions in acidic aqueous solution is given by the following equation:

$$BrO_3^-(aq) + 5Br^-(aq) + 6H^+(aq) \longrightarrow 3Br_2(l) + 3H_2O(l)$$

Table 15.5 gives the results of four experiments involving this reaction. Using these data, determine the orders for all three reactants, the overall reaction order, and the value of the rate constant.

Table 15.5

The Results from Four Experiments to Study the Reaction
$BrO_3^-(aq) + 5Br^-(aq) + 6H^+(aq) \longrightarrow 3Br_2(l) + 3H_2O(l)$

Experiment	Initial Concentration of BrO_3^- (mol/L)	Initial Concentration of Br^- (mol/L)	Initial Concentration of H^+ (mol/L)	Measured Initial Rate (mol L^{-1} s^{-1})
1	0.10	0.10	0.10	8.0×10^{-4}
2	0.20	0.10	0.10	1.6×10^{-3}
3	0.20	0.20	0.10	3.2×10^{-3}
4	0.10	0.10	0.20	3.2×10^{-3}

A solution containing BrO_3^- ions being added to a solution containing Br^- ions to form Br_2.

Solution The general form of the rate law for this reaction is

$$\text{Rate} = k[BrO_3^-]^n[Br^-]^m[H^+]^p$$

We can determine the values of n, m, and p by comparing the rates from the various experiments. To determine the value of n, we use the results from Experiments 1 and 2, in which only $[BrO_3^-]$ changes:

$$\frac{\text{Rate 2}}{\text{Rate 1}} = \frac{1.6 \times 10^{-3} \text{ mol L}^{-1} \text{ s}^{-1}}{8.0 \times 10^{-4} \text{ mol L}^{-1} \text{ s}^{-1}}$$

$$= \frac{k(0.20 \text{ mol/L})^n(0.10 \text{ mol/L})^m(0.10 \text{ mol/L})^p}{k(0.10 \text{ mol/L})^n(0.10 \text{ mol/L})^m(0.10 \text{ mol/L})^p}$$

$$2.0 = \left(\frac{0.20 \text{ mol/L}}{0.10 \text{ mol/L}}\right)^n = (2.0)^n$$

Thus n is equal to 1.

To determine the value of m, we use the results from Experiments 2 and 3, in which only $[Br^-]$ changes:

$$\frac{\text{Rate 3}}{\text{Rate 2}} = \frac{3.2 \times 10^{-3} \text{ mol L}^{-1} \text{ s}^{-1}}{1.6 \times 10^{-3} \text{ mol L}^{-1} \text{ s}^{-1}}$$

$$= \frac{k(0.20 \text{ mol/L})^n(0.20 \text{ mol/L})^m(0.10 \text{ mol/L})^p}{k(0.20 \text{ mol/L})^n(0.10 \text{ mol/L})^m(0.10 \text{ mol/L})^p}$$

$$2.0 = \left(\frac{0.20 \text{ mol/L}}{0.10 \text{ mol/L}}\right)^m = (2.0)^m$$

Thus m is equal to 1.

To determine the value of p, we use the results from Experiments 1 and 4, in which $[BrO_3^-]$ and $[Br^-]$ are constant but $[H^+]$ changes:

$$\frac{\text{Rate 4}}{\text{Rate 1}} = \frac{3.2 \times 10^{-3} \text{ mol L}^{-1} \text{ s}^{-1}}{8.0 \times 10^{-4} \text{ mol L}^{-1} \text{ s}^{-1}}$$

$$= \frac{k(0.10 \text{ mol/L})^n(0.10 \text{ mol/L})^m(0.20 \text{ mol/L})^p}{k(0.10 \text{ mol/L})^n(0.10 \text{ mol/L})^m(0.10 \text{ mol/L})^p}$$

$$4.0 = \left(\frac{0.20 \text{ mol/L}}{0.10 \text{ mol/L}}\right)^p$$

$$4.0 = (2.0)^p = (2.0)^2$$

Thus p is equal to 2.

The rate of this reaction is first order in BrO_3^- and Br^- and second order in H^+. The overall reaction order is $n + m + p = 4$.

The rate law can now be written:

$$\text{Rate} = k[BrO_3^-][Br^-][H^+]^2$$

The value of the rate constant k can be calculated from the results of any of the four experiments. For Experiment 1 the initial rate is 8.0×10^{-4} mol L^{-1} s^{-1}, and $[BrO_3^-] = 0.100$ M, $[Br^-] = 0.100$ M, and $[H^+] = 0.100$ M. Using these values in the rate law gives

$$8.00 \times 10^{-4} \text{ mol L}^{-1} \text{ s}^{-1} = k(0.10 \text{ mol/L})(0.10 \text{ mol/L})(0.10 \text{ mol/L})^2$$

$$8.00 \times 10^{-4} \text{ mol L}^{-1} \text{ s}^{-1} = k(1.0 \times 10^{-4} \text{ mol}^4/\text{L}^4)$$

$$k = \frac{8.0 \times 10^{-4} \text{ mol L}^{-1} \text{ s}^{-1}}{1.0 \times 10^{-4} \text{ mol}^4/\text{L}^4}$$

$$= 8.00 \text{ L}^3 \text{ mol}^{-3} \text{ s}^{-1}$$

Check: Verify that the same value of k can be obtained from the results of the other experiments.

15.4 | The Integrated Rate Law

In the field of kinetics, the rate for this type of reaction is usually defined as

$$\text{Rate} = -\frac{1}{a}\frac{d[A]}{dt}$$

where a is the coefficient of A in the balanced equation. However, to avoid complications, we will leave out the factor of $1/a$, which simply changes the value of the rate constant by a factor of a.

The rate laws we have considered so far express the rate as a function of the reactant concentrations. It is also useful to be able to express the reactant concentrations as a function of time, given the (differential) rate law for the reaction. In this section we will show how this is done.

We will proceed by first looking at reactions involving a single reactant:

$$a\text{A} \longrightarrow \text{products}$$

all of which have a rate law of the form

$$\text{Rate} = -\frac{d[A]}{dt} = k[A]^n$$

We will develop the integrated rate laws individually for the cases $n = 1$ (first order), $n = 2$ (second order), and $n = 0$ (zero order).

First-Order Rate Laws

For the reaction

$$2\text{N}_2\text{O}_5(soln) \longrightarrow 4\text{NO}_2(soln) + \text{O}_2(g)$$

experiments show that the rate law is

$$\text{Rate} = -\frac{d[\text{N}_2\text{O}_5]}{dt} = k[\text{N}_2\text{O}_5]$$

Since the rate of this reaction depends on the concentration of N_2O_5 to the first power, it is a **first-order reaction.** This means that if the concentration of N_2O_5 in a flask were suddenly doubled, the rate of production of NO_2 and O_2 would also double. Using calculus, this differential rate law can be integrated, which yields the expression

$$\ln[\text{N}_2\text{O}_5] = -kt + \ln[\text{N}_2\text{O}_5]_0$$

where ln indicates the natural logarithm, t is the time, $[\text{N}_2\text{O}_5]$ is the concentration of N_2O_5 at time t, and $[\text{N}_2\text{O}_5]_0$ is the initial concentration of N_2O_5 (at $t = 0$, the start of the experiment). Note that such an equation, called the integrated rate law, expresses the *concentration of the reactant as a function of time.*

For a chemical reaction of the form

$$a\text{A} \longrightarrow \text{products}$$

where the kinetics are first order in [A], the differential rate law is of the form

$$\text{Rate} = -\frac{d[A]}{dt} = k[A]$$

and the **integrated first-order rate law** is

$$\ln[A] = -kt + \ln[A]_0 \qquad (15.2)$$

There are three important things to note about Equation (15.2):

1. The equation shows how the concentration of A depends on time. If the initial concentration of A and the value of the rate constant k are known, the concentration of A at any time can be calculated.

2. Equation (15.2) is of the form $y = mx + b$, where a plot of y versus x is a straight line with slope m and intercept b. In this case

$$y = \ln[A] \qquad x = t \qquad m = -k \qquad b = \ln[A]_0$$

The decomposition of N_2O_5 in solution to form NO_2 plus O_2 (bubbles). The brown gas above the solution is escaping NO_2.

An integrated rate law relates concentration to reaction time.

For a first-order reaction, a plot of ln[A] versus t is a straight line.

Thus, for a first-order reaction, plotting the natural logarithm of concentration versus time always gives a straight line. This fact is often used to test whether a reaction is first order. For the reaction of the type

$$aA \longrightarrow products$$

the *reaction is first order in A if a plot of ln[A] versus t is a straight line*. Conversely, if the plot is not a straight line, the reaction is not first order.

3. The integrated rate law for a first-order reaction can also be expressed in terms of the *ratio* of [A] and $[A]_0$ as follows:

$$\ln\left(\frac{[A]_0}{[A]}\right) = kt$$

EXAMPLE 15.2

The decomposition of N_2O_5 in the gas phase was studied at constant temperature:

$$2N_2O_5(g) \longrightarrow 4NO_2(g) + O_2(g)$$

The following results were collected:

$[N_2O_5]$ (mol/L)	Time (s)
0.1000	0
0.0707	50
0.0500	100
0.0250	200
0.0125	300
0.00625	400

Using these data, verify that the rate law is first order in $[N_2O_5]$, and calculate the value of the rate constant, where the rate $= -d[N_2O_5]/dt$.

Solution We can verify that the rate law is first order in $[N_2O_5]$ by constructing a plot of $\ln[N_2O_5]$ versus time. The values of $\ln[N_2O_5]$ at various times are given below, and the plot of $\ln[N_2O_5]$ versus time is shown in Fig. 15.3.

$\ln[N_2O_5]$	Time (s)
−2.303	0
−2.649	50
−2.996	100
−3.689	200
−4.382	300
−5.075	400

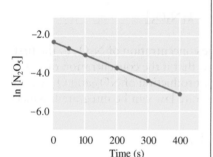

Figure 15.3
A plot of $\ln[N_2O_5]$ versus time.

The plot is a straight line, confirming that the reaction is first order in N_2O_5, since it follows the equation $\ln[N_2O_5] = -kt + \ln[N_2O_5]_0$.

Since the reaction is first order, the slope of the line equals $-k$. In this case

$$k = -(\text{slope}) = 6.93 \times 10^{-3} \text{ s}^{-1}$$

EXAMPLE 15.3

Using the data given in Example 15.2, calculate $[N_2O_5]$ 150. s after the start of the reaction.

Solution We know from Example 15.2 that $[N_2O_5] = 0.0500$ mol/L at 100 s and $[N_2O_5] = 0.0250$ mol/L at 200 s. Since 150 s is halfway between 100 s and

200 s, it is tempting to assume that we can use a simple average to obtain $[N_2O_5]$ at that time. This is incorrect because it is $\ln[N_2O_5]$, not $[N_2O_5]$, that depends directly on t. To calculate $[N_2O_5]$ after 150 s, we must use Equation (15.2):

$$\ln[N_2O_5] = -kt + \ln[N_2O_5]_0$$

where $t = 150.$ s, $k = 6.93 \times 10^{-3}$ s^{-1} (as determined in Example 15.2), and $[N_2O_5]_0 = 0.100$ mol/L.

$$\ln([N_2O_5])_{t=150} = -(6.93 \times 10^{-3} \text{ s}^{-1})(150. \text{ s}) + \ln(0.100)$$

$$= -1.040 - 2.303 = -3.343$$

$$[N_2O_5]_{t=150} = \text{antilog}(-3.343) = 0.0353 \text{ mol/L}$$

Note that this value of $[N_2O_5]$ is *not* halfway between 0.0500 mol/L and 0.0250 mol/L.

Half-Life of a First-Order Reaction

The time required for a reactant to reach half of its original concentration is called the **half-life of a reaction** and is designated by $t_{1/2}$. To illustrate this idea, we can calculate the half-life of the decomposition reaction discussed in Example 15.2. The data plotted in Fig. 15.4 show that the half-life for this reaction is 100 seconds. We can see this by considering the following numbers:

$[N_2O_5]$ (mol/L)	Time (s)		
0.1000	0		
0.0500	100	$\Delta t = 100$ s;	$\dfrac{[N_2O_5]_{t=100}}{[N_2O_5]_{t=0}} = \dfrac{0.050}{0.100} = \dfrac{1}{2}$
0.0250	200	$\Delta t = 100$ s;	$\dfrac{[N_2O_5]_{t=200}}{[N_2O_5]_{t=100}} = \dfrac{0.025}{0.050} = \dfrac{1}{2}$
0.0125	300	$\Delta t = 100$ s;	$\dfrac{[N_2O_5]_{t=300}}{[N_2O_5]_{t=200}} = \dfrac{0.0125}{0.0250} = \dfrac{1}{2}$

Note that it *always* takes 100 seconds for $[N_2O_5]$ to be halved in this reaction.

Figure 15.4
A plot of $[N_2O_5]$ versus time for the decomposition reaction of N_2O_5.

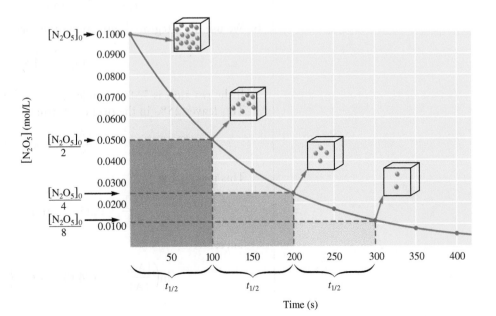

A general formula for the half-life of a first-order reaction can be derived from the integrated rate law for the general reaction,

$$a\text{A} \longrightarrow \text{products}$$

If the reaction is first order in [A],

$$\ln\left(\frac{[\text{A}]_0}{[\text{A}]}\right) = kt$$

By definition, when t = $t_{1/2}$, $[\text{A}] = \dfrac{[\text{A}]_0}{2}$

Then for $t = t_{1/2}$, the integrated rate law becomes

$$\ln\left(\frac{[\text{A}]_0}{[\text{A}]_0/2}\right) = kt_{1/2}$$

or $$\ln(2) = kt_{1/2}$$

Substituting the value of ln(2) and solving for $t_{1/2}$ gives

$$t_{1/2} = \frac{0.693}{k} \tag{15.3}$$

For a first-order reaction, $t_{1/2}$ is independent of the initial concentration.

This is the *general equation for the half-life of a first-order reaction*. Equation (15.3) can be used to calculate $t_{1/2}$ if k is known, or k if $t_{1/2}$ is known. Note that for a first-order reaction *the half-life does not depend on concentration.*

☕WL INTERACTIVE EXAMPLE 15.4

A certain first-order reaction has a half-life of 20.0 minutes.

a. Calculate the rate constant for this reaction.

b. How much time is required for this reaction to be 75% complete?

Solution

a. Solving Equation (15.3) for k gives

$$k = \frac{0.692}{t_{1/2}} = \frac{0.693}{20.0 \text{ min}} = 3.47 \times 10^{-2} \text{ min}^{-1}$$

b. We use the integrated rate law in the form

$$\ln\left(\frac{[\text{A}]_0}{[\text{A}]}\right) = kt$$

If the reaction is 75% complete, 75% of the reactant has been consumed. This leaves 25% in the original form:

$$\frac{[\text{A}]}{[\text{A}]_0} \times 100 = 25$$

This means that

$$\frac{[\text{A}]}{[\text{A}]_0} = 0.25 \quad \text{and} \quad \frac{[\text{A}]_0}{[\text{A}]} = 4.0$$

Therefore,

$$\ln\left(\frac{[\text{A}]_0}{[\text{A}]}\right) = \ln(4.0) = kt = \left(\frac{3.47 \times 10^{-2}}{\text{min}}\right)t$$

and $t = 40.$ min

Thus it takes 40. minutes for this particular reaction to reach 75% completion.
   Let's consider another way of solving this problem by using the definition of half-life. After one half-life the reaction has gone 50% to completion. If the initial concentration were 1.0 mol/L, after one half-life the concentration would be 0.50 mol/L. One more half-life would produce a concentration of 0.25 mol/L. Comparing 0.25 mol/L with the original 1.0 mol/L shows that 25% of the reactant is left after two half-lives. This is a general result. (What percentage of reactant remains after three half-lives?) Two half-lives for this reaction is 2(20.0 min), or 40.0 minutes, which agrees with the above answer.

Second-Order Rate Laws

For a general reaction involving a single reactant,

$$aA \longrightarrow \text{products}$$

Second order: Rate = $k[A]^2$. Doubling the concentration of A quadruples the reaction rate; tripling the concentration of A increases the rate by nine times.

which is second order in A, the rate law can be defined as

$$\text{Rate} = -\frac{d[A]}{dt} = k[A]^2 \tag{15.4}$$

Integration of this differential rate law yields the **integrated second-order rate law:**

$$\frac{1}{[A]} = kt + \frac{1}{[A]_0} \tag{15.5}$$

Note the following characteristics of Equation (15.5):

For a second-order reaction, a plot of $1/[A]$ versus t is linear.

1. A plot of $1/[A]$ versus t will produce a straight line with a slope equal to k.
2. Equation (15.5) shows how [A] depends on time and can be used to calculate [A] at any time t, provided k and $[A]_0$ are known.

   When one half-life of a second-order reaction has elapsed ($t = t_{1/2}$), by definition, $[A] = [A]_0/2$. Equation (15.5) then becomes

$$\frac{1}{\dfrac{[A]_0}{2}} = kt_{1/2} + \frac{1}{[A]_0}$$

and $\dfrac{1}{[A]_0} = kt_{1/2}$

Solving for $t_{1/2}$ gives *the expression for the half-life of a second-order reaction:*

$$t_{1/2} = \frac{1}{k[A]_0} \tag{15.6}$$

EXAMPLE 15.5

When two identical molecules combine, the resulting molecule is called a dimer.

Butadiene reacts to form its dimer according to the equation

$$2C_4H_6(g) \longrightarrow C_8H_{12}(g)$$

The following data were collected for this reaction at a given temperature:

[C_4H_6] (mol/L)	Time (±1 s)
0.01000	0
0.00625	1000
0.00476	1800
0.00370	2800
0.00313	3600
0.00270	4400
0.00241	5200
0.00208	6200

a. Is this reaction first order or second order?
b. What is the value of the rate constant for the reaction?
c. What is the half-life for the reaction under the conditions of this experiment?

Solution

a. To decide whether the rate law for this reaction is first order or second order, we must see whether the plot of $\ln[C_4H_6]$ versus time is a straight line (first order) or the plot of $1/[C_4H_6]$ versus time is a straight line (second order). The data necessary to make these plots are as follows:

t (s)	$\dfrac{1}{[C_4H_6]}$	$\ln[C_4H_6]$
0	100	−4.605
1000	160	−5.075
1800	210	−5.348
2800	270	−5.599
3600	319	−5.767
4400	370	−5.915
5200	415	−6.028
6200	481	−6.175

The resulting plots are shown in Fig. 15.5. Since the $\ln[C_4H_6]$ versus t plot is not a straight line, the reaction is *not* first order. The reaction is,

Butadiene (C_4H_6)

Figure 15.5
(a) A plot of $\ln[C_4H_6]$ versus t.
(b) A plot of $1/[C_4H_6]$ versus t.

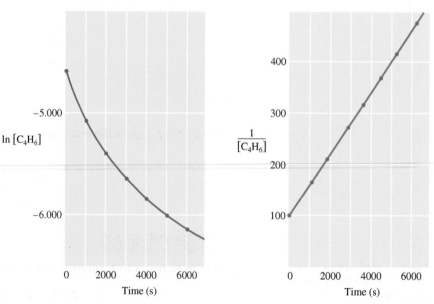

however, second order, as shown by the linearity of the $1/[C_4H_6]$ versus t plot. Thus we can now write the rate law for this second-order reaction:

$$\text{Rate} = -\frac{d[C_4H_6]}{dt} = k[C_4H_6]^2$$

b. For a second-order reaction, a plot of $1/[C_4H_6]$ versus t produces a straight line with slope k. In terms of the standard equation for a straight line, $y = mx + b$, we have $y = 1/[C_4H_6]$ and $x = t$. In this case,

$$k = \text{slope} = 6.14 \times 10^{-2} \text{ L mol}^{-1} \text{ s}^{-1}$$

c. The expression for the half-life of a second-order reaction is

$$t_{1/2} = \frac{1}{k[A]_0}$$

In this case $k = 6.14 \times 10^{-2} \text{ L mol}^{-1} \text{ s}^{-1}$ (from part b) and $[A]_0 = [C_4H_6]_0 = 0.01000 \text{ M}$ (the concentration at $t = 0$). Thus

$$t_{1/2} = \frac{1}{(6.14 \times 10^{-2} \text{ L mol}^{-1} \text{ s}^{-1})(1.000 \times 10^{-2} \text{ mol/L})}$$

$$= 1.63 \times 10^3 \text{ s}$$

The initial concentration of C_4H_6 is halved in 1630 s.

For a second-order reaction, $t_{1/2}$ depends on $[A]_0$. For a first-order reaction, $t_{1/2}$ is independent of $[A]_0$.

It is important to recognize the difference between the half-life for a first-order reaction and the half-life for a second-order reaction. For a second-order reaction, $t_{1/2}$ depends on both k and $[A]_0$; for a first-order reaction, $t_{1/2}$ depends only on k. For a first-order reaction, a constant time is required to reduce the concentration of the reactant by half, and then by half again, and so on, as the reaction proceeds. In Example 15.5 we saw that this is *not* true for a second-order reaction. For that second-order reaction, we found that the first half-life (the time required to go from $[C_4H_6] = 0.010$ M to $[C_4H_6] = 0.0050$ M) is 1630 seconds. We can estimate the second half-life from the concentration data as a function of time. Note that to reach 0.0024 M C_4H_6 (approximately 0.0050/2) requires 5200 seconds of reaction time. Thus, to get from 0.0050 M C_4H_6 to 0.0024 M C_4H_6 takes 3570 seconds (5200 − 1630). The second half-life is much longer than the first. This pattern is characteristic of second-order reactions. In fact, *for a second-order reaction, each successive half-life is double the preceding one* (provided the effects of the reverse reaction can be ignored, as we are assuming here). Prove this to yourself by examining the equation $t_{1/2} = 1/(k[A]_0)$.

For each successive half-life, $[A]_0$ is halved. Since $t_{1/2} = 1/k[A]_0$, $t_{1/2}$ doubles.

Zero-Order Rate Laws

Most reactions involving a single reactant show either first-order or second-order kinetics. However, sometimes such a reaction can be a **zero-order reaction**. The rate law for a zero-order reaction is

$$\text{Rate} = k[A]_0 = k(1) = k$$

A zero-order reaction has a constant rate.

For a zero-order reaction, the rate is a constant. It does not change with concentration as it does for first-order or second-order reactions.

The **integrated rate law for a zero-order reaction** is

$$[A] = -kt + [A]_0 \tag{15.7}$$

In this case a plot of $[A]$ versus t gives a straight line of slope $-k$, as shown in Fig. 15.6.

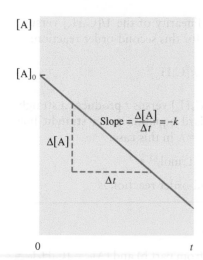

Figure 15.6
A plot of [A] versus t for a zero-order reaction.

The expression for the half-life of a zero-order reaction can be obtained from the integrated rate law. By definition, $[A] = [A]_0/2$ when $t = t_{1/2}$, so

$$\frac{[A]_0}{2} = -kt_{1/2} + [A]_0$$

or

$$kt_{1/2} = \frac{[A]_0}{2}$$

Solving for $t_{1/2}$ gives

$$t_{1/2} = \frac{[A]_0}{2k} \tag{15.8}$$

Zero-order reactions are most often encountered when a substance such as a metal surface or an enzyme is required for the reaction to occur. For example, the decomposition reaction

$$2N_2O(g) \longrightarrow 2N_2(g) + O_2(g)$$

occurs on a hot platinum surface. When the platinum surface is completely covered with N_2O molecules, an increase in the concentration of N_2O has no effect on the rate, since only those N_2O molecules on the surface can react. Under these conditions, *the rate is a constant* because it is controlled by what happens on the platinum surface rather than by the total concentration of N_2O, as illustrated in Fig. 15.7. This reaction can also occur at high temperatures with no platinum surface present, but under these conditions it is not zero order.

Integrated Rate Laws for Reactions with More Than One Reactant

So far we have considered the integrated rate laws for simple reactions with only one reactant. Special techniques are required to deal with more complicated reactions. For example, consider the reaction

$$BrO_3^-(aq) + 5Br^-(aq) + 6H^+(aq) \longrightarrow 3Br_2(l) + 3H_2O(l)$$

From experimental evidence we know that the rate law is

$$\text{Rate} = -\frac{d[BrO_3^-]}{dt} = k[BrO_3^-][Br^-][H^+]^2$$

Suppose we run this reaction under conditions where $[BrO_3^-]_0 = 1.0 \times 10^{-3}\ M$, $[Br^-]_0 = 1.0\ M$, and $[H^+]_0 = 1.0\ M$. As the reaction proceeds, $[BrO_3^-]$

Figure 15.7
The decomposition reaction
$2N_2O(g) \longrightarrow 2N_2(g) + O_2(g)$ takes place on a platinum surface. Although [N₂O] is twice as great in (b) as in (a), the rate of decomposition of N₂O is the same in both cases since the platinum surface can accommodate only a certain number of molecules. As a result, this reaction is zero order.

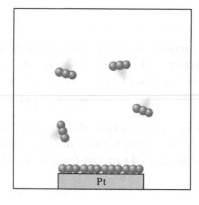

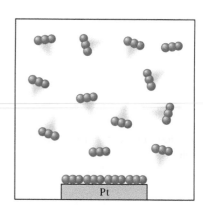

N₂O

(a)   (b)

decreases significantly, but because the Br^- ion and H^+ ion concentrations are so large initially, relatively little of either of these two reactants is consumed. Thus $[Br^-]$ and $[H^+]$ remain *approximately constant*. In other words, under the conditions where the Br^- ion and H^+ ion concentrations are much larger than the BrO_3^- ion concentration, we can assume that throughout the reaction

$$[Br^-] = [Br^-]_0 \quad \text{and} \quad [H^+] = [H^+]_0$$

This means that the rate law can be written as

$$\text{Rate} = k[Br^-]_0[H^+]_0^2[BrO_3^-] = k'[BrO_3^-]$$

where, since $[Br^-]_0$ and $[H^+]_0$ are constant,

$$k' = k[Br^-]_0[H^+]_0^2$$

The rate law

$$\text{Rate} = k'[BrO_3^-]$$

is first order. However, since this rate law was obtained by simplifying a more complicated one, it is called a **pseudo-first-order rate law.** Under the conditions of this experiment, a plot of $\ln[BrO_3^-]$ versus t gives a straight line with a slope equal to $-k'$. Since $[Br^-]_0$ and $[H^+]_0$ are known, the value of k can be calculated from the equation

$$k' = k[Br^-]_0[H^+]_0^2$$

which can be rearranged to give

$$k = \frac{k'}{[Br^-]_0[H^+]_0^2}$$

Note that the kinetics of complicated reactions can be studied by observing the behavior of one reactant at a time. If the concentration of one reactant is much smaller than the concentrations of the others, then the amounts of those reactants present in large concentrations will not change significantly and can be regarded as constant. The change in concentration with time of the reactant present in a relatively small amount can then be used to determine the order of the reaction in that component. This technique allows us to determine rate laws for complex reactions.

15.5 | Rate Laws: A Summary

In the last several sections, we have developed the following important points:

1. To simplify the rate laws for reactions, we have always assumed that the rate is being studied under conditions where only the forward reaction is important. This produces rate laws that contain only reactant concentrations.

2. There are two types of rate laws.

   a. The differential rate law (often called *the rate law*) shows how the rate depends on the concentrations. The forms of the rate laws for zero-order, first-order, and second-order kinetics of reactions with a single reactant are shown in Table 15.6.

   b. The integrated rate law shows how concentration depends on time. The integrated rate laws corresponding to zero-order, first-order, and second-order kinetics of reactions with a single reactant are given in Table 15.6.

3. Whether we determine the differential rate law or the integrated rate law depends on the type of data that can be collected conveniently and accurately. Once we have experimentally determined either type of rate law for a given reaction, we can write the other rate law.

Table 15.6

Summary of the Kinetics for Reactions of the Type $aA \longrightarrow$ Products That Are Zero, First, or Second Order in [A]

	Order		
	Zero	First	Second
Rate law	Rate $= k$	Rate $= k[A]$	Rate $= k[A]^2$
Integrated rate law	$[A] = -kt + [A]_0$	$\ln[A] = -kt + \ln[A]_0$	$\dfrac{1}{[A]} = kt + \dfrac{1}{[A]_0}$
Plot needed to give a straight line	$[A]$ versus t	$\ln[A]$ versus t	$\dfrac{1}{[A]}$ versus t
Relationship of rate constant to the slope of the straight line	Slope $= -k$	Slope $= -k$	Slope $= k$
Half-life	$t_{1/2} = \dfrac{[A]_0}{2k}$	$t_{1/2} = \dfrac{0.693}{k}$	$t_{1/2} = \dfrac{1}{k[A]_0}$

4. The most common method for experimentally determining the differential rate law is the method of initial rates. In this method several experiments are run at different initial concentrations, and the instantaneous rates are determined for each at the same value of t as close to $t = 0$ as possible. The point is to evaluate the rate before the concentrations change significantly from the initial values. From a comparison of the initial rates and the initial concentrations, the dependence of the rate on the concentrations of various reactants can be obtained—that is, the order in each reactant can be determined.

5. To experimentally determine the integrated rate law for a reaction, we measure concentrations at various values of t as the reaction proceeds. Then we see which integrated rate law correctly fits the data. Typically, this is done by ascertaining which type of plot gives a straight line. This information is described for reactions with a single reactant in Table 15.6. Once the correct straight-line plot is found, the correct integrated rate law can be chosen and the value of k obtained from the slope. Also, the (differential) rate law for the reaction can then be written.

6. The integrated rate law for a reaction that involves several reactants can be treated by choosing conditions such that the concentration of only one reactant varies in a given experiment. This is done by having the concentration of one reactant be small compared with the concentrations of all the others, causing a rate law such as

$$\text{Rate} = k[A]^n[B]^m[C]^p$$

to reduce to $\qquad\qquad\text{Rate} = k'[A]^n$

where $k' = k[B]_0^m[C]_0^p$, $[B]_0 \gg [A]_0$, and $[C]_0 \gg [A]_0$. The value of n is obtained by determining whether a plot of $[A]$ versus t is linear ($n = 0$), a plot of $\ln[A]$ versus t is linear ($n = 1$), or a plot of $1/[A]$ versus t is linear ($n = 2$). The value of k' is determined from the slope of the appropriate plot. The values of m, p, and k are found by determining the value of k' at several different concentrations of B and C.

15.6 │ Reaction Mechanisms

Most chemical reactions occur by a *series of steps* called the **reaction mechanism.** To understand a reaction, we must know its mechanism, and one of the main purposes for studying kinetics is to learn as much as possible about the steps involved in a reaction. In this section we explore some of the fundamental characteristics of reaction mechanisms.

Consider the reaction between nitrogen dioxide and carbon monoxide:

$$NO_2(g) + CO(g) \longrightarrow NO(g) + CO_2(g)$$

The rate law for this reaction is known from experiment to be

$$\text{Rate} = k[NO_2]^2$$

As we will see below, this reaction is more complicated than it appears from the balanced equation. This is quite typical; the balanced equation for a reaction tells us the reactants, the products, and the stoichiometry but gives no direct information about the reaction mechanism.

For the reaction between nitrogen dioxide and carbon monoxide, the mechanism is thought to involve the steps shown in Fig. 15.8, where k_1 and k_2 are the rate constants of the individual reactions. In this mechanism gaseous NO_3 is an **intermediate,** a species that is neither a reactant nor a product but that is formed and consumed during the reaction sequence (Fig. 15.8).

Each of these reactions is called an **elementary step,** *a reaction whose rate law can be written from its molecularity.* **Molecularity** is defined as the number of species that must collide to produce the reaction indicated by that step. A reaction involving one molecule is called a **unimolecular step.** Reactions involving the collision of two and three species are termed **bimolecular** and **termolecular,** respectively. Termolecular steps are quite rare because the probability of three molecules colliding simultaneously is very small. Examples of these three types of elementary steps and the corresponding rate laws are shown in Table 15.7. Note from Table 15.7 that the rate law for an elementary step follows *directly* from the molecularity of that step. For example, for a bimolecular step, the rate law is always second order, either of the form $k[A]^2$ for a step with a single reactant or of the form $k[A][B]$ for a step involving two reactants.

We can now define a reaction mechanism more precisely. It is a *series of elementary steps that must satisfy two requirements:*

1. The sum of the elementary steps must give the overall balanced equation for the reaction.

2. The mechanism must agree with the experimentally determined rate law.

A balanced equation does not tell us how the reactants become products.

An intermediate is formed in one step and consumed in a subsequent step and so is never seen as a product.

The prefix uni- means "one," bi- means "two," and ter- means "three."

A unimolecular elementary step is always first order, a bimolecular step is always second order, and so on.

Figure 15.8
A molecular representation of the elementary steps in the reaction of NO_2 and CO.

Step 1

Step 2

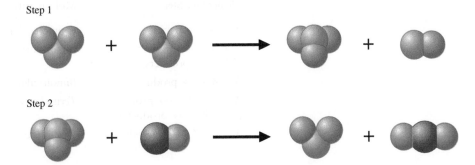

Chemical Insights | Ultracold Reactions

More than 200 years ago the work of Charles Gay-Lussac led to the suspicion that an absolute low temperature exists for matter. In recent years scientists have come close to cooling matter to 0 K. Temperatures of about 10^{-7} K have been achieved by *laser cooling* in which a laser beam is directed against a beam of atoms, dramatically slowing the movement of atoms to near zero.

It is extremely difficult to slow atoms to near absolute zero, but it is even harder to cool molecules to these temperatures. One strategy is to begin with "hot" diatomic molecules and then cool them down using lasers. However, as the velocities of these molecules decrease, they retain high levels of vibrational energy that ultimately cause the molecules to break apart. The other strategy is to cool atoms and then try to get them to form molecules. This is the approach used by physicist Jun Ye and his coworkers at the University of Colorado in Boulder. Ye and his research group were able to form molecules of potassium and rubidium at ultracold temperatures and then encourage the molecules to emit their excess vibrational energy using a laser pulse to produce stable molecules at about 2×10^{-7} K. Because the K-Rb molecule is slightly polar (the potassium atom has a slightly greater electronegativity value than the rubidium atom, which leads to a dipole $^{\delta-}$K-Rb$^{\delta+}$), the mole-

cules can be manipulated by an electric field. Ye and his coworkers have observed the reaction

$$2\text{K-Rb} \longrightarrow \text{K}_2 + \text{Rb}_2$$

at these ultralow temperatures. Because the motions of the molecules are so slow at these temperatures, the researchers have been able to study the details of this reaction. For example, they found that the reaction occurs only when the molecules are head to tail and that the reaction is greatly speeded up when the electric field around the molecule is increased. They also observed that the molecules react with greater certainty when they are within 1 nm of each other.

Theoretical studies by Paul Julienne at the National Institute of Standards and Technology in Maryland and Zbigniew Idziaczek at the University of Warsaw predict how the molecules find each other so that they can react. At these low temperatures, the molecules behave more like diffuse waves than discrete spots, and the waves can spread beyond the individual molecules for hundreds of nanometers. These waves affect how the molecules close in on each other to react. As more of these studies are done at ultracold temperatures, we are certain to learn a lot more about how molecules react with each other.

Table 15.7

Examples of Elementary Steps and Corresponding Rate Laws

Elementary Step	Molecularity	Rate Law
A $\longrightarrow$ products	*Uni*molecular	Rate = $k[\text{A}]$
A + A $\longrightarrow$ products (2A $\longrightarrow$ products)	*Bi*molecular	Rate = $k[\text{A}]^2$
A + B $\longrightarrow$ products	*Bi*molecular	Rate = $k[\text{A}][\text{B}]$
A + A + B $\longrightarrow$ products (2A + B $\longrightarrow$ products)	*Ter*molecular	Rate = $k[\text{A}]^2[\text{B}]$
A + B + C $\longrightarrow$ products	*Ter*molecular	Rate = $k[\text{A}][\text{B}][\text{C}]$

Christopher Rose-Petruck Studies Ultrafast X-ray Spectroscopy

Christopher Rose-Petruck, Associate Professor of Chemistry at Brown University, was educated in Germany, receiving his Ph.D. at the Ludwig-Maximilians University in Munich.

Professor Rose-Petruck's research focuses on the detailed mechanisms of certain important reactions that occur in solution. Because molecules undergo structural changes as they react on the timescale of picoseconds (10^{-12} s) and femtoseconds (10^{-15} s), "seeing" these changes occur requires ultrafast spectroscopic techniques. Professor Rose-Petruck and his group use ultrafast X-ray spectroscopy to study reactions as they occur in solutions. As part of their research, they have designed a reliable laboratory instrument that delivers the ultrashort X-ray pulses needed for ultrafast X-ray spectroscopy. To do this Professor Rose-Petruck developed a high power laser–driven X-ray source.

One system that Professor Rose-Petruck has been investigating involves the reactions of the iron carbonyl compound $Fe(CO)_5$ in solution. He and his students have found that $Fe(CO)_5$ rearranges in solution in a way that allows a solvent molecule to directly attach to the iron atom. This knowledge is important in understanding how $Fe(CO)_5$ and similar compounds react in solution.

Courtesy of Gabriela Petruck/Christopher Rose-Petruck

Christopher Rose-Petruck with his children.

Professor Rose-Petruck plans to continue his studies of chemical reactions with the goal of "seeing" the reactants approach each other, form some sort of activated complex, and follow the products as they separate.

To see how these requirements are applied, we will consider the mechanism given above for the reaction of nitrogen dioxide with carbon monoxide. First, note that the sum of the two steps gives the overall balanced equation:

$$NO_2(g) + NO_2(g) \longrightarrow NO_3(g) + NO(g)$$

$$NO_3(g) + CO(g) \longrightarrow NO_2(g) + CO_2(g)$$

$$\overline{\cancel{NO_2}(g) + NO_2(g) + \cancel{NO_3}(g) + CO(g) \longrightarrow \cancel{NO_3}(g) + NO(g) + \cancel{NO_2}(g) + CO_2(g)}$$

Overall reaction: $NO_2(g) + CO(g) \longrightarrow NO(g) + CO_2(g)$

The first requirement for a correct mechanism is met. To see whether the mechanism meets the second requirement, we need to introduce a new concept: the **rate-determining step.*** Multistep reactions may have one step that is much slower than all the others. Reactants can become products only as fast as they can complete this slowest step. That is, the overall reaction can be no faster than the slowest or rate-determining step in the sequence. An analogy for this situation is the rapid pouring of water through a funnel into a container. The water collects in the container at a rate that is essentially determined by the size of the funnel opening and not by the rate of pouring.

A reaction is only as fast as its slowest step.

---

*The concept of a rate-controlling step in a reaction mechanism is complex and often misleading. For a comprehensive discussion of this issue, see "Rate-Controlling Step: A Necessary or Useful Concept," by Keith J. Laidler, *J. Chem. Ed.* **65** (1988): 250.

The rate at which this colored solution enters the flask is determined by the size of the funnel stem, not how fast the solution is poured.

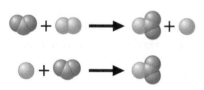

Which is the rate-determining step in the reaction of nitrogen dioxide with carbon monoxide? Let's *assume* that the first step is rate determining and the second step is relatively fast:

$$NO_2(g) + NO_2(g) \longrightarrow NO_3(g) + NO(g) \qquad \text{Slow (rate determining)}$$

$$NO_3(g) + CO(g) \longrightarrow NO_2(g) + CO_2(g) \qquad \text{Fast}$$

What we have really assumed here is that the formation of NO_3 occurs much more slowly than its reaction with CO. The rate of CO_2 production is then controlled by the rate of formation of NO_3 in the first step. Since this is an elementary step, we can write the rate law from the molecularity. The bimolecular first step has the rate law

$$\text{Rate of formation of } NO_3 = \frac{d[NO_3]}{dt} = k_1[NO_2]^2$$

Since the overall reaction rate can be no faster than the slowest step,

$$\text{Overall rate} = k_1[NO_2]^2$$

Note that this rate law agrees with the experimentally determined rate law given earlier. Since the mechanism we assumed above satisfies the two requirements stated earlier, it *may* be the correct mechanism for the reaction.

EXAMPLE 15.6

The balanced equation for the reaction of gaseous nitrogen dioxide and fluorine is

$$2NO_2(g) + F_2(g) \longrightarrow 2NO_2F(g)$$

The experimentally determined rate law is

$$\text{Rate} = k[NO_2][F_2]$$

A suggested mechanism for this reaction is

$$NO_2 + F_2 \xrightarrow{k_1} NO_2F + F \qquad \text{Slow}$$

$$F + NO_2 \xrightarrow{k_2} NO_2F \qquad \text{Fast}$$

Is this an acceptable mechanism? That is, does it satisfy the two requirements?

Solution The first requirement for an acceptable mechanism is that the sum of the steps give the balanced equation:

$$NO_2 + F_2 \longrightarrow NO_2F + F$$

$$\underline{F + NO_2 \longrightarrow NO_2F}$$

$$2NO_2 + F_2 + \cancel{F} \longrightarrow 2NO_2F + \cancel{F}$$

Overall reaction: $\qquad 2NO_2 + F_2 \longrightarrow 2NO_2F$

The first requirement is met.

The second requirement is that the mechanism must agree with the experimentally determined rate law. Since the proposed mechanism states that the first step is rate determining, the overall reaction rate must be that of the first step. The first step is bimolecular, so the rate law is

$$\text{Rate} = k_1[NO_2][F_2]$$

This has the same form as the experimentally determined rate law. The proposed mechanism is acceptable because it satisfies both requirements. (Note that we have not proved it is *the correct* mechanism.)

How does a chemist deduce the mechanism for a given reaction? The rate law is always determined first. Then, using chemical intuition and following the two rules given above, the chemist constructs a possible mechanism. Until recently, we could not prove a mechanism absolutely. We could only say that a mechanism that satisfies the two requirements is *possibly* correct. Recent advances in spectroscopy, however, such as those pioneered by Professor Ahmed Zewail (see "Femtochemistry" on page 721) and the use of STM techniques to study reactions, have provided the means for identifying mechanisms exactly (see "Seeing Reaction Mechanisms" on page 744). Deducing the mechanism for a chemical reaction is difficult; it requires skill and experience. We will only touch on this process in this text.

Mechanisms with Fast Forward and Reverse First Steps

A common type of reaction mechanism is one involving a first step in which *both* the forward and reverse reactions are very fast compared with the reactions in the second step. An example of this type of mechanism is that for the decomposition of ozone to oxygen. The balanced reaction is

$$2O_3(g) \longrightarrow 3O_2(g)$$

The observed rate law is

$$\text{Rate} = k\frac{[O_3]^2}{[O_2]}$$

Note that this rate law is unusual in that it contains the concentration of a *product*. The mechanism proposed for this process is

$$O_3 \underset{k_{-1}}{\overset{k_1}{\rightleftharpoons}} O_2 + O$$

$$O + O_3 \overset{k_2}{\longrightarrow} 2O_2$$

The double arrows in the first step indicate that both the forward and reverse reactions are important. They have the rate constants k_1 and k_{-1}, respectively.

The second step is relatively slow because of the very small concentration of O_3 molecules.

For this mechanism we will assume that *both* the forward and reverse reactions of the first step are very fast compared with the reaction in the second step. This means that the second step is rate determining. Therefore, the rate for the overall reaction is equal to the rate of the second step:

$$\text{Rate} = k_2[O][O_3]$$

This rate law does not have the same form as the experimentally determined rate law. For one thing, it contains the concentration of the intermediate, an oxygen atom. We can remove [O] and obtain a rate law that agrees with the experiment results by making an additional assumption. We assume that the rates of the forward and reverse reactions in the first step are equal. That is, we assume that the initial reversible fast step is at equilibrium, a steady state represented by forward and reverse arrows. This make sense because the rates of both the forward and reverse reactions for the first step are so much faster than the rate of the second step. For the first step,

$$\text{Rate of forward reaction} = k_1[O_3]$$

and $\qquad\qquad$ $$\text{Rate of reverse reaction} = k_{-1}[O_2][O]$$

At equilibrium we have

$$k_1[O_3] = k_{-1}[O_2][O]$$

Chemical Insights   Seeing Reaction Mechanisms

Until very recently chemists could only guess at the details of reaction mechanisms. New developments such as femtosecond spectroscopy (see "Femtochemistry" on page 721) and scanning tunneling microscopy (STM; see "Seeing Atoms" on page 22) have enabled scientists to begin to see the details of chemical reactions.

A perfect example of these new techniques is furnished by the study of the oxidation of carbon monoxide by oxygen to form carbon dioxide by Professor Wilson Ho and his coworkers at the University of California at Irvine. Taking advantage of the single-molecule dexterity of the tip of an STM instrument, Ho and his colleagues maneuvered a single CO molecule on a silver surface until it was near an adsorbed O_2 molecule (Fig. 15.9). At this point an O—CO—O intermediate formed on the surface. A little shot of energy from the STM tip caused the intermediate to form CO_2, which exited the surface while leaving a lone O atom behind. In another study Ho and his coworkers found that CO_2 could be formed by depositing a CO molecule from the STM tip onto an oxygen atom on the surface.

The new techniques of femtosecond spectroscopy and STM are revolutionizing the way chemistry is carried out. We are now at the point where we can "see" the detailed pathways of chemical reactions.

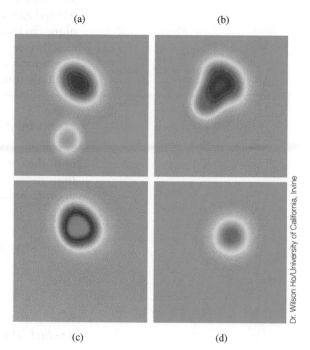

Figure 15.9
The STM images of the reaction of CO and O_2. (a) An O_2 molecule (oval) and a CO molecule (circle) on a surface. As the two molecules approach each other, a reaction occurs (b) to form an O—CO—O complex (c). After an electron pulse is applied to the complex, a newly formed CO_2 molecule exits the surface, leaving behind a single O atom (d).

Dr. Wilson Ho/University of California, Irvine

We solve for [O]:

$$[O] = \frac{k_1[O_3]}{k_{-1}[O_2]}$$

Now we substitute the expression for [O] into the rate law for the second step:

$$\text{Rate} = k_2[O][O_3] = k_2\left(\frac{k_1[O_3]}{k_{-1}[O_2]}\right)[O_3] = \frac{k_2k_1[O_3]^2}{k_{-1}[O_2]}$$

$$= k\frac{[O_3]^2}{[O_2]}$$

where k is a composite constant representing k_2k_1/k_{-1}.

This rate law, *derived* by postulating the two elementary steps and making assumptions about the relative rates of these steps, agrees with the experimental rate law. Since this mechanism (the elementary steps *plus* the assumptions) also gives the correct overall stoichiometry, it is an acceptable mechanism for the decomposition of ozone to oxygen.

EXAMPLE 15.7

The gas-phase reaction of chlorine with chloroform is described by the equation

$$Cl_2(g) + CHCl_3(g) \longrightarrow HCl(g) + CCl_4(g)$$

The rate law determined from experiment has a noninteger order:

$$\text{Rate} = k[Cl_2]^{1/2}[CHCl_3]$$

A proposed mechanism for this reaction follows:

$$Cl_2(g) \underset{k_{-1}}{\overset{k_1}{\rightleftharpoons}} 2Cl(g) \qquad \text{Both fast with equal rates (fast equilibrium)}$$

$$Cl(g) + CHCl_3(g) \xrightarrow{k_2} HCl(g) + CCl_3(g) \qquad \text{Slow}$$

$$CCl_3(g) + Cl(g) \xrightarrow{k_3} CCl_4(g) \qquad \text{Fast}$$

Is this an acceptable mechanism for the reaction?

Solution Two questions must be answered. First, does the mechanism give the correct overall stoichiometry? Adding the three steps does yield the correct balanced equation:

$$Cl_2(g) \rightleftharpoons 2Cl(g)$$

$$Cl(g) + CHCl_3(g) \longrightarrow HCl(g) + CCl_3(g)$$

$$CCl_3(g) + Cl(g) \longrightarrow CCl_4(g)$$

$$Cl_2(g) + \cancel{Cl}(g) + CHCl_3(g) + \cancel{CCl_3}(g) + \cancel{Cl}(g) \longrightarrow 2\cancel{Cl}(g) + HCl(g) + \cancel{CCl_3}(g) + CCl_4(g)$$

Overall reaction: $\quad Cl_2(g) + CHCl_3(g) \longrightarrow HCl(g) + CCl_4(g)$

Second, does the mechanism agree with the observed rate law? Since the overall reaction rate is determined by the rate of the slowest step,

$$\text{Overall rate} = \text{rate of second step} = k_2[Cl][CHCl_3]$$

Since the chlorine atom is an intermediate, we must find a way to eliminate [Cl] in the rate law. This can be done by recognizing that since the first step is at equilibrium, its forward and reverse rates are equal:

$$k_1[Cl_2] = k_{-1}[Cl]^2$$

Solving for $[Cl]^2$ gives

$$[Cl]^2 = \frac{k_1[Cl_2]}{k_{-1}}$$

Taking the square root of both sides yields

$$[Cl] = \left(\frac{k_1}{k_{-1}}\right)^{1/2} [Cl_2]^{1/2}$$

and

$$\text{Rate} = k_2[Cl][CHCl_3] = k_2\left(\frac{k_1}{k_{-1}}\right)^{1/2} [Cl_2]^{1/2}[CHCl_3] = k[Cl_2]^{1/2}[CHCl_3]$$

where

$$k = k_2\left(\frac{k_1}{k_{-1}}\right)^{1/2}$$

The rate law derived from the mechanism agrees with the experimentally observed rate law. This mechanism satisfies the two requirements and thus is an acceptable mechanism.

15.7 | The Steady-State Approximation

In the simplest reaction mechanisms, one particular step is usually rate determining. However, it is not unusual in complex, multistep reaction mechanisms for different steps to be rate determining under different sets of conditions.

In cases where a specific rate-determining step cannot be chosen, an analysis called the **steady-state approximation** is often used. The central feature of this method is the assumption that the concentration of any intermediate remains constant as the reaction proceeds. An intermediate is neither a reactant nor a product but something that is formed and then consumed as the reaction proceeds.

For example, the reaction between nitric oxide and hydrogen,

$$2NO(g) + H_2(g) \longrightarrow N_2O(g) + H_2O(g)$$

may proceed via the following mechanism:

1. $2NO \underset{k_{-1}}{\overset{k_1}{\rightleftharpoons}} N_2O_2$

2. $N_2O_2 + H_2 \xrightarrow{k_2} N_2O + H_2O$

In this mechanism the intermediate is N_2O_2. To apply the steady-state approximation to this mechanism, we assume the concentration of N_2O_2 remains constant. That is,

$$\frac{d[N_2O_2]}{dt} = 0$$

Next, we will identify the steps that produce N_2O_2 and those that consume N_2O_2 and write the rate law for each. Then we will apply the condition that the concentration of N_2O_2 is constant by setting the total rate of production of N_2O_2 equal to the total rate of consumption of N_2O_2. That is, if

Rate of production of N_2O_2 = rate of consumption of N_2O_2

then

$$\frac{d[N_2O_2]}{dt} = 0$$

Rate of Production of N_2O_2

In this mechanism N_2O_2 is produced only in the forward part of the first elementary step,

$$2NO \xrightarrow{k_1} N_2O_2$$

and the rate law for this step is

$$\frac{d[N_2O_2]}{dt} = k_1[NO]^2$$

Rate of Consumption of N_2O_2

In this mechanism N_2O_2 is consumed in the reverse part of the first step,

$$2NO \xleftarrow{k_{-1}} N_2O_2$$

and in the second step,

$$N_2O_2 + H_2 \xrightarrow{k_2} N_2O + H_2O$$

The rate laws for these steps are

$$-\frac{d[N_2O_2]}{dt} = k_{-1}[N_2O_2] \quad \text{and} \quad -\frac{d[N_2O_2]}{dt} = k_2[N_2O_2][H_2]$$

The Steady-State Condition

Now we equate the rates of production and consumption of N_2O_2:

$$k_1[NO]^2 = k_{-1}[N_2O_2] + k_2[N_2O_2][H_2]$$

Rate of production   Total rate of consumption

The Rate Law for the Overall Reaction

Next, we will write the rate law for the overall reaction,

$$2NO + H_2 \longrightarrow N_2O + H_2O$$

We can do this in several ways, depending on which reactant or product we use to represent the rate. In this case we will choose the decomposition of H_2 to define the rate:

$$\text{Rate of reaction} = -\frac{d[H_2]}{dt}$$

Note that H_2 is consumed only in the second step of the mechanism:

$$N_2O_2 + H_2 \xrightarrow{k_1} N_2O + H_2O$$

Thus the rate law is

$$-\frac{d[H_2]}{dt} = k_2[N_2O_2][H_2]$$

However, this is not the final form of the rate law for the overall reaction because it contains the concentration of an intermediate. We can remove this concentration from the rate law by solving the steady-state expression

$$k_1[NO]^2 = k_{-1}[N_2O_2] + k_2[N_2O_2][H_2]$$

for $[N_2O_2]$:

$$[N_2O_2] = \frac{k_1[NO]^2}{k_{-1} + k_2[H_2]}$$

We substitute this expression into the rate law,

$$\text{Rate} = -\frac{d[H_2]}{dt} = k_2[N_2O_2][H_2]$$

to give

$$\text{Rate} = -\frac{d[H_2]}{dt} = k_2[H_2]\left(\frac{k_1[NO]^2}{k_{-1} + k_2[H_2]}\right)$$

or

$$\text{Rate} = -\frac{d[H_2]}{dt} = \frac{k_2k_1[H_2][NO]^2}{k_{-1} + k_2[H_2]}$$

This is the overall rate law for the proposed mechanism based on the steady-state analysis. Note that this rate law is quite complicated, which is common for rate laws obtained by assuming steady-state conditions. The usual practice for testing the validity of a complicated rate law involves choosing concentration conditions that produce a simpler form of the rate law. For example, if the reaction between NO and H_2 is studied under conditions where the concentration of H_2 is large enough so that

$$k_2[H_2] \gg k_{-1}$$

then the full rate law

$$\frac{k_2 k_1 [H_2][NO]^2}{k_{-1} + k_2[H_2]}$$

reduces to

$$\frac{k_2 k_1 [H_2][NO]^2}{k_2[H_2]} = k_1[NO]^2$$

Thus, at sufficiently high concentrations of H_2, the reaction should show second-order dependence on the concentration of nitric oxide if the suggested mechanism is valid.

On the other hand, at low concentrations of H_2, such that

$$k_{-1} \gg k_2[H_2]$$

the rate law reduces to the form

$$\text{Rate} = \frac{k_2 k_1}{k_{-1}}[H_2][NO]^2 = k[H_2][NO]^2$$

Studies of the reaction under these conditions should show first-order dependence on $[H_2]$, as well as second-order dependence on $[NO]$, if the suggested mechanism is valid.

The ideas we have developed above for a specific mechanism can be generalized as follows.

STEPS | **Analyzing a Mechanism Using the Steady-State Approximation**

1 Write the proposed mechanism (the elementary steps).

2 Construct a steady-state expression for each intermediate I by applying the criterion

$$\frac{d[I]}{dt} = 0$$

which means that

Rate of production of I = rate of consumption of I

This condition is implemented by identifying each step that produces or consumes I and writing the appropriate rate law for each. The sum of the rate laws that produce I are then set equal to the sum of the rate laws that consume I.

3 From the steady-state approximation for each intermediate I_1, I_2, ..., solve for $[I_1]$, $[I_2]$, ...

4 Construct the rate law for the overall reaction in terms of one of the reactants or products. The decision about which reactant or product to use in constructing the rate law is based on convenience.

5 Use the expressions from step 3 for $[I_1]$, $[I_2]$, ... to substitute for the concentrations of intermediates found in the rate law for step 4. The goal is to obtain an overall rate law that contains only reactant and/or product concentrations.

15.8 | A Model for Chemical Kinetics

How do chemical reactions occur? We already have given some indications. For example, we have seen that the rates of chemical reactions depend on the concentrations of the reacting species. The initial rate for the reaction

$$a\text{A} + b\text{B} \longrightarrow \text{products}$$

can be described by the rate law

$$\text{Rate} = k[\text{A}]^n[\text{B}]^m$$

where the order of each reactant depends on the detailed reaction mechanism. This explains why reaction rates depend on concentration. But what about some of the other factors affecting reaction rates? For example, how does temperature affect the speed of a reaction?

We can answer this question qualitatively from our experience. We use refrigerators because food spoilage is retarded at low temperatures. The combustion of wood occurs at a measurable rate only at high temperatures. An egg cooks in boiling water much faster at sea level than in Leadville, Colorado (elevation 10,000 feet), where the boiling point of water is about 90°C. These observations and others lead us to conclude that *chemical reactions speed up when the temperature is increased.* Experiments have shown that virtually all rate constants show an exponential increase with absolute temperature, as represented in Fig. 15.10.

In this section we will introduce a model that can be used to account for the observed characteristics of reaction rates. This model, the **collision model,** is built around the central idea that *molecules must collide to react.* We have already seen that this assumption can explain the concentration dependence of reaction rates. Now we need to consider whether this model can also account for the observed temperature dependence of reaction rates.

An increase in temperature increases molecular velocities and so increases the frequency of intermolecular collisions. This agrees with the observation that reaction rates are greater at higher temperatures. Thus there is qualitative agreement between the collision model and experimental observations. However, it is found that the rate of reaction is much smaller than the calculated collision frequency in a given collection of gas particles. This must mean that *only a small fraction of the collisions produces a reaction.* Why?

This question was first addressed in the 1880s by Svante Arrhenius. He proposed the existence of a *threshold energy,* called the **activation energy,** that must be overcome to produce a chemical reaction. We can see that this proposal makes sense by considering the decomposition of BrNO in the gas phase:

$$2\text{BrNO}(g) \longrightarrow 2\text{NO}(g) + \text{Br}_2(g)$$

In this reaction two Br—N bonds must be broken and one Br—Br bond must be formed. Breaking a Br—N bond requires considerable energy (243 kJ/mol), which must come from somewhere. The collision model postulates that the energy required to break the bonds comes from the kinetic energies possessed by the reacting molecules before the collision. This kinetic energy is changed into potential energy as the molecules are distorted during a collision, breaking bonds and rearranging the atoms into the product molecules.

We can envision the reaction progress as shown in Fig. 15.11. The arrangement of atoms found at the top of the potential energy "hill," or barrier, is called the **activated complex,** or **transition state.** The conversion of BrNO to NO and Br$_2$ is exothermic, as indicated by the fact that the products have

Figure 15.10
A plot showing the exponential dependence of the rate constant on absolute temperature. The exact temperature dependence of k is different for each reaction. This plot represents the behavior of a rate constant that doubles for every increase in temperature of 10 K.

k

T (K)

The higher the activation energy, the slower is the reaction at a given temperature.

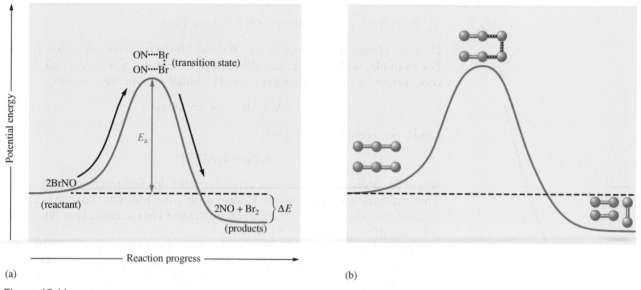

Figure 15.11

(a) The change in potential energy as a function of reaction progress for the reaction $2BrNO \longrightarrow 2NO + Br_2$. The activation energy E_a represents the energy needed to disrupt the BrNO molecules so that they can form products. The quantity ΔE represents the net change in energy in going from reactant to products. (b) A molecular representation of the reaction.

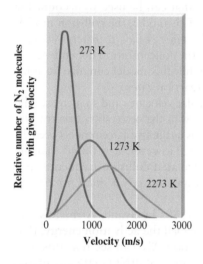

Figure 15.12A

A plot of the relative number of N_2 molecules that have a given velocity at three temperatures. Note that as the tempera-ture increases, both the average velocity and the spread of velocities increase.

lower energy than the reactant. However, ΔE has no effect on the rate of the reaction. Rather, the rate depends on the size of the activation energy E_a.

The main point here is that a certain minimum energy is required for two BrNO molecules to "get over the hill" so that products can form. This is furnished by the collision energy. A collision between two BrNO molecules with small kinetic energies will not have enough energy to get over the barrier, and no reaction occurs. At a given temperature, only a certain fraction of the collisions possess enough energy to be effective and thus to result in product formation.

In a sample of gas the molecules do not have the same velocity. Instead, a distribution of velocities occurs and the distribution changes with temperature as shown in Fig. 15.12A. Therefore, a distribution of collision energies also occurs, as shown in Fig. 15.12B for two different temperatures. Figure 15.12B also shows the activation energy for the reaction in question. Only collisions with energy greater than the activation energy are able to react (get over the barrier). At the lower temperature T_1, the fraction of effective collisions is quite small. However, as the temperature is increased to T_2, the fraction of collisions with the required activation energy increases dramatically. When the temperature is doubled, the fraction of effective collisions much more than doubles. In fact, the fraction of effective collisions increases *exponentially* with temperature. This agrees with the observation that rates of reactions increase exponentially with temperature.

Arrhenius postulated that the number of collisions having an energy equal to or greater than the activation energy is given by the expression

Number of collisions with at least the activation energy

$$= (\text{total number of collisions})e^{-E_a/RT}$$

where E_a is the activation energy, R is the universal gas constant, and T is the Kelvin temperature. The factor $e^{-E_a/RT}$ represents the fraction of collisions with energy E_a or greater at temperature T.

We have seen that not all molecular collisions are effective in producing chemical reactions because a minimum energy is required for the reaction to occur. There is, however, another complication. Experiments show that the

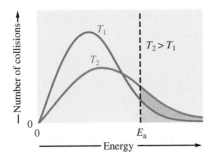

Figure 15.12B
Plot showing the number of collisions with a particular energy at T_1 and T_2, where $T_2 > T_1$.

observed reaction rate is considerably smaller than the rate of collisions with enough energy to surmount the barrier. This means that many collisions, even though they have the required energy, still do not produce a reaction. Why not?

The answer lies in the **molecular orientations** during collisions. We can illustrate this effect by using the reaction between two BrNO molecules, as shown in Fig. 15.13. Some collision orientations can lead to reaction, and others cannot. Therefore, we must include a correction factor to allow for collisions with nonproductive molecular orientations.

To summarize, two requirements must be satisfied for reactants to collide successfully (to rearrange to form products):

1. The collision must involve enough energy to produce the reaction; that is, the collision energy must equal or exceed the activation energy.

2. The relative orientations of the reactants must allow formation of any new bonds necessary to produce products.

Taking these factors into account, we can represent the rate constant as

$$k = zpe^{-E_a/RT}$$

where z is the collision frequency (the total number of collisions per second). The factor p in this expression, called the **steric factor,** reflects the fraction of collisions with effective orientations. Recall that the factor $e^{-E_a/RT}$ represents the fraction of collisions with sufficient energy to produce a reaction. This expression is most often written in the form

$$k = Ae^{-E_a/RT} \qquad (15.9)$$

which is called the **Arrhenius equation.** In this equation A, which replaces zp, is called the **pre-exponential factor,** or **frequency factor,** for the reaction.

Taking the natural logarithm of each side of the Arrhenius equation yields

$$\ln(k) = -\frac{E_a}{R}\left(\frac{1}{T}\right) + \ln(A) \qquad (15.10)$$

Equation (15.10) is a linear equation of the type $y = mx + b$, where $y = \ln(k)$, $m = -E_a/R =$ slope, $x = 1/T$, and $b = \ln(A) =$ intercept. Thus, for a reaction where the rate constant obeys the Arrhenius equation, a plot of $\ln(k)$ versus $1/T$ gives a straight line. The slope and intercept can be used to determine the values of E_a and A characteristic of that reaction. The fact that most rate con-

Figure 15.13
Several possible orientations for a collision between two BrNO molecules. Orientations (a) and (b) can lead to a reaction, but orientation (c) cannot.

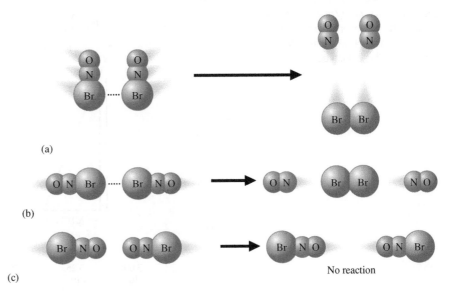

stants obey the Arrhenius equation to a good approximation indicates that the collision model for chemical reactions is physically reasonable.

EXAMPLE 15.8

The reaction

$$2N_2O_5(g) \longrightarrow 4NO_2(g) + O_2(g)$$

was studied at several temperatures and the following values of k were obtained:

k (s^{-1})	T (°C)
2.0×10^{-5}	20
7.3×10^{-5}	30
2.7×10^{-4}	40
9.1×10^{-4}	50
2.9×10^{-3}	60

Calculate the value of E_a for this reaction.

Solution To obtain the value of E_a, we need to construct a plot of $\ln(k)$ versus $1/T$. First, we must calculate values of $\ln(k)$ and $1/T$:

T (°C)	T (K)	$1/T$ (K)	k (s^{-1})	$\ln(k)$
20	293	3.41×10^{-3}	2.0×10^{-5}	-10.82
30	303	3.30×10^{-3}	7.3×10^{-5}	-9.53
40	313	3.19×10^{-3}	2.7×10^{-4}	-8.22
50	323	3.10×10^{-3}	9.1×10^{-4}	-7.00
60	333	3.00×10^{-3}	2.9×10^{-3}	-5.84

The plot of $\ln(k)$ versus $1/T$ is shown in Fig. 15.14. The slope is found to be -1.2×10^4 K. Since

$$\text{Slope} = -\frac{E_a}{R}$$

Figure 15.14
Plot of $\ln(k)$ versus $1/T$ for the reaction $2N_2O_5(g) \longrightarrow 4NO_2(g) + O_2(g)$. The value of the activation energy for this reaction can be obtained from the slope of the line, which equals $-E_a/R$.

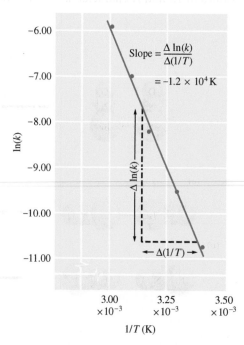

then

$$E_a = -R(\text{slope}) = -(8.3145 \text{ J K}^{-1} \text{ mol}^{-1})(-1.2 \times 10^4 \text{ K})$$
$$= 1.0 \times 10^5 \text{ J/mol}$$

Thus the value of the activation energy for this reaction is 1.0×10^5 J/mol.

The most common procedure for finding E_a for a reaction involves measuring the rate constant k at several temperatures and then plotting $\ln(k)$ versus $1/T$, as shown in Example 15.8. However, E_a can also be calculated from the values of k at only two temperatures using a formula that can be derived as follows from Equation (15.10).

At temperature T_1, the rate constant is k_1; thus

$$\ln(k_1) = -\frac{E_a}{RT_1} + \ln(A)$$

At temperature T_2, the rate constant is k_2; thus

$$\ln(k_2) = -\frac{E_a}{RT_2} + \ln(A)$$

Subtracting the first equation from the second gives

$$\ln\left(\frac{k_2}{k_1}\right) = \frac{E_a}{R}\left(\frac{1}{T_1} - \frac{1}{T_2}\right) \tag{15.11}$$

Therefore, the values of k_1 and k_2 measured at temperatures T_1 and T_2 can be used to calculate E_a.

15.9 | Catalysis

We have seen that the rate of a reaction increases dramatically with temperature. If a particular reaction does not occur fast enough at normal temperatures, we can speed it up by raising the temperature. However, sometimes this is not feasible. For example, since living cells can survive only in a rather narrow temperature range, the human body is designed to operate at an almost constant temperature of 98.6°F. But the many complicated biochemical reactions keeping us alive would be much too slow at this temperature without intervention. We survive only because the body contains many substances called **enzymes** that increase the rates of these reactions even though body temperature remains constant. In fact, almost every biologically important reaction is assisted by a specific enzyme. An important example involves the enzyme carbonic anhydrase, which catalyzes the reaction of carbon dioxide with water:

$$CO_2 + H_2O \rightleftharpoons HCO_3^- + H^+$$

This crucial reaction allows the carbon dioxide that forms in the cells during metabolism to be removed. If the carbon dioxide were allowed to accumulate, it would poison the cell. Carbonic anhydrase is so efficient that one molecule of enzyme can catalyze the reaction of over *600,000 carbon dioxide molecules in one second!*

Although it is possible to use higher temperatures to speed up commercially important reactions, such as the Haber process for synthesizing ammonia, this is very expensive. In a chemical plant an increase in temperature means significantly increased energy costs. The use of an appropriate catalyst allows a reaction to proceed rapidly at a relatively low temperature and therefore can hold down production costs.

Chemical Insights   TiO₂—One of Nature's Most Versatile Materials

Titanium(IV) oxide (commonly called titanium dioxide) is a compound with an amazing array of talents. It is a widely used white pigment for paint, paper, vinyl floor coverings, sunscreens, and synthetic fibers. However, it is much more than a simple pigment. TiO_2, it appears, has an almost unlimited ability to catalyze the breakdown of organic materials. In Japan, scores of companies are scrambling to take advantage of this remarkable talent. TiO_2-impregnated paint used on buildings and in automobile and rail tunnels prevents the buildup of oily dust, TiO_2-impregnated glass prevents oily buildup on chandeliers and automobile windows, and a TiO_2-impregnated fan belt can help break down grease that often clogs kitchen exhaust fans. TiO_2 catalysis can also be used to break down air pollutants such as cigarette smoke and nitrogen oxides. In addition to all these talents, TiO_2 kills bacteria.

TiO_2 is a photocatalyst—it requires light for its catalytic activity. It also requires the presence of oxygen and water. The mechanism for the catalytic behavior of TiO_2 results from its behavior as a semiconductor. When light is absorbed by TiO_2, free electrons and "holes" are created that cause adsorbed water and oxygen molecules to form hydroxyl (OH) and superoxide (O_2^-) radicals,

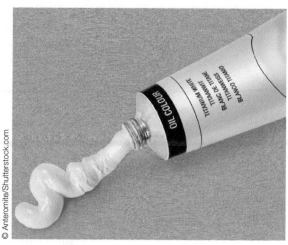

A white paint pigment that contains TiO_2.

© Anteromite/Shutterstock.com

species with unpaired electrons. These extremely reactive radicals can react with and destroy virtually all organic materials. The formation of these radicals also explains the ability of TiO_2 to catalyze the reactions of nitrogen oxides to form nitric acid. These radicals are lethal to microorganisms and explain the ability of TiO_2 to behave as a bactericide.

New uses are being found daily for the many talents of TiO_2.

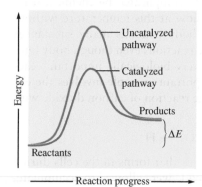

Figure 15.15
Energy plots for catalyzed and uncatalyzed pathways for a given reaction. Note that although the shapes of the catalyzed and uncatalyzed energy profiles are shown here the same for simplicity, they do not have identical shapes for actual reactions.

A **catalyst** is *a substance that speeds up a reaction without being consumed itself.* Just as virtually all vital biological reactions are assisted by enzymes (biological catalysts), almost all industrial processes also benefit from the use of catalysts. For example, the production of sulfuric acid uses vanadium(V) oxide, and the Haber process uses a mixture of iron and iron oxide.

How does a catalyst work? Remember that for each reaction a certain energy barrier must be surmounted. How can we make a reaction occur faster without raising the temperature to increase the molecular kinetic energies? The solution is to provide a new pathway for the reaction, one with a *lower activation energy.* That is what a catalyst does, as shown in Fig. 15.15. Because the catalyst allows the reaction to occur along a pathway with a lower activation energy, a much larger fraction of collisions is effective at a given temperature. Thus the reaction rate is increased. This effect is illustrated in Fig. 15.16. Note from this diagram that although a catalyst lowers the activation energy (E_a) for a reaction, it does not affect the energy difference (ΔE) between products and reactants.

Catalysts are classified as homogeneous or heterogeneous. A **homogeneous catalyst** is one that is *present in the same phase (physical state) as the reacting molecules.* A **heterogeneous catalyst** exists *in a different phase,* usually as a solid.

Figure 15.16

Effect of a catalyst on the number of reaction-producing collisions. Because a catalyst provides a reaction pathway with a lower activation energy, a much greater fraction of the collisions is effective for the catalyzed pathway (b) than for the uncatalyzed pathway (a) (at a given temperature). This allows reactants to become products at a much higher rate, even though there is no temperature increase.

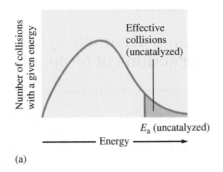
(a)

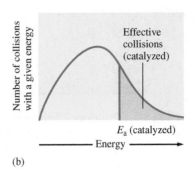
(b)

Heterogeneous Catalysis

Heterogeneous catalysis most often involves gaseous reactants being adsorbed on the surface of a solid catalyst. **Adsorption** refers to the collection of one substance on the surface of another substance; **absorption** refers to the penetration of one substance into another. Water is *absorbed* by a sponge.

One of the earliest examples of heterogeneous catalysis involves the synthesis of ammonia from nitrogen and hydrogen. This process was developed in 1909 by German chemist Fritz Haber—who tested more than 1000 possible catalysts before settling on iron as the best choice. (Today, ammonia manufacturers use a solid catalyst consisting of a mixture of iron, potassium, and calcium that performs better than iron alone.) Although Haber had no means for determining why iron was a good catalyst, it is now understood that the key to iron's effectiveness is that the strong nitrogen–nitrogen and hydrogen–hydrogen bonds are weakened when the H_2 and N_2 molecules are bound to iron atoms on the surface of the metal. Iron turns out to be an ideal catalyst because the iron–nitrogen bond is sufficiently strong that the nitrogen atoms on the surface do not recombine to form N_2 but is weak enough to allow nitrogen and hydrogen atoms on the surface to combine to form ammonia.

An important example of heterogeneous catalysis occurs in the hydrogenation of unsaturated hydrocarbons, compounds composed mainly of carbon and hydrogen and containing some carbon–carbon double bonds. Hydrogenation is an important industrial process used to change unsaturated fats, occurring as oils, to saturated fats (solid shortenings such as Crisco). In this process the C=C bonds are converted to C—C bonds through the addition of hydrogen.

A simple example of hydrogenation involves ethylene:

$$
\begin{array}{c}
\text{H} \\
\backslash \\
\quad\quad \text{C}=\text{C} \quad (g) + \text{H}_2(g) \\
/ \\
\text{H} \quad\quad \text{H}
\end{array}
\longrightarrow
\begin{array}{c}
\text{H H} \\
| \ | \\
\text{H}-\text{C}-\text{C}-\text{H}(g) \\
| \ | \\
\text{H H}
\end{array}
$$

Ethylene   Ethane

This reaction is quite slow at normal temperatures mainly because the strong bond in the hydrogen molecule results in a large activation energy for the reaction. However, the reaction rate can be greatly increased by using a solid catalyst of platinum, palladium, or nickel. The hydrogen and ethylene adsorb on the catalyst surface, where the reaction occurs. The main function of the catalyst apparently is to allow formation of metal–hydrogen interactions that weaken the H—H bonds and facilitate the reaction. The mechanism is illustrated in Fig. 15.17.

Chemistry Explorers

Christopher Arumainayagam Researches the Interactions of Molecules with Surfaces

Professor Christopher Arumainayagam, who has been on the faculty of Wellesley College since 1990, received his B.A. degree from Harvard University and his Ph.D. from Stanford University.

One goal of Professor Arumainayagam's research is to understand the interactions of molecules with solid surfaces in order to learn more about the reaction mechanisms of heterogeneous catalysis. In experiments conducted using molecular beams (narrow streams of molecules that are undisturbed by collisions with other gas molecules), Professor Arumainayagam has studied how adsorption on a solid surface depends on the velocity and angle of approach of the incident molecule. In collaboration with Professor John Yates, Professor Arumainayagam has also studied the production and removal of surface defects (irregularities) that are thought to play a critical role in the performance of heterogeneous catalysts.

Christopher Arumainayagam and a student.

In his current research at Wellesley College, Professor Arumainayagam and his undergraduate students are using surface science techniques and low-energy electron beams to understand how high-energy particles (e.g., electrons, protons, alpha particles) and high-energy photons (e.g., X rays and gamma rays) interact with matter, causing ionization. Results of their studies may provide information that could further cost-efficient destruction of hazardous chemicals and improve our understanding of the electron-induced decomposition of feed gases used in the processing of semiconductor devices.

Figure 15.17

Heterogeneous catalysis of the hydrogenation of ethylene. (a) Hydrogen is adsorbed on the metal surface, forming metal–hydrogen bonds and breaking the H—H bonds. (b) During adsorption, the C—C π bond in ethylene is broken and metal–carbon bonds are formed. (c) The adsorbed molecules and atoms migrate toward each other on the metal surface, forming new C—H bonds. (d) The C atoms in ethane (C_2H_6) have completely saturated bonding capacities and so cannot bind strongly to the metal surfaces. The C_2H_6 molecule thus escapes.

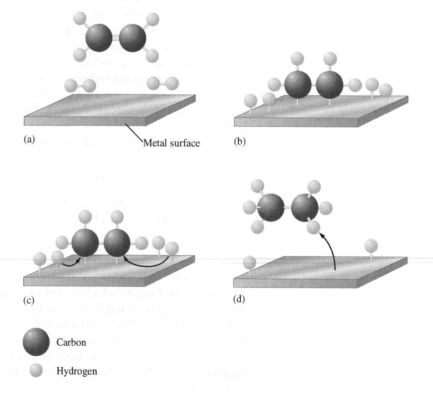

(a)   Metal surface   (b)

(c)   (d)

● Carbon

○ Hydrogen

Typically, heterogeneous catalysis involves four steps:

1. Adsorption and activation of the reactants
2. Migration of the adsorbed reactants on the surface
3. Reaction among the adsorbed substances
4. Escape, or *desorption,* of the products

Heterogeneous catalysis also occurs in the oxidation of gaseous sulfur dioxide to gaseous sulfur trioxide. This process is especially interesting because it illustrates both positive and negative consequences of chemical catalysis.

The negative side is the formation of damaging air pollutants. Recall that sulfur dioxide, a toxic gas with a choking odor, is formed when sulfur-containing fuels are burned. However, it is sulfur trioxide that causes most of the environmental damage, mainly through the production of acid rain. When sulfur trioxide combines with a droplet of water, sulfuric acid is formed:

$$H_2O(l) + SO_3(g) \longrightarrow H_2SO_4(aq)$$

This sulfuric acid can cause considerable damage to vegetation, buildings and statues, and fish populations.

Sulfur dioxide is *not* rapidly oxidized to sulfur trioxide in clean, dry air. Why, then, is there a problem? The answer is catalysis. Dust particles and water droplets catalyze the reaction between SO_2 and O_2 in the air.

On the positive side, the heterogeneous catalysis of the oxidation of SO_2 is used to advantage in the manufacture of sulfuric acid, where the reaction of O_2 and SO_2 to form SO_3 is catalyzed by a solid mixture of platinum and vanadium(V) oxide.

Heterogeneous catalysis is also used in the catalytic converters of automobile exhaust systems. The exhaust gases, containing compounds such as nitric oxide, carbon monoxide, and unburned hydrocarbons, are passed through a converter containing beads of solid catalyst (Fig. 15.18). The catalyst promotes the conversion of carbon monoxide to carbon dioxide, hydrocarbons to carbon dioxide and water, and nitric oxide to nitrogen gas, to lessen the environmental impact of the exhaust gases. This beneficial catalysis can, unfortunately, be accompanied by the unwanted catalysis of the oxidation of SO_2 to SO_3, the latter reacting with the moisture present to form sulfuric acid.

Because of the complex nature of the reactions that take place in the converter, a mixture of catalysts is used. The most effective catalytic materials are transition metal oxides and noble metals such as palladium and platinum. A catalytic converter typically consists of platinum and rhodium particles deposited on a ceramic honeycomb, a configuration that maximizes the contact between the metal particles and the exhaust gases. In studies performed during the last ten years, researchers at General Motors have shown that rhodium

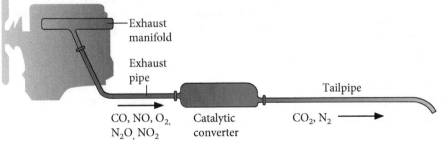
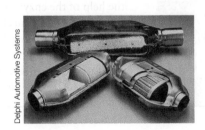

Figure 15.18
The exhaust gases from an automobile engine are passed through a catalytic converter to minimize environmental damage.

The most impressive examples of homogeneous catalysis occur in nature, where the complex reactions necessary for plant and animal life are made possible by enzymes. Enzymes are large molecules specifically tailored to facilitate a given type of reaction. Usually enzymes are proteins, an important class of biomolecules constructed from α-amino acids that have the general structure

where R represents any one of 20 different substituents. These amino acid molecules can be "hooked together" to form a polymer (a word meaning "many parts") called a *protein*. The general structure of a protein can be represented as follows:

Many amino acid fragments	Fragment from an amino acid with substituent R	Fragment from an amino acid with substituent R′	Fragment from an amino acid with substituent R″

Since specific proteins are needed by the human body, the proteins in food must be broken into their constituent amino acids, which are then used to construct new proteins in the body's cells. The reaction in which a protein is broken down one amino acid at a time is shown in Fig. 15.19. Note that in this reaction a water molecule reacts with a protein molecule to produce an amino acid and a new protein containing one fewer amino acid. Without the help of the enzymes found in human cells, this reaction would be much too slow to be useful. One of these enzymes is *carboxypeptidase-A,* a zinc-containing protein (Fig. 15.20).

Carboxypeptidase-A captures the protein to be acted on (called the *substrate*) in a special groove

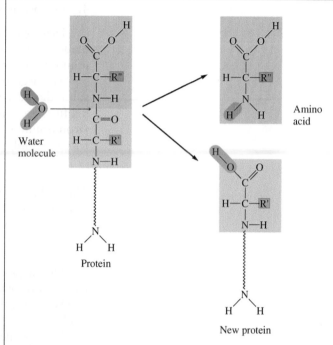

Figure 15.19
The removal of the end amino acid from a protein by reaction with a molecule of water. The products are an amino acid and a new, smaller protein.

and positions the substrate so that the end is in the *active site,* where the catalysis occurs (Fig. 15.21). Note that the Zn^{2+} ion bonds to the oxygen of the $C=O$ (carbonyl) group. This polarizes the electron density in the carbonyl group, allowing the neighboring C—N bond to be broken much more easily. When the reaction is completed, the remaining portion of the substrate protein and the newly formed amino acid are released by the enzyme.

The process just described for carboxypeptidase-A is characteristic of the behavior of other enzymes. Enzyme catalysis can be represented by the series of reactions shown below:

$$E + S \underset{k_{-1}}{\overset{k_1}{\rightleftharpoons}} E \cdot S$$

$$E \cdot S \overset{k_2}{\rightleftharpoons} E + P$$

Figure 15.20

The structure of the enzyme carboxypeptidase-A, which contains 307 amino acids.

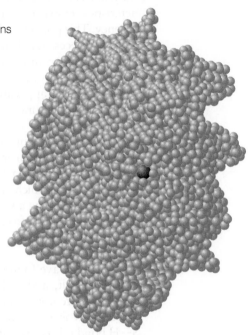

where E represents the enzyme, S represents the substrate, E · S represents the enzyme–substrate complex, and P represents the products. The enzyme and substrate form a complex where the reaction occurs. The enzyme then releases the products and is ready to repeat the process. The most amazing thing about enzymes is their efficiency. Because an enzyme plays its catalytic role over and over and very rapidly, only a tiny amount of enzyme is required. This makes the isolation of enzymes for study quite difficult.

Figure 15.21

Protein–substrate interaction. The substrate is shown in black and red, with the red representing the terminal amino acid. Blue indicates side chains from the enzyme that help bind the substrate.

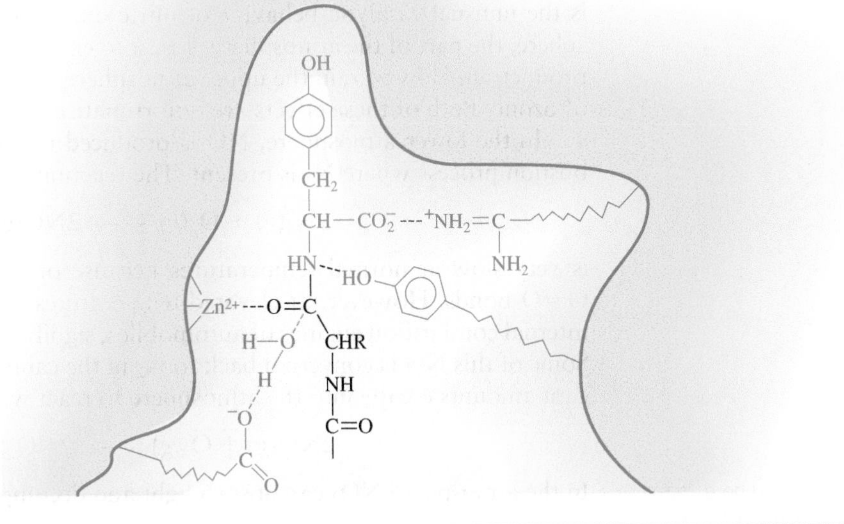

promotes the dissociation of NO molecules adsorbed on its surface, thereby enhancing the conversion of NO, a serious air pollutant, to N_2, a natural component of pure air.

One consequence of the widespread use of catalytic converters has been the need to remove lead from gasoline. Tetraethyl lead was used for more than 50 years as a very effective "octane booster" because of its antiknocking characteristics. However, lead quickly destroys much of a converter's catalytic efficiency. This poisoning effect, along with health concerns about the toxicity of lead, has necessitated the removal of lead from gasoline, which has caused a search for other antiknock additives and the redesigning of engines to run on lower-octane gasoline.

Yet another application of solid-state catalysis occurs in the desulfurization of petroleum. Natural petroleum includes various molecules that contain sulfur atoms. Combustion of this petroleum produces SO_2, which must be removed from the exhaust to prevent air pollution. One way to prevent pollution by SO_2 is to remove the sulfur from the petroleum before it is used for fuel—the desulfurization of petroleum. One type of sulfur-containing molecules found in petroleum are thiols, which can be written R—SH, where R represents a molecular fragment containing a long chain of carbon atoms. In desulfurization the goal is to remove the sulfur from this molecule to produce a hydrocarbon (R—H):

$$R—SH \longrightarrow R—H + S$$

Oil chemists have found that this process is catalyzed by a mixture of molybdenum, cobalt, and sulfur. Because this catalyst is a very complicated substance, we are not certain how it works. It is thought that the desulfurization reaction involves the thiol binding to the catalytic surface. In this process the S—H bond is broken, with the R—S and the H being bound to metal atoms on the surface of the catalyst. The H atom is then transferred to the R fragment to form R—H, which migrates away, leaving the S behind.

Homogeneous Catalysis

A homogeneous catalyst exists in the same phase as the reacting molecules. There are many examples in both the gas and liquid phases. One such example is the unusual catalytic behavior of nitric oxide toward ozone. In the troposphere, the part of the atmosphere closest to earth, nitric oxide catalyzes ozone production. However, in the upper atmosphere, it catalyzes the decomposition of ozone. Both of these effects are unfortunate environmentally.

In the lower atmosphere, NO is produced in any high-temperature combustion process where N_2 is present. The reaction

$$N_2(g) + O_2(g) \longrightarrow 2NO(g)$$

is very slow at normal temperatures because of the very strong N≡N and O=O bonds. However, at elevated temperatures, such as those found in the internal combustion engines of automobiles, significant quantities of NO form. Some of this NO is converted back to N_2 in the catalytic converter, but significant amounts escape into the atmosphere to react with oxygen:

$$2NO(g) + O_2(g) \longrightarrow 2NO_2(g)$$

Although O_2 is represented here as the oxidizing agent for NO, the actual oxidizing agent is probably some type of peroxide compound produced by the reaction of oxygen with pollutants. The direct reaction of NO with O_2 is very slow.

In the atmosphere NO_2 can absorb light and decompose as follows:

$$NO_2(g) \xrightarrow{\text{Light}} NO(g) + O(g)$$

The oxygen atom formed in this process is very reactive and can combine with oxygen molecules to form ozone:

$$O_2(g) + O(g) \longrightarrow O_3(g)$$

Hot, New Enzymes

Enzymes, nature's catalysts, are very attractive to chemical companies: Enzymes are very efficient catalysts and as natural products they tend to be easier on the environment than human-made catalysts. However, one disadvantage of most enzymes is that they can function only near room temperature and at pH values near 7. Because of these limitations, scientists are now looking at the enzymes that occur in organisms that exist in extreme conditions.

The exotic microorganisms that thrive in the scalding temperatures of hot springs, the freezing temperatures of the Arctic, or extremes in pH or salinity are called *extremophiles* and their enzymes are called *extremozymes*. Although the extremozymes are attractive to industry because they can survive in the extreme conditions that often characterize industrial processes, the parent extremophiles are difficult to grow "in captivity" because of the unusual conditions they require. Because of the difficulties in culturing these microorganisms, biotechnology companies are now "shotgun" cloning the DNA from a mix of these extremophiles. The steps in this process are represented below.

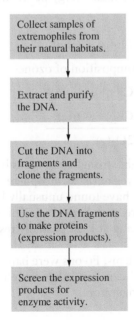

Collect samples of extremophiles from their natural habitats.

↓

Extract and purify the DNA.

↓

Cut the DNA into fragments and clone the fragments.

↓

Use the DNA fragments to make proteins (expression products).

↓

Screen the expression products for enzyme activity.

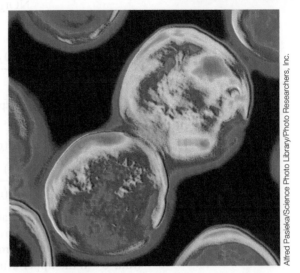

A micrograph of the extremophile *Archaeoglobus fulgidis*, an organism that lives in the hot sediments near submarine hydrothermal vents.

Alfred Pasieka/Science Photo Library/Photo Researchers, Inc.

The DNA fragments are expressed (proteins are made from the genes contained in the fragments) most commonly using *Escherichia coli*. Interestingly, even though *E. coli* must be cultured under the mild conditions necessary for them to survive, the extremozymes formed seem to have their characteristic catalytic activities, indicating that they have the same structures as when they are formed in their native extreme conditions.

The mixtures of extremozymes produced by the expression process are then tested to see if they have catalytic activity for the industrial processes of interest. If a given mixture shows catalytic activity, it is then usually subjected to random DNA mutagenesis or "molecule breeding" to see whether random evolution of the enzymes will lead to improved activities.

The potential market for the extremozymes is huge. Currently, the global market for industrial enzymes is more than $7 billion. The companies developing the extremozymes hope that their products can replace existing industrial catalysts, making processes more efficient by lowering costs and minimizing the formation of by-products.

Ozone is a powerful oxidizing agent that can react with other air pollutants to form substances irritating to the eyes and lungs.

In this series of reactions, nitric oxide is acting as a true catalyst because it assists the production of ozone without being consumed itself. This can be seen by summing the reactions:

$$NO(g) + \tfrac{1}{2}O_2(g) \longrightarrow NO_2(g)$$

$$NO_2(g) \xrightarrow{\text{Light}} NO(g) + O(g)$$

$$\underline{O_2(g) + O(g) \longrightarrow O_3(g)}$$

$$\tfrac{3}{2}O_2(g) \longrightarrow O_3(g)$$

In the upper atmosphere, the presence of nitric oxide has the opposite effect—the depletion of ozone. The series of reactions involved is

$$NO(g) + O_3(g) \longrightarrow NO_2(g) + O_2(g)$$

$$\underline{O(g) + NO_2(g) \longrightarrow NO(g) + O_2(g)}$$

$$O(g) + O_3(g) \longrightarrow 2O_2(g)$$

Nitric oxide is again catalytic, but here its effect is to change O_3 to O_2. This is a potential problem because O_3, which absorbs ultraviolet light, is necessary to protect us from the harmful effects of this high-energy radiation. That is, we want O_3 in the upper atmosphere to block ultraviolet radiation from the sun. However, we do not want it in the lower atmosphere where we have to breathe it and its oxidation products.

Over the last decade, research has shown that the ozone layer in the upper atmosphere is also threatened by *Freons*,* a group of stable, noncorrosive compounds long used as refrigerants and propellants in aerosol cans. The most commonly used substance of this type was Freon-12 (CCl_2F_2). The chemical inertness of Freons makes them more useful but also creates a problem, since they remain for a long time in the environment. Eventually, they migrate into the upper atmosphere to be decomposed by high-energy light. Among the decomposition products are chlorine atoms:

$$CCl_2F_2(g) \xrightarrow{\text{Light}} CClF_2(g) + Cl(g)$$

These chlorine atoms can catalyze the decomposition of ozone:

$$Cl(g) + O_3(g) \longrightarrow ClO(g) + O_2(g)$$

$$\underline{O(g) + ClO(g) \longrightarrow Cl(g) + O_2(g)}$$

$$O(g) + O_3(g) \longrightarrow 2O_2(g)$$

The problem of Freons has been brought strongly into focus by the discovery of a mysterious "hole" in the ozone layer in the stratosphere over Antarctica. Studies to find the reason for the hole have found unusually high levels of chlorine monoxide (ClO) in the atmosphere over Antarctica. This strongly implicates the Freons in the atmosphere as being at least partially responsible for the ozone destruction in the area.

Because they pose environmental problems, Freons were banned years ago by the U.S. government for use in aerosol cans, and they have recently been banned for use in air conditioners and refrigerators.

---

*For more information, see S. Elliott and F. S. Rowland, "Chlorofluorocarbons and Stratospheric Ozone," *J. Chem. Ed.* 64 (1987): 387, and P. S. Zurer, "Ozone Depletion's Recurring Surprises Challenge Atmospheric Scientists," *Chem. Eng. News*, May 24, 1993: 8.

Key Terms

chemical kinetics

Section 15.1
reaction rate
instantaneous rate

Section 15.2
rate law
rate constant
order
differential rate law (rate law)
integrated rate law

Section 15.3
method of initial rates
initial rate
overall reaction order

Section 15.4
first-order reaction
integrated first-order rate law
half-life of a reaction
integrated second-order rate law
zero-order reaction
integrated rate law for a
    zero-order reaction
pseudo-first-order rate law

Section 15.6
reaction mechanism
intermediate
elementary step
molecularity
unimolecular step
bimolecular step
termolecular step
rate-determining step

Section 15.7
steady-state approximation

Section 15.8
collision model
activation energy
activated complex (transition
    state)
molecular orientations
steric factor
Arrhenius equation
pre-exponential (frequency)
    factor

Section 15.9
enzyme
catalyst
homogeneous catalyst
heterogeneous catalyst
adsorption
absorption

For Review

⬤WL and **🄶🄾 Chemistry**

Sign in at **www.cengage.com/owl** to:
• View tutorials and simulations, develop problem-solving skills, and complete online homework assigned by your professor.
• Download Go Chemistry mini lecture modules for quick review and exam prep from OWL (or purchase them at **www.cengagebrain.com**)

Chemical kinetics

■ The study of the factors that control the rate (speed) of a chemical reaction
   ■ Rate is defined in terms of the change in concentration of a given reaction component per unit time
   ■ Kinetic measurements are often made under conditions where the reverse reaction is insignificant
■ The kinetic and thermodynamic properties of a reaction are not fundamentally related

Rate laws

■ Differential rate law: describes the rate as a function of concentration

$$\text{Rate} = -\frac{\Delta[A]}{\Delta t} = k[A]^n$$

   ■ k is the rate constant
   ■ n is the order; not related to the coefficients in the balanced equation
■ Integrated rate law: describes the concentration as a function of time
■ For a reaction of the type

$$aA \longrightarrow \text{products}$$

for which

$$\text{Rate} = k[A]^n$$

$n = 0$: $[A] = -kt + [A]_0$

$$t_{1/2} = \frac{[A]_0}{2k}$$

$n = 1$: $\ln[A] = -kt + \ln[A]_0$

$$t_{1/2} = \frac{0.693}{k}$$

$n = 2$: $\dfrac{1}{[A]} = kt + \dfrac{1}{k[A]_0}$

$$t_{1/2} = \frac{1}{k[A]_0}$$

   ■ The value of k can be determined from the plot of the appropriate function of [A] versus t

Reaction mechanism

■ Series of elementary steps by which an overall reaction occurs
   ■ Elementary step: rate law for the step can be written from the molecularity of the reaction
■ Two requirements for an acceptable mechanism:
   ■ The elementary steps sum to give the correct overall balanced equation
   ■ The mechanism agrees with the experimentally determined rate law

- Simple reactions can have an elementary step that is slower than all of the other steps; which is called the rate-determining step.

Steady state approximation
- Used when a specific rate-determining step cannot be chosen.
- Assumes the concentration of any intermediate remains constant as the reaction proceeds.

Kinetic models
- The simplest model to account for reaction kinetics is the collision model
  - Molecules must collide to react
  - The collision kinetic energy furnishes the potential energy needed to enable the reactants to rearrange to form products
  - A certain threshold energy called the activation energy (E_a) is necessary for a reaction to occur
  - The relative orientations of the colliding reactants are also a determining factor in the reaction rate
  - This model leads to the Arrhenius equation:

$$k = Ae^{-E_a/RT}$$

  - A depends on the collision frequency and relative orientation of the molecules
  - The value of E_a can be found by obtaining the values of k at several temperatures

Catalyst
- Speeds up a reaction without being consumed
- Works by providing a lower-energy pathway for the reaction
- Enzymes are biological catalysts
- Catalysts can be classified as homogeneous or heterogeneous
  - Homogeneous: exist in the same phase as the reactants
  - Heterogeneous: exist in a different phase than the reactants

Discussion Questions*

These questions are designed to be considered by groups of students in class. Often these questions work well for introducing a particular topic in class.

1. Define the term *stability* from both a kinetic and a thermodynamic perspective. Give examples to show the differences in these concepts.

2. Describe at least two experiments you could perform to determine a rate law.

3. Make a graph of [A] versus time for zero-, first-, and second-order reactions. From these graphs, compare successive half-lives.

4. How does temperature affect k, the rate constant? Explain.

5. Consider the following statements: "In general, the rate of a chemical reaction increases at first. After that the rate of the reaction decreases because its rate is depen-

dent on the concentrations of the reactants, and these are decreasing." Indicate everything that is correct in these statements, and indicate everything that is incorrect. Correct the incorrect statements, and explain.

6. For the reaction A + B ⟶ C, explain at least two ways in which the rate law could be zero order in chemical A.

7. A friend of yours states, "A balanced equation tells us how chemicals interact. Therefore, we can determine the rate law directly from the balanced equation." What do you tell your friend?

8. The rate constant (k) depends on which of the following? (There may be more than one answer.)
   a. the concentration of the reactants
   b. the nature of the reactants
   c. the temperature
   d. the order of the reaction
   Explain.

9. Provide a conceptual rationale for the differences in the half-lives of zero-, first-, and second-order reactions.

---

*In the Questions and the Exercises the term *rate law* always means differential rate law.

Exercises*

⚙WL Interactive versions of these problems may be assigned in OWL.

A blue exercise number indicates that the answer to that exercise appears at the back of this book and a solution appears in the *Solutions Guide*.

Reaction Rates

10. Define *reaction rate*. Distinguish between the initial rate, average rate, and instantaneous rate of a chemical reaction. Which of these rates is usually fastest? The initial rate is the rate used by convention. Give a possible explanation as to why.

11. Consider the general reaction

$$aA + bB \longrightarrow cC$$

and the following average rate data over a specific time period Δt:

$$-\frac{\Delta A}{\Delta t} = 0.0080 \text{ mol L}^{-1} \text{ s}^{-1}$$

$$-\frac{\Delta B}{\Delta t} = 0.0120 \text{ mol L}^{-1} \text{ s}^{-1}$$

$$\frac{\Delta C}{\Delta t} = 0.0160 \text{ mol L}^{-1} \text{ s}^{-1}$$

Determine a set of possible coefficients to balance this general reaction.

12. Consider the reaction

$$4PH_3(g) \longrightarrow P_4(g) + 6H_2(g)$$

If, in a certain experiment, over a specific time period, 0.0048 mole of PH_3 is consumed in a 2.0-L container during each second of the reaction, what are the rates of production of P_4 and H_2 in this experiment?

13. In the Haber process for the production of ammonia,

$$N_2(g) + 3H_2(g) \longrightarrow 2NH_3(g)$$

what is the relationship between the rate of production of ammonia and the rate of consumption of hydrogen?

14. What are the units for each of the following if concentrations are expressed in moles per liter and time in seconds?
    a. rate of a chemical reaction
    b. rate constant for a zero-order rate law
    c. rate constant for a first-order rate law
    d. rate constant for a second-order rate law
    e. rate constant for a third-order rate law

15. The rate law for the reaction

$$Cl_2(g) + CHCl_3(g) \longrightarrow HCl(g) + CCl_4(g)$$

is

$$\text{Rate} = k[Cl_2]^{1/2}[CHCl_3]$$

What are the units for k assuming time in seconds?

16. The hydroxyl radical (OH) is an important oxidizing agent in the atmosphere. At 298 K the rate constant for the reaction of OH with benzene is $1.24 \times 10^{-12} \text{ cm}^3$ molecule^{-1} s^{-1}. Calculate the value of the rate constant in L mol^{-1} s^{-1}.

Rate Laws from Experimental Data: Initial-Rates Method

17. The reaction

$$2NO(g) + Cl_2(g) \longrightarrow 2NOCl(g)$$

was studied at $-10°C$. The following results were obtained, where

$$\text{Rate} = -\frac{d[Cl_2]}{dt}$$

$[NO]_0$ (mol/L)	$[Cl_2]_0$ (mol/L)	Initial Rate (mol L^{-1} min^{-1})
0.10	0.10	0.18
0.10	0.20	0.36
0.20	0.20	1.45

a. What is the rate law?
b. What is the value of the rate constant?

18. The following data were obtained for the gas-phase decomposition of dinitrogen pentoxide,

$$2N_2O_5(g) \longrightarrow 4NO_2(g) + O_2(g)$$

$[N_2O_5]_0$ (mol/L)	Initial Rate (mol L^{-1} s^{-1})
0.0750	8.90×10^{-4}
0.190	2.26×10^{-3}
0.275	3.26×10^{-3}
0.410	4.85×10^{-3}

where $\text{Rate} = \frac{-d[N_2O_5]}{dt}$

Write the rate law and calculate the value of the rate constant.

19. The decomposition of nitrosyl chloride was studied:

$$2NOCl(g) \rightleftharpoons 2NO(g) + Cl_2(g)$$

The following data were obtained, where

$$\text{Rate} = \frac{-d[NOCl]}{dt}$$

$[NOCl]_0$ (molecules/cm^3)	Initial Rate (molecules cm^{-3} s^{-1})
3.0×10^{16}	5.98×10^4
2.0×10^{16}	2.66×10^4
1.0×10^{16}	6.64×10^3
4.0×10^{16}	1.06×10^5

---

*In the Questions and the Exercises, the term *rate law* always means differential rate law.

a. What is the rate law?
b. Calculate the rate constant.
c. Calculate the rate constant for the concentrations given in moles per liter.

20. The rate of the reaction between hemoglobin (Hb) and carbon monoxide (CO) was studied at 20°C. The following data were collected, with all concentration units in $\mu mol/L$. (A hemoglobin concentration of 2.21 $\mu mol/L$ is equal to 2.21×10^{-6} mol/L.)

$[Hb]_0$ ($\mu mol/L$)	$[CO]_0$ ($\mu mol/L$)	Initial Rate ($\mu mol\ L^{-1}\ s^{-1}$)
2.21	1.00	0.619
4.42	1.00	1.24
4.42	3.00	3.71

a. Determine the orders of this reaction with respect to Hb and CO.
b. Determine the rate law.
c. Calculate the value of the rate constant.
d. What would be the initial rate for an experiment with $[Hb]_0 = 3.36\ \mu mol/L$ and $[CO]_0 = 2.40\ \mu mol/L$?

21. The following data were obtained for the reaction

$$2ClO_2(aq) + 2OH^-(aq)$$
$$\longrightarrow ClO_3^-(aq) + ClO_2^-(aq) + H_2O(l)$$

where
$$\text{Rate} = -\frac{d[ClO_2]}{dt}$$

$[ClO_2]_0$ (mol/L)	$[OH^-]_0$ (mol/L)	Initial Rate (mol $L^{-1}\ s^{-1}$)
0.0500	0.100	5.75×10^{-2}
0.100	0.100	2.30×10^{-1}
0.100	0.0500	1.15×10^{-1}

a. Determine the rate law and the value of the rate constant.
b. What would be the initial rate for an experiment with $[ClO_2]_0 = 0.175$ mol/L and $[OH^-]_0 = 0.0844$ mol/L?

22. The reaction

$$2NO(g) + O_2(g) \longrightarrow 2NO_2(g)$$

was studied, and the following data were obtained, where

$$\text{Rate} = -\frac{d[O_2]}{dt}$$

$[NO]_0$ (molecules/cm³)	$[O_2]_0$ (molecules/cm³)	Initial Rate (molecules cm^{-3} s^{-1})
1.00×10^{18}	1.00×10^{18}	2.00×10^{16}
3.00×10^{18}	1.00×10^{18}	1.80×10^{17}
2.50×10^{18}	2.50×10^{18}	3.13×10^{17}

What would be the initial rate for an experiment where $[NO]_0 = 6.21 \times 10^{18}$ molecules/cm³ and $[O_2]_0 = 7.36 \times 10^{18}$ molecules/cm³?

23. The reaction

$$H_2SeO_3(aq) + 6I^-(aq) + 4H^+(aq)$$
$$\longrightarrow Se(s) + 2I_3^-(aq) + 3H_2O(l)$$

was studied at 0°C, and the following data were obtained:

$[H_2SeO_3]_0$ (mol/L)	$[H^+]_0$ (mol/L)	$[I^-]_0$ (mol/L)	Initial Rate (mol $L^{-1}\ s^{-1}$)
1.0×10^{-4}	2.0×10^{-2}	2.0×10^{-2}	1.66×10^{-7}
2.0×10^{-4}	2.0×10^{-2}	2.0×10^{-2}	3.33×10^{-7}
3.0×10^{-4}	2.0×10^{-2}	2.0×10^{-2}	4.99×10^{-7}
1.0×10^{-4}	4.0×10^{-2}	2.0×10^{-2}	6.66×10^{-7}
1.0×10^{-4}	1.0×10^{-2}	2.0×10^{-2}	0.42×10^{-7}
1.0×10^{-4}	2.0×10^{-2}	4.0×10^{-2}	13.2×10^{-7}
1.0×10^{-4}	1.0×10^{-2}	4.0×10^{-2}	3.36×10^{-7}

These relationships hold only if there is an insignificant amount of I_3^- present. What is the rate law and the value of the rate constant? $\left(\text{Assume that rate} = -\frac{d[H_2SeO_3]}{dt}.\right)$

24. The initial rate of a reaction doubles as the concentration of one of the reactants is quadrupled. What is the order of this reactant? If a reactant has a -1 order, what happens to the initial rate when the concentration of that reactant increases by a factor of two?

25. A study was made of the effect of the hydroxide concentration on the rate of the reaction

$$I^-(aq) + OCl^-(aq) \longrightarrow IO^-(aq) + Cl^-(aq)$$

The following data were obtained:

$[I^-]_0$ (mol/L)	$[OCl^-]_0$ (mol/L)	$[OH^-]_0$ (mol/L)	Initial Rate (mol $L^{-1}\ s^{-1}$)
0.0013	0.012	0.10	9.4×10^{-3}
0.0026	0.012	0.10	18.7×10^{-3}
0.0013	0.0060	0.10	4.7×10^{-3}
0.0013	0.018	0.10	14.0×10^{-3}
0.0013	0.012	0.050	18.7×10^{-3}
0.0013	0.012	0.20	4.7×10^{-3}
0.0013	0.018	0.20	7.0×10^{-3}

Determine the rate law and the value of the rate constant for this reaction.

Integrated Rate Laws

26. The initial rate for a reaction is equal to the slope of the tangent line at $t \approx 0$ in a plot of [A] versus time. From calculus,

$$\text{Initial rate} = \frac{-d[A]}{dt}$$

Therefore, the differential rate law for a reaction is

$$\text{Rate} = \frac{-d[A]}{dt} = k[A]^n$$

Assuming you have some calculus in your background, derive the zero-, first-, and second-order integrated rate laws using the differential rate law.

27. If the half-life for a reaction is 20. seconds, what would be the second half-life, assuming the reaction is either zero, first, or second order?

28. A certain reaction has the following general form:

$$aA \longrightarrow bB$$

At a particular temperature and $[A]_0 = 2.80 \times 10^{-3}$ M, concentration versus time data were collected for this reaction, and a plot of $1/[A]$ versus time resulted in a straight line with a slope value of $+3.60 \times 10^{-2}$ L mol^{-1} s^{-1}.
   a. Determine the rate law, the integrated rate law, and the value of the rate constant for this reaction.
   b. Calculate the half-life for this reaction.
   c. How much time is required for the concentration of A to decrease to 7.00×10^{-4} M?

29. A certain reaction has the following general form:

$$aA \longrightarrow bB$$

At a particular temperature and $[A]_0 = 2.00 \times 10^{-2}$ M, concentration versus time data were collected for this reaction, and a plot of $\ln[A]$ versus time resulted in a straight line with a slope value of -2.97×10^{-2} min^{-1}.
   a. Determine the rate law, the integrated rate law, and the value of the rate constant for this reaction.
   b. Calculate the half-life for this reaction.
   c. How much time is required for the concentration of A to decrease to 2.50×10^{-3} M?

30. The decomposition of ethanol (C_2H_5OH) on an alumina (Al_2O_3) surface,

$$C_2H_5OH(g) \longrightarrow C_2H_4(g) + H_2O(g)$$

was studied at 600 K. Concentration versus time data were collected for this reaction, and a plot of [A] versus time resulted in a straight line with a slope value of -4.00×10^{-5} mol L^{-1} s^{-1}.
   a. Determine the rate law, the integrated rate law, and the value of the rate constant for this reaction.
   b. If the initial concentration of C_2H_5OH was 1.25×10^{-2} M, calculate the half-life for this reaction.
   c. How much time is required for all of the 1.25×10^{-2} M C_2H_5OH to decompose?

31. The decomposition of hydrogen peroxide was studied at a particular temperature. The following data were obtained, where

$$\text{Rate} = -\frac{d[H_2O_2]}{dt}$$

Time (s)	$[H_2O_2]$ (mol/L)
0	1.00
120 ± 1	0.91
300 ± 1	0.78
600 ± 1	0.59
1200 ± 1	0.37
1800 ± 1	0.22
2400 ± 1	0.13
3000 ± 1	0.082
3600 ± 1	0.050

Determine the integrated rate law, the differential rate law, and the value of the rate constant. Calculate the $[H_2O_2]$ at 4000. s after the start of the reaction.

32. The dimerization of butadiene was studied at 500. K:

$$2C_4H_6(g) \longrightarrow C_8H_{12}(g)$$

The following data were obtained, where

$$\text{Rate} = -\frac{d[C_4H_6]}{dt}$$

Time (s)	$[C_4H_6]$ (mol/L)
195	1.6×10^{-2}
604	1.5×10^{-2}
1246	1.3×10^{-2}
2180	1.1×10^{-2}
6210	0.68×10^{-2}

Determine the forms of the integrated rate law, the differential rate law, and the value of the rate constant for this reaction.

33. The rate of the reaction

$$NO_2(g) + CO(g) \longrightarrow NO(g) + CO_2(g)$$

depends only on the concentration of nitrogen dioxide at temperatures below 225°C. At a temperature below 225°C, the following data were collected:

Time (s)	$[NO_2]$ (mol/L)
0	0.500
1.20×10^3	0.444
3.00×10^3	0.381
4.50×10^3	0.340
9.00×10^3	0.250
1.80×10^4	0.174

Determine the integrated rate law, the differential rate law, and the value of the rate constant at this temperature. Calculate $[NO_2]$ at 2.70×10^4 s after the start of the reaction.

34. The rate of the reaction

$$O(g) + NO_2(g) \longrightarrow NO(g) + O_2(g)$$

was studied at a certain temperature. This reaction is one step of the nitric oxide–catalyzed destruction of ozone in the upper atmosphere.
   a. In one experiment, NO_2 was in large excess at a concentration of 1.0×10^{13} molecules/cm^3 with the following data collected:

Time (s)	[O] (atoms/cm^3)
0	5.0×10^9
1.0×10^{-2}	1.9×10^9
2.0×10^{-2}	6.8×10^8
3.0×10^{-2}	2.5×10^8

What is the order of the reaction with respect to oxygen atoms?

b. The reaction is known to be first order with respect to NO_2. Determine the overall rate law and the value of the rate constant.

35. At 500 K in the presence of a copper surface, ethanol decomposes according to the equation

$$C_2H_5OH(g) \longrightarrow CH_3CHO(g) + H_2(g)$$

The pressure of C_2H_5OH was measured as a function of time, and the following data were obtained:

Time (s)	$P_{C_2H_5OH}$ (torr)
0	250.
100.	237
200.	224
300.	211
400.	198
500.	185

Since the pressure of a gas is directly proportional to the concentration of the gas, we can express the rate law for a gaseous reaction in terms of partial pressures. Using the preceding data, deduce the rate law, the integrated rate law, and the value of the rate constant, all in terms of pressure units in atm and time in seconds. Predict the pressure of C_2H_5OH after 900. s from the start of the reaction. (*Hint:* To determine the order of the reaction with respect to C_2H_5OH, compare how the pressure of C_2H_5OH decreases with each time listing.)

36. Experimental data for the reaction

$$A \longrightarrow 2B + C$$

have been plotted in the following three different ways (with concentration units in mol/L):

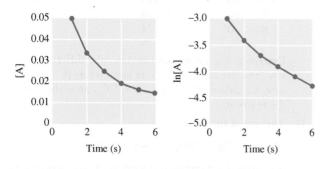

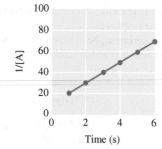

a. What is the order of the reaction with respect to A, and what is the initial concentration of A?
b. What is the concentration of A after 9 s?
c. What are the first three half-lives for this experiment?

37. The reaction

$$NO(g) + O_3(g) \longrightarrow NO_2(g) + O_2(g)$$

was studied by performing two experiments. In the first experiment (results shown in following table), the rate of disappearance of NO was followed in a large excess of O_3. (The $[O_3]$ remains effectively constant at 1.0×10^{14} molecules/cm^3.)

Time (ms)	[NO] (molecules/cm^3)
0	6.0×10^8
100 ± 1	5.0×10^8
500 ± 1	2.4×10^8
700 ± 1	1.7×10^8
1000 ± 1	9.9×10^7

In the second experiment, [NO] was held constant at 2.0×10^{14} molecules/cm^3. The data for the disappearance of O_3 were as follows:

Time (ms)	[O$_3$] (molecules/cm^3)
0	1.0×10^{10}
50 ± 1	8.4×10^9
100 ± 1	7.0×10^9
200 ± 1	4.9×10^9
300 ± 1	3.4×10^9

a. What is the order with respect to each reactant?
b. What is the overall rate law?
c. What is the value of the rate constant obtained from each set of experiments?

$$\text{Rate} = k'[NO]^x \qquad \text{Rate} = k''[O_3]^y$$

d. What is the value of the rate constant for the overall rate law?

$$\text{Rate} = k[NO]^x[O_3]^y$$

38. Determine the forms of the integrated and the differential rate laws for the decomposition of benzene diazonium chloride,

$$C_6H_5N_2Cl(aq) \longrightarrow C_6H_5Cl(l) + N_2(g)$$

from the following data, which were collected at 50.°C and 1.00 atm:

Time (s)	N$_2$ Evolved (mL)
6	19.3
9	26.0
14	36.0
22	45.0
30.	50.4
∞	58.3

The total solution volume was 40.0 mL.

39. You and a coworker have developed a molecule that has shown potential as cobra antivenom (AV). This antivenom

works by binding to the venom (V), thereby rendering it nontoxic. This reaction can be desribed by the rate law

$$Rate = k[AV]^1[V]^1$$

You have been given the following data from your coworker:

$$[V]_0 = 0.20\ M$$

$$[AV]_0 = 1.0 \times 10^{-4}\ M$$

A plot of $\ln[AV]$ versus time gives a straight line with a slope of $-0.32\ s^{-1}$. What is the value of the rate constant (k) for this reaction?

40. Consider the following representation of the reaction $2NO_2(g) \rightarrow 2NO(g) + O_2(g)$.

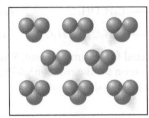 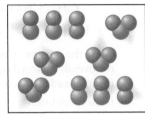 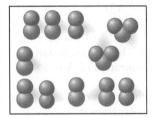

(a) time = 0 minutes   (b) time = 10 minutes   (c) time = ? minutes

Time

Determine the time for the final representation above if the reaction is
a. first order
b. second order
c. zero order

41. The rate law for the decomposition of phosphine (PH_3) is

$$Rate = -\frac{d[PH_3]}{dt} = k[PH_3]$$

It takes 120. s for the concentration of 1.00 M PH_3 to decrease to 0.250 M. How much time is required for 2.00 M PH_3 to decrease to a concentration of 0.350 M?

42. The radioactive isotope ^{32}P decays by first-order kinetics and has a half-life of 14.3 days. How long does it take for 95.0% of a given sample of ^{32}P to decay?

43. Consider the following initial rate data for the decomposition of compound AB to give A and B:

$[AB]_0$ (mol/L)	Initial Rate (mol L^{-1} s^{-1})
0.200	3.20×10^{-3}
0.400	1.28×10^{-2}
0.600	2.88×10^{-2}

Determine the half-life for the decomposition reaction initially having 1.00 M AB present.

44. The rate law for the reaction

$$2NOBr(g) \longrightarrow 2NO(g) + Br_2(g)$$

at some temperature is

$$Rate = -\frac{d[NOBr]}{dt} = k[NOBr]^2$$

a. If the half-life for this reaction is 2.00 s when $[NOBr]_0 = 0.900\ M$, calculate the value of k for this reaction.
b. How much time is required for the concentration of NOBr to decrease to 0.100 M?

45. A first-order reaction is 75.0% complete in 320. s.
a. What are the first and second half-lives for this reaction?
b. How long does it take for 90.0% completion?

46. For the reaction A $\rightarrow$ products, successive half-lives are observed to be 10.0, 20.0, and 40.0 min for an experiment in which $[A]_0 = 0.10\ M$. Calculate the concentration of A at the following times.
a. 80.0 min   b. 30.0 min

47. The decomposition of hydrogen iodide on finely divided gold at 150°C is zero order with respect to HI. The rate defined below is constant at 1.20×10^{-4} mol/L · s.

$$2HI(g) \xrightarrow{\text{Au}} H_2(g) + I_2(g)$$

$$Rate = -\frac{d[HI]}{dt} = k = 1.20 \times 10^{-4}\ mol/L \cdot s$$

a. If the initial HI concentration was 0.250 mol/L, calculate the concentration of HI at 25 minutes after the start of the reaction.
b. How long will it take for all of the 0.250 M HI to decompose?

48. Consider two reaction vessels, one containing A and the other containing B, with equal concentrations at $t = 0$. If both substances decompose by first-order kinectics, where

$$k_A = 4.50 \times 10^{-4}\ s^{-1}$$

$$k_B = 3.70 \times 10^{-3}\ s^{-1}$$

how much time must pass to reach a condition such that $[A] = 4.00[B]$?

49. Theophylline is a phamaceutical drug that is sometimes used to help with lung function. You observe a case where the initial lab results indicate that the concentration of theophylline in a patient's body decreased from 2.0×10^{-3} M to 1.0×10^{-3} M in 24 hours. In another 12 hours, the drug concentration was found to be 5.0×10^{-4} M. What is the value of the rate constant for the metabolism of this drug in the body?

50. Consider the hypothetical reaction

$$A + B + 2C \longrightarrow 2D + 3E$$

where the rate law is

$$\text{Rate} = -\frac{d[A]}{dt} = k[A][B]^2$$

An experiment is carried out where $[A]_0 = 1.0 \times 10^{-2}$ M, $[B]_0 = 3.0$ M, and $[C]_0 = 2.0$ M. The reaction is started, and after 8.0 seconds, the concentration of A is 3.8×10^{-3} M.
   a. Calculate the value of k for this reaction.
   b. Calculate the half-life for this experiment.
   c. Calculate the concentration of A after 13.0 seconds.
   d. Calculate the concentration of C after 13.0 seconds.

51. Consider the reaction

$$3A + B + C \longrightarrow D + E$$

where the rate law is defined as

$$-\frac{d[A]}{dt} = k[A]^2[B][C]$$

An experiment is carried out where $[B]_0 = [C]_0 = 1.00$ M and $[A]_0 = 1.00 \times 10^{-4}$ M.
   a. If after 3.00 minutes $[A] = 3.26 \times 10^{-5}$ M, calculate the value of k.
   b. Calculate the half-life for this experiment.
   c. Calculate the concentration of B and the concentration of A after 10.0 minutes.

Reaction Mechanisms

52. Define each of the following.
   a. elementary step
   b. molecularity
   c. reaction mechanism
   d. intermediate
   e. rate-determining step

53. Define what is meant by unimolecular and bimolecular steps. Why are termolecular steps infrequently seen in chemical reactions?

54. What two requirements must be met to call a mechanism plausible? Why say a "plausible" mechanism instead of the "correct" mechanism? Is it true that most reactions occur by a one-step mechanism? Explain.

55. Write the rate laws for the following elementary reactions.
   a. $CH_3NC(g) \longrightarrow CH_3CN(g)$
   b. $O_3(g) + NO(g) \longrightarrow O_2(g) + NO_2(g)$
   c. $O_3(g) \longrightarrow O_2(g) + O(g)$

   d. $O_3(g) + O(g) \longrightarrow 2O_2(g)$
   e. $^{14}_{6}C \longrightarrow ^{14}_{7}N + \beta$ particle (nuclear decay)

56. A possible mechanism for the decomposition of hydrogen peroxide is

$$H_2O_2 \longrightarrow 2OH$$

$$H_2O_2 + OH \longrightarrow H_2O + HO_2$$

$$HO_2 + OH \longrightarrow H_2O + O_2$$

Using your results fom Exercise 31, specify which step is the rate-determining step. What is the overall balanced equation for the reaction?

57. A proposed mechanism for a reaction is

$$C_4H_9Br \longrightarrow C_4H_9^+ + Br^- \qquad \text{Slow}$$

$$C_4H_9^+ + H_2O \longrightarrow C_4H_9OH_2^+ \qquad \text{Fast}$$

$$C_4H_9OH_2^+ + H_2O \longrightarrow C_4H_9OH + H_3O^+ \qquad \text{Fast}$$

Write the rate law expected for this mechanism. What is the overall balanced equation for the reaction? What are the intermediates in the proposed mechanism?

58. Is the mechanism

$$NO + Cl_2 \xrightarrow{k_1} NOCl_2$$

$$NOCl_2 + NO \xrightarrow{k_2} 2NOCl$$

consistent with the results you obtained in Exercise 17? If so, which step is the rate-determining step?

59. The reaction

$$2NO(g) + O_2(g) \longrightarrow 2NO_2(g)$$

exhibits the rate law

$$\text{Rate} = k[NO]^2[O_2]$$

Which of the following mechanisms is consistent with this rate law?
   a. $NO + O_2 \longrightarrow NO_2 + O$ Slow
       $O + NO \longrightarrow NO_2$ Fast
   b. $NO + O_2 \rightleftharpoons NO_3$ Fast equilibrium
       $NO_3 + NO \longrightarrow 2NO_2$ Slow
   c. $2NO \longrightarrow N_2O_2$ Slow
       $N_2O_2 + O_2 \longrightarrow N_2O_4$ Fast
       $N_2O_4 \longrightarrow 2NO_2$ Fast
   d. $2NO \rightleftharpoons N_2O_2$ Fast equilibrium
       $N_2O_2 \longrightarrow NO_2 + O$ Slow
       $O + NO \longrightarrow NO_2$ Fast

60. The gas-phase reaction between Br_2 and H_2 to form HBr is assumed to proceed by the following mechanism:

$$Br_2 \underset{k_{-1}}{\overset{k_1}{\rightleftharpoons}} 2Br$$

$$Br + H_2 \underset{k_{-2}}{\overset{k_2}{\rightleftharpoons}} HBr + H$$

$$H + Br_2 \xrightarrow{k_3} HBr + Br$$

$$2Br \xrightarrow{k_4} Br_2$$

   a. Under what conditions does the rate law have the form rate = $k'[Br_2]$?

b. Under what conditions does the rate law have the form rate = $k''[H_2][Br_2]^{1/2}$?

c. Give expressions for k' and k'' in terms of the rate constants used to define the mechanism.

61. The reaction

$$5Br^-(aq) + BrO_3^-(aq) + 6H^+(aq) \longrightarrow 3Br_2(l) + 3H_2O(l)$$

is expected to obey the mechanism

$$BrO_3^-(aq) + H^+(aq) \underset{k_{-1}}{\overset{k_1}{\rightleftharpoons}} HBrO_3(aq)$$
Fast equilibrium

$$HBrO_3(aq) + H^+(aq) \underset{k_{-2}}{\overset{k_2}{\rightleftharpoons}} H_2BrO_3^+(aq)$$
Fast equilibrium

$$Br^-(aq) + H_2BrO_3^+(aq) \overset{k_3}{\longrightarrow} (Br{-}BrO_2)(aq) + H_2O(l)$$
Slow

$$(Br{-}BrO_2)(aq) + 4H^+(aq) + 4Br^-(aq) \longrightarrow products$$
Fast

Write the rate law for this reaction.

62. The rate law for the reaction

$$BrO_3^-(aq) + 3SO_3^{2-}(aq) \longrightarrow Br^-(aq) + 3SO_4^{2-}(aq)$$

is   Rate = $k[BrO_3^-][SO_3^{2-}][H^+]$

The first step in a proposed mechanism is

$$SO_3^{2-}(aq) + H^+(aq) \overset{k_1}{\longrightarrow} HSO_3^-(aq) \quad \text{Fast}$$

The second step is rate determining. Write a possible second step for the mechanism.

63. The reaction

$$I^-(aq) + OCl^-(aq) \longrightarrow IO^-(aq) + Cl^-(aq)$$

is believed to occur by the following mechanism:

$$OCl^- + H_2O \underset{k_{-1}}{\overset{k_1}{\rightleftharpoons}} HOCl + OH^- \quad \text{Fast equilibrium}$$

$$I^- + HOCl \overset{k_2}{\longrightarrow} HOI + Cl^- \quad \text{Slow}$$

$$HOI + OH^- \overset{k_1}{\longrightarrow} H_2O + IO^- \quad \text{Fast}$$

Write the rate law for this reaction. *Note:* Since the reaction is in aqueous solution, the effective concentration of water remains constant. Thus the rate of the forward reaction in the first step can be written as

$$\text{Rate} = k[H_2O][OCl^-] = k_1[OCl^-]$$

64. In the gas phase, the production of phosgene from chlorine and carbon monoxide is assumed to proceed by the following mechanism:

$$Cl_2 \underset{k_{-1}}{\overset{k_1}{\rightleftharpoons}} 2Cl \quad \text{Fast equilibrium}$$

$$Cl + CO \underset{k_{-2}}{\overset{k_2}{\rightleftharpoons}} COCl \quad \text{Fast equilibrium}$$

$$COCl + Cl_2 \overset{k_3}{\longrightarrow} COCl_2 + Cl \quad \text{Slow}$$

$$2Cl \overset{k_4}{\longrightarrow} Cl_2 \quad \text{Fast}$$

Overall
reaction: $CO + Cl_2 \longrightarrow COCl_2$

a. Write the rate law for this reaction.
b. Which species are intermediates?

65. The following mechanism is proposed for the reduction of NO_3^- by $MoCl_6^{2-}$:

$$MoCl_6^{2-} \underset{k_{-1}}{\overset{k_1}{\rightleftharpoons}} MoCl_5^- + Cl^-$$

$$NO_3^- + MoCl_5^- \overset{k_2}{\longrightarrow} OMoCl_5^- + NO_2^-$$

a. What is the intermediate?
b. Derive an expression for the rate law (rate = $d[NO_2^-]/dt$) for the overall reaction using the steady-state approximation.

66. The following mechanism has been proposed to account for the rate law of the decomposition of ozone to $O_2(g)$:

$$O_3 + M \underset{k_{-1}}{\overset{k_1}{\rightleftharpoons}} O_2 + O + M$$

$$O + O_3 \overset{k_2}{\longrightarrow} 2O_2$$

Apply the steady-state hypothesis to the concentration of atomic oxygen, and derive the rate law for the decomposition of ozone. (M stands for an atom or molecule that can exchange kinetic energy with the particles undergoing the chemical reaction.)

67. Consider the hypothetical reaction

$$B \longrightarrow E + F$$

which is assumed to occur by the mechanism

$$B + B \underset{k_{-1}}{\overset{k_1}{\rightleftharpoons}} B^* + B$$

$$B^* \overset{k_2}{\longrightarrow} E + F$$

where B^* represents a B molecule with enough energy to surmount the reaction energy barrier.

a. Derive the rate law for the production of E using the steady-state approximation.

b. Assume that this reaction is known to be first order. Under what conditions does your derived rate law (from part a) agree with this observation?

c. Explain how a chemical reaction can be first order, since even in a simple case ($B \longrightarrow E + F$) molecules must collide to build up enough energy to get over the energy barrier. Why aren't all reactions at least second order? In other words, explain the physical significance of the result from part b.

Temperature Dependence of Rate Constants and the Collision Model

68. How is the rate of a reaction affected by each of the following.
a. activation energy
b. temperature
c. frequency of collisions
d. orientation of collisions

69. The central idea of the collision model is that molecules must collide in order to react. Give two reasons why not all collisions of reactant molecules result in product formation.

70. Consider the following potential energy plots

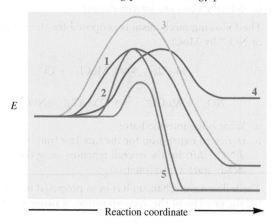

a. Rank the reactions from fastest to slowest, and explain your answer. If any reactions have equal rates, explain why.
b. Label the reactions as endothermic or exothermic, and supply your answer.
c. Rank the exothermic reactions from greatest to least change in potential energy, and support your answer.

71. The graph below shows the number of collisions with a particular energy for two different temperatures.

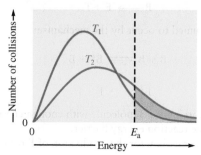

a. Which is greater, T_2 or T_1? How can you tell?
b. What does this graph tell us about the temperature dependence of the rate of a chemical reaction? Explain your answer.

72. Which of the following reactions would you expect to have the larger rate at room temperature? Why? (*Hint:* Think of which would have the lower activation energy.)

$$2Ce^{4+}(aq) + Hg_2^{2+}(aq) \longrightarrow 2Ce^{3+}(aq) + 2Hg^{2+}(aq)$$

$$H_3O^+(aq) + OH^-(aq) \longrightarrow 2H_2O(l)$$

73. The activation energy for the decomposition of HI(g) to $H_2(g)$ and $I_2(g)$ is 186 kJ/mol. The rate constant at 555 K is 3.52×10^{-7} L mol^{-1} s^{-1}. What is the rate constant at 645 K?

74. The decomposition of iodoethane in the gas phase proceeds according to the following equation:

$$C_2H_5I(g) \longrightarrow C_2H_4(g) + HI(g)$$

At 660. K, $k = 7.2 \times 10^{-4}$ s^{-1}; at 720. K, $k = 1.7 \times 10^{-2}$ s^{-1}. What is the rate constant for this first-order decomposition at 325°C? If the initial pressure of iodoethane is 894 torr at 245°C, what is the pressure of iodoethane after three half-lives?

75. A certain reaction has an activation energy of 54.0 kJ/mol. As the temperature is increased from 22°C to a higher temperature, the rate constant increases by a factor of 7.00. Calculate the higher temperature.

76. Chemists commonly use a rule of thumb that an increase of 10 K in temperature doubles the rate of a reaction. What must the activation energy be for this statement to be true for a temperature increase from 25°C to 35°C?

77. The reaction

$$(CH_3)_3CBr + OH^- \longrightarrow (CH_3)_3COH + Br^-$$

in a certain solvent is first order with respect to $(CH_3)_3CBr$ and zero order with respect to OH$^-$. In several experiments the rate constant k was determined at different temperatures. A plot of $\ln(k)$ versus $1/T$ was constructed that resulted in a straight line with a slope of -1.10×10^4 K and a y intercept of 33.5. Assume that k has units of s^{-1}.
a. Determine the activation energy for this reaction.
b. Determine the value of the frequency factor A.
c. Calculate the value of k at 25°C.

78. The rate constant for the gas-phase decomposition of N_2O_5,

$$N_2O_5 \longrightarrow 2NO_2 + \tfrac{1}{2}O_2$$

has the following temperature dependence:

T (K)	k (s^{-1})
338	4.9×10^{-3}
318	5.0×10^{-4}
298	3.5×10^{-5}

Make the appropriate graph using these data, and determine the activation energy for this reaction.

79. Experimental values for the temperature dependence of the rate constant for the gas-phase reaction

$$NO(g) + O_3(g) \longrightarrow NO_2(g) + O_2(g)$$

are as follows:

T (K)	k (L mol^{-1} s^{-1})
195	1.08×10^9
230.	2.95×10^9
260.	5.42×10^9
298	12.0×10^9
369	35.5×10^9

Make the appropriate graph using these data, and determine the activation energy for this reaction.

80. Draw a rough sketch of the energy profile for each of the following cases.
a. $\Delta E = +10$ kJ/mol, $E_a = 25$ kJ/mol
b. $\Delta E = -10$ kJ/mol, $E_a = 50$ kJ/mol
c. $\Delta E = -50$ kJ/mol, $E_a = 50$ kJ/mol

Which reaction will have the greatest rate at 298 K? Assume the frequency factor A is the same for all three reactions.

81. For the following reaction profiles, indicate
    a. the positions of reactants and products.
    b. the activation energy.
    c. ΔE for the reaction.

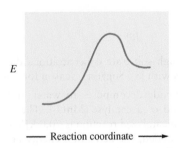

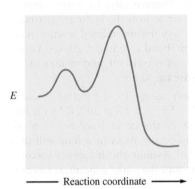

d. The second reaction profile is representative of a reaction that occurs by a two-step mechanism. Which point on the plot represents the energy of the intermediate in the two-step reaction? Which step in the mechanism is rate determining, the first or the second step? Explain.

82. The activation energy for the reaction

$$NO_2(g) + CO(g) \longrightarrow NO(g) + CO_2(g)$$

is 125 kJ/mol, and ΔE for the reaction is -216 kJ/mol. What is the activation energy for the reverse reaction $[NO(g) + CO_2(g) \longrightarrow NO_2(g) + CO(g)]$?

83. The activation energy for the reaction

$$A_2(g) + B_2(g) \longrightarrow 2AB(g)$$

is 167 kJ/mol, and ΔE for the reaction is $+28$ kJ/mol. What is the activation energy for the decomposition of AB?

Catalysis

84. Why does a catalyst increase the rate of a reaction? What is the difference between a homogeneous and a heterogeneous catalyst? Would a given reaction necessarily have the same rate law for both a catalyzed and an uncatalyzed pathway? Explain.

85. Consider the following potential energy plots for a chemical reaction when answering the questions below.

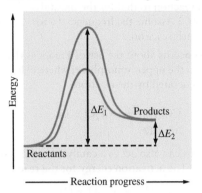

a. Which plot (red or blue) is the catalyzed pathway? How do you know?
b. What does ΔE_1 represent?
c. What does ΔE_2 represent?
d. Is the reaction endothermic or exothermic?

86. Would the slope of a $\ln(k)$ versus $1/T$ (K) plot for a catalyzed reaction be more or less negative than the slope of a $\ln(k)$ versus $1/T$ (K) plot for the uncatalyzed reaction? Assume that both rate laws are first order. Explain.

87. The decomposition of NH_3 to N_2 and H_2 was studied on two surfaces:

Surface	E_a (kJ/mol)
W	163
Os	197

Without a catalyst, the activation energy is 335 kJ/mol.
a. Which surface is the better heterogeneous catalyst for the decomposition of NH_3? Why?
b. How many times faster is the reaction at 298 K on the W surface compared with the reaction with no catalyst present? Assume that the frequency factor A is the same for each reaction.
c. The decomposition reaction on the two surfaces obeys a rate law of the form

$$\text{Rate} = k\frac{[NH_3]}{[H_2]}$$

How can you explain the inverse dependence of the rate on the H_2 concentration?

88. One pathway for the destruction of ozone in the upper atmosphere is

$$O_3(g) + NO(g) \longrightarrow NO_2(g) + O_2(g) \qquad \text{Slow}$$

$$NO_2(g) + O(g) \longrightarrow NO(g) + O_2(g) \qquad \text{Fast}$$

Overall
reaction: $O_3(g) + O(g) \longrightarrow 2O_2(g)$

a. Which species is a catalyst?
b. Which species is an intermediate?
c. E_a for the uncatalyzed reaction

$$O_3(g) + O(g) \longrightarrow 2O_2(g)$$

is 14.0 kJ. E_a for the same reaction when catalyzed is 11.9 kJ. What is the ratio of the rate constant for the catalyzed reaction to that for the uncatalyzed reaction at 25°C? Assume the frequency factor A is the same for each reaction.

89. One of the concerns about the use of Freons is that they will migrate to the upper atmosphere, where chlorine atoms can be generated by the reaction

$$CCl_2F_2 \xrightarrow{h\nu} CF_2Cl + Cl$$

Freon-12

Chlorine atoms can also act as a catalyst for the destruction of ozone. The activation energy for the reaction

$$Cl + O_3 \longrightarrow ClO + O_2$$

is 2.1 kJ/mol. Which is the more effective catalyst for the destruction of ozone, Cl or NO? (See Exercise 88.)

90. Assuming that the mechanism for the hydrogenation of C_2H_4 given in Section 15.9 is correct, would you predict that the product of the reaction of C_2H_4 with D_2 would be CH_2D—CH_2D or CHD_2—CH_3?

91. For enzyme-catalyzed reactions that follow the mechanism

$$E + S \rightleftharpoons E \cdot S$$

$$E \cdot S \rightleftharpoons E + P$$

a graph of the rate as a function of [S], the concentration of the substrate, has the following general appearance:

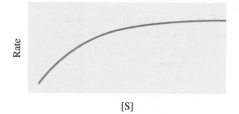

[S]

Note that at high substrate concentrations the rate no longer changes with [S]. Suggest a reason for this.

92. Hydrogen peroxide decomposes to water and oxygen gas with the aid of a catalyst (MnO₂). The activation energy of the uncatalyzed reaction is 70.0 kJ/mol. When the catalyst is added, the activation energy at 20.°C is 42.0 kJ/mol. Theoretically, to what temperature (°C) would one have to heat the hydrogen peroxide solution so that the rate of the uncatalyzed reaction is equal to the rate of the catalyzed reaction at 20.°C? Assume the frequency factor A is constant, and assume the initial concentrations are the same.

93. The activation energy for a reaction is changed from 184 kJ/mol to 59.0 kJ/mol at 600. K by the introduction of a catalyst. If the uncatalyzed reaction takes about 2400 years to occur, about how long will the catalyzed reaction take? Assume the frequency factor A is constant, and assume the initial concentrations are the same.

Additional Exercises

94. The rate law for a reaction can be determined only from experiment and not from the balanced equation. Two experimental procedures were outlined in this chapter. What are these two procedures? Explain how each method is used to determine rate laws.

95. The type of rate law for a reaction, either the differential rate law or the integrated rate law, is usually determined by which data are easiest to collect. Explain.

96. a. Using the free energy profile for a simple one-step reaction, show that at equilibrium $K = k_f/k_r$, where k_f and k_r are the rate constants for the forward and reverse reactions. *Hint:* Use the relationship $\Delta G° = -RT \ln(K)$, and represent k_f and k_r using the Arrhenius equation ($k = Ae^{-E_a/RT}$).

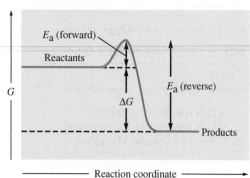

b. Why is the following statement false? "A catalyst can increase the rate of a forward reaction but not the rate of the reverse reaction."

97. Iodomethane (CH₃I) is a commonly used reagent in organic chemistry. When used properly, this reagent allows chemists to introduce methyl groups in many different, useful applications. The chemical does pose a risk as a carcinogen, possibly owing to iodomethane's ability to react with portions of the DNA strand (if they were to come in contact). Consider the following hypothetical initial rates data:

[DNA]₀ (μmol/L)	[CH₃I]₀ (μmol/L)	Initial Rate (μmol L⁻¹ s⁻¹)
0.100	0.100	3.20×10^{-4}
0.100	0.200	6.40×10^{-4}
0.200	0.200	1.28×10^{-3}

Which of the following could be a possible mechanism to explain the initial rate data?

Mechanism I DNA + CH₃I $\longrightarrow$ DNA—CH₃⁺ + I⁻

Mechanism II   CH₃I $\longrightarrow$ CH₃⁺ + I⁻   Slow

DNA + CH₃⁺ $\longrightarrow$ DNA—CH₃⁺   Fast

98. Two isomers (A and B) of a given compound dimerize as follows:

$$2A \xrightarrow{k_1} A_2$$

$$2B \xrightarrow{k_2} B_2$$

Both processes are known to be second order in the reactant, and k_1 is known to be 0.250 L mol^{-1} s^{-1} at 25°C. In a particular experiment A, and B were placed in separate containers at 25°C, where $[A]_0 = 1.00 \times 10^{-2}$ M and $[B]_0 = 2.50 \times 10^{-2}$ M. After each reaction had progressed for 3.00 min, $[A] = 3.00[B]$. In this case the rate laws are defined as follows:

$$\text{Rate} = -\frac{d[A]}{dt} = k_1[A]^2$$

$$\text{Rate} = -\frac{d[B]}{dt} = k_2[B]^2$$

a. Calculate the concentration of A_2 after 3.00 min.
b. Calculate the value of k_2.
c. Calculate the half-life for the experiment involving A.

99. The thermal degradation of silk was studied by Kuruppillai, Hersh, and Tucker ("Historic Textile and Paper Materials," *ACS Advances in Chemistry Series*, No. 212, 1986) by measuring the tensile strength of silk fibers at various times of exposure to elevated temperature. The loss of tensile strength follows first-order kinetics,

$$-\frac{ds}{dt} = ks$$

where s is the strength of the fiber retained after heating and k is the first-order rate constant. The effects of adding a deacidifying agent and an antioxidant to the silk were studied, and the following data were obtained:

Heating Time (days)	Strength Retained (%)		
	Untreated	Deacidifying Agent	Antioxidant
0.00	100.0	100.1	114.6
1.00	67.9	60.8	65.2
2.00	38.9	26.8	28.1
3.00	16.1	—	11.3
6.00	6.8	—	—

a. Determine the first-order rate constants for the thermal degradation of silk for each of the three experiments.
b. Does either of the two additives appear to retard the degradation of silk?
c. Calculate the half-life for the thermal degradation of silk for each of the three experiments.

100. Sulfuryl chloride (SO_2Cl_2) decomposes to sulfur dioxide (SO_2) and chlorine (Cl_2) by reaction in the gas phase. The following data were obtained when a sample containing 5.00×10^{-2} mole of sulfuryl chloride was heated to 600 K ± 1 K in a 5.00×10^{-1} L container.

Time (h)	0.00	1.00	2.00	4.00	8.00	16.00
Pressure (atm)	4.93	5.60	6.34	7.33	8.56	9.52

Define the rate as $-d[SO_2Cl_2]/dt$.
a. Determine the value of the rate constant for the decomposition of sulfuryl chloride at 600 K.
b. What is the half-life of the reaction?
c. What would be the pressure in the vessel after 0.500 h and after 12.0 h?
d. What fraction of the sulfuryl chloride remains after 20.0 h?

101. One reason suggested for the instability of long chains of silicon atoms is that the decomposition involves the following transition state:

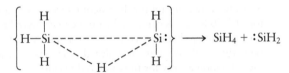

The activation energy for such a process is 210 kJ/mol, which is less than either the Si—Si or the Si—H bond energy. Why would a similar mechanism not be expected to play a very important role in the decomposition of long chains of carbon atoms as seen in organic compounds?

102. The following results were obtained at 600 K for the decomposition of ethanol on an alumina (Al_2O_3) surface,

$$C_2H_5OH(g) \longrightarrow C_2H_4(g) + H_2O(g)$$

t (s)	P_{Total} (torr)
0	250.
10.	265
20.	280.
30.	295
40.	310.
50.	325

a. Predict P_{Total} in torr at $t = 80.$ s.
b. What is the value of the rate constant, and what are its units?
c. What is the order of the reaction?
d. Calculate P_{Total} at $t = 300.$ s.

103. At 620. K butadiene dimerizes at a moderate rate. The following data were obtained in an experiment involving this reaction:

t (s)	$[C_4H_6]$ (mol/L)
0	0.01000
1000.	0.00629
2000.	0.00459
3000.	0.00361

a. Determine the order of the reaction in butadiene.
b. In how many seconds is the dimerization 1.0% complete?
c. In how many seconds is the dimerization 2.0% complete?
d. What is the half-life for the reaction if the initial concentration of butadiene is 0.0200 M?
e. Use the results from this problem and Exercise 32 to calculate the activation energy for the dimerization of butadiene.

104. The decomposition of $NO_2(g)$ occurs by the following bimolecular elementary reaction:

$$2NO_2(g) \longrightarrow 2NO(g) + O_2(g)$$

The rate constant at 273 K is 2.3×10^{-12} L mol^{-1} s^{-1}, and the activation energy is 111 kJ/mol. How long will it take for the concentration of $NO_2(g)$ to decrease from an initial partial pressure of 2.5 atm to 1.5 atm at 500. K? Assume ideal gas behavior.

105. The activation energy for a certain uncatalyzed biochemical reaction is 50.0 kJ/mol. In the presence of a catalyst at 37°C, the rate constant for the reaction increases by a factor of 2.50×10^3 as compared with the uncatalyzed reaction. Assuming that the frequency factor A is the same for both the catalyzed and uncatalyzed reactions, calculate the activation energy for the catalyzed reaction.

106. For the reaction

$$2N_2O_5(g) \longrightarrow 4NO_2(g) + O_2(g)$$

the following data were collected, where

$$\text{Rate} = -\frac{d[N_2O_5]}{dt}$$

t (s)	$T = 338$ K $[N_2O_5]$	$T = 318$ K $[N_2O_5]$
0	1.00×10^{-1} M	1.00×10^{-1} M
100.	6.14×10^{-2} M	9.54×10^{-2} M
300.	2.33×10^{-2} M	8.63×10^{-2} M
600.	5.41×10^{-3} M	7.43×10^{-2} M
900.	1.26×10^{-3} M	6.39×10^{-2} M

Calculate E_a for this reaction.

107. Experiments have shown the average frequency of chirping of individual snowy tree crickets (*Oecanthus fultoni*) to be 178 min^{-1} at 25.0°C, 126 min^{-1} at 20.3°C, and 100. min^{-1} at 17.3°C.

a. What is the apparent activation energy of the reaction that controls the chirping?
b. What chirping rate would be expected at 15.0°C?
c. Compare the observed rates and your calculated rate from part b to the rule of thumb that the Fahrenheit temperature is 42 plus 0.80 times the number of chirps in 15 s.

108. Experiments during a recent summer on a number of fireflies (small beetles, *Lampyridae photinus*) showed that the average interval between flashes of individual insects was 16.3 s at 21.0°C and 13.0 s at 27.8°C.

a. What is the apparent activation energy of the reaction that controls the flashing?
b. What would be the average interval between flashes of an individual firefly at 30.0°C?
c. Compare the observed intervals and the one you calculated in part b to the rule of thumb that the Celsius temperature is 54 minus twice the interval between flashes.

109. The compound NO_2Cl is thought to decompose to NO_2 and Cl_2 by the following mechanism:

$$NO_2Cl \underset{k_{-1}}{\overset{k_1}{\rightleftharpoons}} NO_2 + Cl$$

$$NO_2Cl + Cl \overset{k_2}{\longrightarrow} NO_2 + Cl_2$$

Derive the rate law for the production of Cl_2 using the steady-state approximation.

110. Many biochemical reactions are catalyzed by large protein molecules called enzymes. A typical mechanism for the conversion of a biochemical substrate (S) to product (P) catalyzed by an enzyme (E) involves the following steps:

$$E + S \underset{k_{-1}}{\overset{k_1}{\rightleftharpoons}} ES$$

$$ES \overset{k_2}{\longrightarrow} P$$

The rate-determining step is the decomposition of the intermediate enzyme–substrate complex (ES) to products (P). Under these conditions, show that the overall rate of product formation is

$$\text{Rate} = \frac{d[P]}{dt} = \frac{k_1 k_2 [E]_T [S]}{k_{-1} + k_2 + k_1 [S]}$$

where $[E]_T$ equals the total enzyme concentration:

$$[E]_T = [E] + [ES]$$

Challenge Problems

111. Consider the following reaction:

$$CH_3X + Y \longrightarrow CH_3Y + X$$

At 25°C the following two experiments were run, yielding the following data:

Experiment 1: $[Y]_0 = 3.0$ M

[CH₃X]	Time (h)
7.08×10^{-3} M	1.0
4.52×10^{-3} M	1.5
2.23×10^{-3} M	2.3
4.76×10^{-4} M	4.0
8.44×10^{-5} M	5.7
2.75×10^{-5} M	7.0

Experiment 2: $[Y]_0 = 4.5$ M

[CH₃X]	Time (h)
4.50×10^{-3} M	0
1.70×10^{-3} M	1.0
4.19×10^{-4} M	2.5
1.11×10^{-4} M	4.0
2.81×10^{-5} M	5.5

Experiments were also run at 85°C. The value of the rate constant at 85°C was found to be 7.88×10^8 (with the time in units of hours), where $[CH_3X]_0 = 1.0 \times 10^{-2}$ M and $[Y]_0 = 3.0$ M.
   a. Determine the rate law and the value of k for this reaction at 25°C.
   b. Determine the half-life at 85°C.
   c. Determine E_a for the reaction.
   d. Given that the C—X bond energy is known to be about 325 kJ/mol, suggest a mechanism that explains the results in parts a and c.

112. The following data were collected in two studies of the reaction

$$2A + B \longrightarrow C + D$$

where

$$Rate = \frac{-d[A]}{dt}$$

Time (s)	Experiment 1 [A] (M) × 10⁻²	Experiment 2 [A] (M) × 10⁻²
0	10.0	10.0
20.	6.67	5.00
40.	5.00	3.33
60.	4.00	2.50
80.	3.33	2.00
100.	2.86	1.67
120.	2.50	1.43

In experiment 1, $[B]_0 = 5.0$ M. In experiment 2, $[B]_0 = 10.0$ M.
   a. Why is [B] much greater than [A]?
   b. Give the rate law and value for k for this reaction.
   c. Which of the following mechanisms could be correct for this reaction? Justify your choice.
      i. $A + B \rightleftharpoons E$ (fast equilibrium)
         $E + B \longrightarrow C + D$ (slow)
      ii. $A + B \rightleftharpoons E$ (fast equilibrium)
         $E + A \longrightarrow C + D$ (slow)
      iii. $A + A \longrightarrow E$ (slow)
         $E + B \longrightarrow C + D$ (fast)

113. Consider a reaction of the type aA → products, in which the rate law is found to be rate = $k[A]^3$ (termolecular reactions are improbable but possible). If the first half-life of the reaction is found to be 40. s, what is the time for the second half-life? *Hint:* Using your calculus knowledge, derive the integrated rate law from the differential rate law for a termolecular reaction:

$$Rate = \frac{-d[A]}{dt} = k[A]^3$$

114. For the reaction

$$2A + B \longrightarrow products$$

a friend proposes the following mechanism:

$$A + B \rightleftharpoons M$$

$$A + M \longrightarrow products$$

   a. Assuming that the second step is the rate-determining step and the first step is a fast equilibrium step, determine the rate law. Represent the rate constant in terms of k_1, k_{-1}, and k_2.
   b. Using the steady-state approximation, determine the rate law.
   c. Under what conditions of [A] and [B] do you get the same rate law in parts a and b?

115. Consider the hypothetical reaction

$$A + B + 2C \longrightarrow 2D + 3E$$

In a study of this reaction, three experiments were run at the same temperature. The rate is defined as $-d[B]/dt$.

Experiment 1:

$[A]_0 = 2.0$ M $[B]_0 = 1.0 \times 10^{-3}$ M $[C]_0 = 1.0$ M

[B] (mol/L)	Time (s)
2.7×10^{-4}	1.0×10^5
1.6×10^{-4}	2.0×10^5
1.1×10^{-4}	3.0×10^5
8.5×10^{-5}	4.0×10^5
6.9×10^{-5}	5.0×10^5
5.8×10^{-5}	6.0×10^5

Experiment 2:

$[A]_0 = 1.0 \times 10^{-2} M$ $[B]_0 = 3.0 M$ $[C]_0 = 1.0 M$

[A] (mol/L)	Time (s)
8.9×10^{-3}	1.0
7.1×10^{-3}	3.0
5.5×10^{-3}	5.0
3.8×10^{-3}	8.0
2.9×10^{-3}	10.0
2.0×10^{-3}	13.0

Experiment 3:

$[A]_0 = 10.0 M$ $[B]_0 = 5.0 M$ $[C]_0 = 5.0 \times 10^{-1} M$

[C] (mol/L)	Time (s)
0.43	1.0×10^{-2}
0.36	2.0×10^{-2}
0.29	3.0×10^{-2}
0.22	4.0×10^{-2}
0.15	5.0×10^{-2}
0.08	6.0×10^{-2}

Write the rate law for this reaction, and calculate the rate constant.

116. A reaction represented by the equation

$$3O_2(g) \longrightarrow 2O_3(g)$$

was studied at a specific temperature, and the following data were collected:

Time (s)	Total Pressure (atm)
0	1.000
46.89	0.9500
98.82	0.9033
137.9	0.8733
200.0	0.8333
286.9	0.7900
337.9	0.7700
511.3	0.7233

a. Determine the rate law for this reaction.
b. Determine the value of the rate constant (including units).
c. Calculate the time it would take for the total pressure to be 0.7133 atm.

117. The gas-phase decomposition $2N_2O_5 \rightarrow 4NO_2 + O_2$ is first order but not unimolecular. A possible mechanism is

$$M + N_2O_5 \underset{k_{-1}}{\overset{k_1}{\rightleftarrows}} NO_3 + NO_2 + M$$

$$NO_3 + NO_2 \overset{k_2}{\longrightarrow} NO + O_2 + NO_2$$

$$NO_3 + NO \overset{k_3}{\longrightarrow} 2NO_2$$

Apply the steady-state approximation to the concentrations of the intermediates NO_3 and NO, and derive the rate law for the decomposition of N_2O_5.

118. You are studying the kinetics of the reaction $H_2(g) + F_2(g) \rightarrow 2HF(g)$ and you wish to determine a mechanism for the reaction. You run the reaction twice by keeping one reactant at a much higher pressure than the other reactant (this lower-pressure reactant begins at 1.000 atm). Unfortunately, you neglect to record which reactant was at the higher pressure, and you forget it later. Your data for the first experiment are as follows:

Pressure of HF (atm)	Time (min)
0	0
0.300	30.0
0.600	65.8
0.900	110.4
1.200	169.1
1.500	255.9

When you run the second experiment (in which the higher-pressure reactant is run at a much higher pressure), you determine the values of the apparent rate constants to be the same. It also turns out that you find data taken from another person in the lab. This individual found that the reaction proceeds 40.0 times faster at 55°C than at 35°C. You also know, from the energy-level diagram, that there are three steps to the mechanism, and the first step has the highest activation energy. You look up the bond energies of the species involved and they are (in kJ/mol): H—H (432), F—F (154), and H—F (565).

a. Sketch an energy-level diagram (qualitative) that is consistent with the one described.
b. Develop a reasonable mechanism for the reaction. Support your answer and explain the significance of each piece of information.
c. Which reactant was limiting in the experiments?

119. Hydrogen peroxide and the iodide ion react in acidic solution as follows:

$$H_2O_2(aq) + 3I^-(aq) + 2H^+(aq) \longrightarrow I_3^-(aq) + 2H_2O(l)$$

The kinetics of this reaction were studied by following the decay of the concentration of H_2O_2 and constructing plots of $\ln[H_2O_2]$ versus time. All the plots were linear and all solutions had $[H_2O_2]_0 = 8.0 \times 10^{-4}$ mol/L. The slopes of these straight lines depended on the initial concentrations of I^- and H^+. The results follow:

$[I^-]_0$ (mol/L)	$[H^+]_0$ (mol/L)	Slope (min^{-1})
0.1000	0.0400	−0.120
0.3000	0.0400	−0.360
0.4000	0.0400	−0.480
0.0750	0.0200	−0.0760
0.0750	0.0800	−0.118
0.0750	0.1600	−0.174

The rate law for this reaction has the form

$$\text{Rate} = \frac{-d[H_2O_2]}{dt} = (k_1 + k_2[H^+])[I^-]^m[H_2O_2]^n$$

a. Specify the orders of this reaction with respect to $[H_2O_2]$ and $[I^-]$.
b. Calculate the values of the rate constants k_1 and k_2.
c. What reason could there be for the two-term dependence of the rate on $[H^+]$?

Marathon Problem

120. Consider the following hypothetical data collected in two studies of the reaction

$$2A(g) + 2B(g) \longrightarrow C(g) + 2D(g)$$

Time (s)	Experiment 1 [A] (mol/L)	Experiment 2 [A] (mol/L)
0.	1.0×10^{-2}	1.0×10^{-2}
10.	8.4×10^{-3}	5.0×10^{-3}
20.	7.1×10^{-3}	2.5×10^{-3}
30.	?	1.3×10^{-3}
40.	5.0×10^{-3}	6.3×10^{-4}

In experiment 1, [B] = 10.0 M. In experiment 2, [B] = 20.0 M.

$$\text{Rate} = \frac{-d[A]}{dt}$$

a. Use the concentration versus time data to determine the rate law for the reaction.

b. Solve for the rate constant k for the reaction. Include units.

c. Calculate the concentration of A in experiment 1 at $t = 30.$ s.

d. The following three mechanisms are proposed for this reaction:

   i. $2B \rightleftharpoons B_2$ (Fast equilibrium)

      $B_2 + A \longrightarrow E + D$ (Slow)

      $E + A \longrightarrow C + D$ (Fast)

  ii. $A + B \longrightarrow D + F$ (Slow)

      $F + B \longrightarrow C + G$ (Fast)

      $G + A \longrightarrow D$ (Fast)

 iii. $A + 2B \longrightarrow E + D$ (Slow)

      $E + A \longrightarrow C + D$ (Fast)

Choose the best mechanism(s). Include an explanation of which mechanism(s) you exclude and why. If you believe two (or even all three) mechanisms are equally good, explain why.

5 Gases

chapter

Hot air balloon taking off from the ski resort of Chateau d'Oex in the Swiss Alps.

Matter exists in three distinct physical states: gas, liquid, and solid. Of these, the gaseous state is the easiest to describe both experimentally and theoretically. In particular, the study of gases provides an excellent example of the scientific method in action. It illustrates how observations lead to natural laws, which in turn can be accounted for by models. Then, as more accurate measurements become available, the models are modified.

In addition to providing a good illustration of the scientific method, gases are important in their own right. For example, gases are often produced in chemical reactions and thus must be dealt with in stoichiometric calculations. Also, the earth's atmosphere is a mixture of gases, primarily elemental nitrogen and oxygen; it both supports life and acts as a waste receptacle for the exhaust gases that accompany many industrial processes.

For these reasons, it is important to understand the behavior of gases. We will pursue this goal by considering the properties of gases, the laws and models that describe the behavior of gases, and finally the reactions that occur among the gases in the atmosphere.

5.1 | Early Experiments

Even though the Greeks considered "air" to be one of the four fundamental elements and various alchemists obtained "airs," or "vapors," in their experiments, careful study of these elusive substances proved difficult. The first person to attempt a scientific study of the "vapors" produced in chemical reactions was the Flemish physician Jan Baptista Van Helmont (1577–1644). Thinking that air and similar substances must be akin to the "chaos" from which, according to Greek myth, the universe was created, Van Helmont described these substances using the Flemish word for *chaos,* which was *gas.*

Van Helmont extensively studied a gas he obtained from burning wood, which he called "gas sylvestre" and which we now know as carbon dioxide, and noted that this substance was similar in many ways but not identical to air. By the end of his life, the importance of gases, especially air, was becoming more apparent. In 1643 the Italian physicist Evangelista Torricelli (1608–1647), who had been a student of Galileo, performed experiments that showed that *the air in the atmosphere exerts pressure.* (In fact, as we will see, all gases exert pressure.) Torricelli designed the first **barometer** by filling a tube that was closed at one end with mercury and then inverting it in a dish of mercury (Fig. 5.1). He observed that a column of mercury approximately 760 millimeters long always remained in the tube as a result of the pressure of the atmosphere.

A few years later Otto von Guericke, a German physicist, invented an air pump, often called a vacuum pump, that he used in a famous demonstration for the king of Prussia in 1654. Guericke placed two hemispheres together and pumped the air out of the resulting sphere through a valve, which was subsequently closed. He then dramatically showed that teams of horses could not pull the hemispheres apart. However, after secretly opening the valve to let air in, Guericke was able to separate the hemispheres easily by hand. The king of Prussia was so impressed by Guericke's cleverness that he awarded him a lifetime pension.

Units of Pressure

Because instruments used for measuring pressure, such as the **manometer** (Fig. 5.2), often use columns of mercury because of its high density, the most commonly used units for pressure are based on the height of the mercury column (in millimeters) the gas pressure can support. The unit **millimeters of**

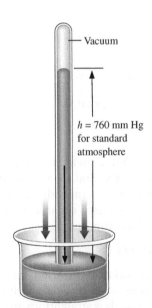

Figure 5.1
A torricellian barometer. The tube, completely filled with mercury, is inverted in a dish of mercury. Mercury flows out of the tube until the pressure of the column of mercury (shown by black arrow) "standing on the surface" of the mercury in the dish is equal to the pressure of the air (shown by purple arrows) on the rest of the surface of the mercury in the dish.

Figure 5.2
A simple manometer, a device for measuring the pressure of a gas in a container. The pressure of the gas is given by h (the difference in mercury levels) in units of torr (equivalent to mm Hg). (a) Gas pressure = atmospheric pressure − h. (b) Gas pressure = atmospheric pressure + h.

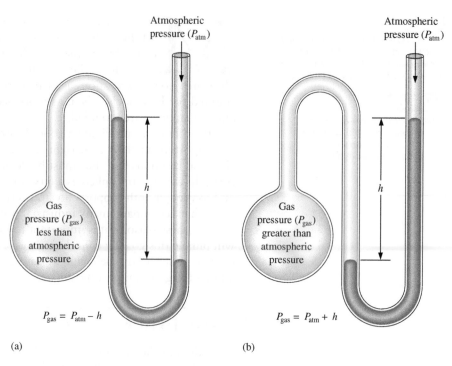

(a)   (b)

1 atm: 760 mm Hg, 760 torr, 101,325 Pa, 29.92 in Hg, 14.7 lb/in²

The International Union of Pure and Applied Chemists (IUPAC) has adopted 1 bar (100,000. Pa) as the standard pressure instead of 1 atm (101,325 Pa). Both standards are now widely used.

mercury (**mm Hg**) is called the **torr** in honor of Torricelli. A related unit for pressure is the **standard atmosphere:**

$$1 \text{ standard atmosphere} = 1 \text{ atm} = 760 \text{ mm Hg} = 760 \text{ torr}$$

However, since pressure is defined as force per unit area, that is,

$$\text{Pressure} = \frac{\text{force}}{\text{area}}$$

the fundamental units of pressure involve units of force divided by units of area. In the SI system, the unit of force is the newton (N) and the unit of area is meters squared (m²). (For a review of the SI system, see Appendix 2.) Thus the unit of pressure in the SI system is newtons per meter squared (N/m²), called the **pascal (Pa)**. In terms of pascals the standard atmosphere is

$$1 \text{ standard atmosphere} = 101,325 \text{ Pa}$$

Thus 1 atm is approximately 10^5 pascals. Since the pascal is so small, and because it is not commonly used in the United States, we will use it sparingly in this book. However, converting from torrs or atmospheres to pascals is straightforward.

5.2 | The Gas Laws of Boyle, Charles, and Avogadro

Boyle's Law

The first quantitative experiments on gases were performed by the Irish chemist Robert Boyle (1627–1691). Using a J-shaped tube closed at one end (Fig. 5.3), which he reportedly set up in the multistory entryway of his house, Boyle studied the relationship between the pressure of the trapped gas and its volume. Representative values from Boyle's experiments are given in Table 5.1. These data show that the product of the pressure and volume for the trapped air sample is constant within the accuracies of Boyle's measurements (note the third column in Table 5.1). This behavior can be represented by the equation

$$PV = k$$

Figure 5.3
A J-tube similar to the one used by Boyle.

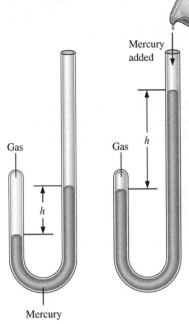

Mercury added

Gas

Gas

h

h

Mercury

Table 5.1

Actual Data from Boyle's Experiments

Volume (in³)	Pressure (in Hg)	Pressure × Volume (in Hg × in³)
48.0	29.1	14.0×10^2
40.0	35.3	14.1×10^2
32.0	44.2	14.1×10^2
24.0	58.8	14.1×10^2
20.0	70.7	14.1×10^2
16.0	87.2	14.0×10^2
12.0	117.5	14.1×10^2

which is called **Boyle's law,** where k is a constant at a specific temperature for a given sample of air.

It is convenient to represent the data in Table 5.1 by using two different plots. Figure 5.4(a) shows a plot of P versus V, which produces a hyperbola. Notice that as the pressure drops by half, the volume doubles. Thus there is an *inverse relationship* between pressure and volume. The second type of plot can be obtained by rearranging Boyle's law to give

$$V = \frac{k}{P}$$

which is the equation for a straight line of the type

$$y = mx + b$$

Graphing is reviewed in Appendix A1.3.

where m represents the slope and b is the intercept of the straight line. In this case, $y = V$, $x = 1/P$, $m = k$, and $b = 0$. Thus a plot of V versus $1/P$ using Boyle's data gives a straight line with an intercept of zero, as shown in Fig. 5.4(b).

Boyle's law only approximately describes the relationship between pressure and volume for a gas. Highly accurate measurements on various gases at a constant temperature have shown that the product PV is not quite constant but changes with pressure. Results for several gases are shown in Fig. 5.5. Note the small changes that occur in the product PV as the pressure is varied. Such changes become very significant at pressures much higher than normal atmospheric pressure. We will discuss these deviations and the reasons for them in detail in Section 5.10. *A gas that obeys Boyle's law is called an* **ideal gas.** We will describe the characteristics of an ideal gas more completely in Section 5.3.

Boyle's law: $V \propto 1/P$ at constant temperature.

Figure 5.4
Plotting Boyle's data from Table 5.1.
(a) A plot of P versus V shows that the volume doubles as the pressure is halved. (b) A plot of V versus $1/P$ gives a straight line. The slope of this line equals the value of the constant k.

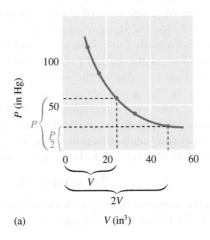

(a)

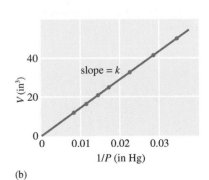

(b)

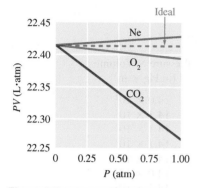

Figure 5.5
A plot of PV versus P for several gases. An ideal gas is expected to have a constant value of PV, as shown by the dashed line. Carbon dioxide shows the largest change in PV, and this change is actually quite small: PV changes from approximately 22.39 L atm at 0.25 atm to 22.26 L atm at 1.00 atm. Thus Boyle's law is a good approximation at these relatively low pressures.

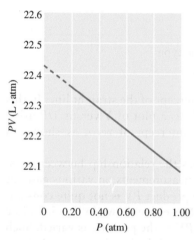

Figure 5.6
A plot of PV versus P for 1 mole of ammonia. The dashed line shows the extrapolation of the data to zero pressure to give the "ideal" value of PV of 22.41 L atm.

As with Boyle's law, Charles's law is obeyed exactly only at relatively low pressures.

One common use of Boyle's law is to predict the new volume of a gas when the pressure is changed (at constant temperature), or vice versa.

We mentioned earlier that Boyle's law is only approximately followed for real gases. To determine the significance of the deviations, studies of the effect of changing pressure on the volume of a gas are often carried out, as shown in Example 5.1.

EXAMPLE 5.1

In a study to see how closely gaseous ammonia obeys Boyle's law, several volume measurements were made at various pressures using 1.0 mole of NH_3 gas at a temperature of 0°C. Using the results listed below, calculate the Boyle's law constant for NH_3 at the various pressures.

Experiment	Pressure (atm)	Volume (L)
1	0.1300	172.1
2	0.2500	89.28
3	0.3000	74.35
4	0.5000	44.49
5	0.7500	29.55
6	1.000	22.08

Solution To determine how closely NH_3 gas follows Boyle's law under these conditions, we calculate the value of k (in L atm) for each set of values:

Experiment	1	2	3	4	5	6
$k = PV$	22.37	22.32	22.31	22.25	22.16	22.08

Although the deviations from true Boyle's law behavior are quite small at these low pressures, the value of k changes regularly in one direction as the pressure is increased. Thus, to calculate the "ideal" value of k for NH_3, plot PV versus P, as shown in Fig. 5.6, and extrapolate (extend the line beyond the experimental points) back to zero pressure, where, for reasons we will discuss later, a gas behaves most ideally. The value of k obtained by this extrapolation is 22.41 L atm. This is the same value obtained from similar plots for the gases CO_2, O_2, and Ne at 0°C, as shown in Fig. 5.5.

Charles's Law

In the century following Boyle's findings, scientists continued to study the properties of gases. One of these scientists was the French physicist Jacques Charles (1746–1823), who was the first person to fill a balloon with hydrogen gas and who made the first solo balloon flight. In 1787 Charles found that the volume of a gas at constant pressure increases *linearly* with the temperature of the gas. That is, a plot of the volume of a gas (at constant pressure) versus its temperature (°C) gives a straight line. This behavior is shown for several gases in Fig. 5.7. One very interesting feature of these plots is that the volumes of all the gases extrapolate to zero at the same temperature, −273.2°C. On the Kelvin temperature scale, this point is defined as 0 K, which leads to the following relationship between the Kelvin and Celsius scales:

$$\text{Temperature (K)} = 0°C + 273$$

When the volumes of the gases shown in Fig. 5.7 are plotted versus temperature on the Kelvin scale, the plots in Fig. 5.8 result. In this case the volume of

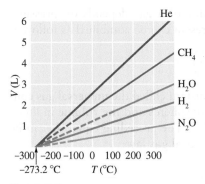

Figure 5.7
Plots of *V* versus *T* (°C) for several gases. The solid lines represent experimental measurements on gases. The dashed lines represent extrapolation of the data into regions where these gases would become liquids or solids. Note that the samples of the various gases contain different numbers of moles.

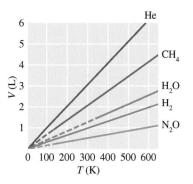

Figure 5.8
Plots of *V* versus *T* as in Fig. 5.7, except that here the Kelvin scale is used for temperature.

each gas is *directly proportional to temperature* and extrapolates to zero when the temperature is 0 K. This behavior is represented by the equation known as **Charles's law,**

$$V = bT$$

where *T* is the temperature (in kelvins) and *b* is a proportionality constant.

Before we illustrate the uses of Charles's law, let's consider the importance of 0 K. At temperatures below this point, the extrapolated volumes would become negative. The fact that a gas cannot have a negative volume suggests that 0 K has a special significance. In fact, 0 K is called **absolute zero,** and much evidence suggests that this temperature cannot be attained. Temperatures of approximately 10^{-6} K have been produced in laboratories, but 0 K has never been reached.

Avogadro's Law

In Chapter 2 we noted that in 1811 the Italian chemist Avogadro postulated that equal volumes of gases at the same temperature and pressure contain the same number of "particles." This observation is called **Avogadro's law** (or **hypothesis**), which can be stated mathematically as

$$V = an$$

where *V* is the volume of the gas, *n* is the number of moles, and *a* is a proportionality constant. This equation states that *for a gas at constant temperature and pressure, the volume is directly proportional to the number of moles of gas.* This relationship is obeyed closely by gases at low pressures.

5.3 | The Ideal Gas Law

We have considered three laws that describe the behavior of gases as revealed by experimental observations:

Boyle's law:	$V = \dfrac{k}{P}$	(at constant *T* and *n*)
Charles's law:	$V = bT$	(at constant *P* and *n*)
Avogadro's law:	$V = an$	(at constant *T* and *P*)

These relationships showing how the volume of a gas depends on pressure, temperature, and number of moles of gas present can be combined as follows:

$$V = R\left(\frac{Tn}{P}\right)$$

where R is the combined proportionality constant called the **universal gas constant.** When the pressure is expressed in atmospheres and the volume in liters, R has the value of 0.08206 L atm K^{-1} mol^{-1}. The preceding equation can be rearranged to the more familiar form of the **ideal gas law:**

$$PV = nRT$$

The ideal gas law is an *equation of state* for a gas, where the state of the gas is its condition at a given time. A particular *state* of a gas is described by its pressure, volume, temperature, and number of moles. Knowledge of any three of these properties is enough to completely define the state of a gas since the fourth property can then be determined from the equation for the ideal gas law.

It is important to recognize that the ideal gas law is an empirical equation—it is based on experimental measurements of the properties of gases. A gas that obeys this equation is said to behave *ideally.* That is, this equation defines the behavior of an ideal gas, which is a hypothetical substance. The ideal gas equation is best regarded as a limiting law—it expresses behavior that real gases *approach* at low pressures and high temperatures. Most gases obey this equation closely enough at pressures below 1 atm that only minimal errors result from assuming ideal behavior. Unless you are given information to the contrary, you should assume ideal gas behavior when solving problems involving gases in this text.

$R = 0.08206$ L atm K^{-1} mol^{-1}

The ideal gas law applies best at pressures below 1 atm.

⊎WL INTERACTIVE EXAMPLE 5.2

A sample of hydrogen gas (H_2) has a volume of 8.56 L at a temperature of 0°C and a pressure of 1.5 atm. Calculate the moles of H_2 present in this gas sample.

Solution Solving the ideal gas law for n gives

$$n = \frac{PV}{RT}$$

In this case $P = 1.5$ atm, $V = 8.56$ L, $T = 0°C + 273 = 273$ K, and $R = 0.08206$ L atm K^{-1} mol^{-1}. Thus

$$n = \frac{(1.5 \text{ atm})(8.56 \text{ L})}{\left(0.08206 \dfrac{\text{L atm}}{\text{K mol}}\right)(273 \text{ K})} = 0.57 \text{ mol}$$

The ideal gas law is often used to calculate the changes that will occur when the conditions of a gas are changed, as described below.

⊎WL INTERACTIVE EXAMPLE 5.3

Suppose we have a sample of ammonia gas with a volume of 3.5 L at a pressure of 1.68 atm. The gas is compressed to a volume of 1.35 L at a constant temperature. Use the ideal gas law to calculate the final pressure.

Solution The basic assumption we make when using the ideal gas law to describe a change in state for a gas is that the equation applies equally well to both the initial and the final states. In dealing with a change in state, we always *place the variables on one side of the equals sign and the constants on the other.* In this case the pressure and volume change, whereas the temperature and the number of moles remain constant (as does R, by definition). Thus we write the ideal gas law as

$$PV = nRT$$

$$\nearrow \qquad \nwarrow$$

Change   Remain constant

Since n and T remain the same in this case, we can write $P_1V_1 = nRT$ and $P_2V_2 = nRT$. Combining these equations gives

$$P_1V_1 = nRT = P_2V_2 \qquad \text{or} \qquad P_1V_1 = P_2V_2$$

We are given $P_1 = 1.68$ atm, $V_1 = 3.5$ L, $V_2 = 1.35$ L. Solving for P_2 gives

$$P_2 = \left(\frac{V_1}{V_2}\right) P_1 = \left(\frac{3.5\ \text{L}}{1.35\ \text{L}}\right) 1.68\ \text{atm} = 4.4\ \text{atm}$$

Check: Does this answer make sense? The volume decreased (at constant temperature), so the pressure should increase, as the result of the calculation indicates. Note that the calculated final pressure is 4.4 atm. Because most gases do not behave ideally above 1 atm, we might find that if we *measured* the pressure of this gas sample, the observed pressure would differ slightly from 4.4 atm.

⬤WL INTERACTIVE EXAMPLE 5.4

A sample of methane gas that has a volume of 3.8 L at 5°C is heated to 86°C at constant pressure. Calculate its new volume.

Solution To solve this problem, we take the ideal gas law and segregate the changing variables and the constants by placing them on opposite sides of the equation. In this case volume and temperature change, and number of moles and pressure (and of course R) remain constant. Thus $PV = nRT$ becomes

$$\frac{V}{T} = \frac{nR}{P}$$

which leads to

$$\frac{V_1}{T_1} = \frac{nR}{P} \qquad \text{and} \qquad \frac{V_2}{T_2} = \frac{nR}{P}$$

Combining these equations gives

$$\frac{V_1}{T_1} = \frac{nR}{P} = \frac{V_2}{T_2} \qquad \text{or} \qquad \frac{V_1}{T_1} = \frac{V_2}{T_2}$$

We are given

$$T_1 = 5°C + 273 = 278\ \text{K} \qquad T_2 = 86°C + 273 = 359\ \text{K}$$

$$V_1 = 3.8\ \text{L} \qquad\qquad\qquad V_2 = ?$$

Thus

$$V_2 = \frac{T_2V_1}{T_1} = \frac{(359\ \text{K})(3.8\ \text{L})}{278\ \text{K}} = 4.9\ \text{L}$$

Check: Is the answer sensible? In this case the temperature was increased (at constant pressure), so the volume should increase. Thus the answer makes sense.

The problem in Example 5.4 can be described as a Charles's law problem, whereas the problem in Example 5.3 can be said to be a Boyle's law problem. In both cases, however, we started with the ideal gas law. The real advantage of using the ideal gas law is that it applies to virtually any problem dealing with gases and is easy to remember.

ⓌWL INTERACTIVE EXAMPLE 5.5

A sample of diborane gas (B_2H_6), a substance that bursts into flames when exposed to air, has a pressure of 345 torr at a temperature of $-15°C$ and a volume of 3.48 L. If conditions are changed so that the temperature is 36°C and the pressure is 468 torr, what will be the volume of the sample?

Solution Since, for this sample, pressure, temperature, and volume all change while the number of moles remains constant, we use the ideal gas law in the form

$$\frac{PV}{T} = nR$$

which leads to

$$\frac{P_1V_1}{T_1} = nR = \frac{P_2V_2}{T_2} \quad \text{or} \quad \frac{P_1V_1}{T_1} = \frac{P_2V_2}{T_2}$$

Then

$$V_2 = \frac{T_2P_1V_1}{T_1P_2}$$

We have

$$P_1 = 345 \text{ torr} \qquad\qquad P_2 = 468 \text{ torr}$$

$$T_1 = -15°C + 273 = 258 \text{ K} \qquad T_2 = 36°C + 273 = 309 \text{ K}$$

$$V_1 = 3.48 \text{ L} \qquad\qquad V_2 = ?$$

Thus

$$V_2 = \frac{(309 \text{ K})(345 \text{ torr})(3.48 \text{ L})}{(258 \text{ K})(468 \text{ torr})} = 3.07 \text{ L}$$

Since the equation used in Example 5.5 involved a *ratio* of pressures, it was unnecessary to convert pressures to units of atmospheres. The units of torr cancel. (You will obtain the same answer by inserting $P_1 = \frac{345}{760}$ and $P_2 = \frac{468}{760}$ into the equation.) However, temperature *must always* be converted to the Kelvin scale; since this conversion involves *addition* of 273, the conversion factor does not cancel. Be careful.

Always convert the temperature to the Kelvin scale when applying the ideal gas law.

5.4 | Gas Stoichiometry

Suppose we have 1 mole of an ideal gas at 0°C (273.2 K) and 1 atm. From the ideal gas law, the volume of the gas is given by

$$V = \frac{nRT}{P} = \frac{(1.000 \text{ mol})(0.08206 \text{ L atm K}^{-1} \text{ mol}^{-1})(273.2 \text{ K})}{1.000 \text{ atm}} = 22.42 \text{ L}$$

This volume of 22.42 liters is called the **molar volume** of an ideal gas. The measured molar volumes of several gases are listed in Table 5.2. Note that the molar volumes of some of the gases are very close to the ideal value, but others deviate significantly. Later in this chapter we will discuss some of the reasons for the deviations.

The conditions 0°C and 1 atm, called **standard temperature and pressure** (abbreviated **STP**), are common reference conditions for the properties of gases. For example, the molar volume of an ideal gas is 22.42 L at STP.

STP: 0°C and 1 atm

Table 5.2

Molar Volumes for Various Gases at 0°C and 1 atm

Gas	Molar Volume (L)
Oxygen (O_2)	22.397
Nitrogen (N_2)	22.402
Hydrogen (H_2)	22.433
Helium (He)	22.434
Argon (Ar)	22.397
Carbon dioxide (CO_2)	22.260
Ammonia (NH_3)	22.079

Many chemical reactions involve gases. By assuming ideal behavior for these gases, we can carry out stoichiometric calculations if the pressure, volume, and temperature of the gases are known.

⬢WL INTERACTIVE EXAMPLE 5.6

Quicklime (CaO) is produced by the thermal decomposition of calcium carbonate ($CaCO_3$). Calculate the volume of CO_2 produced at STP from the decomposition of 152 g of $CaCO_3$ according to the reaction

$$CaCO_3(s) \longrightarrow CaO(s) + CO_2(g)$$

Solution

■ What are we trying to solve?

We are asked to solve for the volume of $CO_2(g)$ produced at STP. We are given the pressure and temperature, so to determine the volume we will need to determine the number of moles of gas produced.

We use the same strategy we used in the stoichiometry problems earlier in the book. That is, we compute the number of moles of $CaCO_3$ consumed and the number of moles of CO_2 produced. The moles of CO_2 can then be converted to volume by using the molar volume of an ideal gas.

Using the molar mass of $CaCO_3$, we can calculate the number of moles of $CaCO_3$:

$$152 \text{ g CaCO}_3 \times \frac{1 \text{ mol CaCO}_3}{100.1 \text{ g CaCO}_3} = 1.52 \text{ mol CaCO}_3$$

Since each mole of $CaCO_3$ produces 1 mole of CO_2, 1.52 moles of CO_2 will be formed. We can compute the volume of CO_2 at STP by using the molar volume:

$$1.52 \text{ mol CO}_2 \times \frac{22.42 \text{ L CO}_2}{1 \text{ mol CO}_2} = 34.1 \text{ L CO}_2$$

Thus the decomposition of 152 g of $CaCO_3$ will produce 34.1 L of CO_2 at STP.

Remember that the molar volume of an ideal gas is 22.42 L at STP.

Note that in Example 5.6 the final step involved calculation of the volume of gas from the number of moles. Since the conditions were specified as STP, we were able to use the molar volume of a gas at STP. If the conditions of a problem are different from STP, the ideal gas law must be used to calculate the volume.

Molar Mass

One very important use of the ideal gas law is in the calculation of the molar mass (molecular weight) of a gas from its measured density. To understand the relationship between gas density and molar mass, note that the number of moles of gas n can be expressed as

$$n = \frac{\text{grams of gas}}{\text{molar mass}} = \frac{\text{mass}}{\text{molar mass}} = \frac{m}{\text{molar mass}}$$

Substitution into the ideal gas equation gives

$$P = \frac{nRT}{V} = \frac{(m/\text{molar mass})RT}{V} = \frac{m(RT)}{V(\text{molar mass})}$$

But m/V is the gas density d in units of grams per liter. Thus

$$P = \frac{dRT}{\text{molar mass}}$$

or $$\text{Molar mass} = \frac{dRT}{P} \tag{5.1}$$

Thus, if the density of a gas at a given temperature and pressure is known, its molar mass can be calculated.

You can memorize the equation involving gas density and molar mass, but it is better simply to remember the ideal gas equation, the definition of density, and the relationship between number of moles and molar mass. You can then derive this equation when you need it. This approach proves that you understand the concepts and means one less equation to memorize.

5.5 | Dalton's Law of Partial Pressures

Among the experiments that led John Dalton to propose the atomic theory were his studies of mixtures of gases. In 1803 Dalton summarized his observations as follows: *For a mixture of gases in a container, the total pressure exerted is the sum of the pressures that each gas would exert if it were alone.* This statement, known as **Dalton's law of partial pressures,** can be expressed as follows:

$$P_{\text{Total}} = P_1 + P_2 + P_3 + \cdots$$

where the subscripts refer to the individual gases (gas 1, gas 2, and so on). The pressures P_1, P_2, P_3, and so on are called **partial pressures;** that is, each one is the pressure that gas would exert if it were alone in the container.

Assuming that each gas behaves ideally, the partial pressure of each gas can be calculated from the ideal gas law:

$$P_1 = \frac{n_1 RT}{V}, \qquad P_2 = \frac{n_2 RT}{V}, \qquad P_3 = \frac{n_3 RT}{V}, \qquad \cdots$$

The total pressure of the mixture P_{Total} can be represented as

$$P_{\text{Total}} = P_1 + P_2 + P_3 + \cdots = \frac{n_1 RT}{V} + \frac{n_2 RT}{V} + \frac{n_3 RT}{V} + \cdots$$

$$= (n_1 + n_2 + n_3 + \cdots)\left(\frac{RT}{V}\right) = n_{\text{Total}}\left(\frac{RT}{V}\right)$$

where n_{Total} is the sum of the numbers of moles of the various gases. Thus, for a mixture of ideal gases, it is the *total number of moles of particles* that is im-

Figure 5.9
The partial pressure of each gas in a mixture of gases depends on the number of moles of that gas. The total pressure is the sum of the partial pressures and depends on the total moles of gas particles present, no matter what their identities.

portant, not the identity or composition of the individual gas particles. This idea is illustrated in Fig. 5.9.

This important result indicates some fundamental characteristics of an ideal gas. The fact that the pressure exerted by an ideal gas is not affected by the identity (structure) of the gas particles reveals two things about ideal gases: (1) the volume of the individual gas particle must not be important, and (2) the forces among the particles must not be important. If these factors were important, the pressure exerted by the gas would depend on the nature of the individual particles. These observations will strongly influence the model that we will eventually construct to explain ideal gas behavior.

At this point we need to define the **mole fraction:** *the ratio of the number of moles of a given component in a mixture to the total number of moles in the mixture.* The Greek letter chi (χ) is used to symbolize the mole fraction. For a given component in a mixture, the mole fraction χ_1 is

$$\chi_1 = \frac{n_1}{n_{\text{Total}}} = \frac{n_1}{n_1 + n_2 + n_3 + \cdots}$$

From the ideal gas equation, we know that the number of moles of a gas is directly proportional to the pressure of the gas, since

$$n = P\left(\frac{V}{RT}\right)$$

That is, for each component in the mixture,

$$n_1 = P_1\left(\frac{V}{RT}\right), \qquad n_2 = P_2\left(\frac{V}{RT}\right), \qquad \cdots$$

Therefore, we can represent the mole fraction in terms of pressures:

$$\chi_1 = \frac{n_1}{n_{\text{Total}}} = \frac{\overbrace{P_1(V/RT)}^{n_1}}{\underbrace{P_1(V/RT)}_{n_1} + \underbrace{P_2(V/RT)}_{n_2} + \underbrace{P_3(V/RT)}_{n_3} + \cdots}$$

$$= \frac{(V/RT)P_1}{(V/RT)(P_1 + P_2 + P_3 + \cdots)}$$

$$= \frac{P_1}{P_1 + P_2 + P_3 + \cdots} = \frac{P_1}{P_{\text{Total}}}$$

Similarly,

$$\chi_2 = \frac{n_2}{n_{\text{Total}}} = \frac{P_2}{P_{\text{Total}}}$$

and so on. Thus the mole fraction of a particular component in a mixture of ideal gases is directly related to its partial pressure.

The expression for the mole fraction,

$$\chi_1 = \frac{P_1}{P_{\text{Total}}}$$

can be rearranged:

$$P_1 = \chi_1 \times P_{\text{Total}}$$

That is, *the partial pressure of a particular component of a gaseous mixture is equal to the mole fraction of that component times the total pressure.*

A mixture of gases occurs whenever a gas is collected by displacement of water. For example, Fig. 5.10 shows the collection of oxygen gas produced by

Chemical Insights   The Chemistry of Air Bags

Most experts agree that air bags represent a very important advance in automobile safety. First patented by American inventor John W. Hetrick in 1953, air bags are now required in all cars and trucks in the United States. These bags, which are stored in the auto's steering wheel or dash, are designed to inflate rapidly (within about 40 ms) in the event of a crash, cushioning the front-seat occupants against impact. The bags then deflate immediately to allow vision and movement after the crash. Air bags are activated when a severe deceleration (an impact) causes a steel ball to compress a spring and electrically ignite a detonator cap, which, in turn, causes sodium azide (NaN_3) to decompose explosively, forming sodium and nitrogen gas:

$$2NaN_3(s) \longrightarrow 2Na(s) + 3N_2(g)$$

This system works very well and requires only a relatively small amount of sodium azide [100 g yields 56 L of $N_2(g)$ at 25°C and 1 atm].

In addition to being located in the steering wheel and dash, air bags are now found in many other sites in motor vehicles. Air bags to protect against side impacts are located above the windows (called *curtain air bags* to protect against head injuries) and in the doors (called *torso air bags*). Some vehicles also have bags to prevent knee injuries. Because the explosive deployment of air bags can cause serious injuries, especially to children, variable force air bags have been devel-

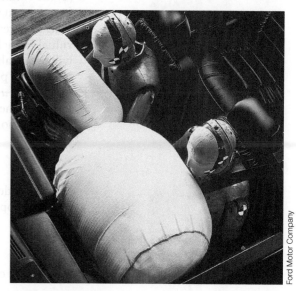

Inflated dual air bags.

oped that depend on the weight of the person occupying the front seat.

When a vehicle containing air bags reaches the end of its useful life, the sodium azide present in the activators must be given proper disposal. Besides being explosive, sodium azide has a toxicity roughly equal to that of sodium cyanide. It also forms hydrazoic acid (HN_3), a toxic and explosive liquid, when treated with acid.

The air bag represents an application of chemistry that has already saved thousands of lives.

Figure 5.10

The production of oxygen by thermal decomposition of $KClO_3$. The MnO_2 catalyst is mixed with the $KClO_3$ to make the reaction faster.

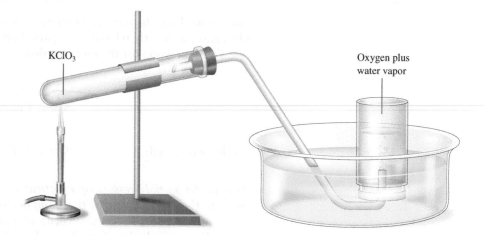

the decomposition of solid potassium chlorate. In this situation the gas in the bottle is a mixture of water vapor and the gas being collected. Water vapor is present because molecules of water escape from the surface of the liquid and collect in the space above the liquid. Molecules of water also return to the liquid. When the rate of escape equals the rate of return, the number of water molecules in the vapor state remains constant, and thus the pressure of water vapor remains constant. This pressure, which depends on temperature, is called the *vapor pressure of water*.

Vapor pressure will be discussed in detail in Chapter 16.

⚈WL INTERACTIVE EXAMPLE 5.7

The mole fraction of nitrogen in air is 0.7808. Calculate the partial pressure of N_2 in air when the atmospheric pressure is 760. torr.

Solution The partial pressure of N_2 can be calculated as follows:

$$P_{N_2} = \chi_{N_2} \times P_{Total} = 0.7808 \times 760. \text{ torr} = 593 \text{ torr}$$

⚈WL INTERACTIVE EXAMPLE 5.8

A sample of solid potassium chlorate ($KClO_3$) was heated in a test tube (Fig. 5.10) and decomposed according to the following reaction:

$$2KClO_3(s) \longrightarrow 2KCl(s) + 3O_2(g)$$

The oxygen produced was collected by displacement of water at 22°C at a total pressure of 754 torr. The volume of the gas collected was 0.650 L, and the vapor pressure of water at 22°C is 21 torr. Calculate the partial pressure of O_2 in the gas collected and the mass of $KClO_3$ in the sample that was decomposed.

Solution

■ What are we trying to solve?

We are asked to find the partial pressure of O_2 in the gas collected and the mass of reactant ($KClO_3$) in the original sample.

We have the balanced equation and are given the volume, temperature, total pressure of the gas mixture, and vapor pressure of the water at that temperature. Since oxygen and water vapor are the only gases in the mixture, we can determine the partial pressure of the oxygen gas from Dalton's law of partial pressures:

$$P_{Total} = P_{O_2} + P_{H_2O} = P_{O_2} + 21 \text{ torr} = 754 \text{ torr}$$

Thus

$$P_{O_2} = 754 \text{ torr} - 21 \text{ torr} = 733 \text{ torr}$$

We now have to determine the mass of $KClO_3$ from the partial pressure of oxygen gas. Recall our strategy used in stoichiometry problems. That is, we can determine the mass of $KClO_3$ from the number of moles of $KClO_3$, which we can determine from the number of moles of O_2. We know the partial pressure of O_2. Along with volume and temperature, we can use the ideal gas law to find the number of moles of O_2:

$$n_{O_2} = \frac{P_{O_2}V}{RT}$$

In this case

$$P_{O_2} = 733 \text{ torr} = \frac{733 \text{ torr}}{760 \text{ torr/atm}} = 0.964 \text{ atm}$$

$$V = 0.650 \text{ L}$$

$$T = 22°C + 273 = 295 \text{ K}$$

$$R = 0.08206 \text{ L atm K}^{-1} \text{ mol}^{-1}$$

Thus

$$n_{O_2} = \frac{(0.964 \text{ atm})(0.650 \text{ L})}{(0.08206 \text{ L atm K}^{-1} \text{ mol}^{-1})(295 \text{ K})} = 2.59 \times 10^{-2} \text{ mol}$$

Next, we calculate the moles of $KClO_3$ needed to produce this quantity of O_2 using the mole ratio from the balanced equation for the decomposition of $KClO_3$:

$$2.59 \times 10^{-2} \text{ mol } O_2 \times \frac{2 \text{ mol } KClO_3}{3 \text{ mol } O_2} = 1.73 \times 10^{-2} \text{ mol } KClO_3$$

Using the molar mass of $KClO_3$, we calculate the grams of $KClO_3$:

$$1.73 \times 10^{-2} \text{ mol } KClO_3 \times \frac{122.6 \text{ g } KClO_3}{1 \text{ mol } KClO_3} = 2.12 \text{ g } KClO_3$$

Thus the original sample contained 2.12 g of $KClO_3$.

5.6 | The Kinetic Molecular Theory of Gases

We have so far considered the behavior of gases from an experimental point of view. Based on observations from different types of experiments, we know that at pressures of less than 1 atm most gases closely approach the behavior described by the ideal gas law. Now we want to construct a model to explain this behavior.

Before we do this, let's briefly review the scientific method. Recall that a law is a way of generalizing behavior that has been observed in many experiments. Laws are very useful, since they allow us to predict the behavior of similar systems. For example, if a chemist prepares a new gaseous compound, a measurement of the gas density at known pressure and temperature can provide a reliable value for the compound's molar mass.

However, although laws summarize observed behavior, they do not tell us *why* nature behaves in the observed fashion. This is the central question for scientists. To try to answer this question, we construct theories (build models). The models in chemistry consist of speculations about what the individual atoms or molecules (microscopic particles) might be doing to cause the observed behavior of the macroscopic systems (collections of very large numbers of atoms and molecules).

A model is considered successful if it explains the observed behavior in question and predicts correctly the results of future experiments. It is important to understand that a model can never be proved absolutely true. In fact, *any model is an approximation* by its very nature and is bound to fail at some point. Models range from the simple to the extraordinarily complex. We use simple models to predict approximate behavior and more complicated models to account very precisely for observed quantitative behavior. In this text we will stress simple models that provide an approximate picture of what might be happening and that fit the most important experimental results.

Separating Gases

Assume you work for an oil company that owns a huge natural gas reservoir containing a mixture of methane and nitrogen gases. In fact, the gas mixture contains so much nitrogen that it is unusable as a fuel. Your job is to separate the nitrogen (N_2) from the methane (CH_4). How might you accomplish this task? You clearly need some sort of "molecular filter" that will stop the slightly larger methane molecules (size ≈ 430 pm) and allow the nitrogen molecules (size ≈ 410 pm) to pass through. To accomplish the separation of molecules so similar in size will require a very precise "filter."

The good news is that such a filter exists. Recent work by Steven Kuznicki and Valerie Bell at Engelhard Corporation in New Jersey and Michael Tsapatsis at the University of Massachusetts has produced a "molecular sieve" in which the pore (passage) sizes can be adjusted precisely enough to separate N_2 molecules from CH_4 molecules. The material involved is a special hydrated titanosilicate (contains H_2O, Ti, Si, O, and Sr)

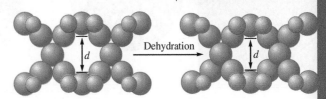

Molecular sieve framework of titanium (blue), silicon (green), and oxygen (red) atoms contracts on heating—at room temperature (left), $d = 4.27$ Å; at 250°C (right), $d = 3.94$ Å.

compound patented by Engelhard and known as ETS-4 (Engelhard TitanoSilicate-4). When sodium ions are substituted for the strontium ions in ETS-4 and the new material is carefully dehydrated, a uniform and controllable pore-size reduction occurs (see figure). The researchers have shown that the material can be used to separate N_2 (≈ 410 pm) from O_2 (≈ 390 pm). They have also shown that it is possible to reduce the nitrogen content of natural gas from 18% to less than 5% with a 90% recovery of methane.

An example of this type of model is the **kinetic molecular theory (KMT)**, a simple model that attempts to explain the properties of an ideal gas. This model is based on speculations about the behavior of the individual gas particles (atoms or molecules). The postulates of the kinetic molecular theory as they relate to the particles of an ideal gas can be stated as follows:

Postulates of the Kinetic Molecular Theory

1. The particles are so small compared with the distances between them that *the volume of the individual particles can be assumed to be negligible* (zero) (Fig. 5.11).

2. *The particles are in constant motion. The collisions of the particles with the walls of the container are the cause of the pressure exerted by the gas.*

3. *The particles are assumed to exert no forces on each other;* they are assumed neither to attract nor to repel each other.

4. *The average kinetic energy of a collection of gas particles is assumed to be directly proportional to the Kelvin temperature of the gas.*

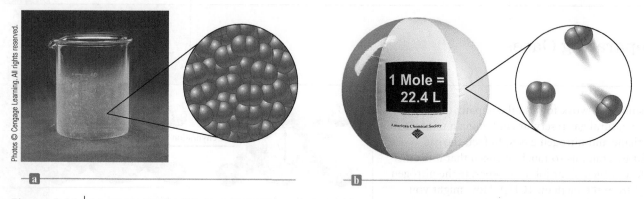

Figure 5.11 | (a) One mole of $N_2(l)$ has a volume of approximately 35 mL and a density of 0.81 g/mL. (b) One mole of $N_2(g)$ has a volume of 22.42 L (STP) and a density of 1.2×10^{-3} g/mL. Thus the ratio of the volumes of gaseous N_2 and liquid N_2 is 22.42/0.035 = 640, and the spacing of the molecules is 9 times farther apart in $N_2(g)$.

Of course, the molecules in a real gas have finite volumes and do exert forces on each other. Thus *real gases* do not conform to these assumptions. However, we will see that these postulates do indeed explain *ideal gas* behavior.

The true test of a model is how well its predictions fit the experimental observations. The postulates of the kinetic molecular model picture an ideal gas as consisting of particles having no volume and no attractions for each other, and the model assumes that the gas produces pressure on its container by collisions with the walls.

Let's consider how this model accounts for the properties of gases as summarized by the ideal gas law: $PV = nRT$.

Pressure and Volume (Boyle's Law)

We have seen that for a given sample of gas at a given temperature (n and T are constant) that if the volume of a gas is decreased, the pressure increases:

$$P = \underbrace{(nRT)}_{\text{Constant}}\frac{1}{V}$$

This makes sense based on the kinetic molecular theory because a decrease in volume means that the gas particles will hit the wall more often, thus increasing pressure (Fig. 5.12).

Pressure and Temperature

From the ideal gas law, we can predict that for a given sample of an ideal gas at a constant volume, the pressure will be directly proportional to the temperature:

$$P = \underbrace{\left(\frac{nR}{V}\right)}_{\text{Constant}}T$$

Figure 5.12 | The effects of decreasing the volume of a sample of gas at constant temperature.

Volume is decreased.

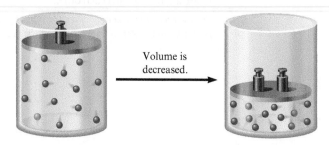

Figure 5.13A | The effects of increasing the temperature of a sample of gas at constant volume.

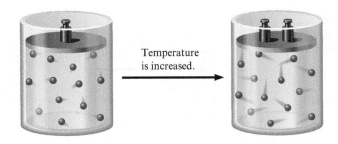

The KMT accounts for this behavior because when the temperature of a gas increases, the speeds of its particles increase, the particles hitting the wall with greater force and greater frequency. Since the volume remains the same, this would result in increased gas pressure (Fig. 5.13A).

Critical Thinking

You have learned the postulates of the KMT. What if we could not assume the third postulate to be true? How would this affect the measured pressure of a gas?

Volume and Temperature (Charles's Law)

The ideal gas law indicates that for a given sample of gas at a constant pressure, the volume of the gas is directly proportional to the temperature in kelvins:

$$V = \underbrace{\left(\frac{nR}{P}\right)}_{\uparrow \text{ Constant}} T$$

This can be visualized from the KMT (Fig. 5.13B). When the gas is heated to a higher temperature, the speeds of its molecules increase and thus they hit the walls more often and with more force. The only way to keep the pressure constant in this situation is to increase the volume of the container. This compensates for the increased particle speeds.

Volume and Number of Moles (Avogadro's Law)

The ideal gas law predicts that the volume of a gas at a constant temperature and pressure depends directly on the number of gas particles present:

$$V = \underbrace{\left(\frac{RT}{P}\right)}_{\uparrow \text{ Constant}} n$$

Figure 5.13B | The effects of increasing the temperature of a sample of gas at constant pressure.

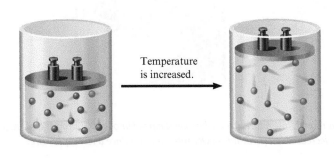

Figure 5.14 | The effects of increasing the number of moles of gas particles at constant temperature and pressure.

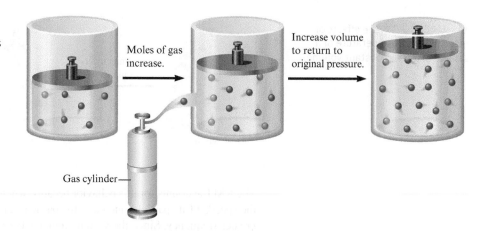

Moles of gas increase.

Increase volume to return to original pressure.

Gas cylinder

This makes sense in terms of the KMT because an increase in the number of gas particles at the same temperature would cause the pressure to increase if the volume were held constant (Fig. 5.14). The only way to return the pressure to its original value is to increase the volume.

It is important to recognize that the volume of a gas (at constant P and T) depends only on the *number* of gas particles present. The individual volumes of the particles are not a factor because the particle volumes are so small compared with the distances between the particles (for a gas behaving ideally).

Mixture of Gases (Dalton's Law)

The observation that the total pressure exerted by a mixture of gases is the sum of the pressures of the individual gases is expected because the KMT assumes that all gas particles are independent of each other and that the volumes of the individual particles are unimportant. Thus the identities of the gas particles do not matter.

Deriving the Ideal Gas Law

We have shown qualitatively that the assumptions of the KMT successfully account for the observed behavior of an ideal gas. We can go further. By applying the principles of physics to the assumptions of the KMT, we can in effect derive the ideal gas law.

Ken O'Donoghue

Ken O'Donoghue

Ken O'Donoghue

(a) A balloon filled with air at room temperature. (b) The balloon is dipped into liquid nitrogen at 77 K. (c) The balloon collapses as the molecules inside slow down due to the decreased temperature. Slower molecules produce a lower pressure.

As shown in detail in Appendix 2, we can apply the definitions of velocity, momentum, force, and pressure to the collection of particles in an ideal gas and *derive* the following expression for pressure:

$$P = \frac{2}{3}\left[\frac{nN_A(\frac{1}{2}m\overline{u^2})}{V}\right]$$

where P is the pressure of the gas, n is the number of moles of gas, N_A is Avogadro's number, m is the mass of each particle, $\overline{u^2}$ is the average of the square of the velocities of the particles, and V is the volume of the container.

The quantity $\frac{1}{2}m\overline{u^2}$ represents the average kinetic energy of a gas particle. If the average kinetic energy of an individual particle is multiplied by N_A, the number of particles in a mole, we get the average kinetic energy for a mole of gas particles:

$$(KE)_{avg} = N_A(\tfrac{1}{2}m\overline{u^2})$$

Kinetic energy (KE) given by the equation $KE = \frac{1}{2}m\overline{u^2}$ is the energy due to the motion of a particle. We will discuss this further in Section 6.1.

Using this definition, we can rewrite the expression for pressure as

$$P = \frac{2}{3}\left[\frac{n(KE)_{avg}}{V}\right] \quad \text{or} \quad \frac{PV}{n} = \frac{2}{3}(KE)_{avg}$$

The fourth postulate of the kinetic molecular theory is that the average kinetic energy of the particles in the gas sample is directly proportional to the temperature in kelvin. Thus, since $(KE)_{avg} \propto T$, we can write

$$\frac{PV}{n} = \frac{2}{3}(KE)_{avg} \propto T \quad \text{or} \quad \frac{PV}{n} \propto T$$

Note that this expression has been *derived* from the assumptions of the kinetic molecular theory. How does it compare to the ideal gas law—the equation obtained from experiment? Compare the ideal gas law,

$$\frac{PV}{n} = RT \quad \text{From experiment}$$

with the result from the kinetic molecular theory,

$$\frac{PV}{n} \propto T \quad \text{From theory}$$

These expressions have exactly the same form if R, the universal gas constant, is considered the proportionality constant in the second case.

The agreement between the ideal gas law and the predictions of the kinetic molecular theory gives us confidence in the validity of the model. The characteristics we have assumed for ideal gas particles must agree, at least under certain conditions, with their actual behavior.

The Meaning of Temperature

We have seen from the kinetic molecular theory that the Kelvin temperature indicates the average kinetic energy of the gas particles. The exact relationship between temperature and average kinetic energy can be obtained by combining the equations:

$$\frac{PV}{n} = RT = \frac{2}{3}(KE)_{avg}$$

which yields the expression

$$(KE)_{avg} = \frac{3}{2}RT$$

This is a very important relationship. It summarizes the meaning of the Kelvin temperature of a gas: The Kelvin temperature is an index of the random motions of the particles of a gas, with higher temperature meaning greater motion. (As we will see in Chapter 10, temperature is an index of the random motions in solids and liquids as well as in gases.)

Root Mean Square Velocity

In the equation from the kinetic molecular theory, the average velocity of the gas particles is a special kind of average. The symbol $\overline{u^2}$ means the average of the *squares* of the particle velocities. The square root of $\overline{u^2}$ is called the **root mean square velocity** and is symbolized by u_{rms}:

$$u_{rms} = \sqrt{\overline{u^2}}$$

We can obtain an expression for u_{rms} from the equations

$$(KE)_{avg} = N_A(\tfrac{1}{2}m\overline{u^2}) \quad \text{and} \quad (KE)_{avg} = \frac{3}{2}RT$$

Combination of these equations gives

$$N_A(\tfrac{1}{2}m\overline{u^2}) = \frac{3}{2}RT \quad \text{or} \quad \overline{u^2} = \frac{3RT}{N_A m}$$

Taking the square root of both sides of the last equation produces

$$\sqrt{\overline{u^2}} = u_{rms} = \sqrt{\frac{3RT}{N_A m}}$$

In this expression m represents the mass in kilograms of a single gas particle. When N_A, the number of particles in a mole, is multiplied by m, the product is the mass of a *mole* of gas particles in *kilograms*. We will call this quantity M. Substituting M for $N_A m$ in the equation for u_{rms}, we obtain

$$u_{rms} = \sqrt{\frac{3RT}{M}}$$

$$R = 0.08206 \frac{L \cdot atm}{K \cdot mol}$$

$$R = 8.3145 \frac{J}{K \cdot mol}$$

   Before we can use this equation, we need to consider the units for R. So far we have used 0.08206 L · atm/K · mol as the value of R. But to obtain the desired units (meters per second) for u_{rms}, R must be expressed in different units. As we will see in more detail in Chapter 6, the energy unit most often used in the SI system is the joule (J). A **joule** is defined as a kilogram meter squared per second squared (kg · m²/s²). When R is converted to include the unit of joules, it has the value 8.3145 J/K · mol. When R in these units is used in the expression $\sqrt{3RT/M}$, u_{rms} is obtained in the units of meters per second as desired.

Interactive Example 5.8A

Sign in at http://login.cengagebrain.com to try this Interactive Example in OWL.

Root Mean Square Velocity

Calculate the root mean square velocity for the atoms in a sample of helium gas at 25°C.

Solution

Where are we going?

To determine the root mean square velocity for the atoms of He

What do we know?

> $T = 25°C + 273 = 298$ K
> $R = 8.3145$ J/K $\cdot$ mol

What information do we need?

> Root mean square velocity is $u_{rms} = \sqrt{\dfrac{3RT}{M}}$

How do we get there?

What is the mass of a mole of He in kilograms?

$$M = 4.00 \frac{g}{mol} \times \frac{1 \text{ kg}}{1000 \text{ g}} = 4.00 \times 10^{-3} \text{ kg/mol}$$

What is the root mean square velocity for the atoms of He?

$$u_{rms} = \sqrt{\frac{3\left(8.3145 \dfrac{J}{K \cdot mol}\right)(298 \text{ K})}{4.00 \times 10^{-3} \dfrac{kg}{mol}}} = \sqrt{1.86 \times 10^6 \frac{J}{kg}}$$

Since the units of J are kg $\cdot$ m²/s², this expression gives

$$\blacksquare \ u_{rms} = \sqrt{1.86 \times 10^6 \frac{kg \cdot m^2}{kg \cdot s^2}} = 1.36 \times 10^3 \text{ m/s}$$

Reality Check | The resulting units are appropriate for velocity.

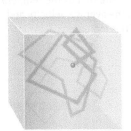

Figure 5.15 | Path of one particle in a gas. Any given particle will continuously change its course as a result of collisions with other particles, as well as with the walls of the container.

So far we have said nothing about the range of velocities actually found in a gas sample. In a real gas, there are large numbers of collisions between particles. For example, as we will see in the next section, when an odorous gas such as ammonia is released in a room, it takes some time for the odor to permeate the air. This delay results from collisions between the NH_3 molecules and the O_2 and N_2 molecules in the air, which greatly slow the mixing process.

If the path of a particular gas particle could be monitored, it would look very erratic, something like that shown in Fig. 5.15. The average distance a particle travels between collisions in a particular gas sample is called the *mean free path*. It is typically a very small distance (1×10^{-7} m for O_2 at STP). One effect of the many collisions among gas particles is to produce a large range of velocities as the particles collide and exchange kinetic energy. Although u_{rms} for oxygen gas at STP is approximately 500 m/s, the majority of O_2 molecules do not have this velocity. The actual distribution of molecular velocities for oxygen gas at STP is shown in Fig. 5.16. This figure shows the relative number of gas molecules having each particular velocity.

We are also interested in the effect of *temperature* on the velocity distribution in a gas. Figure 5.17 shows the velocity distribution (called the Maxwell-Boltzmann distribution) for nitrogen gas at three temperatures. Note that as the temperature is increased, the curve peak moves toward higher values and the range of velocities becomes much larger. The peak of the curve reflects the most probable velocity (the velocity found most often as we sample the movement of the various particles in the gas). Because the kinetic energy increases with temperature, it makes sense that the peak of the curve should move to higher values as the temperature of the gas is increased.

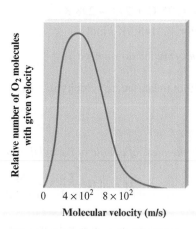

Figure 5.16 | A plot of the relative number of O_2 molecules that have a given velocity at STP.

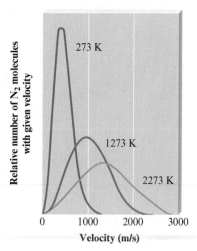

Figure 5.17 | A plot of the relative number of N_2 molecules that have a given velocity at three temperatures. Note that as the temperature increases, both the average velocity and the spread of velocities increase.

5.7 | Effusion and Diffusion

We have seen that the postulates of the kinetic molecular theory, combined with the appropriate physical principles, produce an equation that successfully fits the experimentally observed properties of gases as they approach ideal behavior. Two phenomena involving gases provide further tests of this model.

Diffusion is the term used to describe the mixing of gases. When a small amount of pungent-smelling ammonia is released at the front of a classroom, it takes some time before everyone in the room can smell it because time is required for the ammonia to mix with the air. The rate of diffusion is the rate of the mixing of gases. **Effusion** is the term used to describe the passage of a gas through a tiny orifice into an evacuated chamber (Fig. 5.18). The rate of effusion measures the rate at which the gas is transferred into the chamber.

Figure 5.18
The effusion of a gas into an evacuated chamber. The rate of effusion (the rate at which the gas is transferred across the barrier through the pin hole) is inversely proportional to the square root of the mass of the gas molecules.

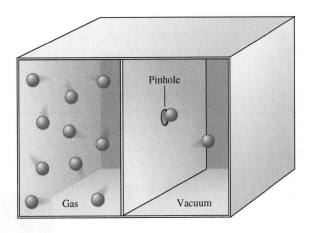

Effusion

Thomas Graham (1805–1869), a Scottish chemist, found experimentally that the rate of effusion of a gas is inversely proportional to the square root of the mass of its particles. Stated in another way, the relative rates of effusion of two gases at the same temperature and pressure are given by the inverse ratio of the square roots of the masses of the gas particles:

$$\frac{\text{Rate of effusion for gas 1}}{\text{Rate of effusion for gas 2}} = \frac{\sqrt{M_2}}{\sqrt{M_1}}$$

In Graham's law, the units for molar mass can be g/mol or kg/mol, since the units cancel in the ratio $\sqrt{M_2}/\sqrt{M_1}$.

where M_1 and M_2 represent the molar masses of the gases. This equation is called **Graham's law of effusion.**

Does the kinetic molecular model for gases correctly predict the relative effusion rates of gases summarized by Graham's law? To answer this question, we must recognize that the effusion rate for a gas depends directly on the average velocity of its particles. The faster the gas particles are moving, the more likely they are to pass through the effusion orifice. This reasoning leads to the following *prediction* for two gases at the same temperature T:

$$\frac{\text{Effusion rate for gas 1}}{\text{Effusion rate for gas 2}} = \frac{u_{\text{avg}} \text{ for gas 1}}{u_{\text{avg}} \text{ for gas 2}} = \frac{\sqrt{8RT/\pi M_1}}{\sqrt{8RT/\pi M_2}} = \frac{\sqrt{M_2}}{\sqrt{M_1}}$$

This equation is Graham's law, and thus the kinetic molecular model fits the experimental results for the effusion of gases.

Diffusion

Diffusion is frequently illustrated by the lecture demonstration represented in Fig. 5.19, in which two cotton plugs, one soaked in ammonia and the other in hydrochloric acid, are simultaneously placed at the ends of a long tube. A white ring of ammonium chloride (NH_4Cl) forms where the NH_3 and HCl molecules meet several minutes later:

$$NH_3(g) + HCl(g) \longrightarrow NH_4Cl(s)$$
White solid

The progress of the gases through the tube is surprisingly slow in light of the fact that the velocities of the HCl and NH_3 molecules at 25°C are approximately 450 and 660 m/s, respectively. Why does it take several minutes for the NH_3 and HCl molecules to meet? The answer is that the tube contains air and thus the NH_3 and HCl molecules undergo many collisions with O_2 and N_2 molecules as they travel through the tube. Although these collisions greatly slow their progress through the tube, it still seems reasonable to expect the

Figure 5.19

(a) A demonstration of the relative diffusion rates of NH_3 and HCl molecules through air. Two cotton plugs, one dipped in HCl(aq) and one dipped in $NH_3(aq)$, are simultaneously inserted into the ends of the tube. Gaseous NH_3 and HCl vaporizing from the cotton plugs diffuse toward each other and, where they meet, react to form $NH_4Cl(s)$.

(b) When HCl(g) and $NH_3(g)$ meet in the tube, a white ring of $NH_4Cl(s)$ forms.

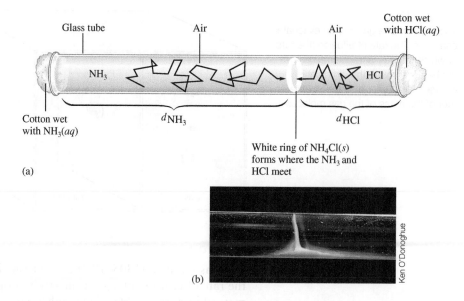

Glass tube　　　　Air　　　　Air　　　Cotton wet with HCl(aq)

NH_3　　　　　　　　　　　HCl

Cotton wet with $NH_3(aq)$　　　d_{NH_3}　　　d_{HCl}

White ring of $NH_4Cl(s)$ forms where the NH_3 and HCl meet

(a)

(b)

Ken O'Donoghue

If no air were present in the tube, the ratio of distances would be 1.5 as predicted from Graham's law.

relative distances traveled by the NH_3 and HCl molecules to be related to their velocities:

$$\frac{d_{NH_3}}{d_{HCl}} = \frac{\text{distance traveled by } NH_3}{\text{distance traveled by HCl}} = \frac{u_{avg(NH_3)}}{u_{avg(HCl)}} = \sqrt{\frac{M_{HCl}}{M_{NH_3}}} = \sqrt{\frac{36.5}{17}} = 1.5$$

However, careful experiments show that this prediction is not borne out—the observed ratio of distances is 1.3, not 1.5 as predicted by Graham's law. This discrepancy is not due to a failure of the kinetic molecular theory or of Graham's law; it exists because this "diffusion" experiment does not involve a simple diffusion process. Rather, it involves a *flow* of ammonia and hydrogen chloride gases through the air in the tube. Because the NH_3 and HCl molecules suffer many collisions with the N_2 and O_2 molecules in the tube, the flow rates of NH_3 and HCl are not directly proportional to their molecular velocities. Higher velocities lead to a higher number of intermolecular collisions, which in turn impedes the flow of the gas. Because of its smaller mass (and thus higher average velocity), the flow of the ammonia gas is impeded more than the flow of the hydrogen chloride gas. Therefore, the $NH_3(g)$ travels a smaller distance to meet the HCl(g) than is expected from Graham's law (the distance ratio is smaller than 1.5).

Although we have given only a qualitative treatment here, the phenomena accompanying the mixing of gases are well understood, and the results of this experiment can be described very accurately by quantitative theories.

Although other technologies are now coming into use for this purpose, gaseous diffusion has played an important role in the enrichment of uranium for use in nuclear reactors. Natural uranium is mostly $^{238}_{92}U$, which cannot be fissioned to produce energy. It contains only about 0.7% of the fissionable nuclide $^{235}_{92}U$. For uranium to be useful as a nuclear fuel, the relative amount of $^{235}_{92}U$ must be increased to about 3%. In the gas diffusion enrichment process, the natural uranium (containing $^{238}_{92}U$ and a small amount of $^{235}_{92}U$) reacts with fluorine to form a mixture of $^{238}UF_6$ and $^{235}UF_6$. Because these molecules have slightly different masses, they will have slightly different velocities at a given temperature, which allows them to be separated by a multistage diffusion process. To understand how this process works, imagine a series of chambers separated by semiporous walls that allow passage of some UF_6 molecules but prevent bulk flow of gas. In effect, each porous wall acts much like a tiny hole in an effusion cell. Assume that the UF_6 from natural uranium is placed in chamber 1. Thus chamber 1 contains 99.3% $^{238}UF_6$ and 0.7% $^{235}UF_6$ (that is, 993 molecules of $^{238}UF_6$ for every 7 molecules of $^{235}UF_6$). Some molecules of this UF_6 diffuse through the semiporous barrier into chamber 2, which was initially empty. Because of its smaller mass, $^{235}UF_6$, which has a slightly greater velocity than $^{238}UF_6$, diffuses at a slightly greater rate. Thus chamber 2 will contain a ratio of $^{235}UF_6$ to $^{238}UF_6$ that is slightly greater than 7 to 993.

Although the process is called *gaseous diffusion* because the chambers are separated by barriers that effectively allow only individual UF_6 molecules to pass through, it behaves like an effusion process. Thus we can find the actual ratio of the two types of UF_6 in chamber 2 from Graham's law:

$$\frac{\text{Diffusion rate for } ^{235}UF_6}{\text{Diffusion rate for } ^{238}UF_6} = \sqrt{\frac{\text{mass}(^{238}UF_6)}{\text{mass}(^{235}UF_6)}}$$

$$= \sqrt{\frac{352.05 \text{ g/mol}}{349.03 \text{ g/mol}}}$$

$$= 1.0043$$

We can use this factor to calculate the ratio of $^{235}UF_6/^{238}UF_6$ in chamber 2:

$$\underset{\underset{\text{Chamber 2}}{\uparrow}}{\frac{^{235}UF_6}{^{238}UF_6}} = 1.0043 \times \underset{\underset{\text{Chamber 1}}{\uparrow}}{\frac{^{235}UF_6}{^{238}UF_6}} = 1.0043\left(\frac{7}{993}\right)$$

$$= 1.0043(7.0493 \times 10^{-3})$$

$$= 7.0797 \times 10^{-3}$$

This very slight increase represents a change from the ratio of 70,493 $^{235}UF_6$ molecules per 10,000,000 $^{238}UF_6$ molecules in chamber 1 to the ratio of 70,797 $^{235}UF_6$ molecules per 10,000,000 $^{238}UF_6$ molecules in chamber 2.

This enrichment process (in $^{235}UF_6$) continues as the slightly enriched gas in chamber 2 diffuses into chamber 3 and is again enriched by a factor of 1.0043. The same process is repeated until sufficient enrichment occurs. Obviously, this process will take many stages. For example, to calculate the number of steps required to enrich from 0.700% ^{235}U to 3.00% ^{235}U, we have the following equation:

$$\underset{\underset{\text{Original ratio}}{\uparrow}}{\frac{0.700 \; ^{235}UF_6}{99.3 \; ^{238}UF_6}} \times (1.0043)^N = \underset{\underset{\text{Desired ratio}}{\uparrow}}{\frac{3.00 \; ^{235}UF_6}{97.0 \; ^{238}UF_6}}$$

where N represents the number of stages. This equation follows from the fact that each stage produces an enrichment by the factor 1.0043. Thus

$$\text{Original ratio} \times \underset{\underset{\text{stage}}{\underset{\text{First}}{\uparrow}}}{1.0043} \times \underset{\underset{\text{stage}}{\underset{\text{Second}}{\uparrow}}}{1.0043} \times \underset{\underset{\text{stage}}{\underset{\text{Third}}{\uparrow}}}{1.0043} \times \cdots = \text{final ratio}$$

Solving this equation for N yields 345. Thus we predict that 345 stages are required to obtain the desired enrichment.

Although we have greatly oversimplified* the actual enrichment process here, this discussion gives you an idea of how it is accomplished. A photo of actual diffusion cells is shown in Fig. 5.20.

Figure 5.20
Uranium-enrichment converters from the Paducah gaseous diffusion plant in Kentucky.

---

*For a more detailed description, see W. Spindel and T. Ishida, "Isotope Separation," *J. Chem. Ed.* 68 (1991): 312.

Enrichment of uranium by gaseous diffusion has become obsolete. Increasingly, a process using gas centrifuges has become the method of choice. Such a process uses a large number of rotating cylinders (centrifuges) that cause the more massive $^{238}UF_6$ to move to the outside of each cylinder relative to the $^{235}UF_6$, which remains closer to the center. Gas centrifuge technology requires much less energy than gaseous diffusion, and each step has a 1.3 separation factor compared to 1.0043 for gaseous diffusion. Other technologies are also being explored for uranium enrichment, but we will not discuss them here.

5.8 | Collisions of Gas Particles with the Container Walls

In the analysis of the kinetic molecular model that led to the ideal gas equation, we assumed that the pressure a gas exerts is caused by the collisions of its particles with the walls of its container. In this section we will consider the details of that phenomenon.

Our goal is to obtain an equation that describes the number of particles that collide per second with a given area of the wall. Although a rigorous derivation of such an equation can be carried out from the details of the kinetic molecular theory, we will not do that. Instead, we will pursue a qualitative strategy, trying to obtain the fundamental relationships from our conceptual understanding of how an ideal gas is expected to behave. We will define the quantity we are looking for as Z_A, the collision rate (per second) of the gas particles with a section of wall that has an area A (in m^2). We expect Z_A to depend on the following factors:

1. The average velocity of the gas particles
2. The size of the area being considered
3. The number of particles in the container

How is Z_A expected to depend on the average velocity of the gas particles? For example, if we double the average velocity, we double the number of wall impacts, so Z_A should double. Thus Z_A depends directly on u_{avg}:

$$Z_A \propto u_{avg}$$

Similarly, Z_A depends directly on A, the area of the wall under consideration. That is, if we double the area being considered, we will double the number of impacts per second that occur within that section of the wall. Thus $Z_A \propto A$.

Likewise, if the number of particles in the container is doubled, the impacts with the wall will double. For a general case, we need to consider not the absolute number of particles but the number of particles per unit volume (the number density of particles), which can be represented by N/V, the number of particles N divided by the volume V (in m^3). Thus Z_A is expected to depend directly on N/V. That is, $Z_A \propto N/V$.

In summary, Z_A should be directly proportional to u_{avg}, A, and N/V:

$$Z_A \propto u_{avg} \times A \times \frac{N}{V}$$

Note that the units for Z_A expected from this relationship are

$$\frac{m}{s} \times m^2 \times \frac{(particles)}{m^3} \longrightarrow \frac{(particles)}{s} \quad or \quad \frac{(collisions)}{s}$$

The parentheses are used here because particles and collisions are understood and are not actual units. The correct units for Z_A are 1/s, or s^{-1}. The fact that the product $u_{avg} \times A \times N/V$ gives the units expected for Z_A indicates that we are considering all the gas properties that influence Z_A. Substituting the expression for u_{avg} gives

$$Z_A \propto \frac{N}{V} A \sqrt{\frac{8RT}{\pi M}}$$

A more detailed analysis of the situation shows that the proportionality constant is $\frac{1}{4}$. Thus the exact equation for Z_A is

$$Z_A = \frac{1}{4} \frac{N}{V} A \sqrt{\frac{8RT}{\pi M}} = A \frac{N}{V} \sqrt{\frac{RT}{2\pi M}}$$

ꙩWL INTERACTIVE EXAMPLE 5.9

Calculate the impact rate on a 1.00-cm² section of a vessel containing oxygen gas at a pressure of 1.00 atm and 27°C.

Solution To calculate Z_A, we must identify the values of the variables in the equation

$$Z_A = A \frac{N}{V} \sqrt{\frac{RT}{2\pi M}}$$

In this case, A is given as 1.00 cm². However, to be inserted into the expression for Z_A, A must have the units m². The appropriate conversion gives $A = 1.00 \times 10^{-4}$ m².

The quantity N/V can be obtained from the ideal gas law by solving for n/V and then converting to the appropriate units:

$$\frac{n}{V} = \frac{P}{RT} = \frac{1.00 \text{ atm}}{\left(0.08206 \frac{\text{L atm}}{\text{K mol}}\right)(300. \text{ K})} = 4.06 \times 10^{-2} \text{ mol/L}$$

To obtain N/V, which has the units (molecules)/m³, from n/V, we make the following conversion:

$$\frac{N}{V} = 4.06 \times 10^{-2} \frac{\text{mol}}{\text{L}} \times 6.022 \times 10^{23} \frac{\text{(molecules)}}{\text{mol}} \times \frac{1000 \text{ L}}{\text{m}^3}$$

$$= 2.44 \times 10^{25} \text{ (molecules)/m}^3$$

The quantity M represents the molar mass of O_2 in kg. Thus

$$M = 32.0 \frac{\text{g}}{\text{mol}} \times \frac{1 \text{ kg}}{1000 \text{ g}} = 3.20 \times 10^{-2} \text{ kg/mol}$$

Next, we insert these quantities into the expression for Z_A:

$$Z_A = A \frac{N}{V} \sqrt{\frac{RT}{2\pi M}} = (1.00 \times 10^{-4} \text{ m}^2)(2.44 \times 10^{25} \text{ m}^{-3})$$

$$\times \sqrt{\frac{\left(8.3145 \frac{\text{J}}{\text{K mol}}\right)(300. \text{ K})}{(2)(3.14)\left(3.20 \times 10^{-2} \frac{\text{kg}}{\text{mol}}\right)}} = 2.72 \times 10^{23} \text{ s}^{-1}$$

That is, in this gas 2.72×10^{23} collisions per second occur on each 1.00-cm² area of the container.

5.9 | Intermolecular Collisions

Recall that the postulates of the kinetic molecular model do not take into account collisions between gas particles. Since this model correctly fits ideal gas behavior (that is, the behavior approached by real gases at high T and low P), our conclusion is that intermolecular collisions apparently do not have an important influence on the pressure, volume, or temperature of a gas behaving ideally. That is, the effects of the collisions must somehow "cancel out" relative to the properties P, V, and T of an ideal gas. However, there is much evidence to suggest that collisions do occur among the gas particles in a real gas. For example, a gas that is somehow disturbed from a Maxwell–Boltzmann distribution of velocities will rapidly change until it again reaches a Maxwell–Boltzmann distribution. This behavior must be caused by energy exchanges through collisions.

In this section we will consider the collision frequency of the particles in a gas. We will start by considering a single spherical gas particle with diameter d (in meters) that is moving with velocity u_{avg}. As this particle moves through the gas in a straight line, it will collide with another particle only if the other particle has its center in a cylinder with radius d, as shown in Fig. 5.21.

Any particle with its center outside this cylinder will not be hit by our particle. Thus our particle "sweeps out" a cylinder of radius d and length $u_{avg} \times 1$ second during every second of its flight. Therefore, the volume of the cylinder swept out per second is

$$V = \text{volume} = \underbrace{(\pi d^2)}_{\substack{\text{Area of} \\ \text{cylinder} \\ \text{slice}}} \underbrace{(u_{avg})(1\text{ s})}_{\substack{\text{Length of} \\ \text{cylinder}}}$$

As the particle travels through this cylinder, the number of collisions depends on the number of gas particles in that volume. To specify the number of gas particles, we use the number density of the gas N/V, which indicates the number of gas particles per unit volume. Thus we can write

$$\frac{\text{Number of collisions}}{\text{per second}} = \left(\frac{\text{volume}}{\text{swept out}}\right) \times \frac{N}{V} = \pi d^2 (u_{avg})\left(\frac{N}{V}\right)$$

$$= \pi d^2 \left(\sqrt{\frac{8RT}{\pi M}}\right)\left(\frac{N}{V}\right) = \frac{N}{V} d^2 \sqrt{\frac{8\pi RT}{M}}$$

Figure 5.21
The cylinder swept out by a gas particle of diameter d.

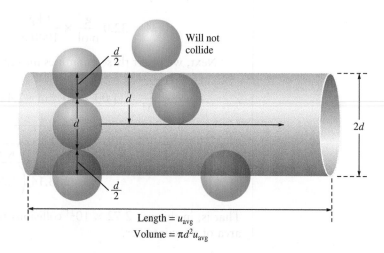

Will not collide

$\frac{d}{2}$

d

d

$\frac{d}{2}$

$2d$

Length $= u_{avg}$

Volume $= \pi d^2 u_{avg}$

This equation is not quite correct. If you are thinking carefully about this situation, you may be asking yourself the question, "What about the motions of the other particles?" That is, we have said that the primary particle has velocity u_{avg}, but we have assumed that the other particles are stationary. Of course, they are not really stationary. They are moving in various directions with various velocities. When the motions of the other particles are accounted for (a derivation we will not show here), the *relative velocity* of the primary particle becomes $\sqrt{2}\, u_{avg}$ rather than the value u_{avg} that we have been using. Thus the expression for the collision rate becomes

$$\text{Collision rate (per second)} = Z = \sqrt{2}\,\frac{N}{V}\,d^2\sqrt{\frac{8\pi RT}{M}} = 4\frac{N}{V}\,d^2\sqrt{\frac{\pi RT}{M}}$$

⍙WL INTERACTIVE EXAMPLE 5.10

Calculate the collision frequency for an oxygen molecule in a sample of pure oxygen gas at 27°C and 1.0 atm. Assume that the diameter of an O_2 molecule is 300 pm.

Solution To obtain the collision frequency, we must identify the quantities in the expression

$$Z = 4\frac{N}{V}\,d^2\sqrt{\frac{\pi RT}{M}}$$

that are appropriate to this case. We can obtain the value of N/V for this sample of oxygen by assuming ideal behavior. From the ideal gas law,

$$\frac{n}{V} = \frac{P}{RT} = \frac{1.0\ \text{atm}}{\left(0.08206\ \dfrac{\text{L atm}}{\text{K mol}}\right)(300.\ \text{K})} = 4.1 \times 10^{-2}\ \text{mol/L}$$

Thus

$$\frac{N}{V} = \left(4.1 \times 10^{-2}\ \frac{\text{mol}}{\text{L}}\right)\left(6.022 \times 10^{23}\ \frac{\text{molecules}}{\text{mol}}\right)\left(\frac{1000\ \text{L}}{\text{m}^3}\right)$$

$$= 2.5 \times 10^{25}\ \text{(molecules)/m}^3$$

From the given information, we know that

$$d = 300\ \text{pm} = 300 \times 10^{-12}\ \text{m}\ \ \text{or}\ \ 3 \times 10^{-10}\ \text{m}$$

Also, for O_2, $M = 3.20 \times 10^{-2}$ kg/mol. Thus

$$Z = 4(2.5 \times 10^{25}\ \text{m}^{-3})(3 \times 10^{-10}\ \text{m})^2 \times \sqrt{\frac{\pi(8.3145\ \text{J K}^{-1}\ \text{mol}^{-1})(300\ \text{K})}{3.20 \times 10^{-2}\ \text{kg/mol}}}$$

$$= 4 \times 10^9\ \text{(collisions)/s} = 4 \times 10^9\ \text{s}^{-1}$$

Notice how large this number is. Each O_2 molecule undergoes approximately 4 billion collisions per second in this gas sample.

Mean Free Path

As we saw earlier, the collision frequency Z represents the number of collisions per second that occur in a given gas sample. On the other hand, the reciprocal of Z gives the time (in seconds) between collisions. Thus, if $Z = 4 \times 10^9$ (collisions) per second, then $1/Z = 2.5 \times 10^{-10}$ seconds between collisions. Now if we multiply $1/Z$ by the average velocity, we obtain the **mean free path** λ:

$$\lambda = \frac{1}{Z} \times u_{avg} = \text{distance between collisions}$$

Time between   Distance traveled
collisions (s)   per second

Substituting the expressions for $1/Z$ and u_{avg} gives

$$\lambda = \left[\frac{1}{4(N/V)(d^2)\sqrt{RT/M}} \right]\left(\sqrt{\frac{8RT}{\pi M}} \right) = \frac{1}{\sqrt{2}(N/V)(\pi d^2)}$$

EXAMPLE 5.11

Calculate the mean free path in a sample of oxygen gas at 27°C and 1.0 atm.

Solution Using data from the preceding example, we have

$$\lambda = \frac{1}{\sqrt{2}(2.5 \times 10^{25}\text{ m}^{-3})(\pi)(3 \times 10^{-10}\text{ m})^2} = 1 \times 10^{-7}\text{ m}$$

Note that an O_2 molecule travels only a very short distance before it collides with another O_2 molecule. This produces a path for a given O_2 molecule like the one represented in Fig. 5.15, where the length of each straight line is $\sim 10^{-7}$ m.

5.10 | Real Gases

An ideal gas is a hypothetical concept. No gas *exactly* follows the ideal gas law, although many gases come very close at low pressures and/or high temperatures. Thus ideal gas behavior can best be thought of as the behavior *approached by real gases* under certain conditions.

We have seen that a very simple model, the kinetic molecular theory, by making some rather drastic assumptions (no interparticle interactions and zero volume for the gas particles), successfully explains ideal behavior. However, it is important that we examine real gas behavior to see how it differs from that predicted by the ideal gas law and to determine what modifications of the kinetic molecular theory are needed to explain the observed behavior. Since a model is an approximation and will inevitably fail, we must be ready to learn from such failures. In fact, we often learn more about nature from the failures of our models than from their successes.

We will examine the experimentally observed behavior of real gases by measuring the pressure, volume, temperature, and number of moles for a gas and noting how the quantity PV/nRT depends on pressure. Plots of PV/nRT versus P are shown for several gases in Fig. 5.22. For an ideal gas, PV/nRT equals 1 under all conditions, but notice that for real gases, PV/nRT approaches 1 only at low pressures (typically 1 atm). To illustrate the effect of temperature, we have plotted PV/nRT versus P for nitrogen gas at several temperatures in Fig. 5.23. Notice that the behavior of the gas appears to become more nearly ideal as the temperature is increased. The most important conclusion to be drawn from these plots is that a real gas typically exhibits behavior that is closest to ideal behavior at *low pressures* and *high temperatures*.

How can we modify the assumptions of the kinetic molecular theory to fit the behavior of real gases? An equation for real gases was developed in 1873 by Johannes van der Waals, a physics professor at the University of Amster-

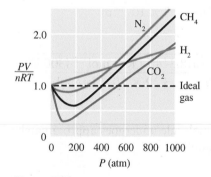

Figure 5.22

Plots of PV/nRT versus P for several gases (200 K). Note the significant deviations from ideal behavior ($PV/nRT = 1$). The behavior is close to ideal only at low pressures (less than 1 atm).

Figure 5.23

Plots of PV/nRT versus P for nitrogen gas at three temperatures. Note that although nonideal behavior is evident in each case, the deviations are smaller at the higher temperatures.

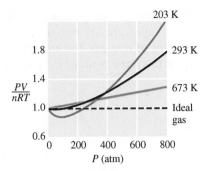

PV/nRT is also 1 at high pressures for many gases because of a canceling of nonideal effects.

P′ is corrected for the finite volume of the particles. The attractive forces have not yet been taken into account.

P_{obs} is usually called just P.

We have now corrected for both the finite volume and the attractive forces of the particles.

dam who in 1910 received a Nobel Prize for his work. To follow his analyses, we start with the ideal gas law,

$$P = \frac{nRT}{V}$$

Remember that this equation describes the behavior of a hypothetical gas consisting of volumeless entities that do not interact with each other. In contrast, a real gas consists of atoms or molecules that have finite volumes. Thus the volume available to a given particle in a real gas is less than the volume of the container because the gas particles themselves take up some of the space. To account for this discrepancy, van der Waals represented the actual volume as the volume of the container V minus a correction factor for the volume of the molecules nb, where n is the number of moles of gas and b is an empirical constant (one determined by fitting the equation to the experimental results). Thus the volume *actually available* to a given gas molecule is given by the difference $V - nb$.

This modification of the ideal gas equation leads to the expression

$$P' = \frac{nRT}{(V - nb)}$$

The volume of the gas particles has now been taken into account.

The next step is to account for the attractions that occur among the particles in a real gas. The effect of these attractions is to make the observed pressure P_{obs} smaller than it would be if the gas particles did not interact:

$$P_{obs} = (P' - \text{correction factor}) = \left(\frac{nRT}{V - nb} - \text{correction factor} \right)$$

This effect can be understood by using the following model. When gas particles come close together, attractive forces occur, which cause the particles to hit the wall slightly less often than they would in the absence of these interactions (Fig. 5.24).

The size of the correction factor depends on the concentration of gas molecules defined in terms of moles of gas particles per liter (n/V). The higher the concentration, the more likely a pair of gas particles will be close enough to attract each other. For large numbers of particles, the number of interacting *pairs* of particles depends on the square of the number of particles and thus on the square of the concentration, or $(n/V)^2$. This reasoning can be justified as follows: In a gas sample containing N particles, there are $N - 1$ partners available for each particle, as shown in Fig. 5.25. Since the $1 \cdots 2$ pair is the same as the $2 \cdots 1$ pair, this analysis counts each pair twice. Thus for N particles there are $N(N - 1)/2$ pairs. If N is a very large number, $N - 1$ approximately equals N, giving $N^2/2$ possible pairs. Thus the correction to the ideal pressure for the attractions of the particles has the form

$$P_{obs} = P' - a\left(\frac{n}{V} \right)^2$$

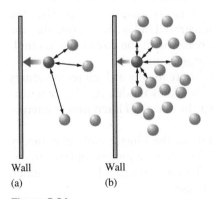

Wall   Wall
(a)   (b)

Figure 5.24

(a) Gas at low concentration—relatively few interactions between particles. The indicated gas particle exerts a pressure on the wall close to that predicted for an ideal gas.
(b) Gas at high concentration—many more interactions between particles. Because of these interactions the collision frequency with the walls is lowered, thus causing the observed pressure to be smaller than if the gas were behaving ideally.

Given particle

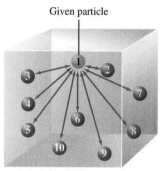

Gas sample with 10 particles

Figure 5.25

Illustration of pairwise interactions among gas particles. In a sample with 10 particles, each particle has 9 possible partners, to give $10(9)/2 = 45$ distinct pairs. The factor of $\frac{1}{2}$ arises because when particle ① is the particle of interest, we count the ①···② pair, and when particle ② is the particle of interest, we count the ②···① pair. However, ①···② and ②···① are the same pair, which we thus have counted twice. Therefore, we must divide by 2 to get the correct number of pairs.

where a is a proportionality constant (which includes the factor of $1\frac{1}{2}$ from $N^2/2$). The value of a for a given real gas can be determined from observing the actual behavior of that gas. Inserting the corrections for both the volume of the particles and the attractions of the particles gives the equation

$$P_{obs} = \frac{nRT}{V - nb} - a\left(\frac{n}{V}\right)^2$$

Observed pressure   Volume of the container   Volume correction   Pressure correction

This equation can be rearranged to give the **van der Waals equation:**

$$\underbrace{\left[P_{obs} + a\left(\frac{n}{V}\right)^2\right]}_{\substack{\text{Corrected pressure} \\ P_{ideal}}} \underbrace{(V - nb)}_{\substack{\text{Corrected volume} \\ V_{ideal}}} = nRT$$

The values of the weighting factors, a and b, are determined for a given gas by fitting experimental behavior. That is, a and b are varied until the best fit of the observed pressure is obtained under all conditions. The values of a and b for various gases are given in Table 5.3.

Experimental studies indicate that the changes van der Waals made in the basic assumptions of the kinetic molecular theory corrected the major flaws in the model. First, consider the effects of volume. For a gas at low pressure (large volume), the volume of the container is very large compared with the volumes of the gas particles. That is, the volume available to the gas is essentially equal to the volume of the container, so the gas behaves ideally. On the other hand, for a gas at high pressure (small volume), the volume of the particles becomes significant so that the volume available to the gas is significantly less than the container volume. These observations are illustrated in Fig. 5.26. Note that the volume-correction constant b generally increases with the size of the gas molecule, which gives further support to these arguments.

The fact that a real gas tends to behave more ideally at high temperatures can also be explained in terms of the van der Waals model. At high temperatures the particles are moving so rapidly that the effects of interparticle interactions are not very important.

The corrections made by van der Waals to the kinetic molecular theory make physical sense, which makes us confident that we understand the fundamentals of gas behavior at the particle level. This is significant because so much important chemistry takes place in the gas phase.

Table 5.3

Values of van der Waals Constants for Some Common Gases

Gas	$a\left(\dfrac{\text{atm L}^2}{\text{mol}^2}\right)$	$b\left(\dfrac{\text{L}}{\text{mol}}\right)$
He	0.034	0.0237
Ne	0.211	0.0171
Ar	1.35	0.0322
Kr	2.32	0.0398
Xe	4.19	0.0511
H_2	0.244	0.0266
N_2	1.39	0.0391
O_2	1.36	0.0318
Cl_2	6.49	0.0562
CO_2	3.59	0.0427
CH_4	2.25	0.0428
NH_3	4.17	0.0371
H_2O	5.46	0.0305

Figure 5.26

The volume occupied by the gas particles themselves is less important at (a) large container volumes (low pressure) than at (b) small container volumes (high pressure).

 (a)

 (b)

Kenneth Suslick Practices Sound Chemistry

Professor Kenneth S. Suslick, who received his B.S. degree from the California Institute of Technology and his Ph.D. from Stanford University, has spent his entire academic career at the University of Illinois at Urbana-Champaign. Although his research interests have spanned the traditional areas of chemistry, Professor Suslick and his group have been especially interested in sonochemistry, the chemical effects of ultrasound in which sound waves (pitched above human hearing) are applied to solutions.

The effects of high-intensity sound waves on solutions come from cavitation: the formation, growth, and implosive collapse of bubbles in a liquid. Cavitational collapse produces very high pressures that lead to local heating so intense that they cause reactions requiring high energies to occur, often accompanied by the emission of light.

In fact, Suslick's research has just shown that as the bubble implodes, the interior can reach temperatures higher than 15,000 K—about three times the temperature of the surface of the sun. At these temperatures atoms come apart to form a plasma, which contains ions and electrons. Thus cavitation can create extraordinarily hot spots in an otherwise cold liquid.

Besides its use for studying high-energy reactions, ultrasound has also proved valuable in the synthesis of nano-structured materials. One example is the formation of liquid-containing protein microspheres that could be injected into the body's circulatory system to deliver drugs. Another application involves surface chemistry. When cavitation occurs near a solid surface, the high-speed jets of liquid and the associated sound waves can alter the surface properties of the solid. This has proved useful in activating the surfaces of metals used as catalysts.

Sonochemistry is indeed sound chemistry.

A humorous photograph of Professor Kenneth S. Suslick. The fog apparently emanating from his head is produced by a very cold vapor from liquid nitrogen, which freezes moisture from the air.

5.11 | Characteristics of Several Real Gases

We can understand gas behavior more completely if we examine the characteristics of several common gases. Note from Fig. 5.22 that the gases H_2, N_2, CH_4, and CO_2 show different behavior when the compressibility PV/nRT is plotted versus P. For example, notice that the plot for $H_2(g)$ never drops below the ideal value (1.0) in contrast to all the other gases. What is special about H_2 compared to these other gases? Recall from Section 5.8 that the reason that the compressibility of a real gas falls below 1.0 is that the actual (observed) pressure is lower than the pressure expected for an ideal gas due to the intermolecular attractions that occur in real gases. This must mean that H_2 molecules have very low attractive forces for each other. This idea is borne out by looking at the van der Waals a value for H_2 in Table 5.3. Note that H_2 has the lowest value among the gases H_2, N_2, CH_4, and CO_2. Remember that the value of a reflects how much of a correction must be made to adjust the observed pressure up to the expected ideal pressure:

$$P_{ideal} = P_{obs} + a\left(\frac{n}{V}\right)^2$$

A low value for a reflects weak intermolecular forces among the gas molecules.

Also notice that although the compressibility for N_2 dips below 1.0, it does not show as much deviation as that for CH_4, which in turn does not show as much deviation as the compressibility for CO_2. Based on this behavior, we can surmise that the importance of intermolecular interactions increases in this order:

$$H_2 < N_2 < CH_4 < CO_2$$

This order is reflected by the relative a values for these gases in Table 5.3. In Section 16.1, we will see how these variations in intermolecular interactions can be explained. The main point to be made here is that real gas behavior can tell us about the relative importance of intermolecular attractions among gas molecules.

5.12 | Chemistry in the Atmosphere

Table 5.4

Atmospheric Composition Near Sea Level (dry air)*

Component	Mole Fraction
N_2	0.78084
O_2	0.20946
Ar	0.00934
CO_2	0.000345
Ne	0.00001818
He	0.00000524
CH_4	0.00000168
Kr	0.00000114
H_2	0.0000005
NO	0.0000005
Xe	0.000000087

*The atmosphere contains various amounts of water vapor, depending on conditions.

The gases that are most important to us are located in the **atmosphere** that surrounds the earth's surface. The principal components are N_2 and O_2, but many other important gases, such as H_2O and CO_2, are also present. The average composition of the earth's atmosphere near sea level, with the water vapor removed, is shown in Table 5.4. Because of gravitational effects, the composition of the earth's atmosphere is not constant: Heavier molecules tend to be near the earth's surface, and light molecules tend to migrate to higher altitudes and eventually to escape into space. The atmosphere is a highly complex and dynamic system, but for convenience, we divide it into several layers based on the way the temperature changes with altitude. (The lowest layer, called the *troposphere,* is shown in Fig. 5.27.) Note that in contrast to the complex temperature profile of the atmosphere in general, the pressure decreases in a regular way with increasing altitude in the troposphere.

The chemistry occurring in the higher levels of the atmosphere is mostly determined by the effects of high-energy radiation and particles from the sun and other sources in space. In fact, the upper atmosphere serves as an important shield to prevent this high-energy radiation from reaching the earth, where it would damage the relatively fragile molecules sustaining life. In particular, the ozone in the upper atmosphere helps prevent high-energy ultraviolet radiation from penetrating to the earth. Intensive research is in progress to determine the natural factors that control the ozone concentration and to understand how it is affected by chemicals released into the atmosphere.

The chemistry occurring in the troposphere is strongly influenced by human activities. Millions of tons of gases and particulates are released into the tropo-

Figure 5.27
The variation of temperature and pressure with altitude. Note that the pressure steadily decreases with increasing altitude but that the temperature does not change monotonically.

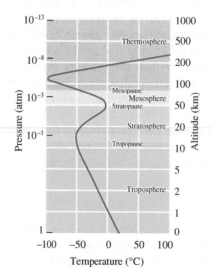

sphere by our highly industrial civilization. Actually, it is amazing that the atmosphere can absorb so much material with relatively small permanent changes.

Significant changes, however, are occurring. Severe **air pollution** is found around many large cities, and it is probable that long-range changes in the planet's weather are taking place. We will deal only with the short-term, localized effects of pollution.

The two main sources of pollution are transportation and the production of electricity. The combustion of petroleum in vehicles produces CO, CO_2, NO, and NO_2, along with unburned molecules from petroleum. When this mixture is trapped close to the ground in stagnant air, reactions occur, producing chemicals that are potentially irritating and harmful to living systems.

The complex chemistry of polluted air appears to center on ozone and the nitrogen oxides (NO_x). At the high temperatures in the gasoline and diesel engines of cars and trucks, N_2 and O_2 react to form a small quantity of NO, which is emitted into the air with the exhaust gases (Fig. 5.28). This NO is oxidized in air to NO_2, which in turn absorbs energy from sunlight and breaks up into nitric oxide and free oxygen atoms:

$$NO_2(g) \xrightarrow{\text{Radiant energy}} NO(g) + O(g)$$

Oxygen atoms are very reactive and can combine with O_2 to form *ozone:*

$$O(g) + O_2(g) \longrightarrow O_3(g)$$

Ozone is also very reactive. It can react with the unburned hydrocarbons in the polluted air to produce chemicals that cause the eyes to water and burn and are harmful to the respiratory system.

The end product of this whole process is often referred to as **photochemical smog,** so called because light is required to initiate some of the reactions. The production of photochemical smog can be more clearly understood by examining as a group the preceding reactions:

$$NO_2(g) \longrightarrow NO(g) + O(g)$$
$$O(g) + O_2(g) \longrightarrow O_3(g)$$
$$NO(g) + \tfrac{1}{2}O_2(g) \longrightarrow NO_2(g)$$

Net reaction:
$$\tfrac{3}{2}O_2(g) \longrightarrow O_3(g)$$

Note that the NO_2 molecules assist in the formation of ozone without being consumed themselves. The ozone then produces other pollutants.

We can observe this process by analyzing polluted air at various times during a day (Fig. 5.28). As people drive to work between 6 and 8 a.m., the amounts of NO, NO_2, and unburned molecules from petroleum increase. Later, as the decomposition of NO_2 occurs, the concentration of ozone and other pollutants builds up. Current efforts to combat the formation of photochemical smog are focused on cutting down the amounts of molecules from unburned fuel in automobile exhaust and designing engines that produce less nitric oxide (Fig. 5.29).

The other major source of pollution results from burning coal to produce electricity. Much of the coal found in the Midwest contains significant quantities of sulfur, which, when burned, produces sulfur dioxide:

$$S \text{ (In coal)} + O_2(g) \longrightarrow SO_2(g)$$

A further oxidation reaction occurs when sulfur dioxide is changed to sulfur trioxide in the air:

$$2SO_2(g) + O_2(g) \longrightarrow 2SO_3(g)$$

Although represented here as O_2, the actual oxidant is an organic peroxide such as CH_3COO, formed by reaction of O_2 with organic pollutants.

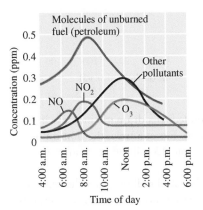

Figure 5.28
Concentration (in molecules per million molecules of "air") of some smog components versus time of day. After P. A. Leighton's classic experiment, "Photochemistry of Air Pollution," in *Physical Chemistry: A Series of Monographs,* ed. Eric Hutchinson and P. Van Rysselberghe, Vol. IX. New York: Academic Press, 1961.

John Lawlor

Figure 5.29
Our various modes of transportation produce large amounts of nitrogen oxides, which facilitate the formation of photochemical smog.

Chemical Insights   The Importance of Oxygen

Oxygen has been present only for the last half of the earth's history—appearing about 2.5 billion years ago in what is called *The Great Oxidation Event*. Before this time the earth's atmosphere contained large quantities of methane, which reacted with oxygen and prevented its buildup. Now there is geological evidence that about 2.7 billion years ago the amount of dissolved nickel in the oceans began to decrease. This was important because the organisms that produced methane required nickel ions to exist. As the methane concentrations in the atmosphere decreased, oxygen produced by chlorophyll-containing organisms began to build up. In contrast, oxygen was removed from the atmosphere by mountain building and erosion as freshly exposed rocks combined with oxygen to form oxygen-containing minerals.

The concentration of oxygen in the atmosphere has varied greatly over the last 600 million years, as shown in the accompanying graph. Note that 300 million years ago (at the end of the Carboniferous period) the air consisted of about 35% oxygen. The fossil record indicates that during this time insects and other arthropods that absorb oxygen through holes in their exoskeletons were extraordinarily large. It is thought that mayflies as big as today's robins and dragonflies as big as modern hawks were commonplace in this period.

About 255 million years ago, the oxygen concentration in the atmosphere was about 30%, but for some reason the oxygen content plunged to about 13% (about the concentration at an elevation of 15,000 feet in today's world) in the relatively short geological time span of 10 million years. Die-offs during this period claimed as many as 95% of the species living in the ocean and about 70% of those living on land. The oxygen content then began to rebound (to about 16%) 200 million

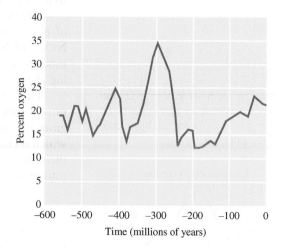

years ago, which led to a dramatic increase in biological innovation. For example, the first dinosaurs appeared only about 15 million years after the mass die-offs.

During the last 200 million years the oxygen content has increased rather steadily, making possible the existence of fuel-intense species such as mammals. In fact about 25 million years ago when oxygen concentration maximized at 23%, many mammals had become gigantic. For example, the relatives of today's rhino stood almost 5 m tall and weighed 15 metric tons—the largest ever land mammals. After peaking at 23%, the oxygen levels dropped to today's level of 21% and the "megamammals" disappeared. If history is any indication, the oxygen levels in the atmosphere will continue to change significantly over time, but this is obviously not a high-priority problem for us in the twenty-first century.

This equation describes only the overall stoichiometry of the process; many different oxidants actually participate in the oxidation of sulfur dioxide (see Chapter 15 for a further discussion). The production of sulfur trioxide is significant because it can combine with droplets of water in the air to form sulfuric acid:

$$SO_3(g) + H_2O(l) \longrightarrow H_2SO_4(aq)$$

Kristie A. Boering and Ronald C. Cohen Study the Earth's Atmosphere

One of the most important areas of research is the study of the chemistry of the earth's atmosphere and how human activities are changing it. Two researchers who are exploring these issues are Kristie A. Boering and Ronald C. Cohen, both faculty members at the University of California at Berkeley. Professor Boering and her research group are studying the earth's atmospheric chemistry through observations from aircraft, balloons, and ground-based platforms; computer simulations; and laboratory experiments. Dr. Boering is particularly interested in the exchange of gases between the biosphere and the atmosphere in modern times and over the past millennium.

Professor Cohen's overall goal is to develop a model for the ways human activity can cause global changes in the atmosphere. His group is particularly interested in what chemical reactions control ozone formation and depletion.

Kristie A. Boering.

Ronald C. Cohen.

Photo by Michael Barnes/University of California at Berkeley

Professors Boering and Cohen hope their efforts to understand the changes in atmospheric chemistry will lead to solutions to problems such as global warming.

Sulfuric acid is very corrosive to both living things and building materials. Another result of this type of pollution is **acid rain** (Fig. 5.30). In many parts of the northeastern United States and southeastern Canada, acid rain has caused some freshwater lakes to become too acidic for fish to live.

Figure 5.30
A helicopter dropping lime in a lake in Sweden to neutralize excess acid from acid rain.

M. Edwards/Peter Arnold, Inc.

Chemical Insights   Acid Rain: An Expensive Problem

Rainwater, even in pristine wilderness areas, is slightly acidic because some of the carbon dioxide present in the atmosphere dissolves in the raindrops to produce H^+ ions by the following reaction:

$$H_2O(l) + CO_2(g) \longrightarrow H^+(aq) + HCO_3^-(aq)$$

This process produces only very small concentrations of H^+ ions in the rainwater. However, gases such as NO_2 and SO_2, which are by-products of energy use, can produce significantly higher H^+ concentrations. Nitrogen dioxide reacts with water to give a mixture of nitrous acid and nitric acid:

$$2NO_2(g) + H_2O(l) \longrightarrow HNO_2(aq) + HNO_3(aq)$$

Sulfur dioxide is oxidized to sulfur trioxide, which then reacts with water to form sulfuric acid:

$$2SO_2(g) + O_2(g) \longrightarrow 2SO_3(g)$$

$$SO_3(g) + H_2O(l) \longrightarrow H_2SO_4(aq)$$

The damage caused by the acid formed in polluted air is a growing worldwide problem. Lakes are dying in Norway, the forests are sick in Germany, and buildings and statues are deteriorating all over the world.

For example, the Field Museum in Chicago contains more white Georgia marble than any other structure in the world. But more than 70 years of exposure to the elements has taken such a toll on it that the building underwent a multimillion-dollar renovation to replace the damaged marble with freshly quarried material.

What is the chemistry of the deterioration of marble by sulfuric acid? Marble is produced by geological processes at high temperatures and pressures from limestone, a sedimentary rock formed by slow deposition of calcium carbonate from the shells of marine organisms. Limestone and marble are chemically identical ($CaCO_3$) but differ in physical properties because limestone is composed of smaller particles of calcium carbonate and is thus more porous and more workable. Although both limestone and marble are used for buildings, marble can be polished to a higher sheen and is often preferred for decorative purposes.

Both marble and limestone react with sulfuric acid to form calcium sulfate. The process can be represented most simply as

$$CaCO_3(s) + H_2SO_4(aq)$$
$$\longrightarrow Ca^{2+}(aq) + SO_4^{2-}(aq) + H_2O(l) + CO_2(g)$$

The problem of sulfur dioxide pollution is further complicated by the energy crisis. As petroleum supplies dwindle and the price increases, our dependence on coal will grow. As supplies of low-sulfur coal are used up, high-sulfur coal will be used. One way to use high-sulfur coal without further harming the air quality is to remove the sulfur dioxide from the exhaust gas by means of a system called a *scrubber* before it is emitted from the power plant stack. A common method of *scrubbing* involves blowing powdered limestone ($CaCO_3$) into the combustion chamber, where it is decomposed to lime and carbon dioxide:

$$CaCO_3(s) \longrightarrow CaO(s) + CO_2(g)$$

The lime then combines with the sulfur dioxide to form calcium sulfite:

$$CaO(s) + SO_2(g) \longrightarrow CaSO_3(s)$$

The calcium sulfite and any remaining unreacted sulfur dioxide are removed by injecting an aqueous suspension of lime into the combustion chamber and the stack, producing a *slurry* (a thick suspension), as shown in Fig. 5.31.

Unfortunately, there are many problems associated with scrubbing. The systems are complicated and expensive and consume a great deal of energy. The large quantities of calcium sulfite produced in the process present a disposal problem. For a typical scrubber approximately 1 ton of calcium sulfite

In this equation the calcium sulfate is represented by separate hydrated ions because calcium sulfate dissolves in rainwater. Thus in areas bathed in rainwater, the marble slowly dissolves away.

In areas of the building protected from the rain, the calcium sulfate can form the mineral gypsum, $CaSO_4 \cdot 2H_2O$. The $\cdot 2H_2O$ in the formula of gypsum indicates the presence of two water molecules (called waters of hydration) for each $CaSO_4$ formula unit in the solid. The smooth surface of the marble is thus replaced by a thin layer of gypsum, a more porous material that binds soot and dust.

What can be done to protect limestone and marble structures from this kind of damage? Of course, one approach is to lower sulfur dioxide and nitrogen oxide emissions from power plants (Fig. 5.31). In addition, scientists are experimenting with coatings to protect marble from the acidic atmosphere. However, a coating can do more harm than good unless it "breathes." If moisture trapped beneath the coating freezes, the expanding ice can fracture the marble. Needless to say, it is difficult to find a coating that will allow water to pass but not allow acid to pass, so the search continues.

The damaging effects of acid rain can be seen by comparing these photos of a decorative statue at the Field Museum in Chicago. The photo on the left was taken c. 1920; the photo on the right was taken in 1990. Recent renovation has since replaced the deteriorating marble.

Figure 5.31

Schematic diagram of the process for scrubbing sulfur dioxide from stack gases in power plants.

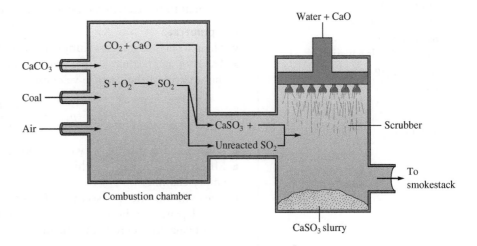

per year is produced per person served by the power plant. Since no use has yet been found for this calcium sulfite, it is usually buried in a landfill. As a result of these difficulties, air pollution by sulfur dioxide continues to be a major problem, one that is expensive in terms of damage to the environment and to human health, as well as in monetary terms.

Key Terms

For Review

OWL and **go Chemistry**

Sign in at **www.cengage.com/owl** to:
- View tutorials and simulations, develop problem-solving skills, and complete online homework assigned by your professor.
- Download Go Chemistry mini lecture modules for quick review and exam prep from OWL (or purchase them at **www.cengagebrain.com**)

State of a gas

- The state of a gas can be described completely by specifying its pressure (P), volume (V), temperature (T), and the amount (moles) of gas present (n).
- Pressure
  - Common units
    - 1 torr = 1 mm Hg
    - 1 atm = 760 torr
  - SI unit: pascal
    - 1 atm = 101,325 Pa

Gas laws

- Discovered by observing the properties of gases
- Boyle's law: $PV = k$
- Charles's law: $V = bT$
- Avogadro's law: $V = an$
- Ideal gas law: $PV = nRT$
- Dalton's law of partial pressures: $P_{\text{Total}} = P_1 + P_2 + P_3 + \cdots$, where P_n represents the partial pressure of component n in a mixture of gases

Kinetic molecular theory (KMT)

- Model that accounts for ideal gas behavior
- Postulates of the KMT:
  - Volume of gas particles is negligible (zero)
  - No particle interactions
  - Particles are in constant motion, colliding with the container walls to produce pressure
  - The average kinetic energy of the gas particles is directly proportional to the Kelvin temperature of the gas

Gas properties

- The particles in any gas sample have a range of velocities
- The root mean square (rms) velocity for a gas represents the average of the squares of the particle velocities

$$\mu_{\text{rms}} = \sqrt{\frac{3RT}{M}}$$

- Diffusion: the mixing of two or more gases
- Effusion: the process in which a gas passes through a small hole into an empty chamber
- The collision rate (per second) of gas particles with the container walls (Z_A) depends on the average velocity of the gas particles, the size of the area being considered, and the number of particles in the container

$$Z_A = A\frac{N}{V}\sqrt{\frac{RT}{1\pi M}}$$

- The intermolecular collision rate (per second) of gas particles (Z) depends on the average velocity of the gas particles, the size of the gas particles, and the number of particles in the container

$$Z = 4\frac{N}{V}d^2\sqrt{\frac{\pi RT}{M}}$$

Real gas behavior
- Real gases approach ideal behavior at high temperatures and low pressures
- Understanding how the ideal gas law must be modified to account for real gas behavior helps us understand how gases behave on a molecular level
- Van der Waals found that to describe real gas behavior we must consider particle interactions and particle volumes

Discussion Questions

These questions are designed to be considered by groups of students in class. Often these questions work well for introducing a particular topic in class.

1. Consider the following apparatus: a test tube covered with a nonpermeable elastic membrane inside a container that is closed with a cork. A syringe goes through the cork.

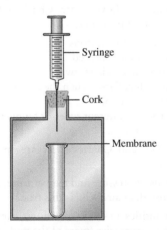

a. As you push down on the syringe, how does the membrane covering the test tube change?
b. You stop pushing the syringe but continue to hold it down. In a few seconds, what happens to the membrane?

2. Figure 5.1 shows a picture of a barometer. Which of the following statements is the best explanation of how this barometer works?
   a. Air pressure outside the tube causes the mercury to move in the tube until the air pressure inside and outside the tube is equal.

b. Air pressure inside the tube causes the mercury to move in the tube until the air pressure inside and outside the tube is equal.
c. Air pressure outside the tube counterbalances the weight of the mercury in the tube.
d. Capillary action of the mercury causes the mercury to go up the tube.
e. The vacuum that is formed at the top of the tube holds up the mercury.

Justify your choice. For choices that you did not pick, explain why they are incorrect. Pictures help!

3. The barometer on the left in the following diagram shows the level of mercury at a given atmospheric pressure. Fill all the other barometers with mercury for that same atmospheric pressure. Explain your answer.

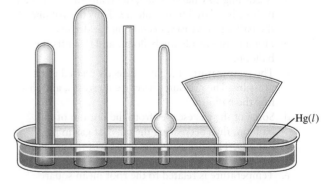

4. As you increase the temperature of a gas in a sealed, rigid container, what happens to the density of the gas? Would the results be the same if you did the same experiment in a container with a piston at constant pressure? Explain.

5. A diagram in a chemistry book shows a magnified view of a flask of air as follows:

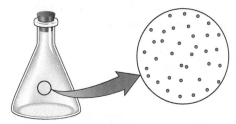

What do you suppose is between the dots (the dots represent air molecules)?
a. air
b. dust
c. pollutants
d. oxygen
e. nothing

6. If you put a drinking straw in water, place your finger over the opening, and lift the straw out of the water, some water stays in the straw. Explain.

7. A chemistry student relates the following story: "I noticed my tires were a bit low and went to the gas station. As I was filling the tires, I thought about the kinetic molecular theory (KMT), and I realized that I was increasing both the pressure and volume of the tires as I filled the tires with air. 'Hmmm,' I thought, 'that goes against what I learned in chemistry, where I was told pressure and volume are inversely proportional.'" What is the fault of the logic of the chemistry student in this situation? Explain *why* we think pressure and volume to be inversely related (draw pictures and use the KMT).

8. Chemicals X and Y (both gases) react to form the gas XY, but it takes a bit of time for the reaction to occur. Both X and Y are placed in a container with a piston (free to move), and you note the volume. As the reaction occurs, what happens to the volume of the container? Explain.

9. Which statement best explains why a hot-air balloon rises when the air in the balloon is heated?
a. According to Charles's law, the temperature of a gas is directly related to its volume. Thus the volume of the balloon increases, decreasing the density.
b. Hot air rises inside the balloon, and this lifts the balloon.
c. The temperature of a gas is directly related to its pressure. The pressure therefore increases, and this lifts the balloon.
d. Some of the gas escapes from the bottom of the balloon, thus decreasing the mass of gas in the balloon. This decreases the density of the gas in the balloon, and this lifts the balloon.
e. Temperature is related to the root mean square velocity of the gas molecules. Thus the molecules are moving faster, hitting the balloon more often, and thus lifting the balloon.

Justify your choice. For those you did not choose, explain why they are incorrect.

10. Draw a highly magnified view of a sealed, rigid container filled with a gas. Then draw what it would look like if you cooled the gas significantly, but kept the temperature above the boiling point of the substance in the container. Also draw what it would look like if you heated the gas significantly. Finally, draw what each situation would look like if you evacuated enough of the gas to decrease the pressure by a factor of 2.

11. If you release a helium balloon, it soars upward and eventually pops. Explain.

12. If you have any two gases in different containers that are the same size at the same pressure and same temperature, what is true about the moles of each gas? Why is this true?

13. Explain the following seeming contradiction: You have two gases, A and B, in two separate containers of equal volume and at equal pressure and temperature. Therefore, you must have the same number of moles of each gas. Because the two temperatures are equal, the average kinetic energies of the two samples are equal. Therefore, since the energy of such a system corresponds to translational motion, the root mean square velocities of the two are equal, and thus the particles in each sample move, on average, with the same relative speed. Since A and B are different gases, each must have a different molar mass. If A has a higher molar mass than B, the particles of A must be hitting the sides of the container with more force. Thus the pressure in the container of gas A must be higher than that in the container with gas B. However, one of our initial assumptions was that the pressures were equal. Explain.

14. Using postulates of the kinetic molecular theory, give a molecular interpretation of Boyle's law, Charles's law, and Dalton's law of partial pressures.

15. Rationalize the following observations.
a. Aerosol cans will explode if heated.
b. You can drink through a soda straw.
c. A thin-walled can will collapse when the air inside is removed by a vacuum pump.
d. Manufacturers produce different types of tennis balls for high and low elevations.

16. Show how Boyle's law and Charles's law are special cases of the ideal gas law.

17. At the same conditions of pressure and temperature, ammonia gas is less dense than air. Why is this true?

18. For each of the quantities (a–f) listed below, explain which of the following properties (mass of the molecule, density of the gas sample, temperature of the gas sample, size of the molecule, and number of moles of gas) must be known to calculate the quantity.
a. average kinetic energy
b. average number of collisions per second with other gas molecules
c. average force of each impact with the wall of the container
d. root mean square velocity
e. average number of collisions with a given area of the container
f. distance between collisions

19. You have two containers each with 1 mole of xenon gas at 15°C. Container A has a volume of 3.0 L, and container B has a volume of 1.0 L. Explain how the following quantities compare between the two containers.
    a. the average kinetic energy of the Xe atoms
    b. the force with which the Xe atoms collide with the container walls
    c. the root mean square velocity of the Xe atoms
    d. the collision frequency of the Xe atoms (with other atoms)
    e. the pressure of the Xe sample

20. You have a balloon covering the mouth of a flask filled with air at 1 atm. You apply heat to the bottom of the flask until the volume of the balloon is equal to that of the flask.
    a. Which has more air in it—the balloon or the flask? Or do both contain the same amount of air? Explain.
    b. In which is the pressure greater—the balloon or the flask? Or is the pressure the same? Explain.

Exercises

OWL Interactive versions of these problems may be assigned in OWL.

A blue exercise number indicates that the answer to that exercise appears at the back of this book and a solution appears in the *Solutions Guide*.

Pressure

21. A sealed-tube manometer as shown below can be used to measure pressures below atmospheric pressure. The tube above the mercury is evacuated. When there is a vacuum in the flask, the mercury levels in both arms of the U-tube are equal. If a gaseous sample is introduced into the flask, the mercury levels are different. The difference h is a measure of the pressure of the gas inside the flask. If h is equal to 4.75 cm, calculate the pressure in the flask in torr, pascals, and atmospheres.

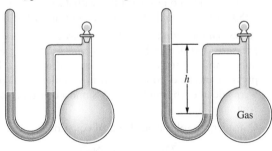

22. A diagram for an open-tube manometer is shown below.

If the flask is open to the atmosphere, the mercury levels are equal. For each of the following situations in which a gas is contained in the flask, calculate the pressure in the flask in torr, atmospheres, and pascals.

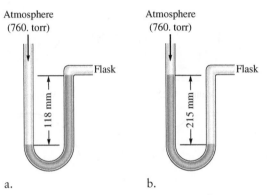

c. Calculate the pressures in the flask in parts a and b (in torr) if the atmospheric pressure is 635 torr.

23. The gravitational force exerted by an object is given by

$$F = mg$$

where F is the force in newtons, m is the mass in kilograms, and g is the acceleration due to gravity, 9.81 m/s². Calculate the force exerted per unit of area by a column of mercury (density = 13.59 g/cm³) that is 76.0 cm high. How high would a column of water (density = 1.00 g/cm³) have to be to exert the same force?

24. a. If the open-tube manometer in Exercise 22 contains a nonvolatile silicone oil (density = 1.30 g/cm³) instead of mercury (density = 13.6 g/cm³), what are the pressures in the flask as shown in parts a and b in torr, atmospheres, and pascals?
    b. What advantage would there be in using a less dense fluid than mercury in a manometer used to measure relatively small differences in pressure?

25. Freon-12 (CF_2Cl_2) is commonly used as the refrigerant in central home air conditioners. The system is initially charged to a pressure of 4.8 atm. Express this pressure in each of the following units (1 atm = 14.7 psi).
    a. mm Hg   b. torr   c. Pa   d. psi

Gas Laws

26. Draw a qualitative graph to show how the first property varies with the second in each of the following (assume 1 mole of an ideal gas and T in kelvins).
    a. PV versus V with constant T
    b. P versus T with constant V

c. *T* versus *V* with constant *P*
d. *P* versus *V* with constant *T*
e. *P* versus 1/*V* with constant *T*
f. *PV/T* versus *P*

27. As weather balloons rise from the earth's surface, the pressure of the atmosphere becomes less, tending to cause the volume of the balloons to expand. However, the temperature is much lower in the upper atmosphere than at sea level. Would this temperature effect tend to make such a balloon expand or contract? Weather balloons do, in fact, expand as they rise. What does this tell you?

28. Consider the flasks in the following diagrams.

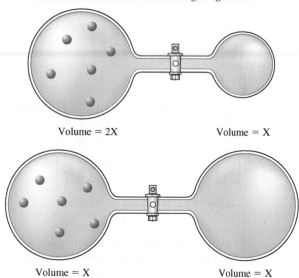

Volume = 2X   Volume = X

Volume = X   Volume = X

Assuming the connecting tube has negligible volume, draw what each diagram will look like after the stopcock between the two flasks is opened. Also, solve for the final pressure in each case, in terms of the original pressure. Assume temperature is constant.

29. Consider the flask diagramed below. What are the final partial pressures of H_2 and N_2 after the stopcock between the two flasks is opened? (Assume the final volume is 3.00 L.) What is the total pressure (in torr)?

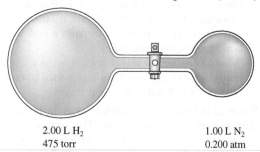

2.00 L H_2 1.00 L N_2
475 torr   0.200 atm

30. Consider the flask apparatus in Exercise 29, which contains 2.00 L of H_2 at a pressure of 360. torr and 1.00 L of N_2 at an unknown pressure. If the total pressure in the flasks is 320. torr after the stopcock is opened, determine the initial pressure of N_2 in the 1.00-L flask.

31. A compressed-gas cylinder contains 1.00×10^3 g of argon gas. The pressure inside the cylinder is 2050. psi (pounds per square inch) at a temperature of 18°C. How

much gas remains in the cylinder if the pressure is decreased to 650. psi at a temperature of 26°C?

32. A sealed balloon is filled with 1.00 L of helium at 23°C and 1.00 atm. The balloon rises to a point in the atmosphere where the pressure is 220. torr and the temperature is −31°C. What is the change in the volume of the balloon as it ascends from 1.00 atm to a pressure of 220. torr?

33. A piece of solid carbon dioxide, with a mass of 22.0 g, is placed in an otherwise empty 4.00-L container at 27°C. What is the pressure in the container after all the carbon dioxide vaporizes? If 22.0 g of solid carbon dioxide was placed in a similar container already containing air at 740. torr, what would be the partial pressure of carbon dioxide and the total pressure in the container after the carbon dioxide had vaporized?

34. An ideal gas is in a cylinder with a volume of 5.0×10^2 mL at a temperature of 30.°C and a pressure of 710. torr. The gas is compressed to a volume of 25 mL, and the temperature is raised to 820°C. What is the new pressure?

35. Suppose two 200.0-L tanks are to be filled separately with the gases helium and hydrogen. What mass of each gas is needed to produce a pressure of 135 atm in its respective tank at 24°C?

36. An ideal gas at 7°C is in a spherical flexible container having a radius of 1.00 cm. The gas is heated at constant pressure to 88°C. Determine the radius of the spherical container after the gas is heated. (Volume of a sphere = $4/3\pi r^3$.)

37. A flask that can withstand an internal pressure of 2500 torr, but no more, is filled with a gas at 21.0°C and 758 torr and heated. At what temperature will it burst?

38. A gas sample containing 1.50 moles at 25°C exerts a pressure of 400. torr. Some gas is *added* to the same container, and the temperature is increased to 50.°C. If the pressure increases to 800. torr, how many moles of gas were added to the container? Assume a constant-volume container.

39. Consider the following chemical equation:

$$2NO_2(g) \longrightarrow N_2O_4(g)$$

If 25.0 mL of NO_2 gas is completely converted to N_2O_4 gas under the same conditions, what volume will the N_2O_4 occupy?

40. A bicycle tire is filled with air to a pressure of 75 psi at a temperature of 19°C. Riding the bike on asphalt on a hot day increases the temperature of the tire to 58°C. The volume of the tire increases by 4.0%. What is the new pressure in the bicycle tire?

41. A hot-air balloon is filled with air to a volume of 4.00×10^3 m³ at 745 torr and 21°C. The air in the balloon is then heated to 62°C, causing the balloon to expand to a volume of 4.20×10^3 m³. What is the ratio of the number of moles of air in the heated balloon to the original number of moles of air in the balloon? (*Hint:* Openings in the balloon allow air to flow in and out. Thus the pressure in the balloon is always the same as that of the atmosphere.)

42. Determine the partial pressure of each gas as shown in the figure below. *Note:* The relative numbers of each type of gas are depicted in the figure.

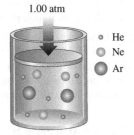

43. Consider the flasks in the following diagrams.

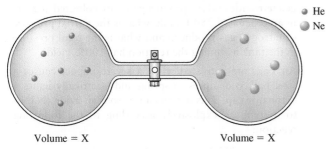

Volume = X   Volume = X

a. Which is greater, the initial pressure of helium or initial pressure of neon? How much greater?
b. Assuming the connecting tube has negligible volume, draw what each diagram will look like after the stopcock between the two flasks is opened.
c. Solve for the final pressure in terms of the original pressures of helium and neon. Assume temperature is constant.
d. Solve for the final partial pressures of helium and neon in terms of their original pressures. Assume the temperature is constant.

44. A sample of nitrogen gas was collected over water at 20.°C and a total pressure of 1.00 atm. A total volume of 2.50×10^2 mL was collected. What mass of nitrogen was collected? (At 20.°C the vapor pressure of water is 17.5 torr.)

45. Helium is collected over water at 25°C and 1.00 atm total pressure. What total volume of gas must be collected to obtain 0.586 g of helium? (At 25°C the vapor pressure of water is 23.8 torr.)

46. A 2.00-L sample of $O_2(g)$ was collected over water at a total pressure of 785 torr and 25°C. When the $O_2(g)$ was dried (water vapor removed), the gas had a volume of 1.94 L at 25°C and 785 torr. Calculate the vapor pressure of water at 25°C.

47. In a mixture of the two gases, the partial pressures of $CH_4(g)$ and $O_2(g)$ are 0.175 atm and 0.250 atm, respectively.
a. What is the mole fraction of each gas in the mixture?
b. If the mixture occupies a volume of 10.5 L at 65°C, calculate the total number of moles of gas in the mixture.
c. Calculate the number of grams of each gas in the mixture.

48. A 1.00-L gas sample at 100.°C and 600. torr contains 50.0% helium and 50.0% xenon by mass. What are the partial pressures of the individual gases?

49. At 0°C a 1.0 L flask contains 5.0×10^{-2} mole of N_2, 1.5×10^2 mg O_2, and 5.0×10^{21} molecules of NH_3. What is the partial pressure of each gas, and what is the total pressure in the flask?

Gas Density, Molar Mass, and Reaction Stoichiometry

50. Given that a sample of air is made up of nitrogen, oxygen, and argon in the mole fractions 78% N_2, 21% O_2, and 1.0% Ar, what is the density of air at standard temperature and pressure?

51. Consider two different containers, each filled with 2 moles of Ne(g). One of the containers is rigid and has constant volume. The other container is flexible (like a balloon) and is capable of changing its volume to keep the external pressure and internal pressure equal to each other. If you raise the temperature in both containers, what happens to the pressure and density of the gas inside each container? Assume a constant external pressure.

52. An unknown diatomic gas has a density of 3.164 g/L at STP. What is the identity of the gas?

53. A compound contains only nitrogen and hydrogen and is 87.4% nitrogen by mass. A gaseous sample of the compound has a density of 0.977 g/L at 710. torr and 100.°C. What is the molecular formula of the compound?

54. A compound has the empirical formula CHCl. A 256-mL flask, at 373 K and 750. torr, contains 0.800 g of the gaseous compound. Give the molecular formula.

55. One of the chemical controversies of the nineteenth century concerned the element beryllium (Be). Berzelius originally claimed that beryllium was a trivalent element (forming Be^{3+} ions) and that it formed an oxide with the formula Be_2O_3. This assumption resulted in a calculated atomic mass of 13.5 for beryllium. In formulating his periodic table, Mendeleev proposed that beryllium was divalent (forming Be^{2+} ions) and that it gave an oxide with the formula BeO. This assumption gives an atomic mass of 9.0. In 1894 A. Combes (*Comptes Rendes*, 1894, p. 1221) reacted beryllium with the anion $C_5H_7O_2^-$ and measured the density of the gaseous product. Combes's data for two different experiments are as follows:

	I	II
Mass	0.2022 g	0.2224 g
Volume	22.6 cm³	26.0 cm³
Temperature	13°C	17°C
Pressure	765.2 torr	764.6 torr

If beryllium is a divalent metal, the molecular formula of the product will be $Be(C_5H_7O_2)_2$; if it is trivalent, the formula will be $Be(C_5H_7O_2)_3$. Show how Combes's data help to confirm that beryllium is a divalent metal.

56. Discrepancies in the experimental values of the molar mass of nitrogen provided some of the first evidence for

the existence of the noble gases. If pure nitrogen is collected from the decomposition of ammonium nitrite,

$$NH_4NO_2(s) \xrightarrow{\text{Heat}} N_2(g) + 2H_2O(g)$$

its measured molar mass is 28.01. If O_2, CO_2, and H_2O are removed from air, the remaining gas has an average molar mass of 28.15. Assuming this discrepancy is solely a result of contamination with argon (atomic mass = 39.95), calculate the ratio of moles of Ar to moles of N_2 in air.

57. A sample of methane (CH_4) gas contains a small amount of helium. Calculate the volume percentage of helium if the density of the sample is 0.70902 g/L at 0.0°C and 1.000 atm.

58. Metallic molybdenum can be produced from the mineral molybdenite (MoS_2). The mineral is first oxidized in air to molybdenum trioxide and sulfur dioxide. Molybdenum trioxide is then reduced to metallic molybdenum using hydrogen gas. The balanced equations are

$$MoS_2(s) + 7/2O_2(g) \longrightarrow MoO_3(s) + 2SO_2(g)$$

$$MoO_3(s) + 3H_2(g) \longrightarrow Mo(s) + 3H_2O(l)$$

Calculate the volumes of air and hydrogen gas at 17°C and 1.00 atm that are necessary to produce 1.00×10^3 kg of pure molybdenum from MoS_2. Assume air contains 21% oxygen by volume and assume 100% yield for each reaction.

59. In 1897 the Swedish explorer Andreé tried to reach the North Pole in a balloon. The balloon was filled with hydrogen gas. The hydrogen gas was prepared from iron splints and diluted sulfuric acid. The reaction is

$$Fe(s) + H_2SO_4(aq) \longrightarrow FeSO_4(aq) + H_2(g)$$

The volume of the balloon was 4800 m³, and the loss of hydrogen gas during filling was estimated at 20.%. What mass of iron splints and 98% (by mass) H_2SO_4 were needed to ensure the complete filling of the balloon? Assume a temperature at 0°C, a pressure of 1.0 atm during filling, and 100% yield.

60. Urea (H_2NCONH_2) is used extensively as a nitrogen source in fertilizers. It is produced commercially from the reaction of ammonia and carbon dioxide:

$$2NH_3(g) + CO_2(g) \xrightarrow[\text{Pressure}]{\text{Heat}} H_2NCONH_2(s) + H_2O(g)$$

Ammonia gas at 223°C and 90. atm flows into a reactor at a rate of 500. L/min. Carbon dioxide at 223°C and 45 atm flows into the reactor at a rate of 600. L/min. What mass of urea is produced per minute by this reaction assuming 100% yield?

61. Methanol (CH_3OH) can be produced by the following reaction:

$$CO(g) + 2H_2(g) \longrightarrow CH_3OH(g)$$

Hydrogen at STP flows into a reactor at a rate of 16.0 L/min. Carbon monoxide at STP flows into the reactor at a rate of 25.0 L/min. If 5.30 g of methanol is produced per minute, what is the percent yield of the reaction?

62. Consider the reaction between 50.0 mL of liquid methanol (CH_3OH; density = 0.850 g/mL) and 22.8 L of O_2 at 27°C and a pressure of 2.00 atm. The products of the reaction are $CO_2(g)$ and $H_2O(g)$. Calculate the number of moles of H_2O formed if the reaction goes to completion.

63. Some very effective rocket fuels are composed of lightweight liquids. The fuel composed of dimethylhydrazine [$(CH_3)_2N_2H_2$] mixed with dinitrogen tetroxide was used to power the lunar lander in its missions to the moon. The two components react according to the following equation:

$$(CH_3)_2N_2H_2(l) + 2N_4O_4(l) \longrightarrow 3N_2(g) + 4H_2O(g) + 2CO_2(g)$$

If 150 g of dimethylhydrazine reacts with excess dinitrogen tetroxide and the product gases are collected at 27°C in an evacuated 250-L tank, what is the partial pressure of nitrogen gas produced and what is the total pressure in the tank assuming the reaction has 100% yield?

64. Air bags are activated when a severe impact causes a steel ball to compress a spring and electrically ignite a detonator cap. This action causes sodium azide (NaN_3) to decompose explosively according to the following reaction:

$$2NaN_3(s) \longrightarrow 2Na(s) + 3N_2(g)$$

What mass of $NaN_3(s)$ must be reacted to inflate an air bag to 70.0 L at STP?

65. At elevated temperatures, sodium chlorate decomposes to produce sodium chloride and oxygen gas. A 0.8765-g sample of impure sodium chlorate was heated until the production of oxygen gas ceased. The oxygen gas collected over water occupied 57.2 mL at a temperature of 22°C and a pressure of 734 torr. Calculate the mass percent of $NaClO_3$ in the original sample. (At 22°C the vapor pressure of water is 19.8 torr.)

66. Xenon and fluorine will react to form binary compounds when a mixture of these two gases is heated to 400°C in a nickel reaction vessel. A 100.0-mL nickel container is filled with xenon and fluorine giving partial pressures of 1.24 atm and 10.10 atm, respectively, at a temperature of 25°C. The reaction vessel is heated to 400°C to cause a reaction to occur and then cooled to a temperature at which F_2 is a gas and the xenon fluoride is a nonvolatile solid. The remaining F_2 gas is transferred to another 100.0-mL nickel container where the pressure of F_2 at 25°C is 7.62 atm. Assuming all of the xenon has reacted, what is the formula of the product?

67. The nitrogen content of organic compounds can be determined by the Dumas method. The compound in question is first reacted by passage over hot $CuO(s)$:

$$\text{Compound} \xrightarrow[\text{CuO}(s)]{\text{Hot}} N_2(g) + CO_2(g) + H_2O(g)$$

The gaseous products are then passed through a concentrated solution of KOH to remove the CO_2. After passage through the KOH solution, the gas contains N_2 and is saturated with water vapor. In a given experiment, a 0.253-g sample of a compound produced 31.8 mL of N_2 saturated with water vapor at 25°C and 726 torr. What is the mass percent of nitrogen in the compound? (The vapor pressure of water at 25°C is 23.8 torr.)

68. An organic compound contains C, H, N, and O. Combustion of 0.1023 g of the compound in excess oxygen yielded 0.2766 g of CO_2 and 0.0991 g of H_2O. A sample of 0.4831 g of the compound was analyzed for nitrogen by the Dumas method (see Exercise 67). At STP, 27.6 mL of dry N_2 was obtained. In a third experiment, the density of the compound as a gas was found to be 4.02 g/L at 127°C and 256 torr. What are the empirical formula and the molecular formula of the compound?

69. Nitric acid is produced commercially by the Ostwald process. In the first step, ammonia is oxidized to nitric oxide:

$$4NH_3(g) + 5O_2(g) \longrightarrow 4NO(g) + 6H_2O(g)$$

Assume this reaction is carried out in the apparatus diagramed below.

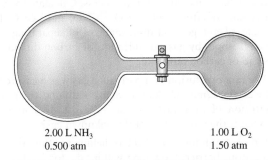

| 2.00 L NH_3 | 1.00 L O_2 |
| 0.500 atm | 1.50 atm |

The stopcock between the two reaction containers is opened, and the reaction proceeds using proper catalysts. Calculate the partial pressure of NO after the reaction is complete. Assume 100% yield for the reaction, assume the final container volume is 3.00 L, and assume the temperature is constant.

70. Consider the following balanced equation in which gas X forms gas X_2:

$$2X(g) \longrightarrow X_2(g)$$

Equal moles of X are placed in two separate containers. One container is rigid, so the volume cannot change; the other container is flexible, so the volume changes to keep the internal pressure equal to the external pressure. The above reaction is run in each container. What happens to the pressure and density of the gas inside each container as reactants are converted to products?

71. As $NH_3(g)$ is decomposed into nitrogen gas and hydrogen gas at constant pressure and temperature, the volume of the product gases collected is twice the volume of NH_3 reacted. Explain. As $NH_3(g)$ is decomposed into nitrogen gas and hydrogen gas at constant volume and temperature, the total pressure increases by some factor. Why does the increase in pressure occur, and by what factor does the total pressure increase when reactants are completely converted into products? How do the partial pressures of the product gases compare to each other and to the initial pressure of NH_3?

Kinetic Molecular Theory and Real Gases

72. Use the postulates of the kinetic molecular theory (KMT) to explain why Boyle's law, Charles's law, Avogadro's law, and Dalton's law of partial pressures hold true for ideal gases. Use the KMT to explain the P versus n (at constant V and T) relationship and the P versus T (at constant V and n) relationship.

73. You have a gas in a container fitted with a piston and you change one of the conditions of the gas such that a change takes place, as shown below:

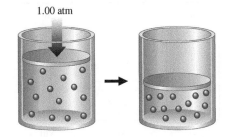

State two distinct changes you can make to accomplish this, and explain why each would work.

74. You have a gas in a container fitted with a piston and you change one of the conditions of the gas such that a change takes place, as shown below:

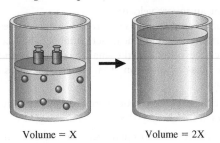

State three distinct changes you can make to accomplish this, and explain why each would work.

75. Consider two gases, A and B, each in a 1.0-L container with both gases at the same temperature and pressure. The mass of gas A in the container is 0.34 g, and the mass of gas B in the container is 0.48 g.

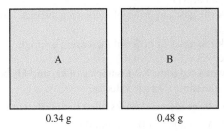

a. Which gas sample has the most molecules present? Explain.
b. Which gas sample has the largest average kinetic energy? Explain.
c. Which gas sample has the fastest average velocity? Explain.

d. How can the pressure in the two containers be equal to each other since the larger gas B molecules collide with the container walls more forcefully?

76. Consider the following samples of gases at the same temperature.

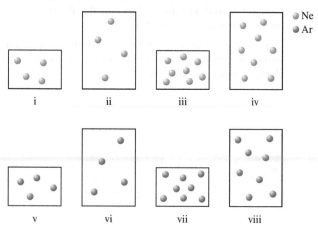

Arrange each of these samples in order from lowest to highest.
a. pressure
b. average kinetic energy
c. density
d. root mean square velocity
Note: Some samples of gases may have equal values for these attributes. Assume the larger containers have a volume twice the volume of the smaller containers and assume the mass of an argon atom is twice the mass of a neon atom.

77. Calculate the average kinetic energies of the CH_4 and N_2 molecules at 273 K and 546 K.

78. Calculate the root mean square velocities of CH_4 and N_2 molecules at 273 K and 546 K.

79. Do all the molecules in a 1-mole sample of $CH_4(g)$ have the same kinetic energy at 273 K? Do all the molecules in a 1-mole sample of $N_2(g)$ have the same velocity at 546 K? Explain.

80. Consider separate 1.0-L gaseous samples of H_2, Xe, Cl_2, and O_2, all at STP.
    a. Rank the gases in order of increasing average kinetic energy.
    b. Rank the gases in order of increasing average velocity.
    c. How can separate 1.0-L samples of O_2 and H_2 both have the same average velocity?

81. Consider three identical flasks filled with different gases.

    Flask A: CO at 760 torr and 0°C

    Flask B: N_2 at 250 torr and 0°C

    Flask C: H_2 at 100 torr and 0°C

    a. In which flask will the molecules have the greatest average kinetic energy?
    b. In which flask will the molecules have the greatest root mean square velocity?
    c. Which flask will have the greatest number of collisions per second with the walls of the container?

82. Consider a 1.0-L container of neon gas at STP. Will the average kinetic energy, root mean square velocity, frequency of collisions of gas molecules with each other, frequency of collisions of gas molecules with the walls of the container, and energy of impact of gas molecules with the container increase, decrease, or remain the same under each of the following conditions?
    a. The temperature is increased to 100°C.
    b. The temperature is decreased to −50°C.
    c. The volume is decreased to 0.5 L.
    d. The number of moles of neon is doubled.

83. Freon-12 is used as a refrigerant in central home air conditioners. The rate of effusion of Freon-12 to Freon-11 (molar mass = 137.4 g/mol) is 1.07:1. The formula of Freon-12 is one of the following: CF_4, CF_3Cl, CF_2Cl_2, $CFCl_3$, or CCl_4. Which formula is correct for Freon-12?

84. One way of separating oxygen isotopes is by gaseous diffusion of carbon monoxide. The gaseous diffusion process behaves like an effusion process. Calculate the relative rates of effusion of $^{12}C^{16}O$, $^{12}C^{17}O$, and $^{12}C^{18}O$. List some advantages and disadvantages of separating oxygen isotopes by gaseous diffusion of carbon dioxide instead of carbon monoxide.

85. The rate of effusion of a particular gas was measured to be 24.0 mL/min. Under the same conditions, the rate of effusion of pure methane gas (CH_4) is 47.8 mL/min. What is the molar mass of the unknown gas?

86. It took 4.5 minutes for 1.0 L of helium to effuse through a porous barrier. How long will it take for 1.0 L of Cl_2 gas to effuse under identical conditions?

87. Calculate the pressure exerted by 0.5000 mole of N_2 in a 1.0000-L container at 25.0°C. (See Table 5.3.)
    a. Use the ideal gas law.
    b. Use the van der Waals equation.
    c. Compare the results from parts a and b.

88. Calculate the pressure exerted by 0.5000 mole of N_2 in a 10.000-L container at 25.0°C. (See Table 5.3.)
    a. Use the ideal gas law.
    b. Use the van der Waals equation.
    c. Compare the results from parts a and b.
    d. Compare the results with those in Exercise 87.

89. Why do real gases not always behave ideally? Under what conditions does a real gas behave most ideally? Why?

90. Consider the following velocity distribution curves *A* and *B*.

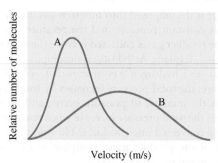

a. If the plots represent the velocity distribution of 1.0 L of He(g) at STP versus 1.0 L of $Cl_2(g)$ at STP, which plot corresponds to each gas? Explain your reasoning.

b. If the plots represent the velocity distribution of 1.0 L of $O_2(g)$ at temperatures of 273 K versus 1273 K, which plot corresponds to each temperature? Explain your reasoning. Under which temperature condition would the $O_2(g)$ sample behave most ideally? Explain.

91. In the van der Waals equation, why is a term added to the observed pressure and why is a term subtracted from the container volume to correct for nonideal gas behavior?

92. Without looking at tables of values, which of the following gases would you expect to have the largest value of the van der Waals constant b: H_2, N_2, CH_4, C_2H_6, or C_3H_8?

93. From the values in Table 5.3 for the van der Waals constant a for the gases H_2, CO_2, N_2, and CH_4, predict which molecule shows the strongest intermolecular attractions.

94. The Maxwell–Boltzmann distribution function $f(u)$ increases at small values of u and decreases at large values of u. Identify the parts of the function responsible for this behavior.

95. Calculate the root mean square, the most probable, and the average velocities for $N_2(g)$ at 227°C.

96. Calculate the kinetic energy possessed by 1.00×10^{20} molecules of methane gas (CH_4) at $T = 27$°C, assuming ideal behavior.

97. A flask contains $\frac{1}{3}$ mole of H_2 and $\frac{2}{3}$ mole of He. Compare the force on the wall per impact of H_2 relative to that for He.

98. A certain sample of uranium is reacted with fluorine to form a mixture of $^{235}UF_6(g)$ and $^{238}UF_6(g)$. After 100 diffusion steps, the gas contains 1526 $^{235}UF_6$ molecules per 1.000×10^5 total number of molecules in the gas ($^{235}UF_6 + ^{238}UF_6$). What is the ratio of ^{235}U to ^{238}U atoms in the original sample of uranium?

99. Consider separate 1.0-L samples of $O_2(g)$ and He(g), both at 25°C and the same pressure. Compare the change in momentum per impact and the number of impacts per second in the two samples.

100. Consider separate 1.00-L samples of Ar(g), both containing the same number of moles, one at 27°C and the other at 77°C. Compare the change in momentum per impact and the number of impacts per second in the two samples.

101. Calculate the intermolecular collision frequency and the mean free path in a sample of helium gas with a volume of 5.0 L at 27°C and 3.0 atm. Assume that the diameter of a helium atom is 50. pm.

Atmosphere Chemistry

102. Use the data in Table 5.4 to calculate the partial pressure of He in dry air assuming that the total pressure is 1.0 atm. Assuming a temperature of 25°C, calculate the number of He atoms per cubic centimeter.

103. Atmospheric scientists often use mixing ratios to express the concentrations of trace compounds in air. Mixing ratios are often expressed as ppmv (parts per million volume):

$$\text{ppmv of } X = \frac{\text{vol of X at STP}}{\text{total vol of air at STP}} \times 10^6$$

On a certain November day, the concentration of carbon monoxide in the air in downtown Denver, Colorado, reached 3.0×10^2 ppmv. The atmospheric pressure at that time was 628 torr and the temperature was 0°C.
a. What was the partial pressure of CO?
b. What was the concentration of CO in molecules per cubic meter?
c. What was the concentration of CO in molecules per cubic centimeter?

104. Write reactions to show how nitric and sulfuric acids are produced in the atmosphere. Write reactions to show how the nitric and sulfuric acids in acid rain react with marble and limestone. (Both marble and limestone are primarily calcium carbonate.)

105. Trace organic compounds in the atmosphere are first concentrated and then measured by gas chromatography. In the concentration step, several liters of air are pumped through a tube containing a porous substance that traps organic compounds. The tube is then connected to a gas chromatograph and heated to release the trapped compounds. The organic compounds are separated in the column and the amounts are measured. In an analysis for benzene and toluene in air, a 3.00-L sample of air at 748 torr and 23°C was passed through the trap. The gas chromatography analysis showed that this air sample contained 89.6 ng of benzene (C_6H_6) and 153 ng of toluene (C_7H_8). Calculate the mixing ratio (see Exercise 103) and number of molecules per cubic centimeter for both benzene and toluene.

Additional Exercises

106. A form of Boyle's law is $PV = k$ (at constant T and n). Table 5.1 contains actual data from pressure–volume experiments conducted by Robert Boyle. The value of k in most experiments is 14.1×10^2 in Hg · in^3. Express k in units of atm · L. In Example 5.1, k was determined for NH_3 at various pressures and volumes. Give some reasons why the k values differ so dramatically between Example 5.1 and Table 5.1.

107. A glass vessel contains 28 g nitrogen gas. Assuming ideal behavior, which of the processes listed below would double the pressure exerted on the walls of the vessel?
a. Adding enough mercury to fill one-half the container.
b. Raising the temperature of the container from 30.°C to 60.°C.
c. Raising the temperature of the container from −73°C to 127°C.
d. Adding 28 g nitrogen gas.

108. Which of the following statements is(are) true? For the false statements, correct them.
    a. At constant temperature, the lighter the gas molecules, the faster the average velocity of the gas molecules.
    b. At constant temperature, the heavier the gas molecules, the larger the average kinetic energy of the gas molecules.
    c. A real gas behaves most ideally when the container volume is relatively large and the gas molecules are moving relatively quickly.
    d. As temperature increases, the effect of interparticle interactions on gas behavior is increased.
    e. At constant V and T, as gas molecules are added into a container, the number of collisions per unit area increases, resulting in a higher pressure.
    f. The kinetic molecular theory predicts that pressure is inversely proportional to temperature at constant volume and moles of gas.

109. A person accidentally swallows a drop of liquid oxygen, $O_2(l)$, which has a density of 1.149 g/mL. Assuming the drop has a volume of 0.050 mL, what volume of gas will be produced in the person's stomach at body temperature (37°C) and a pressure of 1.0 atm?

110. Hydrogen azide, HN_3, decomposes on heating by the following *unbalanced* reaction:

$$HN_3(g) \longrightarrow N_2(g) + H_2(g)$$

If 3.0 atm of pure $HN_3(g)$ is decomposed initially, what is the final total pressure in the reaction container? What are the partial pressures of nitrogen and hydrogen gas? Assume the volume and temperature of the reaction container are constant.

111. A 20.0 L stainless steel container at 25°C was charged with 2.00 atm of hydrogen gas and 3.00 atm of oxygen gas. A spark ignited the mixture, producing water. What is the pressure in the tank at 25°C? If the same experiment were performed, but the temperature was 125°C instead of 25°C, what would be the pressure in the tank?

112. In the "Méthode Champenoise," grape juice is fermented in a wine bottle to produce sparkling wine. The reaction is

$$C_6H_{12}O_6(aq) \longrightarrow 2C_2H_5OH(aq) + 2CO_2(g)$$

Fermentation of 750. mL of grape juice (density = 1.0 g/cm³) is allowed to take place in a bottle with a total volume of 825 mL until 12% by volume is ethanol (C_2H_5OH). Assuming that the CO_2 is insoluble in H_2O (actually a wrong assumption), what would be the pressure of CO_2 inside the wine bottle at 25°C? (The density of ethanol is 0.79 g/cm³.)

113. A 2.747-g sample of manganese metal is reacted with excess HCl gas to produce 3.22 L of $H_2(g)$ at 373 K and 0.951 atm and a manganese chloride compound ($MnCl_x$). What is the formula of the manganese chloride compound produced in the reaction?

114. The total mass that can be lifted by a balloon is given by the difference between the mass of air displaced by the balloon and the mass of the gas inside the balloon. Consider a hot-air balloon that approximates a sphere 5.00 m in diameter and contains air heated to 65°C. The surrounding air temperature is 21°C. The pressure in the balloon is equal to the atmospheric pressure, which is 745 torr.
    a. What total mass can the balloon lift? Assume the average molar mass of air is 29.0 g/mol. (*Hint:* Heated air is less dense than cool air.)
    b. If the balloon is filled with enough helium at 21°C and 745 torr to achieve the same volume as in part a, what total mass can the balloon lift?
    c. What mass could the hot-air balloon (from part a) lift if it were on the ground in Denver, Colorado, where a typical atmospheric pressure is 630. torr?
    d. What mass could the hot-air balloon (from part a) lift if it were a cold day with a temperature of −8°C?

115. At STP, 1.0 L Br_2 reacts completely with 3.0 L F_2, producing 2.0 L of a product. What is the formula of the product? (All substances are gases.)

116. Natural gas is a mixture of hydrocarbons, primarily methane (CH_4) and ethane (C_2H_6). A typical mixture might have $\chi_{methane} = 0.915$ and $\chi_{ethane} = 0.085$. What are the partial pressures of the two gases in a 15.00-L container of natural gas at 20.°C and 1.44 atm? Assuming complete combustion of both gases in the natural gas sample, what is the total mass of water formed?

117. An important process for the production of acrylonitrile (C_3H_3N) (annual U.S. production is greater than 10^9 lb) is given by the following equation:

$$2C_3H_6(g) + 2NH_3(g) + 3O_2(g)$$
$$\longrightarrow 2C_3H_3N(g) + 6H_2O(g)$$

A 150.-L reactor is charged to the following partial pressures at 25°C:

$$P_{C_3H_6} = 0.500 \text{ MPa}$$
$$P_{NH_3} = 0.800 \text{ MPa}$$
$$P_{O_2} = 1.500 \text{ MPa}$$

What mass of acrylonitrile can be produced from this mixture (MPa = 10^6 Pa)?

118. The oxides of Group 2A metals (symbolized by M here) react with carbon dioxide according to the following reaction:

$$MO(s) + CO_2(g) \longrightarrow MCO_3(s)$$

A 2.85-g sample containing only MgO and CuO is placed in a 3.00-L container. The container is filled with CO_2 to a pressure of 740. torr at 20.°C. After the reaction has gone to completion, the pressure inside the flask is 390. torr at 20.°C. What is the mass percent of MgO in the mixture? Assume that only the MgO reacts with CO_2.

119. Small quantities of hydrogen gas can be prepared in the laboratory by the addition of aqueous hydrochloric acid to metallic zinc.

$$Zn(s) + 2HCl(aq) \longrightarrow ZnCl_2(aq) + H_2(g)$$

Typically, the hydrogen gas is bubbled through water for collection and becomes saturated with water vapor. Suppose 240. mL of hydrogen gas is collected at 30.°C and has a total pressure of 1.032 atm by this process. What is the partial pressure of hydrogen gas in the sample? How many grams of zinc must have reacted to produce this quantity of hydrogen? (The vapor pressure of water is 32 torr at 30°C.)

120. Nitrogen gas (N_2) reacts with hydrogen gas (H_2) to form ammonia gas (NH_3). You have nitrogen and hydrogen gases in a 15.0-L container fitted with a movable piston (the piston allows the container volume to change so as to keep the pressure constant inside the container). Initially, the partial pressure of each reactant gas is 1.00 atm. Assume the temperature is constant and the reaction goes to completion.
   a. Calculate the partial pressure of ammonia in the container after the reaction has reached completion.
   b. Calculate the volume of the container after the reaction has reached completion.

121. Consider the three flasks in the diagram below. Assuming the connecting tubes have negligible volume, what is the partial pressure of each gas and the total pressure after all the stopcocks are opened?

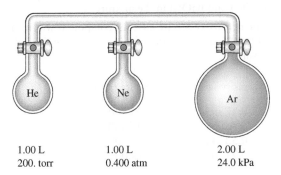

He	Ne	Ar
1.00 L	1.00 L	2.00 L
200. torr	0.400 atm	24.0 kPa

122. Equal moles of sulfur dioxide gas and oxygen gas are mixed in a flexible reaction vessel and then sparked to initiate the formation of gaseous sulfur trioxide. Assuming that the reaction goes to completion, what is the ratio of the final volume of the gas mixture to the initial volume of the gas mixture if both volumes are measured at the same temperature and pressure?

123. Silane (SiH_4) is the silicon analogue of methane (CH_4). It is prepared industrially according to the following equations:

$$Si(s) + 3HCl(g) \longrightarrow HSiCl_3(l) + H_2(g)$$

$$4HSiCl_3(l) \longrightarrow SiH_4(g) + 3SiCl_4(l)$$

   a. If 156 mL of $HSiCl_3$ (d = 1.34 g/mL) is isolated when 15.0 L of HCl at 10.0 atm and 35°C is used, what is the percent yield of $HSiCl_3$?
   b. When 156 mL of $HSiCl_3$ is heated, what volume of SiH_4 at 10.0 atm and 35°C will be obtained if the percent yield of the reaction is 93.1%?

124. A compound containing only C, H, and N yields the following data.
   i. Complete combustion of 35.0 mg of the compound produced 33.5 mg of CO_2 and 41.1 mg of H_2O.

   ii. A 65.2-mg sample of the compound was analyzed for nitrogen by the Dumas method (see Exercise 67), giving 35.6 mL of dry N_2 at 740. torr and 25°C.
   iii. The effusion rate of the compound as a gas was measured and found to be 24.6 mL/min. The effusion rate of argon gas, under identical conditions, is 26.4 mL/min.

   What is the formula of the compound?

125. A 15.0-L tank is filled with H_2 to a pressure of 2.00×10^2 atm. How many balloons (each 2.00 L) can be inflated to a pressure of 1.00 atm from the tank? Assume that there is no temperature change and that the tank cannot be emptied below 1.00 atm pressure.

126. Consider the following diagram.

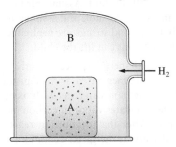

A porous container (A), filled with air at STP, is contained in a large enclosed container (B), which is flushed with $H_2(g)$. What will happen to the pressure inside container A? Explain your answer.

127. A 100.-L flask contains a mixture of methane (CH_4) and argon at 25°C. The mass of argon present is 228 g and the mole fraction of methane in the mixture is 0.650. Calculate the total kinetic energy of the gaseous mixture.

128. Represent the following plots.
   a. PV/n (y axis) versus P (x axis) for a real gas that obeys the equation $PV/n = \alpha + \beta P$
   b. change in momentum per impact versus mass of an individual gas particle for a series of ideal gases all at the same temperature
   c. P versus T (°C) for an ideal gas where n and V are constant

129. A spherical glass container of unknown volume contains helium gas at 25°C and 1.960 atm. When a portion of the helium is withdrawn and adjusted to 1.00 atm at 25°C, it is found to have a volume of 1.75 cm³. The gas remaining in the first container shows a pressure of 1.710 atm. Calculate the volume of the spherical container.

130. A compound Z is known to have a composition of 34.38% Ni, 28.13% C, and 37.48% O. In an experiment 1.00 L of gaseous Z is mixed with 1.00 L of argon, where each gas is at P = 2.00 atm and T = 25°C. When this mixture of gases is put in an effusion chamber, the ratio of Z molecules to Ar molecules in the effused mixture is 0.4837. Using these data, calculate the following.
   a. the empirical formula for Z
   b. the molar mass for Z
   c. the molecular formula for Z
   d. the mole ratio of Z to argon in a sample of gas obtained by five effusion steps (starting with the original mixture)

131. Hydrogen cyanide gas is commercially prepared by the reaction of methane [$CH_4(g)$], ammonia [$NH_3(g)$], and oxygen [$O_2(g)$] at a high temperature. The other product is gaseous water.
    a. Write a balanced chemical equation for the reaction.
    b. Methane and ammonia gases flow into a reactor at a rate of 20.0 L/s. Oxygen gas is introduced at a flow rate of 40.0 L/s. All the reactant gases are at 1.00 atm and 150.°C. What mass of HCN is produced per second by this reaction assuming 100% yield?

Challenge Problems

132. Consider a children's cartoon illustrating a child holding the strings of several helium balloons and being lifted into the sky.
    a. Estimate the minimum number of 10.-L balloons it would take to lift a 50.-lb child. Assume air has an average molar mass of 29 g/mol, and assume the masses of the balloons and strings are negligible.
    b. Explain why the balloons can lift the child.

133. A 16.0-g sample of methane (CH_4) reacts with 64.0 g of oxygen gas in a container fitted with a piston (at 1.00 atm and 425 K). Methane can react with oxygen to form carbon dioxide and water vapor or carbon monoxide and water vapor. After the combustion reaction is complete, the gas density at the given conditions is observed to be 0.7282 g/L. Calculate the mole fraction of methane that reacts to form carbon monoxide rather than carbon dioxide.

134. You have two samples of helium gas at the same pressure in separate steel containers of the same volume. You want the number of collisions of helium atoms with the walls of container 1 to be twice the number of collisions of helium atoms with the walls of container 2. Assume ideal behavior.
    a. How does the temperature in container 1 compare to the temperature in container 2? That is, which temperature is larger and by what factor? Explain your answer and support it mathematically.
    b. If the number of collisions is different in each container, how can the pressure be the same? Provide a written explanation with mathematical support.

135. A mixture of chromium and zinc weighing 0.362 g was reacted with an excess of hydrochloric acid. After all the metals in the mixture reacted, 225 mL of dry hydrogen gas was collected at 27°C and 750. torr. Determine the mass percent of Zn in the metal sample. [Zinc reacts with hydrochloric acid to produce zinc chloride and hydrogen gas; chromium reacts with hydrochloric acid to produce chromium(III) chloride and hydrogen gas.]

136. You have a sealed, flexible balloon filled with argon gas. The atmospheric pressure is 1.00 atm and the temperature is 25°C. The air has a mole fraction of nitrogen of 0.79, the rest being oxygen.
    a. Explain why the balloon would float when heated. Make sure to discuss which factors change and which remain constant, and why this matters. Be complete.
    b. Above what temperature would you heat the balloon so that it would float?

137. Derive a linear relationship between gas density and temperature, and use it to estimate the value of absolute zero temperature (in °C to the nearest 0.1°C) from an air sample whose density is 1.2930 g/L at 0.0°C and 0.9460 g/L at 100.0°C. Assume air obeys the ideal gas law and that the pressure is held constant.

138. A chemist weighed out 5.14 g of a mixture containing unknown amounts of $BaO(s)$ and $CaO(s)$ and placed the sample in a 1.50-L flask containing $CO_2(g)$ at 30.0°C and 750. torr. After the reaction to form $BaCO_3(s)$ and $CaCO_3(s)$ was completed, the pressure of $CO_2(g)$ remaining was 230. torr. Calculate the mass percents of $CaO(s)$ and $BaO(s)$ in the mixture.

139. The density of a pure gaseous compound was measured at 0.00°C as a function of pressure to give the following results:

Density (g/L)	Pressure (atm)
0.17893	0.2500
0.35808	0.5000
0.53745	0.7500
0.71707	1.000

Calculate the molar mass of this compound, corrected for any nonideal behavior of the gas. Assume the nonideal gas obeys the equation $PV/nRT = 1 + \beta P$. (*Hint:* Derive an equation for P/d and plot P/d versus P.)

140. Consider separate 1.0-L samples of $He(g)$ and $UF_6(g)$, both at 1.00 atm and containing the same number of moles. What ratio of temperatures for the two samples would produce the same collision frequency with the vessel walls?

141. The most probable velocity u_{mp} is the velocity possessed by the greatest number of gas particles. At a certain temperature, the probability that a gas particle has the most probable velocity is equal to one-half the probability that the same gas particle has the most probable velocity at 300. K. Is the temperature higher or lower than 300. K? Calculate the temperature.

142. Derive Dalton's law of partial pressures from the kinetic molecular theory of gases. What assumptions are necessary?

143. One of the assumptions of the kinetic molecular theory is that the volume of a gas particle is negligible. If this were the case, the ratio of the number of collisions of gas particles with the walls of the container compared to the

number of collisions a given gas particle experiences with other gas particles should be quite high. Determine the volume of a cube (in L) filled with helium such that the ratio of the number of collisions of helium atoms with the container walls to the number of intermolecular collisions for a given helium atom is 1 quintillion (1 quintillion = 1.00×10^{18}). The atomic radius of helium is 3.2×10^{-11} m.

144. Consider a sample of a hydrocarbon (a compound consisting of only carbon and hydrogen) at 0.959 atm and 298 K. Upon combusting the entire sample in oxygen, you collect a mixture of gaseous carbon dioxide and water vapor at 1.51 atm and 375 K. This mixture has a density of 1.391 g/L and occupies a volume four times as large as that of the pure hydrocarbon. Determine the molecular formula of the hydrocarbon.

145. A steel cylinder contains 5.00 moles of graphite (pure carbon) and 5.00 moles of O_2. The mixture is ignited and all the graphite reacts. Combustion produces a mixture of CO gas and CO_2 gas. After the cylinder has cooled to its original temperature, it is found that the pressure of the cylinder has increased by 17.0%. Calculate the mole fractions of CO, CO_2, and O_2 in the final gaseous mixture.

146. You have an equimolar mixture of the gases SO_2 and O_2, along with some He, in a container fitted with a piston. The density of this mixture at STP is 1.924 g/L. Assume ideal behavior and constant temperature.
    a. What is the mole fraction of He in the original mixture?
    b. The SO_2 and O_2 react to completion to form SO_3. What is the density of the gas mixture after the reaction is complete?

147. Methane (CH_4) gas flows into a combustion chamber at a rate of 200. L/min at 1.50 atm and ambient temperature. Air is added to the chamber at 1.00 atm and the same temperature, and the gases are ignited.
    a. To ensure complete combustion of CH_4 to $CO_2(g)$ and $H_2O(g)$, three times as much oxygen as is necessary is reacted. Assuming air is 21 mole percent O_2 and 79 mole percent N_2, calculate the flow rate of air necessary to deliver the required amount of oxygen.
    b. Under the conditions in part a, combustion of methane was not complete as a mixture of $CO_2(g)$ and $CO(g)$ was produced. It was determined that 95.0% of the carbon in the exhaust gas was present in the CO_2. The remainder was present as carbon in the CO. Calculate the composition of the exhaust gas in terms of mole fractions of CO, CO_2, O_2, N_2, and H_2O. Assume CH_4 is completely reacted and N_2 is unreacted.
    c. Assuming a total pressure of the exhaust gas of 1.00 atm, calculate the partial pressures of the gases in part b.

148. A spherical vessel with a volume of 1.00 L was evacuated and sealed. Twenty-four hours later the pressure of air in the vessel was found to be 1.20×10^{-6} atm. During this 24-h period, the vessel had been surrounded by air at 27°C and 1.00 atm. Assuming that air is 78 mole percent nitrogen and that the remainder is oxygen, calculate the diameter of the tiny circular hole in the vessel that allowed the air to leak in.

149. Calculate the number of stages needed to change a mixture of $^{13}CO_2$ and $^{12}CO_2$ that is originally 0.10% (by moles) $^{13}CO_2$ to a mixture that is 0.010% $^{13}CO_2$ by a gaseous diffusion process. (The mass of ^{13}C is 13.003355 amu.)

150. Two samples of gas are separated in two rectangular 1.00-L chambers by a thin metal wall. One sample is pure helium and the other is pure radon. Both samples are at 27°C and show a pressure of 2.00×10^{-6} atm. Assuming that the metal wall separating the gases suddenly develops a circular hole of radius 1.00×10^{-6} m, calculate the pressure in each chamber after 10.0 h have passed.

151. You have a helium balloon at 1.00 atm and 25°C. You want to make a hot-air balloon with the same volume and same lift as the helium balloon. Assume air is 79.0% nitrogen and 21.0% oxygen by volume. The "lift" of a balloon is given by the difference between the mass of air displaced by the balloon and the mass of gas inside the balloon.
    a. Will the temperature in the hot-air balloon have to be higher or lower than 25°C? Explain.
    b. Calculate the temperature of the air required for the hot-air balloon to provide the same lift as the helium balloon at 1.00 atm and 25°C. Assume atmospheric conditions are 1.00 atm and 25°C.

152. Consider an equimolar mixture (equal number of moles) of two diatomic gases (A_2 and B_2) in a container fitted with a piston. The gases react to form one product (which is also a gas) with the formula A_xB_y. The density of the sample after the reaction is complete (and the temperature returns to its original state) is 1.50 times greater than the density of the reactant mixture.
    a. Specify the formula of the product, and explain if more than one answer is possible based on the given data.
    b. Can you determine the molecular formula of the product with the information given or only the empirical formula?

153. You are given an unknown gaseous binary compound (that is, a compound consisting of two different elements). When 10.0 g of the compound is burned in excess oxygen, 16.3 g of water is produced. The compound has a density 1.38 times that of oxygen gas at the same conditions of temperature and pressure. Give a possible identity for the unknown compound.

Marathon Problem

154.* Use the following information to identify element A and compound B, then answer questions a and b.

An empty glass container has a mass of 658.572 g. It has a mass of 659.452 g after it has been filled with nitrogen gas at a pressure of 790. torr and a temperature of 15°C. When the container is evacuated and refilled with a certain element (A) at a pressure of 745 torr and a temperature of 26°C, it has a mass of 660.59 g.

Compound B, a gaseous organic compound that consists of 85.6% carbon and 14.4% hydrogen by mass, is placed in a stainless steel vessel (10.68 L) with excess oxygen gas. The vessel is placed in a constant-temperature bath at 22°C. The pressure in the vessel is 11.98 atm. In the bottom of the vessel is a container that is packed with Ascarite and a desiccant. Ascarite is asbestos impregnated with sodium hydroxide; it quantitatively absorbs carbon dioxide:

$$2NaOH(s) + CO_2(g) \longrightarrow Na_2CO_3(s) + H_2O(l)$$

The desiccant is anhydrous magnesium perchlorate, which quantitatively absorbs the water produced by the combustion reaction as well as the water produced by the preceding reaction. Neither the Ascarite nor the desiccant reacts with compound B or oxygen. The total mass of the container with the Ascarite and desiccant is 765.3 g.

The combustion reaction of compound B is initiated by a spark. The pressure immediately rises, then begins to decrease, and finally reaches a steady value of 6.02 atm. The stainless steel vessel is carefully opened, and the mass of the container inside the vessel is found to be 846.7 g.

A and B react quantitatively in a 1:1 mole ratio to form 1 mole of gas C.

a. How many grams of C will be produced if 10.0 L of A and 8.60 L of B (each at STP) are reacted by opening a stopcock connecting the two samples?

b. What will be the total pressure in the system?

*From James H. Burness, "The Use of "Marathon" Problems as Effective Vehicles for the Presentation of General Chemistry Lectures," Journal of Chemical Education, 68(11). Copyright © 1991 American Chemical Society. Reprinted by permission.

Appendixes

| ## Mathematical Procedures

A1.1 Exponential Notation

The numbers characteristic of scientific measurements are often very large or very small; thus it is convenient to express them by using powers of 10. For example, the number 1,300,000 can be expressed as 1.3×10^6, which means multiply 1.3 by 10 six times:

$$1.3 \times 10^6 = 1.3 \times \underbrace{10 \times 10 \times 10 \times 10 \times 10 \times 10}_{10^6 = 1 \text{ million}}$$

Note that each multiplication by 10 moves the decimal point one place to the right, and the easiest way to interpret the notation 1.3×10^6 is that it means move the decimal point in 1.3 to the right six times.

In this notation the number 1985 can be expressed as 1.985×10^3. Note that the usual convention is to write the number that appears before the power of 10 as a number between 1 and 10. Some other examples are given below.

Number	Exponential Notation
5.6	5.6×10^0 or 5.6×1
39	3.9×10^1
943	9.43×10^2
1126	1.126×10^3

To represent a number smaller than 1 in exponential notation, start with a number between 1 and 10 and *divide* by the appropriate power of 10:

$$0.0034 = \frac{3.4}{10 \times 10 \times 10} = \frac{3.4}{10^3} = 3.4 \times 10^{-3}$$

Division by 10 moves the decimal point one place to the *left*. Thus the number 0.00000014 can be written as 1.4×10^{-7}.

To summarize, we can write any number in the form

$$N \times 10^{\pm n}$$

where N is between 1 and 10 and the exponent n is an integer. If the sign preceding n is positive, it means the decimal point in N should be moved n places to the right. If a negative sign precedes n, the decimal point in N should be moved n places to the left.

Multiplication and Division

When two numbers expressed in exponential notation are multiplied, the initial numbers are multiplied and the exponents of 10 are added:

$$(M \times 10^m)(N \times 10^n) = (MN) \times 10^{m+n}$$

For example,

$$(3.2 \times 10^4)(2.8 \times 10^3) = 9.0 \times 10^7$$

When the numbers are multiplied, if a result greater than 10 is obtained for the initial number, the number is adjusted to conventional notation:

$$(5.8 \times 10^2)(4.3 \times 10^8) = 24.9 \times 10^{10} = 2.49 \times 10^{11} = 2.5 \times 10^{11}$$

Division of two numbers expressed in exponential notation involves normal division of the initial numbers and *subtraction* of the exponent of the divisor from that of the dividend. For example,

$$\underbrace{\frac{4.8 \times 10^8}{2.1 \times 10^3}}_{\text{Divisor}} = \frac{4.8}{2.1} \times 10^{(8-3)} = 2.3 \times 10^5$$

Addition and Subtraction

When we add or subtract numbers expressed in exponential notation, *the exponents of the numbers must be the same*. For example, to add 1.31×10^5 and 4.2×10^4, rewrite one number so that the exponents of both are the same:

$$13.1 \times 10^4$$
$$+ \quad 4.2 \times 10^4$$
$$\overline{17.3 \times 10^4}$$

In correct exponential notation, the result is expressed as 1.73×10^5.

Powers and Roots

When a number expressed in exponential notation is taken to some power, the initial number is taken to the appropriate power and the exponent of 10 is multiplied by that power:

$$(N \times 10^n)^m = N^m \times 10^{m \cdot n}$$

For example,*

$$(7.5 \times 10^2)^3 = 7.5^3 \times 10^{3 \cdot 2} = 422 \times 10^6 = 4.22 \times 10^8$$
$$= 4.2 \times 10^8 \text{ (rounded to 2 significant figures)}$$

When a root is taken of a number expressed in exponential notation, the root of the initial number is taken and the exponent of 10 is divided by the number representing the root:

$$\sqrt{N \times 10^n} = (N \times 10^n)^{1/2} = \sqrt{N} \times 10^{n/2}$$

For example, $(2.9 \times 10^6)^{1/2} = \sqrt{2.9} \times 10^{6/2} = 1.7 \times 10^3$

Because the exponent of the result must be an integer, we may sometimes have to change the form of the number so that the power divided by the root equals an integer; for example,

$$\sqrt{1.9 \times 10^3} = (1.9 \times 10^3)^{1/2} = (0.19 \times 10^4)^{1/2}$$
$$= \sqrt{0.19} \times 10^2 = 0.44 \times 10^2$$
$$= 4.4 \times 10^1$$

*Refer to the instruction booklet for your calculator for directions concerning how to take roots and powers of numbers.

The same procedure is followed for roots other than square roots; for example,

$$\sqrt[3]{4.6 \times 10^{10}} = (4.6 \times 10^{10})^{1/3} = (46 \times 10^9)^{1/3}$$

$$= \sqrt[3]{46} \times 10^3 = 3.6 \times 10^3$$

A1.2 Logarithms

A logarithm is an exponent. Any number N can be expressed as follows:

$$N = 10^x$$

For example,

$$1000 = 10^3$$

$$100 = 10^2$$

$$10 = 10^1$$

$$1 = 10^0$$

The common, or base 10, logarithm of a number is the power to which 10 must be taken to yield that number. Thus, since $1000 = 10^3$,

$$\log 1000 = 3$$

Similarly,

$$\log 100 = 2$$

$$\log 10 = 1$$

$$\log 1 = 0$$

For a number between 10 and 100, the required exponent of 10 will be between 1 and 2. For example, $65 = 10^{1.8129}$; that is, $\log 65 = 1.8129$. For a number between 100 and 1000, the exponent of 10 will be between 2 and 3. For example, $650 = 10^{2.8129}$ and $\log 650 = 2.8129$.

A number N greater than 0 and less than 1 can be expressed as follows:

$$N = 10^{-x} = \frac{1}{10^x}$$

For example,

$$0.001 = \frac{1}{1000} = \frac{1}{10^3} = 10^{-3}$$

$$0.01 = \frac{1}{100} = \frac{1}{10^2} = 10^{-2}$$

$$0.1 = \frac{1}{10} = \frac{1}{10^1} = 10^{-1}$$

Thus

$$\log 0.001 = -3$$

$$\log 0.01 = -2$$

$$\log 0.1 = -1$$

Although common logs are often tabulated, the most convenient method for obtaining such logs is to use a calculator.

Since logs are simply exponents, they are manipulated according to the rules for exponents. For example, if $A = 10^x$ and $B = 10^y$, then their product is

$$A \cdot B = 10^x \cdot 10^y = 10^{x+y}$$

and

$$\log AB = x + y = \log A + \log B$$

For division we have

$$\frac{A}{B} = \frac{10^x}{10^y} = 10^{x-y}$$

and
$$\log \frac{A}{B} = x - y = \log A - \log B$$

For a number raised to a power, we have
$$A^n = (10^x)^n = 10^{nx}$$

and
$$\log A^n = nx = n \log A$$

It follows that
$$\log \frac{1}{A^n} = \log A^{-n} = -n \log A$$

or for $n = 1$,
$$\log \frac{1}{A} = -\log A$$

When a common log is given, to find the number it represents, we must carry out the process of exponentiation. For example, if the log is 2.673, then $N = 10^{2.673}$. The process of exponentiation is also called taking the antilog, or the inverse logarithm, and is easily carried out by using a calculator.

A second type of logarithm, the natural logarithm, is based on the number 2.7183, which is referred to as e. In this case a number is represented as $N = e^x = 2.7183^x$. For example,

$$N = 7.15 = e^x$$

$$\ln 7.15 = x = 1.967$$

If a natural logarithm is given, to find the number it represents, we must carry out exponentiation to the base e (2.7183) by using a calculator.

A1.3 Graphing Functions

In the interpretation of the results of a scientific experiment, it is often useful to make a graph. It is usually most convenient to graph the function in a form that gives a straight line. The equation for a straight line (a *linear equation*) can be represented by the general form

$$y = mx + b$$

where y is the *dependent variable*, x is the *independent variable*, m is the *slope*, and b is the *intercept* with the y axis.

As an illustration of the characteristics of a linear equation, the function $y = 3x + 4$ is plotted in Fig. A1.1. For this equation, $m = 3$ and $b = 4$. Note that the y intercept occurs when $x = 0$. In this case the intercept is 4, as can be seen from the equation ($b = 4$).

The slope of a straight line is defined as the ratio of the rate of change in y to that in x:

$$m = \text{slope} = \frac{\Delta y}{\Delta x}$$

For the equation $y = 3x + 4$, y changes three times as fast as x (since x has a coefficient of 3). Thus the slope in this case is 3. This can be verified from the graph. For the triangle shown in Fig. A1.1:

$$\text{Slope} = \frac{\Delta y}{\Delta x} = \frac{24}{8} = 3$$

Sometimes an equation that is not in standard form can be changed to the form $y = mx + b$ by rearrangement or mathematical manipulation. An example is the equation $k = Ae^{-E_a/RT}$, where A, E_a, and R are constants, k is the

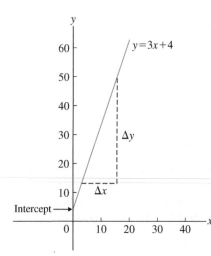

Figure A1.1

Graph of the linear equation $y = 3x + 4$.

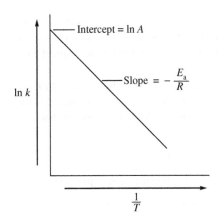

Figure A1.2
Graph of ln k versus $1/T$.

dependent variable, and $1/T$ is the independent variable. This equation can be changed to standard form by taking the natural logarithm of both sides,

$$\ln k = \ln Ae^{-E_a/RT} = \ln A + \ln e^{-E_a/RT} = \ln A - \frac{E_a}{RT}$$

noting that the log of a product is equal to the sum of the logs of the individual terms and that the natural log of $e^{-E_a/RT}$ is simply the exponent $-E_a/RT$. Thus in standard form the equation $k = Ae^{-E_a/RT}$ is written

$$\underbrace{\ln k}_{y} = \underbrace{-\frac{E_a}{R}}_{m} \underbrace{\left(\frac{1}{T}\right)}_{x} + \underbrace{\ln A}_{b}$$

A plot of ln k versus $1/T$ (see Fig. A1.2) gives a straight line with slope $-E_a/R$ and intercept ln A.

Of course, many relationships that arise from the description of natural systems are nonlinear, and the "slope" of a curve is continuously changing. In this case the instantaneous slope is given by the tangent to the curve at that point, which is described by a new function obtained by taking the derivative of the original function. For example, for the function in x, $f = ax^2$, the derivative (df/dx) is $2ax$. Thus the slope at each point on the curve defined by the function ax^2 is given by $2ax$.

A1.4 Solving Quadratic Equations

A *quadratic equation,* a polynomial in which the highest power of x is 2, can be written as

$$ax^2 + bx + c = 0$$

One method for finding the two values of x that satisfy a quadratic equation is to use the *quadratic formula:*

$$x = \frac{-b \pm \sqrt{b^2 - 4ac}}{2a}$$

where a, b, and c represent the coefficients of x^2 and x and the constant, respectively. For example, in the determination of $[H^+]$ in a solution of 1.0×10^{-4} M acetic acid, the following expression arises:

$$1.8 \times 10^{-5} = \frac{x^2}{1.0 \times 10^{-4} - x}$$

which yields

$$x^2 + (1.8 \times 10^{-5})x - 1.8 \times 10^{-9} = 0$$

where $a = 1$, $b = 1.8 \times 10^{-5}$, and $c = -1.8 \times 10^{-9}$. Using the quadratic formula, we have

$$x = \frac{-b \pm \sqrt{b^2 - 4ac}}{2a}$$

$$= \frac{-1.8 \times 10^{-5} \pm \sqrt{3.24 \times 10^{-10} - (4)(1)(-1.8 \times 10^{-9})}}{2(1)}$$

and

$$x = \frac{6.9 \times 10^{-5}}{2} = 3.5 \times 10^{-5}$$

or

$$x = \frac{-10.5 \times 10^{-5}}{2} = -5.2 \times 10^{-5}$$

Note that there are two roots, as there always will be for a polynomial in x^2. In this case x represents a concentration of H^+ (see Section 7.5). Thus the positive root is the one that solves the problem, since a concentration cannot be a negative number.

A second method for solving quadratic equations is by *successive approximations*, a systematic method of trial and error. A value of x is guessed and substituted into the equation everywhere x (or x^2) appears, except for one place. For example, for the equation

$$x^2 + (1.8 \times 10^{-5})x - 1.8 \times 10^{-9} = 0$$

we might guess $x = 2 \times 10^{-5}$. Substituting that value into the equation gives

$$x^2 + (1.8 \times 10^{-5})(2 \times 10^{-5}) - 1.8 \times 10^{-9} = 0$$

or $\qquad x^2 = 1.8 \times 10^{-9} - 3.6 \times 10^{-10} = 1.4 \times 10^{-9}$

Thus $\qquad x = 3.7 \times 10^{-5}$

Note that the guessed value of x (2×10^{-5}) is not the same as the value of x that is calculated (3.7×10^{-5}) after inserting the estimated value. This means that $x = 2 \times 10^{-5}$ is not the correct solution, and we must try another guess.

We take the calculated value (3.7×10^{-5}) as our next guess:

$$x^2 + (1.8 \times 10^{-5})(3.7 \times 10^{-5}) - 1.8 \times 10^{-9} = 0$$

$$x^2 = 1.8 \times 10^{-9} - 6.7 \times 10^{-10} = 1.1 \times 10^{-9}$$

Thus $\qquad x = 3.3 \times 10^{-5}$

Now we compare the two values of x again:

Guessed: $\qquad x = 3.7 \times 10^{-5}$

Calculated: $\qquad x = 3.3 \times 10^{-5}$

These values are closer but still not identical.

Next, we try 3.3×10^{-5} as our guess:

$$x^2 + (1.8 \times 10^{-5})(3.3 \times 10^{-5}) - 1.8 \times 10^{-9} = 0$$

$$x^2 = 1.8 \times 10^{-9} - 5.9 \times 10^{-10} = 1.2 \times 10^{-9}$$

Thus $\qquad x = 3.5 \times 10^{-5}$

Compare:

Guessed: $\qquad x = 3.3 \times 10^{-5}$

Calculated: $\qquad x = 3.5 \times 10^{-5}$

Next, we guess $x = 3.5 \times 10^{-5}$, which leads to

$$x^2 + (1.8 \times 10^{-5})(3.5 \times 10^{-5}) - 1.8 \times 10^{-9} = 0$$

$$x^2 = 1.8 \times 10^{-9} - 6.3 \times 10^{-10} = 1.2 \times 10^{-9}$$

Thus $\qquad x = 3.5 \times 10^{-5}$

Now the guessed value and the calculated value are the same; we have found the correct solution. Note that this agrees with one of the roots found with the quadratic formula in the first method above.

To further illustrate the method of successive approximations, we will solve Example 7.9 by using this procedure. In solving for $[H^+]$ for 0.010 *M* H_2SO_4, we obtain the following expression:

$$1.2 \times 10^{-2} = \frac{x(0.010 + x)}{0.010 - x}$$

which can be rearranged to give

$$x = (1.2 \times 10^{-2})\left(\frac{0.010 - x}{0.010 + x}\right)$$

We will guess a value for x, substitute it into the right side of the equation, and then calculate a value for x. In guessing a value for x, we know it must be less than 0.010, since a larger value would make the calculated value for x negative and the guessed and calculated values will never match. We start by guessing $x = 0.005$.

The results of the successive approximations are shown in the following table:

Trial	Guessed Value for x	Calculated Value for x
1	0.0050	0.0040
2	0.0040	0.0051
3	0.00450	0.00455
4	0.00452	0.00453

Note that the first guess was close to the actual value and that there was oscillation between 0.004 and 0.005 for the guessed and calculated values. For trial 3, an average of these values was used as the guess, and this led rapidly to the correct value (0.0045 to the correct number of significant figures). Also note that it is useful to carry extra digits until the correct value is obtained, which is then rounded off to the correct number of significant figures.

The method of successive approximations is especially useful for solving polynomials containing x to a power of 3 or higher. The procedure is the same as for quadratic equations: Substitute a guessed value for x into the equation for every x term but one, and then solve for x. Continue this process until the guessed and calculated values agree.

A1.5 Uncertainties in Measurements

The number associated with a measurement is obtained by using some measuring device. For example, consider the measurement of the volume of a liquid in a buret, as shown in Fig. A1.3, where the scale is greatly magnified. The volume is about 22.15 mL. Note that the last number must be estimated by interpolating between the 0.1-mL marks. Since the last number is estimated, its value may vary depending on who makes the measurement. If five different people read the same volume, the results might be as follows:

Person	Result of Measurement
1	22.15 mL
2	22.14 mL
3	22.16 mL
4	22.17 mL
5	22.16 mL

Note from these results that the first three numbers (22.1) remain the same regardless of who makes the measurement; these are called certain digits. However, the digit to the right of the 1 must be estimated and thus varies; it is called an uncertain digit. We customarily report a measurement by recording all the certain digits plus the *first* uncertain digit. In our example it would not make any sense to try to record the volume to thousandths of a milliliter because the value for hundredths of a milliliter must be estimated when using the buret.

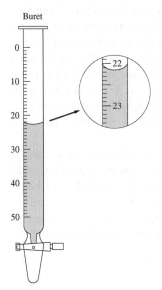

Figure A1.3
Measurement of volume using a buret. The volume is read at the bottom of the liquid curve (called the meniscus).

It is very important to realize that a *measurement always has some degree of uncertainty.* The uncertainty of a measurement depends on the precision of the measuring device. For example, using a bathroom scale, you might estimate that the mass of a grapefruit is about 1.5 pounds. Weighing the same grapefruit on a highly precise balance might produce a result of 1.476 pounds. In the first case the uncertainty occurs in the tenths of a pound place; in the second case the uncertainty occurs in the thousandths of a pound place. Suppose we weigh two similar grapefruit on the two devices and obtain the following results:

	Bathroom Scale	Balance
Grapefruit 1	1.5 lb	1.476 lb
Grapefruit 2	1.5 lb	1.518 lb

Do the two grapefruits have the same mass? The answer depends on which set of results you consider. Thus a conclusion based on a series of measurements depends on the certainty of those measurements. For this reason, it is important to indicate the uncertainty in any measurement. This is done by always recording the certain digits and the first uncertain digit (the estimated number). These numbers are called the **significant figures** of a measurement.

The convention of significant figures automatically gives an indication of the uncertainty in a measurement. The uncertainty in the last number (the estimated number) is usually assumed to be ±1 unless otherwise indicated. For example, the measurement 1.86 kilograms can be interpreted to mean 1.86 ± 0.01 kilograms.

Precision and Accuracy

Two terms often used to describe uncertainty in measurements are *precision* and *accuracy.* Although these words are frequently used interchangeably in everyday life, they have different meanings in the scientific context. **Accuracy** refers to the agreement of a particular value with the true value. **Precision** refers to the degree of agreement among several measurements of the same quantity. Precision reflects the *reproducibility* of a given type of measurement. The difference between these terms is illustrated by the results of three different target practices shown in Fig. A1.4.

Two different types of errors are also introduced in Fig. A1.4. A **random error** (also called an indeterminate error) means that a measurement has an equal probability of being high or low. This type of error occurs in estimating the value of the last digit of a measurement. The second type of error is called **systematic error** (or determinate error). This type of error occurs in the same direction each time; it is either always high or always low. Figure A1.4(a) indicates large random errors (poor technique). Figure A1.4(b) indicates small random errors but a large systematic error, and Fig. A1.4(c) indicates small random errors and no systematic error.

In quantitative work precision is often used as an indication of accuracy; we assume that the *average* of a series of precise measurements (which should "average out" the random errors because of their equal probability of being high or low) is accurate, or close to the "true" value. However, this assumption is valid only if systematic errors are absent. Suppose we weigh a piece of brass five times on a very precise balance and obtain the following results:

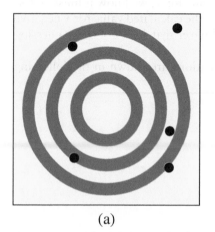

(a)

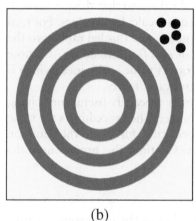

(b)

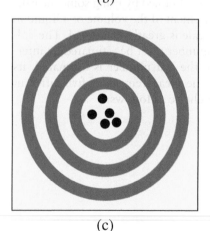

(c)

Figure A1.4

Shooting targets show the difference between *precise* and *accurate.*
(a) Neither accurate nor precise (large random errors). (b) Precise but not accurate (small random errors, large systematic error). (c) Bull's-eye! Both precise and accurate (small random errors, no systematic error).

Weighing	Result
1	2.486 g
2	2.487 g
3	2.485 g
4	2.484 g
5	2.488 g

Normally, we would assume that the true mass of the piece of brass is very close to 2.486 grams, which is the average of the five results. However, if the balance has a defect causing it to give a result that is consistently 1.000 gram too high (a systematic error of $+1.000$ gram), then 2.486 grams would be seriously in error. The point here is that high precision among several measurements is an indication of accuracy *only* if you can be sure that systematic errors are absent.

Expression of Experimental Results

The accuracy of a measurement refers to how close it is to the true value. An inaccurate result occurs as a result of some flaw (systematic error) in the measurement: the presence of an interfering substance, incorrect calibration of an instrument, operator error, and so on. The goal of chemical analysis is to eliminate systematic error, but random errors can only be minimized. In practice, an experiment is almost always done in order to find an unknown value (the true value is not known—someone is trying to obtain that value by doing the experiment). In this case the precision of several replicate determinations is used to assess the accuracy of the result. The results of the replicate experiments are expressed as an average (which we assume is close to the true value) with an error limit that gives some indication of how close the average value may be to the true value. The error limit represents the uncertainty of the experimental result.

To illustrate this procedure, consider a situation that might arise in the pharmaceutical industry. Assume that the specification for a commercial 500-mg acetaminophen (the active painkiller in Tylenol) tablet is that each batch of tablets must contain 450 to 550 mg of acetaminophen per tablet. Suppose that chemical analysis gave the following results for a batch of acetaminophen tablets: 428, 479, 442, and 435 mg. How can these results be used to decide whether the batch of tablets meets the specification? Although the details of how to draw such conclusions from measured data are beyond the scope of this discussion, we will consider some aspects of this process. We will focus here on the types of experimental uncertainty, the expression of experimental results, and a simplified method for estimating experimental uncertainty when several types of measurements contribute to the final result.

There are two common ways of expressing an average: the mean and the median. The mean ($\bar{x}$) is the arithmetic average of the results, or

$$\text{Mean} = \bar{x} = \sum_{i=1}^{n} \frac{x_i}{n} = \frac{x_1 + x_2 + \cdots + x_n}{n}$$

where Σ means take the sum of the values. The mean is equal to the sum of all the measurements divided by the number of measurements. For the acetaminophen results given previously, the mean is

$$\bar{x} = \frac{428 + 479 + 442 + 435}{4} = 446 \text{ mg}$$

The median is the value that lies in the middle among the results. Half of the measurements are above the median and half are below the median. For results of 465, 485, and 492 mg, the median is 485 mg. When there is an even number of results, the median is the average of the two middle results. For the acetaminophen results, the median is

$$\frac{442 + 435}{2} = 439 \text{ mg}$$

There are several advantages to using the median. If a small number of measurements is made, one value can greatly affect the mean. Consider the results for the analysis of acetaminophen: 428, 479, 442, and 435 mg. The mean is 446 mg, which is larger than three of the four results. The median is 439 mg, which lies near the three values that are relatively close to one another.

In addition to expressing an average value for a series of results, we must also express the uncertainty. This usually means expressing either the precision of the measurements or the observed range of the measurements. The range of a series of measurements is defined by the smallest value and the largest value. For the analytical results on the acetaminophen tablets, the range is from 428 to 479 mg. Using this range, we can express the results by saying that the true value lies between 428 and 479 mg. That is, we can express the amount of acetaminophen in a typical tablet as 446 ± 33 mg, where the error limit is chosen to give the observed range (approximately).

The most common way to specify precision is by the standard deviation s, which for a small number of measurements is given by the formula

$$ s = \left[\frac{\sum_{i=1}^{n} (x_i - \bar{x})^2}{n-1} \right]^{1/2} $$

where x_i is an individual result, $\bar{x}$ is the average (either mean or median), and n is the total number of measurements. For the acetaminophen example, we have

$$ s = \left[\frac{(428 - 446)^2 + (479 - 446)^2 + (442 - 446)^2 + (435 - 446)^2}{4-1} \right]^{1/2} = 23 $$

Thus we can say that the amount of acetaminophen in a typical tablet in the batch of tablets is 446 mg with a sample standard deviation of 23 mg. Statistically, this means that any additional measurement has a 68% probability (68 chances out of 100) of being between 423 mg ($446 - 23$) and 469 mg ($446 + 23$). Thus the standard deviation is a measure of the precision of a given type of measurement.

In scientific calculations it is also useful to be able to estimate the precision of a procedure that involves several measurements by combining the precisions of the individual steps. That is, we want to answer the following question: How do the uncertainties propagate when we combine the results of several different types of measurements? There are many ways to deal with the propagation of uncertainty. We will discuss one simple method below.

Worst-Case Method for Estimating Experimental Uncertainty

To illustrate this method, we will consider the determination of the density of an irregularly shaped solid. In this determination we make three measurements. First, we measure the mass of the object on a balance. Next, we must obtain the volume of the solid. The easiest method for doing this is to partially fill a graduated cylinder with a liquid and record the volume. Then we add the solid and record the volume again. The difference in the measured volumes is the volume of the solid. We can then calculate the density of the solid from the equation

$$ D = \frac{M}{V_2 - V_1} $$

where M is the mass of the solid, V_1 is the initial volume of liquid in the graduated cylinder, and V_2 is the volume of liquid plus solid. Suppose we get the following results:

$$ M = 23.06 \text{ g} $$

$$ V_1 = 10.4 \text{ mL} $$

$$ V_2 = 13.5 \text{ mL} $$

The calculated density is

$$\frac{23.06 \text{ g}}{13.5 \text{ mL} - 10.4 \text{ mL}} = 7.44 \text{ g/mL}$$

Now suppose that the precision of the balance used is ± 0.02 g and that the volume measurements are precise to ± 0.05 mL. How do we estimate the uncertainty of the density? We can do this by assuming a worst case. That is, we assume the largest uncertainties in all measurements, and we see what combinations of measurements will give the largest and smallest possible results (the greatest range). Since the density is the mass divided by the volume, the largest value of the density will be that obtained by using the largest possible mass and the smallest possible volume:

Largest possible mass = 23.06 + 0.02

$$D_{max} = \frac{23.08}{13.45 - 10.45} = 7.69 \text{ g/mL}$$

Smallest possible V_2 Largest possible V_1

The smallest value of the density is

Smallest possible mass

$$D_{min} = \frac{23.04}{13.55 - 10.35} = 7.20 \text{ g/mL}$$

Largest possible V_2 Smallest possible V_1

Thus the calculated range is from 7.20 to 7.69, and the average of these values is 7.45. The error limit is the number that gives the high and low range values when added and subtracted from the average. Therefore, we can express the density as 7.45 ± 0.25 g/mL, which is the average value plus or minus the quantity that gives the range calculated by assuming the largest uncertainties.

Analysis of the propagation of uncertainties is useful in drawing qualitative conclusions from the analysis of measurements. For example, suppose that we obtained the preceding results for the density of an unknown alloy and we want to know if it is one of the following alloys:

Alloy A: $D = 7.58$ g/mL

Alloy B: $D = 7.42$ g/mL

Alloy C: $D = 8.56$ g/mL

We can safely conclude that the alloy is not C. But the values of the densities for alloys A and B are both within the inherent uncertainty of our method. To distinguish between A and B, we need to improve the precision of our determination. The obvious choice is to improve the precision of the volume measurement.

The worst-case method is useful for estimating the maximum uncertainty expected when the results of several measurements are combined to obtain a result. We assume the maximum uncertainty in each measurement and then calculate the minimum and maximum possible results. These extreme values describe the range and thus the maximum error limit associated with a particular determination.

	Values of t for Confidence Intervals	
n	90%	95%
2	6.31	12.7
3	2.92	4.30
4	2.35	3.18
5	2.13	2.78
6	2.02	2.57
7	1.94	2.45
8	1.90	2.36
9	1.86	2.31
10	1.83	2.26

Confidence Limits

A more sophisticated method for estimating the uncertainty of a particular type of determination involves the use of confidence limits. A confidence limit is defined as

$$\text{Confidence limit} = \pm\frac{ts}{\sqrt{n}}$$

where t = a weighting factor based on statistical analysis

s = the standard deviation

n = the number of experiments carried out

In this context an experiment may refer to a single type of measurement (for example, weighing an object) or to a procedure that requires various types of measurements to obtain a given final result (for example, obtaining the percentage of iron in a particular sample of iron ore). Some representative values of t are listed in Table A1.1.

A 95% confidence level means that the true value (the *average* obtained if the experiment were repeated an *infinite* number of times) will lie within $\pm ts/\sqrt{n}$ of the *observed* average (obtained from n experiments) with a 95% probability (95 of 100 times). Thus the factor $\pm ts/\sqrt{n}$ represents an error limit for a given set of results from a particular type of experiment. Thus we might represent the result of n determinations as

$$\bar{x} \pm \frac{ts}{\sqrt{n}}$$

where $\bar{x}$ is the average of the results from the n experiments. This type of error limit is expected to be considerably smaller than that obtained from a worst-case analysis.

A1.6 Significant Figures

Calculating the final result for an experiment usually involves adding, subtracting, multiplying, or dividing the results of various types of measurements. Thus it is important to be able to estimate the uncertainty in the final result. In the previous section we have considered this process in some detail. A closely related matter concerns the number of digits that should be retained in the result of a given calculation. In other words, how many of the digits in the result are significant (meaningful) relative to the uncertainty expected in the result? From statistical analyses of how uncertainties accumulate when arithmetic operations are carried out, rules have been developed for determining the correct number of significant figures in a final result. First, we must consider how to count the number of significant figures (digits) represented in a particular number.

Rules for Counting Significant Figures (Digits)

1. *Nonzero integers.* Nonzero integers always count as significant figures.

2. *Zeros.* There are three classes of zeros:

    a. *Leading zeros* are zeros that *precede* all the nonzero digits. They do not count as significant figures. In the number 0.0025 the three zeros simply indicate the position of the decimal point. This number has only two significant figures.

    b. *Captive zeros* are zeros *between* nonzero digits. They always count as significant figures. The number 1.008 has four significant figures.

c. *Trailing zeros* are zeros at the *right end* of the number. They are significant only if the number contains a decimal point. The number 100 has only one significant figure, whereas the number 1.00×10^2 has three significant figures. The number one hundred written as 100. also has three significant figures.

3. *Exact numbers.* Many times calculations involve numbers that were not obtained by using measuring devices but were determined by counting: 10 experiments, 3 apples, 8 molecules. Such numbers are called *exact numbers*. They can be assumed to have an infinite number of significant figures. Other examples of exact numbers are the 2 in $2\pi r$ (the circumference of a circle) and the 4 and the 3 in $\frac{4}{3}\pi r^3$ (the volume of a sphere). Exact numbers can also arise from definitions. For example, one inch is defined as exactly 2.54 centimeters. Thus, in the statement 1 in = 2.54 cm, neither the 2.54 nor the 1 limits the number of significant figures when used in a calculation.

The following rules apply for determining the number of significant figures in the result of a calculation.

Rules for Significant Figures in Mathematical Operations*

1. For *multiplication or division* the number of significant figures in the result is the same as the number in the least precise measurement used in the calculation. For example, consider this calculation:

$$4.56 \times 1.4 = 6.38 \xrightarrow{\text{Corrected}} 6.4$$

Limiting term has two significant figures

Two significant figures

The correct product has only two significant figures, since 1.4 has two significant figures.

2. For *addition or subtraction* the result has the same number of decimal places as the least precise measurement used in the calculation. For example, consider the following sum:

$$
\begin{array}{r}
12.11 \\
18.0 \quad \leftarrow \text{Limiting term has one decimal place} \\
\underline{1.013} \\
31.123 \xrightarrow{\text{Corrected}} 31.1 \\
\end{array}
$$

One decimal place

The correct result is 31.1, since 18.0 has only one decimal place.

Note that for multiplication and division significant figures are counted. For addition and subtraction the decimal places are counted.

In most calculations you will need to round off numbers to obtain the correct number of significant figures. The following rules should be applied for rounding.

---

*Although these rules work well for most cases, they can give misleading results in certain cases. For a discussion of this, see L. M. Schwartz, "Propagation of Significant Figures," *J. Chem. Ed.* **62** (1985):693.

Rules for Rounding

1. In a series of calculations, carry the extra digits through to the final result, *then* round off.*

2. If the digit to be removed†

   a. is less than 5, the preceding digit stays the same. For example, 1.33 rounds to 1.3.

   b. is equal to or greater than 5, the preceding digit is increased by 1. For example, 1.36 rounds to 1.4.

When rounding, use only the first number to the right of the last significant figure. Do not round off sequentially. For example, the number 4.348 when rounded to two significant figures is 4.3, not 4.4.

| Appendix Two | # Units of Measurement and Conversions Among Units |

A2.1 Measurements

Making observations is fundamental to all science. A quantitative observation, or **measurement**, always consists of two parts: a *number* and a scale (a *unit*). Both parts must be present for the measurement to be meaningful.

The two most widely used systems of units are the *English system* used in the United States and the *metric system* used by most of the rest of the industrialized world. This duality obviously causes a good deal of trouble; for example, parts as simple as bolts are not interchangeable between machines built using the different systems. As a result, the United States has begun to adopt the metric system.

For many years, most scientists worldwide have used the metric system. In 1960 an international agreement established a system of units called the *International System* (*le Système International* in French), abbreviated **SI**. This system is based on the metric system and the units derived from the metric system. The fundamental SI units are listed in Table A2.1.

Because the fundamental units are not always convenient (expressing the mass of a pin in kilograms is awkward), the SI system uses prefixes to change the size of the unit. These prefixes are listed in Table A2.2.

Table A2.1

The Fundamental SI Units

Physical Quantity	Name of Unit	Abbreviation
Mass	kilogram	kg
Length	meter	m
Time	second	s
Temperature	Kelvin	K
Electric current	ampere	A
Amount of substance	mole	mol
Luminous intensity	candela	cd

---

*This practice will not usually be followed in the examples in this text because we want to show the correct number of significant figures in each step. However, in the answers to the end-of-chapter exercises, only the final answer is rounded.
†This procedure is consistent with the operation of calculators.

Table A2.2

The Prefixes Used in the SI System

Prefix	Symbol	Meaning	Exponential Notation*
exa	E	1,000,000,000,000,000,000	10^{18}
peta	P	1,000,000,000,000,000	10^{15}
tera	T	1,000,000,000,000	10^{12}
giga	G	1,000,000,000	10^{9}
mega	**M**	**1,000,000**	10^{6}
kilo	**k**	**1000**	10^{3}
hecto	h	100	10^{2}
deka	da	10	10^{1}
—	—	1	10^{0}
deci	d	0.1	10^{-1}
centi	**c**	**0.01**	10^{-2}
milli	**m**	**0.001**	10^{-3}
micro	**μ**	**0.000001**	10^{-6}
nano	**n**	**0.000000001**	10^{-9}
pico	p	0.000000000001	10^{-12}
femto	f	0.000000000000001	10^{-15}
atto	a	0.000000000000000001	10^{-18}

*The most common notations are shown in bold. See Appendix A1.1 if you need a review of exponential notation.

One physical quantity that is very important in chemistry is *volume,* which is not a fundamental SI unit; it is derived from length. A cube with dimensions of 1 m on each edge has a volume of $(1 \text{ m})^3 = 1 \text{ m}^3$. Then, recognizing that there are 10 decimeters (dm) in a meter, the volume of the cube is $(10 \text{ dm})^3 = 1000 \text{ dm}^3$. A cubic decimeter, dm^3, is commonly called a liter (L), which is a unit of volume slightly larger than a quart. Similarly, since 1 dm equals 10 centimeters (cm), the liter $(1 \text{ dm})^3$ contains 1000 cm^3, or 1000 milliliters (mL).

A2.2 Unit Conversions

It is often necessary to convert results from one system of units to another. The most common way of converting units is by the *unit factor method,* more commonly called **dimensional analysis.** To illustrate the use of this method, we will look at a simple unit conversion.

Consider a pin measuring 2.85 cm in length. What is its length in inches? To solve this problem, we must use the equivalence statement

$$2.54 \text{ cm} = 1 \text{ in} \quad \text{(exactly)}$$

If we divide both sides of this equation by 2.54 cm, we get

$$\frac{2.54 \text{ cm}}{2.54 \text{ cm}} = 1 = \frac{1 \text{ in}}{2.54 \text{ cm}}$$

Note that the expression 1 in/2.54 cm equals 1. This expression is called a **unit factor.** Since 1 in and 2.54 cm are exactly equivalent, multiplying any expression by this unit factor will not change its value.

The pin has a length of 2.85 cm. Multiplying this length by the unit factor gives

$$2.85 \text{ cm} \times \frac{1 \text{ in}}{1.54 \text{ cm}} = \frac{2.85}{2.54} \text{ in} = 1.12 \text{ in}$$

Note that the centimeter units cancel to give inches for the result. This is exactly what we wanted to accomplish. Note also that the result has three significant figures, as required by the number 2.85. Recall that the 1 and 2.54 in the conversion factor are exact numbers by definition.

<table>
<tr><td>**STEPS**</td><td>**Converting from One Unit to Another**</td></tr>
</table>

1 To convert from one unit to another, use the equivalence statement that relates the two units.

2 Derive the appropriate unit factor by noting the direction of the required change (to cancel the unwanted units).

3 Multiply the quantity to be converted by the unit factor to give the quantity with the desired units.

In dimensional analysis your verification that everything has been done correctly is that the correct units are obtained in the end. *In doing chemistry problems, you should always include the units for the quantities used.* Always check to see that the units cancel to give the correct units for the final result. This provides a very valuable check, especially for complicated problems.

Appendix Three | Spectral Analysis

Although volumetric and gravimetric analyses are still commonly used, spectroscopy is the technique most often used for modern chemical analysis. *Spectroscopy* is the study of electromagnetic radiation emitted or absorbed by a given chemical species. Since the quantity of radiation absorbed or emitted can be related to the quantity of the absorbing or emitting species present, this technique can be used for quantitative analysis. There are many spectroscopic techniques, since electromagnetic radiation spans a wide range of energies to include microwaves, X rays, and ultraviolet, infrared, and visible light, to name a few of its familiar forms. However, we will consider here only one procedure, which is based on the absorption of visible light.

If a liquid is colored, it is because some component of the liquid absorbs visible light. In a solution the greater the concentration of the light-absorbing substance, the more light is absorbed, and the more intense is the color of the solution.

The quantity of light absorbed by a substance can be measured by a *spectrophotometer,* shown schematically in Fig. A3.1. This instrument consists of a source that emits all wavelengths of light in the visible region (wavelengths of ≈400–700 nm); a monochromator, which selects a given wavelength of light; a sample holder for the solution being measured; and a detector, which compares the intensity of incident light I_0 with the intensity of light after it has passed through the sample I. The ratio I/I_0, called the *transmittance,* is a measure of the fraction of light that passes through the sample. The amount of light absorbed is given by the *absorbance A*, where

$$A = -\log \frac{I}{I_0}$$

The absorbance can be expressed by the *Beer-Lambert law:*

$$A = \epsilon l c$$

Figure A3.1
A schematic diagram of a simple spectrophotometer. The source emits all wavelengths of visible light, which are dispersed by using a prism or grating and then focused, one wavelength at a time, onto the sample. The detector compares the intensity of the incident light (I_0) with the intensity of the light after it has passed through the sample (I).

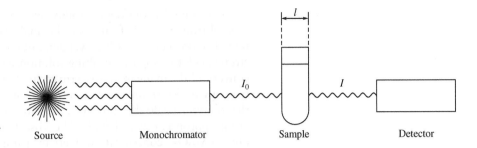

Source   Monochromator   Sample   Detector

where ϵ is the molar absorptivity or the molar extinction coefficient (in L mol^{-1} cm^{-1}), l is the distance the light travels through the solution (in cm), and c is the concentration of the absorbing species (in mol/L). The Beer-Lambert law is the basis for using spectroscopy in quantitative analysis. If ϵ and l are known, determining A for a solution allows us to calculate the concentration of the absorbing species in the solution.

Suppose we have a pink solution containing an unknown concentration of $Co^{2+}(aq)$ ions. A sample of this solution is placed in a spectrophotometer, and the absorbance is measured at a wavelength where ϵ for $Co^{2+}(aq)$ is known to be 12 L mol^{-1} cm^{-1}. The absorbance A is found to be 0.60. The width of the sample tube is 1.0 cm. We want to determine the concentration of $Co^{2+}(aq)$ in the solution. This problem can be solved by a straightforward application of the Beer-Lambert law,

$$A = \epsilon l c$$

where
$$A = 0.60$$

$$\epsilon = \frac{12 \text{ L}}{\text{mol cm}}$$

$$l = \text{light path} = 1.0 \text{ cm}$$

Solving for the concentration gives

$$c = \frac{A}{\epsilon l} = \frac{0.60}{\left(12 \dfrac{\text{L}}{\text{mol cm}}\right)(1.0 \text{ cm})} = 5.0 \times 10^{-2} \text{ mol/L}$$

To obtain the unknown concentration of an absorbing species from the measured absorbance, we must know the product ϵl, since

$$c = \frac{A}{\epsilon l}$$

We can obtain the product ϵl by measuring the absorbance of a solution of *known* concentration, since

Measured using a
$\swarrow$ spectrophotometer

$$\epsilon l = \frac{A}{c}$$

$\nwarrow$ Known from making
up the solution

However, a more accurate value of the product ϵl can be obtained by plotting A versus c for a series of solutions. Note that the equation $A = \epsilon l c$ gives a straight line with slope ϵl when A is plotted against c.

For example, consider the following typical spectroscopic analysis. A sample of steel from a bicycle frame is to be analyzed to determine its manganese content. The procedure involves weighing out a sample of the steel, dissolving it in strong acid, treating the resulting solution with a very strong oxidizing agent to convert all the manganese to permanganate ion (MnO_4^-), and then using spectroscopy to determine the concentration of the intensely purple MnO_4^- ions in the solution. To do this, however, the value of ϵl for MnO_4^- must be determined at an appropriate wavelength. The absorbance values for four solutions with known MnO_4^- concentrations were measured to give the following data:

Solution	Concentration of MnO_4^- (mol/L)	Absorbance
1	7.00×10^{-5}	0.175
2	1.00×10^{-4}	0.250
3	2.00×10^{-4}	0.500
4	3.50×10^{-4}	0.875

A plot of absorbance versus concentration for the solutions of known concentration is shown in Fig. A3.2. The slope of this line (change in A/change in c) is 2.48×10^3 L/mol. This quantity represents the product ϵl.

A sample of the steel weighing 0.1523 g was dissolved, and the unknown amount of manganese was converted to MnO_4^- ions. Water was then added to give a solution with a final volume of 100.0 mL. A portion of this solution was placed in a spectrophotometer, and its absorbance was found to be 0.780. We can use these data to calculate the percent manganese in the steel. The MnO_4^- ions from the manganese in the dissolved steel sample show an absorbance of 0.780. Using the Beer-Lambert law, we calculate the concentration of MnO_4^- in this solution:

$$c = \frac{A}{\epsilon l} = \frac{0.780}{2.48 \times 10^3 \text{ L/mol}} = 3.15 \times 10^{-4} \text{ mol/L}$$

However, there is a more direct way for finding c. Using a graph such as that in Fig. A3.2 (often called a Beer's law plot), we can read the concentration that corresponds to $A = 0.780$. This interpolation is shown by dashed lines on

Figure A3.2
A plot of absorbance versus concentration of MnO_4^- in a series of solutions of known concentration.

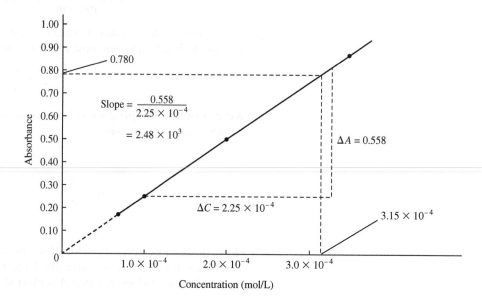

the graph. By this method, $c = 3.15 \times 10^{-4}$ mol/L, which agrees with the value obtained above.

Recall that the original 0.1523-g steel sample was dissolved, the manganese was converted to permanganate, and the volume was adjusted to 100.0 mL. We now know that the $[MnO_4^-]$ in that solution is 3.15×10^{-4} M. Using this concentration, we can calculate the total number of moles of MnO_4^- in that solution:

$$\text{Mol of } MnO_4^- = 100.0 \text{ mL} \times \frac{1 \text{ L}}{1000 \text{ mL}} \times 3.15 \times 10^{-4} \frac{\text{mol}}{\text{L}}$$

$$= 3.15 \times 10^{-5} \text{ mol}$$

Each mole of manganese in the original steel sample yields a mole of MnO_4^-. That is,

$$1 \text{ mol of Mn} \xrightarrow{\text{Oxidation}} 1 \text{ mol of } MnO_4^-$$

so the original steel sample must have contained 3.15×10^{-5} mol of manganese. The mass of manganese present in the sample is

$$3.15 \times 10^{-5} \text{ mol of Mn} \times \frac{54.938 \text{ g of Mn}}{1 \text{ mol of Mn}} = 1.73 \times 10^{-3} \text{ g of Mn}$$

Since the steel sample weighed 0.1523 g, the percent manganese in the steel is

$$\frac{1.73 \times 10^{-3} \text{ g of Mn}}{1.523 \times 10^{-1} \text{ g of sample}} \times 100\% = 1.14\%$$

This example illustrates a typical use of spectroscopy in quantitative analysis. The steps commonly involved are as follows:

1. Preparation of a calibration plot (a Beer's law plot) from the measured absorbance values of a series of solutions with known concentrations.

2. Measurement of the absorbance of the solution of unknown concentration.

3. Use of the calibration plot to determine the unknown concentration.

Appendix Four | Selected Thermodynamic Data*

Substance and State	ΔE_f° (kJ/mol)	ΔG_f° (kJ/mol)	S° (J K^{-1} mol^{-1})	Substance and State	ΔE_f° (kJ/mol)	ΔG_f° (kJ/mol)	S° (J K^{-1} mol^{-1})
Aluminum				**Bromine**			
Al(s)	0	0	28	Br$_2$(l)	0	0	152
Al$_2$O$_3$(s)	−1676	−1582	51	Br$_2$(g)	31	3	245
Al(OH)$_3$(s)	−1277	—	—	Br$_2$(aq)	−3	4	130
AlCl$_3$(s)	−704	−629	111	Br$^-$(aq)	−121	−104	82
Barium				HBr(g)	−36	−53	199
Ba(s)	0	0	67	**Cadmium**			
BaCO$_3$(s)	−1219	−1139	112	Cd(s)	0	0	52
BaO(s)	−582	−552	70	CdO(s)	−258	−228	55
Ba(OH)$_2$(s)	−946	—	—	Cd(OH)$_2$(s)	−561	−474	96
BaSO$_4$(s)	−1465	−1353	132	CdS(s)	−162	−156	65
Beryllium				CdSO$_4$(s)	−935	−823	123
Be(s)	0	0	10	**Calcium**			
BeO(s)	−599	−569	14	Ca(s)	0	0	41
Be(OH)$_2$(s)	−904	−815	47	CaC$_2$(s)	−63	−68	70

*All values are assumed precise to at least ±1.

(continued)

Appendix Four (continued)

Substance and State	ΔE_f° (kJ/mol)	ΔG_f° (kJ/mol)	S° (J K^{-1} mol^{-1})	Substance and State	ΔE_f° (kJ/mol)	ΔG_f° (kJ/mol)	S° (J K^{-1} mol^{-1})
$CaCO_3(s)$	-1207	-1129	93	$H_2O(l)$	-286	-237	70
$CaO(s)$	-635	-604	40	$H_2O(g)$	-242	-229	189
$Ca(OH)_2(s)$	-987	-899	83	Iodine			
$Ca_3(PO_4)_2(s)$	-4126	-3890	241	$I_2(s)$	0	0	116
$CaSO_4(s)$	-1433	-1320	107	$I_2(g)$	62	19	261
$CaSiO_3(s)$	-1630	-1550	84	$I_2(aq)$	23	16	137
Carbon				$I^-(aq)$	-55	-52	106
$C(s)$ (graphite)	0	0	6	Iron			
$C(s)$ (diamond)	2	3	2	$Fe(s)$	0	0	27
$CO(g)$	-110.5	-137	198	$Fe_3C(s)$	21	15	108
$CO_2(g)$	-393.5	-394	214	$Fe_{0.95}O(s)$			
$CH_4(g)$	-75	-51	186	(wustite)	-264	-240	59
$CH_3OH(g)$	-201	-163	240	$FeO(s)$	-272	-255	61
$CH_3OH(l)$	-239	-166	127	$Fe_3O_4(s)$			
$H_2CO(g)$	-116	-110	219	(magnetite)	-1117	-1013	146
$HCOOH(g)$	-363	-351	249	$Fe_2O_3(s)$			
$HCN(g)$	135.1	125	202	(hematite)	-826	-740	90
$C_2H_2(g)$	227	209	201	$FeS(s)$	-95	-97	67
$C_2H_4(g)$	52	68	219	$FeS_2(s)$	-178	-166	53
$CH_3CHO(g)$	-166	-129	250	$FeSO_4(s)$	-929	-825	121
$C_2H_5OH(l)$	-278	-175	161	Lead			
$C_2H_6(g)$	-84.7	-32.9	229.5	$Pb(s)$	0	0	65
$C_3H_6(g)$	20.9	62.7	266.9	$PbO_2(s)$	-277	-217	69
$C_3H_8(g)$	-104	-24	270	$PbS(s)$	-100	-99	91
$C_2H_4O(g)$				$PbSO_4(s)$	-920	-813	149
(ethylene oxide)	-53	-13	242	Magnesium			
$CH_2\text{ P }CHCN(g)$	185.0	195.4	274	$Mg(s)$	0	0	33
$CH_3COOH(l)$	-484	-389	160	$MgCO_3(s)$	-1113	-1029	66
$C_6H_{12}O_6(s)$	-1275	-911	212	$MgO(s)$	-602	-569	27
$CCl_4(l)$	-135	-65	216	$Mg(OH)_2(s)$	-925	-834	64
Chlorine				Manganese			
$Cl_2(g)$	0	0	223	$Mn(s)$	0	0	32
$Cl_2(aq)$	-23	7	121	$MnO(s)$	-385	-363	60
$Cl^-(aq)$	-167	-131	57	$Mn_3O_4(s)$	-1387	-1280	149
$HCl(g)$	-92	-95	187	$Mn_2O_3(s)$	-971	-893	110
Chromium				$MnO_2(s)$	-521	-466	53
$Cr(s)$	0	0	24	$MnO_4^-(aq)$	-543	-449	190
$Cr_2O_3(s)$	-1128	-1047	81	Mercury			
$CrO_3(s)$	-579	-502	72	$Hg(l)$	0	0	76
Copper				$Hg_2Cl_2(s)$	-265	-211	196
$Cu(s)$	0	0	33	$HgCl_2(s)$	-230	-184	144
$CuCO_3(s)$	-595	-518	88	$HgO(s)$	-90	-59	70
$Cu_2O(s)$	-170	-148	93	$HgS(s)$	-58	-49	78
$CuO(s)$	-156	-128	43	Nickel			
$Cu(OH)_2(s)$	-450	-372	108	$Ni(s)$	0	0	30
$CuS(s)$	-49	-49	67	$NiCl_2(s)$	-316	-272	107
Fluorine				$NiO(s)$	-241	-213	38
$F_2(g)$	0	0	203	$Ni(OH)_2(s)$	-538	-453	79
$F^-(aq)$	-333	-279	-14	$NiS(s)$	-93	-90	53
$HF(g)$	-271	-273	174	Nitrogen			
Hydrogen				$N_2(g)$	0	0	192
$H_2(g)$	0	0	131	$NH_3(g)$	-46	-17	193
$H(g)$	217	203	115	$NH_3(aq)$	-80	-27	111
$H^+(aq)$	0	0	0	$NH_4^+(aq)$	-132	-79	113
$OH^-(aq)$	-230	-157	-11	$NO(g)$	90	87	211

Appendix Four (continued)

Substance and State	ΔE_f° (kJ/mol)	ΔG_f° (kJ/mol)	S° (J K^{-1} mol^{-1})	Substance and State	ΔE_f° (kJ/mol)	ΔG_f° (kJ/mol)	S° (J K^{-1} mol^{-1})
$NO_2(g)$	34	52	240	$NaHCO_3(s)$	−948	−852	102
$N_2O(g)$	82	104	220	$NaCl(s)$	−411	−384	72
$N_2O_4(g)$	10	98	304	$NaH(s)$	−56	−33	40
$N_2O_4(l)$	−20	97	209	$NaI(s)$	−288	−282	91
$N_2O_5(s)$	−42	134	178	$NaNO_2(s)$	−359	—	—
$N_2H_4(l)$	51	149	121	$NaNO_3(s)$	−467	−366	116
$N_2H_3CH_3(l)$	54	180	166	$Na_2O(s)$	−416	−377	73
$HNO_3(aq)$	−207	−111	146	$Na_2O_2(s)$	−515	−451	95
$HNO_3(l)$	−174	−81	156	$NaOH(s)$	−427	−381	64
$NH_4ClO_4(s)$	−295	−89	186	$NaOH(aq)$	−470	−419	50
$NH_4Cl(s)$	−314	−203	96	Sulfur			
Oxygen				$S(s)$ (rhombic)	0	0	32
$O_2(g)$	0	0	205	$S(s)$ (monoclinic)	0.3	0.1	33
$O(g)$	249	232	161	$S^{2-}(aq)$	33	86	−15
$O_3(g)$	143	163	239	$S_8(g)$	102	50	431
Phosphorus				$SF_6(g)$	−1209	−1105	292
$P(s)$ (white)	0	0	41	$H_2S(g)$	−21	−34	206
$P(s)$ (red)	−18	−12	23	$SO_2(g)$	−297	−300	248
$P(s)$ (black)	−39	−33	23	$SO_3(g)$	−396	−371	257
$P_4(g)$	59	24	280	$SO_4^{2-}(aq)$	−909	−745	20
$PF_5(g)$	−1578	−1509	296	$H_2SO_4(l)$	−814	−690	157
$PH_3(g)$	5	13	210	$H_2SO_4(aq)$	−909	−745	20
$H_3PO_4(s)$	−1279	−1119	110	Tin			
$H_3PO_4(l)$	−1267	—	—	$Sn(s)$ (white)	0	0	52
$H_3PO_4(aq)$	−1288	−1143	158	$Sn(s)$ (gray)	−2	0.1	44
$P_4O_{10}(s)$	−2984	−2698	229	$SnO(s)$	−285	−257	56
Potassium				$SnO_2(s)$	−581	−520	52
$K(s)$	0	0	64	$Sn(OH)_2(s)$	−561	−492	155
$KCl(s)$	−436	−408	83	Titanium			
$KClO_3(s)$	−391	−290	143	$TiCl_4(g)$	−763	−727	355
$KClO_4(s)$	−433	−304	151	$TiO_2(s)$	−945	−890	50
$K_2O(s)$	−361	−322	98	Uranium			
$K_2O_2(s)$	−496	−430	113	$U(s)$	0	0	50
$KO_2(s)$	−283	−238	117	$UF_6(s)$	−2137	−2008	228
$KOH(s)$	−425	−379	79	$UF_6(g)$	−2113	−2029	380
$KOH(aq)$	−481	−440	9.20	$UO_2(s)$	−1084	−1029	78
Silicon				$U_3O_8(s)$	−3575	−3393	282
$SiO_2(s)$ (quartz)	−911	−856	42	$UO_3(s)$	−1230	−1150	99
$SiCl_4(l)$	−687	−620	240	Xenon			
Silver				$Xe(g)$	0	0	170
$Ag(s)$	0	0	43	$XeF_2(g)$	−108	−48	254
$Ag^+(aq)$	105	77	73	$XeF_4(s)$	−251	−121	146
$AgBr(s)$	−100	−97	107	$XeF_6(g)$	−294	—	—
$AgCN(s)$	146	164	84	$XeO_3(s)$	402	—	—
$AgCl(s)$	−127	−110	96	Zinc			
$Ag_2CrO_4(s)$	−712	−622	217	$Zn(s)$	0	0	42
$AgI(s)$	−62	−66	115	$ZnO(s)$	−348	−318	44
$Ag_2O(s)$	−31	−11	122	$Zn(OH)_2(s)$	−642	—	—
$Ag_2S(s)$	−32	−40	146	$ZnS(s)$			
Sodium				(wurtzite)	−193	—	—
$Na(s)$	0	0	51	$ZnS(s)$			
$Na^+(aq)$	−240	−262	59	(zinc blende)	−206	−201	58
$NaBr(s)$	−360	−347	84	$ZnSO_4(s)$	−983	−874	120
$Na_2CO_3(s)$	−1131	−1048	136				

Appendix Five | Equilibrium Constants and Reduction Potentials

Table A5.1

K_a for Some Common Monoprotic Acids

Name	Formula	Value of K_a
Hydrogen sulfate ion	HSO_4^-	1.2×10^{-2}
Chlorous acid	$HClO_2$	1.2×10^{-2}
Monochloracetic acid	$HC_2H_2ClO_2$	1.35×10^{-3}
Hydrofluoric acid	HF	7.2×10^{-4}
Nitrous acid	HNO_2	4.0×10^{-4}
Formic acid	HCO_2H	1.8×10^{-4}
Lactic acid	$HC_3H_5O_3$	1.38×10^{-4}
Benzoic acid	$HC_7H_5O_2$	6.4×10^{-5}
Acetic acid	$HC_2H_3O_2$	1.8×10^{-5}
Hydrated aluminum(III) ion	$[Al(H_2O)_6]^{3+}$	1.4×10^{-5}
Propanoic acid	$HC_3H_5O_2$	1.3×10^{-5}
Hypochlorous acid	$HOCl$	3.5×10^{-8}
Hypobromous acid	$HOBr$	2×10^{-9}
Hydrocyanic acid	HCN	6.2×10^{-10}
Boric acid	H_3BO_3	5.8×10^{-10}
Ammonium ion	NH_4^+	5.6×10^{-10}
Phenol	HOC_6H_5	1.6×10^{-10}
Hypoiodous acid	HOI	2×10^{-11}

Table A5.2

Stepwise Dissociation Constants for Several Common Polyprotic Acids

Name	Formula	K_{a_1}	K_{a_2}	K_{a_3}
Phosphoric acid	H_3PO_4	7.5×10^{-3}	6.2×10^{-8}	4.8×10^{-13}
Arsenic acid	H_3AsO_4	5×10^{-3}	8×10^{-8}	6×10^{-10}
Carbonic acid	H_2CO_3	4.3×10^{-7}	4.8×10^{-11}	
Sulfuric acid	H_2SO_4	Large	1.2×10^{-2}	
Sulfurous acid	H_2SO_3	1.5×10^{-2}	1.0×10^{-7}	
Hydrosulfuric acid	H_2S	1.0×10^{-7}	$\sim 10^{-19}$	
Oxalic acid	$H_2C_2O_4$	6.5×10^{-2}	6.1×10^{-5}	
Ascorbic acid (vitamin C)	$H_2C_6H_6O_6$	7.9×10^{-5}	1.6×10^{-12}	
Citric acid	$H_3C_6H_5O_7$	8.4×10^{-4}	1.8×10^{-5}	4.0×10^{-6}

Table A5.3

K_b for Some Common Weak Bases

Name	Formula	Conjugate Acid	K_b
Ammonia	NH_3	NH_4^+	1.8×10^{-5}
Methylamine	CH_3NH_2	$CH_3NH_3^+$	4.38×10^{-4}
Ethylamine	$C_2H_5NH_2$	$C_2H_5NH_3^+$	5.6×10^{-4}
Diethylamine	$(C_2H_5)_2NH$	$(C_2H_5)_2NH_2^+$	1.3×10^{-3}
Triethylamine	$(C_2H_5)_3N$	$(C_2H_5)_3NH^+$	4.0×10^{-4}
Hydroxylamine	$HONH_2$	$HONH_3^+$	1.1×10^{-8}
Hydrazine	H_2NNH_2	$H_2NNH_3^+$	3.0×10^{-6}
Aniline	$C_6H_5NH_2$	$C_6H_5NH_3^+$	3.8×10^{-10}
Pyridine	C_5H_5N	$C_5H_5NH^+$	1.7×10^{-9}

Table A5.4

Values of K_{sp} at 25°C for Common Ionic Solids

Ionic Solid	K_{sp} (at 25°C)	Ionic Solid	K_{sp} (at 25°C)	Ionic Solid	K_{sp} (at 25°C)
Fluorides		**Chromates** (*continued*)		**Hydroxides** (*continued*)	
BaF_2	2.4×10^{-5}	Hg_2CrO_4*	2×10^{-9}	$Co(OH)_3$	2.5×10^{-16}
MgF_2	6.4×10^{-9}	$BaCrO_4$	8.5×10^{-11}	$Ni(OH)_2$	1.6×10^{-16}
PbF_2	4×10^{-8}	Ag_2CrO_4	9.0×10^{-12}	$Zn(OH)_2$	4.5×10^{-17}
SrF_2	7.9×10^{-10}	$PbCrO_4$	2×10^{-16}	$Cu(OH)_2$	1.6×10^{-19}
CaF_2	4.0×10^{-11}			$Hg(OH)_2$	3×10^{-26}
		Carbonates		$Sn(OH)_2$	3×10^{-27}
Chlorides		$NiCO_3$	1.4×10^{-7}	$Cr(OH)_3$	6.7×10^{-31}
$PbCl_2$	1.6×10^{-5}	$CaCO_3$	8.7×10^{-9}	$Al(OH)_3$	2×10^{-32}
$AgCl$	1.6×10^{-10}	$BaCO_3$	1.6×10^{-9}	$Fe(OH)_3$	4×10^{-38}
Hg_2Cl_2*	1.1×10^{-18}	$SrCO_3$	7×10^{-10}	$Co(OH)_3$	2.5×10^{-43}
		$CuCO_3$	2.5×10^{-10}		
Bromides		$ZnCO_3$	2×10^{-10}	**Sulfides**	
$PbBr_2$	4.6×10^{-6}	$MnCO_3$	8.8×10^{-11}	MnS	2.3×10^{-13}
$AgBr$	5.0×10^{-13}	$FeCO_3$	2.1×10^{-11}	FeS	3.7×10^{-19}
Hg_2Br_2*	1.3×10^{-22}	Ag_2CO_3	8.1×10^{-12}	NiS	3×10^{-21}
		$CdCO_3$	5.2×10^{-12}	CoS	5×10^{-22}
Iodides		$PbCO_3$	1.5×10^{-15}	ZnS	2.5×10^{-22}
PbI_2	1.4×10^{-8}	$MgCO_3$	1×10^{-15}	SnS	1×10^{-26}
AgI	1.5×10^{-16}	Hg_2CO_3*	9.0×10^{-15}	CdS	1.0×10^{-28}
Hg_2I_2*	4.5×10^{-29}			PbS	7×10^{-29}
		Hydroxides		CuS	8.5×10^{-45}
Sulfates		$Ba(OH)_2$	5.0×10^{-3}	Ag_2S	1.6×10^{-49}
$CaSO_4$	6.1×10^{-5}	$Sr(OH)_2$	3.2×10^{-4}	HgS	1.6×10^{-54}
Ag_2SO_4	1.2×10^{-5}	$Ca(OH)_2$	1.3×10^{-6}		
$SrSO_4$	3.2×10^{-7}	$AgOH$	2.0×10^{-8}	**Phosphates**	
$PbSO_4$	1.3×10^{-8}	$Mg(OH)_2$	8.9×10^{-12}	Ag_3PO_4	1.8×10^{-18}
$BaSO_4$	1.5×10^{-9}	$Mn(OH)_2$	2×10^{-13}	$Sr_3(PO_4)_2$	1×10^{-31}
		$Cd(OH)_2$	5.9×10^{-15}	$Ca_3(PO_4)_2$	1.3×10^{-32}
Chromates		$Pb(OH)_2$	1.2×10^{-15}	$Ba_3(PO_4)_2$	6×10^{-39}
$SrCrO_4$	3.6×10^{-5}	$Fe(OH)_2$	1.8×10^{-15}	$Pb_3(PO_4)_2$	1×10^{-54}

*Contains Hg_2^{2+} ions. $K_{sp} = [Hg_2^{2+}][X^-]^2$ for Hg_2X_2 salts.

Table A5.5

Standard Reduction Potentials at 25°C (298 K) for Many Common Half-Reactions

Half-Reaction	$\mathscr{E}°$ (V)	Half-Reaction	$\mathscr{E}°$ (V)
$F_2 + 2e^- \longrightarrow 2F^-$	2.87	$O_2 + 2H_2O + 4e^- \longrightarrow 4OH^-$	0.40
$Ag^{2+} + e^- \longrightarrow Ag^+$	1.99	$Cu^{2+} + 2e^- \longrightarrow Cu$	0.34
$Co^{3+} + e^- \longrightarrow Co^{2+}$	1.82	$Hg_2Cl_2 + 2e^- \longrightarrow 2Hg + 2Cl^-$	0.27
$H_2O_2 + 2H^+ + 2e^- \longrightarrow 2H_2O$	1.78	$AgCl + e^- \longrightarrow Ag + Cl^-$	0.22
$Ce^{4+} + e^- \longrightarrow Ce^{3+}$	1.70	$SO_4^{2-} + 4H^+ + 2e^- \longrightarrow H_2SO_3 + H_2O$	0.20
$PbO_2 + 4H^+ + SO_4^{2-} + 2e^- \longrightarrow PbSO_4 + 2H_2O$	1.69	$Cu^{2+} + e^- \longrightarrow Cu^+$	0.16
$MnO_4^+ + 4H^+ + 3e^- \longrightarrow MnO_2 + 2H_2O$	1.68	$2H^+ + 2e^- \longrightarrow H_2$	0.00
$IO_4^- + 2H^+ + 2e^- \longrightarrow IO_3^- + H_2O$	1.60	$Fe^{3+} + 3e^- \longrightarrow Fe$	−0.036
$MnO_4^+ + 8H^+ + 5e^- \longrightarrow Mn^{2+} + 4H_2O$	1.51	$Pb^{2+} + 2e^- \longrightarrow Pb$	−0.13
$Au^{3+} + 3e^- \longrightarrow Au$	1.50	$Sn^{2+} + 2e^- \longrightarrow Sn$	−0.14
$PbO_2 + 4H^+ + 2e^- \longrightarrow Pb^{2+} + 2H_2O$	1.46	$Ni^{2+} + 2e^- \longrightarrow Ni$	−0.23
$Cl_2 + 2e^- \longrightarrow 2Cl^-$	1.36	$PbSO_4 + 2e^- \longrightarrow Pb + SO_4^{2-}$	−0.35
$Cr_2O_7^{2-} + 14H^+ + 6e^- \longrightarrow 2Cr^{3+} + 7H_2O$	1.33	$Cd^{2+} + 2e^- \longrightarrow Cd$	−0.40
$O_2 + 4H^+ + 4e^- \longrightarrow 2H_2O$	1.23	$Fe^{2+} + 2e^- \longrightarrow Fe$	−0.44
$MnO_2 + 4H^+ + 2e^- \longrightarrow Mn^{2+} + 2H_2O$	1.21	$Cr^{3+} + e^- \longrightarrow Cr^{2+}$	−0.50
$IO_3^- + 6H^+ + 5e^- \longrightarrow \frac{1}{2}I_2 + 3H_2O$	1.20	$Cr^{3+} + 3e^- \longrightarrow Cr$	−0.73
$Br_2 + 2e^- \longrightarrow 2Br^-$	1.09	$Zn^{2+} + 2e^- \longrightarrow Zn$	−0.76
$VO_2^+ + 2H^+ + e^- \longrightarrow VO^{2+} + H_2O$	1.00	$2H_2O + 2e^- \longrightarrow H_2 + 2OH^-$	−0.83
$AuCl_4^- + 3e^- \longrightarrow Au + 4Cl^-$	0.99	$Mn^{2+} + 2e^- \longrightarrow Mn$	−1.18
$NO_3^- + 4H^+ + 3e^- \longrightarrow NO + 2H_2O$	0.96	$Al^{3+} + 3e^- \longrightarrow Al$	−1.66
$ClO_2 + e^- \longrightarrow ClO_2^-$	0.954	$H_2 + 2e^- \longrightarrow 2H^-$	−2.23
$2Hg^{2+} + 2e^- \longrightarrow Hg_2^{2+}$	0.91	$Mg^{2+} + 2e^- \longrightarrow Mg$	−2.37
$Ag^+ + e^- \longrightarrow Ag$	0.80	$La^{3+} + 3e^- \longrightarrow La$	−2.37
$Hg_2^{2+} + 2e^- \longrightarrow 2Hg$	0.80	$Na^+ + e^- \longrightarrow Na$	−2.71
$Fe^{3+} + e^- \longrightarrow Fe^{2+}$	0.77	$Ca^{2+} + 2e^- \longrightarrow Ca$	−2.76
$O_2 + 2H^+ + 2e^- \longrightarrow H_2O_2$	0.68	$Ba^{2+} + 2e^- \longrightarrow Ba$	−2.90
$MnO_4^- + e^- \longrightarrow MnO_4^{2-}$	0.56	$K^+ + e^- \longrightarrow K$	−2.92
$I_2 + 2e^- \longrightarrow 2I^-$	0.54	$Li^+ + e^- \longrightarrow Li$	−3.05
$Cu^+ + e^- \longrightarrow Cu$	0.52		

Glossary

Note to the Student: The Glossary includes brief definitions of some of the fundamental terms used in chemistry. It does not include complex concepts that require detailed explanation for understanding. Please refer to the appropriate sections of the text for complete discussion of particular topics or concepts.

Accuracy: the agreement of a particular value with the true value. (A1.5)

Acid: a substance that produces hydrogen ions in solution; a proton donor. (4.2)

Acid–base indicator: a substance that marks the endpoint of an acid–base titration by changing color. (8.6)

Acid dissociation constant (K_a): the equilibrium constant for a reaction in which a proton is removed from an acid by H_2O to form the conjugate base and H_3O^+. (7.1)

Acid rain: a result of air pollution by sulfur dioxide. (5.11)

Actinide series: a group of 14 elements following actinium in the periodic table, in which the $5f$ orbitals are being filled. (12.13; 18.1)

Activated complex (transition state): the arrangement of atoms found at the top of the potential energy barrier as a reaction proceeds from reactants to products. (15.8)

Activation energy: the threshold energy that must be overcome to produce a chemical reaction. (15.8)

Addition polymerization: a type of polymerization in which the monomers simply add together to form the polymer, with no other products. (21.5)

Addition reaction: a reaction in which atoms add to a carbon–carbon multiple bond. (21.2)

Adiabatic process: a process that occurs without the transfer of energy as heat. (10.14)

Adsorption: the collection of one substance on the surface of another. (15.9)

Air pollution: contamination of the atmosphere, mainly by the gaseous products of transportation and production of electricity. (5.11)

Alcohol: an organic compound in which the hydroxyl group is a substituent on a hydrocarbon. (21.4)

Aldehyde: an organic compound containing the carbonyl group bonded to at least one hydrogen atom. (21.4)

Alkali metal: a Group 1A metal. (2.8; 18.2)

Alkaline earth metal: a Group 2A metal. (2.8; 18.4)

Alkane: a saturated hydrocarbon with the general formula C_nH_{2n+2}. (21.1)

Alkene: an unsaturated hydrocarbon containing a carbon–carbon double bond. The general formula is C_nH_{2n}. (21.2)

Alkyne: an unsaturated hydrocarbon containing a triple carbon–carbon bond. The general formula is C_nH_{2n-2}. (21.2)

Alloy: a substance that contains a mixture of elements and has metallic properties. (16.4)

Alloy steel: a form of steel containing carbon plus other metals such as chromium, cobalt, manganese, and molybdenum. (19.2)

Alpha (α) particle: a helium nucleus. (20.1)

Alpha-particle production: a common mode of decay for radioactive nuclides in which the mass number changes. (20.1)

Amine: an organic base derived from ammonia in which one or more of the hydrogen atoms are replaced by organic groups. (7.6; 21.4)

α-Amino acid: an organic acid in which an amino group and an R group are attached to the carbon atom next to the carboxyl group. (21.6)

Amorphous solid: a solid with considerable disorder in its structure. (16.3)

Ampere: the unit of electric current equal to one coulomb of charge per second. (11.7)

Amphoteric substance: a substance that can behave either as an acid or as a base. (7.2)

Angular momentum quantum number (ℓ): the quantum number relating to the shape of an atomic orbital, which can assume any integral value from 0 to $n - 1$ for each value of n. (12.9)

Anion: a negative ion. (2.7)

Anode: the electrode in a galvanic cell at which oxidation occurs. (11.1)

Antibonding molecular orbital: an orbital higher in energy than the atomic orbitals of which it is composed. (14.2)

Aqueous solution: a solution in which water is the dissolving medium or solvent. (4)

Aromatic hydrocarbon: one of a special class of cyclic unsaturated hydrocarbons, the simplest of which is benzene. (21.3)

Arrhenius concept: a concept postulating that acids produce hydrogen ions in aqueous solution, whereas bases produce hydroxide ions. (7.1)

Arrhenius equation: the equation representing the rate constant as $k = Ae^{-E_a/RT}$ where A represents the product of the collision frequency and the steric factor, and $e^{-E_a/RT}$ is the fraction of collisions with sufficient energy to produce a reaction. (15.8)

Atmosphere: the mixture of gases that surrounds the earth's surface. (5.11)

Atomic mass (average): the weighted average mass of the atoms in a naturally occurring element. (2.3)

Atomic number: the number of protons in the nucleus of an atom. (2.6)

Atomic radius: half the distance between the nuclei in a molecule consisting of identical atoms. (12.15)

Atomic solid: a solid that contains atoms at the lattice points. (16.3)

Aufbau principle: the principle stating that as protons are added one by one to the nucleus to build up the elements, electrons are similarly added to hydrogenlike orbitals. (12.13)

Autoionization: the transfer of a proton from one molecule to another of the same substance. (7.2)

Avogadro's law: equal volumes of gases at the same temperature and pressure contain the same number of particles. (5.2)

Avogadro's number: the number of atoms in exactly 12 grams of pure ^{12}C, equal to 6.022×10^{23}. (3.2)

Ball-and-stick model: a molecular model that distorts the sizes of atoms, but shows bond relationships clearly. (2.7)

Band model: a molecular model for metals in which the electrons are assumed to travel around the metal crystal in molecular orbitals formed from the valence atomic orbitals of the metal atoms. (16.4)

Barometer: a device for measuring atmospheric pressure. (5.1)

Base: a substance that produces hydroxide ions in aqueous solution, a proton acceptor. (7.2)

Base dissociation constant (K_b): the equilibrium constant for the reaction of a base with water to produce the conjugate acid and hydroxide ion. (7.6)

Basic oxide: an ionic oxide that dissolves in water to produce a basic solution. (18.4)

Battery: a group of galvanic cells connected in series. (11.5)

Beta (β) particle: an electron produced in radioactive decay. (20.1)

Beta-particle production: a decay process for radioactive nuclides in which the mass number remains constant and the atomic number changes. The net effect is to change a neutron to a proton. (20.1)

Bidentate ligand: a ligand that can form two bonds to a metal ion. (19.3)

Bimolecular step: a reaction involving the collision of two molecules. (15.6)

Binary compound: a two-element compound. (2.9)

Binding energy (nuclear): the energy required to decompose a nucleus into its component nucleons. (20.5)

Biomolecule: a molecule responsible for maintaining and/or reproducing life. (22)

Bond energy: the energy required to break a given chemical bond. (13.1)

Bond length: the distance between the nuclei of the two atoms connected by a bond; the distance where the total energy of a diatomic molecule is minimal. (13.1)

Bond order: the difference between the number of bonding electrons and the number of antibonding electrons, divided by two. It is an index of bond strength. (14.2)

Bonding molecular orbital: an orbital lower in energy than the atomic orbitals of which it is composed. (14.2)

Bonding pair: an electron pair found in the space between two atoms. (13.9)

Borane: a covalent hydride of boron. (18.5)

Boyle's law: the volume of a given sample of gas at constant temperature varies inversely with the pressure. (5.2)

Breeder reactor: a nuclear reactor in which fissionable fuel is produced while the reactor runs. (20.6)

Brønsted–Lowry definition (model): a model proposing that an acid is a proton donor, and a base is a proton acceptor. (7.1)

Buffer capacity: the ability of a buffered solution to absorb protons or hydroxide ions without a significant change in pH; determined by the magnitudes of [HA] and [A$^-$] in the solution. (8.4)

Buffered solution: a solution that resists a change in its pH when either hydroxide ions or protons are added. (8.2)

Calorimetry: the science of measuring heat flow. (9.4)

Capillary action: the spontaneous rising of a liquid in a narrow tube. (16.2)

Carbohydrate: a polyhydroxyl ketone or polyhydroxyl aldehyde or a polymer composed of these. (21.6)

Carboxyhemoglobin: a stable complex of hemoglobin and carbon monoxide that prevents normal oxygen uptake in the blood. (19.8)

Carboxyl group: the —COOH group in an organic acid. (7.2; 21.4)

Carboxylic acid: an organic compound containing the carboxyl group; an acid with the general formula RCOOH. (21.4)

Catalyst: a substance that speeds up a reaction without being consumed. (15.9)

Cathode: the electrode in a galvanic cell at which reduction occurs. (11.1)

Cathode rays: the "rays" emanating from the negative electrode (cathode) in a partially evacuated tube; a stream of electrons. (2.5)

Cathodic protection: a method in which an active metal, such as magnesium, is connected to steel to protect it from corrosion. (11.6)

Cation: a positive ion. (2.7)

Cell potential (electromotive force): the driving force in a galvanic cell that pulls electrons from the reducing agent in one compartment to the oxidizing agent in the other. (11.1)

Ceramic: a nonmetallic material made from clay and hardened by firing at high temperature; it contains minute silicate crystals suspended in a glassy cement. (16.5)

Chain reaction (nuclear): a self-sustaining fission process caused by the production of neutrons that proceed to split other nuclei. (20.6)

Charge balance: the positive and negative charges carried by the ions in an aqueous solution must balance. (7.9)

Charles's law: the volume of a given sample of gas at constant pressure is directly proportional to the temperature in kelvins. (5.2)

Chelating ligand (chelate): a ligand having more than one atom with a lone pair that can be used to bond to a metal ion. (19.3)

Chemical bond: the energy that holds two atoms together in a compound. (2.7)

Chemical equation: a representation of a chemical reaction showing the relative numbers of reactant and product molecules. (3.6)

Chemical equilibrium: a dynamic reaction system in which the concentrations of all reactants and products remain constant as a function of time. (6)

Chemical formula: the representation of a molecule in which the symbols for the elements are used to indicate the types of atoms present and subscripts are used to show the relative numbers of atoms. (2.7)

Chemical kinetics: the area of chemistry that concerns reaction rates. (15)

Chemical stoichiometry: the calculation of the quantities of material consumed and produced in chemical reactions. (3)

Chirality: the quality of having nonsuperimposable mirror images. (19.4)

Chlor-alkali process: the process for producing chlorine and sodium hydroxide by electrolyzing brine in a mercury cell. (11.8)

Coagulation: the destruction of a colloid by causing particles to aggregate and settle out. (17.8)

Codons: organic bases in sets of three that form the genetic code. (21.6)

Colligative properties: properties of a solution that depend on the number, and not on the identity, of the solute particles. (17.5)

Collision model: a model based on the idea that molecules must collide to react; used to account for the observed characteristics of reaction rates. (15.8)

Colloid: a suspension of particles in a dispersing medium. (17.8)

Combustion reaction: the vigorous and exothermic reaction that takes place between certain substances, particularly organic compounds, and oxygen. (21.1)

Common ion effect: the shift in an equilibrium position caused by the addition or presence of an ion involved in the equilibrium reaction. (8.1)

Complete ionic equation: an equation that shows all substances that are strong electrolytes as ions. (4.6)

Complex ion: a charged species consisting of a metal ion surrounded by ligands. (8.9; 19.1)

Compound: a substance with constant composition that can be broken down into elements by chemical processes. (2.7)

Concentration cell: a galvanic cell in which both compartments contain the same components, but at different concentrations. (11.4)

Condensation: the process by which vapor molecules re-form a liquid. (16.10)

Condensation polymerization: a type of polymerization in which the formation of a small molecule, such as water, accompanies the extension of the polymer chain. (21.5)

Condensed states of matter: liquids and solids. (16.1)

Conduction bands: the molecular orbitals that can be occupied by mobile electrons, which are free to travel throughout a metal crystal to conduct electricity or heat. (16.4)

Conjugate acid: the species formed when a proton is added to a base. (7.1)

Conjugate acid–base pair: two species related to each other by the donating and accepting of a single proton. (7.1)

Conjugate base: what remains of an acid molecule after a proton is lost. (7.1)

Continuous spectrum: a spectrum that exhibits all the wavelengths of visible light. (12.3)

Control rods: rods in a nuclear reactor composed of substances that absorb neutrons. These rods regulate the power level of the reactor. (20.6)

Coordinate covalent bond: a metal–ligand bond resulting from the interaction of a Lewis base (the ligand) and a Lewis acid (the metal ion). (19.3)

Coordination compound: a compound composed of a complex ion and counter ions sufficient to give no net charge. (19.3)

Coordination isomerism: isomerism in a coordination compound in which the composition of the coordination sphere of the metal ion varies. (19.4)

Coordination number: the number of bonds formed between the metal ion and the ligands in a complex ion. (19.3)

Copolymer: a polymer formed from the polymerization of more than one type of monomer. (21.5)

Core electron: an inner electron in an atom; one not in the outermost (valence) principal quantum level. (12.13)

Corrosion: the process by which metals are oxidized in the atmosphere. (11.6)

Coulomb's law: $E = 2.31 \times 10^{-19} (Q_1 Q_2 / r)$, where E is the energy of interaction between a pair of ions, expressed in joules; r is the distance between the ion centers in nm; and Q_1 and Q_2 are the numerical ion charges. (13.1)

Counter ions: anions or cations that balance the charge on the complex ion in a coordination compound. (19.3)

Covalent bonding: a type of bonding in which electrons are shared by atoms. (2.7; 13.1)

Critical mass: the mass of fissionable material required to produce a self-sustaining chain reaction. (20.6)

Critical point: the point on a phase diagram at which the temperature and pressure have their critical values; the endpoint of the liquid–vapor line. (16.11)

Critical pressure: the minimum pressure required to produce liquefaction of a substance at the critical temperature. (16.11)

Critical reaction (nuclear): a reaction in which exactly one neutron from each fission event causes another fission event, thus sustaining the chain reaction. (20.6)

Critical temperature: the temperature above which vapor cannot be liquefied, no matter what pressure is applied. (16.11)

Crosslinking: the existence of bonds between adjacent chains in a polymer, thus adding strength to the material. (21.5)

Crystal field model: a model used to explain the magnetism and colors of coordination complexes through the splitting of the d orbital energies. (19.6)

Crystalline solid: a solid with a regular arrangement of its components. (16.3)

Cubic closest packed (ccp) structure: a solid modeled by the closest packing of spheres with an *abcabc* arrangement of layers; the unit cell is face-centered cubic. (16.4)

Cyclotron: a type of particle accelerator in which an ion introduced at the center is accelerated in an expanding spiral path by use of alternating electric fields in the presence of a magnetic field. (20.3)

Cytochromes: a series of iron-containing species composed of heme and a protein. Cytochromes are the principal electron-transfer molecules in the respiratory chain. (19.8)

Dalton's law of partial pressures: for a mixture of gases in a container, the total pressure exerted is the sum of the pressures that each gas would exert if it were alone. (5.5)

Degenerate orbitals: a group of orbitals with the same energy. (12.9)

Dehydrogenation reaction: a reaction in which two hydrogen atoms are removed from adjacent carbons of a saturated hydrocarbon, giving an unsaturated hydrocarbon. (21.1)

Delocalization: the condition where the electrons in a molecule are not localized between a pair of atoms but can move throughout the molecule. (13.9)

Denaturation: the breaking down of the three-dimensional structure of a protein resulting in the loss of its function. (21.6)

Denitrification: the return of nitrogen from decomposed matter to the atmosphere by bacteria that change nitrates to nitrogen gas. (18.8)

Deoxyribonucleic acid (DNA): a huge nucleotide polymer having a double-helical structure with complementary bases on the two strands. Its major functions are protein synthesis and the storage and transport of genetic information. (21.6)

Desalination: the removal of dissolved salts from an aqueous solution. (17.6)

Dialysis: a phenomenon in which a semipermeable membrane allows transfer of both solvent molecules and small solute molecules and ions. (17.6)

Diamagnetism: a type of magnetism, associated with paired electrons, that causes a substance to be repelled from the inducing magnetic field. (14.3)

Differential rate law: an expression that gives the rate of a reaction as a function of concentrations; often called the rate law. (15.2)

Diffraction: the scattering of light from a regular array of points or lines, producing constructive and destructive interference. (12.2)

Diffusion: the mixture of gases. (5.7)

Dilution: the process of adding solvent to lower the concentration of solute in a solution. (4.3)

Dimer: a molecule formed by the joining of two identical monomers. (21.5)

Dipole–dipole attraction: the attractive force resulting when polar molecules line up so that the positive and negative ends are close to each other. (16.1)

Dipole moment: a property of a molecule whose charge distribution can be represented by a center of positive charge and a center of negative charge. (13.3)

Disaccharide: a sugar formed from two monosaccharides joined by a glycoside linkage. (21.6)

Disproportionation reaction: a reaction in which a given element is both oxidized and reduced. (18.13)

Disulfide linkage: a S—S bond that stabilizes the tertiary structure of many proteins. (21.6)

Double bond: a bond in which two pairs of electrons are shared by two atoms. (13.8)

Downs cell: a cell used for electrolyzing molten sodium chloride. (11.8)

Dry cell battery: a common battery used in calculators, watches, radios, and portable audio players. (11.5)

Dual nature of light: the statement that light exhibits both wave and particulate properties. (12.2)

$E = mc^2$**:** Einstein's equation proposing that energy has mass; E is energy, m is mass, and c is the speed of light. (12.2)

Effective nuclear charge: the apparent nuclear charge exerted on a particular electron, equal to the actual nuclear charge minus the effect of electron repulsions. (12.11)

Effusion: the passage of a gas through a tiny orifice into an evacuated chamber. (5.7)

Electrical conductivity: the ability to conduct an electric current. (4.2)

Electrochemistry: the study of the interchange of chemical and electrical energy. (11)

Electrolysis: a process that involves forcing a current through a cell to cause a nonspontaneous chemical reaction to occur. (11.7)

Electrolyte: a material that dissolves in water to give a solution that conducts an electric current. (4.2)

Electrolytic cell: a cell that uses electrical energy to produce a chemical change that would otherwise not occur spontaneously. (11.7)

Electromagnetic radiation: radiant energy that exhibits wavelike behavior and travels through space at the speed of light in a vacuum. (12.1)

Electron: a negatively charged particle that moves around the nucleus of an atom. (2.5)

Electron affinity: the energy change associated with the addition of an electron to a gaseous atom. (12.15)

Electron capture: a process in which one of the inner-orbital electrons in an atom is captured by the nucleus. (20.1)

Electron sea model: a model for metals postulating a regular array of cations in a "sea" of electrons. (16.4)

Electron spin quantum number: a quantum number representing one of the two possible values for the electron spin; either $+\frac{1}{2}$ or $-\frac{1}{2}$. (12.10)

Electronegativity: the tendency of an atom in a molecule to attract shared electrons to itself. (13.2)

Element: a substance that cannot be decomposed into simpler substances by chemical or physical means. (2.1)

Elementary step: a reaction whose rate law can be written from its molecularity. (15.6)

Empirical formula: the simplest whole number ratio of atoms in a compound. (3.5)

Enantiomers: isomers that are nonsuperimposable mirror images of each other. (19.4)

Endpoint: the point in a titration at which the indicator changes color. (4.9)

Endothermic: refers to a reaction where energy (as heat) flows into the system. (9.1)

Energy: the capacity to do work or to cause heat flow. (9.1)

Energy: a property of a system equal to $E + PV$, where E is the internal energy of the system, P is the pressure of the system, and V is the volume of the system. At constant pressure, where only PV work is allowed, the change in energy equals the energy flow as heat. (9.2)

Energy of fusion: the energy change that occurs to melt a solid at its melting point. (16.10)

Entropy: a thermodynamic function that measures randomness or disorder. (10.1)

Enzyme: a large molecule, usually a protein, that catalyzes biological reactions. (15.9)

Equilibrium (thermodynamic definition): the position where the free energy of a reaction system has its lowest possible value. (10.11)

Equilibrium constant: the value obtained when equilibrium concentrations of the chemical species are substituted in the equilibrium expression. (6.2)

Equilibrium expression: the expression (from the law of mass action) obtained by multiplying the product concentrations and dividing by the multiplied reactant concentrations, with each concentration raised to a power represented by the coefficient in the balanced equation. (6.2)

Equilibrium position: a particular set of equilibrium concentrations. (6.2)

Equivalence point (stoichiometric point): the point in a titration when enough titrant has been added to react exactly with the substance in solution being titrated. (4.9; 8.4)

Exothermic: refers to a reaction where energy (as heat) flows out of the system. (9.1)

Exponential notation: expresses a number as $N \times 10^M$, a convenient method for representing a very large or very small number and for easily indicating the number of significant figures. (A1.1)

Faraday: a constant representing the charge on one mole of electrons; 96,485 coulombs. (11.3)

First law of thermodynamics: the energy of the universe is constant; same as the law of conservation of energy. (9.1)

Fission: the process of using a neutron to split a heavy nucleus into two nuclei with smaller mass numbers. (20.6)

Formal charge: the charge assigned to an atom in a molecule or polyatomic ion derived from a specific set of rules. (13.12)

Formation constant (stability constant): the equilibrium constant for each step of the formation of a complex ion by the addition of an individual ligand to a metal ion or complex ion in aqueous solution. (8.9)

Fossil fuel: coal, petroleum, or natural gas; consists of carbon-based molecules derived from decomposition of once-living organisms. (9.7)

Frasch process: the recovery of sulfur from underground deposits by melting it with hot water and forcing it to the surface by air pressure. (18.12)

Free energy: a thermodynamic function equal to the energy (H) minus the product of the entropy (S) and the kelvin temperature (T); $G = H - TS$. Under certain conditions the change in free energy for a process is equal to the maximum useful work. (10.7)

Free radical: a species with an unpaired electron. (21.5)

Frequency: the number of waves (cycles) per second that pass a given point in space. (12.1)

Fuel cell: a galvanic cell for which the reactants are continuously supplied. (11.5)

Functional group: an atom or group of atoms in hydrocarbon derivatives that contains elements in addition to carbon and hydrogen. (21.4)

Fusion: the process of combining two light nuclei to form a heavier, more stable nucleus. (20.6)

Galvanic cell: a device in which chemical energy from a spontaneous redox reaction is changed to electrical energy that can be used to do work. (11.1)

Galvanizing: a process in which steel is coated with zinc to prevent corrosion. (11.6)

Gamma (γ) ray: a high-energy photon. (20.1)

Geiger-Müller counter (Geiger counter): an instrument that measures the rate of radioactive decay based on the ions and electrons produced as a radioactive particle passes through a gas-filled chamber. (20.4)

Gene: a given segment of the DNA molecule that contains the code for a specific protein. (21.6)

Geometrical (*cis-trans*) isomerism: isomerism in which atoms or groups of atoms can assume different positions around a rigid ring or bond. (19.4; 21.2)

Glass: an amorphous solid obtained when silica is mixed with other compounds, heated above its melting point, and then cooled rapidly. (16.5)

Glass electrode: an electrode for measuring pH from the potential difference that develops when it is dipped into an aqueous solution containing H^+ ions. (11.4)

Glycosidic linkage: a C—O—C bond formed between the rings of two cyclic monosaccharides by the elimination of water. (21.6)

Graham's law of effusion: the rate of effusion of a gas is inversely proportional to the square root of the mass of its particles. (5.7)

Gravimetric analysis: a method for determining the amount of a given substance in a solution by precipitation, filtration, drying, and weighing. (4.8)

Greenhouse effect: a warming effect exerted by the earth's atmosphere (particularly CO_2 and H_2O) due to thermal energy retained by absorption of infrared radiation. (9.7)

Ground state: the lowest possible energy state of an atom or molecule. (12.4)

Group (of the periodic table): a vertical column of elements having the same valence electron configuration and showing similar properties. (2.8)

Haber process: the manufacture of ammonia from nitrogen and hydrogen, carried out at high pressure and high temperature with the aid of a catalyst. (3.9; 6.1; 18.8)

Half-life (of a radioactive sample): the time required for the number of nuclides in a radioactive sample to reach half of the original value. (20.2)

Half-life (of a reaction): the time required for a reactant to reach half of its original concentration. (15.4)

Half-reactions: the two parts of an oxidation–reduction reaction, one representing oxidation, the other reduction. (4.11; 11.1)

Halogen: a Group 7A element. (2.8; 18.13)

Halogenation: the addition of halogen atoms to unsaturated hydrocarbons. (21.2)

Hard water: water from natural sources that contains relatively large concentrations of calcium and magnesium ions. (18.4)

Heat: energy transferred between two objects caused by a temperature difference between them. (9.1)

Heat capacity: the amount of energy required to raise the temperature of an object by one degree Celsius. (9.4)

Heat of fusion: the energy change that occurs to melt a solid at its melting point. (16.10)

Heat of hydration: the energy change associated with placing gaseous molecules or ions in water; the sum of the energy needed to expand the solvent and the energy released from the solvent–solute interactions. (17.2)

Heat of solution: the energy change associated with dissolving a solute in a solvent; the sum of the energies needed to expand both solvent and solute in a solution and the energy released from the solvent–solute interactions. (17.2)

Heat of vaporization: the energy required to vaporize one mole of a liquid at a pressure of one atmosphere. (16.10)

Heating curve: a plot of temperature versus time for a substance where energy is added at a constant rate. (16.10)

Heisenberg uncertainty principle: a principle stating that there is a fundamental limitation to how precisely both the position and momentum of a particle can be known at a given time. (12.5)

Heme: an iron complex. (19.8)

Hemoglobin: a biomolecule composed of four myoglobin-like units (proteins plus heme) that can bind and transport four oxygen molecules in the blood. (19.8)

Henderson–Hasselbalch equation: an equation giving the relationship between the pH of an acid–base system and the concentrations of base and acid

$$\text{pH} = \text{p}K_a + \log\left(\frac{[\text{base}]}{[\text{acid}]}\right). \text{ (8.2)}$$

Henry's law: the amount of a gas dissolved in a solution is directly proportional to the pressure of the gas above the solution. (17.3)

Hess's law: in going from a particular set of reactants to a particular set of products, the energy change is the same whether the reaction takes place in one step or in a series of steps; in summary, energy is a state function. (9.5)

Heterogeneous equilibrium: an equilibrium involving reactants and/or products in more than one phase. (6.5)

Hexagonal closest packed (hcp) structure: a structure composed of closest packed spheres with an *ababab* arrangement of layers; the unit cell is hexagonal. (16.4)

Homogeneous equilibrium: an equilibrium system where all reactants and products are in the same phase. (6.5)

Homopolymer: a polymer formed from the polymerization of only one type of monomer. (21.5)

Hund's rule: the lowest-energy configuration for an atom is the one having the maximum number of unpaired electrons allowed by the Pauli exclusion principle in a particular set of degenerate orbitals, with all unpaired electrons having parallel spins. (12.13)

Hybrid orbitals: a set of atomic orbitals adopted by an atom in a molecule different from those of the atom in the free state. (14.1)

Hybridization: a mixing of the native orbitals on a given atom to form special atomic orbitals for bonding. (14.1)

Hydration: the interaction between solute particles and water molecules. (4.1)

Hydride: a binary compound containing hydrogen. The hydride ion, H^-, exists in ionic hydrides. The three classes of hydrides are covalent, interstitial, and ionic. (18.3)

Hydrocarbon: a compound composed of carbon and hydrogen. (23.1)

Hydrocarbon derivative: an organic molecule that contains one or more elements in addition to carbon and hydrogen. (21.4)

Hydrogen bonding: unusually strong dipole–dipole attractions that occur among molecules in which hydrogen is bonded to a highly electronegative atom. (16.1)

Hydrogenation reaction: a reaction in which hydrogen is added, with a catalyst present, to a carbon–carbon multiple bond. (21.2)

Hydrohalic acid: an aqueous solution of a hydrogen halide. (18.13)

Hydronium ion: the H_3O^+ ion; a hydrated proton. (7.1)

Hypothesis: one or more assumptions put forth to explain the observed behavior of nature. (1.3)

Ideal gas: a gas that obeys the equation, $PV = nRT$. (5.2)

Ideal gas law: an equation of state for a gas, where the state of the gas is its condition at a given time; expressed by $PV = nRT$, where P = pressure, V = volume, n = moles of the gas, R = the universal gas constant, and T = absolute temperature. This equation expresses behavior approached by real gases at high T and low P. (5.3)

Ideal solution: a solution whose vapor pressure is directly proportional to the mole fraction of solvent present. (17.4)

Indicator: a chemical that changes color and is used to mark the endpoint of a titration. (4.9; 8.5)

Inert pair effect: the tendency for the heavier Group 3A elements to exhibit the +1 as well as the expected +3 oxidation states, and Group 4A elements to exhibit the +2 as well as the +4 oxidation states. (18.5)

Integrated rate law: an expression that shows the concentration of a reactant as a function of time. (15.2)

Intermediate: a species that is neither a reactant nor a product but that is formed and consumed in the reaction sequence. (15.6)

Intermolecular forces: relatively weak interactions that occur between molecules. (16.1)

Internal energy: a property of a system that can be changed by a flow of work, heat, or both; $\Delta E = q + w$, where ΔE is the change in the internal energy of the system, q is heat, and w is work. (9.1)

Ion: an atom or a group of atoms that has a net positive or negative charge. (2.7)

Ion exchange (water softening): the process in which an ion-exchange resin removes unwanted ions (for example, Ca^{2+} and Mg^{2+}) and replaces them with Na^+ ions, which do not interfere with soap and detergent action. (18.4)

Ion pairing: a phenomenon occurring in solution when oppositely charged ions aggregate and behave as a single particle. (17.7)

Ion-product constant (K_w): the equilibrium constant for the autoionization of water; $K_w = [H^+][OH^-]$. At 25°C, K_w equals 1.0×10^{-14}. (7.2)

Ion-selective electrode: an electrode sensitive to the concentration of a particular ion in solution. (11.4)

Ionic bonding: the electrostatic attraction between oppositely charged ions. (2.7; 13.1)

Ionic compound (binary): a compound that results when a metal reacts with a nonmetal to form a cation and an anion. (13.1)

Ionic solid: a solid containing cations and anions that dissolves in water to give a solution containing the separated ions, which are mobile and thus free to conduct electric current. (16.3)

Ionization energy: the quantity of energy required to remove an electron from a gaseous atom or ion. (12.15)

Irreversible process: any real process. When a system undergoes the changes State 1 → State 2 → State 1 by any real pathway, the universe is different than before the cyclic process took place in the system. (10.2)

Isoelectronic ions: ions containing the same number of electrons. (13.4)

Isomers: species with the same formula but different properties. (19.4)

Isothermal process: a process in which the temperature remains constant. (10.2)

Isotonic solutions: solutions having identical osmotic pressures. (17.6)

Isotopes: atoms of the same element (the same number of protons) with different numbers of neutrons. They have identical atomic numbers but different mass numbers. (2.6)

Ketone: an organic compound containing the carbonyl group

bonded to two carbon atoms. (21.4)

Kinetic energy ($\frac{1}{2}mv^2$): energy resulting from the motion of an object; dependent on the mass of the object and the square of its velocity. (9.1)

Kinetic molecular theory: a model that assumes that an ideal gas is composed of tiny particles (molecules) in constant motion. (5.6)

Lanthanide contraction: the decrease in the atomic radii of the lanthanide series elements, going from left to right in the periodic table. (19.1)

Lanthanide series: a group of 14 elements following lanthanum in the periodic table, in which the 4f orbitals are being filled. (12.13; 18.1; 19.1)

Lattice: a three-dimensional system of points designating the positions of the centers of the components of a solid (atoms, ions, or molecules). (16.3)

Lattice energy: the energy change occurring when separated gaseous ions are packed together to form an ionic solid. (13.5)

Law of conservation of energy: energy can be converted from one form to another but can be neither created nor destroyed. (9.1)

Law of conservation of mass: mass is neither created nor destroyed. (2.2)

Law of definite proportion: a given compound always contains exactly the same proportion of elements by mass. (2.2)

Law of mass action: a general description of the equilibrium condition; it defines the equilibrium constant expression. (6.2)

Law of multiple proportions: when two elements form a series of compounds, the ratios of the masses of the second element that combine with one gram of the first element can always be reduced to small whole numbers. (2.2)

Lead storage battery: a battery (used in cars) in which the anode is lead, the cathode is lead coated with lead dioxide, and the electrolyte is a sulfuric acid solution. (11.5)

Le Châtelier's principle: if a change is imposed on a system at equilibrium, the position of the equilibrium will shift in a direction that tends to reduce the effect of that change. (6.8)

Lewis acid: an electron-pair acceptor. (19.3)

Lewis base: an electron-pair donor. (19.3)

Lewis structure: a diagram of a molecule showing how the valence electrons are arranged among the atoms in the molecule. (13.10)

Ligand: a neutral molecule or ion having a lone pair of electrons that can be used to form a bond to a metal ion; a Lewis base. (19.3)

Lime-soda process: a water-softening method in which lime and soda ash are added to water to remove calcium and magnesium ions by precipitation. (7.6)

Limiting reactant (limiting reagent): the reactant that is completely consumed when a reaction is run to completion. (3.9)

Line spectrum: a spectrum showing only certain discrete wavelengths. (12.3)

Linear accelerator: a type of particle accelerator in which a changing electric field is used to accelerate a positive ion along a linear path. (20.3)

Linkage isomerism: isomerism involving a complex ion where the ligands are all the same but the point of attachment of at least one of the ligands differs. (19.4)

Liquefaction: the transformation of a gas into a liquid. (18.1)

Localized electron (LE) model: a model that assumes that a molecule is composed of atoms that are bound together by sharing pairs of electrons using the atomic orbitals of the bound atoms. (13.9)

London dispersion forces: the forces, existing among noble gas atoms and nonpolar molecules, that involve an accidental dipole that induces a momentary dipole in a neighbor. (16.1)

Lone pair: an electron pair that is localized on a given atom; an electron pair not involved in bonding. (13.9)

Magnetic quantum number (m_ℓ): the quantum number relating to the orientation of an orbital in space relative to the other orbitals with the same ℓ quantum number. It can have integral values between ℓ and $-\ell$, including zero. (12.9)

Main-group (representative) elements: elements in the groups labeled 1A, 2A, 3A, 4A, 5A, 6A, 7A, and 8A in the periodic table. The group number gives the sum of valence s and p electrons. (12.13; 18.1)

Major species: the components present in relatively large amounts in a solution. (7.4)

Manometer: a device for measuring the pressure of a gas in a container. (5.1)

Mass defect: the change in mass occurring when a nucleus is formed from its component nucleons. (20.5)

Mass number: the total number of protons and neutrons in the atomic nucleus of an atom. (2.6)

Mass percent: the percent by mass of a component of a mixture (17.1) or of a given element in a compound. (3.4)

Mass spectrometer: an instrument used to determine the relative masses of atoms by the deflection of their ions in a magnetic field. (3.1)

Matter: the material of the universe.

Mean free path: the average distance a molecule in a given gas sample travels between collisions with other molecules. (5.6; 5.9)

Measurement: a quantitative observation. (A1.5)

Messenger RNA (mRNA):   a special RNA molecule built in the cell nucleus that migrates into the cytoplasm and participates in protein synthesis. (21.6)

Metal: an element that gives up electrons relatively easily and is lustrous, malleable, and a good conductor of heat and electricity. (2.8)

Metalloids (semimetals):   elements along the division line in the periodic table between metals and nonmetals. These elements exhibit both metallic and nonmetallic properties. (12.16; 18.1)

Metallurgy: the process of separating a metal from its ore and preparing it for use. (18.1)

Millimeters of mercury (mm Hg):   a unit of pressure, also called a torr; 760 mm Hg = 760 torr = 101,325 Pa = 1 standard atmosphere. (5.1)

Mixture: a material of variable composition that contains two or more substances.

Model (theory):   a set of assumptions put forth to explain the observed behavior of matter. The models of chemistry usually involve assumptions about the behavior of individual atoms or molecules. (1.3)

Moderator: a substance used in a nuclear reactor to slow down the neutrons. (20.6)

Molal boiling-point elevation constant: a constant characteristic of a particular solvent that gives the change in boiling point as a function of solution molality; used in molecular weight determinations. (17.5)

Molal freezing-point depression constant: a constant characteristic of a particular solvent that gives the change in freezing point as a function of the solution molality; used in molecular weight determinations. (17.5)

Molality: the number of moles of solute per kilogram of solvent in a solution. (17.1)

Molar heat capacity: the energy required to raise the temperature of one mole of a substance by one degree Celsius. (9.3; 9.4)

Molar mass: the mass in grams of one mole of molecules or formula units of a substance; also called molecular weight. (3.3)

Molar volume: the volume of one mole of an ideal gas; equal to 22.42 liters at STP. (5.4)

Molarity: moles of solute per volume of solution in liters. (4.3; 17.1)

Mole (mol):   the number equal to the number of carbon atoms in exactly 12 grams of pure ^{12}C; Avogadro's number. One mole represents 6.022×10^{23} units. (3.2)

Mole fraction: the ratio of the number of moles of a given component in a mixture to the total number of moles in the mixture. (5.5; 17.1)

Mole ratio (stoichiometry):   the ratio of moles of one substance to moles of another substance in a balanced chemical equation. (3.8)

Molecular equation: an equation representing a reaction in solution showing the reactants and products in undissociated form, whether they are strong or weak electrolytes. (4.6)

Molecular formula: the exact formula of a molecule, giving the types of atoms and the number of each type. (3.5)

Molecular orbital (MO) model: a model that regards a molecule as a collection of nuclei and electrons, where the electrons are assumed to occupy orbitals much as they do in atoms, but having the orbitals extend over the entire molecule. In this model the electrons are assumed to be delocalized rather than always located between a given pair of atoms. (14.2)

Molecular orientations (kinetics):   orientations of molecules during collisions, some of which can lead to a reaction and some of which cannot. (15.8)

Molecular solid: a solid composed of neutral molecules at the lattice points. (16.3)

Molecular structure: the three-dimensional arrangement of atoms in a molecule. (13.13)

Molecular weight: the mass in grams of one mole of molecules or formula units of a substance; also called molar mass. (3.3)

Molecularity: the number of species that must collide to produce the reaction represented by an elementary step in a reaction mechanism. (15.6)

Molecule: a bonded collection of two or more atoms of the same or different elements. (2.7)

Monodentate (unidentate) ligand: a ligand that can form one bond to a metal ion. (19.3)

Monoprotic acid: an acid with one acidic proton. (7.2)

Monosaccharide (simple sugar):   a polyhydroxy ketone or aldehyde containing from three to nine carbon atoms. (21.6)

Myoglobin: an oxygen-storing biomolecule consisting of a heme complex and a protein. (19.8)

Natural law: a statement that expresses generally observed behavior. (1.3)

Nernst equation: an equation relating the potential of an electrochemical cell to the concentrations of the cell components

$$\mathscr{E} = \mathscr{E}° - \frac{0.0591}{n} \log(Q) \text{ at } 25°C. \text{ (11.4)}$$

Net ionic equation: an equation for a reaction in solution, where strong electrolytes are written as ions, showing only those components that are directly involved in the chemical change. (4.6)

Network solid: an atomic solid containing strong directional covalent bonds. (16.5)

Neutralization reaction: an acid–base reaction. (4.9)

Neutron: a particle in the atomic nucleus with mass virtually equal to the proton's but with no charge. (2.6)

Nitrogen cycle: the conversion of N_2 to nitrogen-containing compounds, followed by the return of nitrogen gas to the atmosphere by natural decay processes. (18.8)

Nitrogen fixation: the process of transforming N_2 to nitrogen-containing compounds useful to plants. (18.8)

Nitrogen-fixing bacteria: bacteria in the root nodules of plants that can convert atmospheric nitrogen to ammonia and other nitrogen-containing compounds useful to plants. (18.8)

Noble gas: a Group 8A element. (2.8; 18.14)

Node: an area of an orbital having zero electron probability. (12.9)

Nonelectrolyte: a substance that, when dissolved in water, gives a nonconducting solution. (4.2)

Nonmetal: an element not exhibiting metallic characteristics. Chemically, a typical nonmetal accepts electrons from a metal. (2.8)

Normal boiling point: the temperature at which the vapor pressure of a liquid is exactly one atmosphere. (16.10)

Normal melting point: the temperature at which the solid and liquid states have the same vapor pressure under conditions where the total pressure on the system is one atmosphere. (16.10)

Normality: the number of equivalents of a substance dissolved in a liter of solution. (17.1)

Nuclear atom: an atom having a dense center of positive charge (the nucleus) with electrons moving around the outside. (2.5)

Nuclear transformation: the change of one element into another. (20.3)

Nucleon: a particle in an atomic nucleus, either a neutron or a proton. (2.6)

Nucleotide: a monomer of the nucleic acids composed of a five-carbon sugar, a nitrogen-containing base, and phosphoric acid. (21.6)

Nucleus: the small, dense center of positive charge in an atom. (2.5)

Nuclide: the general term applied to each unique atom; represented by $^A_Z X$, where X is the symbol for a particular element. (20.2)

Octet rule: the observation that atoms of nonmetals tend to form the most stable molecules when they are surrounded by eight electrons (to fill their valence orbitals). (13.10)

Optical isomerism: isomerism in which the isomers have opposite effects on plane-polarized light. (19.4)

Orbital: a specific wave function for an electron in an atom. The square of this function gives the probability distribution for the electron. (12.5)

d-Orbital splitting: a splitting of the d orbitals of the metal ion in a complex such that the orbitals pointing at the ligands have higher energies than those pointing between the ligands. (19.6)

Order (of reactant):   the positive or negative exponent, determined by experiment, of the reactant concentration in a rate law. (15.2)

Organic acid: an acid with a carbon-atom backbone; often contains the carboxyl group. (7.2)

Organic chemistry: the study of carbon-containing compounds (typically chains of carbon atoms) and their properties. (21)

Osmosis: the flow of solvent into a solution through a semipermeable membrane. (17.6)

Osmotic pressure (π):   the pressure that must be applied to a solution to stop osmosis; $= MRT$. (17.6)

Ostwald process: a commercial process for producing nitric acid by the oxidation of ammonia. (18.8)

Oxidation: an increase in oxidation state (a loss of electrons). (4.10; 11.1)

Oxidation–reduction (redox) reaction: a reaction in which one or more electrons are transferred. (4.4; 4.10; 11.1)

Oxidation states: a concept that provides a way to keep track of electrons in oxidation–reduction reactions according to certain rules. (4.10)

Oxidizing agent (electron acceptor):   a reactant that accepts electrons from another reactant. (4.10; 11.1)

Oxyacid: an acid in which the acidic proton is attached to an oxygen atom. (7.2)

Ozone: O_3, the form of elemental oxygen in addition to the much more common O_2. (18.11)

Paramagnetism: a type of induced magnetism, associated with unpaired electrons, that causes a substance to be attracted into the inducing magnetic field. (14.3)

Partial pressures: the independent pressures exerted by different gases in a mixture. (5.5)

Particle accelerator: a device used to accelerate nuclear particles to very high speeds. (20.3)

Pascal: the SI unit of pressure; equal to newtons per meter squared. (5.1)

Pauli exclusion principle: in a given atom no two electrons can have the same set of four quantum numbers. (12.10)

Penetration effect: the effect whereby a valence electron penetrates the core electrons, thus reducing the shielding effect and increasing the effective nuclear charge. (12.14)

Peptide linkage: the bond resulting from the condensation reaction between amino acids; represented by

$$\underset{\underset{\displaystyle -C-N-}{}}{\overset{\overset{\displaystyle O \quad H}{}}{}} \qquad (22.6)$$

Percent dissociation: the ratio of the amount of a substance that is dissociated at equilibrium to the initial concentration of the substance in a solution, multiplied by 100. (7.5)

Percent yield: the actual yield of a product as a percentage of the theoretical yield. (3.9)

Periodic table: a chart showing all the elements arranged in columns with similar chemical properties. (2.8)

pH curve (titration curve):   a plot showing the pH of a solution being analyzed as a function of the amount of titrant added. (8.5)

pH scale: a log scale based on 10 and equal to $-\log[H^+]$; a convenient way to represent solution acidity. (7.3)

Phase diagram: a convenient way of representing the phases of a substance in a closed system as a function of temperature and pressure. (16.11)

Phenyl group: the benzene molecule minus one hydrogen atom. (21.3)

Photochemical smog: air pollution produced by the action of light on oxygen, nitrogen oxides, and unburned fuel from auto exhaust to form ozone and other pollutants. (5.11)

Photon: a quantum of electromagnetic radiation. (12.2)

Physical change: a change in the form of a substance, but not in its chemical composition; chemical bonds are not broken in a physical change.

Pi (π) bond: a covalent bond in which parallel p orbitals share an electron pair occupying the space above and below the line joining the atoms. (14.1)

Planck's constant: the constant relating the change in energy for a system to the frequency of the electromagnetic radiation absorbed or emitted; equal to 6.626×10^{-34} J s. (12.2)

Polar covalent bond: a covalent bond in which the electrons are not shared equally because one atom attracts them more strongly than the other. (13.1)

Polar molecule: a molecule that has a permanent dipole moment. (4.1)

Polyatomic ion: an ion containing a number of atoms. (2.7)

Polyelectronic atom: an atom with more than one electron. (12.11)

Polymer: a large, usually chainlike molecule built from many small molecules (monomers). (21.5)

Polymerization: a process in which many small molecules (monomers) are joined together to form a large molecule. (21.2)

Polypeptide: a polymer formed from amino acids joined together by peptide linkages. (21.6)

Polyprotic acid: an acid with more than one acidic proton. It dissociates in a stepwise manner, one proton at a time. (7.7)

Porous disk: a disk in a tube connecting two different solutions in a galvanic cell that allows ion flow without extensive mixing of the solutions. (11.1)

Porphyrin: a planar ligand with a central ring structure and various substituent groups at the edges of the ring. (19.8)

Positional probability: a type of probability that depends on the number of arrangements in space that yield a particular state. (10.1)

Positron production: a mode of nuclear decay in which a particle is formed having the same mass as an electron but opposite charge. The net effect is to change a proton to a neutron. (20.1)

Potential energy: energy resulting from position or composition. (9.1)

Precipitation reaction: a reaction in which an insoluble substance forms and separates from the solution. (4.5)

Precision: the degree of agreement among several measurements of the same quantity; the reproducibility of a measurement. (A1.5)

Primary structure (of a protein): the order (sequence) of amino acids in the protein chain. (21.6)

Principal quantum number: the quantum number relating to the size and energy of an orbital; it can have any positive integer value. (12.9)

Probability distribution: the square of the wave function indicating the probability of finding an electron at a particular point in space. (12.8)

Product: a substance resulting from a chemical reaction. It is shown to the right of the arrow in a chemical equation. (3.6)

Protein: a natural high-molecular-weight polymer formed by condensation reactions between amino acids. (21.6)

Proton: a positively charged particle in an atomic nucleus. (2.6; 20)

Qualitative analysis: the separation and identification of individual ions from a mixture. (4.7; 8.9)

Quantization: the concept that energy can occur only in discrete units called quanta. (12.2)

Rad: a unit of radiation dosage corresponding to 10^{-2} J of energy deposited per kilogram of tissue (from *r*adiation *a*bsorbed *d*ose). (20.7)

Radioactive decay (radioactivity): the spontaneous decomposition of a nucleus to form a different nucleus. (20.1)

Radiocarbon dating (carbon-14 dating): a method for dating ancient wood or cloth based on the rate of radioactive decay of the nuclide $^{14}_{6}$C. (20.4)

Radiotracer: a radioactive nuclide, introduced into an organism for diagnostic purposes, whose pathway can be traced by monitoring its radioactivity. (20.4)

Random error: an error that has an equal probability of being high or low. (A1.5)

Raoult's law: the vapor pressure of a solution is directly proportional to the mole fraction of solvent present. (17.4)

Rate constant: the proportionality constant in the relationship between reaction rate and reactant concentrations. (15.2)

Rate of decay: the change in the number of radioactive nuclides in a sample per unit time. (20.2)

Rate-determining step: the slowest step in a reaction mechanism, the one determining the overall rate. (15.6)

Rate law (differential rate law): an expression that shows how the rate of reaction depends on the concentration of reactants. (15.2)

Reactant: a starting substance in a chemical reaction. It appears to the left of the arrow in a chemical equation. (3.6)

Reaction mechanism: the series of elementary steps involved in a chemical reaction. (15.6)

Reaction quotient: a quotient obtained by applying the law of mass action to initial concentrations rather than to equilibrium concentrations. (6.6)

Reaction rate: the change in concentration of a reactant or product per unit time. (15.1)

Reactor core: the part of a nuclear reactor where the fission reaction takes place. (20.6)

Reducing agent (electron donor): a reactant that donates electrons to another substance to reduce the oxidation state of one of its atoms. (4.10; 11.1)

Reduction: a decrease in oxidation state (a gain of electrons). (4.10; 11.1)

Rem: a unit of radiation dosage that accounts for both the energy of the dose and its effectiveness in causing biological damage (from *r*oentgen *e*quivalent for *m*an). (20.7)

Resonance: a condition occurring when more than one valid Lewis structure can be written for a particular molecule. The actual electronic structure is not represented by any one of the Lewis structures but by the average of all of them. (13.11)

Reverse osmosis: the process occurring when the external pressure on a solution causes a net flow of solvent through a semipermeable membrane from the solution to the solvent. (17.6)

Reversible process: a cyclic process carried out by a hypothetical pathway, which leaves the universe exactly the same as it was before the process. No real process is reversible. (10.2)

Ribonucleic acid (RNA): a nucleotide polymer that transmits the genetic information stored in DNA to the ribosomes for protein synthesis. (21.6)

Root mean square velocity: the square root of the average of the squares of the individual velocities of gas particles. (5.6)

Salt: an ionic compound. (7.8)

Salt bridge: a U-tube containing an electrolyte that connects the two compartments of a galvanic cell, allowing ion flow without extensive mixing of the different solutions. (11.1)

Scientific method: the process of studying natural phenomena, involving observations, forming laws and theories, and testing of theories by experimentation. (1.3)

Scintillation counter: an instrument that measures radioactive decay by sensing the flashes of light produced in a substance by the radiation. (20.4)

Second law of thermodynamics: in any spontaneous process, there is always an increase in the entropy of the universe. (10.5)

Secondary structure (of a protein): the three-dimensional structure of the protein chain (for example, α-helix, random coil, or pleated sheet). (21.6)

Selective precipitation: a method of separating metal ions from an aqueous mixture by using a reagent whose anion forms a precipitate with only one or a few of the ions in the mixture. (4.7; 8.8)

Semiconductor: a substance conducting only a slight electric current at room temperature, but showing increased conductivity at higher temperatures. (16.5)

Semipermeable membrane: a membrane that allows solvent but not solute molecules to pass through. (17.6)

Shielding: the effect by which the other electrons screen, or shield, a given electron from some of the nuclear charge. (12.14)

SI units: International System of units based on the metric system and units derived from the metric system. (A2.1)

Side chain (of amino acid): the hydrocarbon group on an amino acid represented by H, CH_3, or a more complex substituent. (21.6)

Sigma (σ) bond: a covalent bond in which the electron pair is shared in an area centered on a line running between the atoms. (14.1)

Significant figures: the certain digits and the first uncertain digit of a measurement. (A1.5)

Silica: the fundamental silicon–oxygen compound, which has the empirical formula SiO_2, and forms the basis of quartz and certain types of sand. (16.5)

Silicates: salts that contain metal cations and polyatomic silicon–oxygen anions that are usually polymeric. (16.5)

Single bond: a bond in which one pair of electrons is shared by two atoms. (13.8)

Solubility: the amount of a substance that dissolves in a given volume of solvent at a given temperature. (4.2)

Solubility product constant: the constant for the equilibrium expression representing the dissolving of an ionic solid in water. (8.8)

Solute: a substance dissolved in a liquid to form a solution. (4.2; 17.1)

Solution: a homogeneous mixture. (17)

Solvent: the dissolving medium in a solution. (4.2)

Somatic damage: radioactive damage to an organism resulting in its sickness or death. (20.7)

Space-filling model: a model of a molecule showing the relative sizes of the atoms and their relative orientations. (2.7)

Specific heat capacity: the energy required to raise the temperature of one gram of a substance by one degree Celsius. (9.4)

Spectator ions: ions present in solution that do not participate directly in a reaction. (4.6)

Spectrochemical series: a listing of ligands in order based on their ability to produce d-orbital splitting. (19.6)

Spectroscopy: the study of the interaction of electromagnetic radiation within matter. (14.7)

Spontaneous fission: the spontaneous splitting of a heavy nuclide into two lighter nuclides. (20.1)

Spontaneous process: a process that occurs without outside intervention. (10.1)

Standard atmosphere: a unit of pressure equal to 760 mm Hg. (5.1)

Standard energy of formation: the energy change that accompanies the formation of one mole of a compound at 25°C from its elements, with all substances in their standard states at that temperature. (9.6)

Standard free energy change: the change in free energy that will occur for one unit of reaction if the reactants in their standard states are converted to products in their standard states. (10.9)

Standard free energy of formation: the change in free energy that accompanies the formation of one mole of a substance from its constituent elements with all reactants and products in their standard states. (10.9)

Standard hydrogen electrode: a platinum conductor in contact with 1 M H^+ ions and bathed by hydrogen gas at one atmosphere. (11.2)

Standard reduction potential: the potential of a half-reaction under standard state conditions, as measured against the potential of the standard hydrogen electrode. (11.2)

Standard solution: a solution whose concentration is accurately known. (4.3)

Standard state: a reference state for a specific substance defined according to a set of conventional definitions. (9.6)

Standard temperature and pressure (STP): the condition 0°C and 1 atm of pressure. (5.4)

Standing wave: a stationary wave as on a string of a musical instrument; in the wave mechanical model, the electron in the hydrogen atom is considered to be a standing wave. (12.5)

State function: a property that is independent of the pathway. (9.1)

States of matter: the three different forms in which matter can exist: solid, liquid, and gas. (5)

Stereoisomerism: isomerism in which all the bonds in the isomers are the same but the spatial arrangements of the atoms are different. (19.4)

Steric factor: the factor (always less than one) that reflects the fraction of collisions with orientations that can produce a chemical reaction. (15.8)

Stoichiometric quantities: quantities of reactants mixed in exactly the correct amounts so that all are used up at the same time. (3.9)

Strong acid: an acid that completely dissociates to produce a H^+ ion and the conjugate base. (4.2; 7.2)

Strong base: a metal hydroxide salt that completely dissociates into its ions in water. (4.2; 7.6)

Strong electrolyte: a material that, when dissolved in water, gives a solution that conducts an electric current very efficiently. (4.2)

Structural formula: the representation of a molecule in which the relative positions of the atoms are shown and the bonds are indicated by lines. (2.7)

Structural isomerism: isomerism in which the isomers contain the same atoms but one or more bonds differ. (19.4; 21.1)

Subcritical reaction (nuclear): a reaction in which less than one neutron causes another fission event and the process dies out. (20.6)

Sublimation: the process by which a substance goes directly from the solid to the gaseous state without passing through the liquid state. (16.10)

Subshell: a set of orbitals with a given angular momentum quantum number. (12.9)

Substitution reaction (hydrocarbons): a reaction in which an atom, usually a halogen, replaces a hydrogen atom in a hydrocarbon. (21.1)

Supercooling: the process of cooling a liquid below its freezing point without its changing to a solid. (16.10)

Supercritical reaction (nuclear): a reaction in which more than one neutron from each fission event causes another fission event. The process rapidly escalates to a violent explosion. (20.6)

Superheating: the process of heating a liquid above its boiling point without its boiling. (16.10)

Superoxide: a compound containing the O_2^- anion. (18.2)

Surface tension: the resistance of a liquid to an increase in its surface area. (16.2)

Surroundings: everything in the universe surrounding a thermodynamic system. (9.1)

Syngas: synthetic gas, a mixture of carbon monoxide and hydrogen, obtained by coal gasification. (9.8)

System (thermodynamic): that part of the universe on which attention is to be focused. (9.1)

Systematic error: an error that always occurs in the same direction. (A1.5)

Termolecular step: a reaction involving the simultaneous collision of three molecules. (15.6)

Tertiary structure (of a protein): the overall shape of a protein, long and narrow or globular, maintained by different types of intramolecular interactions. (21.6)

Theoretical yield: the maximum amount of a given product that can be formed when the limiting reactant is completely consumed. (3.9)

Theory: a set of assumptions put forth to explain some aspect of the observed behavior of matter. (1.3)

Thermal pollution: the oxygen-depleting effect on lakes and rivers of using water for industrial cooling and returning it to its natural source at a higher temperature. (17.3)

Thermodynamic stability (nuclear): the potential energy of a particular nucleus as compared with the sum of the potential energies of its component protons and neutrons. (20.1)

Thermodynamics: the study of energy and its interconversions. (9.1)

Third law of thermodynamics: the entropy of a perfect crystal at 0 K is zero. (10.8)

Titration: a technique in which one solution is used to analyze another. (4.9)

Torr: another name for millimeter of mercury (mm Hg). (5.1)

Transfer RNA (tRNA): a small RNA fragment that finds specific amino acids and attaches them to the protein chain as dictated by the codons in mRNA. (21.6)

Transition metals: several series of elements in which inner orbitals (d or f orbitals) are being filled. (12.13; 18.1)

Transuranium elements: the elements beyond uranium that are made artificially by particle bombardment. (20.3)

Triple bond: a bond in which three pairs of electrons are shared by two atoms. (13.8)

Triple point: the point on a phase diagram at which all three states of a substance are present. (16.11)

Tyndall effect: the scattering of light by particles in a suspension. (17.8)

Uncertainty (in measurement): the characteristics that any measurement involves estimates and cannot be exactly reproduced. (A1.5)

Unimolecular step: a reaction step involving only one molecule. (15.6)

Unit cell: the smallest repeating unit of a lattice. (16.3)

Unit factor: an equivalence statement between units used for converting from one unit to another. (A2.2)

Universal gas constant: the combined proportionality constant in the ideal gas law; 0.08206 L atm/K mol or 8.3145 J/K mol. (5.3)

Valence electrons: the electrons in the outermost principal quantum level of an atom. (12.13)

Valence shell electron-pair repulsion (VSEPR) model: a model whose main postulate is that the structure around a given atom in a molecule is determined principally by minimizing electron-pair repulsions. (13.13)

van der Waals's equation: a mathematical expression for describing the behavior of real gases. (5.10)

van't Hoff factor: the ratio of moles of particles in solution to moles of solute dissolved. (17.7)

Vapor pressure: the pressure of the vapor over a liquid at equilibrium. (16.10)

Vaporization: the change in state that occurs when a liquid evaporates to form a gas. (16.10)

Viscosity: the resistance of a liquid to flow. (16.2)

Volt: the unit of electrical potential defined as one joule of work per coulomb of charge transferred. (11.1)

Voltmeter: an instrument that measures cell potential by drawing electric current through a known resistance. (11.1)

Volumetric analysis: a process involving titration of one solution with another. (4.9)

Wave function: a function of the coordinates of an electron's position in three-dimensional space that describes the properties of the electron. (12.5)

Wave mechanical model: a model for the hydrogen atom in which the electron is assumed to behave as a standing wave. (12.7)

Wavelength: the distance between two consecutive peaks or troughs in a wave. (12.1)

Weak acid: an acid that dissociates only slightly in aqueous solution. (4.2; 7.2)

Weak base: a base that reacts with water to produce hydroxide ions to only a slight extent in aqueous solution. (4.2; 7.6)

Weak electrolyte: a material that, when dissolved in water, gives a solution that conducts only a small electric current. (4.2)

Weight: the force exerted on an object by gravity. (2.3)

Work: force acting over a distance. (9.1)

X-ray diffraction: a technique for establishing the structures of crystalline solids by directing X rays of a single wavelength at a crystal and obtaining a diffraction pattern from which interatomic spaces can be determined. (16.3)

Zone of nuclear stability: the area encompassing the stable nuclides on a plot of their positions as a function of the number of protons and the number of neutrons in the nucleus. (20.1)

Answers to Selected Exercises

The answers listed here are from the *Complete Solutions Guide*, in which rounding is carried out at each intermediate step in a calculation in order to show the correct number of significant figures for that step. Therefore, an answer given here may differ in the last digit from the result obtained by carrying extra digits throughout the entire calculation and rounding at the end (the procedure you should follow).

Chapter 2

19. ClF_5 **21.** NH_3; Avogadro's hypothesis (law) implies that volume ratios are equal to molecule ratios at constant temperature and pressure. Here, 1 volume of N_2 reacts with 3 volumes of H_2 to produce 2 volumes of the gaseous product. Or in terms of molecule ratios, 1 molecule of N_2 reacts with 3 molecules of H_2 to produce 2 molecules of a product. In order for the equation to be balanced, the product must be NH_3. **23.** All the masses of hydrogen in these three compounds can be expressed as simple whole-number ratios. The g H/g N in hydrazine, ammonia, and hydrogen azide are in the ratios 6:9:1. **25.** O, 7.94; Na, 22.8; Mg, 11.9; O and Mg are incorrect by a factor of ≈ 2; correct formulas are H_2O, Na_2O, and MgO. **27.** d(nucleus) $= 3 \times 10^{15}$ g/cm^3; d(atom) $= 0.4$ g/cm^3 **29.** Since all charges are whole-number multiples of 6.40×10^{-13} zirkombs, then the charge on one electron could be 6.40×10^{-13} zirkombs. However, 6.40×10^{-13} zirkombs could be the charge of two electrons (or three electrons, etc.). All one can conclude is that the charge of an electron is 6.40×10^{-13} zirkombs or an integer fraction of 6.40×10^{-13}. **31.** If the plum pudding model were correct (a diffuse positive charge with electrons scattered throughout), then α particles should have traveled through the thin foil with very minor deflections in their path. This was not the case because a few of the α particles were deflected at very large angles. Rutherford reasoned that the large deflections of these α particles could be caused only by a center of concentrated positive charge that contains most of the atom's mass (the nuclear model of the atom). **33.** The atomic number of an element is equal to the number of protons in the nucleus of an atom of that element. The mass number is the sum of the number of protons plus neutrons in the nucleus. The atomic mass is the actual mass of a particular isotope (including electrons). As we will see in Chapter 3, the average mass of an atom is taken from a measurement made on a large number of atoms. The average atomic mass value is listed in the periodic table. **35.** a. The noble gases are He, Ne, Ar, Kr, Xe, and Rn (helium, neon, argon, krypton, xenon, and radon). Radon has only radioactive isotopes. In the periodic table, the whole number enclosed in parentheses is the mass number of the longest-lived isotope of the element. b. promethium (Pm) and technetium (Tc) **37.** a. Cl; halogen; b. Be; alkaline earth metal; c. Eu; lanthanide metal; d. Hf; transition metal; e. He; noble gas; f. U; actinide metal; g. Cs; alkali metal **39.** For lighter, stable isotopes, the number of protons in the nucleus is about equal to the number of neutrons. When the number of protons and neutrons is equal to each other, the mass number (protons + neutrons) will be twice the atomic number (protons). Therefore, for lighter isotopes, the ratio of the mass number to the atomic number is close to 2. For example, con-

sider ^{28}Si, which has 14 protons and $(28 - 14 =)$ 14 neutrons. Here, the mass number to atomic number ratio is 28/14 $= 2.0$. For heavier isotopes, there are more neutrons than protons in the nucleus. Therefore, the ratio of the mass number to the atomic number increases steadily upward from 2 as the isotopes get heavier and heavier. For example, ^{238}U has 92 protons and $(238 - 92 =)$ 146 neutrons. The ratio of the mass number to the atomic number for ^{238}U is 238/92 $= 2.6$. **41.** a. 12 p, 12 n, 12 e; b. 12 p, 12 n, 10 e; c. 27 p, 32 n, 25 e; d. 27 p, 32 n, 24 e; e. 27 p, 32 n, 27 e; f. 34 p, 45 n, 34 e; g. 34 p, 45 n, 36 e; h. 28 p, 35 n, 28 e; i. 28 p, 31 n, 26 e **43.** $^{151}_{63}Eu^{3+}$; $^{118}_{50}Sn^{2+}$ **45.** a. Lose 2 e$^-$ to form Ra^{2+}; b. Lose 3 e$^-$ to form In^{3+}; c. Gain 3 e$^-$ to form P^{3-}; d. Gain 2 e$^-$ to form Te^{2-}; e. Gain 1 e$^-$ to form Br^-; f. Lose 1 e$^-$ to form Rb^+ **47.** $AlCl_3$, aluminum chloride; $CrCl_3$, chromium(III) chloride; ICl_3, iodine trichloride; $AlCl_3$ and $CrCl_3$ are ionic compounds following the rules for naming ionic compounds. The major difference is that $CrCl_3$ contains a transition metal (Cr) that generally exhibits two or more stable charges when in ionic compounds. We need to indicate which charged ion we have in the compound. This is generally true whenever the metal in the ionic compound is a transition metal. ICl_3 is made from only nonmetals and is a covalent compound. Predicting formulas for covalent compounds is extremely difficult. Because of this, we need to indicate the number of each nonmetal in the binary covalent compound. The exception is when there is only one of the first species present in the formula; when this is the case, *mono*- is not used (it is assumed). **49.** a. sulfur difluoride; b. dinitrogen tetroxide; c. iodine trichloride; d. tetraphosphorus hexoxide **51.** a. copper(I) iodide; b. copper(II) iodide; c. cobalt(II) iodide; d. sodium carbonate; e. sodium hydrogen carbonate or sodium bicarbonate; f. tetrasulfur tetranitride; g. selenium tetrabromide; h. sodium hypochlorite; i. barium chromate; j. ammonium nitrate **53.** a. SO_2; b. SO_3; c. Na_2SO_3; d. $KHSO_3$; e. Li_3N; f. $Cr_2(CO_3)_3$; g. $Cr(C_2H_3O_2)_2$; h. SnF_4; i. NH_4HSO_4 (composed of NH_4^+ and HSO_4^- ions); j. $(NH_4)_2HPO_4$; k. $KClO_4$; l. NaH; m. HBrO; n. HBr **55.** a. lead(II) acetate; b. copper(II) sulfate; c. calcium oxide; d. magnesium sulfate; e. magnesium hydroxide; f. calcium sulfate; g. dinitrogen monoxide or nitrous oxide (common) **57.** a. nitric acid, HNO_3; b. perchloric acid, $HClO_4$; c. acetic acid, $HC_2H_3O_2$; d. sulfuric acid, H_2SO_4; e. phosphoric acid, H_3PO_4 **59.** The equation for the reaction would be 2 Na(s) + Cl_2(g) $\rightarrow$ 2 NaCl(s). The sodium reactant exists as singular sodium atoms packed together very tightly and in a very organized fashion. This type of packing of atoms represents the solid phase. The chlorine reactant exists as Cl_2 molecules. In the picture of chlorine, there is a lot of empty space. This occurs only in the gaseous phase. When sodium and chlorine react, the ionic compound NaCl forms. NaCl exists as separate Na^+ and Cl^- ions. Because the ions are packed very closely together and are packed in a very organized fashion, NaCl is depicted in the solid phase. **61.** 299 g **63.** a. True; b. False. The isotope has 34 protons; c. False. The isotope has 45 neutrons; d. False. The identity is selenium, Se. **65.** Ra; 142 n **67.** SeO_4^{2-}: selenate; SeO_3^{2-}: selenite; TeO_4^{2-}: tellurate; TeO_3^{2-}: tellurite **69.** InO, atomic mass of In $= 76.54$; In_2O_3, atomic mass of In $= 114.8$

71. $SbCl_3$; antimony(III) chloride   **73.** chlorine; 18 electrons
75. a. The compounds have the same number and types of atoms (same formula), but the atoms in the molecules are bonded together differently. Therefore, the two compounds are different compounds with different properties. The compounds are called isomers of each other. **b.** When wood burns, most of the solid material in wood is converted to gases, which escape. The gases produced are most likely CO_2 and H_2O. **c.** The atom is not an indivisible particle, but is instead composed of other smaller particles—electrons, neutrons, and protons. **d.** The two hydride samples contain different isotopes of either hydrogen or lithium. Although the compounds are composed of different isotopes, their properties are similar because different isotopes of the same element have similar properties (except, of course, their mass). **77.** The ratio of the masses of R that combine with 1.00 g Q is 3:1, as expected by the law of multiple proportions. R_3Q **79.** C:H ratio = 8:18 or 4:9

Chapter 12

21. 3.0×10^{10} s^{-1}; 2.0×10^{-23} J/photon; 12 J/mol   **23.** 107.1 MHz electromagnetic radiation is FM radio-waves, 2.12×10^{-10} m electromagnetic radiation is X rays, and the 3.97×10^{-19} J/photon electromagnetic radiation is visible (green) light. The order of increasing photon energy and increasing frequency is: FM radiowaves < visible (green) light < X rays.   **25. a.** 5.0×10^{-6} m; **b.** infrared; **c.** 4.0×10^{-20} J/photon; 2.4×10^4 J/mol; **d.** less   **27.** 427.7 nm   **29.** 4.36×10^{-19} J   **31.** The photoelectric effect refers to the phenomenon in which electrons are emitted from the surface of a metal when light strikes it. The light must have a certain minimum frequency (energy) in order to remove electrons from the surface of a metal. Light having a frequency below the minimum results in no electrons being emitted, whereas light at or higher than the minimum frequency does cause electrons to be emitted. For light having a frequency higher than the minimum frequency, the excess energy is transferred into kinetic energy for the emitted electron. Albert Einstein explained the photoelectric effect by applying quantum theory.   **33. a.** 1.32×10^{-13} m; **b.** 5.3×10^3 m/s   **35.** Ca   **37. a.** For hydrogen ($Z = 1$), the energy levels in units of joules are given by the equation $E_n = -2.178 \times 10^{-18}(1/n^2)$. Because the differences between $1/n^2$ values for consecutive energy levels decrease as n increases, the energy levels get closer together as n increases. **b.** In the diagram, the red line is for the $n_i = 3$ to $n_f = 2$ transition. The calculated wavelength for this emission using the Bohr model is 656.7 nm. From Figure 12.3, $\lambda = 656.7$ nm is red light, so the diagram is correct for the red line. The green line is for the $n_i = 4$ to $n_f = 2$ transition. The calculated wavelength for this emission is 486.4 nm. From Figure 12.3, $\lambda = 486.4$ nm is green-blue light. The diagram is consistent with this line. The blue line is for the $n_i = 5$ to $n_f = 2$ transition. The calculated wavelength for this emission is 434.3 nm. From Figure 12.3, $\lambda = 434.3$ nm is blue or blue-violet light. The diagram is consistent with this line also.   **39.** 10   **41. a.** False; It takes less energy to ionize an electron from $n = 3$ than from the ground state. **b.** True; **c.** False; The energy difference between $n = 3$ and $n = 2$ is smaller than the energy difference between $n = 3$ and $n = 1$. Thus the wavelength of light emitted is longer for the $n = 3$ to $n = 2$ electronic transition than for the $n = 3$ to $n = 1$ transition. **d.** True; **e.** False; $n = 2$ is the first excited state and $n = 3$ is the second excited state.   **43.** $n = 7$ **45.** $n = 4$ **47.** $n = 4$ **49. a.** 5.79×10^{-4} m; **b.** 3.64×10^{-33} m; the diameter of an H atom is roughly 2×10^{-8} cm. The uncertainty in the position of the electron is much larger than the size of the atom, whereas the uncertainty in the position of the baseball is insignificant as compared to the size of a baseball.   **51.** At $x = 0$, the value of the square of the wave function must be zero. The particle must be inside the box. For $\psi = A \cos(Lx)$, at $x = 0$, $\cos(0) = 1$ and $\psi^2 = A^2$. This violates the boundary condition.   **53.** 3.50 nm   **55.** As L increases, E_n will decrease and the spacing between energy levels will also decrease.   **57.** Since E_n is inversely proportional to

L^2, the electron in the larger box (10^{-6} m) has the lowest ground-state energy.   **59.** The $2p$ orbitals differ from each other in the direction in which they point in space. The $2p$ and $3p$ orbitals differ from each other in their size, energy, and number of nodes. A nodal surface in an atomic orbital is a surface in which the probability of finding an electron is zero.   **61.** $1p$, $3f$, and $2d$ are all incorrect designations.   **63. a.** For $n = 3$, $\ell = 3$ is not possible. **d.** m_s cannot equal -1. **e.** ℓ cannot be a negative number. **f.** For $\ell = 1$, m_l cannot equal 2.   **65.** $1p$, 0 electrons ($\ell \neq 1$ when $n = 1$); $6d_{x^2-y^2}$, 2 electrons (specifies one atomic orbital); $4f$, 14 electrons (7 orbitals have $4f$ designation); $7p_y$, 2 electrons (specifies one atomic orbital); $2s$, 2 electrons (specifies one atomic orbital); $n = 3$, 18 electrons ($3s$, $3p$, and $3d$ orbitals are possible; there are one $3s$ orbital, three $3p$ orbitals, and five $3d$ orbitals)   **67.** The diagrams of the orbitals in the text give only 90% probabilities of where the electron may reside. We can never be 100% certain of the location of the electrons due to Heisenberg's uncertainty principle.   **69.** $\theta = 0 : 2.46 \times 10^{28}$; $\theta = 90° : 0$ **71.** He: $1s^2$; Ne: $1s^22s^22p^6$; Ar: $1s^22s^22p^63s^23p^6$; each peak in the diagram corresponds to a sublevel with different values of n. Corresponding sublevels are closer to the nucleus for heavier elements because of the increased nuclear charge.   **73.** Valence electrons are the electrons in the outermost principal quantum level of an atom (those electrons in the highest n value orbitals). The electrons in the lower n value orbitals are all inner core or just core electrons. The key is that the outermost electrons are the valence electrons. When atoms interact with each other, it will be the outermost electrons that are involved in these interactions. In addition, how tightly the nucleus holds these outermost electrons determines atomic size, ionization energy, and other properties of atoms. Elements in the same group have similar valence electron configurations and, as a result, have similar chemical properties.   **75. a.** 32; **b.** 8; **c.** 25; **d.** 10; **e.** 6; **f.** 0; **g.** 1; **h.** 9; **i.** 0; **j.** 2   **77.** Sc: $1s^22s^22p^63s^23p^64s^23d^1$; Fe: $1s^22s^22p^63s^23p^64s^23d^6$; P: $1s^22s^22p^63s^23p^3$; Cs: $1s^22s^22p^63s^23p^64s^23d^{10}4p^65s^24d^{10}5p^66s^1$; Eu: $1s^22s^22p^63s^23p^64s^23d^{10}4p^65s^24d^{10}5p^66s^24f^65d^1$ (actual: [Xe]$6s^24f^7$); Pt: $1s^22s^22p^63s^23p^64s^23d^{10}4p^65s^24d^{10}5p^66s^24f^{14}5d^8$ (actual: [Xe]$6s^14f^{14}5d^9$); Xe: $1s^22s^22p^63s^23p^64s^23d^{10}4p^65s^24d^{10}5p^6$; Br: $1s^22s^22p^63s^23p^64s^23d^{10}4p^5$ **79.** Cr, Cu, Nb, Mo, Tc, Ru, Rh, Pd, Ag, Pt, Au   **81.** Cr: $1s^22s^22p^63s^23p^64s^13d^5$; Cr has 6 unpaired electrons.

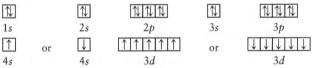

Cu: $1s^22s^22p^63s^23p^64s^13d^{10}$; Cu has 1 unpaired electron.

83. a. 2 valence electrons; $4s^2$; **b.** 6 valence electrons; $2s^22p^4$; **c.** 7 valence electrons; $7s^27p^5$; **d.** 3 valence electrons; $5s^25p^1$; **e.** 8 valence electrons; $3s^23p^6$; **f.** 5 valence electrons; $6s^26p^3$ **85. a.** 32; **b.** 28; **c.** 23; **d.** 56 or 59   **87.** Li (1 unpaired electron), N (3 unpaired electrons), Ni (2 unpaired electrons), and Te (2 unpaired electrons) are paramagnetic.   **89.** H, Li, Na, K, B, Al, Ga, F, Cl, Br, Sc, and Cu all have one unpaired electron in the ground state.   **91.** O, 2; O^+, 3; O^-, 1; Os, 4; Zr, 2; S, 2; F, 1; Ar, 0   **93.** Ionization energy: $P(g) \rightarrow P^+(g) + e^-$; electron affinity: $P(g) + e^- \rightarrow P^-(g)$ **95.** As successive electrons are removed, the net positive charge on the resultant ion increases. This increase in positive charge binds the remaining electrons more firmly, and the ionization energy increases. The electron configuration for Si is $1s^22s^22p^63s^23p^2$. There is a large jump in ionization energy when going from the removal of valence electrons to the removal of core electrons. For silicon, this occurs when the fifth electron is removed since we go from the valence electrons in $n = 3$ to the core electrons in $n = 2$. There should be another big jump when the thirteenth electron is removed (i.e., when a $1s$ electron is removed). **97.** a. S < Se < Te; b. Br < Ni < K; c. F < Si < Ba; d. Be < Na < Rb; e. Ne < Se < Sr; f. O < P < Fe **99.** a. Ba; b. K; c. O; d. S^{2-}; e. Cs **101.** As: $[Ar]4s^23d^{10}4p^3$; Se: $[Ar]4s^23d^{10}4p^4$; The general ionization energy trend predicts that Se should have a higher ionization energy than As. Se is an exception to the general ionization energy trend. There are extra electron–electron repulsions in Se because two electrons are in the same $4p$ orbital, resulting in a lower ionization energy for Se than predicted. **103.** Size also decreases going across a period. Sc and Ti, along with Y and Zr, are adjacent elements. There are 14 elements (the lanthanides) between La and Hf, making Hf considerably smaller. **105.** a. $[Rn]7s^25f^{14}6d^{10}7p^5$; b. At; c. NaUus, Mg(Uus)$_2$, C(Uus)$_4$, O(Uus)$_2$; d. UusO$^-$, UusO$_2^-$, UusO$_3^-$, UusO$_4^-$ **107.** In each case something energetically unfavorable occurs when an electron is added. For Be, the added electron must go into a higher-energy $2p$ atomic orbital because the $2s$ orbital is full. In N, the added electron must pair up with another electron in one of the $2p$ atomic orbitals; this adds electron–electron repulsions. In Ne, the added electron must be added to a much higher-energy $3s$ atomic orbital because the $n = 2$ orbitals are full. **109.** Electron–electron repulsions are much greater in O^- than in S^- because the electron goes into a smaller $2p$ orbital versus the larger $3p$ orbital in sulfur. This results in a more favorable (more exothermic) electron affinity for sulfur. **111.** a. -1445 kJ/mol; b. -580 kJ/mol; c. 348.7 kJ/mol; d. 1255 kJ/mol; e. -1255 kJ/mol **113.** Yes; ionization energy generally decreases down a group, and atomic radius generally increases down a group. The data in Table 12.9 confirm both of these general trends. **115.** a. $6Li(s) + N_2(g) \rightarrow 2Li_3N(s)$; b. $2Rb(s) + S(s) \rightarrow Rb_2S(s)$; c. $2Cs(s) + 2H_2O(l) \rightarrow 2CsOH(aq) + H_2(g)$; d. $2Na(s) + Cl_2(g) \rightarrow 2NaCl(s)$ **117.** For 589.0 nm: 5.090×10^{14} s^{-1}, 3.373×10^{-19} J/photon, 203.1 kJ/mol; for 589.6 nm: 5.085×10^{14} s^{-1}, 3.369×10^{-19} J/photon, 202.9 kJ/mol **119.** 119: $[Rn]7s^25f^{14}6d^{10}7p^68s^1$ **121.** a. n; b. n and ℓ **123.** Size decreases from left to right and increases going down the periodic table. So going one element right and one element down would result in a similar size for the two elements diagonal to each other. The ionization energies will be similar for the diagonal elements since the periodic trends also oppose each other. Electron affinities are harder to predict, but atoms with similar size and ionization energy should also have similar electron affinities. **125.** 200 s (about 3 minutes) **127.** greenish yellow light **129.** When the p and d orbital functions are evaluated at various points in space, the results sometimes have positive values and sometimes have negative values. The term "phase" is often associated with the + and − signs. For example, a sine wave has alternating positive and negative phases. This is analogous to the positive and negative values (phases) in the p and d orbitals. **131.** a. 146 kJ; b. 407 kJ; c. 1117 kJ; d. 1524 kJ **133.** alkaline earth metal family **135.** a. 24; b. 6; c. 12; d. 2; e. 26; f. 24.9 g; g. $1s^22s^22p^63s^23p^64s^13d^5$ **137.** a. 4; b. four elements in the first period and 16 elements in the second period; c. 20; d. 28 **139.** S-type cone receptors detect 400–500 nm light; from Figure 12.3 in the text, this is violet to green light. M-type cone receptors detect 450–630 nm light, which is blue to orange light. L-type cone receptors detect 500–700 nm light, which is green to red light. **141.** a. Line A: 6 → 3; Line B: 5 → 3; b. 121.6 nm **143.** X = carbon; $m = 5(C^{5+})$ **145.** a. The quantum numbers are:

ground state (E_{11})	→ $n_x = 1$, $n_y = 1$
first excited state (E_{21})	→ $n_x = 2$, $n_y = 1$
second excited state (E_{12})	→ $n_x = 1$, $n_y = 2$

b. 4.5×10^{-5} m **147.** a. 2.2×10^{-9}; b. 1.5×10^{-9}; c. 2.9×10^{-10}; d. 1.9×10^{-4}; e. 1×10^{-3} **149.** 2470 nm **151.** a. 43.33; b. Z_{eff} is slightly less than Z. Electrons in other orbitals can penetrate the $1s$ orbital. Thus a $1s$ electron can be slightly shielded from the nucleus, giving a Z_{eff} close to but less than Z.

Chapter 13

11. Electronegativity is the ability of an atom in a molecule to attract electrons to itself. Electronegativity is a bonding term. Electron affinity is the energy change when an electron is added to a substance. Electron affinity deals with isolated atoms in the gas phase. A covalent bond is a sharing of an electron pair in a bond between two atoms. An ionic bond is a complete transfer of electrons from one atom to another to form ions. The electrostatic attraction of the oppositely charged ions is the ionic bond. A pure covalent bond is an equal sharing of a shared electron pair in a bond. A polar covalent bond is an unequal sharing. Ionic bonds form when there is a large difference in electronegativity between the two atoms bonding together. This usually occurs when a metal with a small electronegativity is bonded to a nonmetal having a large electronegativity. A pure covalent bond forms between atoms having identical or nearly identical electronegativities. A polar covalent bond forms when there is an intermediate electronegativity difference. In general, nonmetals bond together by forming covalent bonds, either pure covalent or polar covalent. Ionic bonds form due to the strong electrostatic attraction between two oppositely charged ions. Covalent bonds form because the shared electrons in the bond are attracted to two different nuclei, unlike the isolated atoms, in which electrons are attracted to only one nuclei. The attraction to another nuclei overrides the added electron–electron repulsions.

13.

Halogen	(IE − EA)	(IE − EA)/502	EN(text)
F	2006 kJ/mol	4.0	4.0
Cl	1604 kJ/mol	3.2	3.0
Br	1463 kJ/mol	2.9	2.8
I	1302 kJ/mol	2.6	2.5

$2006/502 = 4.0$; The values calculated from IE and EA show the same trend as (and agree fairly closely) with the values given in the text. **15.** a. C < N < O; b. Se < S < Cl; c. Sn < Ge < Si; d. Tl < Ge < S; e. Rb < K < Na; f. Ga < B < O **17.** a. C (2.5) < N (3.0) < O (3.5), same as predicted; b. Se (2.4) < S (2.5) < Cl (3.0), same; c. Si (1.8) = Ge (1.8) = Sn (1.8), different; d. Tl (1.8) = Ge (1.8) < S (2.5), different; e. Rb (0.8) = K (0.8) < Na (0.9), different; f. Ga (1.6) < B (2.0) < O (3.5), same; Most polar bonds in Exercise 16 using actual EN values: a. Si—F and Ge—F (Ge—F predicted); b. P—Cl (same as predicted); c. S—F (same as predicted); d. Ti—Cl (same as predicted); e. Si—H and Sn—H (Sn—H predicted); f. Al—Br (Tl—Br predicted) **19.** Br—Br < N—O < C—F < Ca—O < K—F **21.** (NH$_4$)$_2$SO$_4$ and Ca$_3$(PO$_4$)$_2$ are the compounds with both ionic and covalent bonds. **23.** Anions are larger than the neutral atom, and cations are smaller than the neutral atom. For anions, the added electrons increase the electron–electron repulsions. To counteract this, the size of the electron cloud increases, placing the electrons further apart from one another. For cations, as electrons are removed, there are fewer electron–electron repulsions, and the electron cloud can be pulled closer to the nucleus. Isoelectronic: same number of electrons. Two variables, the number of protons and the number of electrons, determine the size of an ion. Keeping the number of electrons constant, we have to consider only the number of protons to predict trends in size. The ion with the most protons attracts the same number of electrons most strongly, resulting in a smaller size. **25.** a. Cu > Cu$^+$ > Cu^{2+}; b. Pt^{2+} > Pd^{2+} > Ni^{2+}; c. O^{2-} > O$^-$ > O; d. La^{3+} > Eu^{3+} > Gd^{3+} > Yb^{3+}; e. Te^{2-} > I$^-$ > Cs$^+$ > Ba^{2+} > La^{3+} **27.** Rb$^+$: $[Ar]4s^23d^{10}4p^6$; Ba^{2+}: $[Kr]5s^24d^{10}5p^6$; Se^{2-}: $[Ar]4s^23d^{10}4p^6$; I$^-$: $[Kr]5s^24d^{10}5p^6$ **29.** a. Cs$_2$S is composed of Cs$^+$ and S^{2-}. Cs$^+$ has the same electron configuration as Xe, and S^{2-} has the same configuration as Ar. b. SrF$_2$; Sr^{2+} has the Kr electron configuration and F$^-$ has the Ne configuration. c. Ca$_3$N$_2$; Ca^{2+} has the Ar electron configuration and N^{3-} has the Ne configuration. d. AlBr$_3$; Al^{3+} has the Ne electron configuration and Br$^-$ has the Kr configuration.

31. Se^{2-}, Br^-, Rb^+, Sr^{2+}, Y^{3+}, and Zr^{4+} are some ions that are iso-electronic with Kr (36 electrons). In terms of size, the ion with the most protons will hold the electrons tightest and will be the smallest. The size trend is

$$Zr^{4+} < Y^{3+} < Sr^{2+} < Rb^+ < Br^- < Se^{2-}$$
smallest   largest

33. a. Al_2S_3, aluminum sulfide; **b.** K_3N, potassium nitride; **c.** $MgCl_2$, magnesium chloride; **d.** CsBr, cesium bromide **35.** -411 kJ/mol **37.** 161 kJ/mol **39. a.** From the data given, less energy is required to produce $Mg^+(g) + O^-(g)$ than to produce $Mg^{2+}(g) + O^{2-}(g)$. However, the lattice energy for $Mg^{2+}O^{2-}$ will be much more exother-mic than for Mg^+O^- (because of the greater charges in $Mg^{2+}O^{2-}$). The favorable lattice energy term will dominate and $Mg^{2+}O^{2-}$ forms. **b.** Mg^+ and O^- both have unpaired electrons. In Mg^{2+} and O^{2-}, there are no unpaired electrons. Hence, Mg^+O^- would be para-magnetic; $Mg^{2+}O^{2-}$ would be diamagnetic. Paramagnetism can be detected by measuring the mass of a sample in the presence and absence of a magnetic field. The apparent mass of a paramagnetic substance will be larger in a magnetic field because of the force between the unpaired electrons and the field. **41.** Ca^{2+} has greater charge than Na^+, and Se^{2-} is smaller than Te^{2-}. The effect of charge on the lattice energy is greater than the effect of size. We expect the trend from most exothermic to least exothermic to be

$$CaSe > CaTe > Na_2Se > Na_2Te$$
(-2862) (-2721) (-2130) (-2095 kJ/mol)

43. a. -183 kJ; **b.** -109 kJ; **c.** -158 kJ; **d.** -1169 kJ **45.** -42 kJ **47.** -1228 kJ **49.** -5681 kJ **51.** Since both reactions are highly exothermic, the high temperature is not needed to provide energy. It must be necessary for some other reason. This will be discussed in Chapter 15 on kinetics. **53. a.** 1549 kJ; **b.** 1390. kJ; **c.** 1312 kJ; **d.** 1599 kJ **55.** $D_{calc} = 389$ kJ/mol as compared with 391 kJ/mol in the table.

57. a. H—C≡N: **b.** H—P—H **c.** [diagram] **d.** [diagram]

e. [diagram] **f.** :F—Se—F: **g.** O=C=O **h.** O=O **i.** H—Br:

59. Molecules or ions that have the same number of valence electrons and the same number of atoms will have similar Lewis structures.

61. $\ddot{O}=\ddot{O}—\ddot{O}: \longleftrightarrow :\ddot{O}—\ddot{O}=\ddot{O}$

$\ddot{O}=\ddot{S}—\ddot{O}: \longleftrightarrow :\ddot{O}—\ddot{S}=\ddot{O}$

[three resonance structures of SO3]

63. [resonance structures]

65. [benzene resonance structures]

67. [borazine resonance structures]

69. Statements a and c are true. For statement b, SF_4 has 5 electron pairs around the sulfur in the best Lewis structure; it is an exception to the octet rule. Because OF_4 has the same number of valence electrons as SF_4, OF_4 would also have to be an exception to the octet rule. However, Row 2 elements like O never have more than 8 electrons around them, so OF_4 does not exist. For statement d, two resonance structures can be drawn for ozone:

[ozone resonance structures]

When resonance structures can be drawn, the actual bond lengths and strengths are all equal to each other. Even though each Lewis structure implies the two O—O bonds are different, this is not the case in real life. In real life, both of the O—O bonds are equivalent. When resonance structures can be drawn, you can think of the bonding as an average of all of the resonance structures.

71. [Lewis structures of PF_5, ClF_3, SF_4, Br_3^-]

Row 3 and heavier nonmetals can have more than 8 electrons around them when they have to. Row 3 and heavier elements have empty d orbitals which are close in energy to the valence s and p orbitals. These empty d orbitals can accept extra electrons. **73.** Three resonance structures can be drawn for CO_3^{2-}. The actual structure for CO_3^{2-} is an average of these three resonance structures. That is, the three C—O bond lengths are all equivalent, with a length somewhere between a single bond and a double bond. The actual bond length of 136 pm is consistent with this resonance view of CO_3^{2-}. **75.** $NO^+ < N_2O < NO_2^- < NO_3^- < H_2NOH$

77. :C≡O:

In the CO Lewis structure, carbon has a formal charge of -1 and oxygen has a formal charge of $+1$. Electronegativity predicts the opposite polarization. The two opposing effects seem to partially cancel to give a much less polar molecule than expected. **79.** a–f and h all have similar Lewis structures:

[Lewis structure of YXY₂ type] **g.** ClO_3^- [Lewis structure]

Formal charges: a. +1; b. +2; c. +3; d. +1; e. +2; f. +4;
g. +2; h. +1

81. $\overset{\cdot\cdot}{\underset{\cdot\cdot}{Cl}}-\overset{\cdot\cdot}{\underset{\cdot\cdot}{S}}-\overset{\cdot\cdot}{\underset{\cdot\cdot}{S}}-\overset{\cdot\cdot}{\underset{\cdot\cdot}{Cl}}$

83. $\overset{\cdot\cdot}{\underset{\cdot\cdot}{F}}-\overset{\cdot\cdot}{\underset{\cdot\cdot}{O}}-\overset{\cdot\cdot}{\underset{\cdot\cdot}{O}}-\overset{\cdot\cdot}{\underset{\cdot\cdot}{F}}$

Formal charge:	0	0	0	0
Oxidation state:	−1	+1	+1	−1

Oxidation states are more useful when accounting for the reactivity
of O_2F_2. We are forced to assign +1 as the oxidation state for
oxygen due to the bonding of fluorine. Oxygen is very electronegative, and +1 is not a stable oxidation state for this element.
85. a. V-shaped or bent; b. see-saw; c. trigonal pyramid;
d. trigonal bipyramid; e. tetrahedral **87.** [57] a. linear, 180°;
b. trigonal pyramid, < 109.5°; c. tetrahedral, 109.5°; d. tetrahedral, 109.5°; e. trigonal planar, 120°; f. V-shaped, < 109.5°;
g. linear, 180°; h. and i. linear, no bond angle in diatomic molecules;
[58] a. All are tetrahedral, 109.5°; b. All are trigonal pyramid,
< 109.5°; c. All are V-shaped, < 109.5°; [60] a. NO_2^-: V-shaped,
≈ 120°; NO_3^-: trigonal planar, 120°; N_2O_4: trigonal planar about
both nitrogens, 120°; b. All are linear; 180° **89.** Br_3^- is linear; ClF_3
is T-shaped; SF_4 is see-saw. **91.** a. linear, 180°; b. T-shaped, ≈ 90°;
c. see-saw, ≈ 120° and ≈ 90°; d. trigonal bipyramid, 120° and
90° **93.** SeO_2, PCl_3, and SCl_2 have net dipole moments (are polar).
95. The two general requirements for a polar molecule are (1) polar
bonds and (2) a structure such that the bond dipoles of the polar
bonds do not cancel. In CF_4, the fluorines are symmetrically arranged
about the central carbon atom. The net result is for all of the individual C—F bond dipoles to cancel each other out, giving a nonpolar
molecule. In XeF_4 the 4 Xe—F bond dipoles are also symmetrically
arranged and XeF_4 is also nonpolar. The individual bond dipoles
cancel out when summed together. In SF_4 we also have 4 polar bonds.
But in SF_4 the bond dipoles are not symmetrically arranged and they
do not cancel each other out. SF_4 is polar. It is the positioning of
the lone pair that disrupts the symmetry in SF_4. CO_2 is nonpolar because
the individual bond dipoles cancel each other out, but COS is polar.
By replacing an O with a less electronegative S atom, the molecule is
not symmetric any more. The individual bond dipoles do not cancel
since the C—S bond dipole is smaller than the C—O bond dipole,
resulting in a polar molecule. **97.** Only statement c is true. The
bond dipoles in CF_4 and KrF_4 are arranged in a manner that they all
cancel each other out, making them nonpolar molecules (CF_4 has a
tetrahedral molecular structure, while KrF_4 has a square planar
molecular structure). In SeF_4 the bond dipoles in this see-saw molecule do not cancel each other out, so SeF_4 is polar. For statement a,
all the molecules have either a trigonal planar geometry or a trigonal
bipyramidal geometry, both of which have 120-degree bond angles.
However, $XeCl_2$ has three lone pairs and two bonded chlorine atoms
around it. $XeCl_2$ has a linear molecular structure with a 180-degree
bond angle. With three lone pairs, we no longer have a 120-degree
bond angle in $XeCl_2$. For statement b, SO_2 has a V-shaped molecular
structure with a bond angle of about 120 degrees. CS_2 is linear with a
180-degree bond angle, and SCl_2 is V-shaped but with an approximately 109.5-degree bond angle. The three compounds do not have
the same bond angle. For statement d, central atoms adopt a geometry to minimize electron repulsions, not maximize them.
99. Element E must belong to the Group 6A elements because it has
6 valence electrons. E must also be a Period 3 or heavier element
since this ion has more than 8 electrons around the central E atom
(Period 2 elements never have more than 8 electrons around them).
Some possible identities for E are S, Se, and Te. The ion has a
T-shaped molecular structure with bond angles of ≈ 90°.

101. a. OCl_2 V-shaped, polar

KrF_2 $:\overset{\cdot\cdot}{\underset{\cdot\cdot}{F}}-Kr-\overset{\cdot\cdot}{\underset{\cdot\cdot}{F}}:$ Linear, nonpolar

BeH_2 H—Be—H   Linear, nonpolar

SO_2 V-shaped, polar

(One other resonance structure possible)

b. SO_3 Trigonal planar, nonpolar

(Two other resonance structures possible)

NF_3 Trigonal pyramid, polar

IF_3 T-shaped, polar

c. CF_4 Tetrahedral, nonpolar

SeF_4 See-saw, polar

KrF_4 Square planar, nonpolar

d. IF_5 Square pyramid, polar

AsF_5 Trigonal bipyramid, nonpolar

103. All these molecules have polar bonds that are symmetrically
arranged around the central atom. In each molecule, the individual
bond dipoles cancel to give no net overall dipole moment.

105.

$\Delta E = -83$ kJ; the carbon–oxygen double bond is stronger than two carbon–oxygen single bonds; hence CO_2 and H_2O are more stable than H_2CO_3. **107.** As the halogen atoms get larger, it becomes more difficult to fit three halogen atoms around the small nitrogen atom, and the NX_3 molecule becomes less stable. **109. a.** NaBr: In $NaBr_2$ the sodium ion would have a +2 charge assuming each bromine has a −1 charge. Sodium doesn't form stable Na^{2+} compounds. **b.** ClO_4^-: ClO_4 has 31 valence electrons so it is impossible to satisfy the octet rule for all atoms in ClO_4. The extra electron from the −1 charge in ClO_4^- allows for complete octets for all atoms. **c.** XeO_4: We can't draw a Lewis structure that obeys the octet rule for SO_4 (30 electrons), unlike with XeO_4 (32 electrons). **d.** SeF_4: Both compounds require the central atom to expand its octet. O is too small and doesn't have low-energy d orbitals to expand its octet (which is true for all Period 2 elements). **111. a.** radius: $N^+ < N < N^-$; IE: $N^- < N < N^+$; **b.** radius: $Cl^+ < Cl < Se < Se^-$; IE: $Se^- < Se < Cl < Cl^+$; **c.** radius: $Sr^{2+} < Rb^+ < Br^-$; IE: $Br^- < Rb^+ < Sr^{2+}$. **113.** I; square pyramid **115.** Yes; each structure has the same number of effective pairs around the central atom, giving the same predicted molecular structure for each compound/ion. (A multiple bond is counted as a single group of electrons.) **117.** From VSEPR, the molecular structure would be linear. Using hyperconjugation, the resonance structures are

119. -562 kJ   **121. a.** The most likely structures are

There are other possible resonance structures, but these are most likely. **b.** The NNN, ONN, and ONO bond angles should be about 120°. **c.** $NH_4N(NO_2)_2(s) \rightarrow 2N_2(g) + 2H_2O(g) + O_2(g)$, $\Delta E = -893$ kJ; **d.** To estimate ΔE, we ignored the ionic interactions between NH_4^+ and $N(NO_2)_2^-$. In addition, we assumed the bond energies in Table 13.6 applied to the $N(NO_2)_2^-$ bonds in any one of the resonance structures above. This is a bad assumption since molecules that exhibit resonance generally have stronger overall bonds than predicted. All of these assumptions give an estimated ΔE value that is too negative. **123. a. i.** -2636 kJ; **ii.** -3471 kJ; **iii.** -3543 kJ; **b.** reaction iii, -8085 kJ/kg **125.** 17 kJ/mol

Chapter 3

23. 47.88 amu; Ti   **25.** 108.9 amu   **27.** 185 amu   **29.** There are three peaks in the mass spectrum, each two mass units apart. This is consistent with two isotopes, differing in mass by two mass units. The peak at 157.84 corresponds to a Br_2 molecule composed of two atoms of the lighter isotope. This isotope has mass equal to 157.84/2 or 78.92, which corresponds to ^{79}Br. The second isotope is ^{81}Br with mass equal to 161.84/2 = 80.92. The peaks in the mass spectrum correspond to $^{79}Br_2$, $^{79}Br^{81}Br$, and $^{81}Br_2$, in order of increasing mass. The intensities of the highest and lowest masses tell us the two isotopes are present at about equal abundance. The actual abundance is 50.68% ^{79}Br and 49.32% ^{81}Br.   **31.** GaAs can be either $^{69}GaAs$ or

$^{71}GaAs$. The mass spectrum for GaAs will have 2 peaks at 144 (69 + 75) and 146 (71 + 75) with intensities in the ratio of 60:40 or 3:2. Ga_2As_2 can be $^{69}Ga_2As_2$, $^{69}Ga^{71}GaAs_2$, or $^{71}Ga_2As_2$. The mass spectrum will have 3 peaks at 288, 290, and 292 with intensities in the ratio of 36:48:16 or 9:12:4.   **33. a.** 180.158 g/mol; **b.** 2.78×10^{-3} mol; 1.67×10^{21} molecules   **35. a.** 1.03×10^{-4} mol; **b.** 4.52×10^{-3} mol; **c.** 3.41×10^{-2} mol   **37.** 4.0 g He < 1.0 mol F_2 < 44.0 g CO_2 < 4.0 g H_2 < 146 g SF_6 **39. a.** 165.39 g/mol; **b.** 3.023 mol; **c.** 3.3 g; **d.** 5.5×10^{22} atoms; **e.** 1.6 g; **f.** 1.373×10^{-19} g   **41.** 71.40% C; 8.689% H; 5.648% F; 14.26% O   **43.** 13.35% Y, 41.22% Ba, 28.62% Cu, and 16.81% O   **45.** Only NO is 46.7% N by mass, so NO could be this species. Any other compound having NO as an empirical formula could also be the compound.   **47.** 6.54×10^4 g/mol   **49. a.** 40.002% C, 6.7135% H, 53.285% O; **b.** 40.002% C, 6.7136% H, 53.284% O; **c.** 40.002% C, 6.7135% H, 53.285% O; All three compounds have the same empirical formula, CH_2O, but different molecular formulas. The composition of all three in mass percent is also the same (within rounding differences). Therefore, elemental analysis will give us only the empirical formula.   **51. a.** $S_4N_4H_4$; **b.** $N_3P_3Cl_6$; **c.** $Co_2C_8O_8$; **d.** S_4N_4 **53.** HgO and Hg_2O **55.** $C_7H_5N_3O_6$ **57.** $P_5N_5Cl_{10}$ **59.** $C_3H_4O_3$; $C_6H_8O_6$ **61.** Only one product is formed in this representation. This product has two Ys bonded to an X. The other substance present in the product mixture is just the excess of one of the reactants (Y). The best equation has smallest whole numbers. Here, answer c would be this smallest whole number equation (X + 2Y → XY_2). Answers a and b have incorrect products listed, and for answer d, an equation includes only the reactants that go to produce the product; excess reactants are not shown in an equation.   **63. a.** $C_6H_{12}O_6(s) + 6O_2(g) \rightarrow 6CO_2(g) + 6H_2O(g)$; **b.** $Fe_2S_3(s) + 6HCl(g) \rightarrow 2FeCl_3(s) + 3H_2S(g)$; **c.** $CS_2(l) + 2NH_3(g) \rightarrow H_2S(g) + NH_4SCN(s)$ **65. a.** $16Cr(s) + 3S_8(s) \rightarrow 8Cr_2S_3(s)$; **b.** $2NaHCO_3(s) \rightarrow Na_2CO_3(s) + CO_2(g) + H_2O(g)$; **c.** $2KClO_3(s) \rightarrow 2KCl(s) + 3O_2(g)$; **d.** $2Eu(s) + 6HF(g) \rightarrow 2EuF_3(s) + 3H_2(g)$; **e.** $2C_6H_6(l) + 15O_2(g) \rightarrow 12CO_2(g) + 6H_2O(g)$ **67.** 4355 g   **69.** 21.5 g Fe_2O_3; 7.26 g Al; 13.7 g Al_2O_3 **71.** 2.8 days   **73.** 150 g   **75.** $2NO(g) + O_2(g) \rightarrow 2NO_2(g)$; NO is limiting.   **77.** 0.301 g H_2O_2; 3.6×10^{-2} g HCl   **79.** 1.20 metric tons   **81.** 2.81×10^6 g HCN; 5.63×10^6 g H_2O **83.** 99.8 g F_2 **85.** 4.30×10^{-2} mol; 2.50 g   **87.** M is yttrium, and X is chlorine. Yttrium(III) chloride; 1.84 g   **89.** 5   **91.** Al_2Se_3 **93.** 42.8%   **95.** 83.40%   **97.** 86.2%   **99.** 86.92 amu   **101.** I. NH_3; II. N_2H_4; III. HN_3; If we set the atomic mass of H equal to 1.008, then the atomic mass of N is 14.01.   **103.** 87.8 amu   **105.** $C_{20}H_{30}O$ **107.** The gas mixture consists of $^{16}O^{16}O$, $^{16}O^{18}O$, and ^{40}Ar. The isotope composition is 42.82% ^{16}O, 8.6×10^{-2}% ^{18}O, and 57.094% ^{40}Ar.   **109.** 207 amu; Pb   **111.** Ge   **113.** 184 amu   **115.** 1.05 mol   **117.** 10.% La^{2+}, 90.% La^{3+} **119.** 32.9%   **121.** 0.48 mol

Chapter 4

11. Solution A has the most molecules per unit volume so solution A is most concentrated. This is followed by solution D, then solution C. Solution B has the fewest molecules per unit volume, so solution B is least concentrated.   **13. a.** *Polarity* is a term applied to covalent compounds. Polar covalent compounds have an unequal sharing of electrons in bonds that results in unequal charge distribution in the overall molecule. Polar molecules have a partial negative end and a partial positive end. These are not full charges as in ionic compounds but are charges much smaller in magnitude. Water is a polar molecule and dissolves other polar solutes readily. The oxygen end of water (the partial negative end of the polar water molecule) aligns with the partial positive end of the polar solute, whereas the hydrogens of water (the partial positive end of the polar water molecule) align with the partial negative end of the solute. These opposite-charge attractions stabilize polar solutes in water. This process is called *hydration.* Nonpolar solutes do not have permanent partial negative and partial positive ends; nonpolar solutes are not stabilized in water and do not dissolve. b. KF is a soluble ionic compound, so it is a strong electrolyte. KF(aq) actually exists as separate hydrated K^+ ions and hydrated F^- ions in solution: $C_6H_{12}O_6$ is a polar covalent molecule that is a nonelectrolyte. $C_6H_{12}O_6$ is hydrated as described in part a. c. RbCl is a soluble ionic compound, so it exists as separate hydrated Rb^+ ions and hydrated Cl^- ions in solution. AgCl is an insoluble ionic compound, so the ions stay together in solution and fall to the bottom of the container as a precipitate. d. HNO_3 is a strong acid and exists as separate hydrated H^+ ions and hydrated NO_3^- ions in solution. CO is a polar covalent molecule and is hydrated as explained in part a. **15.** a. picture iv; b. picture ii; c. picture iii; d. picture i; **17.** a. Place 20.0 g NaOH in a 2-L volumetric flask; add water to dissolve the NaOH, and fill to the mark with water, mixing several times along the way. b. Add 500. mL of 1.00 M NaOH stock solution to a 2-L volumetric flask; fill to the mark with water, mixing several times along the way. c. Similar to the solution made in part a, instead using 38.8 g K_2CrO_4. d. Similar to the solution made in part b, instead using 114 mL of the 1.75 M K_2CrO_4 stock solution. **19.** 4.00 g **21.** 100.0 mL of 0.30 M $AlCl_3$ contains the most moles of Cl^- ions. **23.** 4.5 M **25.** 5.95×10^{-8} M **27.** a. 2.5×10^{-8} M; b. 8.4×10^{-9} M; c. 1.33×10^{-4} M; d. 2.8×10^{-7} M **29.** Bromides: NaBr, KBr, and NH_4Br (and others) would be soluble, and AgBr, $PbBr_2$, and Hg_2Br_2 would be insoluble. Sulfates: Na_2SO_4, K_2SO_4, and $(NH_4)_2SO_4$ (and others) would be soluble, and $BaSO_4$, $CaSO_4$, and $PbSO_4$ (or Hg_2SO_4) would be insoluble. Hydroxides: NaOH, KOH, $Ca(OH)_2$ (and others) would be soluble, and $Al(OH)_3$, $Fe(OH)_3$, and $Cu(OH)_2$ (and others) would be insoluble. Phosphates: Na_3PO_4, K_3PO_4, $(NH_4)_3PO_4$ (and others) would be soluble, and Ag_3PO_4, $Ca_3(PO_4)_2$, and $FePO_4$ (and others) would be insoluble. Lead: $PbCl_2$, $PbBr_2$, PbI_2, $Pb(OH)_2$, $PbSO_4$, and PbS (and others) would be insoluble. $Pb(NO_3)_2$ would be a soluble Pb^{2+} salt. **31.** a. precipitate = Hg_2SO_4; b. no precipitate forms; c. precipitate = $MgCO_3$; d. precipitate = $Al_2(CrO_4)_3$ **33.** a. $(NH_4)_2SO_4(aq) + Ba(NO_3)_2(aq) \rightarrow 2NH_4NO_3(aq) + BaSO_4(s)$; $2NH_4^+(aq) + SO_4^{2-}(aq) + Ba^{2+}(aq) + 2NO_3^-(aq) \rightarrow 2NH_4^+(aq) + 2NO_3^-(aq) + BaSO_4(s)$; $Ba^{2+}(aq) + SO_4^{2-}(aq) \rightarrow BaSO_4(s)$; b. $Pb(NO_3)_2(aq) + 2NaCl(aq) \rightarrow PbCl_2(s) + 2NaNO_3(aq)$; $Pb^{2+}(aq) + 2NO_3^-(aq) + 2Na^+(aq) + 2Cl^-(aq) \rightarrow PbCl_2(s) + 2Na^+(aq) + 2NO_3^-(aq)$; $Pb^{2+}(aq) + 2Cl^-(aq) \rightarrow PbCl_2(s)$; c. No reaction occurs since all possible products are soluble. d. No reaction occurs since all possible products are soluble. e. $CuCl_2(aq) + 2NaOH(aq) \rightarrow Cu(OH)_2(s) + 2NaCl(aq)$; $Cu^{2+}(aq) + 2Cl^-(aq) + 2Na^+(aq) + 2OH^-(aq) \rightarrow Cu(OH)_2(s) + 2Na^+(aq) + 2Cl^-(aq)$; $Cu^{2+}(aq) + 2OH^-(aq) \rightarrow Cu(OH)_2(s)$ **35.** a. When $CuSO_4(aq)$ is added to $Na_2S(aq)$, the precipitate that forms is CuS(s). Therefore, Na^+ (the gray spheres) and SO_4^{2-} (the bluish green spheres) are the spectator ions. $CuSO_4(aq) + Na_2S(aq) \rightarrow CuS(s) + Na_2SO_4(aq)$; $Cu^{2+}(aq) + S^{2-}(aq) \rightarrow CuS(s)$ b. When $CoCl_2(aq)$ is added to NaOH(aq), the precipitate that forms is $Co(OH)_2(s)$. Therefore, Na^+ (the gray spheres) and Cl^- (the green spheres) are the spectator ions. $CoCl_2(aq) + 2NaOH(aq) \rightarrow Co(OH)_2(s) + 2NaCl(aq)$; $Co^{2+}(aq) + 2OH^-(aq) \rightarrow Co(OH)_2(s)$ c. When $AgNO_3(aq)$ is added to KI(aq), the precipitate that forms is AgI(s). Therefore, K^+ (the red spheres) and NO_3^- (the blue spheres) are the spectator ions. $AgNO_3(aq) + KI(aq) \rightarrow AgI(s) + KNO_3(aq)$; $Ag^+(aq) + I^-(aq) \rightarrow AgI(s)$ **37.** From the solubility rules in Table 4.1, the possible cations could be Ba^{2+} and Ca^{2+}. **39.** 2.9 g AgCl; 0.050 M Cl^-; 0.10 M NO_3^-; 0.075 M Ca^{2+} **41.** 0.607 g **43.** 16.2% **45.** 39.49 mg/tablet; 67.00% **47.** 23 amu; Na **49.** a. Perchloric acid reacted with potassium hydroxide is a possibility. $HClO_4(aq) + KOH(aq) \rightarrow H_2O(l) + KClO_4(aq)$; b. Nitric acid reacted with cesium hydroxide is a possibility. $HNO_3(aq) + CsOH(aq) \rightarrow H_2O(l) + CsNO_3(aq)$;

c. Hydroiodic acid reacted with calcium hydroxide is a possibility. $2HI(aq) + Ca(OH)_2(aq) \rightarrow 2H_2O(l) + CaI_2(aq)$ **51.** a. 50.0 mL; b. 25.0 mL; c. 8.33 mL; d. 33.3 mL; e. 25.0 mL; f. 8.33 mL **53.** The acid is a diprotic acid (H_2A), meaning that it has two H^+ ions in the formula to donate to a base. The reaction is $H_2A(aq) + 2NaOH(aq) \rightarrow 2H_2O(l) + Na_2A(aq)$, where A^{2-} is what is left over from the acid formula when the two protons (H^+ ions) are reacted. For the HCl reaction, the base has the ability to accept two protons. The most common examples are $Ca(OH)_2$, $Sr(OH)_2$, and $Ba(OH)_2$. A possible reaction would be $2HCl(aq) + Ca(OH)_2(aq) \rightarrow 2H_2O(l) + CaCl_2(aq)$. **55.** 4.7×10^{-2} M **57.** a. 0.8393 M; b. 5.010% **59.** The resulting solution is not neutral. 5.9×10^{-3} M OH^- **61.** 2.0×10^{-2} M OH^- **63.** a. The species reduced is the element that gains electrons. The reducing agent causes reduction to occur by itself being oxidized. The reducing agent generally refers to the entire formula of the compound/ion that contains the element oxidized. b. The species oxidized is the element that loses electrons. The oxidizing agent causes oxidation to occur by being reduced itself. The oxidizing agent generally refers to the entire formula of the compound/ion that contains the element reduced. c. For simple binary ionic compounds, the actual charge on the ions are the oxidation states. For covalent substances, nonzero oxidation states are imaginary charges the elements would have if they were held together by ionic bonds (assuming the bond is between two different nonmetals). Nonzero oxidation states for elements in covalent compounds are not actual charges. Oxidation states for covalent compounds are a bookkeeping method to keep track of electrons in a reaction. **65.** a. K, +1; O, −2; Mn, +7; b. Ni, +4; O, −2; c. Fe, +2; d. H, +1; O, −2; N, −3; P, +5; e. P, +3; O, −2; f. O, −2; Fe, $+\frac{8}{3}$; g. O, −2; F, −1; Xe, +6; h. S, +4; F, −1; i. C, +2; O, −2; j. C, 0; H, +1; O, −2 **67.** a. Sr, +2; O, −2; Cr, +6; b. Cu, +2; Cl, −1; c. O, 0; d. H, +1; O, −1; e. Mg, +2; O, −2; C, +4; f. Ag, 0; g. Pb, +2; O, −2; S, +4; h. O, −2; Pb, +4; i. Na, +1; O, −2; C, +3; j. O, −2; C, +4; k. H, +1; N, −3; O, −2; S, +6; Ce, +4; l. O, −2; Cr, +3 **69.** a. $2Al(s) + 6HCl(aq) \rightarrow 2AlCl_3(aq) + 3H_2(g)$; H is reduced, and Al is oxidized. b. $CH_4(g) + 4S(s) \rightarrow CS_2(l) + 2H_2S(g)$; S is reduced, and C is oxidized. c. $C_3H_8(g) + 5O_2(g) \rightarrow 3CO_2(g) + 4H_2O(l)$; O is reduced, and C is oxidized. d. $Cu(s) + 2Ag^+(aq) \rightarrow 2Ag(s) + Cu^{2+}(aq)$; Ag is reduced, and Cu is oxidized. **71.** a. $3Cu(s) + 8H^+(aq) + 2NO_3^-(aq) \rightarrow 3Cu^{2+}(aq) + 2NO(g) + 4H_2O(l)$; b. $14H^+(aq) + Cr_2O_7^{2-}(aq) + 6Cl^-(aq) \rightarrow 3Cl_2(g) + 2Cr^{3+}(aq) + 7H_2O(l)$; c. $Pb(s) + 2H_2SO_4(aq) + PbO_2(s) \rightarrow 2PbSO_4(s) + 2H_2O(l)$; d. $14H^+(aq) + 2Mn^{2+}(aq) + 5NaBiO_3(s) \rightarrow 2MnO_4^-(aq) + 5Bi^{3+}(aq) + 5Na^+(aq) + 7H_2O(l)$; e. $8H^+(aq) + H_3AsO_4(aq) + 4Zn(s) \rightarrow 4Zn^{2+}(aq) + AsH_3(g) + 4H_2O(l)$; f. $7H_2O(l) + 4H^+(aq) + 3As_2O_3(s) + 4NO_3^-(aq) \rightarrow 4NO(g) + 6H_3AsO_4(aq)$; g. $16H^+(aq) + 2MnO_4^-(aq) + 10Br^-(aq) \rightarrow 5Br_2(l) + 2Mn^{2+}(aq) + 8H_2O(l)$; h. $8H^+(aq) + 3CH_3OH(aq) + Cr_2O_7^{2-}(aq) \rightarrow 2Cr^{3+}(aq) + 3CH_2O(aq) + 7H_2O(l)$ **73.** a. $8HCl(aq) + 2Fe(s) \rightarrow 2HFeCl_4(aq) + 3H_2(g)$; b. $6H^+(aq) + 8I^-(aq) + IO_3^-(aq) \rightarrow 3I_3^-(aq) + 3H_2O(l)$; c. $97Ce^{4+}(aq) + 54H_2O(l) + Cr(NCS)_6^{4-}(aq) \rightarrow 97Ce^{3+}(aq) + Cr^{3+}(aq) + 6NO_3^-(aq) + 6CO_2(g) + 6SO_4^{2-}(aq) + 108H^+(aq)$; d. $64OH^-(aq) + 2CrI_3(s) + 27Cl_2(g) \rightarrow 54Cl^-(aq) + 2CrO_4^{2-}(aq) + 6IO_4^-(aq) + 32H_2O(l)$; e. $258OH^-(aq) + Fe(CN)_6^{4-}(aq) + 61Ce^{4+}(aq) \rightarrow Fe(OH)_3(s) + 61Ce(OH)_3(s) + 6CO_3^{2-}(aq) + 6NO_3^-(aq) + 36H_2O(l)$ **75.** 1.622×10^{-2} M **77.** 34.6% **79.** 49.4 mL **81.** 173 mL **83.** a. 14.2%; b. 8.95 mL **85.** a. 24.8% Co, 29.7% Cl, 5.09% H, 40.4% O; b. $CoCl_2 \cdot 6H_2O$; c. $CoCl_2 \cdot 6H_2O(aq) + 2AgNO_3(aq) \rightarrow 2AgCl(s) + Co(NO_3)_2(aq) + 6H_2O(l)$, $CoCl_2 \cdot 6H_2O(aq) + 2NaOH(aq) \rightarrow Co(OH)_2(s) + 2NaCl(aq) + 6H_2O(l)$, $4Co(OH)_2(s) + O_2(g) \rightarrow 2Co_2O_3(s) + 4H_2O(l)$ **87.** 72.4% KCl; 27.6% NaCl **89.** 2.00 M **91.** 0.0785 ± 0.0002 M **93.** three acidic hydrogens **95.** 3.442% **97.** a. 31.3%; b. 6.00 M

99. 14.6 g Zn, 14.4 g Ag **101.** 77.1% KCl; 22.9% KBr

103. a. $\dfrac{\text{mass of AgCl}}{\text{mass of PCB}} = \dfrac{143.4\,n}{154.20 + 34.44\,n}$ or

$\text{mass}_{\text{AgCl}}(154.20 + 34.44\,n) = \text{mass}_{\text{PCB}}(143.4\,n)$; **b.** 7.097
105. a. 5.35×10^4 L/s; **b.** 4.25 ppm; **c.** 1.69×10^6 g; **d.** 10.3 ppm
107. a. $YBa_2Cu_3O_{6.5}$: +2; only Cu^{2+} present; $YBa_2Cu_3O_7$: +2.33;
two Cu^{2+} and one Cu^{3+} present; $YBa_2Cu_3O_8$: +3; only Cu^{3+} present;
b. $2Cu^{2+}(aq) + 5I^-(aq) \rightarrow 2CuI(s) + I_3^-(aq)$; $Cu^{3+}(aq) + 4I^-(aq) \rightarrow$
$CuI(s) + I_3^-(aq)$; $2S_2O_3^{2-}(aq) + I_3^-(aq) \rightarrow 3I^-(aq) + S_4O_6^{2-}(aq)$;
c. $YBa_2Cu_3O_{7.25}$; +2.50 **109.** 24.99% $AgNO_3$; 40.07% $CuCl_2$;
34.94% $FeCl_3$

Chapter 15

11. A possible balanced equation is $2A + 3B \rightarrow 4C$.
13. $\dfrac{d[NH_3]}{dt} = -\dfrac{2}{3}\dfrac{d[H_2]}{dt}$ **15.** $L^{1/2}\,mol^{-1/2}\,s^{-1}$
17. a. Rate $= k[NO]^2[Cl_2]$; **b.** $k_{\text{mean}} = 1.8 \times 10^2\,L^2\,mol^{-2}\,min^{-1}$
19. a. Rate $= k[NOCl]^2$; **b.** $k_{\text{mean}} = 6.6 \times 10^{-29}\,cm^3\,molecules^{-1}$
s^{-1}; **c.** $4.0 \times 10^{-8}\,L\,mol^{-1}\,s^{-1}$ **21. a.** Rate $= k[ClO_2]^2[OH^-]$;
$k_{\text{mean}} = 2.30 \times 10^2\,L^2\,mol^{-2}\,s^{-1}$; **b.** $0.594\,mol\,L^{-1}\,s^{-1}$
23. Rate $= k[H_2SeO_3][H^+]^2[I^-]^3$; $k_{\text{mean}} = 5.2 \times 10^5\,L^5\,mol^{-5}\,s^{-1}$
25. Rate $= \dfrac{k[I^-][OCl^-]}{[OH^-]}$; $k_{\text{mean}} = 60.\,s^{-1}$ **27.** The first-order half-life
is independent of concentration, the zero-order half-life is directly
related to the concentration, and the second-order half-life is
inversely related to concentration. For a first-order reaction, if the
first half-life equals 20. s, the second half-life will also be 20. s
because the half-life for a first-order reaction is concentration-
independent. The second half-life for a zero-order reaction will be
$1/2(20.) = 10.$ s. This is so because the half-life for a zero-order reaction has a direct relationship with concentration (as the concentration decreases by a factor of 2, the half-life decreases by a factor of
2). Because a second-order reaction has an inverse relationship
between $t_{1/2}$ and $[A]_0$, the second half-life will be 40. s (twice the
first half-life value). **29. a.** Rate $= k[A]$; $\ln[A] = -kt + \ln[A]_0$;
$k = 2.97 \times 10^{-2}\,min^{-1}$; **b.** 23.3 min; **c.** 69.9 min **31.** $\ln[H_2O_2] =$
$-kt + \ln[H_2O_2]_0$; Rate $= k[H_2O_2]$; $k = 8.3 \times 10^{-4}\,s^{-1}$; $0.037\,M$
33. $\dfrac{1}{[NO_2]} = kt + \dfrac{1}{[NO_2]_0}$; Rate $= k[NO_2]^2$; $k = 2.08 \times 10^{-4}$
$L\,mol^{-1}\,s^{-1}$; $0.131\,M$ **35.** The rate law and integrated rate law are
Rate $= k = 1.7 \times 10^{-4}\,atm/s$; $P_{C_2H_5OH} = -kt + 250.\,torr\left(\dfrac{1\,atm}{760\,torr}\right)$
$= -kt + 0.329\,atm$; At 900. s, $P_{C_2H_5OH} = 130$ torr **37. a.** The reac-
tion is first order with respect to NO and first order with respect to
O_3. **b.** Rate $= k[NO][O_3]$; **c.** $k' = 1.8\,s^{-1}$; $k'' = 3.6\,s^{-1}$; **d.** $1.8 \times$
$10^{-14}\,cm^3\,molecules^{-1}\,s^{-1}$ **39.** $1.6\,L\,mol^{-1}\,s^{-1}$ **41.** 150. s
43. 12.5 s **45. a.** 160. s for both; **b.** 532 s **47. a.** 0.07 M;
b. 34.7 min **49.** $4.2 \times 10^{-5}\,mol\,L^{-1}\,h^{-1}$ **51. a.** 1.15×10^2
$L^3\,mol^{-3}\,s^{-1}$; **b.** 87.0 s; **c.** $[B] = 1.00\,M$; $[A] = 1.27 \times 10^{-5}\,M$
53. In a unimolecular reaction, a single-reactant molecule decom-
poses to products. In a bimolecular reaction, two molecules collide
to give products. The probability of the simultaneous collision of
three molecules with enough energy and proper orientation is very
small, making termolecular steps very unlikely. **55. a.** Rate $=$
$k[CH_3NC]$; **b.** Rate $= k[O_3][NO]$; **c.** Rate $= k[O_3]$; **d.** Rate $=$
$k[O_3][O]$; **e.** Rate $= k[_6^{14}C]$ or rate $= kN$ where $N =$ the number of
$_6^{14}C$ atoms **57.** Rate $= k[C_4H_9Br]$; $C_4H_9Br + 2H_2O \rightarrow C_4H_9OH +$
$Br^- + H_3O^+$; the intermediates are $C_4H_9^+$ and $C_4H_9OH_2^+$
59. mechanism b **61.** Rate $= \dfrac{k_3k_2k_1}{k_{-2}k_{-1}}[Br^-][BrO_3^-][H^+]^2 =$
$k[Br^-][BrO_3^-][H^+]^2$ **63.** Rate $= \dfrac{k_2k_1[I^-][OCl^-]}{k_{-1}[OH^-]} = \dfrac{k[I^-][OCl^-]}{[OH^-]}$
65. a. $MoCl_5^-$; **b.** Rate $= \dfrac{d[NO_2^-]}{dt} = \dfrac{k_1k_2[NO_3^-][MoCl_6^{2-}]}{k_{-1}[Cl^-] + k_2[NO_3^-]}$

67. a. Rate $= \dfrac{d[E]}{dt} = \dfrac{k_1k_2[B]^2}{k_{-1}[B] + k_2}$; **b.** When $k_2 << k_{-1}[B]$, then
the reaction is first order in B. **c.** Collisions between B molecules
only transfer energy from one B to another. This occurs at a much
faster rate than the decomposition of an energetic B molecule (B^*).
69. Two reasons are: **a.** The collision must involve enough energy to
produce the reaction; that is, the collision energy must be equal to or
exceed the activation energy. **b.** The relative orientation of the reactants when they collide must allow formation of any new bonds necessary to produce products. **71. a.** $T_2 > T_1$; as temperature
increases, the distribution of collision energies shifts to the right. That
is, as temperature increases, there are fewer collision energies with
small energies and more collisions with large energies. **b.** As temperature increases, more of the collisions have the required activation
energy necessary to convert reactants into products. Hence, the rate
of the reaction increases with increasing temperature. **73.** $9.5 \times$
$10^{-5}\,L\,mol^{-1}\,s^{-1}$ **75.** 51°C **77. a.** 91.5 kJ/mol; **b.** $3.54 \times 10^{14}\,s^{-1}$;
c. $3.24 \times 10^{-2}\,s^{-1}$ **79.** A plot of $\ln(k)$ versus $\dfrac{1}{T}$ gives a straight line
with negative slope equal to $-E_a/R$ (see *Solutions Guide* for plot).
$E_a = 11.2$ kJ/mol

81.

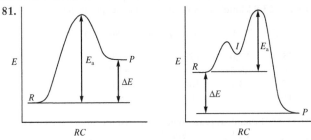

d. See plot for the intermediate plateau, which represents the energy
of the intermediate. The two steps in the mechanism are $R \rightarrow I$ and
$I \rightarrow P$. In a mechanism, the rate of the slowest step determines the
rate of the reaction. The activation energy for the slowest step will be
the largest energy barrier that the reaction must overcome. Since the
second hump in the diagram is at the highest energy, then the second
step ($I \rightarrow P$) has the largest activation energy and will be the rate-
determining step (the slow step). **83.** 139 kJ/mol **85. a.** The blue
plot is the catalyzed pathway. The catalyzed pathway has the lower
activation. This is why the catalyzed pathway is faster. **b.** ΔE_1 represents the activation energy for the uncatalyzed pathway. **c.** ΔE_2 represents the energy difference between the reactants and products.
Note that ΔE_2 is the same for both the catalyzed and the uncatalyzed
pathways. It is the activation energy that is different for a catalyzed
pathway versus an uncatalyzed pathway. **d.** Because the products
have a higher total energy as compared to reactants, this is an endothermic reaction. **87. a.** W, because it has a lower activation energy
than the Os catalyst. **b.** The W-catalyzed reaction is approximately
10^{30} times faster than the uncatalyzed reaction. **c.** Because $[H_2]$ is in
the denominator of the rate law, the presence of H_2 decreases the rate
of the reaction. For the decomposition to occur, NH_3 molecules must
be adsorbed on the surface of the catalyst. If H_2 is also adsorbed on
the catalyst surface, then there are fewer sites for NH_3 molecules to
be adsorbed, and the rate decreases. **89.** Since the chlorine atom–
catalyzed reaction has a lower activation energy, then the Cl-catalyzed
rate is faster. Hence, Cl is a more effective catalyst. **91.** At high $[S]$,
the enzyme is completely saturated with substrate. Once the enzyme
is completely saturated, the rate of decomposition of ES can no longer
increase and the overall rate remains constant. **93.** ~1 second
95. The most common method to experimentally determine the differential rate law is the method of initial rates. Once the differential
rate law is determined experimentally, the integrated rate law can be
derived. However, sometimes it is more convenient and more accurate to collect concentration versus time data for a reactant. When
this is the case, then we do "proof" plots to determine the integrated

rate law. Once the integrated rate law is determined, the differential rate law can be determined. Either experimental procedure allows determination of both the integrated and the differential rate; which rate law is determined by experiment and which is derived is usually decided by which data is easiest and most accurately collected. 97. The experimentally determined rate law is Rate = k[DNA][CH$_3$I]. Mechanism I is possible because the derived rate law from the mechanism (Rate = k[DNA][CH$_3$I]) agrees with the experimentally determined rate law. The derived rate law for Mechanism II will equal the rate of the slowest step. This is step 1 in the mechanism, giving a derived rate law that is Rate = k[CH$_3$I]. Because this rate law does not agree with experiment, Mechanism II would not be a possible mechanism for the reaction. 99. a. untreated: $k = 0.465$ day^{-1}; deacidifying agent: $k = 0.659$ day^{-1}; antioxidant: $k = 0.779$ day^{-1}; b. No, the silk degrades more rapidly with the additives; c. untreated: $t_{1/2} = 1.49$ day; deacidifying agent: $t_{1/2} = 1.05$ day; antioxidant: $t_{1/2} = 0.890$ day 101. Carbon cannot form the fifth bond necessary for the transition state because of the small atomic size of carbon and because carbon doesn't have low-energy d orbitals available to expand the octet. 103. a. Second order; b. 17.1 s ≈ 20 s; c. 34.6 s ≈ 30 s; d. 847 s; e. 31 kJ/mol 105. 29.8 kJ/mol 107. a. 53.9 kJ/mol; b. 83 chirps per minute per insect;

T (°C)	T (°F)	k (min^{-1})	42 + 0.80 (k/4)
25.0	77.0	178	78°F
20.3	68.5	126	67°F
17.3	63.1	100.	62°F
15.0	59.0	83	59°F

The rule of thumb appears to be fairly accurate, about ±1°F. 109. Rate = $\dfrac{d[Cl_2]}{dt} = \dfrac{k_1 k_2 [NO_2Cl]^2}{k_{-1}[NO_2] + k_2[NO_2Cl]}$ 111. a. Rate = k[CH$_3$X], $k = 0.93$ h^{-1}; b. 8.80 × 10^{-10} h; c. 3.0 × 10^2 kJ/mol; d. The activation energy is close to the C—X bond energy. A plausible mechanism is

$$CH_3X \longrightarrow CH_3 + X \quad \text{(slow)}$$
$$CH_3 + Y \longrightarrow CH_3Y \quad \text{(fast)}$$

113. 160 s 115. Rate = k[A][B]^2, $k = 1.4 \times 10^{-2}$ L^2 mol^{-2} s^{-1} 117. Rate = $\dfrac{-d[N_2O_5]}{dt} = \dfrac{2k_1 k_2 [M][N_2O_5]}{k_{-1}[M] + 2k_2}$ 119. a. Both are first order. b. $k_1 = 0.82$ L mol^{-1} min^{-1}; $k_2 = 9.5$ L^2 mol^{-2} min^{-1} c. There are two pathways, one involving H$^+$ with rate = k_2[H$^+$][I$^-$][H$_2$O$_2$] and another pathway not involving H$^+$ with rate = k_1[I$^-$][H$_2$O$_2$]. The overall rate of reaction depends on which of these two pathways dominates, and this depends on the H$^+$ concentration.

Chapter 5

21. 47.5 torr; 6.33 × 10^3 Pa; 6.25 × 10^{-2} atm 23. 1.01 × 10^5 Pa; 10.3 m 25. a. 3.6 × 10^3 mm Hg; b. 3.6 × 10^3 torr; c. 4.9 × 10^5 Pa; d. 71 psi 27. The decrease in temperature causes the balloon to contract (V and T are directly related). Because weather balloons do expand, the effect of the decrease in pressure must be dominant. 29. $P_{H_2} = 317$ torr; $P_{N_2} = 50.7$ torr; $P_{Total} = 368$ torr 31. 309 g 33. 3.08 atm; $P_{CO_2} = 3.08$ atm, $P_{Total} = 4.05$ atm 35. 4.44 × 10^3 g He; 2.24 × 10^3 g H$_2$ 37. 7.0 × 10^2°C 39. 12.5 mL 41. $n_2/n_1 = 0.921$ 43. a. The He flask has 1.5 times as many atoms of gas present as the Ne flask, so the pressure in the He flask will be 1.5 times greater (assuming a constant temperature). b. Because the flask volumes are the same, your drawing should have the various atoms equally distributed between the two flasks. So each flask should have 3 He atoms and 2 Ne atoms. c. $P_{final} = \frac{5}{6}P_{He, initial} = \frac{5}{4}P_{Ne, initial}$; d. $P_{He, final} = \dfrac{P_{He, initial}}{2}$; $P_{Ne, final} = \dfrac{P_{Ne, initial}}{2}$ 45. 3.69 L

47. a. $\chi_{CH_4} = 0.412$, $\chi_{O_2} = 0.588$; b. 0.161 mol; c. 1.06 g CH$_4$, 3.03 g O$_2$ 49. $P_{N_2} = 1.1$ atm; $P_{O_2} = 0.10$ atm; $P_{NH_3} = 0.18$ atm; $P_{total} = 1.4$ atm 51. Rigid container: pressure increases, density is constant; flexible container: pressure is constant, density decreases 53. N$_2$H$_4$ 55. The calculated molar masses are 209 g/mol from data set I and 202 g/mol from data set II. These values are close to the expected molar mass (207 g/mol) for the divalent metal compound, Be(C$_5$H$_7$O$_2$)$_2$. 57. 1.16% 59. 1.5 × 10^7 g Fe; 2.6 × 10^7 g 98% H$_2$SO$_4$ 61. 46.5% 63. $P_{N_2} = 0.74$ atm; $P_{Total} = 2.2$ atm 65. 18.0% 67. 13.3% 69. 0.333 atm 71. 2NH$_3(g) \rightarrow$ N$_2(g) +$ 3H$_2(g)$: As reactants are converted into products, we go from 2 mol of gaseous reactants to 4 mol of gaseous products (1 mol N$_2$ + 3 mol H$_2$). Because the moles of gas double as reactants are converted into products, the volume of the gases will double (at constant P and T). Pressure is directly related to n at constant T and V. As the reaction occurs, the moles of gas will double, so the pressure will double. Because 1 mol of N$_2$ is produced for every 2 mol of NH$_3$ reacted, $P_{N_2} = \frac{1}{2}P°_{NH_3}$. Due to the 3:2 mole ratio in the balanced equation, $P_{H_2} = \frac{3}{2}P°_{NH_3}$. Note: $P_{Total} = P_{H_2} + P_{N_2} = \frac{3}{2}P°_{NH_3} + \frac{1}{2}P°_{NH_3} = 2P°_{NH_3}$. As said earlier, the total pressure will double from the initial pressure of NH$_3$ as the reactants are completely converted into products. 73. The number of gas particles is constant, so at constant moles of gas, either a temperature change or a pressure change results in the smaller volume. If the temperature is constant, an increase in the external pressure would cause the volume to decrease. Gases are mostly empty space, so gases are easily compressible. If the pressure is constant, a decrease in temperature would cause the volume to decrease. As the temperature is lowered, the gas particles move with a slower average velocity and don't collide with the container walls as frequently and as forcefully. As a result, the internal pressure decreases. In order to keep the pressure constant, the volume of the container must decrease in order to increase the gas particle collisions per unit area. 75. a. Both gas samples have the same number of molecules present (n is constant); b. Since T is constant, (KE)$_{avg}$ must be the same for both gases [(KE)$_{avg} = \frac{3}{2}RT$]; c. The lighter gas A molecules will have the faster average velocity; d. The heavier gas B molecules do collide more forcefully, but gas A molecules, with the faster average velocity, collide more frequently. The end result is that P is constant between the two containers. 77. 3.40 × 10^3 J/mol = 5.65 × 10^{-21} J/molecule (for each gas at 273 K); 6.81 × 10^3 J/mol = 1.13 × 10^{-20} J/molecule (for each gas at 546 K) 79. No; there is a distribution of energies with only the average kinetic energy equal to $\frac{3}{2}RT$. Similarly, there is always a distribution of velocities for a gas sample at some temperature. 81. a. All the same; b. Flask C; c. Flask A 83. CF$_2$Cl$_2$ 85. 63.7 g/mol 87. a. 12.24 atm; b. 12.13 atm; c. The ideal gas law is high by 0.91%. 89. The kinetic molecular theory assumes that gas particles do not exert forces on each other and that gas particles are volumeless. Real gas particles do exert attractive forces on each other, and real gas particles do have volumes. A gas behaves most ideally at low pressures and high temperatures. The effect of attractive forces is minimized at high temperatures since the gas particles are moving very rapidly. At low pressure, the container volume is relatively large (P and V are inversely related), so the volume of the container taken up by the gas particles is negligible. 91. The pressure measured for real gases is too low compared to ideal gases. This is due to the attractions gas particles do have for each other; these attractions "hold" them back from hitting the container walls as forcefully. To make up for this slight decrease in pressure for real gases, a factor is added to the measured pressure. The measured volume is too large. A fraction of the space of the container volume is taken up by the volume of gas of the molecules themselves. Therefore, the actual volume available to real gas molecules is slightly less than the container volume. A term is subtracted from the container volume to correct for the volume taken up by real gas molecules.

93. CO_2 since it has the largest a value. **95.** $u_{rms} = 667$ m/s; $u_{mp} = 545$ m/s; $u_{avg} = 615$ m/s **97.** Impact force (H_2)/impact force $(He) = 0.7097$ **99.** The change in momentum per impact is 2.827 times larger for O_2 molecules than for He atoms. There are 2.827 times as many impacts per second for He as compared with those for O_2. **101.** 1.0×10^9 collisions/s; 1.3×10^{-6} m **103.** a. 0.19 torr; b. 6.6×10^{21} molecules/m^3; c. 6.6×10^{15} molecules/cm^3 **105.** Benzene: 9.47×10^{-3} ppmv; 2.31×10^{11} molecules/cm^3; toluene: 1.37×10^{-2} ppmv; 3.33×10^{11} molecules/cm^3 **107.** Processes a, c, and d will all result in a doubling of the pressure. Process a has the effect of halving the volume, which would double the pressure (Boyle's law). Process c doubles the pressure because the absolute temperature is doubled (from 200. K to 400. K). Process d doubles the pressure because the moles of gas are doubled (28 g N_2 is 1 mol of N_2). Process b won't double the pressure because the absolute temperature is not doubled (303 K to 333 K). **109.** 46 mL **111.** at 25°C: 2.00 atm; at 125°C: 4.00 atm **113.** $MnCl_4$ **115.** BrF_3 **117.** 1.61×10^3 g **119.** 0.990 atm; 0.625 g Zn **121.** $P_{He} = 50.0$ torr; $P_{Ne} = 76.0$ torr; $P_{Ar} = 90.0$ torr; $P_{Total} = 216.0$ torr **123.** a. 78.0%; b. 0.907 L **125.** 1490 **127.** 60.6 kJ

129. 7.00 mL **131.** a. $2CH_4(g) + 2NH_3(g) + 3O_2(g) \rightarrow 2HCN(g) + 6H_2O(g)$ b. 15.6 g/s **133.** 30.% **135.** 29.0% **137.** $dT = \dfrac{P(\text{molar mass})}{R} = \text{constant so } d = \text{constant}\left(\dfrac{1}{T}\right)$; -272.6°C **139.** 16.03 g/mol **141.** From Figure 5.16 of the text, as temperature increases, the probability that a gas particle has the most probable velocity decreases. Since the probability of the gas particle with the most probable velocity decreased by one-half, the temperature must be higher than 300. K. The temperature is 1.20×10^3 K. **143.** 1.3 L **145.** $\chi_{CO} = 0.291$; $\chi_{CO_2} = 0.564$; $\chi_{O_2} = 0.145$ **147.** a. 8.7×10^3 L air/min; b. $\chi_{CO} = 0.0017$, $\chi_{CO_2} = 0.032$, $\chi_{O_2} = 0.13$, $\chi_{N_2} = 0.77$, $\chi_{H_2O} = 0.067$; c. $P_{CO} = 0.0017$ atm, $P_{CO_2} = 0.032$ atm, $P_{O_2} = 0.13$ atm, $P_{N_2} = 0.77$ atm, $P_{H_2O} = 0.067$ atm **149.** 2.1×10^2 stages **151.** a. A given volume of air at a given set of conditions has a larger density than helium at those conditions. We need to heat the air to greater than 25°C to lower the air density (by driving air out of the hot-air balloon) until the density is the same as that for helium (at 25°C and 1.00 atm). b. 2150 K **153.** C_3H_8 is possible.

Index

TABLE OF CONTENTS

Page

TO THE STUDENT: HOW TO USE THIS GUIDE

Solutions to odd-numbered chapter exercises are in this manual. This "Solutions Guide" can be a valuable resource if you use it properly. The way <u>NOT</u> to use it is to look at an exercise in the book and then immediately check the solution, often saying to yourself, "That's easy, I can do it." Developing problem solving skills takes practice. Don't look up a solution to a problem until you have tried to work it on your own. If you are completely stuck, see if you can find a similar problem in the Sample Exercises in the chapter. Only look up the solution as a last resort. If you do this for a problem, look for a similar problem in the end of chapter exercises and try working it. The more problems you do, the easier chemistry becomes. It is also in your self interest to try to work as many problems as possible. Most exams that you will take in chemistry will involve a lot of problem solving. If you have worked several problems similar to the ones on an exam, you will do much better than if the exam is the first time you try to solve a particular type of problem. No matter how much you read and study the text, or how well you think you understand the material, you don't really understand it until you have taken the information in the text and applied the principles to problem solving. You will make mistakes, but the good students learn from their mistakes.

In this manual we have worked problems as in the textbook. We have shown intermediate answers to the correct number of significant figures and used the rounded answer in later calculations. Thus, some of your answers may differ slightly from ours. When we have not followed this convention, we have usually noted this in the solution. The most common exception is when working with the natural logarithm (ln) function, where we usually carried extra significant figures in order to reduce round-off error. In addition, we tried to use constants and conversion factors reported to at least one more significant figure as compared to numbers given in the problem. For some problems, this required the use of more precise atomic masses for H, C, N, and O as given in Chapter 3. This practice of carrying one extra significant figure in constants helps minimize round-off error.

TJH
SSZ

CHAPTER 2

ATOMS, MOLECULES, AND IONS

Development of the Atomic Theory

19. From Avogadro's hypothesis (law), volume ratios are equal to molecule ratios at constant temperature and pressure. Therefore, we can write a balanced equation using the volume data, $Cl_2 + 5 F_2 \rightarrow 2 X$. Two molecules of X contain 10 atoms of F and two atoms of Cl. The formula of X is ClF_5 for a balanced equation.

21. Avogadro's hypothesis (law) implies that volume ratios are equal to molecule ratios at constant temperature and pressure. Here, 1 volume of N_2 reacts with 3 volumes of H_2 to produce 2 volumes of the gaseous product or in terms of molecule ratios:

$$1 N_2 + 3 H_2 \rightarrow 2 \text{ product}$$

In order for the equation to be balanced, the product must be NH_3.

23. Hydrazine: 1.44×10^{-1} g H/g N; ammonia: 2.16×10^{-1} g H/g N; hydrogen azide: 2.40×10^{-2} g H/g N. Let's try all of the ratios:

$$\frac{0.144}{0.0240} = 6.00; \quad \frac{0.216}{0.0240} = 9.00; \quad \frac{0.0240}{0.0240} = 1.00; \quad \frac{0.216}{0.144} = 1.50 = \frac{3}{2}$$

All the masses of hydrogen in these three compounds can be expressed as simple whole-number ratios. The g H/g N in hydrazine, ammonia, and hydrogen azide are in the ratios $6 : 9 : 1$.

25. To get the atomic mass of H to be 1.00, we divide the mass that reacts with 1.00 g of oxygen by 0.126, that is, 0.126/0.126 = 1.00. To get Na, Mg, and O on the same scale, we do the same division.

$$\text{Na: } \frac{2.875}{0.126} = 22.8; \quad \text{Mg: } \frac{1.500}{0.126} = 11.9; \quad \text{O: } \frac{1.00}{0.126} = 7.94$$

	H	O	Na	Mg
Relative value	1.00	7.94	22.8	11.9
Accepted value	1.0079	15.999	22.99	24.31

1

The atomic masses of O and Mg are incorrect. The atomic masses of H and Na are close. Something must be wrong about the assumed formulas of the compounds. It turns out that the correct formulas are H_2O, Na_2O, and MgO. The smaller discrepancies result from the error in the assumed atomic mass of H.

The Nature of the Atom

27.   From section 2.6, the nucleus has "a diameter of about 10^{-13} cm" and the electrons "move about the nucleus at an average distance of about 10^{-8} cm from it." We will use these statements to help determine the densities. Density of hydrogen nucleus (contains one proton only):

$$V_{nucleus} = \frac{4}{3}\pi r^3 = \frac{4}{3}(3.14)(5 \times 10^{-14}\,cm)^3 = 5 \times 10^{-40}\,cm^3$$

$$d = density = \frac{1.67 \times 10^{-24}\,g}{5 \times 10^{-40}\,cm^3} = 3 \times 10^{15}\,g/cm^3$$

Density of H atom (contains one proton and one electron):

$$V_{atom} = \frac{4}{3}(3.14)(1 \times 10^{-8}\,cm)^3 = 4 \times 10^{-24}\,cm^3$$

$$d = \frac{1.67 \times 10^{-24}\,g + 9 \times 10^{-28}\,g}{4 \times 10^{-24}\,cm^3} = 0.4\,g/cm^3$$

29.   First, divide all charges by the smallest quantity, 6.40×10^{-13}.

$$\frac{2.56 \times 10^{-12}}{6.40 \times 10^{-13}} = 4.00; \quad \frac{7.68}{0.640} = 12.00; \quad \frac{3.84}{0.640} = 6.00$$

Because all charges are whole-number multiples of 6.40×10^{-13} zirkombs, the charge on one electron could be 6.40×10^{-13} zirkombs. However, 6.40×10^{-13} zirkombs could be the charge of two electrons (or three electrons, etc.). All one can conclude is that the charge of an electron is 6.40×10^{-13} zirkombs or an integer fraction of 6.40×10^{-13}.

31.   If the plum pudding model were correct (a diffuse positive charge with electrons scattered throughout), then α particles should have traveled through the thin foil with very minor deflections in their path. This was not the case because a few of the α particles were deflected at very large angles. Rutherford reasoned that the large deflections of these α particles could be caused only by a center of concentrated positive charge that contains most of the atom's mass (the nuclear model of the atom).

Elements, Ions, and the Periodic Table

33.   The atomic number of an element is equal to the number of protons in the nucleus of an atom of that element. The mass number is the sum of the number of protons plus neutrons in the nucleus. The atomic mass is the actual mass of a particular isotope (including electrons). As is discussed in Chapter 3, the average mass of an atom is taken from a measurement made on a large number of atoms. The average atomic mass value is listed in the periodic table.

35.   a.   The noble gases are He, Ne, Ar, Kr, Xe, and Rn (helium, neon, argon, krypton, xenon, and radon). Radon has only radioactive isotopes. In the periodic table, the whole number enclosed in parentheses is the mass number of the longest-lived isotope of the element.

       b.   promethium (Pm) and technetium (Tc)

37.   Use the periodic table to identify the elements.

       a.   Cl; halogen   b.   Be; alkaline earth metal

       c.   Eu; lanthanide metal   d.   Hf; transition metal

       e.   He; noble gas   f.   U; actinide metal

       g.   Cs; alkali metal

39.   For lighter, stable isotopes, the number of protons in the nucleus is about equal to the number of neutrons. When the number of protons and neutrons is equal to each other, the mass number (protons + neutrons) will be twice the atomic number (protons). Therefore, for lighter isotopes, the ratio of the mass number to the atomic number is close to 2. For example, consider ^{28}Si, which has 14 protons and (28 – 14 =) 14 neutrons. Here, the mass number to atomic number ratio is 28/14 = 2.0. For heavier isotopes, there are more neutrons than protons in the nucleus. Therefore, the ratio of the mass number to the atomic number increases steadily upward from 2 as the isotopes get heavier and heavier. For example, ^{238}U has 92 protons and (238 – 92 =) 146 neutrons. The ratio of the mass number to the atomic number for ^{238}U is 238/92 = 2.6.

41.   a. $^{24}_{12}Mg$: 12 protons, 12 neutrons, 12 electrons

       b. $^{24}_{12}Mg^{2+}$: 12 p, 12 n, 10 e   c. $^{59}_{27}Co^{2+}$: 27 p, 32 n, 25 e

       d. $^{59}_{27}Co^{3+}$: 27 p, 32 n, 24 e   e. $^{59}_{27}Co$: 27 p, 32 n, 27 e

       f. $^{79}_{34}Se$: 34 p, 45 n, 34 e   g. $^{79}_{34}Se^{2-}$: 34 p, 45 n, 36 e

       h. $^{63}_{28}Ni$: 28 p, 35 n, 28 e   i. $^{59}_{28}Ni^{2+}$: 28 p, 31 n, 26 e

43.   Atomic number = 63 (Eu); net charge = +63 – 60 = 3+; mass number = 63 + 88 = 151; symbol: $^{151}_{63}Eu^{3+}$

Atomic number = 50 (Sn); mass number = 50 + 68 = 118; net charge = +50 − 48 = 2+; symbol: $^{118}_{50}Sn^{2+}$.

45. In ionic compounds, metals lose electrons to form cations, and nonmetals gain electrons to form anions. Group 1A, 2A, and 3A metals form stable 1+, 2+, and 3+ charged cations, respectively. Group 5A, 6A, and 7A nonmetals form 3−, 2−, and 1− charged anions, respectively.

     a. Lose $2\,e^-$ to form Ra^{2+}.   b. Lose $3\,e^-$ to form In^{3+}.   c. Gain $3\,e^-$ to form P^{3-}.

     d. Gain $2\,e^-$ to form Te^{2-}.   e. Gain $1\,e^-$ to form Br^-.   f. Lose $1\,e^-$ to form Rb^+.

Nomenclature

47. $AlCl_3$, aluminum chloride; $CrCl_3$, chromium(III) chloride; ICl_3, iodine trichloride; $AlCl_3$ and $CrCl_3$ are ionic compounds following the rules for naming ionic compounds. The major difference is that $CrCl_3$ contains a transition metal (Cr) that generally exhibits two or more stable charges when in ionic compounds. We need to indicate which charged ion we have in the compound. This is generally true whenever the metal in the ionic compound is a transition metal. ICl_3 is made from only nonmetals and is a covalent compound. Predicting formulas for covalent compounds is extremely difficult. Because of this, we need to indicate the number of each nonmetal in the binary covalent compound. The exception is when there is only one of the first species present in the formula; when this is the case, mono- is not used (it is assumed).

49.   a. sulfur difluoride   b. dinitrogen tetroxide

       c. iodine trichloride   d. tetraphosphorus hexoxide

51.   a. copper(I) iodide   b. copper(II) iodide   c. cobalt(II) iodide

       d. sodium carbonate   e. sodium hydrogen carbonate or sodium bicarbonate

       f. tetrasulfur tetranitride   g. selenium tetrabromide   h. sodium hypochlorite

       i. barium chromate   j. ammonium nitrate

53.   a. SO_2 b. SO_3 c. Na_2SO_3 d. $KHSO_3$

       e. Li_3N f. $Cr_2(CO_3)_3$ g. $Cr(C_2H_3O_2)_2$ h. SnF_4

       i. NH_4HSO_4: composed of NH_4^+ and HSO_4^- ions

       j. $(NH_4)_2HPO_4$ k. $KClO_4$ l. NaH

       m. $HBrO$ n. HBr

55.   a. $Pb(C_2H_3O_2)_2$; lead(II) acetate   b. $CuSO_4$; copper(II) sulfate

       c. CaO; calcium oxide   d. $MgSO_4$; magnesium sulfate

       e. $Mg(OH)_2$; magnesium hydroxide   f. $CaSO_4$; calcium sulfate

       g. N_2O; dinitrogen monoxide or nitrous oxide (common name)

57.   a. nitric acid, HNO_3 b. perchloric acid, $HClO_4$ c. acetic acid, $HC_2H_3O_2$

       d. sulfuric acid, H_2SO_4 e. phosphoric acid, H_3PO_4

Additional Exercises

59.   The equation for the reaction between the elements of sodium and chlorine is $2\ Na(s) + Cl_2(g)$ $\rightarrow$ $2\ NaCl(s)$. The sodium reactant exists as singular sodium atoms packed together very tightly and in a very organized fashion. This type of packing of atoms represents the solid phase. The chlorine reactant exists as Cl_2 molecules. In the picture of chlorine, there is a lot of empty space present. This only occurs in the gaseous phase. When sodium and chlorine react, the ionic compound NaCl is the product. NaCl exists as separate Na^+ and Cl^- ions. Because the ions are packed very closely together and are packed in a very organized fashion, NaCl is depicted in the solid phase.

61.   From the law of definite proportions, a given compound always contains exactly the same proportion of elements by mass. The first sample of chloroform has a total mass of 12.0 g C + 106.4 g Cl + 1.01 g H = 119.41 g (carrying extra significant figures). The mass percent of carbon in this sample of chloroform is:

$$\frac{12.0\,\text{g C}}{119.41\,\text{g total}} \times 100 = 10.05\%\ \text{C by mass}$$

       From the law of definite proportions, the second sample of chloroform must also contain 10.05% C by mass. Let x = mass of chloroform in the second sample:

$$\frac{30.0\,\text{g C}}{x} \times 100 = 10.05, \quad x = 299\ \text{g chloroform}$$

63.   From the Na_2X formula, X has a 2– charge. Because 36 electrons are present, X has 34 protons, 79 – 34 = 45 neutrons, and is selenium.

       a. True. Nonmetals bond together using covalent bonds and are called covalent compounds.

       b. False. The isotope has 34 protons.

       c. False. The isotope has 45 neutrons.

       d. False. The identity is selenium, Se.

65.   From the XBr_2 formula, the charge on element X is 2+. Therefore, the element has 88 protons, which identifies it as radium, Ra. 230 – 88 = 142 neutrons.

67.   In the case of sulfur, SO_4^{2-} is sulfate, and SO_3^{2-} is sulfite. By analogy:

       SeO_4^{2-}: selenate; SeO_3^{2-}: selenite; TeO_4^{2-}: tellurate; TeO_3^{2-}: tellurite

69.   If the formula is InO, then one atomic mass of In would combine with one atomic mass of O, or:

$$\frac{A}{16.00} = \frac{4.784 \text{ g In}}{1.000 \text{ g O}}, \quad A = \text{atomic mass of In} = 76.54$$

If the formula is In_2O_3, then two times the atomic mass of In will combine with three times the atomic mass of O, or:

$$\frac{2A}{(3)16.00} = \frac{4.784 \text{ g In}}{1.000 \text{ g O}}, \quad A = \text{atomic mass of In} = 114.8$$

The latter number is the atomic mass of In used in the modern periodic table.

71.   The cation has 51 protons and 48 electrons. The number of protons corresponds to the atomic number. Thus this is element 51, antimony. There are 3 fewer electrons than protons. Therefore, the charge on the cation is 3+. The anion has one-third the number of protons of the cation which corresponds to 17 protons; this is element 17, chlorine. The number of electrons in this anion of chlorine is 17 + 1 = 18 electrons. The anion must have a charge of 1−.

The formula of the compound formed between Sb^{3+} and Cl^- is $SbCl_3$. The name of the compound is antimony(III) chloride. The Roman numeral is used to indicate the charge of Sb because the predicted charge is not obvious from the periodic table.

73.   Because this is a relatively small number of neutrons, the number of protons will be very close to the number of neutrons present. The heavier elements have significantly more neutrons than protons in their nuclei. Because this element forms anions, it is a nonmetal and will be a halogen because halogens form stable 1− charged ions in ionic compounds. From the halogens listed, chlorine, with an average atomic mass of 35.45, fits the data. The two isotopes are ^{35}Cl and ^{37}Cl, and the number of electrons in the 1− ion is 18. Note that because the atomic mass of chlorine listed in the periodic table is closer to 35 than 37, we can assume that ^{35}Cl is the more abundant isotope. This is discussed in Chapter 3.

Challenge Problems

75.   a.   Both compounds have C_2H_6O as the formula. Because they have the same formula, their mass percent composition will be identical. However, these are different compounds with different properties because the atoms are bonded together differently. These compounds are called isomers of each other.

b.   When wood burns, most of the solid material in wood is converted to gases, which escape. The gases produced are most likely CO_2 and H_2O.

c.   The atom is not an indivisible particle but is instead composed of other smaller particles, for example, electrons, neutrons, and protons.

d.   The two hydride samples contain different isotopes of either hydrogen and/or lithium. Although the compounds are composed of different isotopes, their properties are similar because different isotopes of the same element have similar properties (except, of course, their mass).

77.   Compound I: $\dfrac{14.0 \text{ g R}}{3.00 \text{ g Q}} = \dfrac{4.67 \text{ g R}}{1.00 \text{ g Q}}$;   Compound II: $\dfrac{7.00 \text{ g R}}{4.50 \text{ g Q}} = \dfrac{1.56 \text{ g R}}{1.00 \text{ g Q}}$

The ratio of the masses of R that combines with 1.00 g Q is $\dfrac{4.67}{1.56} = 2.99 \approx 3$.

As expected from the law of multiple proportions, this ratio is a small whole number.

Because compound I contains three times the mass of R per gram of Q as compared with compound II (RQ), the formula of compound I should be R_3Q.

79.   Avogadro proposed that equal volumes of gases (at constant temperature and pressure) contain equal numbers of molecules. In terms of balanced equations, Avogadro's hypothesis (law) implies that volume ratios will be identical to molecule ratios. Assuming one molecule of octane reacts, then 1 molecule of C_xH_y produces 8 molecules of CO_2 and 9 molecules of H_2O. $C_xH_y + n\ O_2 \rightarrow 8\ CO_2 + 9\ H_2O$. Because all the carbon in octane ends up as carbon in CO_2, octane must contain 8 atoms of C. Similarly, all hydrogen in octane ends up as hydrogen in H_2O, so one molecule of octane must contain $9 \times 2 = 18$ atoms of H. Octane formula $= C_8H_{18}$ and the ratio of C:H $= 8{:}18$ or $4{:}9$.

CHAPTER 12

QUANTUM MECHANICS AND ATOMIC THEORY

Light and Matter

21. $\nu = \dfrac{c}{\lambda} = \dfrac{3.00 \times 10^8 \text{ m/s}}{1.0 \times 10^{-2} \text{ m}} = 3.0 \times 10^{10} \text{ s}^{-1}$

$E = h\nu = 6.63 \times 10^{-34} \text{ J s} \times 3.0 \times 10^{10} \text{ s}^{-1} = 2.0 \times 10^{-23} \text{ J/photon}$

$\dfrac{2.0 \times 10^{-23} \text{ J}}{\text{photon}} = \dfrac{6.02 \times 10^{23} \text{ photons}}{\text{mol}} = 12 \text{ J/mol}$

23.   Referencing Figure 12.3 of the text, 2.12×10^{-10} m electromagnetic radiation is X rays.

$\lambda = \dfrac{c}{\nu} = \dfrac{2.9979 \times 10^8 \text{ m/s}}{107.1 \times 10^6 \text{ s}^{-1}} = 2.799 \text{ m}$

From the wavelength calculated above, 107.1 MHz electromagnetic radiation is FM radio-waves.

$\lambda = \dfrac{hc}{E} = \dfrac{6.626 \times 10^{-34} \text{ J s} \times 2.998 \times 10^8 \text{ m/s}}{3.97 \times 10^{-19} \text{ J}} = 5.00 \times 10^{-7} \text{ m}$

The 3.97×10^{-19} J/photon electromagnetic radiation is visible (green) light.

The photon energy and frequency order will be the exact opposite of the wavelength ordering because E and ν are both inversely related to λ. From the previously calculated wavelengths, the order of photon energy and frequency is:

FM radiowaves < visible (green) light < X rays
longest λ shortest λ
lowest ν highest ν
smallest E   largest E

25.   a. $\lambda = \dfrac{c}{\nu} = \dfrac{3.00 \times 10^8 \text{ m/s}}{6.0 \times 10^{13} \text{ s}^{-1}} = 5.0 \times 10^{-6} \text{ m}$

　　　b. From Figure 12.3, this is infrared EMR.

　　　c. $E = h\nu = 6.63 \times 10^{-34} \text{ J s} \times 6.0 \times 10^{13} \text{ s}^{-1} = 4.0 \times 10^{-20} \text{ J/photon}$

$$\dfrac{4.0 \times 10^{-20} \text{ J}}{\text{photon}} \times \dfrac{6.022 \times 10^{23} \text{ photons}}{\text{mol}} = 2.4 \times 10^{4} \text{ J/mol}$$

　　　d. Frequency and photon energy are directly related ($E = h\nu$). Because $5.4 \times 10^{13} \text{ s}^{-1}$ EMR has a lower frequency than $6.0 \times 10^{13} \text{ s}^{-1}$ EMR, the $5.4 \times 10^{13} \text{ s}^{-1}$ EMR will have less energetic photons.

27.   The energy needed to remove a single electron is:

$$\dfrac{279.7 \text{ kJ}}{\text{mol}} \times \dfrac{1 \text{ mol}}{6.0221 \times 10^{23}} = 4.645 \times 10^{-22} \text{ kJ} = 4.645 \times 10^{-19} \text{ J}$$

$$E = \dfrac{hc}{\lambda}, \ \lambda = \dfrac{hc}{E} = \dfrac{6.6261 \times 10^{-34} \text{ J s} \times 2.9979 \times 10^8 \text{ m/s}}{4.645 \times 10^{-19} \text{ J}} = 4.277 \times 10^{-7} \text{ m} = 427.7 \text{ nm}$$

29.   The energy to remove a single electron is:

$$\dfrac{208.4 \text{ kJ}}{\text{mol}} \times \dfrac{1 \text{ mol}}{6.022 \times 10^{23}} = 3.461 \times 10^{-22} \text{ kJ} = 3.461 \times 10^{-19} \text{ J} = E_w$$

Energy of 254-nm light is:

$$E = \dfrac{hc}{\lambda} = \dfrac{(6.626 \times 10^{-34} \text{ J s})(2.998 \times 10^8 \text{ m/s})}{254 \times 10^{-9} \text{ m}} = 7.82 \times 10^{-19} \text{ J}$$

$E_{photon} = E_K + E_w, \ E_K = 7.82 \times 10^{-19} \text{ J} - 3.461 \times 10^{-19} \text{ J} = 4.36 \times 10^{-19} \text{ J} = \text{maximum KE}$

31.   The photoelectric effect refers to the phenomenon in which electrons are emitted from the surface of a metal when light strikes it. The light must have a certain minimum frequency (energy) in order to remove electrons from the surface of a metal. Light having a frequency below the minimum results in no electrons being emitted, whereas light at or higher than the minimum frequency does cause electrons to be emitted. For light having a frequency higher than the minimum frequency, the excess energy is transferred into kinetic energy for the emitted electron. Albert Einstein explained the photoelectric effect by applying quantum theory.

33.   a. $\lambda = \dfrac{h}{mv} = \dfrac{6.626 \times 10^{-34} \text{ J s}}{1.675 \times 10^{-27} \text{ kg} \times (0.0100 \times 2.998 \times 10^8 \text{ m/s})} = 1.32 \times 10^{-13} \text{ m}$

b. $\lambda = \dfrac{h}{mv}$, $v = \dfrac{h}{\lambda m} = \dfrac{6.626 \times 10^{-34} \text{ J s}}{75 \times 10^{-12} \text{ m} \times 1.675 \times 10^{-27} \text{ kg}} = 5.3 \times 10^{3} \text{ m/s}$

35. $m = \dfrac{h}{\lambda v} = \dfrac{6.626 \times 10^{-34} \text{ kg m}^{2}/\text{s}}{3.31 \times 10^{-15} \text{ m} \times (0.0100 \times 2.998 \times 10^{8} \text{ m/s})} = 6.68 \times 10^{-26} \text{ kg/atom}$

$\dfrac{6.68 \times 10^{-26} \text{ kg}}{\text{atom}} \times \dfrac{6.022 \times 10^{23} \text{ atoms}}{\text{mol}} \times \dfrac{1000 \text{ g}}{\text{kg}} = 40.2 \text{ g/mol}$

The element is calcium (Ca).

Hydrogen Atom: The Bohr Model

37. a. For hydrogen (Z = 1), the energy levels in units of joules are given by the equation $E_n = -2.178 \times 10^{-18}(1/n^2)$. As n increases, the differences between $1/n^2$ for consecutive energy levels becomes smaller and smaller. Consider the difference between $1/n^2$ values for $n = 1$ and $n = 2$ as compared to $n = 3$ and $n = 4$.

For $n = 1$ and $n = 2$:   For $n = 3$ and $n = 4$:

$\dfrac{1}{1^2} - \dfrac{1}{2^2} = 1 - 0.25 = 0.75$ $\dfrac{1}{3^2} - \dfrac{1}{4^2} = 0.1111 - 0.0625 = 0.0486$

Because the differences between $1/n^2$ values for consecutive energy levels decrease as n increases, the energy levels get closer together as n increases.

b. For a spectral transition for hydrogen, $\Delta E = E_f - E_i$:

$$\Delta E = -2.178 \times 10^{-18} \text{ J} \left(\frac{1}{n_f^2} - \frac{1}{n_i^2} \right)$$

where n_i and n_f are the levels of the initial and final states, respectively. A positive value of ΔE always corresponds to an absorption of light, and a negative value of ΔE always corresponds to an emission of light.

In the diagram, the red line is for the $n_i = 3$ to $n_f = 2$ transition.

$$\Delta E = -2.178 \times 10^{-18} \text{ J}\left(\frac{1}{2^2} - \frac{1}{3^2} \right) = -2.178 \times 10^{-18} \text{ J}\left(\frac{1}{4} - \frac{1}{9} \right)$$

$\Delta E = -2.178 \times 10^{-18} \text{ J} \times (0.2500 - 0.1111) = -3.025 \times 10^{-19} \text{ J}$

The photon of light must have precisely this energy (3.025×10^{-19} J).

$$|\Delta E| = E_{photon} = h\nu = \frac{hc}{\lambda}$$

$$\lambda = \frac{hc}{|\Delta E|} = \frac{6.6261 \times 10^{-34} \text{ J s} \times 2.9979 \times 10^8 \text{ m/s}}{3.025 \times 10^{-19} \text{ J}} = 6.567 \times 10^{-7} \text{ m} = 656.7 \text{ nm}$$

From Figure 12.3, $\lambda = 656.7$ nm is red light so the diagram is correct for the red line.

In the diagram, the green line is for the $n_i = 4$ to $n_f = 2$ transition.

$$\Delta E = -2.178 \times 10^{-18} \text{ J} \left(\frac{1}{2^2} - \frac{1}{4^2} \right) = -4.084 \times 10^{-19} \text{ J}$$

$$\lambda = \frac{hc}{|\Delta E|} = \frac{6.6261 \times 10^{-34} \text{ J s} \times 2.9979 \times 10^8 \text{ m/s}}{4.084 \times 10^{-19} \text{ J}} = 4.864 \times 10^{-7} \text{ m} = 486.4 \text{ nm}$$

From Figure 12.3, $\lambda = 486.4$ nm is green-blue light. The diagram is consistent with this line.

In the diagram, the blue line is for the $n_i = 5$ to $n_f = 2$ transition.

$$\Delta E = -2.178 \times 10^{-18} \text{ J} \left(\frac{1}{2^2} - \frac{1}{5^2} \right) = -4.574 \times 10^{-19} \text{ J}$$

$$\lambda = \frac{hc}{|\Delta E|} = \frac{6.6261 \times 10^{-34} \text{ J s} \times 2.9979 \times 10^8 \text{ m/s}}{4.574 \times 10^{-19} \text{ J}} = 4.343 \times 10^{-7} \text{ m} = 434.3 \text{ nm}$$

From Figure 12.3, $\lambda = 434.3$ nm is blue or blue-violet light. The diagram is consistent with this line also.

39.   There are 4 possible transitions for an electron in the $n = 5$ level ($5 \rightarrow 4$, $5 \rightarrow 3$, $5 \rightarrow 2$, and $5 \rightarrow 1$). If an electron initially drops to the $n = 4$ level, three additional transitions can occur ($4 \rightarrow 3$, $4 \rightarrow 2$, and $4 \rightarrow 1$). Similarly, there are two more transitions from the $n = 3$ level ($3 \rightarrow 2$, $3 \rightarrow 1$) and one more transition for the $n = 2$ level ($2 \rightarrow 1$). There are a total of 10 possible transitions for an electron in the $n = 5$ level for a possible total of 10 different wavelength emissions.

41.   a.   False;   it takes less energy to ionize an electron from $n = 3$ than from the ground state.

        b.   True

        c.   False;   the energy difference between $n = 3$ and $n = 2$ is smaller than the energy difference to $n = 2$ electronic transition than for the $n = 3$ to $n = 1$ transition. E and λ are inversely proportional to each other (E = hc/λ).

        d.   True

        e.   False;   the ground state in hydrogen is $n = 1$ and all other allowed energy states are called excited states; $n = 2$ is the first excited state, and $n = 3$ is the second excited state.

43. $|\Delta E| = E_{photon} = \dfrac{hc}{\lambda} = \dfrac{6.6261 \times 10^{-34} \text{ J s} \times 2.9979 \times 10^8 \text{ m/s}}{397.2 \times 10^{-9} \text{ m}} = 5.001 \times 10^{-19} \text{ J}$

$\Delta E = -5.001 \times 10^{-19} \text{ J because we have an emission.}$

$-5.001 \times 10^{-19} \text{ J} = E_2 - E_n = -2.178 \times 10^{-18} \text{ J} \left(\dfrac{1}{2^2} - \dfrac{1}{n^2} \right)$

$0.2296 = \dfrac{1}{4} - \dfrac{1}{n^2}, \quad \dfrac{1}{n^2} = 0.0204, \quad n = 7$

45. $\Delta E = E_4 - E_n = -E_n = 2.178 \times 10^{-18} \text{ J} \left(\dfrac{1}{n^2} \right)$

$E_{photon} = \dfrac{hc}{\lambda} = \dfrac{6.626 \times 10^{-34} \text{ J s} \times 2.9979 \times 10^8 \text{ m/s}}{1460 \times 10^{-9} \text{ m}} = 1.36 \times 10^{-19} \text{ J}$

$E_{photon} = \Delta E = 1.36 \times 10^{-19} \text{ J} = 2.178 \times 10^{-18} \left(\dfrac{1}{n^2} \right), \quad n^2 = 16.0, \quad n = 4$

47. $E_{photon} = \dfrac{hc}{\lambda} = \dfrac{6.6261 \times 10^{-34} \text{ J s} \times 2.9979 \times 10^8 \text{ m/s}}{253.4 \times 10^{-9} \text{ m}} = 7.839 \times 10^{-19} \text{ J}$

$\Delta E = -7.839 \times 10^{-19} \text{ J because we have an emission.}$

The general energy equation for one-electron ions is $E_n = -2.178 \times 10^{-18} \text{ J } (Z^2)/n^2$, where Z = atomic number.

$\Delta E = -2.178 \times 10^{-18} \text{ J } (Z)^2 \left(\dfrac{1}{n_f^2} - \dfrac{1}{n_i^2} \right), \quad Z = 4 \text{ for Be}^{3+}$

$\Delta E = -7.839 \times 10^{-19} \text{ J} = -2.178 \times 10^{-18} (4)^2 \left(\dfrac{1}{n_f^2} - \dfrac{1}{5^2} \right)$

$\dfrac{7.839 \times 10^{-19}}{2.178 \times 10^{-18} \times 16} + \dfrac{1}{25} = \dfrac{1}{n_f^2}, \quad \dfrac{1}{n_f^2} = 0.06249, \quad n_f = 4$

This emission line corresponds to the $n = 5 \rightarrow n = 4$ electronic transition.

Wave Mechanics and Particle in a Box

49.   a. $\Delta p = m\Delta v = 9.11 \times 10^{-31} \text{ kg} \times 0.100 \text{ m/s} = \dfrac{9.11 \times 10^{-32} \text{ kg m}}{\text{s}}$

$\Delta p \Delta x \geq \dfrac{h}{4\pi}, \quad \Delta x = \dfrac{h}{4\pi \Delta p} = \dfrac{6.626 \times 10^{-34} \text{ J s}}{4 \times 3.142 \times (9.11 \times 10^{-32} \text{ kg m/s})} = 5.79 \times 10^{-4} \text{ m}$

b. $\Delta x = \dfrac{h}{4\pi\,\Delta p} = \dfrac{6.626 \times 10^{-34}\ \text{J s}}{4 \times 3.142 \times 0.145\ \text{kg} \times 0.100\ \text{m/s}} = 3.64 \times 10^{-33}\ \text{m}$

The diameter of an H atom is roughly 2×10^{-8} cm. The uncertainty in the position of the electron is much larger than the size of the atom, whereas, the uncertainty in the position of the baseball is insignificant as compared to the size of a baseball.

51.   At $x = 0$, the value of the square of the wave function must be zero. The particle must be inside the box. For $\psi = A\,\cos(Lx)$, at $x = 0$, $\cos(0) = 1$ and $\psi^2 = A^2$. This violates the boundary condition for a particle in a one-dimensional box.

53. $E_n = \dfrac{n^2 h^2}{8mL^2}$; $\Delta E = E_3 - E_2 = \dfrac{9h^2}{8mL^2} - \dfrac{4h^2}{8mL^2} = \dfrac{5h^2}{8mL^2}$

$\Delta E = \dfrac{hc}{\lambda} = \dfrac{(6.626 \times 10^{-34}\ \text{J s})(2.998 \times 10^8\ \text{m/s})}{8080 \times 10^{-9}\ \text{m}} = 2.46 \times 10^{-20}\ \text{J}$

$\Delta E = 2.46 \times 10^{-20}\ \text{J} = \dfrac{5h^2}{8mL^2} = \dfrac{5(6.626 \times 10^{-34}\ \text{J s})^2}{8(9.109 \times 10^{-31}\ \text{kg})\,L^2}$, $L = 3.50 \times 10^{-9}$ m = 3.50 nm

55. $E_n = \dfrac{n^2 h^2}{8mL^2}$;   as L increases, E_n will decrease, and the spacing between energy levels will also decrease.

57. $E_n = \dfrac{n^2 h^2}{8mL^2}$, $n = 1$ for ground state; from equation, as L increases, E_n decreases.

Using numbers: 10^{-6} m box: $E_1 = \dfrac{h^2}{8m}\,(1 \times 10^{12}\ \text{m}^{-2})$; 10^{-10} m box: $E_1 = \dfrac{h^2}{8m}\,(1 \times 10^{20}\ \text{m}^{-2})$

As expected, the electron in the 1×10^{-6} m box has the lowest ground state energy.

Orbitals and Quantum Numbers

59.   The 2p orbitals differ from each other in the direction in which they point in space. The 2p and 3p orbitals differ from each other in their size, energy, and number of nodes. A nodal surface in an atomic orbital is a surface in which the probability of finding an electron is zero.

61.   1p: $n = 1$, $\ell = 1$ is not possible; 3f: $n = 3$, $\ell = 3$ is not possible; 2d: $n = 2$, $\ell = 2$ is not possible; in all three incorrect cases, $n = \ell$. The maximum value ℓ can have is $n - 1$, not n.

63.   a.   For $n = 3$, $\ell = 3$ is not possible.

      d. m_s cannot equal -1.

e. ℓ cannot be a negative number.   f. For $\ell = 1$, m_ℓ cannot equal 2.

The quantum numbers in parts b and c are allowed.

65.   1p, 0 electrons ($\ell \neq 1$ when $n = 1$); $6d_{x^2-y^2}$, 2 electrons (specifies one atomic orbital); 4f, 14 electrons (7 orbitals have 4f designation); $7p_y$, 2 electrons (specifies one atomic orbital); 2s, 2 electrons (specifies one atomic orbital); $n = 3$, 18 electrons (3s, 3p, and 3d orbitals are possible; there are one 3s orbital, three 3p orbitals, and five 3d orbitals).

67.   The diagrams of the orbitals in the text give only 90% probabilities of where the electron may reside. We can never be 100% certain of the location of the electrons due to Heisenberg's uncertainty principle.

69.   For $r = a_o$ and $\theta = 0°$ ($Z = 1$ for H):

$$\psi_{2p_z} = \frac{1}{4(2\pi)^{1/2}}\left(\frac{1}{5.29 \times 10^{-11}}\right)^{3/2} (1)\, e^{-1/2} \cos 0 = 1.57 \times 10^{14};\ \psi^2 = 2.46 \times 10^{28}$$

For $r = a_o$ and $\theta = 90°$: $\psi_{2p_z} = 0$ because $\cos 90° = 0$; $\psi^2 = 0$; the xy plane is a node for the $2p_z$ atomic orbital.

Polyelectronic Atoms

71.   He: $1s^2$; Ne: $1s^2 2s^2 2p^6$; Ar: $1s^2 2s^2 2p^6 3s^2 3p^6$; each peak in the diagram corresponds to a subshell with different values of n. Corresponding subshells are closer to the nucleus for heavier elements because of the increased nuclear charge.

73.   Valence electrons are the electrons in the outermost principal quantum level of an atom (those electrons in the highest n value orbitals). The electrons in the lower n value orbitals are all inner core or just core electrons. The key is that the outermost electrons are the valence electrons. When atoms interact with each other, it will be the outermost electrons that are involved in these interactions. In addition, how tightly the nucleus holds these outermost electrons determines atomic size, ionization energy, and other properties of atoms. Elements in the same group have similar valence electron configurations and, as a result, have similar chemical properties.

75.   a. $n = 4$: ℓ can be 0, 1, 2, or 3. Thus we have s (2 e⁻), p (6 e⁻), d (10 e⁻) and f (14 e⁻) orbitals present. Total number of electrons to fill these orbitals is 32.

b. $n = 5$, $m_\ell = +1$: for $n = 5$, $\ell = 0, 1, 2, 3, 4$; for $\ell = 1, 2, 3, 4$, all can have $m_\ell = +1$. Four distinct orbitals which can hold a maximum of 8 electrons.

c. $n = 5$, $m_s = +1/2$: for $n = 5$, $\ell = 0, 1, 2, 3, 4$. Number of orbitals = 1, 3, 5, 7, 9 for each value of ℓ, respectively. There are 25 orbitals with $n = 5$. They can hold 50 electrons, and 25 of these electrons can have $m_s = +1/2$.

d. $n = 3$, $\ell = 2$: these quantum numbers define a set of 3d orbitals. There are 5 degenerate 3d orbitals that can hold a total of 10 electrons.

e. $n = 2$, $\ell = 1$: these define a set of 2p orbitals. There are 3 degenerate 2p orbitals that can hold a total of 6 electrons.

f.   It is impossible for $n = 0$. Thus no electrons can have this set of quantum numbers.

g.   The four quantum numbers completely specify a single electron.

h. $n = 3$: 3s, 3p, and 3d orbitals all have $n = 3$. These orbitals can hold 18 electrons, and 9 of these electrons can have $m_s = +1/2$.

i. $n = 2$, $\ell = 2$: this combination is not possible ($\ell \neq 2$ for $n = 2$). Zero electrons in an atom can have these quantum numbers.

j. $n = 1$, $\ell = 0$, $m_\ell = 0$: these define a 1s orbital that can hold 2 electrons.

77.   The following are complete electron configurations. Noble gas shorthand notation could also be used.

Sc: $1s^2 2s^2 2p^6 3s^2 3p^6 4s^2 3d^1$; Fe: $1s^2 2s^2 2p^6 3s^2 3p^6 4s^2 3d^6$

P: $1s^2 2s^2 2p^6 3s^2 3p^3$; Cs: $1s^2 2s^2 2p^6 3s^2 3p^6 4s^2 3d^{10} 4p^6 5s^2 4d^{10} 5p^6 6s^1$

Eu: $1s^2 2s^2 2p^6 3s^2 3p^6 4s^2 3d^{10} 4p^6 5s^2 4d^{10} 5p^6 6s^2 4f^6 5d^1$*

Pt: $1s^2 2s^2 2p^6 3s^2 3p^6 4s^2 3d^{10} 4p^6 5s^2 4d^{10} 5p^6 6s^2 4f^{14} 5d^8$*

Xe: $1s^2 2s^2 2p^6 3s^2 3p^6 4s^2 3d^{10} 4p^6 5s^2 4d^{10} 5p^6$; Br: $1s^2 2s^2 2p^6 3s^2 3p^6 4s^2 3d^{10} 4p^5$

Note: These electron configurations were written down using only the periodic table. The actual electron configurations are: Eu: $[Xe]6s^2 4f^7$ and Pt: $[Xe]6s^1 4f^{14} 5d^9$

79.   Exceptions: Cr, Cu, Nb, Mo, Tc, Ru, Rh, Pd, Ag, Pt, and Au; Tc, Ru, Rh, Pd, and Pt do not correspond to the supposed extra stability of half-filled and filled subshells.

81.   The two exceptions are Cr and Cu. Cr: $1s^2 2s^2 2p^6 3s^2 3p^6 4s^1 3p^5$; Cr has 6 unpaired electrons.

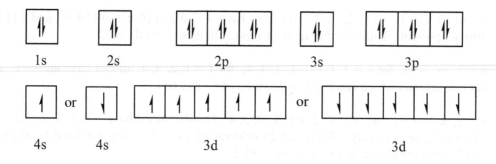

Cu: $1s^22s^22p^63s^23p^64s^13d^{10}$; Cu has 1 unpaired electron.

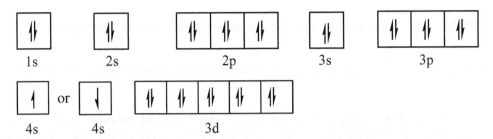

$\underset{4s}{\boxed{\uparrow}}$ or $\underset{4s}{\boxed{\downarrow}}$ $\underset{3d}{\boxed{\uparrow\downarrow}\,\boxed{\uparrow\downarrow}\,\boxed{\uparrow\downarrow}\,\boxed{\uparrow\downarrow}\,\boxed{\uparrow\downarrow}}$

83.   a. 2 valence electrons; $4s^2$ b. 6 valence electrons; $2s^22p^4$

      c. 7 valence electrons; $7s^27p^5$ d. 3 valence electrons; $5s^25p^1$

      e. 8 valence electrons; $3s^23p^6$ f. 5 valence electrons; $6s^26p^3$

85.   Element 115, Uup, is in Group 5A under Bi (bismuth):

      Uup: $1s^22s^22p^63s^23p^64s^23d^{10}4p^65s^24d^{10}5p^66s^24f^{14}5d^{10}6p^67s^25f^{14}6d^{10}7p^3$

      a. $5s^2$, $5p^6$, $5d^{10}$, and $5f^{14}$; 32 electrons have $n = 5$ as one of their quantum numbers

      b. $\ell = 3$ are f orbitals. $4f^{14}$ and $5f^{14}$ are the f orbitals used. They are all filled so 28 electrons have $\ell = 3$.

      c. p, d, and f orbitals all have one of the degenerate orbitals with $m_\ell = 1$. There are 6 orbitals with $m_\ell = 1$ for the various p orbitals used; there are 4 orbitals with $m_\ell =1$ for the various d orbitals used; and there are 2 orbitals with $m_\ell = 1$ for the various f orbitals used. We have a total of $6 + 4 + 2 = 12$ orbitals with $m_\ell = 1$. Eleven of these orbitals are filled with 2 electrons, and the 7p orbitals are only half-filled. The number of electrons with $m_\ell = 1$ is $11 \times (2\ e^-) + 1 \times (1\ e^-) = 23$ electrons.

      d. The first 112 electrons are all paired; one-half of these electrons ($56\ e^-$) will have $m_s = -1/2$. The 3 electrons in the 7p orbitals singly occupy each of the three degenerate 7p orbitals; the three electrons are spin parallel, so the 7p electrons either have $m_s = +1/2$ or $m_s = -1/2$. Therefore, either 56 electrons have $m_s = -1/2$ or 59 electrons have $m_s = -1/2$.

87.   We get the number of unpaired electrons by examining the incompletely filled subshells. The paramagnetic substances have unpaired electrons, and the ones with no unpaired electrons are not paramagnetic (they are called diamagnetic).

      Li: $1s^22s^1$ $\underset{2s}{\uparrow}$; paramagnetic with 1 unpaired electron.

      N: $1s^22s^22p^3$ $\underset{2p}{\uparrow\,\uparrow\,\uparrow}$; paramagnetic with 3 unpaired electrons.

      Ni: [Ar]$4s^23d^8$ $\underset{3d}{\uparrow\downarrow\,\uparrow\downarrow\,\uparrow\downarrow\,\uparrow\,\uparrow}$; paramagnetic with 2 unpaired electrons.

Te: $[Kr]5s^24d^{10}5p^4$ ⇅ ↑ ↑ ; paramagnetic with 2 unpaired electrons.
    5p

Ba: $[Xe]6s^2$ ⇅ ; not paramagnetic because no unpaired electrons are present.
    6s

Hg: $[Xe]6s^24f^{14}5d^{10}$ ⇅ ⇅ ⇅ ⇅ ⇅ ; not paramagnetic because no unpaired electrons.
    5d

89.   The s block elements with ns^1 for a valence electron configuration have one unpaired electrons. These are elements H, Li, Na, and K for the first 36 elements. The p block elements with ns^2np^1 or ns^2np^5 valence electron configurations have one unpaired electron. These are elements B, Al, and Ga (ns^2np^1) and elements F, Cl, and Br (ns^2np^5) for the first 36 elements. In the d block, Sc ($[Ar]4s^23d^1$) and Cu ($[Ar]4s^13d^{10}$) each have one unpaired electron. A total of 12 elements from the first 36 elements have one unpaired electron in the ground state.

91.   We get the number of unpaired electrons by examining the incompletely filled subshells.

O: $[He]2s^22p^4$ $2p^4$: ⇅ ↑ ↑   Two unpaired e⁻

O⁺: $[He]2s^22p^3$ $2p^3$: ↑ ↑ ↑   Three unpaired e⁻

O⁻: $[He]2s^22p^5$ $2p^5$: ⇅ ⇅ ↑   One unpaired e⁻

Os: $[Xe]6s^24f^{14}5d^6$ $5d^6$: ⇅ ↑ ↑ ↑ ↑   Four unpaired e⁻

Zr: $[Kr]5s^24d^2$ $4d^2$: ↑ ↑ _ _ _   Two unpaired e⁻

S: $[Ne]3s^23p^4$ $3p^4$: ⇅ ↑ ↑   Two unpaired e⁻

F: $[He]2s^22p^5$ $2p^5$: ⇅ ⇅ ↑   One unpaired e⁻

Ar: $[Ne]3s^23p^6$ $3p^6$: ⇅ ⇅ ⇅   Zero unpaired e⁻

The Periodic Table and Periodic Properties

93.   Ionization energy: $P(g) \rightarrow P^+(g) + e^-$; electron affinity: $P(g) + e^- \rightarrow P^-(g)$

95.   As successive electrons are removed, the net positive charge on the resulting ion increases. This increase in positive charge binds the remaining electrons more firmly, and the ionization energy increases.

The electron configuration for Si is $1s^22s^22p^63s^23p^2$. There is a large jump in ionization energy when going from the removal of valence electrons to the removal of core electrons. For silicon, this occurs when the fifth electron is removed since we go from the valence electrons in $n = 3$ to the core electrons in $n = 2$. There should be another big jump when the thirteenth electron is removed, i.e., when a 1s electron is removed.

97.   Size (radius) decreases left to right across the periodic table, and size increases from top to bottom of the periodic table.

   a. S < Se < Te   b. Br < Ni < K   c. F < Si < Ba

   d. Be < Na < Rb   e. Ne < Se < Sr   f. O < P < Fe

   All follow the general radius trend.

99.   a. Ba   b. K

   c. O; in general, Group 6A elements have a lower ionization energy than neighboring Group 5A elements. This is an exception to the general ionization energy trend across the periodic table.

   d. S^{2-}; this ion has the most electrons compared to the other sulfur species present. S^{2-} has the largest number of electron-electron repulsions, which leads to S^{2-} having the largest size and smallest ionization energy.

   e. Cs; this follows the general ionization energy trend.

101.   As: $[Ar]4s^2 3d^{10} 4p^3$; Se: $[Ar]4s^2 3d^{10} 4p^4$; the general ionization energy trend predicts that Se should have a higher ionization energy than As. Se is an exception to the general ionization energy trend. There are extra electron-electron repulsions in Se because two electrons are in the same 4p orbital, resulting in a lower ionization energy for Se than predicted.

103.   Size also decreases going across a period. Sc and Ti along with Y and Zr are adjacent elements. There are 14 elements (the lanthanides) between La and Hf, making Hf considerably smaller.

105.   a. Uus will have 117 electrons. $[Rn]7s^2 5f^{14} 6d^{10} 7p^5$

   b. It will be in the halogen family and will be most similar to astatine (At).

   c. Like the other halogens: NaUus, $Mg(Uus)_2$, $C(Uus)_4$, $O(Uus)_2$

   d. Like the other halogens: $UusO^-$, $UusO_2^-$, $UusO_3^-$, $UusO_4^-$

107.   Electron affinity refers to the energy associated with the process of adding an electron to a gaseous substance. Be, N, and Ne all have positive (unfavorable) electron affinity values. In order to add an electron to Be, N, or Ne, energy must be added. Another way of saying this is that Be, N, and Ne become less stable (have a higher energy) when an electron is added to each. To rationalize why those three atoms have positive (unfavorable) electron affinity values, let's see what happens to the electron configuration as an electron is added.

   $Be(g)$ + e^- → $Be^-(g)$ $N(g)$ + e^- → $N^-(g)$
   $[He]2s^2$ $[He]2s^2 2p^1$ $[He]2s^2 2p^3$ $[He]2s^2 2p^4$

$Ne(g) + e^- \rightarrow Ne^-(g)$
$[He]2s^22p^6$ $[He]2s^22p^63s^1$

In each case something energetically unfavorable occurs when an electron is added. For Be, the added electron must go into a higher-energy 2p atomic orbital because the 2s orbital is full. In N, the added electron must pair up with another electron in one of the 2p atomic orbitals; this adds electron-electron repulsions. In Ne, the added electron must be added to a much higher 3s atomic orbital because the n = 2 orbitals are full.

109.   Electron-electron repulsions are much greater in O^- than in S^- because the electron goes into a smaller 2p orbital versus the larger 3p orbital in sulfur. This results in a more favorable (more exothermic) EA for sulfur.

111.   a.   The electron affinity of Mg^{2+} is ΔE for $Mg^{2+}(g) + e^- \rightarrow Mg^+(g)$; this is just the reverse of the second ionization energy for Mg. $EA(Mg^{2+}) = -IE_2(Mg) = -1445$ kJ/mol (Table 12.6)

        b.   EA of Al^+ is ΔE for $Al^+(g) + e^- \rightarrow Al(g)$; $EA(Al^+) = -IE_1(Al) =$
                                                            -580 kJ/mol (Table 12.6)

        c.   IE of Cl^- is ΔE for $Cl^-(g) \rightarrow Cl(g) + e^-$; $IE(Cl^-) = -EA(Cl) = +348.7$ kJ/mol
                                                            (Table 12.8)

        d. $Cl(g) \rightarrow Cl^+(g) + e^-$ $\Delta E = IE_1(Cl) = 1255$ kJ/mol (Table 12.6)

        e. $Cl^+(g) + e^- \rightarrow Cl(g)$ $\Delta E = -IE_1(Cl) = -1255$ kJ/mol $= EA(Cl^+)$

The Alkali Metals

113.   Yes; the ionization energy general trend is to decrease down a group, and the atomic radius trend is to increase down a group. The data in Table 12.9 confirm both of these general trends.

115.   a. $6 Li(s) + N_2(g) \rightarrow 2 Li_3N(s)$ b. $2 Rb(s) + S(s) \rightarrow Rb_2S(s)$

        c. $2 Cs(s) + 2 H_2O(l) \rightarrow 2 CsOH(aq) + H_2(g)$ d. $2 Na(s) + Cl_2(g) \rightarrow 2 NaCl(s)$

117.   For 589.0 nm: $\nu = \dfrac{c}{\lambda} = \dfrac{2.9979 \times 10^8 \text{ m/s}}{589.0 \times 10^{-9} \text{ m}} = 5.090 \times 10^{14} \text{ s}^{-1}$

        $E = h\nu = 6.6261 \times 10^{-34}$ J s $\times 5.090 \times 10^{14}$ s$^{-1} = 3.373 \times 10^{-19}$ J

        For 589.6 nm: $\nu = c/\lambda = 5.085 \times 10^{14}$ s^{-1}; $E = h\nu = 3.369 \times 10^{-19}$ J

        The energies in kJ/mol are:

$$3.373 \times 10^{-19} \text{ J} \times \frac{1 \text{ kJ}}{1000 \text{ J}} \times \frac{6.0221 \times 10^{23}}{\text{mol}} = 203.1 \text{ kJ/mol}$$

$$3.369 \times 10^{-19} \text{ J} \times \frac{1 \text{ kJ}}{1000 \text{ J}} \times \frac{6.0221 \times 10^{23}}{\text{mol}} = 202.9 \text{ kJ/mol}$$

119.   It should be element 119 with ground state electron configuration: $[Rn]7s^2 5f^{14} 6d^{10} 7p^6 8s^1$

Additional Exercises

121.   a. n b. n and ℓ

123.   Size decreases from left to right and increases going down the periodic table. Thus going one element right and one element down would result in a similar size for the two elements diagonal to each other. The ionization energies will be similar for the diagonal elements since the periodic trends also oppose each other. Electron affinities are harder to predict, but atoms with similar sizes and ionization energies should also have similar electron affinities.

125. $$60 \times 10^6 \text{ km} \times \frac{1000 \text{ m}}{\text{km}} \times \frac{1 \text{ s}}{3.00 \times 10^8 \text{ m}} = 200 \text{ s} \text{ (about 3 minutes)}$$

127. $$\lambda = \frac{hc}{E} = \frac{6.626 \times 10^{-34} \text{ J s} \times 2.998 \times 10^8 \text{ m/s}}{3.59 \times 10^{-19} \text{ J}} = 5.53 \times 10^{-7} \text{ m} \times \frac{100 \text{ cm}}{\text{m}}$$

$$= 5.53 \times 10^{-5} \text{ cm}$$

From the spectrum, $\lambda = 5.53 \times 10^{-5}$ cm is greenish yellow light.

129.   When the p and d orbital functions are evaluated at various points in space, the results sometimes have positive values and sometimes have negative values. The term phase is often associated with the + and − signs. For example, a sine wave has alternating positive and negative phases. This is analogous to the positive and negative values (phases) in the p and d orbitals.

131.   a.

$Na(g) \rightarrow Na^+(g) + e^-$	$IE_1 = 495 \text{ kJ}$
$Cl(g) + e^- \rightarrow Cl^-(g)$	$EA = -348.7 \text{ kJ}$
$Na(g) + Cl(g) \rightarrow Na^+(g) + Cl^-(g)$	$\Delta E = 146 \text{ kJ}$

b.

$Mg(g) \rightarrow Mg^+(g) + e^-$	$IE_1 = 735 \text{ kJ}$
$F(g) + e^- \rightarrow F^-(g)$	$EA = -327.8 \text{ kJ}$
$Mg(g) + F(g) \rightarrow Mg^+(g) + F^-(g)$	$\Delta E = 407 \text{ kJ}$

c.

$Mg^+(g) \rightarrow Mg^{2+}(g) + e^-$	$IE_2 = 1445 \text{ kJ}$
$F(g) + e^- \rightarrow F^-(g)$	$EA = -327.8 \text{ kJ}$
$Mg^+(g) + F(g) \rightarrow Mg^{2+}(g) + F^-(g)$	$\Delta E = 1117 \text{ kJ}$

d. From parts b and c, we get:

$$Mg(g) + F(g) \rightarrow Mg^+(g) + F^-(g) \qquad \Delta E = 407 \text{ kJ}$$
$$Mg^+(g) + F(g) \rightarrow Mg^{2+}(g) + F^-(g) \qquad \Delta E = 1117 \text{ kJ}$$

$$Mg(g) + 2\,F(g) \rightarrow Mg^{2+}(g) + 2\,F^-(g) \qquad \Delta E = 1524 \text{ kJ}$$

133.   Valence electrons are easier to remove than inner core electrons. The large difference in energy between I_2 and I_3 indicates that this element has two valence electrons. This element is most likely an alkaline earth metal since alkaline earth metal elements all have two valence electrons.

135.   a. The 4+ ion contains 20 electrons. Thus the electrically neutral atom will contain 24 electrons. The atomic number is 24 which identifies it as chromium.

b. The ground state electron configuration of the ion must be: $1s^2 2s^2 2p^6 3s^2 3p^6 4s^0 3d^2$; there are 6 electrons in s orbitals.

c. 12

d. 2

e. This is the isotope $^{50}_{24}\text{Cr}$. There are 26 neutrons in the nucleus.

f. 3.01×10^{23} atoms $\times \dfrac{1 \text{ mol}}{6.022 \times 10^{23} \text{ atoms}} \times \dfrac{49.9 \text{ g}}{\text{mol}} = 24.9 \text{ g}$

g. $1s^2 2s^2 2p^6 3s^2 3p^6 4s^1 3d^5$ is the ground state electron configuration for Cr. Cr is an exception to the normal filling order.

137.   a. Each orbital could hold 4 electrons.

b. The first period corresponds to $n = 1$, which can only have 1s orbitals. The 1s orbital could hold 4 electrons; hence the first period would have four elements. The second period corresponds to $n = 2$, which has 2s and 2p orbitals. These four orbitals can each hold four electrons. A total of 16 elements would be in the second period.

c. 20

d. 28

139.   S-type cone receptors: $\lambda = \dfrac{c}{\nu} = \dfrac{2.998 \times 10^8 \text{ m/s}}{6.00 \times 10^{14} \text{ s}^{-1}} = 5.00 \times 10^{-7} \text{ m} = 500. \text{ nm}$

$$\lambda = \dfrac{2.998 \times 10^8 \text{ m/s}}{7.49 \times 10^{14} \text{ s}^{-1}} = 4.00 \times 10^{-7} \text{ m} = 400. \text{ nm}$$

S-type cone receptors detect 400–500 nm light. From Figure 12.3 in the text, this is violet to green light, respectively.

M-type cone receptors: $\lambda = \dfrac{2.998 \times 10^8 \text{ m/s}}{4.76 \times 10^{14} \text{ s}^{-1}} = 6.30 \times 10^{-7}$ m $= 630.$ nm

$$\lambda = \dfrac{2.998 \times 10^8 \text{ m/s}}{6.62 \times 10^{14} \text{ s}^{-1}} = 4.53 \times 10^{-7} \text{ m} = 453 \text{ nm}$$

M-type cone receptors detect 450-630 nm light. From Figure 12.3 in the text, this is blue to orange light, respectively.

L-type cone receptors: $\lambda = \dfrac{2.998 \times 10^8 \text{ m/s}}{4.28 \times 10^{14} \text{ s}^{-1}} = 7.00 \times 10^{-7}$ m $= 700.$ nm

$$\lambda = \dfrac{2.998 \times 10^8 \text{ m/s}}{6.00 \times 10^{14} \text{ s}^{-1}} = 5.00 \times 10^{-7} \text{ m} = 500. \text{ nm}$$

L-type cone receptors detect 500-700 nm light.   This represents green to red light, respectively.

141.   a.   Because wavelength is inversely proportional to energy, the spectral line to the right of B (at a larger wavelength) represents the lowest possible energy transition; this is $n = 4$ to $n = 3$. The B line represents the next lowest energy transition, which is $n = 5$ to $n = 3$, and the A line corresponds to the $n = 6$ to $n = 3$ electronic transition.

b.   Because this spectrum is for a one-electron ion, $E_n = -2.178 \times 10^{-18}$ J (Z^2/n^2). To determine ΔE and, in turn, the wavelength of spectral line A, we must determine Z, the atomic number of the one electron species. Use spectral line B data to determine Z.

$$\Delta E_{5 \to 3} = -2.178 \times 10^{-18} \text{ J} \left(\frac{Z^2}{3^2} - \frac{Z^2}{5^2} \right) = -2.178 \times 10^{-18} \left(\frac{16Z^2}{9 \times 25} \right)$$

$$E = \frac{hc}{\lambda} = \frac{6.6261 \times 10^{-34} \text{ J s}(2.9979 \times 10^8 \text{ m/s})}{142.5 \times 10^{-9} \text{ m}} = 1.394 \times 10^{-18} \text{ J}$$

Because an emission occurs, $\Delta E_{5 \to 3} = -1.394 \times 10^{-18}$ J.

$$\Delta E = -1.394 \times 10^{-18} \text{ J} = -2.178 \times 10^{-18} \text{ J} \left(\frac{16\,Z^2}{9 \times 25} \right), \ Z^2 = 9.001, \ Z = 3; \text{ the ion is Li}^{2+}.$$

Solving for the wavelength of line A:

$$\Delta E_{6 \to 3} = -2.178 \times 10^{-18} (3)^2 \left(\frac{1}{3^2} - \frac{1}{6^2} \right) = -1.634 \times 10^{-18} \text{ J}$$

$$\lambda = \frac{hc}{|\Delta E|} = \frac{6.6261 \times 10^{-34} \text{ J s}(2.9979 \times 10^8 \text{ m/s})}{1.634 \times 10^{-18} \text{ J}} = 1.216 \times 10^{-7} \text{ m} = 121.6 \text{ nm}$$

Challenge Problems

143.   For one-electron species, $E_n = -R_HZ^2/n^2$. IE is for the $n = 1 \rightarrow n = \infty$ transition. So:

$$IE = E_\infty - E_1 = -E_1 = R_HZ^2/n^2 = R_HZ^2$$

$$\frac{4.72 \times 10^4 \text{ kJ}}{\text{mol}} \times \frac{1 \text{ mol}}{6.022 \times 10^{23}} \times \frac{1000 \text{ J}}{\text{kJ}} = 2.178 \times 10^{-18} \text{ J } (Z^2); \text{ solving: } Z = 6$$

Element 6 is carbon (X = carbon), and the charge for a one-electron carbon ion is 5+ (m = 5). The one-electron ion is C^{5+}.

145.   a.   Because the energy levels E_{xy} are inversely proportional to L^2, the $n_x = 2$, $n_y = 1$ energy level will be lower in energy than the $n_x = 1$, $n_y = 2$ energy level since $L_x > L_y$. The first three energy levels E_{xy} in order of increasing energy are:

$$E_{11} < E_{21} < E_{12}$$

The quantum numbers are:

Ground state (E_{11}) $\rightarrow$ $n_x = 1, n_y = 1$
First excited state (E_{21}) $\rightarrow$ $n_x = 2, n_y = 1$
Second excited state (E_{12}) $\rightarrow$ $n_x = 1, n_y = 2$

b. $E_{21} \rightarrow E_{12}$ is the transition. $E_{xy} = \dfrac{h^2}{8m}\left(\dfrac{n_x^2}{L_x^2} + \dfrac{n_y^2}{L_y^2}\right)$

$$E_{12} = \frac{h^2}{8m}\left[\frac{1^2}{(8.00 \times 10^{-9} \text{ m})^2} + \frac{2^2}{(5.00 \times 10^{-9} \text{ m})^2}\right] = \frac{1.76 \times 10^{17} \text{ h}^2}{8m}$$

$$E_{21} = \frac{h^2}{8m}\left[\frac{2^2}{(8.00 \times 10^{-9} \text{ m})^2} + \frac{1^2}{(5.00 \times 10^{-9} \text{ m})^2}\right] = \frac{1.03 \times 10^{17} \text{ h}^2}{8m}$$

$$\Delta E = E_{12} - E_{21} = \frac{1.76 \times 10^{17} \text{ h}^2}{8m} - \frac{1.03 \times 10^{17} \text{ h}^2}{8m} = \frac{7.3 \times 10^{16} \text{ h}^2}{8m}$$

$$\Delta E = \frac{(7.3 \times 10^{16} \text{ m}^{-2})(6.626 \times 10^{-34} \text{ J s})^2}{8(9.11 \times 10^{-31} \text{ kg})} = 4.4 \times 10^{-21} \text{ J}$$

$$\lambda = \frac{hc}{\Delta E} = \frac{6.626 \times 10^{-34} \text{ J s}(2.998 \times 10^8 \text{ m/s})}{4.4 \times 10^{-21} \text{ J}} = 4.5 \times 10^{-5} \text{ m}$$

147. $\psi_{1s} = \dfrac{1}{\sqrt{\pi}} \left(\dfrac{Z}{a_0} \right)^{3/2} e^{-\sigma}$; Z = 1 for H, $\sigma = \dfrac{Zr}{a_0} = \dfrac{-r}{a_0}$, $a_0 = 5.29 \times 10^{-11}$ m

$\psi_{1s} = \dfrac{1}{\sqrt{\pi}} \left(\dfrac{1}{a_0} \right)^{3/2} \exp \left(\dfrac{-r}{a_0} \right)$

Probability is proportional to ψ^2: $\psi_{1s}^2 = \dfrac{1}{\pi} \left(\dfrac{1}{a_0} \right)^3 \exp \left(\dfrac{-2r}{a_0} \right)$ (units of $\psi^2 = m^{-3}$)

a. ψ_{1s}^2 (at nucleus) $= \dfrac{1}{\pi} \left(\dfrac{1}{a_0} \right)^3 \exp \left[\dfrac{-2(0)}{a_0} \right] = 2.15 \times 10^{30}$ m^{-3}

If we assume this probability is constant throughout the 1×10^{-3} pm^3 volume, then the total probability p is $\psi_{1s}^2 \times V$.

1.0×10^{-3} pm$^3 = (1.0 \times 10^{-3}$ pm$) \times (1 \times 10^{-12}$ m/pm$)^3 = 1.0 \times 10^{-39}$ m^3

Total probability $= p = (2.15 \times 10^{30}$ m$^{-3}) \times (1.0 \times 10^{-39}$ m$^3) = 2.2 \times 10^{-9}$

b.   For an electron that is 1.0×10^{-11} m from the nucleus:

$\psi_{1s}^2 = \dfrac{1}{\pi} \left(\dfrac{1}{5.29 \times 10^{-11}} \right)^3 \exp \left[\dfrac{-2(1.0 \times 10^{-11})}{(5.29 \times 10^{-11})} \right] = 1.5 \times 10^{30}$ m^{-3}

$V = 1.0 \times 10^{-39}$ m^3; $p = \psi_{1s}^2 \times V = 1.5 \times 10^{-9}$

c. $\psi_{1s}^2 = 2.15 \times 10^{30}$ m^{-3} $\exp \left[\dfrac{-2(53 \times 10^{-12})}{(5.29 \times 10^{-11})} \right] = 2.9 \times 10^{29}$; $V = 1.0 \times 10^{-39}$ m^3

$p = \psi_{1s}^2 \times V = 2.9 \times 10^{-10}$

d. $V = \dfrac{4}{3} \pi [(10.05 \times 10^{-12}$ m$)^3 - (9.95 \times 10^{-12}$ m$)^3] = 1.3 \times 10^{-34}$ m^3

We shall evaluate ψ_{1s}^2 at the middle of the shell, r = 10.00 pm, and assume ψ_{1s}^2 is constant from r = 9.95 to 10.05 pm. The concentric spheres are assumed centered about the nucleus.

$\psi_{1s}^2 = 2.15 \times 10^{30}$ m^{-3} $\exp \left[\dfrac{-2(10.0 \times 10^{-12}$ m$)}{(5.29 \times 10^{-11}$ m$)} \right] = 1.47 \times 10^{30}$ m^{-3}

$p = (1.47 \times 10^{30}$ m$^{-3})(1.3 \times 10^{-34}$ m$^3) = 1.9 \times 10^{-4}$

e. $V = \dfrac{4}{3}\pi\,[(52.95 \times 10^{-12}\text{ m})^3 - (52.85 \times 10^{-12}\text{ m})^3] = 4 \times 10^{-33}\text{ m}^3$

Evaluate ψ_{1s}^2 at $r = 52.90$ pm: $\psi_{1s}^2 = 2.15 \times 10^{30}\text{ m}^{-3}\,(\text{e}^{-2}) = 2.91 \times 10^{29}\text{ m}^{-3}$; $p = 1 \times 10^{-3}$

149. $E_{xyz} = \dfrac{h^2\,(n_x^2 + n_y^2 + n_z^2)}{8mL^2}$, where $L = L_x = L_y = L_z$.

The first four energy levels will be filled with the 8 electrons. The first four energy levels are:

$$E_{111} = \frac{h^2\,(1^2 + 1^2 + 1^2)}{8mL^2} = \frac{3h^2}{8mL^2}$$

$$E_{211} = E_{121} = E_{112} = \frac{6h^2}{8mL^2} \quad \text{(These three energy levels are degenerate.)}$$

The next energy levels correspond to the first excited state. The energy for these levels are:

$$E_{221} = E_{212} = E_{122} = \frac{9h^2}{8mL^2} \quad \text{(These three energy levels are degenerate.)}$$

The electronic transition in question is from one of the degenerate E_{211}, E_{121}, or E_{112} levels to one of the degenerate E_{221}, E_{212}, or E_{122} levels.

$$\Delta E = \frac{9h^2}{8mL^2} - \frac{6h^2}{8mL^2} = \frac{3h^2}{8mL^2}$$

$$\Delta E = \frac{3(6.626 \times 10^{-34}\text{ J s})^2}{8(9.109 \times 10^{-31}\text{ kg})(1.50 \times 10^{-9}\text{ m})^2} = 8.03 \times 10^{-20}\text{ J}$$

$$\lambda = \frac{hc}{\Delta E} = \frac{(6.626 \times 10^{-34}\text{ J s})(2.998 \times 10^{8}\text{ m/s})}{8.03 \times 10^{-20}\text{ J}} = 2.47 \times 10^{-6}\text{ m} = 2470\text{ nm}$$

151.   a. Assuming the Bohr model applies to the 1s electron, $E_{1s} = -R_H Z^2/n^2 = -R_H Z^2_{\text{eff}}$, where $n = 1$.

IE $= E_\infty - E_{1s} = 0 - E_{1s} = R_H Z^2_{\text{eff}}$

$$\frac{2.462 \times 10^6 \text{ kJ}}{\text{mol}} \times \frac{1\text{ mol}}{6.0221 \times 10^{23}} \times \frac{1000\text{ J}}{\text{kJ}} = 2.178 \times 10^{-18}\text{ J }(Z_{\text{eff}})^2,\ Z_{\text{eff}} = 43.33$$

b. Silver is element 47, so $Z = 47$ for silver. Our calculated Z_{eff} value is slightly less than 47. Electrons in other orbitals can penetrate the 1s orbital. Thus a 1s electron can be slightly shielded from the nucleus, giving a Z_{eff} close to but less than Z.

CHAPTER 13

BONDING: GENERAL CONCEPTS

Chemical Bonds and Electronegativity

11. Electronegativity is the ability of an atom in a molecule to attract electrons to itself. Electronegativity is a bonding term. Electron affinity is the energy change when an electron is added to a substance. Electron affinity deals with isolated atoms in the gas phase.

   A covalent bond is a sharing of electron pair(s) in a bond between two atoms. An ionic bond is a complete transfer of electrons from one atom to another to form ions. The electrostatic attraction of the oppositely charged ions is the ionic bond.

   A pure covalent bond is an equal sharing of shared electron pair(s) in a bond. A polar covalent bond is an unequal sharing.

   Ionic bonds form when there is a large difference in electronegativity between the two atoms bonding together. This usually occurs when a metal with a small electronegativity is bonded to a nonmetal having a large electronegativity. A pure covalent bond forms between atoms having identical or nearly identical eletronegativities. A polar covalent bond forms when there is an intermediate electronegativity difference. In general, nonmetals bond together by forming covalent bonds, either pure covalent or polar covalent.

   Ionic bonds form due to the strong electrostatic attraction between two oppositely charged ions. Covalent bonds form because the shared electrons in the bond are attracted to two different nuclei, unlike the isolated atoms where electrons are only attracted to one nuclei. The attraction to another nuclei overrides the added electron-electron repulsions.

13.

	(IE – EA)	(IE – EA)/502	EN (text)	$2006/502 = 4.0$
F	2006 kJ/mol	4.0	4.0	
Cl	1604 kJ/mol	3.2	3.0	
Br	1463 kJ/mol	2.9	2.8	
I	1302 kJ/mol	2.6	2.5	

   The values calculated from IE and EA show the same trend as (and agree fairly closely) with the values given in the text.

15.   Using the periodic table, we expect the general trend for electronegativity to be:

   1. Increase as we go from left to right across a period

   2. Decrease as we go down a group

   a. $C < N < O$ b. $Se < S < Cl$ c. $Sn < Ge < Si$

   d. $Tl < Ge < S$ e. $Rb < K < Na$ f. $Ga < B < O$

17.   The general trends in electronegativity used in Exercises 13.15 and 13.16 are only rules of thumb. In this exercise we use experimental values of electronegativities and can begin to see several exceptions. The order of EN using Figure 13.3 is:

   a. $C (2.5) < N (3.0) < O (3.5)$ same as predicted

   b. $Se (2.4) < S (2.5) < Cl (3.0)$ same

   c. $Si (1.8) = Ge (1.8) = Sn (1.8)$ different   d. $Tl (1.8) = Ge (1.8) < S (2.5)$ different

   e. $Rb (0.8) = K (0.8) < Na (0.9)$ different   f. $Ga (1.6) < B (2.0) < O (3.5)$ same

Most polar bonds using actual EN values:

   a. Si–F and Ge–F (Ge–F predicted)   b. P–Cl (same as predicted)

   c. S–F (same as predicted)   d. Ti–Cl (same as predicted)

   e. Si–H and Sn–H (Sn–H predicted)   f. Al–Br (Tl–Br predicted)

19.   Ionic character is proportional to the difference in electronegativity values between the two elements forming the bond. Using the trend in electronegativity, the order will be:

   Br–Br < N–O < C–F < Ca–O < K–F
   least   most
   ionic character   ionic character

Note that Br–Br, N–O and C–F bonds are all covalent bonds since the elements are all non-metals. The Ca–O and K–F bonds are ionic, as is generally the case when a metal forms a bond with a nonmetal.

21.   Of the compounds listed, P_2O_5 is the only compound containing only covalent bonds. $(NH_4)_2SO_4$, $Ca_3(PO_4)_2$, K_2O, and KCl are all compounds composed of ions, so they exhibit ionic bonding. The polyatomic ions in $(NH_4)_2SO_4$ are NH_4^+ and SO_4^{2-}. Covalent bonds exist between the N and H atoms in NH_4^+ and between the S and O atoms in SO_4^{2-}. Therefore, $(NH_4)_2SO_4$ contains both ionic and covalent bonds. The same is true for $Ca_3(PO_4)_2$. The bonding is ionic between the Ca^{2+} and PO_4^{3-} ions and covalent between the P and O atoms in PO_4^{3-}. Therefore, $(NH_4)_2SO_4$ and $Ca_3(PO_4)_2$ are the compounds with both ionic and covalent bonds.

Ions and Ionic Compounds

23.   Anions are larger than the neutral atom, and cations are smaller than the neutral atom. For anions, the added electrons increase the electron-electron repulsions. To counteract this, the size of the electron cloud increases, placing the electrons further apart from one another. For cations, as electrons are removed, there are fewer electron-electron repulsions, and the electron cloud can be pulled closer to the nucleus.

Isoelectronic: same number of electrons. Two variables, the number of protons and the number of electrons, determine the size of an ion. Keeping the number of electrons constant, we only have to consider the number of protons to predict trends in size. The ion with the most protons attracts the same number of electrons most strongly, resulting in a smaller size.

25.   a. $Cu > Cu^+ > Cu^{2+}$ b. $Pt^{2+} > Pd^{2+} > Ni^{2+}$ c. $O^{2-} > O^- > O$

d. $La^{3+} > Eu^{3+} > Gd^{3+} > Yb^{3+}$ e. $Te^{2-} > I^- > Cs^+ > Ba^{2+} > La^{3+}$

For answer a, as electrons are removed from an atom, size decreases. Answers b and d follow the radius trend. For answer c, as electrons are added to an atom, size increases. Answer e follows the trend for an isoelectronic series, i.e., the smallest ion has the most protons.

27. Rb^+: $[Ar]4s^23d^{10}4p^6$; Ba^{2+}: $[Kr]5s^24d^{10}5p^6$; Se^{2-}: $[Ar]4s^23d^{10}4p^6$

I^-: $[Kr]5s^24d^{10}5p^6$

29.   a. Cs_2S is composed of Cs^+ and S^{2-}. Cs^+ has the same electron configuration as Xe, and S^{2-} has the same configuration as Ar.

b. SrF_2; Sr^{2+} has the Kr electron configuration, and F^- has the Ne configuration.

c. Ca_3N_2; Ca^{2+} has the Ar electron configuration, and N^{3-} has the Ne configuration.

d. $AlBr_3$; Al^{3+} has the Ne electron configuration, and Br^- has the Kr configuration.

31. Se^{2-}, Br^-, Rb^+, Sr^{2+}, Y^{3+}, and Zr^{4+} are some ions that are isoelectronic with Kr (36 electrons). In terms of size, the ion with the most protons will hold the electrons tightest and will be the smallest. The size trend is:

$$Zr^{4+} < Y^{3+} < Sr^{2+} < Rb^+ < Br^- < Se^{2-}$$
        smallest   largest

33.   a. Al^{3+} and S^{2-} are the expected ions. The formula of the compound would be Al_2S_3 (aluminum sulfide).

b. K^+ and N^{3-}; K_3N, potassium nitride

c. Mg^{2+} and Cl^-; $MgCl_2$, magnesium chloride

d. Cs^+ and Br^-; CsBr, cesium bromide

35.

$$K(s) \rightarrow K(g) \qquad \Delta E = 90. \text{ kJ} \quad \text{(sublimation)}$$

$$K(g) \rightarrow K^+(g) + e^- \qquad \Delta E = 419 \text{ kJ} \quad \text{(ionization energy)}$$

$$1/2 \, Cl_2(g) \rightarrow Cl(g) \qquad \Delta E = 239/2 \text{ kJ (bond energy)}$$

$$Cl(g) + e^- \rightarrow Cl^-(g) \qquad \Delta E = -349 \text{ kJ} \quad \text{(electron affinity)}$$

$$K^+(g) + Cl^-(g) \rightarrow KCl(s) \qquad \Delta E = -690. \text{ kJ} \quad \text{(lattice energy)}$$

$$K(s) + 1/2 \, Cl_2(g) \rightarrow KCl(s) \qquad \Delta E_f^o = -411 \text{ kJ/mol}$$

37.   Use Figure 13.11 as a template for this problem.

$$Li(s) \rightarrow Li(g) \qquad \Delta E_{sub} = ?$$

$$Li(g) \rightarrow Li^+(g) + e^- \qquad \Delta E = 520. \text{ kJ}$$

$$1/2 \, I_2(g) \rightarrow I(g) \qquad \Delta E = 151/2 \text{ kJ}$$

$$I(g) + e^- \rightarrow I^-(g) \qquad \Delta E = -295 \text{ kJ}$$

$$Li^+(g) + I^-(g) \rightarrow LiI(s) \qquad \Delta E = -753 \text{ kJ}$$

$$Li(s) + 1/2 \, I_2(g) \rightarrow LiI(s) \qquad \Delta E = -292 \text{ kJ}$$

$$\Delta E_{sub} + 520. + 151/2 - 295 - 753 = -292, \ \Delta E_{sub} = 161 \text{ kJ}$$

39.   a.   From the data given, less energy is required to produce $Mg^+(g) + O^-(g)$ than to produce $Mg^{2+}(g) + O^{2-}(g)$. However, the lattice energy for $Mg^{2+}O^{2-}$ will be much more exothermic than for Mg^+O^- (due to the greater charges in $Mg^{2+}O^{2-}$). The favorable lattice energy term will dominate and $Mg^{2+}O^{2-}$ forms.

b. Mg^+ and O^- both have unpaired electrons. In Mg^{2+} and O^{2-} there are no unpaired electrons. Hence Mg^+O^- would be paramagnetic; $Mg^{2+}O^{2-}$ would be diamagnetic. Paramagnetism can be detected by measuring the mass of a sample in the presence and absence of a magnetic field. The apparent mass of a paramagnetic substance will be larger in a magnetic field because of the force between the unpaired electrons and the field.

41. Ca^{2+} has a greater charge than Na^+, and Se^{2-} is smaller than Te^{2-}. The effect of charge on the lattice energy is greater than the effect of size. We expect the trend from most exothermic to least exothermic to be:

$$CaSe \ > \ CaTe \ > \ Na_2Se \ > \ Na_2Te$$

$$(-2862) \quad (-2721) \quad (-2130) \quad (-2095 \text{ kJ/mol}) \qquad \text{This is what we observe.}$$

Bond Energies

43. a. 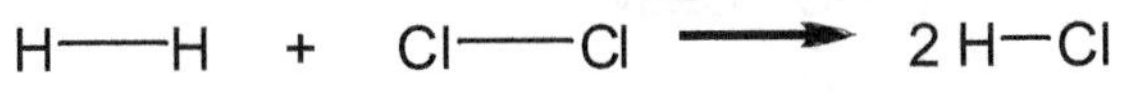   H—H + Cl—Cl ⟶ 2 H—Cl

Bonds broken: Bonds formed:

   1 H–H (432 kJ/mol)   2 H–Cl (427 kJ/mol)
   1 Cl–Cl (239 kJ/mol)

$\Delta E = \Sigma D_{broken} - \Sigma D_{formed}$, $\Delta E = 432\ kJ + 239\ kJ - 2(427)\ kJ = -183\ kJ$

b. 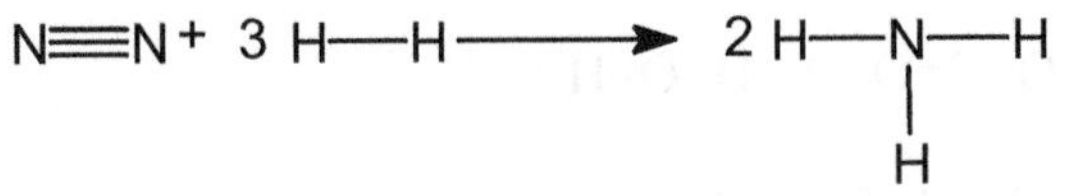   N≡N + 3 H—H ⟶ 2 H—N—H
                              |
                              H

Bonds broken: Bonds formed:

   1 N ≡ N (941 kJ/mol)   6 N–H (391 kJ/mol)
   3 H–H (432 kJ/mol)

$\Delta E = 941\ kJ + 3(432)\ kJ - 6(391)\ kJ = -109\ kJ$

c.   Sometimes some of the bonds remain the same between reactants and products. To save time, only break and form bonds that are involved in the reaction.

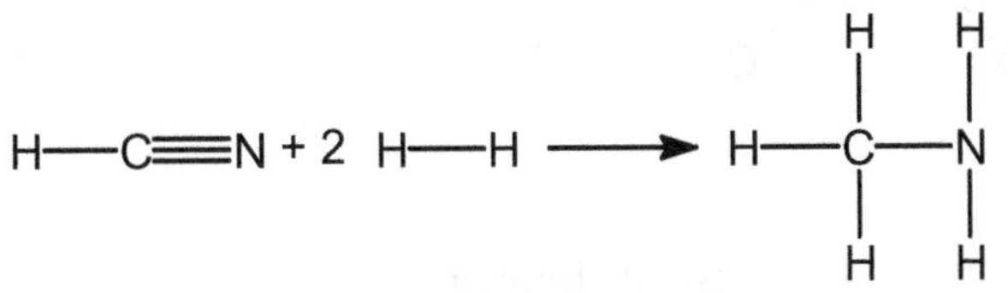

                              H   H
                              | |
H—C≡N + 2 H—H ⟶ H—C—N
                              | |
                              H   H

Bonds broken: Bonds formed:

   1 C≡N (891 kJ/mol)   1 C–N (305 kJ/mol)
   2 H–H (432 kJ/mol)   2 C–H (413 kJ/mol)
                                  2 N–H (391 kJ/mol)

$\Delta E = 891\ kJ + 2(432\ kJ) - [305\ kJ + 2(413\ kJ) + 2(391\ kJ)] = -158\ kJ$

d. 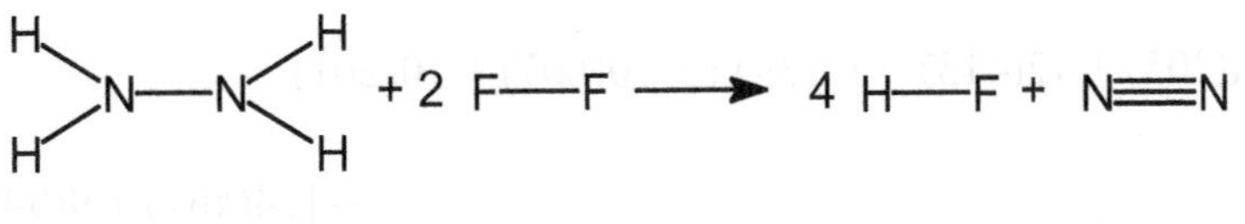   H   H
      \   /
       N—N   + 2 F—F ⟶ 4 H—F + N≡N
      /   \
     H   H

Bonds broken: Bonds formed:

   1 N–N (160. kJ/mol)   4 H–F (565 kJ/mol)
   4 N–H (391 kJ/mol)   1 N≡N (941 kJ/mol)
   2 F–F (154 kJ/mol)

$\Delta E = 160.\ kJ + 4(391\ kJ) + 2(154\ kJ) - [4(565\ kJ) + 941\ kJ] = -1169\ kJ$

45.

$$H-\overset{\overset{\displaystyle H}{|}}{\underset{\underset{\displaystyle H}{|}}{C}}-N\equiv C \longrightarrow H-\overset{\overset{\displaystyle H}{|}}{\underset{\underset{\displaystyle H}{|}}{C}}-C\equiv N$$

Bonds broken: 1 C–N (305 kJ/mol)   Bonds formed: 1 C–C (347 kJ/mol)

$\Delta E = \Sigma D_{broken} - \Sigma D_{formed}$, $\Delta E = 305 - 347 = -42$ kJ

Note: Sometimes some of the bonds remain the same between reactants and products. To save time, only break and form bonds that are involved in the reaction.

47. $H-C\equiv C-H + 5/2\ O=O \rightarrow 2\ O=C=O + H-O-H$

Bonds broken: Bonds formed:

    2 C–H (413 kJ/mol)   2 × 2 C=O (799 kJ/mol)
    1 C≡C (839 kJ/mol)   2 O–H (467 kJ/mol)
    5/2 O=O (495 kJ/mol)

$\Delta H = 2(413\ \text{kJ}) + 839\ \text{kJ} + 5/2\ (495\ \text{kJ}) - [4(799\ \text{kJ}) + 2(467\ \text{kJ})] = -1228$ kJ

49.

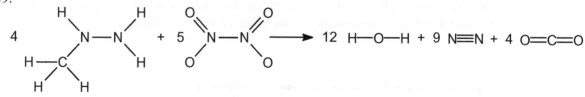

Bonds broken: Bonds formed:

    9 N–N (160. kJ/mol)   24 O–H (467 kJ/mol)
    4 N–C (305 kJ/mol)   9 N≡N (941 kJ/mol)
    12 C–H (413 kJ/mol)   8 C=O (799 kJ/mol)
    12 N–H (391 kJ/mol)
    10 N=O (607 kJ/mol)
    10 N–O (201 kJ/mol)

$\Delta E = 9(160.) + 4(305) + 12(413) + 12(391) + 10(607) + 10(201)$

$- [24(467) + 9(941) + 8(799)]$

$\Delta E = 20{,}388\ \text{kJ} - 26{,}069\ \text{kJ} = -5681$ kJ

51.   Because both reactions are highly exothermic, the high temperature is not needed to provide energy. It must be necessary for some other reason. The reason is to increase the speed of the reaction. This will be discussed in Chapter 15 on kinetics.

53.   a. $HF(g) \rightarrow H(g) + F(g)$ $\Delta E = 565$ kJ
           $H(g) \rightarrow H^+(g) + e^-$ $\Delta E = 1312$ kJ
           $F(g) + e^- \rightarrow F^-(g)$ $\Delta E = -327.8$ kJ
           _____
           $HF(g) \rightarrow H^+(g) + F^-(g)$ $\Delta E = 1549$ kJ

      b. $HCl(g) \rightarrow H(g) + Cl(g)$ $\Delta E = 427$ kJ
           $H(g) \rightarrow H^+(g) + e^-$ $\Delta E = 1312$ kJ
           $Cl(g) + e^- \rightarrow Cl^-(g)$ $\Delta E = -348.7$ kJ
           _____
           $HCl(g) \rightarrow H^+(g) + Cl^-(g)$ $\Delta E = 1390.$ kJ

      c. $HI(g) \rightarrow H(g) + I(g)$ $\Delta E = 295$ kJ
           $H(g) \rightarrow H^+(g) + e^-$ $\Delta E = 1312$ kJ
           $I(g) + e^- \rightarrow I^-(g)$ $\Delta E = -295.2$ kJ
           _____
           $HI(g) \rightarrow H^+(g) + I^-(g)$ $\Delta E = 1312$ kJ

      d. $H_2O(g) \rightarrow OH(g) + H(g)$ $\Delta E = 467$ kJ
           $H(g) \rightarrow H^+(g) + e^-$ $\Delta E = 1312$ kJ
           $OH(g) + e^- \rightarrow OH^-(g)$ $\Delta E = -180.$ kJ
           _____
           $H_2O(g) \rightarrow H^+(g) + OH^-(g)$ $\Delta E = 1599$ kJ

55. $NH_3(g) \rightarrow N(g) + 3\,H(g)$

      $\Delta E° = 3D_{NH} = 472.7$ kJ $+ 3(216.0$ kJ$) - (-46.1$ kJ$) = 1166.8$ kJ

      $$D_{NH} = \frac{1166.8 \text{ kJ}}{3 \text{ mol NH bonds}} = 388.93 \text{ kJ/mol}$$

      $D_{calc} = 389$ kJ/mol compared with 391 kJ/mol in the table. There is good agreement.

Lewis Structures and Resonance

57.   Drawing Lewis structures is mostly trial and error. However, the first two steps are always the same. These steps are (1) count the valence electrons available in the molecule/ion, and (2) attach all atoms to each other with single bonds (called the skeletal structure). Unless noted otherwise, the atom listed first is assumed to be the atom in the middle, called the central atom, and all other atoms in the formula are attached to this atom. The most notable exceptions to the rule are formulas that begin with H, e.g., H_2O, H_2CO, etc. Hydrogen can never be a central atom since this would require H to have more than two electrons. In these compounds, the atom listed second is assumed to be the central atom.

After counting valence electrons and drawing the skeletal structure, the rest is trial and error. We place the remaining electrons around the various atoms in an attempt to satisfy the octet rule (or duet rule for H). Keep in mind that practice makes perfect. After practicing, you can (and will) become very adept at drawing Lewis structures.

a.   HCN has $1 + 4 + 5 = 10$ valence electrons.

b. PH_3 has $5 + 3(1) = 8$ valence electrons.

H—C—N   H—C≡N:

Skeletal   Lewis
structure   structure

H—P—H   H—P—H
      | |
      H   H

Skeletal   Lewis
structure   structure

Skeletal structure uses 4 e⁻; 6 e⁻ remain

Skeletal structures uses 6 e⁻; 2 e⁻ remain

c. $CHCl_3$ has $4 + 1 + 3(7) = 26$ valence electrons.

d. NH_4^+ has $5 + 4(1) ! 1 = 8$ valence electrons.

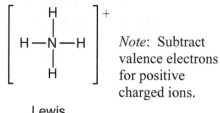

H
|
Cl—C—Cl
|
Cl

H
|
:Cl—C—Cl:
|
:Cl:

Skeletal   Lewis
structure   structure

[H]⁺
|
H—N—H
|
H

Lewis
structure

Note: Subtract valence electrons for positive charged ions.

e. H_2CO has $2(1) + 4 + 6 = 12$ valence electrons.

f. SeF_2 has $6 + 2(7) = 20$ valence electrons.

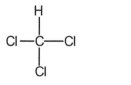

:O:
||
C
H   H

:F—Se—F:

g. CO_2 has $4 + 2(6) = 16$ valence electrons.

h. O_2 has $2(6) = 12$ valence electrons.

O=C=O

O=O

i.   HBr has $1 + 7 = 8$ valence electrons.

H—Br:

59.   Molecules/ions that have the same number of valence electrons and the same number of atoms will have similar Lewis structures.

61.   Ozone: O_3 has 3(6) = 18 valence electrons. Two resonance structures can be drawn.

Sulfur dioxide: SO_2 has 6 + 2(6) = 18 valence electrons.   Two resonance structures are possible.

Sulfur trioxide: SO_3 has 6 + 3(6) = 24 valence electrons.   Three resonance structures are possible.

63. CH_3NCO has 4 + 3(1) + 5 + 4 + 6 = 22 valence electrons. The order of the elements in the formula give the skeletal structure.

65.   Benzene has 6(4) + 6(1) = 30 valence electrons. Two resonance structures can be drawn for benzene. The actual structure of benzene is an average of these two resonance structures; i.e., all carbon-carbon bonds are equivalent with a bond length and bond strength somewhere between a single and a double bond.

67.   Borazine ($B_3N_3H_6$) has $3(3) + 3(5) + 6(1) = 30$ valence electrons. The possible resonance structures are similar to those of benzene in Exercise 13.65.

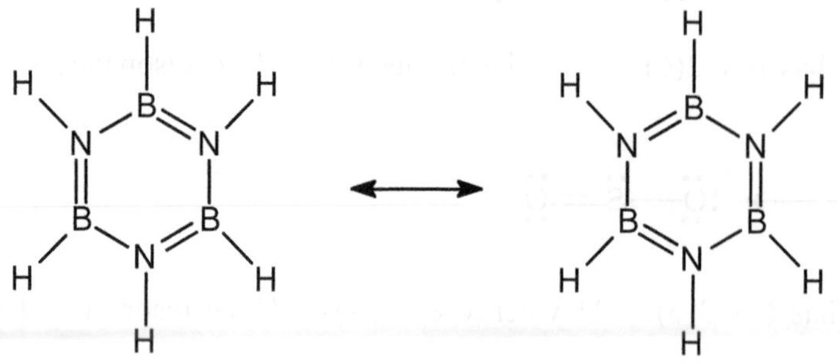

69.   Statements a and c are true. For statement a, XeF_2 has 22 valence electrons and it is impossible to satisfy the octet rule for all atoms with this number of electrons. The best Lewis structure is:

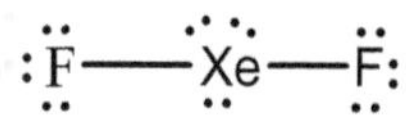

For statement c, NO^+ has 10 valence electrons, whereas NO^- has 12 valence electrons. The Lewis structures are:

Because a triple bond is stronger than a double bond, NO^+ has a stronger bond.

For statement b, SF_4 has five electron pairs around the sulfur in the best Lewis structure; it is an exception to the octet rule. Because OF_4 has the same number of valence electrons as SF_4, OF_4 would also have to be an exception to the octet rule. However, Row 2 elements such as O never have more than 8 electrons around them, so OF_4 does not exist. For statement d, two resonance structures can be drawn for ozone:

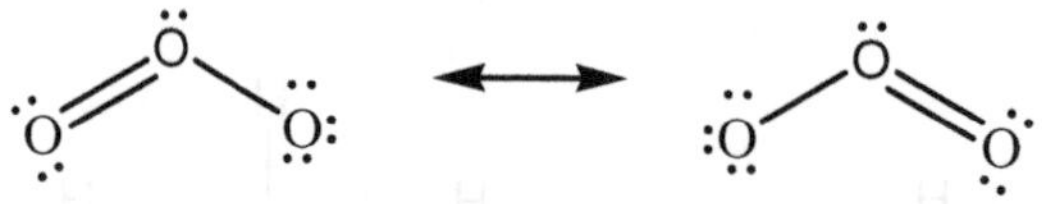

When resonance structures can be drawn, the actual bond lengths and strengths are all equal to each other. Even though each Lewis structure implies the two O–O bonds are different, this is not the case in real life. In real life, both of the O–O bonds are equivalent. When resonance structures can be drawn, you can think of the bonding as an average of all of the resonance structures.

71.   PF₅, 5 +5(7) = 40 valence electrons   SF₄, 6 + 4(7) = 34 e⁻

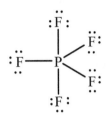   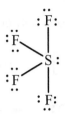

ClF₃, 7 + 3(7) = 28 e⁻   Br₃⁻, 3(7) + 1 = 22 e⁻

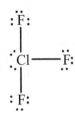 $$\left[:\ddot{Br}\!-\!\ddot{Br}\!-\!\ddot{Br}: \right]^{-}$$

Row 3 and heavier nonmetals can have more than 8 electrons around them when they have to. Row 3 and heavier elements have empty d orbitals that are close in energy to valence s and p orbitals. These empty d orbitals can accept extra electrons.

For example, P in PF₅ has its five valence electrons in the 3s and 3p orbitals. These s and p orbitals have room for three more electrons, and if it has to, P can use the empty 3d orbitals for any electrons above 8.

73.   CO₃²⁻ has 4 + 3(6) + 2 = 24 valence electrons.

Three resonance structures can be drawn for CO₃²⁻. The actual structure for CO₃²⁻ is an average of these three resonance structures. That is, the three C–O bond lengths are all equivalent, with a length somewhere between a single and a double bond. The actual bond length of 136 pm is consistent with this resonance view of CO₃²⁻.

75.   H₂NOH (14 e⁻):

H——N——O——H   Single bond between N and O

        |
        H

N_2O (16 e$^-$): $\ddot{N}=N=\ddot{O}$ ⟷ $:N\equiv N-\ddot{O}:$ ⟷ $:\ddot{N}-N\equiv O:$

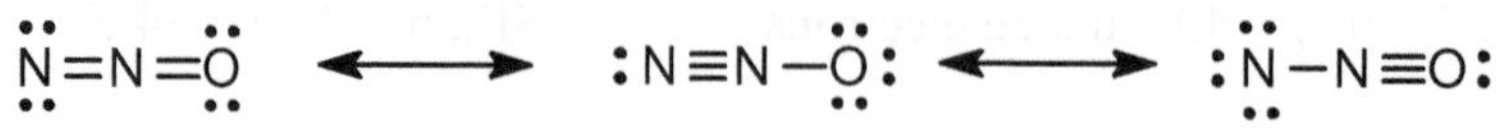

Average of a double bond between N and O

NO^+ (10 e$^-$): $\left[:N\equiv O:\right]^+$ Triple bond between N and O

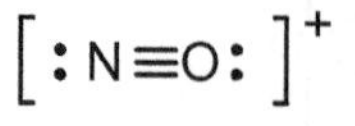

NO_2^- (18 e$^-$): $\left[\ddot{O}=\ddot{N}-\ddot{O}:\right]^-$ ⟷ $\left[:\ddot{O}-\ddot{N}=\ddot{O}\right]^-$

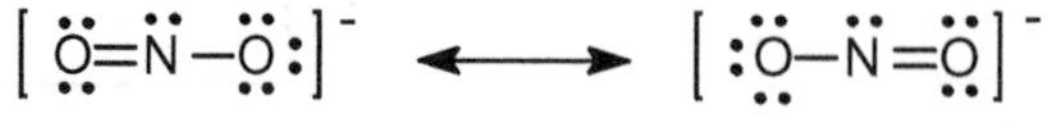

Average of 1 1/2 bond between N and O

NO_3^- (24 e$^-$):

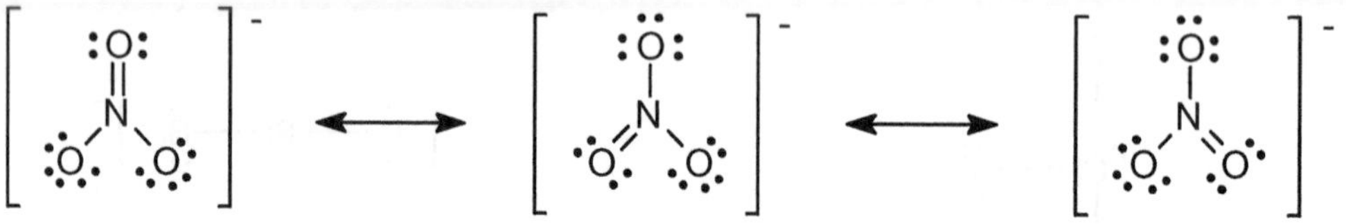

Average of 1 1/3 bond between N and O

From the Lewis structures, the order from shortest → longest N–O bond is:

$$NO^+ < N_2O < NO_2^- < NO_3^- < H_2NOH$$

Formal Charge

77.  $:C\equiv O:$ Carbon: FC = 4 – 2 – 1/2(6) = –1; oxygen: FC = 6 – 2 – 1/2(6) = +1

Electronegativity predicts the opposite polarization. The two opposing effects seem to partially cancel to give a much less polar molecule than expected.

79.   See Exercise 13.58a for the Lewis structures of $POCl_3$, SO_4^{2-}, ClO_4^- and PO_4^{3-}. All of these compounds/ions have similar Lewis structures to those of SO_2Cl_2 and XeO_4 shown below.

a. $POCl_3$: P, FC = 5 – 1/2(8) = +1   b. SO_4^{2-}: S, FC = 6 – 1/2(8) = +2

c. ClO_4^-: Cl, FC = 7 – 1/2(8) = +3   d. PO_4^{3-}: P, FC = 5 – 1/2(8) = +1

e. SO_2Cl_2, 6 + 2(6) + 2(7) = 32 e$^-$ f. XeO_4, 8 + 4(6) = 32 e$^-$

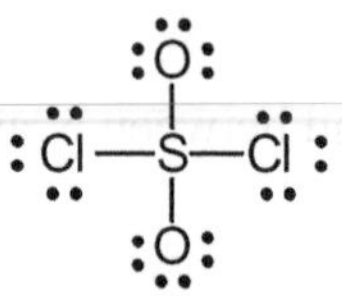

S, FC = 6 – 1/2(8) = +2 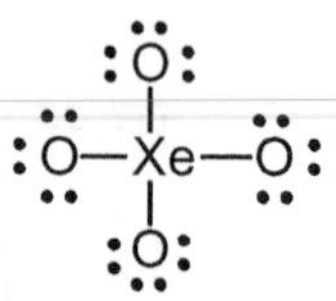   Xe, FC = 8 – 1/2(8) = +4

g. ClO_3^-, $7 + 3(6) + 1 = 26$ e⁻   h. NO_4^{3-}, $5 + 4(6) + 3 = 32$ e⁻

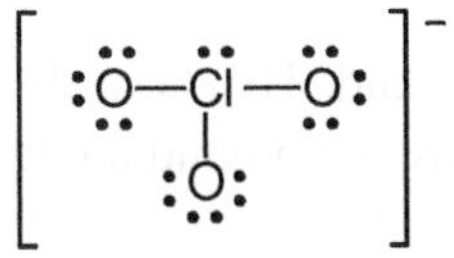

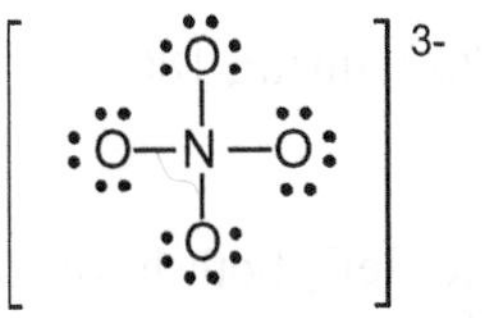

Cl, FC = $7 - 2 - 1/2(6) = +2$ N, FC = $5 - 1/2(8) = +1$

81.   SCl, $6 + 7 = 13$; the formula could be SCl (13 valence electrons), S_2Cl_2 (26 valence electrons), S_3Cl_3 (39 valence electrons), etc. For a formal charge of zero on S, we will need each sulfur in the Lewis structure to have two bonds to it and two lone pairs [FC = $6 - 4 - 1/2(4) = 0$]. Cl will need one bond and three lone pairs for a formal charge of zero [FC = $7 - 6 - 1/2(2) = 0$]. Since chlorine wants only one bond to it, it will not be a central atom here. With this in mind, only S_2Cl_2 can have a Lewis structure with a formal charge of zero on all atoms. The structure is:

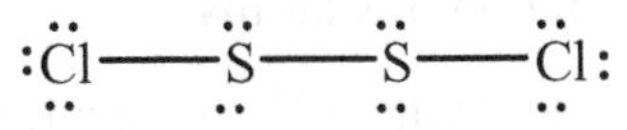

83. O_2F_2 has $2(6) + 2(7) = 26$ valence e⁻. The formal charge and oxidation number (state) of each atom is below the Lewis structure of O_2F_2.

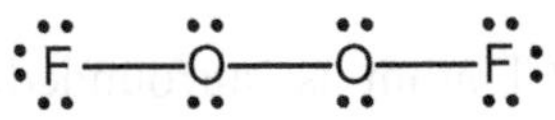

Formal Charge	0 0	0 0	
Oxid. Number	-1 +1	+1 -1	

Oxidation states are more useful when accounting for the reactivity of O_2F_2. We are forced to assign +1 as the oxidation state for oxygen due to the bonding to fluorine. Oxygen is very electronegative, and +1 is not a stable oxidation state for this element.

Molecular Structure and Polarity

85.   a. V-shaped or bent   b. see-saw   c. trigonal pyramid

d. trigonal bipyramid   e. tetrahedral

87.   The first step always is to draw a valid Lewis structure when predicting molecular structure. When resonance is possible, only one of the possible resonance structures is necessary to predict the correct structure because all resonance structures give the same structure. The Lewis structures are in Exercises 13.57, 13.58 and 13.60. The structures and bond angles for each follow.

13.57   a. HCN: linear, 180°   b. PH₃: trigonal pyramid, <109.5°

c. $CHCl_3$: tetrahedral, 109.5°   d. NH_4^+: tetrahedral, 109.5°

e. H_2CO: trigonal planar, 120°   f. SeF_2: V-shaped or bent, <109.5°

g. CO_2: linear, 180°   h and i. O_2 and HBr are both linear, but
                                                        there is no bond angle in either.

Note: PH_3 and SeF_2 both have lone pairs of electrons on the central atom, which result in bond angles that are something less than predicted from a tetrahedral arrangement (109.5°). However, we cannot predict the exact number. For these cases we will just insert a less than sign to indicate this phenomenon.

13.58   a.   All are tetrahedral; 109.5°

        b.   All are trigonal pyramid; <109.5°

        c.   All are V-shaped; <109.5°

13.60   a. NO_2^-: V-shaped, ≈120°; NO_3^-: trigonal planar, 120°

             N_2O_4: trigonal planar, 120° about both N atoms

        b. OCN^-, SCN^-, and N_3^- are all linear with 180° bond angles.

89.   From the Lewis structures (see Exercise 13.71), Br_3^- would have a linear molecular structure, ClF_3 would have a T-shaped molecular structure, and SF_4 would have a see-saw molecular structure. For example, consider ClF_3 (28 valence electrons):

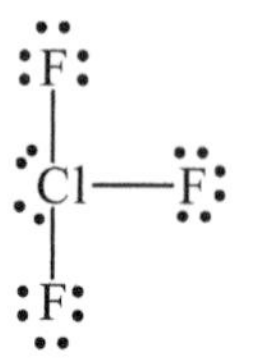

The central Cl atom is surrounded by five electron pairs, which requires a trigonal bipyramid geometry. Since there are three bonded atoms and two lone pairs of electrons about Cl, we describe the molecular structure of ClF_3 as T-shaped with predicted bond angles of about 90°. The actual bond angles will be slightly less than 90° due to the stronger repulsive effect of the lone pair electrons as compared to the bonding electrons.

91.   a. $XeCl_2$ has $8 + 2(7) = 22$ valence electrons.

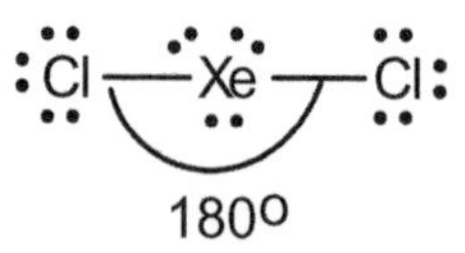

            There are five pairs of electrons about the central Xe atom. The structure will be based on a trigonal bipyramid geometry. The most stable arrangement of the atoms in $XeCl_2$ is a linear molecular structure with a 180° bond angle.

       b. ICl_3 has $7 + 3(7) = 28$ valence electrons.

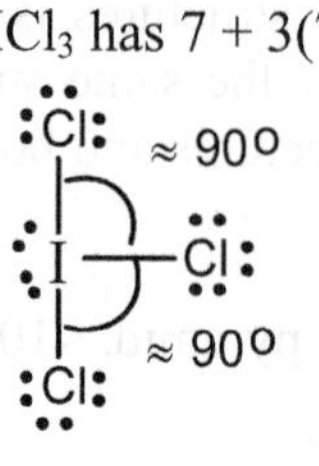

            T-shaped; The ClICl angles are ≈ 90°. Since the lone pairs will take up more space, the ClICl bond angles will probably be slightly less than 90°.

c.   TeF$_4$ has 6 + 4(7) = 34
     valence electrons.

d.   PCl$_5$ has 5 + 5(7) = 40
     valence electrons.

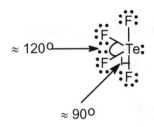

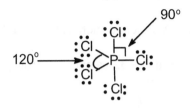

See-saw or teeter-totter
or distorted tetrahedron

Trigonal bipyramid

All the species in this exercise have five pairs of electrons around the central atom. All the structures are based on a trigonal bipyramid geometry, but only in PCl$_5$ are all the pairs bonding pairs. Thus PCl$_5$ is the only one we describe the molecular structure as trigonal bipyramid. Still, we had to begin with the trigonal bipyramid geometry to get to the structures (and bond angles) of the others.

93.   Let us consider the molecules with three pairs of electrons around the central atom first; these molecules are SeO$_3$ and SeO$_2$, and both have a trigonal planar arrangement of electron pairs. Both these molecules have polar bonds, but only SeO$_2$ has an overall net dipole moment. The net effect of the three bond dipoles from the three polar Se–O bonds in SeO$_3$ will be to cancel each other out when summed together. Hence SeO$_3$ is nonpolar since the overall molecule has no resulting dipole moment. In SeO$_2$, the two Se–O bond dipoles do not cancel when summed together; hence SeO$_2$ has a net dipole moment (is polar). Since O is more electronegative than Se, the negative end of the dipole moment is between the two O atoms, and the positive end is around the Se atom. The arrow in the following illustration represents the overall dipole moment in SeO$_2$. Note that to predict polarity for SeO$_2$, either of the two resonance structures can be used.

The other molecules in Exercise 13.88 (PCl$_3$, SCl$_2$, and SiF$_4$) have a tetrahedral arrangement of electron pairs. All have polar bonds; in SiF$_4$ the individual bond dipoles cancel when summed together, and in PCl$_3$ and SCl$_2$ the individual bond dipoles do not cancel. Therefore, SiF$_4$ has no net dipole moment (is nonpolar), and PCl$_3$ and SCl$_2$ have net dipole moments (are polar). For PCl$_3$, the negative end of the dipole moment is between the more electronegative chlorine atoms, and the positive end is around P. For SCl$_2$, the negative end is between the more electronegative Cl atoms, and the positive end of the dipole moment is around S.

95.   The two general requirements for a polar molecule are:

1.   Polar bonds

2.   A structure such that the bond dipoles of the polar bonds do not cancel

CF$_4$, 4 + 4(7) = 32 valence electrons   XeF$_4$, 8 + 4(7) = 36 e⁻

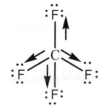   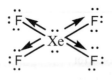

        Tetrahedral, 109.5°   Square planar, 90°

SF$_4$, 6 + 4(7) = 34 e⁻

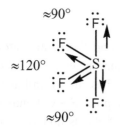   See-saw, ≈ 90°, ≈ 120°

The arrows indicate the individual bond dipoles in the three molecules (the arrows point to the more electronegative atom in the bond, which will be the partial negative end of the bond dipole). All three of these molecules have polar bonds. To determine the polarity of the overall molecule, we sum the effect of all of the individual bond dipoles. In CF$_4$, the fluorines are symmetrically arranged about the central carbon atom. The net result is for all the individual C–F bond dipoles to cancel each other out, giving a nonpolar molecule. In XeF$_4$, the 4 Xe–F bond dipoles are also symmetrically arranged, and XeF$_4$ is also nonpolar. The individual bond dipoles cancel out when summed together. In SF$_4$, we also have four polar bonds. But in SF$_4$ the bond dipoles are not symmetrically arranged, and they do not cancel each other out. SF$_4$ is polar. It is the positioning of the lone pair that disrupts the symmetry in SF$_4$.

CO$_2$, 4 + 2(6) = 16 e⁻   COS, 4 + 6 + 6 = 16 e⁻

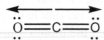

CO$_2$ and COS both have a linear molecular structure with a 180° bond angle. CO$_2$ is nonpolar because the individual bond dipoles cancel each other out, but COS is polar. By replacing an O with a less electronegative S atom, the molecule is not symmetric any more. The individual bond dipoles do not cancel because the C–S bond dipole is smaller than the C–O bond dipole resulting in a polar molecule.

97.   Only statement c is true. The bond dipoles in CF_4 and KrF_4 are arranged in a manner that they all cancel each other out, making them nonpolar molecules (CF_4 has a tetrahedral molecular structure, whereas KrF_4 has a square planar molecular structure). In SeF_4 the bond dipoles in this see-saw molecule do not cancel each other out, so SeF_4 is polar. For statement a, all the molecules have either a trigonal planar geometry or a trigonal bipyramid geometry, both of which have 120° bond angles. However, $XeCl_2$ has three lone pairs and two bonded chlorine atoms around it. $XeCl_2$ has a linear molecular structure with a 180° bond angle. With three lone pairs, we no longer have a 120° bond angle in $XeCl_2$. For statement b, SO_2 has a V-shaped molecular structure with a bond angle of about 120°. CS_2 is linear with a 180° bond angle and SCl_2 is V-shaped but with an approximate 109.5° bond angle. The three compounds do not have the same bond angle. For statement d, central atoms adopt a geometry to minimize electron repulsions, not maximize them.

99.   The formula is EF_2O^{2-}, and the Lewis structure has 28 valence electrons.

$$28 = x + 2(7) + 6 + 2, \ x = 6 \text{ valence electrons for element E}$$

Element E must belong to the Group 6A elements since E has six valence electrons. E must also be a Row 3 or heavier element since this ion has more than eight electrons around the central E atom (Row 2 elements never have more than eight electrons around them). Some possible identities for E are S, Se and Te. The ion has a T-shaped molecular structure (see Exercise 13.89) with bond angles of $\approx 90°$.

101.   Molecules that have an overall dipole moment are called polar molecules, and molecules that do not have an overall dipole moment are called nonpolar molecules.

   a. OCl_2, $6 + 2(7) = 20 \ e^-$ KrF_2, $8 + 2(7) = 22 \ e^-$

   V-shaped, polar; OCl_2 is polar because   Linear, nonpolar; The molecule is
   the two O–Cl bond dipoles don't cancel   nonpolar because the two Kr–F
   each other. The resulting dipole moment   bond dipoles cancel each other.
   is shown in the drawing.

   BeH_2, $2 + 2(1) = 4 \ e^-$ SO_2, $6 + 2(6) = 18 \ e^-$

   Linear, nonpolar; Be–H bond dipoles   V-shaped, polar; The S–O bond
   are equal and point in opposite directions.   dipoles do not cancel, so SO_2 is polar
   They cancel each other. BeH_2 is nonpolar.   (has a net dipole moment). Only one
                                                    resonance structure is shown.

Note: All four species contain three atoms. They have different structures because the number of lone pairs of electrons around the central atom are different in each case.

b. SO_3, $6 + 3(6) = 24$ e⁻ NF_3, $5 + 3(7) = 26$ e⁻

Trigonal planar, nonpolar;   Trigonal pyramid, polar;
bond dipoles cancel. Only one   bond dipoles do not cancel.
resonance structure is shown.

IF_3 has $7 + 3(7) = 28$ valence electrons.

T-shaped, polar; bond dipoles do not cancel.

Note: Each molecule has the same number of atoms but different structures because of differing numbers of lone pairs around each central atom.

c. CF_4, $4 + 4(7) = 32$ e⁻ SeF_4, $6 + 4(7) = 34$ e⁻

Tetrahedral, nonpolar;   See-saw, polar;
bond dipoles cancel.   bond dipoles do not cancel.

KrF_4, $8 + 4(7) = 36$ valence electrons

Square planar, nonpolar;
bond dipoles cancel.

Note: Again, each molecule has the same number of atoms but different structures because of differing numbers of lone pairs around the central atom.

d. IF_5, $7 + 5(7) = 42 \ e^-$ AsF_5, $5 + 5(7) = 40 \ e^-$

Square pyramid, polar;   Trigonal bipyramid, nonpolar;
bond dipoles do not cancel.   bond dipoles cancel.

Note: Yet again, the molecules have the same number of atoms but different structures because of the presence of differing numbers of lone pairs.

103.   All these molecules have polar bonds that are symmetrically arranged about the central atoms. In each molecule the individual bond dipoles cancel to give no net overall dipole moment. All these molecules are nonpolar even though they all contain polar bonds.

Additional Exercises

105. CO_3^{2-} has $4 + 3(6) + 2 = 24$ valence electrons.

HCO_3^- has $1 + 4 + 3(6) + 1 = 24$ valence electrons.

H_2CO_3 has $2(1) + 4 + 3(6) = 24$ valence electrons.

The Lewis structures for the reactants and products are:

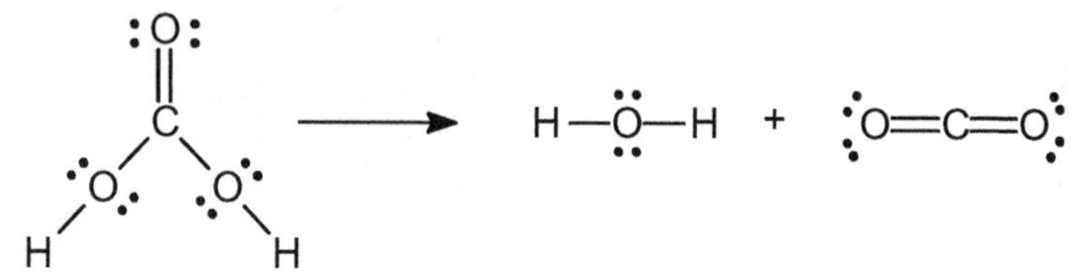

Bonds broken: Bonds formed:

   2 C–O (358 kJ/mol)   1 C=O (799 kJ/mol)
   1 O–H (467 kJ/mol)   1 O–H (467 kJ/mol)

$\Delta E = 2(358) + 467 - (799 + 467) = -83$ kJ; the carbon-oxygen double bond is stronger than two carbon-oxygen single bonds; hence CO_2 and H_2O are more stable than H_2CO_3.

107.   As the halogen atoms get larger, it becomes more difficult to fit three halogen atoms around the small nitrogen atom, and the NX_3 molecule becomes less stable.

109.   The stable species are:

   a.   NaBr: In $NaBr_2$, the sodium ion would have a 2+ charge, assuming that each bromine has a 1– charge. Sodium doesn't form stable Na^{2+} compounds.

   b. ClO_4^-: ClO_4 has 31 valence electrons, so it is impossible to satisfy the octet rule for all atoms in ClO_4. The extra electron from the 1– charge in ClO_4^- allows for complete octets for all atoms.

   c. XeO_4: We can't draw a Lewis structure that obeys the octet rule for SO_4 (30 electrons), unlike with XeO_4 (32 electrons).

   d. SeF_4: Both compounds require the central atom to expand its octet. O is too small and doesn't have low-energy d orbitals to expand its octet (which is true for all Row 2 elements).

111.   a.   Radius: $N^+ < N < N^-$;   IE: $N^- < N < N^+$

        N^+ has the fewest electrons held by the seven protons in the nucleus whereas N^- has the most electrons held by the seven protons. The seven protons in the nucleus will hold the electrons most tightly in N^+ and least tightly in N^-. Therefore, N^+ has the smallest radius with the largest ionization energy (IE), and N^- is the largest species with the smallest IE.

        b.   Radius: $Cl^+ < Cl < Se < Se^-$;   IE: $Se^- < Se < Cl < Cl^+$

        The general trends tell us that Cl has a smaller radius than Se and a larger IE than Se. Cl^+, with fewer electron-electron repulsions than Cl, will be smaller than Cl and have a larger IE. Se^-, with more electron-electron repulsions than Se, will be larger than Se and have a smaller IE.

c.   Radius: $Sr^{2+} < Rb^+ < Br^-$; IE: $Br^- < Rb^+ < Sr^{2+}$

These ions are isoelectronic. The species with the most protons (Sr^{2+}) will hold the electrons most tightly and will have the smallest radius and largest IE. The ion with the fewest protons (Br^-) will hold the electrons least tightly and will have the largest radius and smallest IE.

113.   Assuming 100.00 g of compound: $42.81 \text{ g F} \times \dfrac{1 \text{ mol F}}{19.00 \text{ g F}} = 2.253 \text{ mol F}$

The number of moles of X in XF_5 is: $2.253 \text{ mol F} \times \dfrac{1 \text{ mol X}}{5 \text{ mol F}} = 0.4506 \text{ mol X}$

This number of moles of X has a mass of 57.19 g (= 100.00 g − 42.81 g). The molar mass of X is:

$$\dfrac{57.19 \text{ g X}}{0.4506 \text{ mol X}} = 126.9 \text{ g/mol}; \text{This is element I.}$$

IF_5, $7 + 5(7) = 42 \text{ e}^-$

The molecular structure is square pyramid.

115.   Yes, each structure has the same number of effective pairs around the central atom, giving the same predicted molecular structure for each compound/ion. (A multiple bond is counted as a single group of electrons.)

Challenge Problems

117. KrF_2, $8 + 2(7) = 22 \text{ e}^-$; from the Lewis structure, we have a trigonal bipyramid arrangement of electron pairs with a linear molecular structure.

Hyperconjugation assumes that the overall bonding in KrF_2 is a combination of covalent and ionic contributions (see Section 13.12 of the text for discussion of hyperconjugation). Using hyperconjugation, two resonance structures are possible that keep the linear structure.

119. $2 \text{ Li}^+(g) + 2 \text{ Cl}^-(g) \rightarrow 2 \text{ LiCl}(s)$ $\Delta H = 2(-829 \text{ kJ})$

         $2 \text{ Li}(g) \rightarrow 2 \text{ Li}^+(g) + 2 \text{ e}^-$ $\Delta H = 2(520. \text{ kJ})$

         $2 \text{ Li}(s) \rightarrow 2 \text{ Li}(g)$ $\Delta H = 2(166 \text{ kJ})$

         $2 \text{ HCl}(g) \rightarrow 2 \text{ H}(g) + 2 \text{ Cl}(g)$ $\Delta H = 2(427 \text{ kJ})$

         $2 \text{ Cl}(g) + 2 \text{ e}^- \rightarrow 2 \text{ Cl}^-(g)$ $\Delta H = 2(-349 \text{ kJ})$

         $2 \text{ H}(g) \rightarrow \text{ H}_2(g)$ $\Delta H = -(432 \text{ kJ})$

         _____

         $2 \text{ Li}(s) + 2 \text{ HCl}(g) \rightarrow 2 \text{ LiCl}(s) + \text{ H}_2(g)$ $\Delta H = -562 \text{ kJ}$

121.   a. $\text{N(NO}_2)_2^-$ contains $5 + 2(5) + 4(6) + 1 = 40$ valence electrons.

         The most likely structures are:

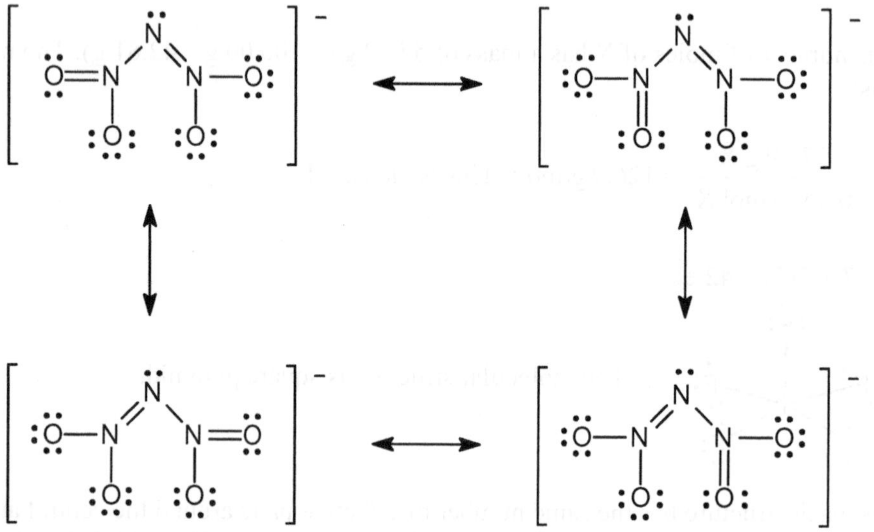

         There are other possible resonance structures, but these are most likely.

    b.   The NNN and all ONN and ONO bond angles should be about 120°.

    c. $\text{NH}_4\text{N(NO}_2)_2(s) \rightarrow 2 \text{ N}_2(g) + 2 \text{ H}_2\text{O}(g) + \text{ O}_2(g)$; break and form all bonds.

         Bonds broken: Bonds formed:

         4 N–H (391 kJ/mol)   2 N≡N (941 kJ/mol)

         1 N–N (160. kJ/mol)   4 H–O (467 kJ/mol)

         1 N=N (418 kJ/mol)   1 O=O (495 kJ/mol)

         3 N–O (201 kJ/mol)   _____

         1 N=O (607 kJ/mol) $\Sigma D_{formed} = 4245 \text{ kJ}$

         _____

         $\Sigma D_{broken} = 3352 \text{ kJ}$

         $\Delta E = \Sigma D_{broken} - \Sigma D_{formed} = 3352 \text{ kJ} - 4245 \text{ kJ} = -893 \text{ kJ}$

d. To estimate ΔE, we completely ignored the ionic interactions between NH_4^+ and $N(NO_2)_2^-$ in the solid phase. In addition, we assumed the bond energies in Table 13.6 applied to the $N(NO_2)^-$ bonds in any one of the resonance structures above. This is a bad assumption since molecules that exhibit resonance generally have stronger overall bonds than predicted. All these assumptions give an estimated ΔE value which is too negative.

123. a. i. $C_6H_6N_{12}O_{12} \rightarrow 6\ CO + 6\ N_2 + 3\ H_2O + 3/2\ O_2$

The NO_2 groups have one N–O single bond and one N=O double bond, and each carbon atom has one C–H single bond. We must break and form all bonds.

Bonds broken:	Bonds formed:
3 C–C (347 kJ/mol)	6 C≡O (1072 kJ/mol)
6 C–H (413 kJ/mol)	6 N≡N (941 kJ/mol)
12 C–N (305 kJ/mol)	6 H–O (467 kJ/mol)
6 N–N (160. kJ/mol)	3/2 O=O (495 kJ/mol)
6 N–O (201 kJ/mol)	
6 N=O (607 kJ/mol)	ΣD_{formed} = 15,623 kJ

ΣD_{broken} = 12,987 kJ

$\Delta E = \Sigma D_{broken} - \Sigma D_{formed}$ = 12,987 kJ – 15,623 kJ = –2636 kJ

ii. $C_6H_6N_{12}O_{12} \rightarrow 3\ CO + 3\ CO_2 + 6\ N_2 + 3\ H_2O$

Note: The bonds broken will be the same for all three reactions.

Bonds formed:

3 C≡O (1072 kJ/mol)
6 C=O (799 kJ/mol)
6 N≡N (941 kJ/mol)
6 H–O (467 kJ/mol)

ΣD_{formed} = 16,458 kJ

ΔE = 12,987 kJ – 16,458 kJ = –3471 kJ

iii. $C_6H_6N_{12}O_{12} \rightarrow 6\ CO_2 + 6\ N_2 + 3\ H_2$

Bonds formed:

12 C=O (799 kJ/mol)
6 N≡N (941 kJ/mol)
3 H–H (432 kJ/mol)

ΣD_{formed} = 16,530. kJ

ΔE = 12,987 kJ – 16,530. kJ = –3543 kJ

b. Reaction iii yields the most energy per mole of CL-20, so it will yield the most energy per kilogram.

$$\frac{-3543\ \text{kJ}}{\text{mol}} \times \frac{1\ \text{mol}}{438.23\ \text{g}} \times \frac{1000\ \text{g}}{\text{kg}} = -8085\ \text{kJ/kg}$$

125.   The reaction is: $1/2\ I_2(s) + 1/2\ Cl_2(g) \rightarrow ICl(g)$ $\Delta E_f^\circ = ?$

Using Hess's law:

$1/2\ I_2(s) \rightarrow 1/2\ I_2(g)$	$\Delta H = 1/2\ (62\ \text{kJ})$	(Appendix 4)
$1/2\ I_2(g) \rightarrow I(g)$	$\Delta H = 1/2\ (149\ \text{kJ})$	(Table 13.6)
$1/2\ Cl_2(g) \rightarrow Cl(g)$	$\Delta H = 1/2\ (239\ \text{kJ})$	(Table 13.6)
$I(g) + Cl(g) \rightarrow ICl(g)$	$\Delta H = -208\ \text{kJ}$	(Table 13.6)

$1/2\ I_2(s) + 1/2\ Cl_2(g) \rightarrow ICl(g)$	$\Delta H = 17\ \text{kJ}$ so $\Delta E_f^\circ = 17\ \text{kJ/mol}$

CHAPTER 3

STOICHIOMETRY

Atomic Masses and the Mass Spectrometer

23. Average atomic mass = A = 0.0800(45.95269) + 0.0730(46.951764) + 0.7380(47.947947)

    $$+ 0.0550(48.947841) + 0.0540(49.944792) = 47.88 \text{ amu}$$

    This is element Ti (titanium).

25. If silver is 51.82% ^{107}Ag, then the remainder is ^{109}Ag (48.18%). Determining the atomic mass (A) of ^{109}Ag:

    $$107.868 = \frac{51.82(106.905) + 48.18(A)}{100}$$

    $10786.8 = 5540. + (48.18)A$, A = 108.9 amu = atomic mass of ^{109}Ag

27. $186.207 = 0.6260(186.956) + 0.3740(A)$, $186.207 - 117.0 = 0.3740(A)$

    $$A = \frac{69.2}{0.3740} = 185 \text{ amu} \ (A = 184.95 \text{ amu without rounding to proper significant figures})$$

29. There are three peaks in the mass spectrum, each 2 mass units apart. This is consistent with two isotopes, differing in mass by two mass units. The peak at 157.84 corresponds to a Br_2 molecule composed of two atoms of the lighter isotope. This isotope has mass equal to 157.84/2, or 78.92. This corresponds to ^{79}Br. The second isotope is ^{81}Br with mass equal to 161.84/2 = 80.92. The peaks in the mass spectrum correspond to $^{79}Br_2$, $^{79}Br^{81}Br$, and $^{81}Br_2$ in order of increasing mass. The intensities of the highest and lowest masses tell us the two isotopes are present at about equal abundance. The actual abundance is 50.68% ^{79}Br and 49.32% ^{81}Br.

31. GaAs can be either ^{69}GaAs or ^{71}GaAs. The mass spectrum for GaAs will have two peaks at 144 (= 69 + 75) and 146 (= 71 + 75) with intensities in the ratio of 60 : 40 or 3 : 2.

144   146

8

Ga_2As_2 can be $^{69}Ga_2As_2$, $^{69}Ga^{71}GaAs_2$, or $^{71}Ga_2As_2$. The mass spectrum will have three peaks at 288, 290, and 292 with intensities in the ratio of 36 : 48 : 16 or 9 : 12 : 4. We get this ratio from the following probability table:

	^{69}Ga (0.60)	^{71}Ga (0.40)
^{69}Ga (0.60)	0.36	0.24
^{71}Ga (0.40)	0.24	0.16

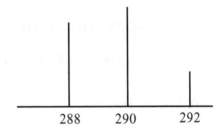

Moles and Molar Masses

33.   a. $9(12.011) + 8(1.0079) + 4(15.999) = 180.158$ g/mol

b. $500.\ \text{mg} \times \dfrac{1\,g}{1000\,mg} \times \dfrac{1\,mol}{180.16\,g} = 2.78 \times 10^{-3}$ mol

2.78×10^{-3} mol $\times \dfrac{6.022 \times 10^{23}\ \text{molecules}}{mol} = 1.67 \times 10^{21}$ molecules

35.   a. $20.0\ \text{mg}\ C_8H_{10}N_4O_2 \times \dfrac{1\,g}{1000\,mg} \times \dfrac{1\,mol}{194.20\,g} = 1.03 \times 10^{-4}$ mol $C_8H_{10}N_4O_2$

b. $2.72 \times 10^{21}\ \text{molecules}\ C_2H_5OH \times \dfrac{1\,mol}{6.022 \times 10^{23}\ \text{molecules}} = 4.52 \times 10^{-3}$ mol C_2H_5OH

c. $1.50\ \text{g}\ CO_2 \times \dfrac{1\,mol}{44.01\,g} = 3.41 \times 10^{-2}$ mol CO_2

37. $4.0\ \text{g}\ H_2 \times \dfrac{1\,mol\,H_2}{2.016\,g\,H_2} \times \dfrac{2\,mol\,H}{1\,mol\,H_2} \times \dfrac{6.022 \times 10^{23}\ \text{atoms}\ H}{1\,mol\,H} = 2.4 \times 10^{24}$ atoms

$4.0\ \text{g}\ He \times \dfrac{1\,mol\,He}{4.003\,g\,He} \times \dfrac{6.022 \times 10^{23}\ \text{atoms}\ He}{1\,mol\,He} = 6.0 \times 10^{23}$ atoms

$$1.0 \text{ mol } F_2 \times \frac{2 \text{ mol F}}{1 \text{ mol } F_2} \times \frac{6.022 \times 10^{23} \text{ atoms F}}{1 \text{ mol F}} = 1.2 \times 10^{24} \text{ atoms}$$

$$44.0 \text{ g } CO_2 \times \frac{1 \text{ mol } CO_2}{44.01 \text{ g } CO_2} \times \frac{3 \text{ mol atoms}(1 \text{ C} + 2 \text{ O})}{1 \text{ mol } CO_2} \times \frac{6.022 \times 10^{23} \text{ atoms}}{1 \text{ mol atoms}}$$
$$= 1.81 \times 10^{24} \text{ atoms}$$

$$146 \text{ g } SF_6 \times \frac{1 \text{ mol } SF_6}{146.07 \text{ g } SF_6} \times \frac{7 \text{ mol atoms}(1 \text{ S} + 6 \text{ F})}{1 \text{ mol } SF_6} \times \frac{6.022 \times 10^{23} \text{ atoms}}{1 \text{ mol atoms}} = 4.21 \times 10^{24} \text{ atoms}$$

The order is: $4.0 \text{ g He} < 1.0 \text{ mol } F_2 < 44.0 \text{ g } CO_2 < 4.0 \text{ g } H_2 < 146 \text{ g } SF_6$

39.   a. $2(12.01) + 3(1.008) + 3(35.45) + 2(16.00) = 165.39 \text{ g/mol}$

       b. $500.0 \text{ g} \times \dfrac{1 \text{ mol}}{165.39 \text{ g}} = 3.023 \text{ mol } C_2H_3Cl_3O_2$

       c. $2.0 \times 10^{-2} \text{ mol} \times \dfrac{165.39 \text{ g}}{\text{mol}} = 3.3 \text{ g } C_2H_3Cl_3O_2$

       d. $5.0 \text{ g } C_2H_3Cl_3O_2 \times \dfrac{1 \text{ mol}}{165.39 \text{ g}} \times \dfrac{6.02 \times 10^{23} \text{ molecules}}{\text{mol}} \times \dfrac{3 \text{ atoms Cl}}{\text{molecule}}$
$$= 5.5 \times 10^{22} \text{ atoms of chlorine}$$

       e. $1.0 \text{ g Cl} \times \dfrac{1 \text{ mol Cl}}{35.45 \text{ g}} \times \dfrac{1 \text{ mol } C_2H_3Cl_3O_2}{3 \text{ mol Cl}} \times \dfrac{165.39 \text{ g } C_2H_3Cl_3O_2}{\text{mol } C_2H_3Cl_3O_2} = 1.6 \text{ g chloral hydrate}$

       f. $500 \text{ molecules} \times \dfrac{1 \text{ mol}}{6.022 \times 10^{23} \text{ molecules}} \times \dfrac{165.39 \text{ g}}{\text{mol}} = 1.373 \times 10^{-19} \text{ g}$

Percent Composition

41.   Molar mass $= 20(12.01) + 29(1.008) + 19.00 + 3(16.00) = 336.43 \text{ g/mol}$

       $\text{Mass \% C} = \dfrac{20(12.01) \text{ g C}}{336.43 \text{ g compound}} \times 100 = 71.40\% \text{ C}$

       $\text{Mass \% H} = \dfrac{29(1.008) \text{ g H}}{336.43 \text{ g compound}} \times 100 = 8.689\% \text{ H}$

$$\text{Mass \% F} = \frac{19.00 \text{ g F}}{336.43 \text{ g compound}} \times 100 = 5.648\% \text{ F}$$

$$\text{Mass \% O} = 100.00 - (71.40 + 8.689 + 5.648) = 14.26\% \text{ O or:}$$

$$\text{Mass \% O} = \frac{3(16.00) \text{ g O}}{336.43 \text{ g compound}} \times 100 = 14.27\% \text{ O}$$

43.   In 1 mole of $YBa_2Cu_3O_7$, there are 1 mole of Y, 2 moles of Ba, 3 moles of Cu, and 7 moles of O.

$$\text{Molar mass} = 1 \text{ mol Y} \left(\frac{88.91 \text{ g Y}}{\text{mol Y}} \right) + 2 \text{ mol Ba} \left(\frac{137.3 \text{ g Ba}}{\text{mol Ba}} \right)$$

$$+ 3 \text{ mol Cu} \left(\frac{63.55 \text{ g Cu}}{\text{mol Cu}} \right) + 7 \text{ mol O} \left(\frac{16.00 \text{ g O}}{\text{mol O}} \right)$$

$$\text{Molar mass} = 88.91 + 274.6 + 190.65 + 112.00 = 666.2 \text{ g/mol}$$

$$\text{Mass \% Y} = \frac{88.91 \text{ g}}{666.2 \text{ g}} \times 100 = 13.35\% \text{ Y}; \quad \text{mass \% Ba} = \frac{274.6 \text{ g}}{666.2 \text{ g}} \times 100 = 41.22\% \text{ Ba}$$

$$\text{Mass \% Cu} = \frac{190.65 \text{ g}}{666.2 \text{ g}} \times 100 = 28.62\% \text{ Cu}; \quad \text{mass \% O} = \frac{112.0 \text{ g}}{666.2 \text{ g}} \times 100 = 16.81\% \text{ O}$$

45.   NO: $\text{Mass \% N} = \dfrac{14.01 \text{ g N}}{30.01 \text{ g NO}} \times 100 = 46.68\% \text{ N}$

NO_2: $\text{Mass \% N} = \dfrac{14.01 \text{ g N}}{46.01 \text{ g NO}_2} \times 100 = 30.45\% \text{ N}$

N_2O: $\text{Mass \% N} = \dfrac{2(14.01) \text{ g N}}{44.02 \text{ g N}_2\text{O}} \times 100 = 63.65\% \text{ N}$

From the calculated mass percents, only NO is 46.7% N by mass, so NO could be this species. Any other compound having NO as an empirical formula could also be the compound.

47.   There are 0.390 g Cu for every 100.000 g of fungal laccase. Let's assume 100.000 g fungal laccase.

$$\text{Mol fungal laccase} = 0.390 \text{ g Cu} \times \frac{1 \text{ mol Cu}}{63.55 \text{ g Cu}} \times \frac{1 \text{ mol fungal laccase}}{4 \text{ mol Cu}} = 1.53 \times 10^{-3} \text{ mol}$$

$$\frac{x \text{ g fungal laccase}}{1 \text{ mol fungal laccase}} = \frac{100.000 \text{ g}}{1.53 \times 10^{-3} \text{ mol}}, \quad x = \text{molar mass} = 6.54 \times 10^4 \text{ g/mol}$$

Empirical and Molecular Formulas

49.   a.   Molar mass of $CH_2O = 1$ mol $C\left(\dfrac{12.011\ g}{mol\ C}\right) + 2$ mol $H\left(\dfrac{1.0079\ g}{mol\ H}\right)$

$$+ 1\ mol\ O\left(\dfrac{15.999\ g}{mol\ O}\right) = 30.026\ g/mol$$

$$\%\ C = \dfrac{12.011\ g\ C}{30.026\ g\ CH_2O} \times 100 = 40.002\%\ C;\ \ \%\ H = \dfrac{2.0158\ g\ H}{30.026\ g\ CH_2O} \times 100 = 6.7135\%\ H$$

$$\%\ O = \dfrac{15.999\ g\ O}{30.026\ g\ CH_2O} \times 100 = 53.284\%\ O\ \ or\ \%\ O = 100.000 - (40.002 + 6.7135)$$

$$= 53.285\%$$

b.   Molar mass of $C_6H_{12}O_6 = 6(12.011) + 12(1.0079) + 6(15.999) = 180.155\ g/mol$

$$\%\ C = \dfrac{72.066\ g\ C}{180.155\ g\ C_6H_{12}O_6} \times 100 = 40.002\%;\ \ \ \%\ H = \dfrac{12(1.0079)\ g}{180.155\ g} \times 100 = 6.7136\%$$

$$\%\ O = 100.00 - (40.002 + 6.7136) = 53.284\%$$

c.   Molar Mass of $HC_2H_3O_2 = 2(12.011) + 4(1.0079) + 2(15.999) = 60.052\ g/mol$

$$\%\ C = \dfrac{24.022\ g}{60.052\ g} \times 100 = 40.002\%;\ \ \ \%\ H = \dfrac{4.0316\ g}{60.052\ g} \times 100 = 6.7135\%$$

$$\%\ O = 100.000 - (40.002 + 6.7135) = 53.285\%$$

All three compounds have the same empirical formula, CH_2O, and different molecular formulas. The composition of all three in mass percent is also the same (within rounding differences). Therefore, elemental analysis will give us only the empirical formula.

51.   a.   SNH: Empirical formula mass $= 32.07 + 14.01 + 1.008 = 47.09\ g/mol$

$$\dfrac{188.35\ g}{47.09\ g} = 4.000;\ \ so\ the\ molecular\ formula\ is\ (SNH)_4\ or\ S_4N_4H_4.$$

b. $NPCl_2$: Empirical formula mass $= 14.01 + 30.97 + 2(35.45) = 115.88\ g/mol$

$$\dfrac{347.64\ g}{115.88\ g} = 3.0000;\ \ molecular\ formula\ is\ (NPCl_2)_3\ or\ N_3P_3Cl_6.$$

c. CoC_4O_4: $58.93 + 4(12.01) + 4(16.00) = 170.97$ g/mol

$$\frac{341.94 \text{ g}}{170.97 \text{ g}} = 2.0000; \text{ molecular formula: } Co_2C_8O_8$$

d. SN: $32.07 + 14.01 = 46.08$ g/mol; $\dfrac{184.32 \text{ g}}{46.08 \text{ g}} = 4.000$; molecular formula: S_4N_4

53.   Compound I: mass O $= 0.6498$ g $Hg_xO_y - 0.6018$ g Hg $= 0.0480$ g O

$$0.6018 \text{ g Hg} \times \frac{1 \text{ mol Hg}}{200.6 \text{ g Hg}} = 3.000 \times 10^{-3} \text{ mol Hg}$$

$$0.0480 \text{ g O} \times \frac{1 \text{ mol O}}{16.00 \text{ g O}} = 3.00 \times 10^{-3} \text{ mol O}$$

The mole ratio between Hg and O is 1 : 1, so the empirical formula of compound I is HgO.

Compound II: mass Hg $= 0.4172$ g $Hg_xO_y - 0.016$ g O $= 0.401$ g Hg

$$0.401 \text{ g Hg} \times \frac{1 \text{ mol Hg}}{200.6 \text{ g Hg}} = 2.00 \times 10^{-3} \text{ mol Hg}; \ 0.016 \text{ g O} \times \frac{1 \text{ mol O}}{16.00 \text{ g O}} = 1.0 \times 10^{-3} \text{ mol O}$$

The mole ratio between Hg and O is 2 : 1, so the empirical formula is Hg_2O.

55.   First, we will determine composition in mass percent. We assume that all the carbon in the 0.213 g CO_2 came from the 0.157 g of the compound and that all the hydrogen in the 0.0310 g H_2O came from the 0.157 g of the compound.

$$0.213 \text{ g CO}_2 \times \frac{12.01 \text{ g C}}{44.01 \text{ g CO}_2} = 0.0581 \text{ g C}; \ \% \text{ C} = \frac{0.0581 \text{ g C}}{0.157 \text{ g compound}} \times 100 = 37.0\% \text{ C}$$

$$0.0310 \text{ g H}_2\text{O} \times \frac{2.016 \text{ g H}}{18.02 \text{ g H}_2\text{O}} = 3.47 \times 10^{-3} \text{ g H}; \ \% \text{ H} = \frac{3.47 \times 10^{-3} \text{ g}}{0.157 \text{ g}} \times 100 = 2.21\% \text{ H}$$

We get the mass percent of N from the second experiment:

$$0.0230 \text{ g NH}_3 \times \frac{14.01 \text{ g N}}{17.03 \text{ g NH}_3} = 1.89 \times 10^{-2} \text{ g N}$$

$$\% \text{ N} = \frac{1.89 \times 10^{-2} \text{ g}}{0.103 \text{ g}} \times 100 = 18.3\% \text{ N}$$

The mass percent of oxygen is obtained by difference:

$$\% \text{ O} = 100.00 - (37.0 + 2.21 + 18.3) = 42.5\% \text{ O}$$

So, out of 100.00 g of compound, there are:

$$37.0 \text{ g C} \times \frac{1 \text{ mol C}}{12.01 \text{ g C}} = 3.08 \text{ mol C}; \quad 2.21 \text{ g H} \times \frac{1 \text{ mol H}}{1.008 \text{ g H}} = 2.19 \text{ mol H}$$

$$18.3 \text{ g N} \times \frac{1 \text{ mol N}}{14.01 \text{ g N}} = 1.31 \text{ mol N}; \quad 42.5 \text{ g O} \times \frac{1 \text{ mol O}}{16.00 \text{ g O}} = 2.66 \text{ mol O}$$

Lastly, and often the hardest part, we need to find simple whole number ratios. Divide all mole values by the smallest number:

$$\frac{3.08}{1.31} = 2.35; \quad \frac{2.19}{1.31} = 1.67; \quad \frac{1.31}{1.31} = 1.00; \quad \frac{2.66}{1.31} = 2.03$$

Multiplying all these ratios by 3 gives an empirical formula of $C_7H_5N_3O_6$.

57.   Assuming 100.0 g of compound:

$$26.7 \text{ g P} \times \frac{1 \text{ mol P}}{30.97 \text{ g P}} = 0.862 \text{ mol P}; \quad 12.1 \text{ g N} \times \frac{1 \text{ mol N}}{14.01 \text{ g N}} = 0.864 \text{ mol N}$$

$$61.2 \text{ g Cl} \times \frac{1 \text{ mol Cl}}{35.45 \text{ g Cl}} = 1.73 \text{ mol Cl}$$

$$\frac{1.73}{0.862} = 2.01; \text{ the empirical formula is } PNCl_2.$$

The empirical formula mass is $\approx 31.0 + 14.0 + 2(35.5) = 116$ g/mol.

$$\frac{\text{Molar mass}}{\text{Empirical formula mass}} = \frac{580}{116} = 5.0; \text{ the molecular formula is } (PNCl_2)_5 = P_5N_5Cl_{10}.$$

59.   First, we will determine composition by mass percent:

$$16.01 \text{ mg CO}_2 \times \frac{1 \text{ g}}{1000 \text{ mg}} \times \frac{12.011 \text{ g C}}{44.009 \text{ g CO}_2} \times \frac{1000 \text{ mg}}{\text{g}} = 4.369 \text{ mg C}$$

$$\% \text{ C} = \frac{4.369 \text{ mg C}}{10.68 \text{ mg compound}} \times 100 = 40.91\% \text{ C}$$

$$4.37 \text{ mg H}_2\text{O} \times \frac{1 \text{ g}}{1000 \text{ mg}} \times \frac{2.016 \text{ g H}}{18.02 \text{ g H}_2\text{O}} \times \frac{1000 \text{ mg}}{\text{g}} = 0.489 \text{ mg H}$$

$$\% \text{ H} = \frac{0.489 \text{ mg}}{10.68 \text{ mg}} \times 100 = 4.58\% \text{ H}; \ \% \text{ O} = 100.00 - (40.91 + 4.58) = 54.51\% \text{ O}$$

So, in 100.00 g of the compound, we have:

$$40.91 \text{ g C} \times \frac{1 \text{ mol C}}{12.011 \text{ g C}} = 3.406 \text{ mol C}; \ 4.58 \text{ g H} \times \frac{1 \text{ mol H}}{1.008 \text{ g H}} = 4.54 \text{ mol H}$$

$$54.51 \text{ g O} \times \frac{1 \text{ mol O}}{15.999 \text{ g O}} = 3.407 \text{ mol O}$$

Dividing by the smallest number: $\dfrac{4.54}{3.406} = 1.33 \ . \ \dfrac{4}{3}$; the empirical formula is $C_3H_4O_3$.

The empirical formula mass of $C_3H_4O_3$ is $\approx 3(12) + 4(1) + 3(16) = 88$ g.

Because $\dfrac{176.1}{88} = 2.0$, the molecular formula is $C_6H_8O_6$.

Balancing Chemical Equations

61.   Only one product is formed in this representation. This product has two Ys bonded to an X. The other substance present in the product mixture is just the excess of one of the reactants (Y). The best equation has smallest whole numbers. Here, answer c would be this smallest whole number equation ($X + 2 \text{ Y} \rightarrow XY_2$). Answers a and b have incorrect products listed, and for answer d, an equation only includes the reactants that go to produce the product; excess reactants are not shown in an equation.

63.   When balancing reactions, start with elements that appear in only one of the reactants and one of the products, and then go on to balance the remaining elements.

   a. $C_6H_{12}O_6(s) + O_2(g) \rightarrow CO_2(g) + H_2O(g)$

        Balance C atoms: $C_6H_{12}O_6 + O_2 \rightarrow 6 \ CO_2 + H_2O$

        Balance H atoms: $C_6H_{12}O_6 + O_2 \rightarrow 6 \ CO_2 + 6 \ H_2O$

        Lastly, balance O atoms: $C_6H_{12}O_6(s) + 6 \ O_2(g) \rightarrow 6 \ CO_2(g) + 6 \ H_2O(g)$

   b. $Fe_2S_3(s) + HCl(g) \rightarrow FeCl_3(s) + H_2S(g)$

        Balance Fe atoms: $Fe_2S_3 + HCl \rightarrow 2 \ FeCl_3 + H_2S$

        Balance S atoms: $Fe_2S_3 + HCl \rightarrow 2 \ FeCl_3 + 3 \ H_2S$

        There are 6 H and 6 Cl on right, so balance with 6 HCl on left:

            $Fe_2S_3(s) + 6 \ HCl(g) \rightarrow 2 \ FeCl_3(s) + 3 \ H_2S(g)$

c. $CS_2(l) + NH_3(g) \rightarrow H_2S(g) + NH_4SCN(s)$

C and S are balanced; balance N:

$CS_2 + 2\ NH_3 \rightarrow H_2S + NH_4SCN$

H is also balanced. $CS_2(l) + 2\ NH_3(g) \rightarrow H_2S(g) + NH_4SCN(s)$.

65.   a. $16\ Cr(s) + 3\ S_8(s) \rightarrow 8\ Cr_2S_3(s)$

       b. $2\ NaHCO_3(s) \rightarrow Na_2CO_3(s) + CO_2(g) + H_2O(g)$

       c. $2\ KClO_3(s) \rightarrow 2\ KCl(s) + 3\ O_2(g)$

       d. $2\ Eu(s) + 6\ HF(g) \rightarrow 2\ EuF_3(s) + 3\ H_2(g)$

       e. $2\ C_6H_6(l) + 15\ O_2(g) \rightarrow 12\ CO_2(g) + 6\ H_2O(g)$

Reaction Stoichiometry

67. $1.000\ kg\ Al \times \dfrac{1000\ g\ Al}{kg\ Al} \times \dfrac{1\ mol\ Al}{26.98\ g\ Al} \times \dfrac{3\ mol\ NH_4ClO_4}{3\ mol\ Al} \times \dfrac{117.49\ g\ NH_4ClO_4}{mol\ NH_4ClO_4}$

$$= 4355\ g\ NH_4ClO_4$$

69. $Fe_2O_3(s) + 2\ Al(s) \rightarrow 2\ Fe(l) + Al_2O_3(s)$

$15.0\ g\ Fe \times \dfrac{1\ mol\ Fe}{55.85\ g\ Fe} = 0.269\ mol\ Fe;\ \ 0.269\ mol\ Fe \times \dfrac{2\ mol\ Al}{2\ mol\ Fe} \times \dfrac{26.98\ g\ Al}{mol\ Al} = 7.26\ g\ Al$

$0.269\ mol\ Fe \times \dfrac{1\ mol\ Fe_2O_3}{2\ mol\ Fe} \times \dfrac{159.70\ g\ Fe_2O_3}{mol\ Fe_2O_3} = 21.5\ g\ Fe_2O_3$

$0.269\ mol\ Fe \times \dfrac{1\ mol\ Al_2O_3}{2\ mol\ Fe} \times \dfrac{101.96\ g\ Al_2O_3}{mol\ Al_2O_3} = 13.7\ g\ Al_2O_3$

71. $2\ LiOH(s) + CO_2(g) \rightarrow Li_2CO_3(aq) + H_2O(l)$

The total volume of air exhaled each minute for the 7 astronauts is $7 \times 20. = 140\ L/min$.

$25{,}000\ g\ LiOH \times \dfrac{1\ mol\ LiOH}{23.95\ g\ LiOH} \times \dfrac{1\ mol\ CO_2}{2\ mol\ LiOH} \times \dfrac{44.01\ g\ CO_2}{mol\ CO_2} \times \dfrac{100\ g\ air}{4.0\ g\ CO_2} \times$

$\dfrac{1\ mL\ air}{0.0010\ g\ air} \times \dfrac{1\ L}{1000\ mL} \times \dfrac{1\ min}{140\ L\ air} \times \dfrac{1\ h}{60\ min} = 68\ h = 2.8\ days$

73. 1.0×10^3 g phosphorite $\times \dfrac{75 \text{ g Ca}_3(\text{PO}_4)_2}{100 \text{ g phosphorite}} \times \dfrac{1 \text{ mol Ca}_3(\text{PO}_4)_2}{310.18 \text{ g Ca}_3(\text{PO}_4)_2} \times$

$$\dfrac{1 \text{ mol P}_4}{2 \text{ mol Ca}_3(\text{PO}_4)_2} \times \dfrac{123.88 \text{ g P}_4}{\text{mol P}_4} = 150 \text{ g P}_4$$

Limiting Reactants and Percent Yield

75.   The product formed in the reaction is NO_2; the other species present in the product picture is excess O_2. Therefore, NO is the limiting reactant. In the pictures, 6 NO molecules react with 3 O_2 molecules to form 6 NO_2 molecules.

$$6 \text{ NO(g)} + 3 \text{ O}_2\text{(g)} \rightarrow 6 \text{ NO}_2\text{(g)}$$

For smallest whole numbers, the balanced reaction is:

$$2 \text{ NO(g)} + \text{O}_2\text{(g)} \rightarrow 2 \text{ NO}_2\text{(g)}$$

77. $1.50 \text{ g BaO}_2 \times \dfrac{1 \text{ mol BaO}_2}{169.3 \text{ g BaO}_2} = 8.86 \times 10^{-3} \text{ mol BaO}_2$

$25.0 \text{ mL} \times \dfrac{0.0272 \text{ g HCl}}{\text{mL}} \times \dfrac{1 \text{ mol HCl}}{36.46 \text{ g HCl}} = 1.87 \times 10^{-2} \text{ mol HCl}$

The required mole ratio from the balanced reaction is 2 mol HCl to 1 mol BaO_2. The actual mole ratio is:

$$\dfrac{1.87 \times 10^{-2} \text{ mol HCl}}{8.86 \times 10^{-3} \text{ mol BaO}_2} = 2.11$$

Because the actual mole ratio is larger than the required mole ratio, the denominator (BaO_2) is the limiting reagent.

$8.86 \times 10^{-3} \text{ mol BaO}_2 \times \dfrac{1 \text{ mol H}_2\text{O}_2}{\text{mol BaO}_2} \times \dfrac{34.02 \text{ g H}_2\text{O}_2}{\text{mol H}_2\text{O}_2} = 0.301 \text{ g H}_2\text{O}_2$

The amount of HCl reacted is:

$8.86 \times 10^{-3} \text{ mol BaO}_2 \times \dfrac{2 \text{ mol HCl}}{\text{mol BaO}_2} = 1.77 \times 10^{-2} \text{ mol HCl}$

Excess mol HCl = 1.87×10^{-2} mol $- 1.77 \times 10^{-2}$ mol $= 1.0 \times 10^{-3}$ mol HCl

Mass of excess HCl = 1.0×10^{-3} mol HCl $\times \dfrac{36.46 \text{ g HCl}}{\text{mol HCl}} = 3.6 \times 10^{-2}$ g HCl

79.   2.50 metric tons $Cu_3FeS_3 \times \dfrac{1000\text{ kg}}{\text{metric ton}} \times \dfrac{1000\text{ g}}{\text{kg}} \times \dfrac{1\text{ mol }Cu_3FeS_3}{342.71\text{ g}} \times \dfrac{3\text{ mol }Cu}{1\text{ mol }Cu_3FeS_3} \times$

$$\dfrac{63.55\text{ g}}{\text{mol }Cu} = 1.39 \times 10^6 \text{ g Cu (theoretical)}$$

1.39×10^6 g Cu (theoretical) $\times \dfrac{86.3\text{ g Cu (actual)}}{100.\text{ g Cu (theoretical)}} = 1.20 \times 10^6$ g Cu $= 1.20 \times 10^3$ kg Cu

$$= 1.20 \text{ metric tons Cu (actual)}$$

81.   An alternative method to solve limiting-reagent problems is to assume that each reactant is limiting and then calculate how much product could be produced from each reactant. The reactant that produces the smallest amount of product will run out first and is the limiting reagent.

$$5.00 \times 10^6 \text{ g NH}_3 \times \dfrac{1\text{ mol NH}_3}{17.03\text{ g NH}_3} \times \dfrac{2\text{ mol HCN}}{2\text{ mol NH}_3} = 2.94 \times 10^5 \text{ mol HCN}$$

$$5.00 \times 10^6 \text{ g O}_2 \times \dfrac{1\text{ mol O}_2}{32.00\text{ g O}_2} \times \dfrac{2\text{ mol HCN}}{3\text{ mol O}_2} = 1.04 \times 10^5 \text{ mol HCN}$$

$$5.00 \times 10^6 \text{ g CH}_4 \times \dfrac{1\text{ mol CH}_4}{16.04\text{ g CH}_4} \times \dfrac{2\text{ mol HCN}}{2\text{ mol CH}_4} = 3.12 \times 10^5 \text{ mol HCN}$$

O_2 is limiting because it produces the smallest amount of HCN. Although more product could be produced from NH_3 and CH_4, only enough O_2 is present to produce 1.04×10^5 mol HCN. The mass of HCN that can be produced is:

$$1.04 \times 10^5 \text{ mol HCN} \times \dfrac{27.03\text{ g HCN}}{\text{mol HCN}} = 2.81 \times 10^6 \text{ g HCN}$$

$$5.00 \times 10^6 \text{ g O}_2 \times \dfrac{1\text{ mol O}_2}{32.00\text{ g O}_2} \times \dfrac{6\text{ mol H}_2O}{3\text{ mol O}_2} \times \dfrac{18.02\text{ g H}_2O}{1\text{ mol H}_2O} = 5.63 \times 10^6 \text{ g H}_2O$$

83. $P_4(s) + 6\ F_2(g) \rightarrow 4\ PF_3(g)$; the theoretical yield of PF_3 is:

$$120.\text{ g PF}_3 \text{ (actual)} \times \dfrac{100.0\text{ g PF}_3 \text{ (theoretical)}}{78.1\text{ g PF}_3 \text{ (actual)}} = 154 \text{ g PF}_3 \text{ (theoretical)}$$

$$154 \text{ g PF}_3 \times \dfrac{1\text{ mol PF}_3}{87.97\text{ g PF}_3} \times \dfrac{6\text{ mol F}_2}{4\text{ mol PF}_3} \times \dfrac{38.00\text{ g F}_2}{\text{mol F}_2} = 99.8 \text{ g F}_2$$

99.8 g F_2 are needed to actually produce 120. g of PF_3 if the percent yield is 78.1%.

Additional Exercises

85. $17.3 \text{ g H} \times \dfrac{1 \text{ mol H}}{1.008 \text{ g H}} = 17.2 \text{ mol H}; \quad 82.7 \text{ g C} \times \dfrac{1 \text{ mol C}}{12.01 \text{ g C}} = 6.89 \text{ mol C}$

$\dfrac{17.2}{6.89} = 2.50;$ the empirical formula is C_2H_5.

The empirical formula mass is ~29 g, so two times the empirical formula would put the compound in the correct range of the molar mass. Molecular formula = $(C_2H_5)_2 = C_4H_{10}$

$2.59 \times 10^{23} \text{ atoms H} \times \dfrac{1 \text{ molecule } C_4H_{10}}{10 \text{ atoms H}} \times \dfrac{1 \text{ mol } C_4H_{10}}{6.022 \times 10^{23} \text{ molecules}}$

$$= 4.30 \times 10^{-2} \text{ mol } C_4H_{10}$$

$4.30 \times 10^{-2} \text{ mol } C_4H_{10} \times \dfrac{58.12 \text{ g}}{\text{mol } C_4H_{10}} = 2.50 \text{ g } C_4H_{10}$

87.   Molar mass $X_2 = \dfrac{0.105 \text{ g}}{8.92 \times 10^{20} \text{ molecules} \times \dfrac{1 \text{ mol}}{6.022 \times 10^{23} \text{ molecules}}} = 70.9 \text{ g/mol}$

The mass of X = 1/2(70.9 g/mol) = 35.5 g/mol. This is the element chlorine.

Assuming 100.00 g of MX_3 compound:

$54.47 \text{ g Cl} \times \dfrac{1 \text{ mol}}{35.45 \text{ g}} = 1.537 \text{ mol Cl}$

$1.537 \text{ mol Cl} \times \dfrac{1 \text{ mol M}}{3 \text{ mol Cl}} = 0.5123 \text{ mol M}$

Molar mass of M $= \dfrac{45.53 \text{ g M}}{0.5123 \text{ mol M}} = 88.87 \text{ g/mol M}$

M is the element yttrium (Y), and the name of YCl_3 is yttrium(III) chloride.

The balanced equation is $2 \text{ Y} + 3 \text{ Cl}_2 \rightarrow 2 \text{ YCl}_3$.

Assuming Cl_2 is limiting:

$1.00 \text{ g Cl}_2 \times \dfrac{1 \text{ mol Cl}_2}{70.90 \text{ g Cl}_2} \times \dfrac{2 \text{ mol YCl}_3}{3 \text{ mol Cl}_2} \times \dfrac{195.26 \text{ g YCl}_3}{1 \text{ mol YCl}_3} = 1.84 \text{ g YCl}_3$

Assuming Y is limiting:

$$1.00 \text{ g Y} \times \frac{1 \text{ mol Y}}{88.91 \text{ g Y}} \times \frac{2 \text{ mol YCl}_3}{2 \text{ mol Y}} \times \frac{195.26 \text{ g YCl}_3}{1 \text{ mol YCl}_3} = 2.20 \text{ g YCl}_3$$

Because Cl_2, when it all reacts, produces the smaller amount of product, Cl_2 is the limiting reagent, and the theoretical yield is 1.84 g YCl_3.

89.   Mass of H_2O = 0.755 g $CuSO_4 \bullet xH_2O$ – 0.483 g $CuSO_4$ = 0.272 g H_2O

$$0.483 \text{ g CuSO}_4 \times \frac{1 \text{ mol CuSO}_4}{159.62 \text{ g CuSO}_4} = 0.00303 \text{ mol CuSO}_4$$

$$0.272 \text{ g H}_2\text{O} \times \frac{1 \text{ mol H}_2\text{O}}{18.02 \text{ g H}_2\text{O}} = 0.0151 \text{ mol H}_2\text{O}$$

$$\frac{0.0151 \text{ mol H}_2\text{O}}{0.00303 \text{ mol CuSO}_4} = \frac{4.98 \text{ mol H}_2\text{O}}{1 \text{ mol CuSO}_4} ; \text{ compound formula} = \text{CuSO}_4 \bullet 5\text{H}_2\text{O}, \ x = 5$$

91.   Consider the case of aluminum plus oxygen. Aluminum forms Al^{3+} ions; oxygen forms O^{2-} anions. The simplest compound of the two elements is Al_2O_3. Similarly, we would expect the formula of a Group 6A element with Al to be Al_2X_3. Assuming this, out of 100.00 g of compound, there are 18.56 g Al and 81.44 g of the unknown element, X. Let's use this information to determine the molar mass of X, which will allow us to identify X from the periodic table.

$$18.56 \text{ g Al} \times \frac{1 \text{ mol Al}}{26.98 \text{ g Al}} \times \frac{3 \text{ mol X}}{2 \text{ mol Al}} = 1.032 \text{ mol X}$$

81.44 g of X must contain 1.032 mol of X.

$$\text{Molar mass of X} = \frac{81.44 \text{ g X}}{1.032 \text{ mol X}} = 78.91 \text{ g/mol}$$

From the periodic table, the unknown element is selenium, and the formula is Al_2Se_3.

93. $$1.20 \text{ g CO}_2 \times \frac{1 \text{ mol CO}_2}{44.01 \text{ g}} \times \frac{1 \text{ mol C}}{\text{mol CO}_2} \times \frac{1 \text{ mol C}_{24}\text{H}_{30}\text{N}_3\text{O}}{24 \text{ mol C}} \times \frac{376.51 \text{ g}}{\text{mol C}_{24}\text{H}_{30}\text{N}_3\text{O}}$$
$$= 0.428 \text{ g C}_{24}\text{H}_{30}\text{N}_3\text{O}$$

$$\frac{0.428 \text{ g C}_{24}\text{H}_{30}\text{N}_3\text{O}}{1.00 \text{ g sample}} \times 100 = 42.8\% \text{ C}_{24}\text{H}_{30}\text{N}_3\text{O (LSD)}$$

95.   2 $NaNO_3(s) \rightarrow$ 2 $NaNO_2(s) + O_2(g)$;   the amount of $NaNO_3$ in the impure sample is:

$$0.2864 \text{ g NaNO}_2 \times \frac{1 \text{ mol NaNO}_2}{69.00 \text{ g NaNO}_2} \times \frac{2 \text{ mol NaNO}_3}{2 \text{ mol NaNO}_2} \times \frac{85.00 \text{ g NaNO}_3}{\text{mol NaNO}_3}$$
$$= 0.3528 \text{ g NaNO}_3$$

$$\text{Mass percent NaNO}_3 = \frac{0.3528 \text{ g NaNO}_3}{0.4230 \text{ g sample}} \times 100 = 83.40\%$$

97. $$453 \text{ g Fe} \times \frac{1 \text{ mol Fe}}{55.85 \text{ g Fe}} \times \frac{1 \text{ mol Fe}_2\text{O}_3}{2 \text{ mol Fe}} \times \frac{159.70 \text{ g Fe}_2\text{O}_3}{\text{mol Fe}_2\text{O}_3} = 648 \text{ g Fe}_2\text{O}_3$$

$$\text{Mass \% Fe}_2\text{O}_3 = \frac{648 \text{ g Fe}_2\text{O}_3}{752 \text{ g ore}} \times 100 = 86.2\%$$

99. $$\frac{^{85}\text{Rb atoms}}{^{87}\text{Rb atoms}} = 2.591;$$ If we had exactly 100 atoms, x = number of ^{85}Rb atoms and $100 - x$ = number of ^{87}Rb atoms.

$$\frac{x}{100 - x} = 2.591, \quad x = 259.1 - (2.591)x, \quad x = \frac{259.1}{3.591} = 72.15; \quad 72.15\% \, ^{85}\text{Rb}$$

$$0.7215(84.9117) + 0.2785(A) = 85.4678, \quad A = \frac{85.4678 - 61.26}{0.2785} = 86.92 \text{ amu}$$

101.   The volume of a gas is proportional to the number of molecules of gas. Thus the formulas are:

I: NH_3 II: N_2H_4 III: HN_3

The mass ratios are:

I: $\dfrac{4.634 \text{ g N}}{\text{g H}}$ II: $\dfrac{6.949 \text{ g N}}{\text{g H}}$ III: $\dfrac{41.7 \text{ g N}}{\text{g H}}$

If we set the atomic mass of H equal to 1.008, then the atomic mass, A, for nitrogen is:

I: 14.01   II: 14.01   III. 14.0

For example, for compound I: $\dfrac{A}{3(1.008)} = \dfrac{4.634}{1}$, A = 14.01

103. $$1.375 \text{ g AgI} \times \frac{1 \text{ mol AgI}}{234.8 \text{ g AgI}} = 5.856 \times 10^{-3} \text{ mol AgI} = 5.856 \times 10^{-3} \text{ mol I}$$

$$1.375 \text{ g AgI} \times \frac{126.9 \text{ g I}}{234.8 \text{ g AgI}} = 0.7431 \text{ g I}; \quad \text{XI}_2 \text{ contains } 0.7431 \text{ g I and } 0.257 \text{ g X}.$$

$$5.856 \times 10^{-3} \text{ mol I} \times \frac{1 \text{ mol X}}{2 \text{ mol I}} = 2.928 \times 10^{-3} \text{ mol X}$$

$$\text{Molar mass} = \frac{0.257 \text{ g X}}{2.928 \times 10^{-3} \text{ mol X}} = \frac{87.8 \text{ g}}{\text{mol}}; \quad \text{atomic mass} = 87.8 \text{ amu (X is Sr.)}$$

105.   Assuming 1 mole of vitamin A (286.4 g vitamin A):

$$\text{mol C} = 286.4 \text{ g vitamin A} \times \frac{0.8396 \text{ g C}}{\text{g vitamin A}} \times \frac{1 \text{ mol C}}{12.011 \text{ g C}} = 20.00 \text{ mol C}$$

$$\text{mol H} = 286.4 \text{ g vitamin A} \times \frac{0.1056 \text{ g H}}{\text{g vitamin A}} \times \frac{1 \text{ mol H}}{1.0079 \text{ g H}} = 30.01 \text{ mol H}$$

Because 1 mole of vitamin A contains 20 mol C and 30 mol H, the molecular formula of vitamin A is $C_{20}H_{30}E$. To determine E, lets calculate the molar mass of E:

$$286.4 \text{ g} = 20(12.01) + 30(1.008) + \text{molar mass E},\ \text{molar mass E} = 16.0 \text{ g/mol}$$

From the periodic table, E = oxygen, and the molecular formula of vitamin A is $C_{20}H_{30}O$.

Challenge Problems

107.   When the discharge voltage is low, the ions present are in the form of molecules. When the discharge voltage is increased, the bonds in the molecules are broken, and the ions present are in the form of individual atoms. Therefore, the high discharge data indicate that the ions $^{16}O^+$, $^{18}O^+$, and $^{40}Ar^+$ are present. The only combination of these individual ions that can explain the mass data at low discharge is $^{16}O^{16}O^+$ (mass = 32), $^{16}O^{18}O^+$ (mass = 34), and $^{40}Ar^+$ (mass = 40). Therefore, the gas mixture contains $^{16}O^{16}O$, $^{16}O^{18}O$, and ^{40}Ar. To determine the percent composition of each isotope, we use the relative intensity data from the high discharge data to determine the percentage that each isotope contributes to the total relative intensity. For ^{40}Ar:

$$\frac{1.0000}{0.7500 + 0.0015 + 1.0000} \times 100 = \frac{1.0000}{1.7515} \times 100 = 57.094\% \ ^{40}Ar$$

For ^{16}O: $\dfrac{0.7500}{1.7515} \times 100 = 42.82\% \ ^{16}O$; for ^{18}O: $\dfrac{0.0015}{1.7515} \times 100 = 8.6 \times 10^{-2}\% \ ^{18}O$

Note: ^{18}F instead of ^{18}O could also explain the data. However, OF(g) is not a stable compound. This is why ^{18}O is the best choice because O_2(g) does form.

109. $10.00 \text{ g } XCl_2 + \text{excess } Cl_2 \rightarrow 12.55 \text{ g } XCl_4$; 2.55 g Cl reacted with XCl_2 to form XCl_4. XCl_4 contains 2.55 g Cl and 10.00 g XCl_2. From mole ratios, 10.00 g XCl_2 must also contain 2.55 g Cl; mass X in $XCl_2 = 10.00 - 2.55 = 7.45$ g X.

$$2.55 \text{ g Cl} \times \frac{1 \text{ mol Cl}}{35.45 \text{ g Cl}} \times \frac{1 \text{ mol } XCl_2}{2 \text{ mol Cl}} \times \frac{1 \text{ mol X}}{\text{mol } XCl_2} = 3.60 \times 10^{-2} \text{ mol X}$$

So, 3.60×10^{-2} mol X has a mass equal to 7.45 g X. The molar mass of X is:

$$\frac{7.45 \text{ g X}}{3.60 \times 10^{-2} \text{ mol X}} = 207 \text{ g/mol X; atomic mass} = 207 \text{ amu, so X is Pb.}$$

111.   For a gas, density and molar mass are directly proportional to each other.

$$\text{Molar mass } XH_n = 2.393(32.00) = \frac{76.58 \text{ g}}{\text{mol}}$$

$$0.803 \text{ g H}_2\text{O} \times \frac{2 \text{ mol H}}{18.02 \text{ g H}_2\text{O}} = 8.91 \times 10^{-2} \text{ mol H}$$

$$\frac{8.91 \times 10^{-2} \text{ mol H}}{2.23 \times 10^{-2} \text{ mol } XH_n} = \frac{4 \text{ mol H}}{\text{mol } XH_n}$$

Molar mass X = 76.58 – 4(1.008 g) = 72.55 g/mol;   the element is Ge.

113. $4.000 \text{ g M}_2\text{S}_3 \rightarrow 3.723 \text{ g MO}_2$

There must be twice as many moles of MO_2 as moles of M_2S_3 in order to balance M in the reaction. Setting up an equation for 2(mol M_2S_3) = mol MO_2 where A = molar mass M:

$$2\left(\frac{4.000 \text{ g}}{2A + 3(32.07)}\right) = \frac{3.723 \text{ g}}{A + 2(16.00)}, \quad \frac{8.000}{2A + 96.21} = \frac{3.723}{A + 32.00}$$

(8.000)A + 256.0 = (7.446)A + 358.2, (0.554)A = 102.2, A = 184 g/mol; atomic mass
= 184 amu

115.   The balanced equations are:

$$C(s) + 1/2 \ O_2(g) \rightarrow CO(g) \text{ and } C(s) + O_2(g) \rightarrow CO_2(g)$$

If we have 100.0 mol of products, then we have 72.0 mol CO_2, 16.0 mol CO, and 12.0 mol O_2. The initial moles of C equals 72.0 (from CO_2) + 16.00 (from CO) = 88.0 mol C and the initial moles of O_2 equals 72.0 (from CO_2) + 16.0/2 (from CO) + 12.0 (unreacted O_2) = 92.0 mol O_2. The initial reaction mixture contained:

$$\frac{92.0 \text{ mol O}_2}{88.0 \text{ mol C}} = 1.05 \text{ mol O}_2/\text{mol C}$$

117. $LaH_{2.90}$ is the formula. If only La^{3+} is present, LaH_3 would be the formula. If only La^{2+} is present, LaH_2 would be the formula. Let x = mol La^{2+} and y = mol La^{3+}:

$$(La^{2+})_x(La^{3+})_yH_{(2x + 3y)} \text{ where } x + y = 1.00 \text{ and } 2x + 3y = 2.90$$

Solving by simultaneous equations:

$$2x + 3y = 2.90$$
$$\underline{-2x - 2y = -2.00}$$
$$y = 0.90 \text{ and } x = 0.10$$

$LaH_{2.90}$ contains $\dfrac{1}{10}$ La^{2+}, or 10.% La^{2+}, and $\dfrac{9}{10}$ La^{3+}, or 90.% La^{3+}.

119.   Let x = mass KCl and y = mass KNO_3. Assuming 100.0 g of mixture, $x + y = 100.0$ g.

Molar mass KCl = 74.55 g/mol; molar mass KNO_3 = 101.11 g/mol

Mol KCl = $\dfrac{x}{74.55}$; mol KNO_3 = $\dfrac{y}{101.11}$

Knowing that the mixture is 43.2% K, then in the 100.0 g mixture:

$$39.10\left(\dfrac{x}{74.55} + \dfrac{y}{101.11}\right) = 43.2$$

We have two equations and two unknowns:

$$(0.5245)x + (0.3867)y = 43.2$$
$$x + y = 100.0$$

Solving, $x = 32.9$ g KCl; $\dfrac{32.9 \text{ g}}{100.0 \text{ g}} \times 100 = 32.9\%$ KCl

121.   The balanced equations are:

$$4 \text{ NH}_3(g) + 5 \text{ O}_2(g) \rightarrow 4 \text{ NO}(g) + 6 \text{ H}_2\text{O}(g) \text{ and } 4 \text{ NH}_3(g) + 7 \text{ O}_2(g) \rightarrow 4 \text{ NO}_2(g)$$
$$+ 6 \text{ H}_2\text{O}(g)$$

Let $4x$ = number of moles of NO formed, and let $4y$ = number of moles of NO_2 formed. Then:

$$4x \text{ NH}_3 + 5x \text{ O}_2 \rightarrow 4x \text{ NO} + 6x \text{ H}_2\text{O} \text{ and } 4y \text{ NH}_3 + 7y \text{ O}_2 \rightarrow 4y \text{ NO}_2 + 6y \text{ H}_2\text{O}$$

All the NH_3 reacted, so $4x + 4y = 2.00$.

$10.00 - 6.75 = 3.25$ mol O_2 reacted, so $5x + 7y = 3.25$.

Solving by the method of simultaneous equations:

$$20x + 28y = 13.0$$
$$\underline{-20x - 20y = -10.0}$$
$$8y = 3.0, \quad y = 0.38; \quad 4x + 4 \times 0.38 = 2.00, \quad x = 0.12$$

Mol NO = $4x = 4 \times 0.12 = 0.48$ mol NO formed

CHAPTER 4

TYPES OF CHEMICAL REACTIONS AND SOLUTION STOICHIOMETRY

Aqueous Solutions: Strong and Weak Electrolytes

11. Solution A: $\dfrac{4\ \text{molecules}}{1.0\ \text{L}}$; solution B: $\dfrac{6\ \text{molecules}}{4.0\ \text{L}} = \dfrac{1.5\ \text{molecules}}{1.0\ \text{L}}$

 Solution C: $\dfrac{4\ \text{molecules}}{2.0\ \text{L}} = \dfrac{2\ \text{molecules}}{1.0\ \text{L}}$; solution D: $\dfrac{6\ \text{molecules}}{2.0\ \text{L}} = \dfrac{3\ \text{molecules}}{1.0\ \text{L}}$

 Solution A has the most molecules per unit volume so solution A is most concentrated. This is followed by solution D, then solution C. Solution B has the fewest molecules per unit volume, so solution B is least concentrated.

13. a. Polarity is a term applied to covalent compounds. Polar covalent compounds have an unequal sharing of electrons in bonds that results in unequal charge distribution in the overall molecule. Polar molecules have a partial negative end and a partial positive end. These are not full charges as in ionic compounds but are charges much smaller in magnitude. Water is a polar molecule and dissolves other polar solutes readily. The oxygen end of water (the partial negative end of the polar water molecule) aligns with the partial positive end of the polar solute, whereas the hydrogens of water (the partial positive end of the polar water molecule) align with the partial negative end of the solute. These opposite charge attractions stabilize polar solutes in water. This process is called hydration. Nonpolar solutes do not have permanent partial negative and partial positive ends; nonpolar solutes are not stabilized in water and do not dissolve.

 b. KF is a soluble ionic compound, so it is a strong electrolyte. KF(aq) actually exists as separate hydrated K^+ ions and hydrated F^- ions in solution. $C_6H_{12}O_6$ is a polar covalent molecule that is a nonelectrolyte. $C_6H_{12}O_6$ is hydrated as described in part a.

 c. RbCl is a soluble ionic compound, so it exists as separate hydrated Rb^+ ions and hydrated Cl^- ions in solution. AgCl is an insoluble ionic compound so the ions stay together in solution and fall to the bottom of the container as a precipitate.

 d. HNO_3 is a strong acid and exists as separate hydrated H^+ ions and hydrated NO_3^- ions in solution. CO is a polar covalent molecule and is hydrated as explained in part a.

15. a. $Ba(NO_3)_2(aq) \rightarrow Ba^{2+}(aq) + 2\ NO_3^-(aq)$; picture iv represents the Ba^{2+} and NO_3^- ions present in $Ba(NO_3)_2(aq)$.

25

   b. $NaCl(aq) \rightarrow Na^+(aq) + Cl^-(aq)$;   picture ii represents $NaCl(aq)$.

   c. $K_2CO_3(aq) \rightarrow 2\ K^+(aq) + CO_3^{2-}(aq)$;   picture iii represents $K_2CO_3(aq)$.

   d. $MgSO_4(aq) \rightarrow Mg^{2+}(aq) + SO_4^{2-}(aq)$;   picture i represents $MgSO_4(aq)$.

Solution Concentration: Molarity

17.   a. $2.00\ L \times \dfrac{0.250\ mol\ NaOH}{L} \times \dfrac{40.00\ g\ NaOH}{mol} = 20.0\ g\ NaOH$

   Place 20.0 g NaOH in a 2-L volumetric flask; add water to dissolve the NaOH, and fill to the mark with water, mixing several times along the way.

   b. $2.00\ L \times \dfrac{0.250\ mol\ NaOH}{L} \times \dfrac{1\ L\ stock}{1.00\ mol\ NaOH} = 0.500\ L$

   Add 500. mL of 1.00 *M* NaOH stock solution to a 2-L volumetric flask; fill to the mark with water, mixing several times along the way.

   c. $2.00\ L \times \dfrac{0.100\ mol\ K_2CrO_4}{L} \times \dfrac{194.20\ g\ K_2CrO_4}{mol\ K_2CrO_4} = 38.8\ g\ K_2CrO_4$

   Similar to the solution made in part a, instead using 38.8 g K_2CrO_4.

   d. $2.00\ L \times \dfrac{0.100\ mol\ K_2CrO_4}{L} \times \dfrac{1\ L\ stock}{1.75\ mol\ K_2CrO_4} = 0.114\ L$

   Similar to the solution made in part b, instead using 114 mL of the 1.75 *M* K_2CrO_4 stock solution.

19.   Molar mass of NaOH = 22.99 + 16.00 + 1.008 = 40.00 g/mol

   $Mass\ NaOH = 0.2500\ L \times \dfrac{0.400\ mol\ NaOH}{L} \times \dfrac{40.00\ g\ NaOH}{mol\ NaOH} = 4.00\ g\ NaOH$

21.   Mol solute = volume (L) × molarity $\left(\dfrac{mol}{L}\right)$; $AlCl_3(s) \rightarrow Al^{3+}(aq) + 3\ Cl^-(aq)$

   $Mol\ Cl^- = 0.1000\ L \times \dfrac{0.30\ mol\ AlCl_3}{L} \times \dfrac{3\ mol\ Cl^-}{mol\ AlCl_3} = 9.0 \times 10^{-2}\ mol\ Cl^-$

   $MgCl_2(s) \rightarrow Mg^{2+}(aq) + 2\ Cl^-(aq)$

   $Mol\ Cl^- = 0.0500\ L \times \dfrac{0.60\ mol\ MgCl_2}{L} \times \dfrac{2\ mol\ Cl^-}{mol\ MgCl_2} = 6.0 \times 10^{-2}\ mol\ Cl^-$

$$NaCl(s) \rightarrow Na^+(aq) + Cl^-(aq)$$

$$Mol\ Cl^- = 0.2000\ L \times \frac{0.40\ mol\ NaCl}{L} \times \frac{1\ mol\ Cl^-}{mol\ NaCl} = 8.0 \times 10^{-2}\ mol\ Cl^-$$

100.0 mL of 0.30 M AlCl$_3$ contains the most moles of Cl$^-$ ions.

23. $$Mol\ Na_2CO_3 = 0.0700\ L \times \frac{3.0\ mol\ Na_2CO_3}{L} = 0.21\ mol\ Na_2CO_3$$

$$Na_2CO_3(s) \rightarrow 2\ Na^+(aq) + CO_3^{2-}(aq);\ mol\ Na^+ = 2(0.21\ mol) = 0.42\ mol$$

$$Mol\ NaHCO_3 = 0.0300\ L \times \frac{1.0\ mol\ NaHCO_3}{L} = 0.030\ mol\ NaHCO_3$$

$$NaHCO_3(s) \rightarrow Na^+(aq) + HCO_3^-(aq);\ mol\ Na^+ = 0.030\ mol$$

$$M_{Na^+} = \frac{total\ mol\ Na^+}{total\ volume} = \frac{0.42\ mol + 0.030\ mol}{0.0700\ L + 0.0300\ L} = \frac{0.45\ mol}{0.1000\ L} = 4.5\ M\ Na^+$$

25. $$Stock\ solution = \frac{10.0\ mg}{500.0\ mL} = \frac{10.0 \times 10^{-3}\ g}{500.0\ mL} = \frac{2.00 \times 10^{-5}\ g\ steroid}{mL}$$

$$100.0 \times 10^{-6}\ L\ stock \times \frac{1000\ mL}{L} \times \frac{2.00 \times 10^{-5}\ g\ steroid}{mL} = 2.00 \times 10^{-6}\ g\ steroid$$

This is diluted to a final volume of 100.0 mL.

$$\frac{2.00 \times 10^{-6}\ g\ steroid}{100.0\ mL} \times \frac{1000\ mL}{L} \times \frac{1\ mol\ steroid}{336.4\ g\ steroid} = 5.95 \times 10^{-8}\ M\ steroid$$

27.   a. $$5.0\ ppb\ Hg\ in\ water = \frac{5.0\ ng\ Hg}{mL\ H_2O} = \frac{5.0 \times 10^{-9}\ g\ Hg}{mL\ H_2O}$$

$$\frac{5.0 \times 10^{-9}\ g\ Hg}{mL} \times \frac{1\ mol\ Hg}{200.6\ g\ Hg} \times \frac{1000\ mL}{L} = 2.5 \times 10^{-8}\ M\ Hg$$

b. $$\frac{1.0 \times 10^{-9}\ g\ CHCl_3}{mL} \times \frac{1\ mol\ CHCl_3}{119.4\ g\ CHCl_3} \times \frac{1000\ mL}{L} = 8.4 \times 10^{-9}\ M\ CHCl_3$$

c. $$10.0\ ppm\ As = \frac{10.0\ \mu g\ As}{mL} = \frac{10.0 \times 10^{-6}\ g\ As}{mL}$$

$$\frac{10.0 \times 10^{-6}\ g\ As}{mL} \times \frac{1\ mol\ As}{74.92\ g\ As} \times \frac{1000\ mL}{L} = 1.33 \times 10^{-4}\ M\ As$$

d. $\dfrac{0.10 \times 10^{-6} \text{ g DDT}}{\text{mL}} \times \dfrac{1 \text{ mol DDT}}{354.5 \text{ g DDT}} \times \dfrac{1000 \text{ mL}}{\text{L}} = 2.8 \times 10^{-7} \, M \text{ DDT}$

Precipitation Reactions

29. Use the solubility rules in Table 4.1. Some soluble bromides by Rule 2 would be NaBr, KBr, and NH_4Br (there are others). The insoluble bromides by Rule 3 would be AgBr, $PbBr_2$, and Hg_2Br_2. Similar reasoning is used for the other parts to this problem.

Sulfates: Na_2SO_4, K_2SO_4, and $(NH_4)_2SO_4$ (and others) would be soluble, and $BaSO_4$, $CaSO_4$, and $PbSO_4$ (or Hg_2SO_4) would be insoluble.

Hydroxides: NaOH, KOH, $Ca(OH)_2$ (and others) would be soluble, and $Al(OH)_3$, $Fe(OH)_3$, and $Cu(OH)_2$ (and others) would be insoluble.

Phosphates: Na_3PO_4, K_3PO_4, $(NH_4)_3PO_4$ (and others) would be soluble, and Ag_3PO_4, $Ca_3(PO_4)_2$, and $FePO_4$ (and others) would be insoluble.

Lead: $PbCl_2$, $PbBr_2$, PbI_2, $Pb(OH)_2$, $PbSO_4$, and PbS (and others) would be insoluble. $Pb(NO_3)_2$ would be a soluble Pb^{2+} salt.

31. Use Table 4.1 to predict the solubility of the possible products.

a. Possible products = Hg_2SO_4 and $Cu(NO_3)_2$; precipitate = Hg_2SO_4

b. Possible products = $NiCl_2$ and $Ca(NO_3)_2$; both salts are soluble so no precipitate forms.

c. Possible products = KI and $MgCO_3$; precipitate = $MgCO_3$

d. Possible products = NaBr and $Al_2(CrO_4)_3$; precipitate = $Al_2(CrO_4)_3$

33. For the following answers, the balanced molecular equation is first, followed by the complete ionic equation, and then the net ionic equation.

a. $(NH_4)_2SO_4(aq) + Ba(NO_3)_2(aq) \rightarrow 2\ NH_4NO_3(aq) + BaSO_4(s)$

$2\ NH_4^{+}(aq) + SO_4^{2-}(aq) + Ba^{2+}(aq) + 2\ NO_3^{-}(aq) \rightarrow 2\ NH_4^{+}(aq) + 2\ NO_3^{-}(aq) + BaSO_4(s)$

$Ba^{2+}(aq) + SO_4^{2-}(aq) \rightarrow BaSO_4(s)$ is the net ionic equation (spectator ions omitted).

b. $Pb(NO_3)_2(aq) + 2\ NaCl(aq) \rightarrow PbCl_2(s) + 2\ NaNO_3(aq)$

$Pb^{2+}(aq) + 2\ NO_3^{-}(aq) + 2\ Na^{+}(aq) + 2\ Cl^{-}(aq) \rightarrow PbCl_2(s) + 2\ Na^{+}(aq) + 2\ NO_3^{-}(aq)$

$Pb^{2+}(aq) + 2\ Cl^{-}(aq) \rightarrow PbCl_2(s)$

c. The possible products, potassium phosphate and sodium nitrate, are both soluble in water. Therefore, no reaction occurs.

d. No reaction occurs because all possible products are soluble.

e. $CuCl_2(aq) + 2\ NaOH(aq) \rightarrow Cu(OH)_2(s) + 2\ NaCl(aq)$

$Cu^{2+}(aq) + 2\ Cl^-(aq) + 2\ Na^+(aq) + 2\ OH^-(aq) \rightarrow Cu(OH)_2(s) + 2\ Na^+(aq) + 2\ Cl^-(aq)$

$Cu^{2+}(aq) + 2\ OH^-(aq) \rightarrow Cu(OH)_2(s)$

35.   a. When $CuSO_4(aq)$ is added to $Na_2S(aq)$, the precipitate that forms is $CuS(s)$. Therefore, Na^+ (the gray spheres) and SO_4^{2-} (the bluish green spheres) are the spectator ions.

$CuSO_4(aq) + Na_2S(aq) \rightarrow CuS(s) + Na_2SO_4(aq);\ Cu^{2+}(aq) + S^{2-}(aq) \rightarrow CuS(s)$

b. When $CoCl_2(aq)$ is added to $NaOH(aq)$, the precipitate that forms is $Co(OH)_2(s)$. Therefore, Na^+ (the gray spheres) and Cl^- (the green spheres) are the spectator ions.

$CoCl_2(aq) + 2\ NaOH(aq) \rightarrow Co(OH)_2(s) + 2\ NaCl(aq)$

$Co^{2+}(aq) + 2\ OH^-(aq) \rightarrow Co(OH)_2(s)$

c. When $AgNO_3(aq)$ is added to $KI(aq)$, the precipitate that forms is $AgI(s)$. Therefore, K^+ (the red spheres) and NO_3^- (the blue spheres) are the spectator ions.

$AgNO_3(aq) + KI(aq) \rightarrow AgI(s) + KNO_3(aq);\ Ag^+(aq) + I^-(aq) \rightarrow AgI(s)$

37.   Because a precipitate formed with Na_2SO_4, the possible cations are Ba^{2+}, Pb^{2+}, Hg_2^{2+}, and Ca^{2+} (from the solubility rules). Because no precipitate formed with KCl, Pb^{2+}, and Hg_2^{2+} cannot be present. Because both Ba^{2+} and Ca^{2+} form soluble chlorides and soluble hydroxides, both these cations could be present. Therefore, the cations could be Ba^{2+} and Ca^{2+} (by the solubility rules in Table 4.1). For students who do a more rigorous study of solubility, Sr^{2+} could also be a possible cation (it forms an insoluble sulfate salt, whereas the chloride and hydroxide salts of strontium are soluble).

39. $2\ AgNO_3(aq) + CaCl_2(aq) \rightarrow 2\ AgCl(s) + Ca(NO_3)_2(aq)$

$$\text{Mol } AgNO_3 = 0.1000\ L \times \frac{0.20\ \text{mol } AgNO_3}{L} = 0.020\ \text{mol } AgNO_3$$

$$\text{Mol } CaCl_2 = 0.1000\ L \times \frac{0.15\ \text{mol } CaCl_2}{L} = 0.015\ \text{mol } CaCl_2$$

The required mol $AgNO_3$ to mol $CaCl_2$ ratio is 2 : 1 (from the balanced equation). The actual mole ratio present is $0.020/0.015 = 1.3$ (1.3 : 1). Therefore, $AgNO_3$ is the limiting reagent.

$$\text{Mass } AgCl = 0.020\ \text{mol } AgNO_3 \times \frac{1\ \text{mol } AgCl}{1\ \text{mol } AgNO_3} \times \frac{143.4\ \text{g } AgCl}{\text{mol } AgCl} = 2.9\ \text{g } AgCl$$

The net ionic equation is $Ag^+(aq) + Cl^-(aq) \rightarrow AgCl(s)$. The ions remaining in solution are the unreacted Cl^- ions and the spectator ions, NO_3^- and Ca^{2+} (all Ag^+ is used up in forming $AgCl$). The moles of each ion present initially (before reaction) can be easily determined from the moles of each reactant. 0.020 mol $AgNO_3$ dissolves to form 0.020 mol Ag^+ and 0.020 mol NO_3^-. 0.015 mol $CaCl_2$ dissolves to form 0.015 mol Ca^{2+} and 2(0.015) = 0.030 mol Cl^-.

Mol unreacted Cl^- = 0.030 mol Cl^- initially – 0.020 mol Cl^- reacted

Mol unreacted Cl^- = 0.010 mol Cl^-

$$M_{Cl^-} = \frac{0.010 \text{ mol } Cl^-}{\text{total volume}} = \frac{0.010 \text{ mol } Cl^-}{0.1000 \text{ L} + 0.1000 \text{ L}} = 0.050 \ M \ Cl^-$$

The molarity of the spectator ions are:

$$M_{NO_3^-} = \frac{0.020 \text{ mol } NO_3^-}{0.2000 \text{ L}} = 0.10 \ M \ NO_3^-; \ \ M_{Ca_2^+} = \frac{0.015 \text{ mol } Ca^{2+}}{0.2000 \text{ L}} = 0.075 \ M \ Ca^{2+}$$

41. $2 \ AgNO_3(aq) + Na_2CrO_4(aq) \rightarrow Ag_2CrO_4(s) + 2 \ NaNO_3(aq)$

$$0.0750 \text{ L} \times \frac{0.100 \text{ mol } AgNO_3}{L} \times \frac{1 \text{ mol } Na_2CrO_4}{2 \text{ mol } AgNO_3} \times \frac{161.98 \text{ g } Na_2CrO_4}{\text{mol } Na_2CrO_4} = 0.607 \text{ g } Na_2CrO_4$$

43.   Use aluminum in the formulas to convert from mass of $Al(OH)_3$ to mass of $Al_2(SO_4)_3$ in the mixture.

$$0.107 \text{ g } Al(OH)_3 \times \frac{1 \text{ mol } Al(OH)_3}{78.00 \text{ g}} \times \frac{1 \text{ mol } Al^{3+}}{\text{mol } Al(OH)_3} \times \frac{1 \text{ mol } Al_2(SO_4)_3}{2 \text{ mol } Al^{3+}} \times$$

$$\frac{342.17 \text{ g } Al_2(SO_4)_3}{\text{mol } Al_2(SO_4)_3} = 0.235 \text{ g } Al_2(SO_4)_3$$

Mass % $Al_2(SO_4)_3 = \dfrac{0.235 \text{ g}}{1.45 \text{ g}} \times 100 = 16.2\%$

45.   All the sulfur in $BaSO_4$ came from the saccharin. The conversion from $BaSO_4$ to saccharin uses the molar masses and formulas of each compound.

$$0.5032 \text{ g } BaSO_4 \times \frac{32.07 \text{ g S}}{233.4 \text{ g } BaSO_4} \times \frac{183.9 \text{ g saccharin}}{32.07 \text{ g S}} = 0.3949 \text{ g saccharin}$$

$$\frac{\text{Average mass}}{\text{Tablet}} = \frac{0.3949 \text{ g}}{10 \text{ tablets}} = \frac{3.949 \times 10^{-2} \text{ g}}{\text{tablet}} = \frac{39.49 \text{ mg}}{\text{tablet}}$$

$$\text{Average mass \%} = \frac{0.3949 \text{ g saccharin}}{0.5894 \text{ g}} \times 100 = 67.00\% \text{ saccharin by mass}$$

47. $M_2SO_4(aq) + CaCl_2(aq) \rightarrow CaSO_4(s) + 2 \ MCl(aq)$

$$1.36 \text{ g } CaSO_4 \times \frac{1 \text{ mol } CaSO_4}{136.15 \text{ g } CaSO_4} \times \frac{1 \text{ mol } M_2SO_4}{\text{mol } CaSO_4} = 9.99 \times 10^{-3} \text{ mol } M_2SO_4$$

From the problem, 1.42 g M_2SO_4 was reacted, so:

$$\text{molar mass} = \frac{1.42 \text{ g } M_2SO_4}{9.99 \times 10^{-3} \text{ mol } M_2SO_4} = 142 \text{ g/mol}$$

142 amu = 2(atomic mass M) + 32.07 + 4(16.00), atomic mass M = 23 amu

From periodic table, M is Na (sodium).

Acid-Base Reactions

49.   a. Perchloric acid reacted with potassium hydroxide is a possibility.

$$HClO_4(aq) + KOH(aq) \rightarrow H_2O(l) + KClO_4(aq)$$

b. Nitric acid reacted with cesium hydroxide is a possibility.

$$HNO_3(aq) + CsOH(aq) \rightarrow H_2O(l) + CsNO_3(aq)$$

c. Hydroiodic acid reacted with calcium hydroxide is a possibility.

$$2 \text{ HI}(aq) + Ca(OH)_2(aq) \rightarrow 2 \text{ H}_2O(l) + CaI_2(aq)$$

51.   If we begin with 50.00 mL of 0.100 M NaOH, then:

$$50.00 \times 10^{-3} \text{ L} \times \frac{0.100 \text{ mol}}{L} = 5.00 \times 10^{-3} \text{ mol NaOH to be neutralized.}$$

a. $NaOH(aq) + HCl(aq) \rightarrow NaCl(aq) + H_2O(l)$

$$5.00 \times 10^{-3} \text{ mol NaOH} \times \frac{1 \text{ mol HCl}}{\text{mol NaOH}} \times \frac{1 \text{ L soln}}{0.100 \text{ mol}} = 5.00 \times 10^{-2} \text{ L or 50.0 mL}$$

b. $2 \text{ NaOH}(aq) + H_2SO_3(aq) \rightarrow 2 \text{ H}_2O(l) + Na_2SO_3(aq)$

$$5.00 \times 10^{-3} \text{ mol NaOH} \times \frac{1 \text{ mol } H_2SO_3}{2 \text{ mol NaOH}} \times \frac{1 \text{ L soln}}{0.100 \text{ mol } H_2SO_3} = 2.50 \times 10^{-2} \text{ L or 25.0 mL}$$

c. $3 \text{ NaOH}(aq) + H_3PO_4(aq) \rightarrow Na_3PO_4(aq) + 3 \text{ H}_2O(l)$

$$5.00 \times 10^{-3} \text{ mol NaOH} \times \frac{1 \text{ mol } H_3PO_4}{3 \text{ mol NaOH}} \times \frac{1 \text{ L soln}}{0.200 \text{ mol } H_3PO_4} = 8.33 \times 10^{-3} \text{ L or 8.33 mL}$$

d. $HNO_3(aq) + NaOH(aq) \rightarrow H_2O(l) + NaNO_3(aq)$

$$5.00 \times 10^{-3} \text{ mol NaOH} \times \frac{1 \text{ mol } HNO_3}{\text{mol NaOH}} \times \frac{1 \text{ L soln}}{0.150 \text{ mol } HNO_3} = 3.33 \times 10^{-2} \text{ L or 33.3 mL}$$

e. $HC_2H_3O_2(aq) + NaOH(aq) \rightarrow H_2O(l) + NaC_2H_3O_2(aq)$

$$5.00 \times 10^{-3} \text{ mol NaOH} \times \frac{1 \text{ mol } HC_2H_3O_2}{\text{mol NaOH}} \times \frac{1 \text{ L soln}}{0.200 \text{ mol } HC_2H_3O_2} = 2.50 \times 10^{-2} \text{ L}$$

$$\text{or } 25.0 \text{ mL}$$

f. $H_2SO_4(aq) + 2 \text{ NaOH}(aq) \rightarrow 2 H_2O(l) + Na_2SO_4(aq)$

$$5.00 \times 10^{-3} \text{ mol NaOH} \times \frac{1 \text{ mol } H_2SO_4}{2 \text{ mol NaOH}} \times \frac{1 \text{ L soln}}{0.300 \text{ mol } H_2SO_4} = 8.33 \times 10^{-3} \text{ L or } 8.33 \text{ mL}$$

53.   The acid is a diprotic acid (H_2A) meaning that it has two H^+ ions in the formula to donate to a base. The reaction is $H_2A(aq) + 2 \text{ NaOH}(aq) \rightarrow 2 H_2O(l) + Na_2A(aq)$, where A^{2-} is what is left over from the acid formula when the two protons (H^+ ions) are reacted.

For the HCl reaction, the base has the ability to accept two protons. The most common examples are $Ca(OH)_2$, $Sr(OH)_2$, and $Ba(OH)_2$. A possible reaction would be $2 \text{ HCl}(aq) + Ca(OH)_2(aq) \rightarrow 2 H_2O(l) + CaCl_2(aq)$.

55.   The pertinent reactions are:

$$2 \text{ NaOH}(aq) + H_2SO_4(aq) \rightarrow Na_2SO_4(aq) + 2 H_2O(l)$$

$$HCl(aq) + NaOH(aq) \rightarrow NaCl(aq) + H_2O(l)$$

$$\text{Amount of NaOH added} = 0.0500 \text{ L} \times \frac{0.213 \text{ mol}}{\text{L}} = 1.07 \times 10^{-2} \text{ mol NaOH}$$

Amount of NaOH neutralized by HCl:

$$0.01321 \text{ L HCl} \text{ H } \frac{0.103 \text{ mol HCl}}{\text{L HCl}} \times \frac{1 \text{ mol NaOH}}{\text{mol HCl}} = 1.36 \times 10^{-3} \text{ mol NaOH}$$

The difference, 9.3×10^{-3} mol, is the amount of NaOH neutralized by the sulfuric acid.

$$9.3 \times 10^{-3} \text{ mol NaOH} \times \frac{1 \text{ mol } H_2SO_4}{2 \text{ mol NaOH}} = 4.7 \times 10^{-3} \text{ mol } H_2SO_4$$

$$\text{Concentration of } H_2SO_4 = \frac{4.7 \times 10^{-3} \text{ mol}}{0.1000 \text{ L}} = 4.7 \times 10^{-2} \text{ } M \text{ } H_2SO_4$$

57. $HC_2H_3O_2(aq) + NaOH(aq) \rightarrow H_2O(l) + NaC_2H_3O_2(aq)$

a. $16.58 \times 10^{-3} \text{ L soln H } \dfrac{0.5062 \text{ mol NaOH}}{\text{L soln}} \times \dfrac{1 \text{ mol acetic acid}}{\text{mol NaOH}}$

$$= 8.393 \times 10^{-3} \text{ mol acetic acid}$$

$$\text{Concentration of acetic acid} = \frac{8.393 \times 10^{-3} \text{ mol}}{0.01000 \text{ L}} = 0.8393 \text{ } M \text{ } HC_2H_3O_2$$

b. If we have 1.000 L of solution: total mass = 1000. mL $\times \dfrac{1.006\,g}{mL}$ = 1006 g solution

Mass of $HC_2H_3O_2$ = 0.8393 mol $\times \dfrac{60.052\,g}{mol}$ = 50.40 g $HC_2H_3O_2$

Mass % acetic acid = $\dfrac{50.40\,g}{1006\,g} \times 100$ = 5.010%

59.   HCl and HNO_3 are strong acids; $Ca(OH)_2$ and RbOH are strong bases. The net ionic equation that occurs is $H^+(aq) + OH^-(aq) \rightarrow H_2O(l)$.

Mol H^+ = 0.0500 L $\times \dfrac{0.100\,mol\,HCl}{L} \times \dfrac{1\,mol\,H^+}{mol\,HCl}$ +

0.1000 L $\times \dfrac{0.200\,mol\,HNO_3}{L} \times \dfrac{1\,mol\,H^+}{mol\,HNO_3}$ = 0.00500 + 0.0200 = 0.0250 mol H^+

Mol OH^- = 0.5000 L $\times \dfrac{0.0100\,mol\,Ca(OH)_2}{L} \times \dfrac{2\,mol\,OH^-}{mol\,Ca(OH)_2}$ +

0.2000 L $\times \dfrac{0.100\,mol\,RbOH}{L} \times \dfrac{1\,mol\,OH^-}{mol\,RbOH}$ = 0.0100 + 0.0200 = 0.0300 mol OH^-

We have an excess of OH^-, so the solution is basic (not neutral). The moles of excess OH^- = 0.0300 mol OH^- initially – 0.0250 mol OH^- reacted (with H^+) = 0.0050 mol OH^- excess.

$$M_{OH^-} = \dfrac{0.0050\,mol\,OH^-}{(0.05000 + 0.1000 + 0.5000 + 0.2000)\,L} = \dfrac{0.0050\,mol}{0.8500\,L} = 5.9 \times 10^{-3}\,M$$

61. $Ba(OH)_2(aq) + 2\,HCl(aq) \rightarrow BaCl_2(aq) + 2\,H_2O(l);\ H^+(aq) + OH^-(aq) \rightarrow H_2O(l)$

75.0 $\times 10^{-3}$ L $\times \dfrac{0.250\,mol\,HCl}{L}$ = 1.88 $\times 10^{-2}$ mol HCl = 1.88 $\times 10^{-2}$ mol H^+ +
1.88 $\times 10^{-2}$ mol Cl^-

225.0 $\times 10^{-3}$ L $\times \dfrac{0.0550\,mol\,Ba(OH)_2}{L}$ = 1.24 $\times 10^{-2}$ mol $Ba(OH)_2$ = 1.24 $\times 10^{-2}$ mol Ba^{2+} +
2.48 $\times 10^{-2}$ mol OH^-

The net ionic equation requires a 1 : 1 mol ratio between OH^- and H^+. The actual mol OH^- to mol H^+ ratio is greater than 1 : 1, so OH^- is in excess. Because 1.88 $\times 10^{-2}$ mol OH^- will be neutralized by the H^+, we have (2.48 – 1.88) $\times 10^{-2}$ = 0.60 $\times 10^{-2}$ mol OH^- in excess.

$$M_{OH^-} = \dfrac{mol\,OH^-\,excess}{total\,volume} = \dfrac{6.0 \times 10^{-3}\,mol\,OH^-}{0.0750\,L + 0.2250\,L} = 2.0 \times 10^{-2}\,M\,OH^-$$

Oxidation-Reduction Reactions

63.   a.   The species reduced is the element that gains electrons. The reducing agent causes reduction to occur by itself being oxidized. The reducing agent generally refers to the entire formula of the compound/ion that contains the element oxidized.

        b.   The species oxidized is the element that loses electrons. The oxidizing agent causes oxidation to occur by itself being reduced. The oxidizing agent generally refers to the entire formula of the compound/ion that contains the element reduced.

        c.   For simple binary ionic compounds, the actual charge on the ions are the same as the oxidation states. For covalent compounds and ions, nonzero oxidation states are imaginary charges the elements would have if they were held together by ionic bonds (assuming the bond is between two different nonmetals). Nonzero oxidation states for elements in covalent compounds are not actual charges. Oxidation states for covalent compounds are a bookkeeping method to keep track of electrons in a reaction.

65.   Apply rules in Table 4.3.

        a. $KMnO_4$ is composed of K^+ and MnO_4^- ions. Assign oxygen an oxidation state value of -2, which gives manganese a $+7$ oxidation state because the sum of oxidation states for all atoms in MnO_4^- must equal the $1-$ charge on MnO_4^-. K, $+1$; O, -2; Mn, $+7$.

        b.   Assign O a -2 oxidation state, which gives nickel a $+4$ oxidation state. Ni, $+4$; O, -2.

        c. $K_4Fe(CN)_6$ is composed of K^+ cations and $Fe(CN)_6^{4-}$ anions. $Fe(CN)_6^{4-}$ is composed of iron and CN^- anions. For an overall anion charge of $4-$, iron must have a $+2$ oxidation state.

        d. $(NH_4)_2HPO_4$ is made of NH_4^+ cations and HPO_4^{2-} anions. Assign $+1$ as oxidation state of H and -2 as the oxidation state of O. For N in NH_4^+: $x + 4(+1) = +1$, $x = -3 =$ oxidation state of N. For P in HPO_4^{2-}: $+1 + y + 4(-2) = -2$, $y = +5 =$ oxidation state of P.

        e.   O, -2; P, $+3$ f.   O, -2; Fe, $+ 8/3$

        g.   O, -2; F, -1; Xe, $+6$ h.   F, -1; S, $+4$

        i.   O, -2; C, $+2$ j.   H, $+1$; O, -2; C, 0

67.   a. $SrCr_2O_7$: Composed of Sr^{2+} and $Cr_2O_7^{2-}$ ions. Sr, $+2$; O, -2; Cr, $2x + 7(-2) = -2$, $x = +6$

        b.   Cu, $+2$; Cl, -1;   c.   O, 0;   d.   H, $+1$; O, -1

        e. Mg^{2+} and CO_3^{2-} ions present. Mg, $+2$; O, -2; C, $+4$;   f.   Ag, 0

        g. Pb^{2+} and SO_3^{2-} ions present. Pb, $+2$; O, -2; S, $+4$;   h.   O, -2; Pb, $+4$

        i. Na^+ and $C_2O_4^{2-}$ ions present. Na, $+1$; O, -2; C, $2x + 4(-2) = -2$, $x = +3$

j.   O, –2; C, +4

k.   Ammonium ion has a 1+ charge (NH_4^+), and sulfate ion has a 2– charge (SO_4^{2-}). Therefore, the oxidation state of cerium must be +4 (Ce^{4+}). H, +1; N, –3; O, –2; S, +6

l.   O, –2; Cr, +3

69.   a. $Al(s) + 3\ HCl(aq) \rightarrow AlCl_3(aq) + 3/2\ H_2(g)$ or $2\ Al(s) + 6\ HCl(aq) \rightarrow 2\ AlCl_3(aq) +$

$$3\ H_2(g)$$

Hydrogen is reduced (goes from the +1 oxidation state to the 0 oxidation state), and aluminum Al is oxidized (0 → +3).

b.   Balancing S is most complicated because sulfur is in both products. Balance C and H first; then worry about S.

$CH_4(g) + 4\ S(s) \rightarrow CS_2(l) + 2\ H_2S(g)$

Sulfur is reduced (0 → –2), and carbon is oxidized (–4 → +4).

c.   Balance C and H first; then balance O.

$C_3H_8(g) + 5\ O_2(g) \rightarrow 3\ CO_2(g) + 4\ H_2O(l)$

Oxygen is reduced (0 → –2), and carbon is oxidized (–8/3 → +4).

d.   Although this reaction is mass balanced, it is not charge balanced. We need 2 mol of silver on each side to balance the charge.

$Cu(s) + 2\ Ag^+(aq) \rightarrow 2\ Ag(s) + Cu^{2+}(aq)$

Silver is reduced (+1 → 0), and copper is oxidized (0 → +2).

71.   a.   Review Section 4.11 of the text for rules on balancing by the half-reaction method. The first step is to separate the reaction into two half-reactions, and then balance each half-reaction separately.

$(Cu \rightarrow Cu^{2+} + 2\ e^-) \times 3$ $\qquad\qquad\qquad NO_3^- \rightarrow NO + 2\ H_2O$
$$(3\ e^- + 4\ H^+ + NO_3^- \rightarrow NO + 2\ H_2O) \times 2$$

Adding the two balanced half-reactions so electrons cancel:

$$3\ Cu \rightarrow 3\ Cu^{2+} + 6\ e^-$$
$$6\ e^- + 8\ H^+ + 2\ NO_3^- \rightarrow 2\ NO + 4\ H_2O$$

$$\overline{3\ Cu(s) + 8\ H^+(aq) + 2\ NO_3^-(aq) \rightarrow 3\ Cu^{2+}(aq) + 2\ NO(g) + 4\ H_2O(l)}$$

The final step is to simplify the equation by cancelling identical species on both sides of the equations. Other than the electrons, this equation has no identical species to cancel, so this is the balanced equation. Typically, H^+ and H_2O are the species which can be cancelled in this final step (other than the electrons).

b. $(2 \, Cl^- \rightarrow Cl_2 + 2 \, e^-) \times 3$ $Cr_2O_7^{2-} \rightarrow 2 \, Cr^{3+} + 7 \, H_2O$

$$6 \, e^- + 14 \, H^+ + Cr_2O_7^{2-} \rightarrow 2 \, Cr^{3+} + 7 \, H_2O$$

Add the two balanced half-reactions with six electrons transferred:

$$6 \, Cl^- \rightarrow 3 \, Cl_2 + 6 \, e^-$$
$$6 \, e^- + 14 \, H^+ + Cr_2O_7^{2-} \rightarrow 2 \, Cr^{3+} + 7 \, H_2O$$

$$\overline{14 \, H^+(aq) + Cr_2O_7^{2-}(aq) + 6 \, Cl^-(aq) \rightarrow 3 \, Cl_2(g) + 2 \, Cr^{3+}(aq) + 7 \, H_2O(l)}$$

c. $Pb \rightarrow PbSO_4$ $PbO_2 \rightarrow PbSO_4$

$Pb + H_2SO_4 \rightarrow PbSO_4 + 2 \, H^+$ $PbO_2 + H_2SO_4 \rightarrow PbSO_4 + 2 \, H_2O$

$Pb + H_2SO_4 \rightarrow PbSO_4 + 2 \, H^+ + 2 \, e^-$ $2 \, e^- + 2 \, H^+ + PbO_2 + H_2SO_4 \rightarrow PbSO_4 + 2 \, H_2O$

Add the two half-reactions with two electrons transferred:

$$2 \, e^- + 2 \, H^+ + PbO_2 + H_2SO_4 \rightarrow PbSO_4 + 2 \, H_2O$$
$$Pb + H_2SO_4 \rightarrow PbSO_4 + 2 \, H^+ + 2 \, e^-$$

$$\overline{Pb(s) + 2 \, H_2SO_4(aq) + PbO_2(s) \rightarrow 2 \, PbSO_4(s) + 2 \, H_2O(l)}$$

This is the reaction that occurs in an automobile lead storage battery.

d. $Mn^{2+} \rightarrow MnO_4^-$

$(4 \, H_2O + Mn^{2+} \rightarrow MnO_4^- + 8 \, H^+ + 5 \, e^-) \times 2$

$$NaBiO_3 \rightarrow Bi^{3+} + Na^+$$
$$6 \, H^+ + NaBiO_3 \rightarrow Bi^{3+} + Na^+ + 3 \, H_2O$$
$$(2 \, e^- + 6 \, H^+ + NaBiO_3 \rightarrow Bi^{3+} + Na^+ + 3 \, H_2O) \times 5$$

$$8 \, H_2O + 2 \, Mn^{2+} \rightarrow 2 \, MnO_4^- + 16 \, H^+ + 10 \, e^-$$
$$10 \, e^- + 30 \, H^+ + 5 \, NaBiO_3 \rightarrow 5 \, Bi^{3+} + 5 \, Na^+ + 15 \, H_2O$$

$$\overline{8 \, H_2O + 30 \, H^+ + 2 \, Mn^{2+} + 5 \, NaBiO_3 \rightarrow 2 \, MnO_4^- + 5 \, Bi^{3+} + 5 \, Na^+ + 15 \, H_2O + 16 \, H^+}$$

Simplifying:

$$14 \, H^+(aq) + 2 \, Mn^{2+}(aq) + 5 \, NaBiO_3(s) \rightarrow 2 \, MnO_4^-(aq) + 5 \, Bi^{3+}(aq) + 5 \, Na^+(aq) + 7 \, H_2O(l)$$

e. $H_3AsO_4 \rightarrow AsH_3$ $(Zn \rightarrow Zn^{2+} + 2 \, e^-) \times 4$

$$H_3AsO_4 \rightarrow AsH_3 + 4 \, H_2O$$
$$8 \, e^- + 8 \, H^+ + H_3AsO_4 \rightarrow AsH_3 + 4 \, H_2O$$

$$8 \, e^- + 8 \, H^+ + H_3AsO_4 \rightarrow AsH_3 + 4 \, H_2O$$
$$4 \, Zn \rightarrow 4 \, Zn^{2+} + 8 \, e^-$$

$$\overline{8 \, H^+(aq) + H_3AsO_4(aq) + 4 \, Zn(s) \rightarrow 4 \, Zn^{2+}(aq) + AsH_3(g) + 4 \, H_2O(l)}$$

f. $As_2O_3 \rightarrow H_3AsO_4$

                    $As_2O_3 \rightarrow 2\ H_3AsO_4$

   $(5\ H_2O + As_2O_3 \rightarrow 2\ H_3AsO_4 + 4\ H^+ + 4\ e^-) \times 3$

                                                   $NO_3^- \rightarrow NO + 2\ H_2O$

                                          $4\ H^+ + NO_3^- \rightarrow NO + 2\ H_2O$

                                  $(3\ e^- + 4\ H^+ + NO_3^- \rightarrow NO + 2\ H_2O) \times 4$

                    $12\ e^- + 16\ H^+ + 4\ NO_3^- \rightarrow 4\ NO + 8\ H_2O$

                      $15\ H_2O + 3\ As_2O_3 \rightarrow 6\ H_3AsO_4 + 12\ H^+ + 12\ e^-$

_____

   $7\ H_2O(l) + 4\ H^+(aq) + 3\ As_2O_3(s) + 4\ NO_3^-(aq) \rightarrow 4\ NO(g) + 6\ H_3AsO_4(aq)$

g. $(2\ Br^- \rightarrow Br_2 + 2\ e^-) \times 5$ $MnO_4^- \rightarrow Mn^{2+} + 4\ H_2O$

                                              $(5\ e^- + 8\ H^+ + MnO_4^- \rightarrow Mn^{2+} + 4\ H_2O) \times 2$

                    $10\ Br^- \rightarrow 5\ Br_2 + 10\ e^-$

         $10\ e^- + 16\ H^+ + 2\ MnO_4^- \rightarrow 2\ Mn^{2+} + 8\ H_2O$

_____

   $16\ H^+(aq) + 2\ MnO_4^-(aq) + 10\ Br^-(aq) \rightarrow 5\ Br_2(l) + 2\ Mn^{2+}(aq) + 8\ H_2O(l)$

h. $CH_3OH \rightarrow CH_2O$ $Cr_2O_7^{2-} \rightarrow Cr^{3+}$

   $(CH_3OH \rightarrow CH_2O + 2\ H^+ + 2\ e^-) \times 3$ $14\ H^+ + Cr_2O_7^{2-} \rightarrow 2\ Cr^{3+} + 7\ H_2O$

                                              $6\ e^- + 14\ H^+ + Cr_2O_7^{2-} \rightarrow 2\ Cr^{3+} + 7\ H_2O$

                    $3\ CH_3OH \rightarrow 3\ CH_2O + 6\ H^+ + 6\ e^-$

              $6\ e^- + 14\ H^+ + Cr_2O_7^{2-} \rightarrow 2\ Cr^{3+} + 7\ H_2O$

_____

   $8\ H^+(aq) + 3\ CH_3OH(aq) + Cr_2O_7^{2-}(aq) \rightarrow 2\ Cr^{3+}(aq) + 3\ CH_2O(aq) + 7\ H_2O(l)$

73.   a.   HCl(aq) dissociates to $H^+(aq) + Cl^-(aq)$. For simplicity, let's use H^+ and Cl^- separately.

                    $H^+ \rightarrow H_2$ $Fe \rightarrow HFeCl_4$

         $(2\ H^+ + 2\ e^- \rightarrow H_2) \times 3$ $(H^+ + 4\ Cl^- + Fe \rightarrow HFeCl_4 + 3\ e^-) \times 2$

                    $6\ H^+ + 6\ e^- \rightarrow 3\ H_2$

           $2\ H^+ + 8\ Cl^- + 2\ Fe \rightarrow 2\ HFeCl_4 + 6\ e^-$

_____

           $8\ H^+ + 8\ Cl^- + 2\ Fe \rightarrow 2\ HFeCl_4 + 3\ H_2$

      or $8\ HCl(aq) + 2\ Fe(s) \rightarrow 2\ HFeCl_4(aq) + 3\ H_2(g)$

b.
$$IO_3^- \rightarrow I_3^-$$
$$3\ IO_3^- \rightarrow I_3^-$$
$$3\ IO_3^- \rightarrow I_3^- + 9\ H_2O$$
$$16\ e^- + 18\ H^+ + 3\ IO_3^- \rightarrow I_3^- + 9\ H_2O$$

$$I^- \rightarrow I_3^-$$
$$(3\ I^- \rightarrow I_3^- + 2\ e^-) \times 8$$

$$16\ e^- + 18\ H^+ + 3\ IO_3^- \rightarrow I_3^- + 9\ H_2O$$
$$24\ I^- \rightarrow 8\ I_3^- + 16\ e^-$$

$$18\ H^+ + 24\ I^- + 3\ IO_3^- \rightarrow 9\ I_3^- + 9\ H_2O$$

Reducing: $6\ H^+(aq) + 8\ I^-(aq) + IO_3^-(aq) \rightarrow 3\ I_3^-(aq) + 3\ H_2O(l)$

c. $(Ce^{4+} + e^- \rightarrow Ce^{3+}) \times 97$
$$Cr(NCS)_6^{4-} \rightarrow Cr^{3+} + NO_3^- + CO_2 + SO_4^{2-}$$
$$54\ H_2O + Cr(NCS)_6^{4-} \rightarrow Cr^{3+} + 6\ NO_3^- + 6\ CO_2 + 6\ SO_4^{2-} + 108\ H^+$$

Charge on left $= -4$. Charge on right $= +3 + 6(-1) + 6(-2) + 108(+1) = +93$. Add 97 e⁻ to the product side, and then add the two balanced half-reactions with a common factor of 97 e⁻ transferred.

$$54\ H_2O + Cr(NCS)_6^{4-} \rightarrow Cr^{3+} + 6\ NO_3^- + 6\ CO_2 + 6\ SO_4^{2-} + 108\ H^+ + 97\ e^-$$
$$97\ e^- + 97\ Ce^{4+} \rightarrow 97\ Ce^{3+}$$

$$97\ Ce^{4+}(aq) + 54\ H_2O(l) + Cr(NCS)_6^{4-}(aq) \rightarrow 97\ Ce^{3+}(aq) + Cr^{3+}(aq) + 6\ NO_3^-(aq)$$
$$+ 6\ CO_2(g) + 6\ SO_4^{2-}(aq) + 108\ H^+(aq)$$

This is very complicated. A check of the net charge is a good check to see if the equation is balanced. Left: charge $= 97(+4) - 4 = +384$. Right: charge $= 97(+3) + 3 + 6(-1) + 6(-2) + 108(+1) = +384$.

d.
$$CrI_3 \rightarrow CrO_4^{2-} + IO_4^-$$
$$(16\ H_2O + CrI_3 \rightarrow CrO_4^{2-} + 3\ IO_4^- + 32\ H^+ + 27\ e^-) \times 2$$

$$Cl_2 \rightarrow Cl^-$$
$$(2\ e^- + Cl_2 \rightarrow 2\ Cl^-) \times 27$$

Common factor is a transfer of 54 e⁻.

$$54\ e^- + 27\ Cl_2 \rightarrow 54\ Cl^-$$
$$32\ H_2O + 2\ CrI_3 \rightarrow 2\ CrO_4^{2-} + 6\ IO_4^- + 64\ H^+ + 54\ e^-$$

$$32\ H_2O + 2\ CrI_3 + 27\ Cl_2 \rightarrow 54\ Cl^- + 2\ CrO_4^{2-} + 6\ IO_4^- + 64\ H^+$$

Add 64 OH⁻ to both sides and convert 64 H⁺ into 64 H₂O.

$$64\ OH^- + 32\ H_2O + 2\ CrI_3 + 27\ Cl_2 \rightarrow 54\ Cl^- + 2\ CrO_4^{2-} + 6\ IO_4^- + 64\ H_2O$$

Reducing gives:

$$64\ OH^-(aq) + 2\ CrI_3(s) + 27\ Cl_2(g) \rightarrow 54\ Cl^-(aq) + 2\ CrO_4^{2-}(aq) + 6\ IO_4^-(aq)$$
$$+ 32\ H_2O(l)$$

e. $Ce^{4+} \rightarrow Ce(OH)_3$
$$(e^- + 3\ H_2O + Ce^{4+} \rightarrow Ce(OH)_3 + 3\ H^+) \times 61$$

$$Fe(CN)_6^{4-} \rightarrow Fe(OH)_3 + CO_3^{2-} + NO_3^-$$
$$Fe(CN)_6^{4-} \rightarrow Fe(OH)_3 + 6\ CO_3^{2-} + 6\ NO_3^-$$

There are 39 extra O atoms on right. Add 39 H_2O to left, then add 75 H^+ to right to balance H^+.

$$39\ H_2O + Fe(CN)_6^{4-} \rightarrow Fe(OH)_3 + 6\ CO_3^{2-} + 6\ NO_3^- + 75\ H^+$$
$$\text{net charge} = 4-\qquad\qquad \text{net charge} = 57+$$

Add 61 e^- to the product side, and then add the two balanced half-reactions with a common factor of 61 e^- transferred.

$$39\ H_2O + Fe(CN)_6^{4-} \rightarrow Fe(OH)_3 + 6\ CO_3^- + 6\ NO_3^- + 75\ H^+ + 61\ e^-$$
$$61\ e^- + 183\ H_2O + 61\ Ce^{4+} \rightarrow 61\ Ce(OH)_3 + 183\ H^+$$

$$222\ H_2O + Fe(CN)_6^{4-} + 61\ Ce^{4+} \rightarrow 61\ Ce(OH)_3 + Fe(OH)_3 + 6\ CO_3^{2-} + 6\ NO_3^- + 258\ H^+$$

Adding 258 OH^- to each side, and then reducing gives:

$$258\ OH^-(aq) + Fe(CN)_6^{4-}(aq) + 61\ Ce^{4+}(aq) \rightarrow 61\ Ce(OH)_3(s) + Fe(OH)_3(s)$$
$$+\ 6\ CO_3^{2-}(aq) + 6\ NO_3^-(aq) + 36\ H_2O(l)$$

75. $(H_2C_2O_4 \rightarrow 2\ CO_2 + 2\ H^+ + 2\ e^-) \times 5 \qquad\qquad (5\ e^- + 8\ H^+ + MnO_4^- \rightarrow Mn^{2+} + 4\ H_2O) \times 2$

$$5\ H_2C_2O_4 \rightarrow 10\ CO_2 + 10\ H^+ + 10\ e^-$$
$$10\ e^- + 16\ H^+ + 2\ MnO_4^- \rightarrow 2\ Mn^{2+} + 8\ H_2O$$

$$6\ H^+(aq) + 5\ H_2C_2O_4(aq) + 2\ MnO_4^-(aq) \rightarrow 10\ CO_2(g) + 2\ Mn^{2+}(aq) + 8\ H_2O(l)$$

$$0.1058\ g\ H_2C_2O_4 \times \frac{1\ mol\ H_2C_2O_4}{90.034\ g} \times \frac{2\ mol\ MnO_4^-}{5\ mol\ H_2C_2O_4} = 4.700 \times 10^{-4}\ mol\ MnO_4^-$$

$$Molarity = \frac{4.700 \times 10^{-4}\ mol\ MnO_4^-}{28.97\ mL} \times \frac{1000\ mL}{L} = 1.622 \times 10^{-2}\ M\ MnO_4^-$$

77. $(Fe^{2+} \rightarrow Fe^{3+} + e^-) \times 5$
$$5\ e^- + 8\ H^+ + MnO_4^- \rightarrow Mn^{2+} + 4\ H_2O$$

$$8\ H^+(aq) + MnO_4^-(aq) + 5\ Fe^{2+}(aq) \rightarrow 5\ Fe^{3+}(aq) + Mn^{2+}(aq) + 4\ H_2O(l)$$

From the titration data we can get the number of moles of Fe^{2+}. We then convert this to a mass of iron and calculate the mass percent of iron in the sample.

$$38.37 \times 10^{-3} \text{ L MnO}_4^- \times \frac{0.0198 \text{ mol MnO}_4^-}{\text{L}} \times \frac{5 \text{ mol Fe}^{2+}}{\text{mol MnO}_4^-} = 3.80 \times 10^{-3} \text{ mol Fe}^{2+}$$

$$= 3.80 \times 10^{-3} \text{ mol Fe present}$$

$$3.80 \times 10^{-3} \text{ mol Fe} \times \frac{55.85 \text{ g Fe}}{\text{mol Fe}} = 0.212 \text{ g Fe}$$

$$\text{Mass \% Fe} = \frac{0.212 \text{ g}}{0.6128 \text{ g}} \times 100 = 34.6\% \text{ Fe}$$

79. $Mg(s) + 2 HCl(aq) \rightarrow MgCl_2(aq) + H_2(g)$

$$3.00 \text{ g Mg} \times \frac{1 \text{ mol Mg}}{24.31 \text{ g Mg}} \times \frac{2 \text{ mol HCl}}{\text{mol Mg}} \times \frac{1 \text{ L HCl}}{5.0 \text{ mol HCl}} = 0.0494 \text{ L} = 49.4 \text{ mL HCl}$$

Additional Exercises

81. $\text{Mol CaCl}_2 \text{ present} = 0.230 \text{ L CaCl}_2 \times \dfrac{0.275 \text{ mol CaCl}_2}{\text{L CaCl}_2} = 6.33 \times 10^{-2} \text{ mol CaCl}_2$

The volume of $CaCl_2$ solution after evaporation is:

$$6.33 \times 10^{-2} \text{ mol CaCl}_2 \times \frac{1 \text{ L CaCl}_2}{1.10 \text{ mol CaCl}_2} = 5.75 \times 10^{-2} \text{ L} = 57.5 \text{ mL CaCl}_2$$

Volume H_2O evaporated = 230. mL – 57.5 mL = 173 mL H_2O evaporated

83.   a. $MgCl_2(aq) + 2 AgNO_3(aq) \rightarrow 2 AgCl(s) + Mg(NO_3)_2(aq)$

$$0.641 \text{ g AgCl} \times \frac{1 \text{ mol AgCl}}{143.4 \text{ g AgCl}} \times \frac{1 \text{ mol MgCl}_2}{2 \text{ mol AgCl}} \times \frac{95.21 \text{ g}}{\text{mol MgCl}_2} = 0.213 \text{ g MgCl}_2$$

$$\frac{0.213 \text{ g MgCl}_2}{1.50 \text{ g mixture}} \times 100 = 14.2\% \text{ MgCl}_2$$

b. $0.213 \text{ g MgCl}_2 \times \dfrac{1 \text{ mol MgCl}_2}{95.21 \text{ g}} \times \dfrac{2 \text{ mol AgNO}_3}{\text{mol MgCl}_2} \times \dfrac{1 \text{ L}}{0.500 \text{ mol AgNO}_3} \times \dfrac{1000 \text{ mL}}{1 \text{ L}}$

$$= 8.95 \text{ mL AgNO}_3$$

85.   a. $0.308 \text{ g AgCl} \times \dfrac{35.45 \text{ g Cl}}{143.4 \text{ g AgCl}} = 0.0761 \text{ g Cl};$ $\% \text{ Cl} = \dfrac{0.0761 \text{ g}}{0.256 \text{ g}} \times 100 = 29.7\% \text{ Cl}$

Cobalt(III) oxide, Co_2O_3: 2(58.93) + 3(16.00) = 165.86 g/mol

$$0.145 \text{ g Co}_2\text{O}_3 \times \frac{117.86 \text{ g Co}}{165.86 \text{ g Co}_2\text{O}_3} = 0.103 \text{ g Co}; \quad \% \text{ Co} = \frac{0.103 \text{ g}}{0.416 \text{ g}} \times 100 = 24.8\% \text{ Co}$$

The remainder, $100.0 - (29.7 + 24.8) = 45.5\%$, is water.

Assuming 100.0 g of compound:

$$45.5 \text{ g H}_2\text{O} \times \frac{2.016 \text{ g H}}{18.02 \text{ g H}_2\text{O}} = 5.09 \text{ g H}; \quad \% \text{ H} = \frac{5.09 \text{ g H}}{100.0 \text{ g compound}} \times 100 = 5.09\% \text{ H}$$

$$45.5 \text{ g H}_2\text{O} \times \frac{16.00 \text{ g O}}{18.02 \text{ g H}_2\text{O}} = 40.4 \text{ g O}; \quad \% \text{ O} = \frac{40.4 \text{ g O}}{100.0 \text{ g compound}} \times 100 = 40.4\% \text{ O}$$

The mass percent composition is 24.8% Co, 29.7% Cl, 5.09% H, and 40.4% O.

b. Out of 100.0 g of compound, there are:

$$24.8 \text{ g Co} \times \frac{1 \text{ mol}}{58.93 \text{ g Co}} = 0.421 \text{ mol Co}; \quad 29.7 \text{ g Cl} \times \frac{1 \text{ mol}}{35.45 \text{ g Cl}} = 0.838 \text{ mol Cl}$$

$$5.09 \text{ g H} \times \frac{1 \text{ mol}}{1.008 \text{ g H}} = 5.05 \text{ mol H}; \quad 40.4 \text{ g O} \times \frac{1 \text{ mol}}{16.00 \text{ g O}} = 2.53 \text{ mol O}$$

Dividing all results by 0.421, we get $CoCl_2 \bullet 6H_2O$ for the empirical formula, which is also the molecular formula.

c. $CoCl_2 \bullet 6H_2O(aq) + 2 \text{ AgNO}_3(aq) \rightarrow 2 \text{ AgCl}(s) + Co(NO_3)_2(aq) + 6 H_2O(l)$

$CoCl_2 \bullet 6H_2O(aq) + 2 \text{ NaOH}(aq) \rightarrow Co(OH)_2(s) + 2 \text{ NaCl}(aq) + 6 H_2O(l)$

$Co(OH)_2 \rightarrow Co_2O_3$ This is an oxidation-reduction reaction. Thus we also need to include an oxidizing agent. The obvious choice is O_2.

$4 \text{ Co(OH)}_2(s) + O_2(g) \rightarrow 2 \text{ Co}_2\text{O}_3(s) + 4 H_2O(l)$

87. $Ag^+(aq) + Cl^-(aq) \rightarrow \text{AgCl}(s)$; let $x = $ mol NaCl and $y = $ mol KCl.

$(22.90 \times 10^{-3} \text{ L}) \times 0.1000 \text{ mol/L} = 2.290 \times 10^{-3} \text{ mol Ag}^+ = 2.290 \times 10^{-3} \text{ mol Cl}^-$ total

$x + y = 2.290 \times 10^{-3} \text{ mol Cl}^-, \quad x = 2.290 \times 10^{-3} - y$

Because the molar mass of NaCl is 58.44 g/mol and the molar mass of KCl is 74.55 g/mol:

$(58.44)x + (74.55)y = 0.1586 \text{ g}$

$$58.44(2.290 \times 10^{-3} - y) + (74.55)y = 0.1586, \; (16.11)y = 0.0248, \; y = 1.54 \times 10^{-3} \text{ mol KCl}$$

$$\text{Mass \% KCl} = \frac{1.54 \times 10^{-3} \text{ mol} \times 74.55 \text{ g/mol}}{0.1586 \text{ g}} \times 100 = 72.4\% \text{ KCl}$$

% NaCl = 100.0 − 72.4 = 27.6% NaCl

89. $Cr(NO_3)_3(aq) + 3 \, NaOH(aq) \rightarrow Cr(OH)_3(s) + 3 \, NaNO_3(aq)$

$$\text{Mol NaOH used} \atop \text{to form precipitate} = 2.06 \text{ g } Cr(OH)_3 \times \frac{1 \text{ mol } Cr(OH)_3}{103.02 \text{ g}} \times \frac{3 \text{ mol NaOH}}{\text{mol } Cr(OH)_3} = 6.00 \times 10^{-2} \text{ mol}$$

$NaOH(aq) + HCl(aq) \rightarrow NaCl(aq) + H_2O(l)$

$$\text{Mol NaOH used} \atop \text{to react with HCl} = 0.1000 \text{ L} \times \frac{0.400 \text{ mol HCl}}{\text{L}} \times \frac{1 \text{ mol NaOH}}{\text{mol HCl}} = 4.00 \times 10^{-2} \text{ mol}$$

$$M_{\text{NaOH}} = \frac{\text{total mol NaOH}}{\text{volume}} = \frac{6.00 \times 10^{-2} \text{ mol} + 4.00 \times 10^{-2} \text{ mol}}{0.0500 \text{ L}} = 2.00 \; M \text{ NaOH}$$

91.   Mol KHP used = 0.4016 g × 1 mol/204.22 g = 1.967×10^{-3} mol KHP

Because 1 mole of NaOH reacts completely with 1 mole of KHP, the NaOH solution contains 1.967×10^{-3} mol NaOH.

$$\text{Molarity of NaOH} = \frac{1.967 \times 10^{-3} \text{ mol}}{25.06 \times 10^{-3} \text{ L}} = \frac{7.849 \times 10^{-2} \text{ mol NaOH}}{\text{L}}$$

$$\text{Maximum molarity} = \frac{1.967 \times 10^{-3} \text{ mol}}{25.01 \times 10^{-3} \text{ L}} = \frac{7.865 \times 10^{-2} \text{ mol NaOH}}{\text{L}}$$

$$\text{Minimum molarity} = \frac{1.967 \times 10^{-3} \text{ mol}}{25.11 \times 10^{-3} \text{ L}} = \frac{7.834 \times 10^{-2} \text{ mol NaOH}}{\text{L}}$$

We can express this as 0.07849 ±0.00016 M. An alternate way is to express the molarity as 0.0785 ±0.0002 M. This second way shows the actual number of significant figures in the molarity.   The advantage of the first method is that it shows that we made all our individual measurements to four significant figures.

93. $$\text{Mol } C_6H_8O_7 = 0.250 \text{ g } C_6H_8O_7 \times \frac{1 \text{ mol } C_6H_8O_7}{192.1 \text{ g } C_6H_8O_7} = 1.30 \times 10^{-3} \text{ mol } C_6H_8O_7$$

Let H_xA represent citric acid, where x is the number of acidic hydrogens. The balanced neutralization reaction is:

$$H_xA(aq) + x\ OH^-(aq) \rightarrow x\ H_2O(l) + A^{x-}(aq)$$

$$\text{Mol } OH^-\text{ reacted} = 0.0372\ L \times \frac{0.105\ \text{mol } OH^-}{L} = 3.91 \times 10^{-3}\ \text{mol } OH^-$$

$$x = \frac{\text{mol } OH^-}{\text{mol citric acid}} = \frac{3.91 \times 10^{-3}\ \text{mol}}{1.30 \times 10^{-3}\ \text{mol}} = 3.01$$

Therefore, the general acid formula for citric acid is H_3A, meaning that citric acid has three acidic hydrogens per citric acid molecule (citric acid is a triprotic acid).

95. $H_2SO_4(aq) + 2\ NaOH(aq) \rightarrow Na_2SO_4(aq) + 2\ H_2O(l)$

$$0.02844\ L \times \frac{0.1000\ \text{mol NaOH}}{L} \times \frac{1\ \text{mol } H_2SO_4}{2\ \text{mol NaOH}} \times \frac{1\ \text{mol } SO_2}{\text{mol } H_2SO_4} \times \frac{32.07\ \text{g S}}{\text{mol } SO_2}$$

$$= 4.560 \times 10^{-2}\ \text{g S}$$

$$\text{Mass \% S} = \frac{0.04560\ \text{g}}{1.325\ \text{g}} \times 100 = 3.442\%$$

Challenge Problems

97.   a.   Let x = mass of Mg, so $10.00 - x$ = mass of Zn. $Ag^+(aq) + Cl^-(aq) \rightarrow AgCl(s)$.

From the given balanced equations, there is a 2 : 1 mole ratio between mol Mg and mol Cl^-. The same is true for Zn. Because mol Ag^+ = mol Cl^- present, one can setup an equation relating mol Cl^- present to mol Ag^+ added.

$$x\ \text{g Mg} \times \frac{1\ \text{mol Mg}}{24.31\ \text{g Mg}} \times \frac{2\ \text{mol } Cl^-}{\text{mol Mg}} + (10.00 - x)\ \text{g Zn} \times \frac{1\ \text{mol Zn}}{65.38\ \text{g Zn}} \times \frac{2\ \text{mol } Cl^-}{\text{mol Zn}}$$

$$= 0.156\ L \times \frac{3.00\ \text{mol } Ag^+}{L} \times \frac{1\ \text{mol } Cl^-}{\text{mol } Ag^+} = 0.468\ \text{mol } Cl^-$$

$$\frac{2x}{24.31} + \frac{2(10.00 - x)}{65.38} = 0.468,\ \ 24.31 \times 65.38 \left(\frac{2x}{24.31} + \frac{20.00 - 2x}{65.38} = 0.468 \right)$$

$(130.8)x + 486.2 - (48.62)x = 743.8$ (carrying 1 extra significant figure)

$(82.2)x = 257.6,\ \ x = 3.13\ \text{g Mg};\ \ \ \% \text{Mg} = \dfrac{3.13\ \text{g Mg}}{10.00\ \text{g mixture}} \times 100 = 31.3\%\ \text{Mg}$

b. $0.156\ L \times \dfrac{3.00\ \text{mol } Ag^+}{L} \times \dfrac{1\ \text{mol } Cl^-}{\text{mol } Ag^+} = 0.468\ \text{mol } Cl^- = 0.468\ \text{mol HCl added}$

$$M_{HCl} = \frac{0.468\ \text{mol}}{0.0780\ L} = 6.00\ M\ \text{HCl}$$

99. $Zn(s) + 2\ AgNO_2(aq) \rightarrow 2\ Ag(s) + Zn(NO_2)_2(aq)$

Let x = mass of Ag and y = mass of Zn after the reaction has stopped. Then $x + y = 29.0$ g.
Because the moles of Ag produced will equal two times the moles of Zn reacted:

$$(19.0 - y)\ \text{g Zn} \times \frac{1\ \text{mol Zn}}{65.38\ \text{g Zn}} \times \frac{2\ \text{mol Ag}}{1\ \text{mol Zn}} = x\ \text{g Ag} \times \frac{1\ \text{mol Ag}}{107.9\ \text{g Ag}}$$

Simplifying:

$$3.059 \times 10^{-2}(19.0 - y) = (9.268 \times 10^{-3})x$$

Substituting $x = 29.0 - y$ into the equation gives:

$$3.059 \times 10^{-2}(19.0 - y) = 9.268 \times 10^{-3}(29.0 - y)$$

Solving:

$$0.581 - (3.059 \times 10^{-2})y = 0.269 - (9.268 \times 10^{-3})y, \ (2.132 \times 10^{-2})y = 0.312, \ y = 14.6\ \text{g Zn}$$

14.6 g Zn are present, and 29.0 − 14.6 = 14.4 g Ag are also present after the reaction is
stopped.

101.   Molar masses: KCl, 39.10 + 35.45 = 74.55 g/mol; KBr, 39.10 + 79.90 = 119.00 g/mol,
AgCl, 107.9 + 35.45 = 143.4 g/mol; AgBr, 107.9 + 79.90 = 187.8 g/mol

Let x = number of moles of KCl in mixture and y = number of moles of KBr in mixture.
$Ag^+ + Cl^- \rightarrow AgCl$ and $Ag^+ + Br^- \rightarrow AgBr$; so, x = moles AgCl and y = moles AgBr.

Setting up two equations from the given information:

$$0.1024\ \text{g} = (74.55)x + (119.0)y \ \text{ and } \ 0.1889\ \text{g} = (143.4)x + (187.8)y$$

Multiply the first equation by $\dfrac{187.8}{119.0}$, and then subtract from the second.

$$\begin{array}{ll} 0.1889 = & (143.4)x + (187.8)y \\ \underline{-0.1616 = -(117.7)x - (187.8)y} \\ 0.0273 = & (25.7)x, \qquad\qquad x = 1.06 \times 10^{-3}\ \text{mol KCl} \end{array}$$

$$1.06 \times 10^{-3}\ \text{mol KCl} \times \frac{74.55\ \text{g KCl}}{\text{mol KCl}} = 0.0790\ \text{g KCl}$$

$$\text{Mass \% KCl} = \frac{0.0790\ \text{g}}{0.1024\ \text{g}} \times 100 = 77.1\%, \ \% \text{ KBr} = 100.0 - 77.1 = 22.9\%$$

103.   a. $C_{12}H_{10-n}Cl_n + n\,Ag^+ \to n\,AgCl$; molar mass of AgCl = 143.4 g/mol

Molar mass of PCB = $12(12.01) + (10 - n)(1.008) + n(35.45) = 154.20 + (34.44)n$

Because n mol AgCl are produced for every 1 mol PCB reacted, $n(143.4)$ g of AgCl will be produced for every $[154.20 + (34.44)n]$ g of PCB reacted.

$$\frac{\text{Mass of AgCl}}{\text{Mass of PCB}} = \frac{(143.4)n}{154.20 + (34.44)n} \text{ or } \text{mass}_{AgCl}[154.20 + (34.44)n] = \text{mass}_{PCB}(143.4)n$$

   b. $0.4971[154.20 + (34.44)n] = 0.1947(143.4)n,\ \ 76.65 + (17.12)n = (27.92)n$

$76.65 = (10.80)n,\ \ n = 7.097$

105.   a.   Flow rate = 5.00×10^4 L/s + 3.50×10^3 L/s = 5.35×10^4 L/s

   b. $C_{HCl} = \dfrac{3.50 \times 10^3(65.0)}{5.35 \times 10^4} = 4.25$ ppm HCl

   c.   1 ppm = 1 mg/kg H_2O = 1 mg/L   (assuming density = 1.00 g/mL)

$$8.00\ \text{h} \times \frac{60\ \text{min}}{\text{h}} \times \frac{60\ \text{s}}{\text{min}} \times \frac{1.80 \times 10^4\ \text{L}}{\text{s}} \times \frac{4.25\ \text{mg HCl}}{\text{L}} \times \frac{1\ \text{g}}{1000\ \text{mg}} = 2.20 \times 10^6\ \text{g HCl}$$

$$2.20 \times 10^6\ \text{g HCl} \ \times \frac{1\ \text{mol HCl}}{36.46\ \text{g HCl}} \times \frac{1\ \text{mol CaO}}{2\ \text{mol HCl}} \times \frac{56.08\ \text{g Ca}}{\text{mol CaO}} = 1.69 \times 10^6\ \text{g CaO}$$

   d.   The concentration of Ca^{2+} going into the second plant was:

$$\frac{5.00 \times 10^4(10.2)}{5.35 \times 10^4} = 9.53\ \text{ppm}$$

The second plant used: 1.80×10^4 L/s $\times$ $(8.00 \times 60 \times 60)$ s = 5.18×10^8 L of water.

$$1.69 \times 10^6\ \text{g CaO}\ \times \frac{40.08\ \text{g Ca}^{2+}}{56.08\ \text{g CaO}} = 1.21 \times 10^6\ \text{g Ca}^{2+} \text{ was added to this water.}$$

$$C_{Ca^{2+}}\ \text{(plant water)} = 9.53 + \frac{1.21 \times 10^9\ \text{mg}}{5.18 \times 10^8\ \text{L}} = 9.53 + 2.34 = 11.87\ \text{ppm}$$

Because 90.0% of this water is returned, $(1.80 \times 10^4) \times 0.900 = 1.62 \times 10^4$ L/s of water with 11.87 ppm Ca^{2+} is mixed with $(5.35 - 1.80) \times 10^4 = 3.55 \times 10^4$ L/s of water containing 9.53 ppm Ca^{2+}.

$$C_{Ca^{2+}}\ \text{(final)} = \frac{(1.62 \times 10^4\ \text{L/s})(11.87\ \text{ppm}) + (3.55 \times 10^4\ \text{L/s})(9.53\ \text{ppm})}{1.62 \times 10^4\ \text{L/s} + 3.55 \times 10^4\ \text{L/s}} = 10.3\ \text{ppm}$$

107.   a. $YBa_2Cu_3O_{6.5}$:

$$+3 + 2(+2) + 3x + 6.5(-2) = 0$$

$$7 + 3x - 13 = 0, \quad 3x = 6, \quad x = +2 \qquad \text{Only } Cu^{2+} \text{ present.}$$

$YBa_2Cu_3O_7$:

$$+3 + 2(+2) + 3x + 7(-2) = 0, \quad x = +2\ 1/3 \text{ or } 2.33$$

This corresponds to two Cu^{2+} and one Cu^{3+} present.

$YBa_2Cu_3O_8$:

$$+3 + 2(+2) + 3x + 8(-2) = 0, \quad x = +3; \quad \text{Only } Cu^{3+} \text{ present.}$$

b.

$$(e^- + Cu^{2+} + I^- \rightarrow CuI) \times 2 \qquad\qquad 2\,e^- + Cu^{3+} + I^- \rightarrow CuI$$
$$3\,I^- \rightarrow I_3^- + 2\,e^- \qquad\qquad\qquad\qquad 3\,I^- \rightarrow I_3^- + 2\,e^-$$

$$\overline{2\,Cu^{2+}(aq) + 5\,I^-(aq) \rightarrow 2\,CuI(s) + I_3^-(aq)} \qquad \overline{Cu^{3+}(aq) + 4\,I^-(aq) \rightarrow CuI(s) + I_3^-(aq)}$$

$$2\,S_2O_3^{2-} \rightarrow S_4O_6^{2-} + 2\,e^-$$
$$2\,e^- + I_3^- \rightarrow 3\,I^-$$

$$\overline{2\,S_2O_3^{2-}(aq) + I_3^-(aq) \rightarrow 3\,I^-(aq) + S_4O_6^{2-}(aq)}$$

c.   Step II data: All Cu is converted to Cu^{2+}. *Note*: Superconductor abbreviated as "123."

$$22.57 \times 10^{-3}\ L \times \frac{0.1000\ \text{mol}\ S_2O_3^{2-}}{L} \times \frac{1\ \text{mol}\ I_3^-}{2\ \text{mol}\ S_2O_3^{2-}} \times \frac{2\ \text{mol}\ Cu^{2+}}{\text{mol}\ I_3^-}$$
$$= 2.257 \times 10^{-3}\ \text{mol}\ Cu^{2+}$$

$$2.257 \times 10^{-3}\ \text{mol}\ Cu \times \frac{1\ \text{mol "123"}}{3\ \text{mol}\ Cu} = 7.523 \times 10^{-4}\ \text{mol "123"}$$

$$\text{Molar mass of } YBa_2Cu_3O_x = \frac{0.5402\ g}{7.523 \times 10^{-4}\ \text{mol}} = 670.2\ \text{g/mol}$$

$$670.2 = 88.91 + 2(137.3) + 3(63.55) + x(16.00), \quad 670.2 = 554.2 + x(16.00)$$

$x = 7.250$; formula is $YBa_2Cu_3O_{7.25}$.

Check with Step I data: Both Cu^{2+} and Cu^{3+} present.

$$37.77 \times 10^{-3}\ L \times \frac{0.1000\ \text{mol}\ S_2O_3^{2-}}{L} \times \frac{1\ \text{mol}\ I_3^-}{2\ \text{mol}\ S_2O_3^{2-}} = 1.889 \times 10^{-3}\ \text{mol}\ I_3^-$$

We get 1 mol I_3^- per mol Cu^{3+} and 1 mol I_3^- per 2 mol Cu^{2+}. Let $n_{Cu^{3+}} = \text{mol}\ Cu^{3+}$ and $n_{Cu^{2+}} = \text{mol}\ Cu^{2+}$, then:

$$n_{Cu^{3+}} + \frac{n_{Cu^{2+}}}{2} = 1.889 \times 10^{-3} \text{ mol}$$

In addition: $\dfrac{0.5625 \text{ g}}{670.2 \text{ g/mol}} = 8.393 \times 10^{-4}$ mol "123"; this amount of "123" contains:

$$3(8.393 \times 10^{-4}) = 2.518 \times 10^{-3} \text{ mol Cu total} = n_{Cu^{3+}} + n_{Cu^{2+}}$$

Solving by simultaneous equations:

$$n_{Cu^{3+}} + n_{Cu^{2+}} = 2.518 \times 10^{-3}$$

$$-n_{Cu^{3+}} - \frac{n_{Cu^{2+}}}{2} = -1.889 \times 10^{-3}$$

$$\rule{6cm}{0.4pt}$$

$$\frac{n_{Cu^{2+}}}{2} = 6.29 \times 10^{-4}$$

$n_{Cu^{2+}} = 1.26 \times 10^{-3}$ mol Cu^{2+}; $n_{Cu^{3+}} = 2.518 \times 10^{-3} - 1.26 \times 10^{-3} = 1.26 \times 10^{-3}$ mol Cu^{3+}

This sample of superconductor contains equal moles of Cu^{2+} and Cu^{3+}. Therefore, 1 mole of $YBa_2Cu_3O_x$ contains 1.50 mol Cu^{2+} and 1.50 mol Cu^{3+}. Solving for x using oxidation states:

$$+3 + 2(+2) + 1.50(+2) + 1.50(+3) + x(-2) = 0, \quad 14.50 = 2x, \quad x = 7.25$$

The two experiments give the same result, $x = 7.25$ with formula $YBa_2Cu_3O_{7.25}$.

Average oxidation state of Cu:

$$+3 + 2(+2) + 3(x) + 7.25(-2) = 0, \quad 3x = 7.50, \quad x = +2.50$$

As determined from Step I data, this superconductor sample contains equal moles of Cu^{2+} and Cu^{3+}, giving an average oxidation state of +2.50.

109.   There are three unknowns so we need three equations to solve for the unknowns. Let $x =$ mass $AgNO_3$, $y =$ mass $CuCl_2$, and $z =$ mass $FeCl_3$. Then $x + y + z = 1.0000$ g. The Cl^- in $CuCl_2$ and $FeCl_3$ will react with the excess $AgNO_3$ to form the precipitate AgCl(s). Assuming silver has an atomic mass of 107.90:

$$\text{Mass of Cl in mixture} = 1.7809 \text{ g AgCl} \times \frac{35.45 \text{ g Cl}}{143.35 \text{ g AgCl}} = 0.4404 \text{ g Cl}$$

$$\text{Mass of Cl from } CuCl_2 = y \text{ g } CuCl_2 \times \frac{2(35.45) \text{ g Cl}}{134.45 \text{ g } CuCl_2} = (0.5273)y$$

$$\text{Mass of Cl from } FeCl_3 = z \text{ g } FeCl_3 \times \frac{3(35.45) \text{ g Cl}}{162.20 \text{ g } FeCl_3} = (0.6557)z$$

The second equation is: 0.4404 g Cl $= (0.5273)y + (0.6557)z$

Similarly, let's calculate the mass of metals in each salt.

Mass of Ag in $AgNO_3 = x$ g $AgNO_3 \times \dfrac{107.9 \text{ g Ag}}{169.91 \text{ g } AgNO_3} = (0.6350)x$

For $CuCl_2$ and $FeCl_3$, we already calculated the amount of Cl in each initial amount of salt; the remainder must be the mass of metal in each salt.

Mass of Cu in $CuCl_2 = y - (0.5273)y = (0.4727)y$

Mass of Fe in $FeCl_3 = z - (0.6557)z = (0.3443)z$

The third equation is: 0.4684 g metals $= (0.6350)x + (0.4727)y + (0.3443)z$

We now have three equations with three unknowns. Solving:

$$
\begin{array}{rcccccc}
-0.6350\,(1.0000 = & x & + & y & + & z) \\
0.4684 = & (0.6350)x & + & (0.4727)y & + & (0.3443)z \\
\hline
-0.1666 = & & & -(0.1623)y & - & (0.2907)z
\end{array}
$$

$$
\dfrac{0.5273}{0.1623}\,[-0.1666 = -(0.1623)y - (0.2907)z]
$$

$$
\begin{array}{rcc}
0.4404 = & (0.5273)y & + & (0.6557)z \\
\hline
-0.1009 = & -(0.2888)z, & z = \dfrac{0.1009}{0.2888} = 0.3494 \text{ g } FeCl_3
\end{array}
$$

$0.4404 = (0.5273)y + 0.6557(0.3494)$, $y = 0.4007$ g $CuCl_2$

$x = 1.0000 - y - z = 1.0000 - 0.4007 - 0.3494 = 0.2499$ g $AgNO_3$

Mass % $AgNO_3 = \dfrac{0.2499 \text{ g}}{1.0000 \text{ g}} \times 100 = 24.99\%$ $AgNO_3$

Mass % $CuCl_2 = \dfrac{0.4007 \text{ g}}{1.0000 \text{ g}} \times 100 = 40.07\%$ $CuCl_2$; mass % $FeCl_3 = 34.94\%$

CHAPTER 15

CHEMICAL KINETICS

Reaction Rates

11. $0.0120/0.0080 = 1.5$; reactant B is used up 1.5 times faster than reactant A. This corresponds to a 3 to 2 mole ratio between B and A in the balanced equation. $0.0160/0.0080 = 2$; product C is produced twice as fast as reactant A is used up. So the coefficient for C is twice the coefficient for A. A possible balanced equation is $2A + 3B \rightarrow 4C$.

13. Using the coefficients in the balanced equation to relate the rates:

$$\frac{d[H_2]}{dt} = 3\frac{d[N_2]}{dt} \text{ and } \frac{d[NH_3]}{dt} = -2\frac{d[N_2]}{dt}$$

$$\text{So}: \frac{1}{3}\frac{d[H_2]}{dt} = -\frac{1}{2}\frac{d[NH_3]}{dt} \text{ or } \frac{d[NH_3]}{dt} = -\frac{2}{3}\frac{d[H_2]}{dt}$$

Ammonia is produced at a rate equal to 2/3 of the rate of consumption of hydrogen.

15. $\text{Rate} = k[Cl]^{1/2}[CHCl_3]$, $\frac{mol}{L\,s} = k\left(\frac{mol}{L}\right)^{1/2}\left(\frac{mol}{L}\right)$; k must have units of $L^{1/2}\,mol^{-1/2}\,s^{-1}$.

Rate Laws from Experimental Data: Initial Rates Method

17.   a.   In the first two experiments, [NO] is held constant and $[Cl_2]$ is doubled. The rate also doubled. Thus the reaction is first order with respect to Cl_2. Or mathematically: Rate = $k[NO]^x[Cl_2]^y$

$$\frac{0.36}{0.18} = \frac{k(0.10)^x(0.20)^y}{k(0.10)^x(0.10)^y} = \frac{(0.20)^y}{(0.10)^y}, \ 2.0 = 2.0^y, \ y = 1$$

We can get the dependence on NO from the second and third experiments. Here, as the NO concentration doubles (Cl_2 concentration is constant), the rate increases by a factor of four. Thus, the reaction is second order with respect to NO. Or mathematically:

$$\frac{1.45}{0.36} = \frac{k(0.20)^x(0.20)}{k(0.10)^x(0.20)} = \frac{(0.20)^x}{(0.10)^x}, \ 4.0 = 2.0^x, \ x = 2; \ \text{so, Rate} = k[NO]^2[Cl_2].$$

Try to examine experiments where only one concentration changes at a time. The more variables that change, the harder it is to determine the orders. Also, these types of problems can usually be solved by inspection. In general, we will solve using a mathematical approach, but keep in mind that you probably can solve for the orders by simple inspection of the data.

b. The rate constant k can be determined from the experiments. From experiment 1:

$$\frac{0.18 \ mol}{L \ min} = k\left(\frac{0.10 \ mol}{L}\right)^2\left(\frac{0.10 \ mol}{L}\right), \ k = 180 \ L^2 \ mol^{-2} \ min^{-1}$$

From the other experiments:

$$k = 180 \ L^2 \ mol^{-2} \ min^{-1} \ (\text{second exp.}); \ k = 180 \ L^2 \ mol^{-2} \ min^{-1} \ (\text{third exp.})$$

The average rate constant is $k_{mean} = 1.8 \times 10^2 \ L^2 \ mol^{-2} \ min^{-1}$.

19.   a. Rate $= k[NOCl]^n$; using experiments two and three:

$$\frac{2.66 \times 10^4}{6.64 \times 10^3} = \frac{k(2.0 \times 10^{16})^n}{k(1.0 \times 10^{16})^n}, \ 4.01 = 2.0^n, \ n = 2; \ \text{Rate} = k[NOCl]^2$$

b. $$\frac{5.98 \times 10^4 \ molecules}{cm^3 \ s} = k\left(\frac{3.0 \times 10^{16} \ molecules}{cm^3}\right)^2, \ k = 6.6 \times 10^{-29} \ cm^3 \ molecules^{-1} \ s^{-1}$$

The other three experiments give $(6.7, 6.6, \text{and } 6.6) \times 10^{-29} \ cm^3 \ molecules^{-1} \ s^{-1}$, respectively. The mean value for k is $6.6 \times 10^{-29} \ cm^3 \ molecules^{-1} \ s^{-1}$.

c. $$\frac{6.6 \times 10^{-29} \ cm^3}{molecules \ s} \times \frac{1 \ L}{1000 \ cm^3} \times \frac{6.022 \times 10^{23} \ molecules}{mol} = \frac{4.0 \times 10^{-8} \ L}{mol \ s}$$

21.   a. Rate $= k[ClO_2]^x[OH^-]^y$; From the first two experiments:

$$2.30 \times 10^{-1} = k(0.100)^x(0.100)^y \ \text{and} \ 5.75 \times 10^{-2} = k(0.0500)^x(0.100)^y$$

Dividing the two rate laws: $4.00 = \dfrac{(0.100)^x}{(0.0500)^x} = 2.00^x, \ x = 2$

Comparing the second and third experiments:

$$2.30 \times 10^{-1} = k(0.100)(0.100)^y \ \text{and} \ 1.15 \times 10^{-1} = k(0.100)(0.0500)^y$$

Dividing: $2.00 = \dfrac{(0.100)^y}{(0.050)^y} = 2.0^y$, $y = 1$

The rate law is: Rate = $k[ClO_2]^2[OH^-]$

2.30×10^{-1} mol L^{-1} s^{-1} = $k(0.100$ mol/L$)^2(0.100$ mol/L$)$, $k = 2.30 \times 10^2$ L^2 mol^{-2} s^{-1}

$= k_{mean}$

b.   Rate = $\dfrac{2.30 \times 10^2 \, L^2}{mol^2 \, s} \times \left(\dfrac{0.175 \, mol}{L}\right)^2 \times \dfrac{0.0844 \, mol}{L} = 0.594$ mol L^{-1} s^{-1}

23.   Rate = $k[H_2SeO_3]^x[H^+]^y[I^-]^z$; comparing the first and second experiments:

$\dfrac{3.33 \times 10^{-7}}{1.66 \times 10^{-7}} = \dfrac{k(2.0 \times 10^{-4})^x(2.0 \times 10^{-2})^y(2.0 \times 10^{-2})^z}{k(1.0 \times 10^{-4})^x(2.0 \times 10^{-2})^y(2.0 \times 10^{-2})^z}$, $2.01 = 2.0^x$, $x = 1$

Comparing the first and fourth experiments:

$\dfrac{6.66 \times 10^{-7}}{1.66 \times 10^{-7}} = \dfrac{k(1.0 \times 10^{-4})(4.0 \times 10^{-2})^y(2.0 \times 10^{-2})^z}{k(1.0 \times 10^{-4})(2.0 \times 10^{-2})^y(2.0 \times 10^{-2})^z}$, $4.01 = 2.0^y$, $y = 2$

Comparing the first and sixth experiments:

$\dfrac{13.2 \times 10^{-7}}{1.66 \times 10^{-7}} = \dfrac{k(1.0 \times 10^{-4})(2.0 \times 10^{-2})^2(4.0 \times 10^{-2})^z}{k(1.0 \times 10^{-4})(2.0 \times 10^{-2})^2(2.0 \times 10^{-2})^z}$

$7.95 = 2.0^z$, $\log(7.95) = z \log(2.0)$, $z = \dfrac{\log(7.95)}{\log(2.0)} = 2.99 \approx 3$

Rate = $k[H_2SeO_3][H^+]^2[I^-]^3$

Experiment 1:

$\dfrac{1.66 \times 10^{-7} \, mol}{L \, s} = k\left(\dfrac{1.0 \times 10^{-4} \, mol}{L}\right)\left(\dfrac{2.0 \times 10^{-2} \, mol}{L}\right)^2\left(\dfrac{2.0 \times 10^{-2} \, mol}{L}\right)^3$

$k = 5.19 \times 10^5$ L^5 mol^{-5} s^{-1} = 5.2×10^5 L^5 mol^{-5} s^{-1} = k_{mean}

25.   Rate = $k[I^-]^x[OCl^-]^y[OH^-]^z$; Comparing the first and second experiments:

$\dfrac{18.7 \times 10^{-3}}{9.4 \times 10^{-3}} = \dfrac{k(0.0026)^x(0.012)^y(0.10)^z}{k(0.0013)^x(0.012)^y(0.10)^z}$, $2.0 = 2.0^x$, $x = 1$

Comparing the first and third experiments:

$$\frac{9.4 \times 10^{-3}}{4.7 \times 10^{-3}} = \frac{k(0.0013)(0.012)^y(0.10)^z}{k(0.0013)(0.0060)^y(0.10)^z}, \ 2.0 = 2.0^y, \ y = 1$$

Comparing the first and sixth experiments:

$$\frac{4.8 \times 10^{-3}}{9.4 \times 10^{-3}} = \frac{k(0.0013)(0.012)(0.20)^z}{k(0.0013)(0.012)(0.10)^z}, \ 1/2 = 2.0^z, \ z = -1$$

Rate $= \dfrac{k[I^-][OCl^-]}{[OH^-]}$; the presence of OH^- decreases the rate of the reaction.

For the first experiment:

$$\frac{9.4 \times 10^{-3} \ mol}{L \ s} = k\frac{(0.0013 \ mol/L)(0.012 \ mol/L)}{(0.10 \ mol/L)}, \ k = 60.3 \ s^{-1} = 60. \ s^{-1}$$

For all experiments, $k_{mean} = 60. \ s^{-1}$.

Integrated Rate Laws

27.   Zero order: $t_{1/2} = \dfrac{[A]_0}{2k}$;   first order: $t_{1/2} = \dfrac{\ln 2}{k}$;   second order: $t_{1/2} = \dfrac{1}{k[A]_0}$

For a first-order reaction, if the first half-life equals 20. s, the second half-life will also be 20. s because the half-life for a first-order reaction is concentration-independent. The second half-life for a zero-order reaction will be 1/2(20.) = 10. s. This is because the half-life for a zero-order reaction has a direct relationship with concentration (as the concentration decreases by a factor of 2, the half-life decreases by a factor of 2). Because a second-order reaction has an inverse relationship between $t_{1/2}$ and $[A]_0$, the second half-life will be 40. s (twice the first half-life value).

29.   a.   Because the ln[A] versus time plot was linear, the reaction is first order in A. The slope of the ln[A] versus time plot equals $-k$. Therefore, the rate law, the integrated rate law, and the rate constant value are:

Rate $= k[A]$; $\ln[A] = -kt + \ln[A]_0$; $k = 2.97 \times 10^{-2} \ min^{-1}$

b.   The half-life expression for a first order rate law is:

$$t_{1/2} = \frac{\ln 2}{k} = \frac{0.6931}{k}, \ t_{1/2} = \frac{0.6931}{2.97 \times 10^{-2} \ min^{-1}} = 23.3 \ min$$

c. 2.50×10^{-3} M is 1/8 of the original amount of A present initially, so the reaction is 87.5% complete. When a first-order reaction is 87.5% complete (or 12.5% remains), then the reaction has gone through 3 half-lives:

$$100\% \; \underset{t_{1/2}}{\rightarrow} \; 50.0\% \; \underset{t_{1/2}}{\rightarrow} \; 25.0\% \; \underset{t_{1/2}}{\rightarrow} \; 12.5\%; \quad t = 3 \times t_{1/2} = 3 \times 23.3 \text{ min} = 69.9 \text{ min}$$

Or we can use the integrated rate law:

$$\ln\left(\frac{[A]}{[A]_0}\right) = -kt, \; \ln\left(\frac{2.50 \times 10^{-3} \, M}{2.00 \times 10^{-2} \, M}\right) = -(2.97 \times 10^{-2} \text{ min}^{-1})t$$

$$t = \frac{\ln(0.125)}{-2.97 \times 10^{-2} \text{ min}^{-1}} = 70.0 \text{ min}$$

31. The first assumption to make is that the reaction is first order. For a first order reaction, a graph of $\ln[H_2O_2]$ versus time will yield a straight line. If this plot is not linear, then the reaction is not first order, and we make another assumption.

Time (s)	[H$_2$O$_2$] (mol/L)	ln[H$_2$O$_2$]
0	1.00	0.000
120.	0.91	−0.094
300.	0.78	−0.25
600.	0.59	−0.53
1200.	0.37	−0.99
1800.	0.22	−1.51
2400.	0.13	−2.04
3000.	0.082	−2.50
3600.	0.050	−3.00

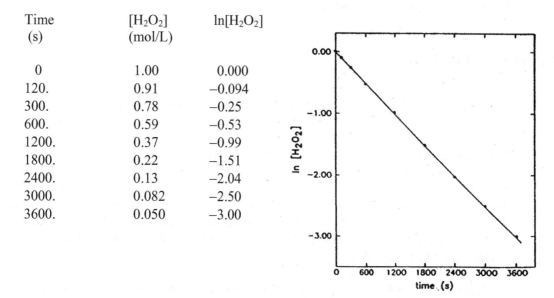

Note: We carried extra significant figures in some of the natural log values in order to reduce round-off error. For the plots, we will do this most of the time when the natural log function is involved.

The plot of $\ln[H_2O_2]$ versus time is linear. Thus the reaction is first order. The differential rate law and integrated rate law are Rate $= \dfrac{-d[H_2O_2]}{dt} = k[H_2O_2]$ and $\ln[H_2O_2] = -kt + \ln[H_2O_2]_0$.

We determine the rate constant k by determining the slope of the $\ln[H_2O_2]$ versus time plot (slope = −k). Using two points on the curve gives:

$$slope = -k = \frac{\Delta y}{\Delta x} = \frac{0 - (3.00)}{0 - 3600.} = -8.3 \times 10^{-4} \, s^{-1}, \ k = 8.3 \times 10^{-4} \, s^{-1}$$

To determine $[H_2O_2]$ at 4000. s, use the integrated rate law, where $[H_2O_2]_0 = 1.00 \, M$.

$$\ln[H_2O_2] = -kt + \ln[H_2O_2]_0 \ \text{ or } \ \ln\left(\frac{[H_2O_2]}{[H_2O_2]_0}\right) = -kt$$

$$\ln\left(\frac{[H_2O_2]}{1.00}\right) = -8.3 \times 10^{-4} \, s^{-1} \times 4000. \, s, \ \ln[H_2O_2] = -3.3, \ [H_2O_2] = e^{-3.3} = 0.037 \, M$$

33.   Assume the reaction is first order and see if the plot of $\ln[NO_2]$ versus time is linear. If this isn't linear, try the second order plot of $1/[NO_2]$ versus time. The data and plots follow.

Time (s)	$[NO_2]$ (M)	$\ln[NO_2]$	$1/[NO_2]$ (M^{-1})
0	0.500	−0.693	2.00
1.20×10^3	0.444	−0.812	2.25
3.00×10^3	0.381	−0.965	2.62
4.50×10^3	0.340	−1.079	2.94
9.00×10^3	0.250	−1.386	4.00
1.80×10^4	0.174	−1.749	5.75

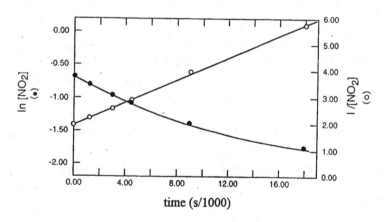

The plot of $1/[NO_2]$ versus time is linear. The reaction is second order in NO_2. The differential rate law and integrated rate law are $Rate = k[NO_2]^2$ and $\dfrac{1}{[NO_2]} = kt + \dfrac{1}{[NO_2]_0}$.

The slope of the plot $1/[NO_2]$ versus time gives the value of k. Using a couple of points on the plot:

$$slope = k = \frac{\Delta y}{\Delta x} = \frac{(5.75 - 2.00) \, M^{-1}}{(1.80 \times 10^4 - 0) \, s} = 2.08 \times 10^{-4} \, L \, mol^{-1} \, s^{-1}$$

To determine $[NO_2]$ at 2.70×10^4 s, use the integrated rate law, where $1/[NO_2]_0 = 1/0.500\ M = 2.00\ M^{-1}$.

$$\frac{1}{[NO_2]} = kt + \frac{1}{[NO_2]_0}, \quad \frac{1}{[NO_2]} = \frac{2.08 \times 10^{-4}\ L}{mol\ s} \times 2.70 \times 10^4\ s + 2.00\ M^{-1}$$

$$\frac{1}{[NO_2]} = 7.62, \quad [NO_2] = 0.131\ M$$

35.   From the data, the pressure of C_2H_5OH decreases at a constant rate of 13 torr for every 100. s. Since the rate of disappearance of C_2H_5OH is not dependent on concentration, the reaction is zero order in C_2H_5OH.

$$k = \frac{13\ torr}{100.\ s} \times \frac{1\ atm}{760\ torr} = 1.7 \times 10^{-4}\ atm/s$$

The rate law and integrated rate law are:

$$Rate = k = 1.7 \times 10^{-4}\ atm/s; \quad P_{C_2H_5OH} = -kt + 250.\ torr \left(\frac{1\ atm}{760\ torr} \right) = -kt + 0.329\ atm$$

At 900. s:

$$P_{C_2H_5OH} = -1.7 \times 10^{-4}\ atm/s \times 900.\ s + 0.329\ atm = 0.176\ atm = 0.18\ atm = 130\ torr$$

37.   a. We check for first-order dependence by graphing ln[concentration] versus time for each set of data. The rate dependence on NO is determined from the first set of data since the ozone concentration is relatively large compared to the NO concentration, so it is effectively constant.

Time (ms)	[NO] (molecules/cm³)	ln[NO]
0	6.0×10^8	20.21
100.	5.0×10^8	20.03
500.	2.4×10^8	19.30
700.	1.7×10^8	18.95
1000.	9.9×10^7	18.41

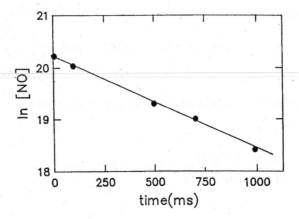

Because ln[NO] versus t is linear, the reaction is first order with respect to NO.

We follow the same procedure for ozone using the second set of data. The data and plot are:

Time (ms)	$[O_3]$ (molecules/cm^3)	$\ln[O_3]$
0	1.0×10^{10}	23.03
50.	8.4×10^9	22.85
100.	7.0×10^9	22.67
200.	4.9×10^9	22.31
300.	3.4×10^9	21.95

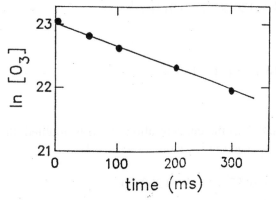

The plot of ln[O$_3$] versus t is linear. Hence the reaction is first order with respect to ozone.

b. Rate = k[NO][O$_3$] is the overall rate law.

c. For NO experiment, Rate = k′[NO] and k′ = –(slope from graph of ln[NO] versus t).

$$k' = -\text{slope} = -\frac{18.41 - 20.21}{(1000. - 0) \times 10^{-3} \text{ s}} = 1.8 \text{ s}^{-1}$$

For ozone experiment, Rate = k″[O$_3$] and k″ = –(slope from ln[O$_3$] versus t).

$$k'' = -\text{slope} = -\frac{(21.95 - 23.03)}{(300. - 0) \times 10^{-3} \text{ s}} = 3.6 \text{ s}^{-1}$$

d. From NO experiment, Rate = k[NO][O$_3$] = k′[NO] where k′ = k[O$_3$].

$k' = 1.8 \text{ s}^{-1} = k(1.0 \times 10^{14} \text{ molecules/cm}^3)$, $k = 1.8 \times 10^{-14} \text{ cm}^3 \text{ molecules}^{-1} \text{ s}^{-1}$

We can check this from the ozone data. Rate = k″[O$_3$] = k[NO][O$_3$], where k″ = k[NO].

$k'' = 3.6 \text{ s}^{-1} = k(2.0 \times 10^{14} \text{ molecules/cm}^3)$, $k = 1.8 \times 10^{-14} \text{ cm}^3 \text{ molecules}^{-1} \text{ s}^{-1}$

Both values of k agree.

39.   Because $[V]_0 >> [AV]_0$, the concentration of V is essentially constant in this experiment. We have a pseudo-first-order reaction in AV:

$$\text{Rate} = k[AV][V] = k'[AV], \text{ where } k' = k[V]_0$$

The slope of the $\ln[AV]$ versus time plot is equal to $-k'$.

$$k' = -\text{slope} = 0.32 \text{ s}^{-1}; \quad k = \frac{k'}{[V]_0} = \frac{0.32 \text{ s}^{-1}}{0.20 \text{ mol/L}} = 1.6 \text{ L mol}^{-1} \text{ s}^{-1}$$

41.   For a first-order reaction, the integrated rate law is $\ln([A]/[A]_0) = -kt$. Solving for k:

$$\ln\left(\frac{0.250 \text{ mol/L}}{1.00 \text{ mol/L}}\right) = -k \times 120. \text{ s}, \quad k = 0.0116 \text{ s}^{-1}$$

$$\ln\left(\frac{0.350 \text{ mol/L}}{2.00 \text{ mol/L}}\right) = -0.0116 \text{ s}^{-1} \times t, \quad t = 150. \text{ s}$$

43.   Comparing experiments 1 and 2, as the concentration of AB is doubled, the initial rate increases by a factor of 4. The reaction is second order in AB.

$$\text{Rate} = k[AB]^2, \quad 3.20 \times 10^{-3} \text{ mol L}^{-1} \text{s}^{-1} = k_1(0.200 \, M)^2$$

$$k = 8.00 \times 10^{-2} \text{ L mol}^{-1} \text{s}^{-1} = k_{mean}$$

For a second-order reaction:

$$t_{1/2} = \frac{1}{k[AB]_0} = \frac{1}{8.00 \times 10^{-2} \text{ L mol}^{-1} \text{s}^{-1} \times 1.00 \text{ mol/L}} = 12.5 \text{ s}$$

45.   a.   When a reaction is 75.0% complete (25.0% of reactant remains), this represents two half-lives (100% $\rightarrow$ 50% $\rightarrow$ 25%). The first-order half-life expression is $t_{1/2} = (\ln 2)/k$. Because there is no concentration dependence for a first-order half-life, 320. s = two half-lives, $t_{1/2} = 320./2 = 160.$ s. This is both the first half-life, the second half-life, etc.

       b. $t_{1/2} = \dfrac{\ln 2}{k}, \quad k = \dfrac{\ln 2}{t_{1/2}} = \dfrac{\ln 2}{160. \text{ s}} = 4.33 \times 10^{-3} \text{ s}^{-1}$

       At 90.0% complete, 10.0% of the original amount of the reactant remains, so $[A] = 0.100[A]_0$.

$$\ln\left(\frac{[A]}{[A]_0}\right) = -kt, \quad \ln\frac{0.100[A]_0}{[A]_0} = -(4.33 \times 10^{-3} \text{ s}^{-1})t, \quad t = \frac{\ln(0.100)}{-4.33 \times 10^{-3} \text{ s}^{-1}} = 532 \text{ s}$$

47.   a.   The integrated rate law for this zero-order reaction is $[HI] = -kt + [HI]_0$.

$$[HI] = -kt + [HI]_0, \quad [HI] = -\left(\frac{1.20 \times 10^{-4} \text{ mol}}{\text{L s}}\right) \times \left(25 \text{ min} \times \frac{60 \text{ s}}{\text{min}}\right) + \frac{0.250 \text{ mol}}{\text{L}}$$

$$[HI] = -0.18 \text{ mol/L} + 0.250 \text{ mol/L} = 0.07 \ M$$

b. $[HI] = 0 = -kt + [HI]_0, \quad kt = [HI]_0, \quad t = \dfrac{[HI]_0}{k}$

$$t = \frac{0.250 \text{ mol/L}}{1.20 \times 10^{-4} \text{ mol L}^{-1} \text{ s}^{-1}} = 2080 \text{ s} = 34.7 \text{ min}$$

49.   The consecutive half-life values of 24 hours, then 12 hours, show a direct relationship with concentration; as the concentration decreases, the half-life decreases. Assuming the drug reaction is either zero, first, or second order, only a zero order reaction shows this direct relationship between half-life and concentration. Therefore, assume the reaction is zero order in the drug.

$$t_{1/2} = \frac{[A]_0}{2k}, \quad k = \frac{[A]_0}{2t_{1/2}} = \frac{2.0 \times 10^{-3} \text{ mol/L}}{2(24 \text{ h})} = 4.2 \times 10^{-5} \text{ mol L}^{-1} \text{ h}^{-1}$$

51.   a.   Because $[A]_0 << [B]_0$ or $[C]_0$, the B and C concentrations remain constant at $1.00 \ M$ for this experiment. Thus, rate $= k[A]^2[B][C] = k'[A]^2$ where $k' = k[B][C]$.

For this pseudo-second-order reaction:

$$\frac{1}{[A]} = k't + \frac{1}{[A]_0}, \quad \frac{1}{3.26 \times 10^{-5} \ M} = k'(3.00 \text{ min}) + \frac{1}{1.00 \times 10^{-4} \ M}$$

$$k' = 6890 \text{ L mol}^{-1} \text{ min}^{-1} = 115 \text{ L mol}^{-1} \text{ s}^{-1}$$

$$k' = k[B][C], \quad k = \frac{k'}{[B][C]}, \quad k = \frac{115 \text{ L mol}^{-1} \text{ s}^{-1}}{(1.00 \ M)(1.00 \ M)} = 115 \text{ L}^3 \text{ mol}^{-3} \text{ s}^{-1}$$

b.   For this pseudo-second-order reaction:

$$\text{Rate} = k'[A]^2, \quad t_{1/2} = \frac{1}{k'[A]_0} = \frac{1}{115 \text{ L mol}^{-1} \text{ s}^{-1}(1.00 \times 10^{-4} \text{ mol/L})} = 87.0 \text{ s}$$

c. $\dfrac{1}{[A]} = k't + \dfrac{1}{[A]_0} = 115 \text{ L mol}^{-1} \text{ s}^{-1} \times 600. \text{ s} + \dfrac{1}{1.00 \times 10^{-4} \text{ mol/L}} = 7.90 \times 10^4 \text{ L/mol}$

$$[A] = 1/7.90 \times 10^4 \text{ L/mol} = 1.27 \times 10^{-5} \text{ mol/L}$$

From the stoichiometry in the balanced reaction, 1 mol of B reacts with every 3 mol of A.

Amount A reacted = $1.00 \times 10^{-4} M - 1.27 \times 10^{-5} M = 8.7 \times 10^{-5} M$

Amount B reacted = 8.7×10^{-5} mol/L $\times \dfrac{1 \text{ mol B}}{3 \text{ mol A}} = 2.9 \times 10^{-5} M$

$[B] = 1.00 \ M - 2.9 \times 10^{-5} \ M = 1.00 \ M$

As we mentioned in part a, the concentration of B (and C) remain constant because the A concentration is so small compared to the B (or C) concentration.

Reaction Mechanisms

53.   In a unimolecular reaction, a single reactant molecule decomposes to products. In a bimolecular reaction, two molecules collide to give products. The probability of the simultaneous collision of three molecules with enough energy and the proper orientation is very small, making termolecular steps very unlikely.

55.   For elementary reactions, the rate law can be written using the coefficients in the balanced equation to determine the orders.

   a.   Rate = $k[CH_3NC]$ b.   Rate = $k[O_3][NO]$

   c.   Rate = $k[O_3]$ d.   Rate = $k[O_3][O]$

   e.   Rate = $k\left[{}^{14}_{6}C\right]$ or Rate = kN, where N = the number of ${}^{14}_{6}C$ atoms (convention)

57.   A mechanism consists of a series of elementary reactions in which the rate law for each step can be determined using the coefficients in the balanced equations. For a plausible mechanism, the rate law derived from a mechanism must agree with the rate law determined from experiment. To derive the rate law from the mechanism, the rate of the reaction is assumed to equal the rate of the slowest step in the mechanism.

Because step 1 is the rate determining step, the rate law for this mechanism is Rate = $k[C_4H_9Br]$. To get the overall reaction, we sum all the individual steps of the mechanism. Summing all steps gives:

$$C_4H_9Br \rightarrow C_4H_9{}^+ + Br^-$$
$$C_4H_9{}^+ + H_2O \rightarrow C_4H_9OH_2{}^+$$
$$C_4H_9OH_2{}^+ + H_2O \rightarrow C_4H_9OH + H_3O^+$$
$$\overline{}$$
$$C_4H_9Br + 2 H_2O \rightarrow C_4H_9OH + Br^- + H_3O^+$$

Intermediates in a mechanism are species that are neither reactants nor products but that are formed and consumed during the reaction sequence in the mechanism. The intermediates for this mechanism are $C_4H_9{}^+$ and $C_4H_9OH_2{}^+$.

59.   Let's determine the rate law for each mechanism. If the rate law derived from the mechanism is the same as the experimental rate law, then the mechanism is possible (assuming the sum of all the steps in the mechanism gives the overall balanced equation). When deriving rate laws from a mechanism, we must substitute for all intermediate concentrations.

   a.   Rate = $k_1[NO][O_2]$;   <u>not possible</u>

   b.   Rate = $k_2[NO_3][NO]$ and $k_1[NO][O_2] = k_{-1}[NO_3]$ or $[NO_3] = \dfrac{k_1}{k_{-1}}[NO][O_2]$

        Rate = $\dfrac{k_2 k_1}{k_{-1}}[NO]^2[O_2]$;   <u>possible</u>

   c.   Rate = $k_1[NO]^2$;   <u>not possible</u>   d.   Rate = $k_2[N_2O_2]$ and $[N_2O_2] = \dfrac{k_1}{k_{-1}}[NO]^2$

                                                            Rate = $\dfrac{k_2 k_1}{k_{-1}}[NO]^2$; <u>not possible</u>

   Only the mechanism in b is consistent, so only mechanism b is a possible mechanism for this reaction.

61.   Rate = $k_3[Br^-][H_2BrO_3^+]$; we must substitute for the intermediate concentration. Because steps 1 and 2 are fast-equilibrium steps, rate forward reaction = rate reverse reaction.

   $k_2[HBrO_3][H^+] = k_{-2}[H_2BrO_3^+]$; $k_1[BrO_3^-][H^+] = k_{-1}[HBrO_3]$

   $[HBrO_3] = \dfrac{k_1}{k_{-1}}[BrO_3^-][H^+]$; $[H_2BrO_3^+] = \dfrac{k_2}{k_{-2}}[HBrO_3][H^+] = \dfrac{k_2 k_1}{k_{-2}k_{-1}}[BrO_3^-][H^+]^2$

   Rate = $\dfrac{k_3 k_2 k_1}{k_{-2}k_{-1}}[Br^-][BrO_3^-][H^+]^2 = k[Br^-][BrO_3^-][H^+]^2$

63.   Rate = $k_2[I^-][HOCl]$; from the fast-equilibrium first step:

        $k_1[OCl^-] = k_{-1}[HOCl][OH^-]$, $[HOCl] = \dfrac{k_1[OCl^-]}{k_{-1}[OH^-]}$; substituting into the rate equation:

        Rate = $\dfrac{k_2 k_1[I^-][OCl^-]}{k_{-1}[OH^-]} = \dfrac{k[I^-][OCl^-]}{[OH^-]}$

65.   a. $MoCl_5^-$

   b.   Rate = $\dfrac{d[NO_2^-]}{dt} = k_2[NO_3^-][MoCl_5^-]$ (Only the last step contains NO_2^-.)

        We use the steady-state assumption to substitute for the intermediate concentration in the rate law.   The steady-state approximation assumes that the concentration of an intermediate remains constant; i.e., d[intermediate]/dt = 0. To apply the steady-state assumption, we write rate laws for all steps where the intermediate is produced and equate the sum of these rate laws to the sum of the rate laws where the intermediate is consumed. Applying the steady-state approximation to $MoCl_5^-$:

$$\frac{d[MoCl_5^-]}{dt} = 0, \text{ so } k_1[MoCl_6^{2-}] = k_{-1}[MoCl_5^-][Cl^-] + k_2[NO_3^-][MoCl_5^-]$$

$$[MoCl_5^-] = \frac{k_1[MoCl_6^{2-}]}{k_{-1}[Cl^-] + k_2[NO_3^-]}; \text{ Rate} = \frac{d[NO_2^-]}{dt} = \frac{k_1 k_2[NO_3^-][MoCl_6^{2-}]}{k_{-1}[Cl^-] + k_2[NO_3^-]}$$

67. a. Rate $= \dfrac{d[E]}{dt} = k_2[B^*]$; assume $\dfrac{d[B^*]}{dt} = 0$, then $k_1[B]^2 = k_{-1}[B][B^*] + k_2[B^*]$.

$[B^*] = \dfrac{k_1[B]^2}{k_{-1}[B] + k_2}$; the rate law is: Rate $= \dfrac{d[E]}{dt} = \dfrac{k_1 k_2[B]^2}{k_{-1}[B] + k_2}$

b. When $k_2 \ll k_{-1}[B]$, then Rate $= \dfrac{d[E]}{dt} = \dfrac{k_1 k_2[B]^2}{k_{-1}[B]} = \dfrac{k_1 k_2}{k_{-1}}[B]$.

The reaction is first order when the rate of the second step is very slow (when k_2 is very small).

c. Collisions between B molecules only transfer energy from one B to another. This occurs at a much faster rate than the decomposition of an energetic B molecule (B*).

Temperature Dependence of Rate Constants and the Collision Model

69. Two reasons are:

1) The collision must involve enough energy to produce the reaction; i.e., the collision energy must be equal to or exceed the activation energy.

2) The relative orientation of the reactants when they collide must allow formation of any new bonds necessary to produce products.

71. a. $T_2 > T_1$; as temperature increases, the distribution of collision energies shifts to the right. That is, as temperature increases, there are fewer collision energies with small energies and more collisions with large energies.

b. As temperature increases, more of the collisions have the required activation energy necessary to convert reactants into products. Hence, the rate of the reaction increases with increasing temperature.

73. $k = A \exp(-E_a/RT)$ or $\ln k = \dfrac{-E_a}{RT} + \ln A$ (the Arrhenius equation)

For two conditions: $\ln\left(\dfrac{k_2}{k_1}\right) = \dfrac{E_a}{R}\left(\dfrac{1}{T_1} - \dfrac{1}{T_2}\right)$ (Assuming A is temperature independent.)

Let $k_1 = 3.52 \times 10^{-7}$ L mol^{-1}s^{-1}, $T_1 = 555$ K; $k_2 = ?$, $T_2 = 645$ K; $E_a = 186 \times 10^3$ J/mol

$$\ln\left(\dfrac{k_2}{3.52 \times 10^{-7}}\right) = \dfrac{1.86 \times 10^5 \text{ J/mol}}{8.3145 \text{ J K}^{-1} \text{ mol}^{-1}}\left(\dfrac{1}{555 \text{ K}} - \dfrac{1}{645 \text{ K}}\right) = 5.6$$

$$\dfrac{k_2}{3.52 \times 10^{-7}} = e^{5.6} = 270, \quad k_2 = 270(3.52 \times 10^{-7}) = 9.5 \times 10^{-5} \text{ L mol}^{-1} \text{ s}^{-1}$$

75. $\ln\left(\dfrac{k_2}{k_1}\right) = \dfrac{E_a}{R}\left(\dfrac{1}{T_1} - \dfrac{1}{T_2}\right);$ $\dfrac{k_2}{k_1} = 7.00$, $T_1 = 295$ K, $E_a = 54.0 \times 10^3$ J/mol

$$\ln(7.00) = \dfrac{54.0 \times 10^3 \text{ J/mol}}{8.3145 \text{ J K}^{-1} \text{ mol}^{-1}}\left(\dfrac{1}{295 \text{ K}} - \dfrac{1}{T_2}\right), \quad \dfrac{1}{295 \text{ K}} - \dfrac{1}{T_2} = 3.00 \times 10^{-4}$$

$$\dfrac{1}{T_2} = 3.09 \times 10^{-3}, \quad T_2 = 324 \text{ K} = 51°C$$

77.   From the Arrhenius equation in logarithmic form ($\ln k = -E_a/RT + \ln A$), a graph of $\ln k$ versus. $1/T$ should yield a straight line with a slope equal to $-E_a/R$ and a y intercept equal to $\ln A$.

a.   Slope $= -E_a/R$, $E_a = 1.10 \times 10^4$ K $\times \dfrac{8.3145 \text{ J}}{\text{K mol}} = 9.15 \times 10^4$ J/mol $= 91.5$ kJ/mol

b.   The units for A are the same as the units for k (s^{-1}).

y intercept $= \ln A$, $A = e^{33.5} = 3.54 \times 10^{14}$ s^{-1}

c. $\ln k = -E_a/RT + \ln A$ or $k = A \exp(-E_a/RT)$

$$k = 3.54 \times 10^{14} \text{ s}^{-1} \times \exp\left(\dfrac{-9.15 \times 10^{-4} \text{ J/mol}}{8.3145 \text{ J K}^{-1} \text{ mol}^{-1} \times 298 \text{ K}}\right) = 3.24 \times 10^{-2} \text{ s}^{-1}$$

79.   The Arrhenius equation is $k = A\exp(-E_a/RT)$ or, in logarithmic form, $\ln k = -E_a/RT + \ln A$. Hence a graph of $\ln k$ versus $1/T$ should yield a straight line with a slope equal to $-E_a/R$ since the logarithmic form of the Arrhenius equation is in the form of a straight-line equation, $y = mx + b$. *Note:* We carried one extra significant figure in the following $\ln k$ values in order to reduce round-off error.

T (K)	1/T (K^{-1})	k (L mol^{-1} s^{-1})	ln k
195	5.13×10^{-3}	1.08×10^9	20.80
230.	4.35×10^{-3}	2.95×10^9	21.81
260.	3.85×10^{-3}	5.42×10^9	22.41
298	3.36×10^{-3}	12.0×10^9	23.21
369	2.71×10^{-3}	35.5×10^9	24.29

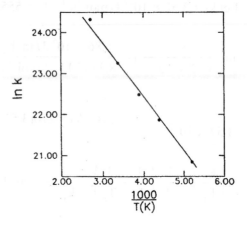

Using a couple of points on the plot:

$$\text{slope} = \frac{20.95 - 23.65}{5.00 \times 10^{-3} - 3.00 \times 10^{-3}} = \frac{-2.70}{2.00 \times 10^{-3}} = -1.35 \times 10^3 \text{ K} = \frac{-E_a}{R}$$

$E_a = 1.35 \times 10^3 \text{ K} \times 8.3145 \text{ J K}^{-1} \text{ mol}^{-1} = 1.12 \times 10^4 \text{ J/mol} = 11.2 \text{ kJ/mol}$

From the best straight line (by calculator): slope $= -1.43 \times 10^3$ K and $E_a = 11.9$ kJ/mol

81.   In the following reaction profiles R = reactants, P = products, E$_a$ = activation energy, ΔE = overall energy change for the reaction, and RC = reaction coordinate, which is the same as reaction progress.

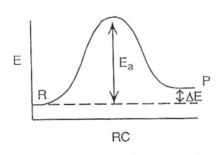

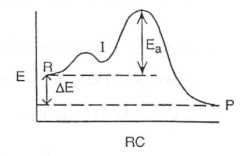

The second reaction profile represents a two-step reaction since an intermediate plateau appears between the reactants and the products. This plateau (see I in plot) represents the energy of the intermediate. The general reaction mechanism for this reaction is:

$$\begin{array}{c} R \rightarrow I \\ \underline{I \rightarrow P} \\ R \rightarrow P \end{array}$$

In a mechanism, the rate of the slowest step determines the rate of the reaction. The activation energy for the slowest step will be the largest energy barrier that the reaction must overcome. Since the second hump in the diagram is at the highest energy, the second step has the largest activation energy and will be the rate determining step (the slow step).

83.

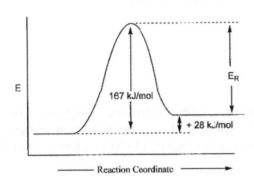

The activation energy for the reverse reaction is E_R in the diagram.

$E_R = 167 - 28 = 139$ kJ/mol

Catalysis

85.   a.   The blue plot is the catalyzed pathway. The catalyzed pathway has the lower activation. This is why the catalyzed pathway is faster.

b. ΔE_1 represents the activation energy for the uncatalyzed pathway.

c. ΔE_2 represents the energy difference between the reactants and products. Note that ΔE_2 is the same for both the catalyzed and the uncatalyzed pathways. It is the activation energy that is different for a catalyzed pathway versus an uncatalyzed pathway.

d.   Because the products have a higher total energy as compared to reactants, this is an endothermic reaction.

87.   a.   W because it has a lower activation energy than the Os catalyst.

b. $k_w = A_w \exp[-E_a(W)/RT]$; $k_{uncat} = A_{uncat} \exp[-E_a(uncat)/RT]$; assume $A_w = A_{uncat}$.

$$\frac{k_w}{k_{uncat}} = \exp\left(\frac{-E_a(W)}{RT} + \frac{E_a(uncat)}{RT}\right)$$

$$\frac{k_w}{k_{uncat}} = \exp\left(\frac{-163{,}000\ J/mol + 335{,}000\ J/mol}{8.3145\ J\ K^{-1}\ mol^{-1} \times 298\ K}\right) = 1.41 \times 10^{30}$$

The W-catalyzed reaction is approximately 10^{30} times faster than the uncatalyzed reaction.

c. Because $[H_2]$ is in the denominator of the rate law, the presence of H_2 decreases the rate of the reaction. For the decomposition to occur, NH_3 molecules must be adsorbed on the surface of the catalyst. If H_2 is also adsorbed on the catalyst surface, then there are fewer sites for NH_3 molecules to be adsorbed, and the rate decreases.

89.   The mechanism for the chlorine catalyzed destruction of ozone is:

$$O_3 + Cl \rightarrow O_2 + ClO \quad \text{(slow)}$$
$$ClO + O \rightarrow O_2 + Cl \quad \text{(fast)}$$

$$\overline{}$$

$$O_3 + O \rightarrow 2\, O_2$$

Because the chlorine atom-catalyzed reaction has a lower activation energy, the Cl-catalyzed rate is faster. Hence Cl is a more effective catalyst. Using the activation energy, we can estimate the efficiency that Cl atoms destroy ozone compared to NO molecules (see Exercise 15.88c).

At 25°C: $\dfrac{k_{Cl}}{k_{NO}} = \exp\left[\dfrac{-E_a(Cl)}{RT} + \dfrac{E_a(NO)}{RT}\right] = \exp\left[\dfrac{(-2100 + 11,900)\,\text{J/mol}}{(8.3145 \times 298)\,\text{J/mol}}\right] = e^{3.96} = 52$

At 25°C, the Cl catalyzed reaction is roughly 52 times faster than the NO-catalyzed reaction, assuming the frequency factor A is the same for each reaction.

91.   At high [S], the enzyme is completely saturated with substrate. Once the enzyme is completely saturated, the rate of decomposition of ES can no longer increase, and the overall rate remains constant.

93.   Rate $= \dfrac{-d[A]}{dt} = k[A]^x$

Assuming the catalyzed and uncatalyzed reaction have the same form and orders and because concentrations are assumed equal, rate $\propto 1/\Delta t$, where $\Delta t = \Delta \text{time}$.

$$\dfrac{\text{Rate}_{cat}}{\text{Rate}_{un}} = \dfrac{\Delta t_{un}}{\Delta t_{cat}} = \dfrac{2400\ \text{yr}}{\Delta t_{cat}} \quad \text{and} \quad \dfrac{\text{rate}_{cat}}{\text{rate}_{un}} = \dfrac{k_{cat}}{k_{un}}$$

$$\dfrac{\text{Rate}_{cat}}{\text{Rate}_{un}} = \dfrac{k_{cat}}{k_{un}} = \dfrac{A \exp[-E_a(cat)/RT]}{A \exp[-E_a(un)/RT]} = \exp\left[\dfrac{-E_a(cat) + E_a(un)}{RT}\right]$$

$$\dfrac{k_{cat}}{k_{un}} = \exp\left(\dfrac{-5.90 \times 10^4\ \text{J/mol} + 1.84 \times 10^5\ \text{J/mol}}{8.3145\ \text{J K}^{-1}\ \text{mol}^{-1} \times 600.\ \text{K}}\right) = 7.62 \times 10^{10}$$

$$\dfrac{\Delta t_{un}}{\Delta t_{cat}} = \dfrac{\text{rate}_{cat}}{\text{rate}_{un}} = \dfrac{k_{cat}}{k_{un}}, \quad \dfrac{2400\ \text{yr}}{\Delta t_{cat}} = 7.62 \times 10^{10}, \quad \Delta t_{cat} = 3.15 \times 10^{-8}\ \text{yr} \approx 1\ \text{s}$$

Additional Exercises

95.   The most common method to experimentally determine the differential rate law is the method of initial rates. Once the differential rate law is determined experimentally, the integrated rate law can be derived. However, sometimes it is more convenient and more accurate to collect concentration versus time data for a reactant. When this is the case, then we do "proof" plots to determine the integrated rate law. Once the integrated rate law is determined, the differential rate law can be determined. Either experimental procedure allows determination of both the integrated and the differential rate law; and which rate law is determined by experiment and which is derived is usually decided by which data are easiest and most accurately collected.

97.   Rate = $k[DNA]^x[CH_3I]^y$; comparing the second and third experiments:

$$\frac{1.28 \times 10^{-3}}{6.40 \times 10^{-4}} = \frac{k(0.200)^x(0.200)^y}{k(0.100)^x(0.200)^y}, \; 2.00 = 2.00^x, \; x = 1$$

Comparing the first and second experiments:

$$\frac{6.40 \times 10^{-4}}{3.20 \times 10^{-4}} = \frac{k(0.100)(0.200)^y}{k(0.100)(0.100)^y}, \; 2.00 = 2.00^y, \; y = 1$$

The rate law is Rate = $k[DNA][CH_3I]$.

Mechanism I is possible because the derived rate law from the mechanism (Rate = $k[DNA][CH_3I]$) agrees with the experimentally determined rate law. The derived rate law for Mechanism II will equal the rate of the slowest step. This is step 1 in the mechanism giving a derived rate law that is Rate = $k[CH_3I]$. Because this rate law does not agree with experiment, Mechanism II would not be a possible mechanism for the reaction.

99.

Heating Time	Untreated		Deacidifying		Antioxidant	
(days)	s	ln s	s	ln s	s	ln s
0.00	100.0	4.605	100.1	4.606	114.6	4.741
1.00	67.9	4.218	60.8	4.108	65.2	4.177
2.00	38.9	3.661	26.8	3.288	28.1	3.336
3.00	16.1	2.779	–	–	11.3	2.425
6.00	6.8	1.92	–	–	–	–

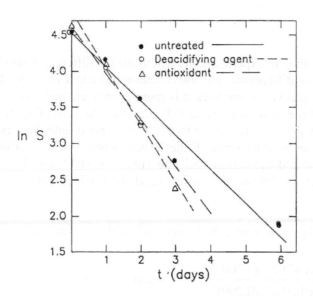

a.   We used a calculator to fit the data by least squares. The results follow.

Untreated: $\ln s = -(0.465)t + 4.55$, $k = 0.465 \text{ d}^{-1}$

Deacidifying agent: $\ln s = -(0.659)t + 4.66$, $k = 0.659 \text{ d}^{-1}$

Antioxidant: $\ln s = -(0.779)t + 4.84$, $k = 0.779 \text{ d}^{-1}$

b.   No, the silk degrades more rapidly with the additives since k increases.

c. $t_{1/2} = (\ln 2)/k$; untreated: $t_{1/2} = 1.49$ day; deacidifying agent: $t_{1/2} = 1.05$ day;

antioxidant: $t_{1/2} = 0.890$ day.

101.   Carbon cannot form the fifth bond necessary for the transition state because of the small atomic size of carbon and because carbon doesn't have low-energy d orbitals available to expand the octet.

103.   a.

t (s)	$[C_4H_6]$ (M)	$\ln[C_4H_6]$	$1/[C_4H_6]$ (M^{-1})
0	0.01000	−4.6052	1.000×10^2
1000.	0.00629	−5.069	1.59×10^2
2000.	0.00459	−5.384	2.18×10^2
3000.	0.00361	−5.624	2.77×10^2

The plot of $1/[C_4H_6]$ versus t is linear, thus the reaction is second order in butadiene. From the plot (not included), the integrated rate law is:

$$\frac{1}{[C_4H_6]} = (5.90 \times 10^{-2} \text{ L mol}^{-1} \text{ s}^{-1})t + 100.0 \, M^{-1}$$

b. When dimerization is 1.0% complete, 99.0% of C_4H_6 is left.

$$[C_4H_6] = 0.990(0.01000) = 0.00990 \ M; \quad \frac{1}{0.00990} = (5.90 \times 10^{-2})t + 100.0$$

$$t = 17.1 \ s \approx 20 \ s$$

c. 2.0% complete, $[C_4H_6] = 0.00980 \ M; \quad \frac{1}{0.00980} = (5.90 \times 10^{-2})t + 100.0,$

$$t = 34.6 \ s \approx 30 \ s$$

d. $\dfrac{1}{[C_4H_6]} = kt + \dfrac{1}{[C_4H_6]_0}$; $[C_4H_6]_0 = 0.0200 \ M$; at $t = t_{1/2}$, $[C_4H_6] = 0.0100 \ M$.

$$\frac{1}{0.0100} = (5.90 \times 10^{-2})t_{1/2} + \frac{1}{0.0200} , \quad t_{1/2} = 847 \ s = 850 \ s$$

Or: $t_{1/2} = \dfrac{1}{k[A]_0} = \dfrac{1}{(5.90 \times 10^{-2} \ L \ mol^{-1} \ s^{-1})(2.00 \times 10^{-2} \ M)} = 847 \ s$

e. From Exercise 15.32, $k = 1.4 \times 10^{-2} \ L \ mol^{-1} \ s^{-1}$ at 500. K. From this problem, $k = 5.90 \times 10^{-2} \ L \ mol^{-1} \ s^{-1}$ at 620. K.

$$\ln\left(\frac{k_2}{k_1}\right) = \frac{E_a}{R}\left(\frac{1}{T_1} - \frac{1}{T_2}\right), \quad \ln\left(\frac{5.90 \times 10^{-2}}{1.4 \times 10^{-2}}\right) = \frac{E_a}{8.3145 \ J \ K^{-1} \ mol^{-1}}\left(\frac{1}{500. \ K} - \frac{1}{620. \ K}\right)$$

$$12 = E_a(3.9 \times 10^{-4}), \ E_a = 3.1 \times 10^4 \ J/mol = 31 \ kJ/mol$$

105. $k = A \ exp(-E_a/RT); \quad \dfrac{k_{cat}}{k_{uncat}} = \dfrac{A_{cat} \ exp(-E_{a, cat}/RT)}{A_{uncat} \ exp(-E_{a, uncat}/RT)} = exp\left(\dfrac{-E_{a, cat} + E_{a, uncat}}{RT}\right)$

$$2.50 \times 10^3 = \frac{k_{cat}}{k_{uncat}} = exp\left(\frac{-E_{a, cat} + 5.00 \times 10^4 \ J/mol}{8.3145 \ J \ K^{-1} \ mol^{-1} \times 310. \ K}\right)$$

$$\ln(2.50 \times 10^3) \times 2.58 \times 10^3 \ J/mol = -E_{a, cat} + 5.00 \times 10^4 \ J/mol$$

$$E_{a, cat} = 5.00 \times 10^4 \ J/mol - 2.02 \times 10^4 \ J/mol = 2.98 \times 10^4 \ J/mol = 29.8 \ kJ/mol$$

107. a.

T (K)	1/T (K^{-1})	k (min^{-1})	ln k
298.2	3.353×10^{-3}	178	5.182
293.5	3.407×10^{-3}	126	4.836
290.5	3.442×10^{-3}	100.	4.605

A plot of ln k versus 1/T gives a straight line (plot not included). The equation for the straight line is:

$$\ln k = -6.48 \times 10^3 (1/T) + 26.9$$

For the ln k versus 1/T plot, slope $= -E_a/R = -6.48 \times 10^3$ K.

$$-6.48 \times 10^3 \text{ K} = -E_a/8.3145 \text{ J K}^{-1} \text{ mol}^{-1}, \quad E_a = 5.39 \times 10^4 \text{ J/mol} = 53.9 \text{ kJ/mol}$$

b. $\ln k = -6.48 \times 10^3 (1/288.2) + 26.9 = 4.42, \quad k = e^{4.42} = 83 \text{ min}^{-1}$

About 83 chirps per minute per insect. Note: We carried extra significant figures.

c. k gives the number of chirps per minute. The number or chirps in 15 s is k/4.

T (°C)	T (°F)	k (min^{-1})	42 + 0.80(k/4)
25.0	77.0	178	78° F
20.3	68.5	126	67°F
17.3	63.1	100.	62°F
15.0	59.0	83	59°F

The rule of thumb appears to be fairly accurate, almost ±1°F.

109. Rate $= \dfrac{d[Cl_2]}{dt} = k_2[NO_2Cl][Cl];$ Assume $\dfrac{d[Cl]}{dt} = 0$, then:

$$k_1[NO_2Cl] = k_{-1}[NO_2][Cl] + k_2[NO_2Cl][Cl], \quad [Cl] = \frac{k_1[NO_2Cl]}{k_{-1}[NO_2] + k_2[NO_2Cl]}$$

$$\text{Rate} = \frac{d[Cl_2]}{dt} = \frac{k_1 k_2 [NO_2Cl]^2}{k_{-1}[NO_2] + k_2[NO_2Cl]}$$

Challenge Problems

111. a. Rate $= k[CH_3X]^x[Y]^y$; for experiment 1, [Y] is in large excess, so its concentration will be constant. Rate $= k'[CH_3X]^x$, where $k' = k(3.0 \text{ M})^y$.

A plot (not included) of $\ln[CH_3X]$ versus t is linear ($x = 1$). The integrated rate law is:

$$\ln[CH_3X] = -(0.93)t - 3.99; \quad k' = 0.93 \text{ h}^{-1}$$

For experiment 2, [Y] is again constant, with Rate $= k''[CH_3X]^x$, where $k'' = k(4.5 \text{ M})^y$. The natural log plot is linear again with an integrated rate law:

$$\ln[CH_3X] = -(0.93)t - 5.40; \quad k'' = 0.93 \text{ h}^{-1}$$

Dividing the rate-constant values: $\dfrac{k'}{k''} = \dfrac{0.93}{0.93} = \dfrac{k(3.0)^y}{k(4.5)^y},\quad 1.0 = (0.67)^y,\ y = 0$

Reaction is first order in CH_3X and zero order in Y. The overall rate law is:

$$Rate = k[CH_3X], \text{ where } k = 0.93 \text{ h}^{-1} \text{ at } 25°C$$

b. $t_{1/2} = (\ln 2)/k = 0.6931/(7.88 \times 10^8 \text{ h}^{-1}) = 8.80 \times 10^{-10} \text{ hour}$

c. $\ln\left(\dfrac{k_2}{k_1}\right) = \dfrac{E_a}{R}\left(\dfrac{1}{T_1} - \dfrac{1}{T_2}\right), \quad \ln\left(\dfrac{7.88 \times 10^8}{0.93}\right) = \dfrac{E_a}{8.3145 \text{ J K}^{-1} \text{ mol}^{-1}}\left(\dfrac{1}{298 \text{ K}} - \dfrac{1}{358 \text{ K}}\right)$

$E_a = 3.0 \times 10^5 \text{ J/mol} = 3.0 \times 10^2 \text{ kJ/mol}$

d.   From part a, the reaction is first order in CH_3X and zero order in Y. From part c, the activation energy is close to the C-X bond energy. A plausible mechanism that explains the results in parts a and c is:

$$CH_3X \rightarrow CH_3 + X \quad \text{(slow)}$$

$$CH_3 + Y \rightarrow CH_3Y \quad \text{(fast)}$$

Note: This is a possible mechanism because the derived rate law is the same as the experimental rate law (and the sum of the steps gives the overall balanced equation).

113. $\dfrac{-d[A]}{dt} = k[A]^3, \quad \displaystyle\int_{[A]_0}^{[A]_t} \dfrac{d[A]}{[A]^3} = -\int_0^t k \, dt$

$\displaystyle\int x^n \, dx = \dfrac{x^{n+1}}{n+1}; \text{ so: } \left. -\dfrac{1}{2[A]^2}\right|_{[A]_0}^{[A]_t} = -kt, \quad -\dfrac{1}{2[A]_t^2} + \dfrac{1}{2[A]_0^2} = -kt$

For the half-life equation, $[A]_t = 1/2[A]_0$:

$$-\dfrac{1}{2\left(\dfrac{1}{2}[A]_0\right)^2} + \dfrac{1}{2[A]_0^2} = -kt_{1/2}, \quad -\dfrac{4}{2[A]_0^2} + \dfrac{1}{2[A]_0^2} = -kt_{1/2}$$

$$-\dfrac{3}{2[A]_0^2} = -kt_{1/2}, \quad t_{1/2} = \dfrac{3}{2[A]_0^2 k}$$

The first half-life is $t_{1/2} = 40.$ s and corresponds to going from $[A]_0$ to $1/2[A]_0$. The second half-life corresponds to going from $1/2 [A]_0$ to $1/4 [A]_0$.

First half-life $= \dfrac{3}{2[A]_0^2 k}$;   second half-life $= \dfrac{3}{2\left(\dfrac{1}{2}[A]_0\right)^2 k} = \dfrac{6}{[A]_0^2 k}$

$$\frac{\text{First half} - \text{life}}{\text{Second half} - \text{life}} = \frac{\dfrac{3}{2[A]_0^2 k}}{\dfrac{6}{[A]_0^2 k}} = 3/12 = 1/4$$

Because the first half-life is 40. s, the second half-life will be four times this, or 160 s.

115.   Rate = $k[A]^x[B]^y[C]^z$; during the course of experiment 1, [A] and [C] are essentially constant, and Rate = $k'[B]^y$, where $k' = k[A]_0^x[C]_0^z$.

[B] (M)	time (s)	ln[B]	1/[B] (M^{-1})
1.0×10^{-3}	0	−6.91	1.0×10^3
2.7×10^{-4}	1.0×10^5	−8.22	3.7×10^3
1.6×10^{-4}	2.0×10^5	−8.74	6.3×10^3
1.1×10^{-4}	3.0×10^5	−9.12	9.1×10^3
8.5×10^{-5}	4.0×10^5	−9.37	12×10^3
6.9×10^{-5}	5.0×10^5	−9.58	14×10^3
5.8×10^{-5}	6.0×10^5	−9.76	17×10^3

A plot of 1/[B] versus t is linear (plot not included). The reaction is second order in B, and the integrated rate equation is:

$$1/[B] = (2.7 \times 10^{-2}\ \text{L mol}^{-1}\ \text{s}^{-1})t + 1.0 \times 10^3\ M^{-1};\ k' = 2.7 \times 10^{-2}\ \text{L mol}^{-1}\ \text{s}^{-1}$$

For experiment 2, [B] and [C] are essentially constant, and Rate = $k''[A]^x$, where $k'' = k[B]_0^y[C]_0^z = k[B]_0^2[C]_0^z$.

[A] (M)	time (s)	ln[A]	1/[A] (M^{-1})
1.0×10^{-2}	0	−4.61	1.0×10^2
8.9×10^{-3}	1.0	−4.72	110
7.1×10^{-3}	3.0	−4.95	140
5.5×10^{-3}	5.0	−5.20	180
3.8×10^{-3}	8.0	−5.57	260
2.9×10^{-3}	10.0	−5.84	340
2.0×10^{-3}	13.0	−6.21	5.0×10^2

A plot of ln[A] versus t is linear. The reaction is first order in A, and the integrated rate law is:

$$\ln[A] = -(0.123\ \text{s}^{-1})t - 4.61;\ k'' = 0.123\ \text{s}^{-1}$$

Note: We will carry an extra significant figure in k''.

Experiment 3:   [A] and [B] are constant; Rate = $k'''[C]^z$

The plot of [C] versus t is linear. Thus $z = 0$.

The overall rate law is Rate = $k[A][B]^2$.

From experiment 1 (to determine k):

$$k' = 2.7 \times 10^{-2} \text{ L mol}^{-1} \text{ s}^{-1} = k[A]_0^x[C]_0^z = k[A]_o = k(2.0 \text{ } M), \text{ } k = 1.4 \times 10^{-2} \text{ L}^2 \text{ mol}^{-2} \text{ s}^{-1}$$

From experiment 2: $k'' = 0.123 \text{ s}^{-1} = k[B]_0^2, \text{ } k = \dfrac{0.123 \text{ s}^{-1}}{(3.0 \text{ } M)^2} = 1.4 \times 10^{-2} \text{ L}^2 \text{ mol}^{-2} \text{ s}^{-1}$

Thus Rate = $k[A][B]^2$ and $k = 1.4 \times 10^{-2} \text{ L}^2 \text{ mol}^{-2} \text{ s}^{-1}$.

117.   Rate = $\dfrac{-d[N_2O_5]}{dt} = k_1[M][N_2O_5] - k_{-1}[NO_3][NO_2][M]$

Assume $d[NO_3]/dt = 0$, so $k_1[N_2O_5][M] = k_{-1}[NO_3][NO_2][M] + k_2[NO_3][NO_2] +$

$$k_3[NO_3][NO].$$

$$[NO_3] = \dfrac{k_1[N_2O_5][M]}{k_{-1}[NO_2][M] + k_2[NO_2] + k_3[NO]}$$

Assume $\dfrac{d[NO]}{dt} = 0$, so $k_2[NO_3][NO_2] = k_3[NO_3][NO], \text{ } [NO] = \dfrac{k_2}{k_3} [NO_2].$

Substituting: $[NO_3] = \dfrac{k_1[N_2O_5][M]}{k_{-1}[NO_2][M] + k_2[NO_2] + \dfrac{k_2 k_3}{k_3}[NO_2]} = \dfrac{k_1[N_2O_5][M]}{[NO_2](k_{-1}[M] + 2k_2)}$

Solving for the rate law:

$$\text{Rate} = \dfrac{-d[N_2O_5]}{dt} = k_1[N_2O_5][M] - \dfrac{k_{-1}k_1[NO_2][N_2O_5][M]^2}{[NO_2](k_{-1}[M] + 2k_2)} = k_1[N_2O_5][M]$$

$$- \dfrac{k_{-1}k_1[M]^2[N_2O_5]}{k_{-1}[M] + 2k_2}$$

$$\text{Rate} = \dfrac{-d[N_2O_5]}{dt} = \left(k_1 - \dfrac{k_{-1}k_1[M]}{k_{-1}[M] + 2k_2} \right)[N_2O_5][M]; \text{ simplifying:}$$

$$\text{Rate} = \dfrac{-d[N_2O_5]}{dt} = \dfrac{2k_1k_2[M][N_2O_5]}{k_{-1}[M] + 2k_2}$$

119.   a.   Rate $= (k_1 + k_2[H^+])[I^-]^m[H_2O_2]^n$

In all the experiments the concentration of H_2O_2 is small compared to the concentrations of I^- and H^+. Therefore, the concentrations of I^- and H^+ are effectively constant, and the rate law reduces to:

Rate $= k_{obs}[H_2O_2]^n$, where $k_{obs} = (k_1 + k_2[H^+])[I^-]^m$

Because all plots of $\ln[H_2O_2]$ versus time are linear, the reaction is first order with respect to H_2O_2 ($n = 1$). The slopes of the $\ln[H_2O_2]$ versus time plots equal $-k_{obs}$, which equals $-(k_1 + k_2[H^+])[I^-]^m$. To determine the order of I^-, compare the slopes of two experiments in which I^- changes and H^+ is constant. Comparing the first two experiments:

$$\frac{\text{slope (exp. 2)}}{\text{slope (exp. 1)}} = \frac{-0.360}{-0.120} = \frac{-[k_1 + k_2(0.0400\ M)](0.3000\ M)^m}{-[k_1 + k_2(0.0400\ M)](0.1000\ M)^m}$$

$$3.00 = \left(\frac{0.3000\ M}{0.1000\ M}\right)^m = (3.000)^m,\ m = 1$$

The reaction is also first order with respect to I^-.

b.   The slope equation has two unknowns, k_1 and k_2. To solve for k_1 and k_2, we must have two equations. We need to take one of the first set of three experiments and one of the second set of three experiments to generate the two equations in k_1 and k_2.

Experiment 1: slope $= -(k_1 + k_2[H^+])[I^-]$

$-0.120\ \text{min}^{-1} = -[k_1 + k_2(0.0400\ M)](0.1000\ M)$ or $1.20 = k_1 + k_2(0.0400)$

Experiment 4:

$-0.0760\ \text{min}^{-1} = -[k_1 + k_2(0.0200\ M)](0.0750\ M)$ or $1.01 = k_1 + k_2(0.0200)$

Subtracting 4 from 1:

$$\begin{array}{l} 1.20 = k_1 + k_2(0.0400) \\ -1.01 = -k_1 - k_2(0.0200) \\ \hline 0.19 = k_2(0.0200),\ \ k_2 = 9.5\ \text{L}^2\ \text{mol}^{-2}\ \text{min}^{-1} \end{array}$$

$1.20 = k_1 + 9.5(0.0400),\ k_1 = 0.82\ \text{L mol}^{-1}\ \text{min}^{-1}$

c.   There are two pathways, one involving H^+ with rate $= k_2[H^+][I^-][H_2O_2]$ and another not involving H^+ with rate $= k_1[I^-][H_2O_2]$. The overall rate of reaction depends on which of these two pathways dominates, and this depends on the H^+ concentration.

CHAPTER 5

GASES

Pressure

21. $4.75 \text{ cm} \times \dfrac{10 \text{ mm}}{\text{cm}} = 47.5 \text{ mm Hg or } 47.5 \text{ torr}; \quad 47.5 \text{ torr} \times \dfrac{1 \text{ atm}}{760 \text{ torr}} = 6.25 \times 10^{-2} \text{ atm}$

$6.25 \times 10^{-2} \text{ atm} \times \dfrac{1.013 \times 10^5 \text{ Pa}}{\text{atm}} = 6.33 \times 10^3 \text{ Pa}$

23. Suppose we have a column of mercury $1.00 \text{ cm} \times 1.00 \text{ cm} \times 76.0 \text{ cm} = \text{V} = 76.0 \text{ cm}^3$:

$\text{mass} = 76.0 \text{ cm}^3 \times 13.59 \text{ g/cm}^3 = 1.03 \times 10^3 \text{ g} \times \dfrac{1 \text{ kg}}{1000 \text{ g}} = 1.03 \text{ kg}$

$\text{F} = \text{mg} = 1.03 \text{ kg} \times 9.81 \text{ m/s}^2 = 10.1 \text{ kg m/s}^2 = 10.1 \text{ N}$

$\dfrac{\text{Force}}{\text{Area}} = \dfrac{10.1 \text{ N}}{\text{cm}^2} \times \left(\dfrac{100 \text{ cm}}{\text{m}}\right)^2 = 1.01 \times 10^5 \dfrac{\text{N}}{\text{m}^2} \text{ or } 1.01 \times 10^5 \text{ Pa}$

(*Note*: $76.0 \text{ cm Hg} = 1 \text{ atm} = 1.01 \times 10^5 \text{ Pa.}$)

To exert the same pressure, a column of water will have to contain the same mass as the 76.0-cm column of mercury. Thus the column of water will have to be 13.59 times taller or $76.0 \text{ cm} \times 13.59 = 1.03 \times 10^3 \text{ cm} = 10.3 \text{ m}$.

25. a. $4.8 \text{ atm} \times \dfrac{760 \text{ mm Hg}}{\text{atm}} = 3.6 \times 10^3 \text{ mm Hg};$ b. $3.6 \times 10^3 \text{ mm Hg} \times \dfrac{1 \text{ torr}}{\text{mm Hg}}$

$= 3.6 \times 10^3 \text{ torr}$

c. $4.8 \text{ atm} \times \dfrac{1.013 \times 10^5 \text{ Pa}}{\text{atm}} = 4.9 \times 10^5 \text{ Pa};$ d. $4.8 \text{ atm} \times \dfrac{14.7 \text{ psi}}{\text{atm}} = 71 \text{ psi}$

Gas Laws

27.   The decrease in temperature causes the balloon to contract (V and T are directly related). Because weather balloons do expand, the effect of the decrease in pressure must be dominant.

29.   Treat each gas separately, and use the relationship $P_1V_1 = P_2V_2$ (n and T are constant).

For H_2: $P_2 = \dfrac{P_1V_1}{V_2} = 475 \text{ torr} \times \dfrac{2.00 \text{ L}}{3.00 \text{ L}} = 317 \text{ torr}$

For N_2: $P_2 = 0.200 \text{ atm} \times \dfrac{1.00 \text{ L}}{3.00 \text{ L}} = 0.0667 \text{ atm}$; $0.0667 \text{ atm} \times \dfrac{760 \text{ torr}}{\text{atm}} = 50.7 \text{ torr}$

$P_{total} = P_{H_2} + P_{N_2} = 317 + 50.7 = 368 \text{ torr}$

31. $PV = nRT$, $\dfrac{nT}{P} = \dfrac{V}{R} = \text{constant}$, $\dfrac{n_1T_1}{P_1} = \dfrac{n_2T_2}{P_2}$;   moles × molar mass = mass

$\dfrac{n_1(\text{molar mass})T_1}{P_1} = \dfrac{n_2(\text{molar mass})T_2}{P_2}$, $\dfrac{\text{mass}_1 \times T_1}{P_1} = \dfrac{\text{mass}_2 \times T_2}{P_2}$

$\text{mass}_2 = \dfrac{\text{mass}_1 \times T_1P_2}{T_2P_1} = \dfrac{1.00 \times 10^3 \text{ g} \times 291 \text{ K} \times 650.\text{ psi}}{299 \text{ K} \times 2050.\text{ psi}} = 309 \text{ g}$

33. $P = P_{CO_2} = \dfrac{n_{CO_2}RT}{V} = \dfrac{\left(22.0 \text{ g} \times \dfrac{1 \text{ mol}}{44.01 \text{ g}}\right) \times \dfrac{0.08206 \text{ L atm}}{\text{K mol}} \times 300.\text{ K}}{4.00 \text{ L}} = 3.08 \text{ atm}$

With air present, the partial pressure of CO_2 will still be 3.08 atm. The total pressure will be the sum of the partial pressures.

$P_{total} = P_{CO_2} + P_{air} = 3.08 \text{ atm} + \left(740.\text{ torr} \times \dfrac{1 \text{ atm}}{760 \text{ torr}}\right) = 3.08 + 0.974 = 4.05 \text{ atm}$

35. $n = \dfrac{PV}{RT} = \dfrac{135 \text{ atm} \times 200.0 \text{ L}}{\dfrac{0.08206 \text{ L atm}}{\text{K mol}} \times (273 + 24) \text{ K}} = 1.11 \times 10^3 \text{ mol}$

For He: $1.11 \times 10^3 \text{ mol} \times \dfrac{4.003 \text{ g He}}{\text{mol}} = 4.44 \times 10^3 \text{ g He}$

For H_2: $1.11 \times 10^3 \text{ mol} \times \dfrac{2.016 \text{ g } H_2}{\text{mol}} = 2.24 \times 10^3 \text{ g } H_2$

37. $\dfrac{PV}{nT} = R$; for a gas at two conditions:

$$\dfrac{P_1V_1}{n_1T_1} = \dfrac{P_2V_2}{n_2T_2}; \text{ because n and V are constant: } \dfrac{P_1}{T_1} = \dfrac{P_2}{T_2}$$

$$T_2 = \dfrac{P_2T_1}{P_1} = \dfrac{2500 \text{ torr} \times 294.2 \text{ K}}{758 \text{ torr}} = 970 \text{ K} = 7.0 \times 10^2 \,^\circ\text{C}$$

For two-condition problems, units for P and V just need to be the same units for both conditions, not necessarily atm and L. The unit conversions from other P or V units would cancel when applied to both conditions. However, temperature always must be converted to the Kelvin scale. The temperature conversions between other units and Kelvin will not cancel each other.

39.   As NO_2 is converted completely into N_2O_4, the moles of gas present will decrease by a factor of one-half (from the 2 : 1 mol ratio in the balanced equation). Using Avogadro's law:

$$\dfrac{V_1}{n_1} = \dfrac{V_2}{n_2}, \quad V_2 = V_1 \times \dfrac{n_2}{n_1} = 25.0 \text{ mL} \times \dfrac{1}{2} = 12.5 \text{ mL}$$

$N_2O_4(g)$ will occupy one-half the original volume of $NO_2(g)$.

41. $PV = nRT$, P is constant. $\dfrac{nT}{V} = \dfrac{P}{R} = \text{constant}, \dfrac{n_1T_1}{V_1} = \dfrac{n_2T_2}{V_2}$

$$\dfrac{n_2}{n_1} = \dfrac{T_1V_2}{T_2V_1} = \dfrac{294 \text{ K}}{335 \text{ K}} \times \dfrac{4.20 \times 10^3 \,\text{m}^3}{4.00 \times 10^3 \,\text{m}^3} = 0.921$$

43.   a.   There are 6 He atoms and 4 Ne atoms, and each flask has the same volume. The He flask has 1.5 times as many atoms of gas present as the Ne flask, so the pressure in the He flask will be 1.5 times greater (assuming a constant temperature).

        b.   Because the flask volumes are the same, your drawing should have the various atoms equally distributed between the two flasks. So each flask should have 3 He atoms and 2 Ne atoms.

        c.   After the stopcock is opened, each flask will have 5 total atoms and the pressures will be equal. If six atoms of He gave an initial pressure of $P_{\text{He, initial}}$, then 5 total atoms will have a pressure of $5/6 \times P_{\text{He, initial}}$.

             Using similar reasoning, 4 atoms of Ne gave an initial pressure of $P_{\text{Ne, initial}}$, so 5 total atoms will have a pressure of $5/4 \times P_{\text{Ne, initial}}$. Summarizing:

$$P_{\text{final}} = \dfrac{5}{6}P_{\text{He, initial}} = \dfrac{5}{4}P_{\text{Ne, initial}}$$

d. For the partial pressures, treat each gas separately. For helium, when the stopcock is opened, the six atoms of gas are now distributed over a larger volume. To solve for the final partial pressures, use Boyle's law for each gas.

For He: $P_2 = \dfrac{P_1 V_1}{V_2} = P_{\text{He, initial}} \times \dfrac{X}{2X} = \dfrac{P_{\text{He, initial}}}{2}$

The partial pressure of helium is exactly halved. The same result occurs with neon so that when the volume is doubled, the partial pressure is halved. Summarizing:

$$P_{\text{He, final}} = \dfrac{P_{\text{He, initial}}}{2}; \ P_{\text{Ne, final}} = \dfrac{P_{\text{Ne, initial}}}{2}$$

45. $P_{\text{He}} + P_{\text{H}_2\text{O}} = 1.00 \text{ atm} = 760. \text{ torr} = P_{\text{He}} + 23.8 \text{ torr}, \ P_{\text{He}} = 736 \text{ torr}$

$$n_{\text{He}} = 0.586 \text{ g} \times \dfrac{1 \text{ mol}}{4.003 \text{ g}} = 0.146 \text{ mol He}$$

$$V = \dfrac{n_{\text{He}} RT}{P_{\text{He}}} = \dfrac{0.146 \text{ mol} \times \dfrac{0.08206 \text{ L atm}}{\text{K mol}} \times 298 \text{ K}}{736 \text{ torr} \times \dfrac{1 \text{ atm}}{760 \text{ torr}}} = 3.69 \text{ L}$$

47. a. Mole fraction $CH_4 = \chi_{\text{CH}_4} = \dfrac{P_{\text{CH}_4}}{P_{\text{total}}} = \dfrac{0.175 \text{ atm}}{0.175 \text{ atm} + 0.250 \text{ atm}} = 0.412$

$\chi_{\text{O}_2} = 1.000 - 0.412 = 0.588$

b. $PV = nRT, \ n_{\text{total}} = \dfrac{P_{\text{total}} \times V}{RT} = \dfrac{0.425 \text{ atm} \times 10.5 \text{ L}}{\dfrac{0.08206 \text{ L atm}}{\text{K mol}} \times 338 \text{ K}} = 0.161 \text{ mol}$

c. $\chi_{\text{CH}_4} = \dfrac{n_{\text{CH}_4}}{n_{\text{total}}}, \ n_{\text{CH}_4} = \chi_{\text{CH}_4} \times n_{\text{total}} = 0.412 \times 0.161 \text{ mol} = 6.63 \times 10^{-2} \text{ mol CH}_4$

$6.63 \times 10^{-2} \text{ mol CH}_4 \times \dfrac{16.04 \text{ g CH}_4}{\text{mol CH}_4} = 1.06 \text{ g CH}_4$

$n_{\text{O}_2} = 0.588 \times 0.161 \text{ mol} = 9.47 \times 10^{-2} \text{ mol O}_2; \ 9.47 \times 10^{-2} \text{ mol O}_2 \times \dfrac{32.00 \text{ g O}_2}{\text{mol O}_2}$

$= 3.03 \text{ g O}_2$

49.   We can use the ideal gas law to calculate the partial pressure of each gas or to calculate the total pressure. There will be less math if we calculate the total pressure from the ideal gas law.

$$n_{O_2} = 1.5 \times 10^2 \text{ mg } O_2 \times \frac{1 \text{ g}}{1000 \text{ mg}} \times \frac{1 \text{ mol } O_2}{32.00 \text{ g } O_2} = 4.7 \times 10^{-3} \text{ mol } O_2$$

$$n_{NH_3} = 5.0 \times 10^{21} \text{ molecules } NH_3 \times \frac{1 \text{ mol } NH_3}{6.022 \times 10^{23} \text{ molecules } NH_3} = 8.3 \times 10^{-3} \text{ mol } NH_3$$

$$n_{total} = n_{N_2} + n_{O_3} + n_{NH_3} = 5.0 \times 10^{-2} + 4.7 \times 10^{-3} + 8.3 \times 10^{-3} = 6.3 \times 10^{-2} \text{ mol total}$$

$$P_{total} = \frac{n_{total} \times RT}{V} = \frac{6.3 \times 10^{-2} \text{ mol} \times \dfrac{0.08206 \text{ L atm}}{\text{K mol}} \times 273 \text{ K}}{1.0 \text{ L}} = 1.4 \text{ atm}$$

$$P_{N_2} = \chi_{N_2} \times P_{total}, \ \chi_{N_2} = \frac{n_{N_2}}{n_{total}}; \ P_{N_2} = \frac{5.0 \times 10^{-2} \text{ mol}}{6.3 \times 10^{-2} \text{ mol}} \times 1.4 \text{ atm} = 1.1 \text{ atm}$$

$$P_{O_2} = \frac{4.7 \times 10^{-3}}{6.3 \times 10^{-2}} \times 1.4 \text{ atm} = 0.10 \text{ atm}; \ P_{NH_3} = \frac{8.3 \times 10^{-3}}{6.3 \times 10^{-2}} \times 1.4 \text{ atm} = 0.18 \text{ atm}$$

Gas Density, Molar Mass, and Reaction Stoichiometry

51.   Rigid container: As temperature is increased, the gas molecules move with a faster average velocity. This results in more frequent and more forceful collisions, resulting in an increase in pressure. Density = mass/volume; the moles of gas are constant, and the volume of the container is constant, so density in this case must be temperature-independent (density is constant).

Flexible container: The flexible container is a constant-pressure container. Therefore, the final internal pressure will be unaffected by an increase in temperature. The density of the gas, however, will be affected because the container volume is affected. As T increases, there is an immediate increase in P inside the container. The container expands its volume to reduce the internal pressure back to the external pressure. We have the same mass of gas in a larger volume. Gas density will decrease in the flexible container as T increases.

53.   Out of 100.0 g of compound, there are:

$$87.4 \text{ g N} \times \frac{1 \text{ mol N}}{14.01 \text{ g N}} = 6.24 \text{ mol N}; \ \frac{6.24}{6.24} = 1.00$$

$$12.6 \text{ g H} \times \frac{1 \text{ mol H}}{1.008 \text{ g H}} = 12.5 \text{ mol H}; \ \frac{12.5}{6.24} = 2.00$$

Empirical formula is NH_2. $P \times$ (molar mass) = dRT, where d = density.

$$\text{Molar mass} = \frac{dRT}{P} = \frac{\dfrac{0.977\ g}{L} \times \dfrac{0.08206\ L\ atm}{K\ mol} \times 373\ K}{710.\ torr \times \dfrac{1\ atm}{760\ torr}} = 32.0\ g/mol$$

Empirical formula mass of $NH_2 = 16.0$ g. Therefore, the molecular formula is N_2H_4.

55.   If Be^{3+}, the formula is $Be(C_5H_7O_2)_3$ and molar mass $\approx 13.5 + 15(12) + 21(1) + 6(16)$
$= 311$ g/mol. If Be^{2+}, the formula is $Be(C_5H_7O_2)_2$ and molar mass $\approx 9.0 + 10(12) + 14(1) + 4(16) = 207$ g/mol.

Data set I (molar mass = dRT/P and d = mass/V):

$$\text{molar mass} = \frac{mass \times RT}{PV} = \frac{0.2022\ g \times \dfrac{0.08206\ L\ atm}{K\ mol} \times 286\ K}{(765.2\ torr \times \dfrac{1\ atm}{760\ torr}) \times (22.6 \times 10^{-3}\ L)} = 209\ g/mol$$

Data set II:

$$\text{molar mass} = \frac{mass \times RT}{PV} = \frac{0.2224\ g \times \dfrac{0.08206\ L\ atm}{K\ mol} \times 290.\ K}{(764.6\ torr \times \dfrac{1\ atm}{760\ torr}) \times (26.0 \times 10^{-3}\ L)} = 202\ g/mol$$

These results are close to the expected value of 207 g/mol for $Be(C_5H_7O_2)_2$. Thus we conclude from these data that beryllium is a divalent element with an atomic weight (mass) of 9.0 g/mol.

57. $$\text{Molar mass} = \frac{dRT}{P} = \frac{\dfrac{0.70902\ g}{L} \times \dfrac{0.08206\ L\ atm}{K\ mol} \times 273.2\ K}{1.000\ atm} = 15.90\ g/mol$$

15.90 g/mol is the average molar mass of the mixture of methane and helium. Assume 100.00 mol of total gas present, and let x = mol of CH_4 in the 100.00 mol mixture. This value of x is also equal to the volume percentage of CH_4 in 100.00 L of mixture because T and P are constant.

$$15.90 = \frac{x(16.04) + (100.00 - x)(4.003)}{100.00}, \quad 1590. = (16.04)x + 400.3 - (4.003)x$$

$1190. = (12.04)x, \quad x = 98.84\%\ CH_4$ by volume; % He $= 100.00 - x = 1.16\%$ He by volume

59. $n_{H_2} = \dfrac{PV}{RT} = \dfrac{1.0\,\text{atm} \times \left[4800\,\text{m}^3 \times \left(\dfrac{100\,\text{cm}}{\text{m}} \right)^3 \times \dfrac{1\,\text{L}}{1000\,\text{cm}^3} \right]}{\dfrac{0.08206\,\text{L atm}}{\text{K mol}} \times 273\,\text{K}} = 2.1 \times 10^5\,\text{mol}$

2.1×10^5 mol H_2 are in the balloon. This is 80.% of the total amount of H_2 that had to be generated:

$0.80(\text{total mol } H_2) = 2.1 \times 10^5, \quad \text{total mol } H_2 = 2.6 \times 10^5 \text{ mol } H_2$

$2.6 \times 10^5 \text{ mol } H_2 \times \dfrac{1\,\text{mol Fe}}{\text{mol } H_2} \times \dfrac{55.85\,\text{g Fe}}{\text{mol Fe}} = 1.5 \times 10^7 \text{ g Fe}$

$2.6 \times 10^5 \text{ mol } H_2 \times \dfrac{1\,\text{mol } H_2SO_4}{\text{mol } H_2} \times \dfrac{98.09\,\text{g } H_2SO_4}{\text{mol } H_2SO_4} \times \dfrac{100\,\text{g reagent}}{98\,\text{g } H_2SO_4} = 2.6 \times 10^7 \text{ g of } 98\%$ sulfuric acid

61.   Because P and T are constant, V and n are directly proportional. The balanced equation requires 2 L of H_2 to react with 1 L of CO (2 : 1 volume ratio due to 2 : 1 mole ratio in the balanced equation). The actual volume ratio present in 1 minute is 16.0 L/25.0 L = 0.640 (0.640 : 1). Because the actual volume ratio present is smaller than the required volume ratio, H_2 is the limiting reactant. The volume of CH_3OH produced at STP will be one-half the volume of H_2 reacted due to the 1 : 2 mole ratio in the balanced equation. In 1 minute, 16.0 L/2 = 8.00 L CH_3OH are produced (theoretical yield).

$n_{CH_3OH} = \dfrac{PV}{RT} = \dfrac{1.00\,\text{atm} \times 8.00\,\text{L}}{\dfrac{0.08206\,\text{L atm}}{\text{K mol}} \times 273\,\text{K}} = 0.357 \text{ mol } CH_3OH \text{ in 1 minute}$

$0.357 \text{ mol } CH_3OH \times \dfrac{32.04\,\text{g } CH_3OH}{\text{mol } CH_3OH} = 11.4 \text{ g } CH_3OH \text{ (theoretical yield per minute)}$

$\text{Percent yield} = \dfrac{\text{actual yield}}{\text{theoretical yield}} \times 100 = \dfrac{5.30\,\text{g}}{11.4\,\text{g}} \times 100 = 46.5\% \text{ yield}$

63. $150 \text{ g } (CH_3)_2N_2H_2 \times \dfrac{1\,\text{mol } (CH_3)_2N_2H_2}{60.10\,\text{g}} \times \dfrac{3\,\text{mol } N_2}{\text{mol } (CH_3)_2N_2H_2} = 7.5 \text{ mol } N_2 \text{ produced}$

$P_{N_2} = \dfrac{nRT}{V} = \dfrac{7.5\,\text{mol} \times \dfrac{0.08206\,\text{L atm}}{\text{K mol}} \times 300.\,\text{K}}{250\,\text{L}} = 0.74 \text{ atm}$

We could do a similar calculation for P_{H_2O} and P_{CO_2} and then calculate P_{total} $(= P_{N_2} + P_{H_2O} + P_{CO_2})$. Or we can recognize that 9 total moles of gaseous products form for every mole of $(CH_3)_2N_2H_2$ reacted. This is three times the moles of N_2 produced. Therefore, P_{total} will be three times larger than P_{N_2}. $P_{total} = 3 \times P_{N_2} = 3 \times 0.74 \text{ atm} = 2.2 \text{ atm}$.

65. $2\ NaClO_3(s) \rightarrow 2\ NaCl(s) + 3\ O_2(g)$

$P_{total} = P_{O_2} + P_{H_2O}$, $P_{O_2} = P_{total} - P_{H_2O} = 734\ torr - 19.8\ torr = 714\ torr$

$$n_{O_2} = \frac{P_{O_2} \times V}{RT} = \frac{\left(714\ torr \times \dfrac{1\ atm}{760\ torr}\right) \times 0.0572\ L}{\dfrac{0.08206\ L\ atm}{K\ mol} \times (273 + 22)\ K} = 2.22 \times 10^{-3}\ mol\ O_2$$

Mass $NaClO_3$ decomposed $= 2.22 \times 10^{-3}\ mol\ O_2 \times \dfrac{2\ mol\ NaClO_3}{3\ mol\ O_2} \times \dfrac{106.44\ g\ NaClO_3}{mol\ NaClO_3}$

$= 0.158\ g\ NaClO_3$

Mass % $NaClO_3 = \dfrac{0.158\ g}{0.8765\ g} \times 100 = 18.0\%$

67. $P_{total} = P_{N_2} + P_{H_2O}$, $P_{N_2} = 726\ torr - 23.8\ torr = 702\ torr\ H\ \dfrac{1\ atm}{760\ torr} = 0.924\ atm$

$$n_{N_2} = \frac{P_{N_2} \times V}{RT} = \frac{0.924\ atm \times 31.8 \times 10^{-3}\ L}{\dfrac{0.08206\ L\ atm}{K\ mol} \times 298\ K} = 1.20 \times 10^{-3}\ mol\ N_2$$

Mass of N in compound $= 1.20 \times 10^{-3}\ mol\ N_2 \times \dfrac{28.02\ g\ N_2}{mol} = 3.36 \times 10^{-2}\ g\ nitrogen$

Mass % N $= \dfrac{3.36 \times 10^{-2}\ g}{0.253\ g} \times 100 = 13.3\%\ N$

69.   For NH_3: $P_2 = \dfrac{P_1 V_1}{V_2} = 0.500\ atm \times \dfrac{2.00\ L}{3.00\ L} = 0.333\ atm$

For O_2: $P_2 = \dfrac{P_1 V_1}{V_2} = 1.50\ atm \times \dfrac{1.00\ L}{3.00\ L} = 0.500\ atm$

After the stopcock is opened, V and T will be constant, so P ∝ n. The balanced equation requires:

$$\frac{n_{O_2}}{n_{NH_3}} = \frac{P_{O_2}}{P_{NH_3}} = \frac{5}{4} = 1.25$$

The actual ratio present is: $\dfrac{P_{O_2}}{P_{NH_3}} = \dfrac{0.500\ atm}{0.333\ atm} = 1.50$

The actual ratio is larger than the required ratio, so NH_3 in the denominator is limiting. Because equal moles of NO will be produced as NH_3 reacted, the partial pressure of NO produced is 0.333 atm (the same as P_{NH_3} reacted).

71. $2 NH_3(g) \rightarrow N_2(g) + 3 H_2(g)$; as reactants are converted into products, we go from 2 moles of gaseous reactants to 4 moles of gaseous products (1 mol N_2 + 3 mol H_2). Because the moles of gas doubles as reactants are converted into products, the volume of the gases will double (at constant P and T).

$$PV = nRT, \; P = \left(\frac{RT}{V}\right)n = (constant)n; \; \text{pressure is directly related to n at constant T and V.}$$

As the reaction occurs, the moles of gas will double, so the pressure will double. Because 1 mol of N_2 is produced for every 2 mol of NH_3 reacted, $P_{N_2} = 1/2 \, P^o_{NH_3}$. Owing to the 3 to 2 mole ratio in the balanced equation, $P_{H_2} = 3/2 \, P^o_{NH_3}$.

Note: $P_{total} = P_{H_2} + P_{N_2} = 3/2 \, P^o_{NH_3} + 1/2 \, P^o_{NH_3} = 2 \, P^o_{NH_3}$. As we said earlier, the total pressure doubles as reactants are completely converted into products for this reaction.

Kinetic Molecular Theory and Real Gases

73.   The number of gas particles is constant, so at constant moles of gas, either a temperature change or a pressure change results in the smaller volume. If the temperature is constant, an increase in the external pressure would cause the volume to decrease. Gases are mostly empty space so gases are easily compressible.

If the pressure is constant, a decrease in temperature would cause the volume to decrease. As the temperature is lowered, the gas particles move with a slower average velocity and don't collide with the container walls as frequently and as forcefully. As a result, the internal pressure decreases. In order to keep the pressure constant, the volume of the container must decrease in order to increase the gas particle collisions per unit area.

75.   V, T, and P are all constant, so n must be constant. Because we have equal moles of gas in each container, gas B molecules must be heavier than gas A molecules.

a.   Both gas samples have the same number of molecules present (n is constant).

b.   Because T is constant, KE_{ave} must be the same for both gases ($KE_{ave} = 3/2 \, RT$).

c.   The lighter gas A molecules will have the faster average velocity.

d.   The heavier gas B molecules do collide more forcefully, but gas A molecules, with the faster average velocity, collide more frequently. The end result is that P is constant between the two containers.

77. $(KE)_{avg} = 3/2\ RT$; KE depends only on temperature. At each temperature CH_4 and N_2 will have the same average KE. For energy units of joules (J), use $R = 8.3145\ J\ K^{-1}\ mol^{-1}$. To determine average KE per molecule, divide by Avogadro's number, 6.022×10^{23} molecules/mol.

At 273 K: $(KE)_{avg} = \dfrac{3}{2} \times \dfrac{8.3145\ J}{K\ mol} \times 273\ K = 3.40 \times 10^3\ J/mol = 5.65 \times 10^{-21}\ J/molecule$

At 546 K: $(KE)_{avg} = \dfrac{3}{2} \times \dfrac{8.3145\ J}{K\ mol} \times 546\ K = 6.81 \times 10^3\ J/mol = 1.13 \times 10^{-20}\ J/molecule$

79.   No; the numbers calculated in Exercise 77 are the average kinetic energies at the various temperatures. At each temperature, there is a distribution of energies. Similarly, the numbers calculated in Exercise 78 are a special kind of average velocity. There is a distribution of velocities as shown in Figs. 5.15 to 5.17 of the text. Note that the major reason there is a distribution of kinetic energies is because there is a distribution of velocities for any gas sample at some temperature.

81.   a.   They will all have the same average kinetic energy because they are all at the same temperature. Average kinetic energy depends only on temperature.

       b.   Flask C; at constant T, $u_{rms} \propto (1/M)^{1/2}$. In general, the lighter the gas molecules, the greater is the root mean square velocity (at constant T).

       c.   Flask A: collision frequency is proportional to average velocity $\times$ n/V (as the average velocity doubles, the number of collisions will double, and as the number of molecules in the container doubles, the number of collisions again doubles). At constant T and V, n is proportional to P, and average velocity is proportional to $(1/M)^{1/2}$. We use these relationships and the data in the exercise to determine the following relative values.

	n (relative)	u_{avg} (relative)	Coll. Freq. (relative) = n $\times$ u_{avg}
A	1.0	1.0	1.0
B	0.33	1.0	0.33
C	0.13	3.7	0.48

83.   Graham's law of effusion: $\dfrac{Rate_1}{Rate_2} = \left(\dfrac{M_2}{M_1}\right)^{1/2}$

Let Freon-12 = gas 1 and Freon-11 = gas 2:

$\dfrac{1.07}{1.00} = \left(\dfrac{137.4}{M_1}\right)^{1/2}$, $1.14 = \dfrac{137.4}{M_1}$, $M_1 = 121\ g/mol$

The molar mass of CF_2Cl_2 is equal to 121 g/mol, so Freon-12 is CF_2Cl_2.

85. $\dfrac{\text{Rate}_1}{\text{Rate}_2} = \left(\dfrac{M_2}{M_1}\right)^{1/2}$; $\text{rate}_1 = \dfrac{24.0\,\text{mL}}{\text{min}}$; $\text{rate}_2 = \dfrac{47.8\,\text{mL}}{\text{min}}$; $M_2 = \dfrac{16.04\,\text{g}}{\text{mol}}$; $M_1 = ?$

$\dfrac{24.0}{47.8} = \left(\dfrac{16.04}{M_1}\right)^{1/2} = 0.502$, $16.04 = (0.502)^2 \times M_1$, $M_1 = \dfrac{16.04}{0.252} = \dfrac{63.7\,\text{g}}{\text{mol}}$

87.   a. $PV = nRT$

$P = \dfrac{nRT}{V} = \dfrac{0.5000\,\text{mol} \times \dfrac{0.08206\,\text{L atm}}{\text{K mol}} \times (25.0 + 273.2)\,\text{K}}{1.0000\,\text{L}} = 12.24\,\text{atm}$

b. $\left[P + a\left(\dfrac{n}{V}\right)^2\right](V - nb) = nRT$;   for N_2: $a = 1.39\ \text{atm L}^2/\text{mol}^2$ and $b = 0.0391\ \text{L/mol}$

$\left[P + 1.39\left(\dfrac{0.5000}{1.0000}\right)^2\,\text{atm}\right](1.0000\,\text{L} - 0.5000 \times 0.0391\,\text{L}) = 12.24\,\text{L atm}$

$(P + 0.348\,\text{atm})(0.9805\,\text{L}) = 12.24\,\text{L atm}$

$P = \dfrac{12.24\,\text{L atm}}{0.9805\,\text{L}} - 0.348\,\text{atm} = 12.48 - 0.348 = 12.13\,\text{atm}$

c.   The ideal gas law is high by 0.11 atm, or $\dfrac{0.11}{12.13} \times 100 = 0.91\%$.

89.   The kinetic molecular theory assumes that gas particles do not exert forces on each other and that gas particles are volumeless. Real gas particles do exert attractive forces for each other, and real gas particles do have volumes. A gas behaves most ideally at low pressures and high temperatures. The effect of attractive forces is minimized at high temperatures because the gas particles are moving very rapidly. At low pressure, the container volume is relatively large (P and V are inversely related), so the volume of the container taken up by the gas particles is negligible.

91.   The pressure measured for real gases is too low compared to ideal gases. This is due to the attractions gas particles do have for each other; these attractions "hold" them back from hitting the container walls as forcefully. To make up for this slight decrease in pressure for real gases, a factor is added to the measured pressure. The measured volume is too large. A fraction of the space of the container volume is taken up by the volume of the molecules themselves. Therefore, the actual volume available to real gas molecules is slightly less than the container volume. A term is subtracted from the container volume to correct for the volume taken up by real gas molecules.

93.   The values of a are: H_2, $\dfrac{0.244 \text{ atm L}^2}{\text{mol}^2}$; CO_2, 3.59; N_2, 1.39; CH_4, 2.25

Because a is a measure of intermolecular attractions, the attractions are greatest for CO_2.

95. $u_{rms} = \left(\dfrac{3RT}{M}\right)^{1/2} = \left[\dfrac{3\left(\dfrac{8.3145 \text{ kg m}^2}{\text{s}^2 \text{ K mol}}\right)(227 + 273)\text{ K}}{28.02 \times 10^{-3} \text{ kg/mol}}\right]^{1/2} = 667 \text{ m/s}$

$u_{mp} = \left(\dfrac{2RT}{M}\right)^{1/2} = \left[\dfrac{2\left(\dfrac{8.3145 \text{ kg m}^2}{\text{s}^2 \text{ K mol}}\right)(500.\text{ K})}{28.02 \times 10^{-3} \text{ kg/mol}}\right]^{1/2} = 545 \text{ m/s}$

$u_{avg} = \left(\dfrac{8RT}{\pi M}\right)^{1/2} = \left[\dfrac{8\left(\dfrac{8.3145 \text{ kg m}^2}{\text{s}^2 \text{ K mol}}\right)(500.\text{ K})}{\pi(28.02 \times 10^{-3} \text{ kg/mol})}\right]^{1/2} = 615 \text{ m/s}$

97.   The force per impact is proportional to $\Delta(mu) = 2mu$. Because m $\propto$ M, the molar mass, and u $\propto (1/M)^{1/2}$ at constant T, the force per impact at constant T is proportional to M $\times (1/M)^{1/2} = \sqrt{M}$.

$\dfrac{\text{Impact force (H}_2)}{\text{Impact force (He)}} = \sqrt{\dfrac{M_{H_2}}{M_{He}}} = \sqrt{\dfrac{2.016}{4.003}} = 0.7097$

99. $\Delta(mu) = 2mu$ = change in momentum per impact. Because m is proportional to M, the molar mass, and u is proportional to $(T/M)^{1/2}$:

$\Delta(mu)_{O_2} \propto 2M_{O_2}\left(\dfrac{T}{M_{O_2}}\right)^{1/2}$ and $\Delta(mu)_{He} \propto 2M_{He}\left(\dfrac{T}{M_{He}}\right)^{1/2}$

$\dfrac{\Delta(mu)_{O_2}}{\Delta(mu)_{He}} = \dfrac{2M_{O_2}\left(\dfrac{T}{M_{O_2}}\right)^{1/2}}{2M_{He}\left(\dfrac{T}{M_{He}}\right)^{1/2}} = \dfrac{M_{O_2}}{M_{He}}\left(\dfrac{M_{He}}{M_{O_2}}\right)^{1/2} = \dfrac{31.998}{4.003}\left(\dfrac{4.003}{31.998}\right)^{1/2} = 2.827$

The change in momentum per impact is 2.827 times larger for O_2 molecules than for He atoms.

$$Z_A = A \frac{N}{V} \left(\frac{RT}{2\pi M} \right)^{1/2} = \text{collision rate}$$

$$\frac{Z_{O_2}}{Z_{He}} = \frac{A \left(\dfrac{N}{V} \right) \left(\dfrac{RT}{2\pi M_{O_2}} \right)^{1/2}}{A \left(\dfrac{N}{V} \right) \left(\dfrac{RT}{2\pi M_{He}} \right)^{1/2}} = \frac{\left(\dfrac{1}{M_{O_2}} \right)^{1/2}}{\left(\dfrac{1}{M_{He}} \right)^{1/2}} = 0.3537; \quad \frac{Z_{He}}{Z_{O_2}} = 2.827$$

There are 2.827 times as many impacts per second for He as for O_2.

101.   Intermolecular collision frequency $= Z = 4 \dfrac{N}{V} d^2 \left(\dfrac{\pi RT}{M} \right)^{1/2}$, where d = diameter of He atom

$$\frac{n}{V} = \frac{P}{RT} = \frac{3.0 \text{ atm}}{\dfrac{0.08206 \text{ L atm}}{\text{K mol}} \times 300. \text{ K}} = 0.12 \text{ mol/L}$$

$$\frac{N}{V} = \frac{0.12 \text{ mol}}{L} \times \frac{6.022 \times 10^{23} \text{ molecules}}{\text{mol}} \times \frac{1000 \text{ L}}{m^3} = \frac{7.2 \times 10^{25} \text{ molecules}}{m^3}$$

$$Z = 4 \times \frac{7.2 \times 10^{25} \text{ molecules}}{m^3} \times (50. \times 10^{-12} \text{ m})^2 \times \left(\frac{\pi (8.3145)(300.)}{4.00 \times 10^{-3}} \right)^{1/2}$$
$$= 1.0 \times 10^9 \text{ collisions/s}$$

Mean free path $= \lambda = \dfrac{u_{avg}}{Z}$; $u_{avg} = \left(\dfrac{8RT}{\pi M} \right)^{1/2} = 1260 \text{ m/s}$; $\lambda = \dfrac{1260 \text{ m/s}}{1.0 \times 10^9 \text{ s}^{-1}} = 1.3 \times 10^{-6} \text{ m}$

Atmospheric Chemistry

103.   a.   If we have 1.0×10^6 L of air, then there are 3.0×10^2 L of CO.

$$P_{CO} = \chi_{CO} P_{total}; \quad \chi_{CO} = \frac{V_{CO}}{V_{total}} \text{ because V } \% \text{ n}; \quad P_{CO} = \frac{3.0 \times 10^2}{1.0 \times 10^6} \times 628 \text{ torr} = 0.19 \text{ torr}$$

b. $n_{CO} = \dfrac{P_{CO} V}{RT}$; Assuming 1.0 m^3 air, $1 \text{ m}^3 = 1000 \text{ L}$:

$$n_{CO} = \frac{\dfrac{0.19}{760} \text{ atm} \times (1.0 \times 10^3 \text{ L})}{\dfrac{0.08206 \text{ L atm}}{\text{K mol}} \times 273 \text{ K}} = 1.1 \times 10^{-2} \text{ mol CO}$$

$$1.1 \times 10^{-2} \text{ mol} \times \frac{6.02 \times 10^{23} \text{ molecules}}{\text{mol}} = 6.6 \times 10^{21} \text{ CO molecules in 1.0 m}^3 \text{ of air}$$

c. $$\frac{6.6 \times 10^{21} \text{ molecules}}{\text{m}^3} \times \left(\frac{1 \text{ m}}{100 \text{ cm}}\right)^3 = \frac{6.6 \times 10^{15} \text{ molecules CO}}{\text{cm}^3}$$

105.   For benzene:

$$89.6 \times 10^{-9} \text{ g} \times \frac{1 \text{ mol}}{78.11 \text{ g}} = 1.15 \times 10^{-9} \text{ mol benzene}$$

$$V_{\text{benzene}} = \frac{n_{\text{benzene}} RT}{P} = \frac{1.15 \times 10^{-9} \text{ mol} \times \dfrac{0.08206 \text{ L atm}}{\text{K mol}} \times 296 \text{ K}}{748 \text{ torr} \times \dfrac{1 \text{ atm}}{760 \text{ torr}}} = 2.84 \times 10^{-8} \text{ L}$$

$$\text{Mixing ratio} = \frac{2.84 \times 10^{-8} \text{ L}}{3.00 \text{ L}} \times 10^6 = 9.47 \times 10^{-3} \text{ ppmv}$$

$$\text{or } ppbv = \frac{\text{vol. of X} \times 10^9}{\text{total vol.}} = \frac{2.84 \times 10^{-8} \text{ L}}{3.00 \text{ L}} \times 10^9 = 9.47 \text{ ppbv}$$

$$\frac{1.15 \times 10^{-9} \text{ mol benzene}}{3.00 \text{ L}} \times \frac{1 \text{ L}}{1000 \text{ cm}^3} \times \frac{6.022 \times 10^{23} \text{ molecules}}{\text{mol}}$$

$$= 2.31 \times 10^{11} \text{ molecules benzene/cm}^3$$

For toluene:

$$153 \times 10^{-9} \text{ g C}_7\text{H}_8 \times \frac{1 \text{ mol}}{92.13 \text{ g}} = 1.66 \times 10^{-9} \text{ mol toluene}$$

$$V_{\text{toluene}} = \frac{n_{\text{toluene}} RT}{P} = \frac{1.66 \times 10^{-9} \text{ mol} \times \dfrac{0.08206 \text{ L atm}}{\text{K mol}} \times 296 \text{ K}}{748 \text{ torr} \times \dfrac{1 \text{ atm}}{760 \text{ torr}}} = 4.10 \times 10^{-8} \text{ L}$$

$$\text{Mixing ratio} = \frac{4.10 \times 10^{-8} \text{ L}}{3.00 \text{ L}} \times 10^6 = 1.37 \times 10^{-2} \text{ ppmv (or 13.7 ppbv)}$$

$$\frac{1.66 \times 10^{-9} \text{ mol toluene}}{3.00 \text{ L}} \times \frac{1 \text{ L}}{1000 \text{ cm}^3} \times \frac{6.022 \times 10^{23} \text{ molecules}}{\text{mol}}$$

$$= 3.33 \times 10^{11} \text{ molecules toluene/cm}^3$$

Additional Exercises

107.   Processes a, c, and d will all result in a doubling of the pressure. Process a has the effect of halving the volume, which would double the pressure (Boyle's law). Process c doubles the pressure because the absolute temperature is doubled (from 200. K to 400. K). Process d doubles the pressure because the moles of gas are doubled (28 g N_2 is 1 mol of N_2). Process b won't double the pressure since the absolute temperature is not doubled (303 K to 333 K).

109. $0.050 \text{ mL} \times \dfrac{1.149 \text{ g}}{\text{mL}} \times \dfrac{1 \text{ mol O}_2}{32.0 \text{ g}} = 1.8 \times 10^{-3} \text{ mol O}_2$

$$V = \frac{nRT}{P} = \frac{1.8 \times 10^{-3} \text{ mol} \times \dfrac{0.08206 \text{ L atm}}{\text{K mol}} \times 310.\,\text{K}}{1.0 \text{ atm}} = 4.6 \times 10^{-2} \text{ L} = 46 \text{ mL}$$

111. $PV = nRT$, V and T are constant. $\dfrac{P_1}{n_1} = \dfrac{P_2}{n_2}$ or $\dfrac{P_1}{P_2} = \dfrac{n_1}{n_2}$

When V and T are constant, then pressure is directly proportional to moles of gas present, and pressure ratios are identical to mole ratios.

At 25°C: $2 \text{ H}_2(g) + \text{O}_2(g) \rightarrow 2 \text{ H}_2\text{O}(l)$, $H_2O(l)$ is produced at 25°C.

The balanced equation requires 2 mol H_2 for every mol O_2 reacted. The same ratio (2 : 1) holds true for pressure units. The actual pressure ratio present is 2 atm H_2 to 3 atm O_2, well below the required 2 : 1 ratio. Therefore, H_2 is the limiting reagent. The only gas present at 25°C after the reaction goes to completion will be the excess O_2.

$$P_{O_2} \text{ (reacted)} = 2.00 \text{ atm H}_2 \times \frac{1 \text{ atm O}_2}{2 \text{ atm H}_2} = 1.00 \text{ atm O}_2$$

$$P_{O_2} \text{ (excess)} = P_{O_2} \text{ (initial)} - P_{O_2} \text{ (reacted)} = 3.00 \text{ atm} - 1.00 \text{ atm} = 2.00 \text{ atm O}_2 = P_{\text{total}}$$

At 125°C: $2 \text{ H}_2(g) + \text{O}_2(g) \rightarrow 2 \text{ H}_2\text{O}(g)$, $H_2O(g)$ is produced at 125°C.

The major difference in the problem is that gaseous H_2O is now a product (instead of liquid H_2O), which will increase the total pressure because an additional gas is present.

$$P_{H_2O} \text{ (produced)} = 2.00 \text{ atm H}_2 \times \frac{2 \text{ atm H}_2\text{O}}{2 \text{ atm H}_2} = 2.00 \text{ atm H}_2\text{O}$$

$$P_{\text{total}} = P_{O_2} \text{ (excess)} + P_{H_2O} \text{ (produced)} = 2.00 \text{ atm O}_2 + 2.00 \text{ atm H}_2\text{O} = 4.00 \text{ atm}$$

113. $Mn(s) + x \, HCl(g) \rightarrow MnCl_x(s) + \dfrac{x}{2} H_2(g)$

$$n_{H_2} = \dfrac{PV}{RT} = \dfrac{0.951 \, atm \times 3.22 \, L}{\dfrac{0.08206 \, L \, atm}{K \, mol} \times 373 \, K} = 0.100 \, mol \, H_2$$

Mol Cl in compound = mol HCl = $0.100 \, mol \, H_2 \times \dfrac{x \, mol \, Cl}{\dfrac{x}{2} \, mol \, H_2} = 0.200 \, mol \, Cl$

$$\dfrac{Mol \, Cl}{Mol \, Mn} = \dfrac{0.200 \, mol \, Cl}{2.747 \, g \, Mn \times \dfrac{1 \, mol \, Mn}{54.94 \, g \, Mn}} = \dfrac{0.200 \, mol \, Cl}{0.05000 \, mol \, Mn} = 4.00$$

The formula of compound is $MnCl_4$.

115.   At constant T and P, Avogadro's law applies; that is, equal volumes contain equal moles of molecules. In terms of balanced equations, we can say that mole ratios and volume ratios between the various reactants and products will be equal to each other. $Br_2 + 3 \, F_2 \rightarrow 2 \, X$; 2 moles of X must contain 2 moles of Br and 6 moles of F; X must have the formula BrF_3 for a balanced equation.

117. $PV = nRT$, V and T are constant. $\dfrac{P_1}{n_1} = \dfrac{P_2}{n_2}, \quad \dfrac{P_2}{P_1} = \dfrac{n_2}{n_1}$

We will do this limiting-reagent problem using an alternative method than described in Chapter 3. Let's calculate the partial pressure of C_3H_3N that can be produced from each of the starting materials assuming each reactant is limiting. The reactant that produces the smallest amount of product will run out first and is the limiting reagent.

$$P_{C_3H_3N} = 0.500 \, MPa \times \dfrac{2 \, MPa \, C_3H_3N}{2 \, MPa \, C_3H_6} = 0.500 \, MPa \text{ if } C_3H_6 \text{ is limiting}$$

$$P_{C_3H_3N} = 0.800 \, MPa \times \dfrac{2 \, MPa \, C_3H_3N}{2 \, MPa \, NH_3} = 0.800 \, MPa \text{ if } NH_3 \text{ is limiting}$$

$$P_{C_3H_3N} = 1.500 \, MPa \times \dfrac{2 \, MPa \, C_3H_3N}{3 \, MPa \, O_2} = 1.000 \, MPa \text{ if } O_2 \text{ is limiting}$$

C_3H_6 is limiting. Although more product could be produced from NH_3 and O_2, there is only enough C_3H_6 to produce 0.500 MPa of C_3H_3N. The partial pressure of C_3H_3N in atmospheres after the reaction is:

$$0.500 \times 10^6 \text{ Pa} \times \frac{1 \text{ atm}}{1.013 \times 10^5 \text{ Pa}} = 4.94 \text{ atm}$$

$$n = \frac{PV}{RT} = \frac{4.94 \text{ atm} \times 150. \text{ L}}{\dfrac{0.08206 \text{ L atm}}{\text{K mol}} \times 298 \text{ K}} = 30.3 \text{ mol C}_3\text{H}_3\text{N}$$

$$30.3 \text{ mol} \times \frac{53.06 \text{ g}}{\text{mol}} = 1.61 \times 10^3 \text{ g C}_3\text{H}_3\text{N can be produced.}$$

119. $P_{total} = P_{H_2} + P_{H_2O}$, $1.032 \text{ atm} = P_{H_2} + 32 \text{ torr} \times \dfrac{1 \text{ atm}}{760 \text{ torr}}$, $1.032 - 0.042 = 0.990 \text{ atm} = P_{H_2}$

$$n_{H_2} = \frac{P_{H_2} V}{RT} = \frac{0.990 \text{ atm} \times 0.240 \text{ L}}{\dfrac{0.08206 \text{ L atm}}{\text{K mol}} \times 303 \text{ K}} = 9.56 \times 10^{-3} \text{ mol H}_2$$

$$9.56 \times 10^{-3} \text{ mol H}_2 \times \frac{1 \text{ mol Zn}}{\text{mol H}_2} \times \frac{65.38 \text{ g Zn}}{\text{mol Zn}} = 0.625 \text{ g Zn}$$

121. $P_1V_1 = P_2V_2$; the total volume is $1.00 \text{ L} + 1.00 \text{ L} + 2.00 \text{ L} = 4.00 \text{ L}.$

For He: $P_2 = \dfrac{P_1 V_1}{V_2} = 200. \text{ torr} \times \dfrac{1.00 \text{ L}}{4.00 \text{ L}} = 50.0 \text{ torr He}$

For Ne: $P_2 = 0.400 \text{ atm} \times \dfrac{1.00 \text{ L}}{4.00 \text{ L}} = 0.100 \text{ atm}$; $0.100 \text{ atm} \times \dfrac{760 \text{ torr}}{\text{atm}} = 76.0 \text{ torr Ne}$

For Ar: $P_2 = 24.0 \text{ kPa} \times \dfrac{2.00 \text{ L}}{4.00 \text{ L}} = 12.0 \text{ kPa}$; $12.0 \text{ kPa} \times \dfrac{1 \text{ atm}}{101.3 \text{ kPa}} \times \dfrac{760 \text{ torr}}{\text{atm}}$

$$= 90.0 \text{ torr Ar}$$

$P_{total} = 50.0 + 76.0 + 90.0 = 216.0 \text{ torr}$

123.   a. $156 \text{ mL} \times 1.34 \text{ g/mL} = 209 \text{ g HSiCl}_3 = \text{actual yield of HSiCl}_3$

$$n_{HCl} = \frac{PV}{RT} = \frac{10.0 \text{ atm} \times 15.0 \text{ L}}{\dfrac{0.08206 \text{ L atm}}{\text{K mol}} \times 308 \text{ K}} = 5.93 \text{ mol HCl}$$

$$5.93 \text{ mol HCl} \times \frac{1 \text{ mol HSiCl}_3}{3 \text{ mol HCl}} \times \frac{135.45 \text{ g HSiCl}_3}{\text{mol HSiCl}_3} = 268 \text{ g HSiCl}_3$$

$$\text{Percent yield} = \frac{\text{actual yield}}{\text{theoretical yield}} \times 100 = \frac{209 \text{ g}}{268 \text{ g}} \times 100 = 78.0\%$$

b. $209 \text{ g HiSCl}_3 \times \dfrac{1 \text{ mol HSiCl}_3}{135.45 \text{ g HSiCl}_3} \times \dfrac{1 \text{ mol SiH}_4}{4 \text{ mol HSiCl}_3} = 0.386 \text{ mol SiH}_4$

This is the theoretical yield. If the percent yield is 93.1%, then the actual yield is:

$0.386 \text{ mol SiH}_4 \times 0.931 = 0.359 \text{ mol SiH}_4$

$$V_{\text{SiH}_4} = \dfrac{nRT}{P} = \dfrac{0.359 \text{ mol} \times \dfrac{0.08206 \text{ L atm}}{\text{K mol}} \times 308 \text{ K}}{10.0 \text{ atm}} = 0.907 \text{ L} = 907 \text{ mL SiH}_4$$

125.   We will apply Boyle's law to solve. $PV = nRT = \text{constant}, \ P_1V_1 = P_2V_2$

Let condition (1) correspond to He from the tank that can be used to fill balloons. We must leave 1.0 atm of He in the tank, so $P_1 = 200. - 1.00 = 199$ atm and $V_1 = 15.0$ L. Condition (2) will correspond to the filled balloons with $P_2 = 1.00$ atm and $V_2 = N(2.00 \text{ L})$, where N is the number of filled balloons, each at a volume of 2.00 L.

199 atm × 15.0 L = 1.00 atm × N(2.00 L), N = 1492.5; we can't fill 0.5 of a balloon, so N = 1492 balloons, or to 3 significant figures, 1490 balloons.

127. $n_{\text{Ar}} = \dfrac{228 \text{ g}}{39.95 \text{ g/mol}} = 5.71 \text{ mol Ar}; \quad \chi_{\text{CH}_4} = \dfrac{n_{\text{CH}_4}}{n_{\text{CH}_4} + n_{\text{Ar}}}, \quad 0.650 = \dfrac{n_{\text{CH}_4}}{n_{\text{CH}_4} + 5.71}$

$0.650(n_{\text{CH}_4} + 5.71) = n_{\text{CH}_4}, \quad 3.71 = (0.350)n_{\text{CH}_4}, \quad n_{\text{CH}_4} = 10.6 \text{ mol CH}_4$

$KE_{\text{avg}} = \dfrac{3}{2}RT$ for 1 mol

Thus $KE_{\text{total}} = (10.6 + 5.71 \text{ mol}) \times 3/2 \times 8.3145 \text{ J K}^{-1} \text{ mol}^{-1} \times 298 \text{ K} = 6.06 \times 10^4 \text{ J} = 60.6 \text{ kJ}$

129.   Mol of He removed $= \dfrac{PV}{RT} = \dfrac{1.00 \text{ atm} \times (1.75 \times 10^{-3} \text{ L})}{\dfrac{0.08206 \text{ L atm}}{\text{K mol}} \times 298 \text{ K}} = 7.16 \times 10^{-5} \text{ mol He}$

In the original flask, 7.16×10^{-5} mol of He exerted a partial pressure of $1.960 - 1.710 = 0.250$ atm.

$$V = \dfrac{nRT}{V} = \dfrac{(7.16 \times 10^{-5} \text{ mol}) \times 0.08206 \text{ L atm K}^{-1} \text{ mol}^{-1} \times 298 \text{ K}}{0.250 \text{ atm}} = 7.00 \times 10^{-3} \text{ L}$$
$$= 7.00 \text{ mL}$$

131.   a. $2 CH_4(g) + 2 NH_3(g) + 3 O_2(g) \rightarrow 2 HCN(g) + 6 H_2O(g)$

   b.   Volumes of gases are proportional to moles at constant T and P. Using the balanced equation, methane and ammonia are in stoichiometric amounts and oxygen is in excess. In 1 second:

$$n_{CH_4} = \frac{PV}{RT} = \frac{1.00 \text{ atm} \times 20.0 \text{ L}}{0.08206 \text{ L atm K}^{-1} \text{mol}^{-1} \times 423 \text{ K}} = 0.576 \text{ mol CH}_4$$

$$\frac{0.576 \text{ mol CH}_4}{s} \times \frac{2 \text{ mol HCN}}{2 \text{ mol CH}_4} \times \frac{27.03 \text{ g HCN}}{\text{mol HCN}} = 15.6 \text{ g HCN/s}$$

Challenge Problems

133.   Initially we have 1.00 mol CH_4 (16.0 g/mol = molar mass) and 2.00 mol O_2 (32.0 g/mol = molar mass).

$$CH_4(g) + a O_2(g) \rightarrow b CO(g) + c CO_2(g) + d H_2O(g)$$

$b + c = 1.00$ (C balance); $2a = b + 2c + d$ (O balance)

$2d = 4$ (H balance), $d = 2 = 2.00$ mol H_2O

$$V_{initial} = \frac{nRT}{P} = \frac{3.00 \text{ mol} \times 0.08206 \text{ L atm K}^{-1} \text{mol}^{-1} \times 425 \text{ K}}{1.00 \text{ atm}} = 104.6 \text{ L (1 extra sig .fig.)}$$

$$Density_{initial} = \frac{80.0 \text{ g}}{104.6 \text{ L}} = 0.7648 \text{ g/L (1 extra significant figure)}$$

Because mass is constant:

$$\text{mass} = V_{initial} \times d_{initial} = V_{final} \times d_{final}, V_{final} = V_{initial} \times \frac{d_{initial}}{d_{final}} = 104.6 \text{ L} \times \frac{0.7648 \text{ g/L}}{0.7282 \text{ g/L}}$$

$V_{final} = 109.9$ L (1 extra significant figure)

$$n_{final} = \frac{PV}{RT} = \frac{1.00 \text{ atm} \times 109.9 \text{ L}}{\dfrac{0.08206 \text{ L atm}}{\text{K mol}} \times 425 \text{ K}} = 3.15 \text{ total moles of gas}$$

Assuming an excess of O_2 is present after reaction, an expression for the total moles of gas present at completion is:

$b + c + 2.00 + (2.00 - a) = 3.15$; *Note:* $d = 2.00$ mol H_2O was determined previously.

Because $b + c = 1.00$, solving gives $a = 1.85$ mol O_2 reacted. Indeed, O_2 is in excess.

From the O balance equation:

$$2a = 3.70 = b + 2c + 2.00, \ b + 2c = 1.70$$

Because $b + c = 1.00$, solving gives $b = 0.30$ mol CO and $c = 0.70$ mol CO_2.

The fraction of methane that reacts to form CO is 0.30 mol CO/1.00 mol CH_4 = 0.30 (or 30.% by moles of the reacted methane forms CO).

135. $Cr(s) + 3\ HCl(aq) \rightarrow CrCl_3(aq) + 3/2\ H_2(g); \ Zn(s) + 2\ HCl(aq) \rightarrow ZnCl_2(aq) + H_2(g)$

$$\text{Mol } H_2 \text{ produced} = n = \frac{PV}{RT} = \frac{\left(750.\ \text{torr} \times \dfrac{1\ \text{atm}}{760\ \text{torr}}\right) \times 0.225\ \text{L}}{\dfrac{0.08206\ \text{L atm}}{\text{K mol}} \times (273 + 27)\ \text{K}} = 9.02 \times 10^{-3}\ \text{mol } H_2$$

9.02×10^{-3} mol H_2 = mol H_2 from Cr reaction + mol H_2 from Zn reaction

From the balanced equation: 9.02×10^{-3} mol H_2 = mol Cr × (3/2) + mol Zn × 1

Let x = mass of Cr and y = mass of Zn, then:

$$x + y = 0.362\ \text{g and } 9.02 \times 10^{-3} = \frac{(1.5)x}{52.00} + \frac{y}{65.38}$$

We have two equations and two unknowns. Solving by simultaneous equations:

$$9.02 \times 10^{-3} = (0.02885)x + (0.01530)y$$
$$\underline{-0.01530 \times 0.362 = -(0.01530)x - (0.01530)y}$$
$$3.48 \times 10^{-3} = (0.01355)x, \qquad x = \text{mass of Cr} = \frac{3.48 \times 10^{-3}}{0.01355} = 0.257\ \text{g}$$

y = mass of Zn = 0.362 g − 0.257 g = 0.105 g Zn; mass % Zn = $\dfrac{0.105\ \text{g}}{0.362\ \text{g}} \times 100$ = 29.0% Zn

137.   Molar mass = $\dfrac{dRT}{P}$, P and molar mass are constant; $dT = \dfrac{P \times \text{molar mass}}{R}$ = constant

$d = \text{constant}(1/T)$ or $d_1T_1 = d_2T_2$, where T is in kelvin (K).

$T = x + {}^\circ C; \ 1.2930(x + 0.0) = 0.9460(x + 100.0)$

$(1.2930)x = (0.9460)x + 94.60, \ (0.3470)x = 94.60, \ x = 272.6$

From these data, absolute zero would be −272.6°C. The actual value is −273.15°C.

139. $\dfrac{PV}{nRT} = 1 + \beta P;\quad \dfrac{n}{V} \times$ molar mass $= d$

$\dfrac{\text{molar mass}}{RT} \times \dfrac{P}{d} = 1 + \beta P,\quad \dfrac{P}{d} = \dfrac{RT}{\text{molar mass}} + \dfrac{\beta RTP}{\text{molar mass}}$

This is in the equation for a straight line: $y = b + mx$. If we plot P/d versus P and extrapolate to P = 0, we get a y intercept = b = 1.398 = RT/molar mass.

At 0.00°C, molar mass $= \dfrac{0.08206 \times 273.15}{1.398} = 16.03$ g/mol.

141.   Figure 5.16 shows the effect of temperature on the Maxwell-Boltzmann distribution of velocities of molecules. Note that as temperature increases, the probability that a gas particle has the most probable velocity decreases. Thus, since the probability of the gas particle with the most probable velocity decreased by one-half, then the temperature must be higher than 300. K.

The equation that determines the probability that a gas molecule has a certain velocity is:

$$f(u) = 4\pi \left(\dfrac{m}{2\pi k_B T} \right)^{3/2} u^2 e^{-mu^2/2k_B T}$$

Let T_x = the unknown temperature, then:

$$\dfrac{f(u_{mp,x})}{f(u_{mp,300})} = \dfrac{1}{2} = \dfrac{4\pi \left(\dfrac{m}{2\pi k_B T_x} \right)^{3/2} u_{mp,x}^2 \, e^{-mu_{mp,x}^2/2k_B T_x}}{4\pi \left(\dfrac{m}{2\pi k_B T_{300}} \right)^{3/2} u_{mp,300}^2 \, e^{-mu_{mp,300}^2/2k_B T_{300}}}$$

Because $u_{mp} = \sqrt{\dfrac{2k_B T}{m}}$, the equation reduces to:

$$\dfrac{1}{2} = \dfrac{\left(\dfrac{1}{T_x} \right)^{3/2} (T_x)}{\left(\dfrac{1}{T_{300}} \right)^{3/2} (T_{300})} = \left(\dfrac{T_{300}}{T_x} \right)^{1/2}$$

Note that the overall exponent term cancels from the expression when $2k_B T/m$ is substituted for u_{mp}^2 in the exponent term; the temperatures cancel. Solving for T_x:

$$\dfrac{1}{2} = \left(\dfrac{300.\,K}{T_x} \right),\quad T_x = 1.20 \times 10^3 \text{ K; as expected, } T_x \text{ is higher than 300. K.}$$

143.   From the problem, we want $Z_A/Z = 1.00 \times 10^{18}$ where Z_A is the collision frequency of the gas particles with the walls of the container and Z is the intermolecular collision frequency.

From the text:
$$\frac{Z_A}{Z} = \frac{A\dfrac{N}{V}\sqrt{\dfrac{RT}{2\pi M}}}{4\dfrac{N}{V}d^2\sqrt{\dfrac{\pi RT}{M}}} = 1.00 \times 10^{18}, \quad 1.00 \times 10^{18} = \frac{A}{4\,d^2\,\pi\sqrt{2}}$$

If l = length of the cube edge container, then the area A of one cube face is l^2 and the total area in the cube is $6l^2$ (6 faces/cube). He diameter = $d = 2(3.2 \times 10^{-11}$ m$) = 6.4 \times 10^{-11}$ m.

Solving the above expression for A, and then for l gives $l = 0.11$ m $= 1.1$ dm.

Volume $= l^3 = (1.1$ dm$)^3 = 1.3$ dm$^3 = 1.3$ L

145.   The reactions are:

$$C(s) + 1/2\, O_2(g) \rightarrow CO(g) \quad \text{and} \quad C(s) + O_2(g) \rightarrow CO_2(g)$$

$$PV = nRT, \quad P = n\left(\frac{RT}{V}\right) = n(\text{constant})$$

Because the pressure has increased by 17.0%, the number of moles of gas has also increased by 17.0%.

$n_{final} = (1.170)n_{initial} = 1.170(5.00) = 5.85$ mol gas $= n_{O_2} + n_{CO} + n_{CO_2}$

$n_{CO} + n_{CO_2} = 5.00$ (balancing moles of C).   Solving by simultaneous equations:

$$
\begin{aligned}
n_{O_2} + n_{CO} + n_{CO_2} &= 5.85 \\
-(n_{CO} + n_{CO_2} &= 5.00) \\
\hline
n_{O_2} \phantom{+ n_{CO} + n_{CO_2}} &= 0.85
\end{aligned}
$$

If all C were converted to CO_2, no O_2 would be left. If all C were converted to CO, we would get 5 mol CO and 2.5 mol excess O_2 in the reaction mixture. In the final mixture, moles of CO equals twice the moles of O_2 present ($n_{CO} = 2n_{O_2}$).

$n_{CO} = 2n_{O_2} = 1.70$ mol CO; $1.70 + n_{CO_2} = 5.00$, $n_{CO_2} = 3.30$ mol CO_2

$$\chi_{CO} = \frac{1.70}{5.85} = 0.291; \quad \chi_{CO_2} = \frac{3.30}{5.85} = 0.564; \quad \chi_{O_2} = 1.000 - 0.291 - 0.564 = 0.145$$

147.   a.   The reaction is: $CH_4(g) + 2\,O_2(g) \rightarrow CO_2(g) + 2\,H_2O(g)$

$$PV = nRT, \quad \frac{PV}{n} = RT = \text{constant}, \quad \frac{P_{CH_4} V_{CH_4}}{n_{CH_4}} = \frac{P_{air} V_{air}}{n_{air}}$$

The balanced equation requires 2 mol O_2 for every mol of CH_4 that reacts. For three times as much oxygen, we would need 6 mol O_2 per mol of CH_4 reacted ($n_{O_2} = 6n_{CH_4}$). Air is 21% mole percent O_2, so $n_{O_2} = (0.21)n_{air}$. Therefore, the moles of air we would need to deliver the excess O_2 are:

$$n_{O_2} = (0.21)n_{air} = 6n_{CH_4}, \quad n_{air} = 29n_{CH_4}, \quad \frac{n_{air}}{n_{CH_4}} = 29$$

In 1 minute:

$$V_{air} = V_{CH_4} \times \frac{n_{air}}{n_{CH_4}} \times \frac{P_{CH_4}}{P_{air}} = 200.\ \text{L} \times 29 \times \frac{1.50\ \text{atm}}{1.00\ \text{atm}} = 8.7 \times 10^3\ \text{L air/min}$$

b.   If x mol of CH_4 were reacted, then $6x$ mol O_2 were added, producing $(0.950)x$ mol CO_2 and $(0.050)x$ mol of CO. In addition, $2x$ mol H_2O must be produced to balance the hydrogens.

$$CH_4(g) + 2\,O_2(g) \rightarrow CO_2(g) + 2\,H_2O(g); \quad CH_4(g) + 3/2\,O_2(g) \rightarrow CO(g) + 2\,H_2O(g)$$

Amount O_2 reacted:

$$(0.950)x\ \text{mol CO}_2 \times \frac{2\ \text{mol O}_2}{\text{mol CO}_2} = (1.90)x\ \text{mol O}_2$$

$$(0.050)x\ \text{mol CO} \times \frac{1.5\ \text{mol O}_2}{\text{mol CO}} = (0.075)x\ \text{mol O}_2$$

Amount of O_2 left in reaction mixture $= (6.00)x - (1.90)x - (0.075)x = (4.03)x\ \text{mol O}_2$

Amount of $N_2 = (6.00)x\ \text{mol O}_2 \times \frac{79\ \text{mol N}_2}{21\ \text{mol O}_2} = (22.6)x \approx 23x\ \text{mol N}_2$

The reaction mixture contains:

$$(0.950)x\ \text{mol CO}_2 + (0.050)x\ \text{mol CO} + (4.03)x\ \text{mol O}_2 + (2.00)x\ \text{mol H}_2O$$
$$+\ 23x\ \text{mol N}_2 = (30.)x\ \text{mol of gas total}$$

$$\chi_{CO} = \frac{(0.050)x}{(30.)x} = 0.0017; \quad \chi_{CO_2} = \frac{(0.950)x}{(30.)x} = 0.032; \quad \chi_{O_2} = \frac{(4.03)x}{(30.)x} = 0.13$$

$$\chi_{H_2O} = \frac{(2.00)x}{(30.)x} = 0.067; \quad \chi_{N_2} = \frac{23x}{(30.)x} = 0.77$$

c.   The partial pressures are determined by $P = \chi P_{total}$. Because $P_{total} = 1.00$ atm, $P_{CO} = 0.0017$ atm, $P_{CO_2} = 0.032$ atm, $P_{O_2} = 0.13$ atm, $P_{H_2O} = 0.067$ atm, and $P_{N_2} = 0.77$ atm.

149.   Each stage will give an enrichment of:

$$\frac{\text{Diffusion rate } {}^{12}CO_2}{\text{Diffusion rate } {}^{13}CO_2} = \left(\frac{M_{{}^{13}CO_2}}{M_{{}^{12}CO_2}}\right)^{1/2} = \left(\frac{45.001}{43.998}\right) = 1.0113$$

Because ${}^{12}CO_2$ moves slightly faster, each successive stage will have less ${}^{13}CO_2$.

$$\frac{99.90 \ {}^{12}CO_2}{0.10 \ {}^{13}CO_2} \times 1.0113^N = \frac{99.990 \ {}^{12}CO_2}{0.010 \ {}^{13}CO_2}$$

$$1.0113^N = \frac{9,999.0}{999.00} = 10.009 \quad \text{(carrying extra significant figures)}$$

$$N \log(1.0113) = \log(10.009), \ N = \frac{1.000391}{4.88 \times 10^{-3}} = 2.05 \times 10^2 \approx 2.1 \times 10^2 \text{ stages are needed.}$$

151.   a.   Average molar mass of air $= 0.790 \times 28.02$ g/mol $+ 0.210 \times 32.00$ g/mol $= 28.9$ g/mol; molar mass of helium $= 4.003$ g/mol

A given volume of air at a given set of conditions has a larger density than helium at those conditions. We need to heat the air to a temperature greater than 25°C in order to lower the air density (by driving air out of the hot air balloon) until the density is the same as that for helium (at 25°C and 1.00 atm).

b.   To provide the same lift as the helium balloon (assume $V = 1.00$ L), the mass of air in the hot-air balloon ($V = 1.00$ L) must be the same as that in the helium balloon. Let MM = molar mass:

$$P \bullet MM = dRT, \ \text{mass} = \frac{MM \bullet PV}{RT}; \ \text{solving: mass He} = 0.164 \text{ g}$$

$$\text{Mass air} = 0.164 \text{ g} = \frac{28.9 \text{ g/mol} \times 1.00 \text{ atm} \times 1.00 \text{ L}}{\dfrac{0.08206 \text{ L atm}}{K \text{ mol}} \times T}, \ T = 2150 \text{ K} \ \text{(a very high temperature)}$$

153. $d = $ molar mass(P/RT); at constant P and T, the density of gas is directly proportional to the molar mass of the gas. Thus the molar mass of the gas has a value which is 1.38 times that of the molar mass of O_2.

Molar mass $= 1.38(32.00$ g/mol$) = 44.2$ g/mol

Because H_2O is produced when the unknown binary compound is combusted, the unknown must contain hydrogen. Let A_xH_y be the formula for unknown compound.

$$\text{Mol } A_xH_y = 10.0 \text{ g } A_xH_y \times \frac{1 \text{ mol } A_xH_y}{44.2 \text{ g}} = 0.226 \text{ mol } A_xH_y$$

$$\text{Mol H} = 16.3 \text{ g } H_2O \times \frac{1 \text{ mol } H_2O}{18.02 \text{ g}} \times \frac{2 \text{ mol H}}{\text{mol } H_2O} = 1.81 \text{ mol H}$$

$$\frac{1.81 \text{ mol H}}{0.226 \text{ mol } A_xH_y} = 8 \text{ mol H/mol } A_xH_y \text{ ; } A_xH_y = A_xH_8$$

The mass of the x moles of A in the A_xH_8 formula is:

$$44.2 \text{ g} - 8(1.008 \text{ g}) = 36.1 \text{ g}$$

From the periodic table and by trial and error, some possibilities for A_xH_8 are ClH_8, F_2H_8, C_3H_8, and Be_4H_8. C_3H_8 and Be_4H_8 fit the data best and because C_3H_8 (propane) is a known substance, C_3H_8 is the best possible identity from the data in this problem.

Because H_2O is produced when the unknown binary compound is combusted, the unknown must contain hydrogen. Let A_xH_y be the formula for unknown compound.

$$\text{Mol A·H} = 10.0 \text{ g/L H}_2 \times \frac{1 \text{ mol A·H}}{44.2 \text{ g}} = 0.226 \text{ mol A·H}$$

$$\text{Mol H} = 16.3 \text{ g H}_2O \times \frac{1 \text{ mol H}_2O}{18.02 \text{ g}} \times \frac{2 \text{ mol H}}{\text{mol H}_2O} = 1.81 \text{ mol H}$$

$$\frac{1.81 \text{ mol H}}{0.226 \text{ mol A·H}} = 8 \text{ mol H per mol A·H, } A_xH_8$$

The mass of the x moles of A in the A_xH_8 formula is:

$$44.2 \text{ g} - 8(1.008 \text{ g}) = 36.1 \text{ g}$$

From the procedure outlined by trial and error, some possible data for A_xH_8 are CH_4, C_2H_8, C_3H_8 and B_2H_6, but the data best fit the data best and because C_3H_8 (propane) is a known substance. C_3H_8 is the best possible identity from the data in this problem.